Single Variable Essential Calculus

Early Transcendentals

University of California, Berkeley

James Stewart

CENGAGE
Learning™

Australia • Brazil • Japan • Korea • Mexico • Singapore • Spain • United Kingdom • United States

Single Variable Essential Calculus: Early Transcendentals, University of California, Berkeley

James Stewart

Executive Editors:
Michele Baird

Maureen Staudt

Michael Stranz

Project Development Manager:
Linda deStefano

Senior Marketing Coordinators:
Sara Mercurio

Lindsay Shapiro

Production/Manufacturing Manager:
Donna M. Brown

PreMedia Services Supervisor:
Rebecca A. Walker

Rights & Permissions Specialist:
Kalina Hintz

Cover Image:
Getty Images*

* Unless otherwise noted, all cover images used by Custom Solutions, a part of Cengage Learning, have been supplied courtesy of Getty Images with the exception of the Earthview cover image, which has been supplied by the National Aeronautics and Space Administration (NASA).

ISBN-13: 978-0-495-43845-5

ISBN-10: 0-495-43945-2

Cengage Learning
5191 Natorp Boulevard
Mason, Ohio 45040
USA

Cengage Learning is a leading provider of customized learning solutions with office locations around the globe, including Singapore, the United Kingdom, Australia, Mexico, Brazil, and Japan. Locate your local office at:
international.cengage.com/region

Cengage Learning products are represented in Canada by Nelson Education, Ltd.

For your lifelong learning solutions, visit **custom.cengage.com**

Visit our corporate website at **cengage.com**

Printed in the United States of America

Custom Contents

ANCILLARIES FOR INSTRUCTORS

COMPLETE SOLUTIONS MANUAL
ISBN 0495014303

The Complete Solutions Manual provides worked-out solutions to all of the problems in the text.

SOLUTIONS BUILDER CD
ISBN 0495106925

This CD is an electronic version of the complete solutions manual. It provides instructors with an efficient method for creating solution sets to homework or exams. Instructors can easily view, select, and save solution sets that can then be printed or posted.

 ### TOOLS FOR ENRICHING CALCULUS
ISBN 0495107638

TEC contains Visuals and Modules for use as classroom demonstrations. Exercises for each Module allow instructors to make assignments based on the classroom demonstration. TEC also includes Homework Hints for representative exercises. Students can benefit from this additional help when instructors assign these exercises.

Thomson™ ThomsonNOW™

ThomsonNOW allows instructors to assign machine-gradable homework problems that motivate students by providing feedback and help as they work problems. That assistance is available through worked-out solutions that guide students through the steps of problem solving, or via live online tutoring at *vMentor*™. The tutors at this online service will skillfully guide students through a problem, using unique two-way audio and whiteboard features.

ANCILLARIES FOR STUDENTS

STUDENT SOLUTIONS MANUAL
ISBN 049501429X

The Student Solutions Manual provides completely worked-out solutions to all odd-numbered exercises within the text, giving students a way to check their answers and ensure that they took the correct steps to arrive at an answer.

INTERACTIVE VIDEO SKILLBUILDER CD
ISBN 0495113719

The Interactive Video Skillbuilder CD-ROM contains more than eight hours of instruction. To help students evaluate their progress, each section contains a ten-question web quiz (the results of which can be e-mailed to the instructor) and each chapter contains a chapter test, with the answer to each problem on each test.

 ### TOOLS FOR ENRICHING CALCULUS
ISBN 0495107638

TEC provides a laboratory environment in which students can enrich their understanding by revisiting and exploring selected topics. TEC also includes Homework Hints for representative exercises.

Thomson™ ThomsonNOW™

Students like to use ThomsonNOW because they find they are studying more efficiently, spending their time on what they still need to master rather than on information they have already learned.

Ancillaries for students are available for purchase at
www.thomsonedu.com

∫ TO THE STUDENT

Reading a calculus textbook is different from reading a newspaper or a novel, or even a physics book. Don't be discouraged if you have to read a passage more than once in order to understand it. You should have pencil and paper and calculator at hand to sketch a diagram or make a calculation.

Some students start by trying their homework problems and read the text only if they get stuck on an exercise. I suggest that a far better plan is to read and understand a section of the text before attempting the exercises. In particular, you should look at the definitions to see the exact meanings of the terms. And before you read each example, I suggest that you cover up the solution and try solving the problem yourself. You'll get a lot more from looking at the solution if you do so.

Part of the aim of this course is to train you to think logically. Learn to write the solutions of the exercises in a connected, step-by-step fashion with explanatory sentences—not just a string of disconnected equations or formulas.

The answers to the odd-numbered exercises appear at the back of the book, in Appendix E. Some exercises ask for a verbal explanation or interpretation or description. In such cases there is no single correct way of expressing the answer, so don't worry that you haven't found the definitive answer. In addition, there are often several different forms in which to express a numerical or algebraic answer, so if your answer differs from mine, don't immediately assume you're wrong. For example, if the answer given in the back of the book is $\sqrt{2} - 1$ and you obtain $1/(1 + \sqrt{2})$, then you're right and rationalizing the denominator will show that the answers are equivalent.

The icon ⌾ indicates an exercise that definitely requires the use of either a graphing calculator or a computer with graphing software. But that doesn't mean that graphing devices can't be used to check your work on the other exercises as well. The symbol CAS is reserved for problems in which the full resources of a computer algebra system (like Derive, Maple, Mathematica, or the TI-89/92) are required. You will also encounter the symbol ⊘, which warns you against committing an error. I have placed this symbol in the margin in situations where I have observed that a large proportion of my students tend to make the same mistake.

The CD-ROM *Tools for Enriching™ Calculus* is referred to by means of the symbol TEC . It directs you to *Visuals* and *Modules* in which you can explore aspects of calculus for which the computer is particularly useful. TEC also provides *Homework Hints* for representative exercises that are indicated by printing the exercise number in blue: **43.** These homework hints ask you questions that allow you to make progress toward a solution without actually giving you the answer. You need to pursue each hint in an active manner with pencil and paper to work out the details. If a particular hint doesn't enable you to solve the problem, you can click to reveal the next hint. (See the front endsheet for information on how to purchase this and other useful tools.)

The *Interactive Video Skillbuilder CD-ROM* contains videos of instructors explaining two or three of the examples in every section of the text. (The symbol **V** has been placed beside these examples in the text.) Also on the CD is a video in which I offer advice on how to succeed in your calculus course.

I also want to draw your attention to the website **www.stewartcalculus.com**. There you will find an *Algebra Review* (in case your precalculus skills are weak) as well as *Additional Examples, Challenging Problems, Projects, Lies My Calculator and Computer Told Me* (explaining why calculators sometimes give the wrong answer), *History of Mathematics, Additional Topics,* chapter quizzes, and links to outside resources.

I recommend that you keep this book for reference purposes after you finish the course. Because you will likely forget some of the specific details of calculus, the book will serve as a useful reminder when you need to use calculus in subsequent courses. And, because this book contains more material than can be covered in any one course, it can also serve as a valuable resource for a working scientist or engineer.

Calculus is an exciting subject, justly considered to be one of the greatest achievements of the human intellect. I hope you will discover that it is not only useful but also intrinsically beautiful.

JAMES STEWART

1 FUNCTIONS AND LIMITS

Calculus is fundamentally different from the mathematics that you have studied previously. Calculus is less static and more dynamic. It is concerned with change and motion; it deals with quantities that approach other quantities. So in this first chapter we begin our study of calculus by investigating how the values of functions change and approach limits.

1.1 FUNCTIONS AND THEIR REPRESENTATONS

Functions arise whenever one quantity depends on another. Consider the following four situations.

A. The area A of a circle depends on the radius r of the circle. The rule that connects r and A is given by the equation $A = \pi r^2$. With each positive number r there is associated one value of A, and we say that A is a *function* of r.

B. The human population of the world P depends on the time t. The table gives estimates of the world population $P(t)$ at time t, for certain years. For instance,

$$P(1950) \approx 2,560,000,000$$

But for each value of the time t there is a corresponding value of P, and we say that P is a function of t.

C. The cost C of mailing a first-class letter depends on the weight w of the letter. Although there is no simple formula that connects w and C, the post office has a rule for determining C when w is known.

D. The vertical acceleration a of the ground as measured by a seismograph during an earthquake is a function of the elapsed time t. Figure 1 shows a graph generated by seismic activity during the Northridge earthquake that shook Los Angeles in 1994. For a given value of t, the graph provides a corresponding value of a.

Year	Population (millions)
1900	1650
1910	1750
1920	1860
1930	2070
1940	2300
1950	2560
1960	3040
1970	3710
1980	4450
1990	5280
2000	6080

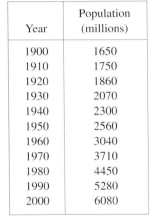

Calif. Dept. of Mines and Geology

FIGURE I

Vertical ground acceleration during the Northridge earthquake

Each of these examples describes a rule whereby, given a number (r, t, w, or t), another number (A, P, C, or a) is assigned. In each case we say that the second number is a function of the first number.

I

> A **function** f is a rule that assigns to each element x in a set A exactly one element, called $f(x)$, in a set B.

We usually consider functions for which the sets A and B are sets of real numbers. The set A is called the **domain** of the function. The number $f(x)$ is the **value of f at x** and is read "f of x." The **range** of f is the set of all possible values of $f(x)$ as x varies throughout the domain. A symbol that represents an arbitrary number in the *domain* of a function f is called an **independent variable**. A symbol that represents a number in the *range* of f is called a **dependent variable**. In Example A, for instance, r is the independent variable and A is the dependent variable.

It's helpful to think of a function as a **machine** (see Figure 2). If x is in the domain of the function f, then when x enters the machine, it's accepted as an input and the machine produces an output $f(x)$ according to the rule of the function. Thus we can think of the domain as the set of all possible inputs and the range as the set of all possible outputs.

Another way to picture a function is by an **arrow diagram** as in Figure 3. Each arrow connects an element of A to an element of B. The arrow indicates that $f(x)$ is associated with x, $f(a)$ is associated with a, and so on.

The most common method for visualizing a function is its graph. If f is a function with domain A, then its **graph** is the set of ordered pairs

$$\{(x, f(x)) \mid x \in A\}$$

(Notice that these are input-output pairs.) In other words, the graph of f consists of all points (x, y) in the coordinate plane such that $y = f(x)$ and x is in the domain of f.

The graph of a function f gives us a useful picture of the behavior or "life history" of a function. Since the y-coordinate of any point (x, y) on the graph is $y = f(x)$, we can read the value of $f(x)$ from the graph as being the height of the graph above the point x. (See Figure 4.) The graph of f also allows us to picture the domain of f on the x-axis and its range on the y-axis as in Figure 5.

FIGURE 2
Machine diagram for a function f

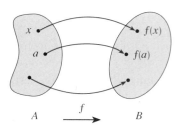

FIGURE 3
Arrow diagram for f

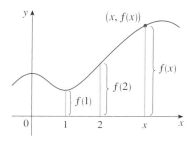

FIGURE 4

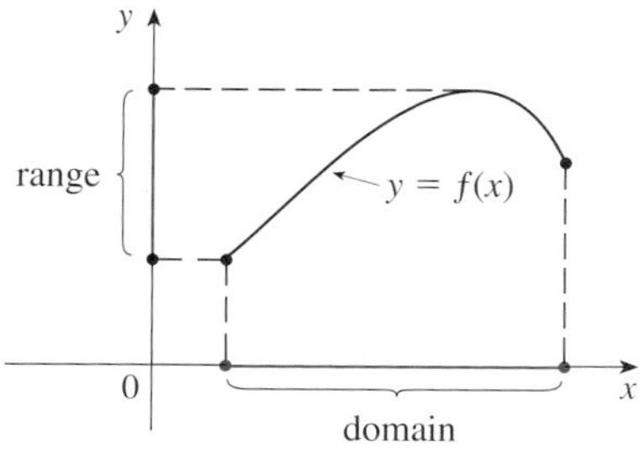

FIGURE 5

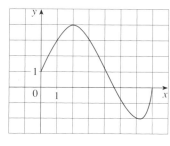

FIGURE 6

EXAMPLE I The graph of a function f is shown in Figure 6.
(a) Find the values of $f(1)$ and $f(5)$.
(b) What are the domain and range of f?

SOLUTION
(a) We see from Figure 6 that the point $(1, 3)$ lies on the graph of f, so the value of f at 1 is $f(1) = 3$. (In other words, the point on the graph that lies above $x = 1$ is 3 units above the x-axis.)

When $x = 5$, the graph lies about 0.7 unit below the x-axis, so we estimate that $f(5) \approx -0.7$.

■ The notation for intervals is given on Reference Page 3. The Reference Pages are located at the front and back of the book.

(b) We see that $f(x)$ is defined when $0 \leqslant x \leqslant 7$, so the domain of f is the closed interval $[0, 7]$. Notice that f takes on all values from -2 to 4, so the range of f is

$$\{y \mid -2 \leqslant y \leqslant 4\} = [-2, 4]$$ ■

REPRESENTATIONS OF FUNCTIONS

There are four possible ways to represent a function:

- verbally (by a description in words)
- visually (by a graph)
- numerically (by a table of values)
- algebraically (by an explicit formula)

If a single function can be represented in all four ways, it is often useful to go from one representation to another to gain additional insight into the function. But certain functions are described more naturally by one method than by another. With this in mind, let's reexamine the four situations that we considered at the beginning of this section.

A. The most useful representation of the area of a circle as a function of its radius is probably the algebraic formula $A(r) = \pi r^2$, though it is possible to compile a table of values or to sketch a graph (half a parabola). Because a circle has to have a positive radius, the domain is $\{r \mid r > 0\} = (0, \infty)$, and the range is also $(0, \infty)$.

Year	Population (millions)
1900	1650
1910	1750
1920	1860
1930	2070
1940	2300
1950	2560
1960	3040
1970	3710
1980	4450
1990	5280
2000	6080

B. We are given a description of the function in words: $P(t)$ is the human population of the world at time t. The table of values of world population provides a convenient representation of this function. If we plot these values, we get the graph (called a *scatter plot*) in Figure 7. It too is a useful representation; the graph allows us to absorb all the data at once. What about a formula? Of course, it's impossible to devise an explicit formula that gives the exact human population $P(t)$ at any time t. But it is possible to find an expression for a function that *approximates* $P(t)$. In fact, we could use a graphing calculator with exponential regression capabilities to obtain the approximation

$$P(t) \approx f(t) = (0.008079266) \cdot (1.013731)^t$$

and Figure 8 shows that it is a reasonably good "fit." The function f is called a *mathematical model* for population growth. In other words, it is a function with an explicit formula that approximates the behavior of our given function. We will see, however, that the ideas of calculus can be applied to a table of values; an explicit formula is not necessary.

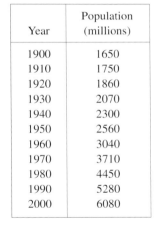

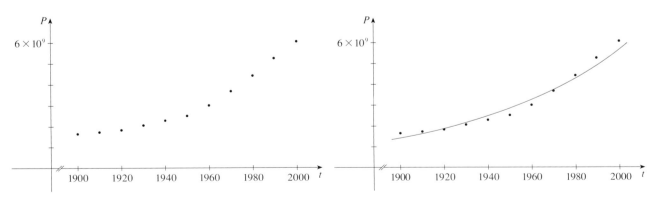

FIGURE 7 Scatter plot of data points for population growth

FIGURE 8 Graph of a mathematical model for population growth

The function P is typical of the functions that arise whenever we attempt to apply calculus to the real world. We start with a verbal description of a function. Then we may be able to construct a table of values of the function, perhaps from instrument readings in a scientific experiment. Even though we don't have complete knowledge of the values of the function, we will see throughout the book that it is still possible to perform the operations of calculus on such a function.

▪ A function defined by a table of values is called a *tabular* function.

w (ounces)	$C(w)$ (dollars)
$0 < w \leq 1$	0.39
$1 < w \leq 2$	0.63
$2 < w \leq 3$	0.87
$3 < w \leq 4$	1.11
$4 < w \leq 5$	1.35
⋮	⋮
$12 < w \leq 13$	3.27

C. Again the function is described in words: $C(w)$ is the cost of mailing a first-class letter with weight w. The rule that the US Postal Service used as of 2006 is as follows: The cost is 39 cents for up to one ounce, plus 24 cents for each successive ounce up to 13 ounces. The table of values shown in the margin is the most convenient representation for this function, though it is possible to sketch a graph (see Example 6).

D. The graph shown in Figure 1 is the most natural representation of the vertical acceleration function $a(t)$. It's true that a table of values could be compiled, and it is even possible to devise an approximate formula. But everything a geologist needs to know—amplitudes and patterns—can be seen easily from the graph. (The same is true for the patterns seen in electrocardiograms of heart patients and polygraphs for lie-detection.)

In the next example we sketch the graph of a function that is defined verbally.

EXAMPLE 2 When you turn on a hot-water faucet, the temperature T of the water depends on how long the water has been running. Draw a rough graph of T as a function of the time t that has elapsed since the faucet was turned on.

SOLUTION The initial temperature of the running water is close to room temperature because the water has been sitting in the pipes. When the water from the hot-water tank starts flowing from the faucet, T increases quickly. In the next phase, T is constant at the temperature of the heated water in the tank. When the tank is drained, T decreases to the temperature of the water supply. This enables us to make the rough sketch of T as a function of t in Figure 9. ▪

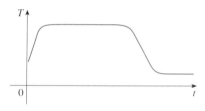

FIGURE 9

EXAMPLE 3 Find the domain of each function.

(a) $f(x) = \sqrt{x + 2}$ (b) $g(x) = \dfrac{1}{x^2 - x}$

SOLUTION

▪ If a function is given by a formula and the domain is not stated explicitly, the convention is that the domain is the set of all numbers for which the formula makes sense and defines a real number.

(a) Because the square root of a negative number is not defined (as a real number), the domain of f consists of all values of x such that $x + 2 \geq 0$. This is equivalent to $x \geq -2$, so the domain is the interval $[-2, \infty)$.

(b) Since

$$g(x) = \frac{1}{x^2 - x} = \frac{1}{x(x - 1)}$$

and division by 0 is not allowed, we see that $g(x)$ is not defined when $x = 0$ or $x = 1$. Thus the domain of g is $\{x \mid x \neq 0, x \neq 1\}$, which could also be written in interval notation as $(-\infty, 0) \cup (0, 1) \cup (1, \infty)$. ▪

The graph of a function is a curve in the xy-plane. But the question arises: Which curves in the xy-plane are graphs of functions? This is answered by the following test.

THE VERTICAL LINE TEST A curve in the xy-plane is the graph of a function of x if and only if no vertical line intersects the curve more than once.

The reason for the truth of the Vertical Line Test can be seen in Figure 10. If each vertical line $x = a$ intersects a curve only once, at (a, b), then exactly one functional value is defined by $f(a) = b$. But if a line $x = a$ intersects the curve twice, at (a, b) and (a, c), then the curve can't represent a function because a function can't assign two different values to a.

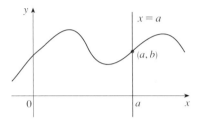
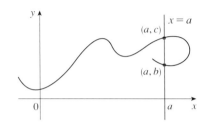

FIGURE 10

PIECEWISE DEFINED FUNCTIONS

The functions in the following three examples are defined by different formulas in different parts of their domains.

V EXAMPLE 4 A function f is defined by

$$f(x) = \begin{cases} 1 - x & \text{if } x \leq 1 \\ x^2 & \text{if } x > 1 \end{cases}$$

Evaluate $f(0)$, $f(1)$, and $f(2)$ and sketch the graph.

SOLUTION Remember that a function is a rule. For this particular function the rule is the following: First look at the value of the input x. If it happens that $x \leq 1$, then the value of $f(x)$ is $1 - x$. On the other hand, if $x > 1$, then the value of $f(x)$ is x^2.

Since $0 \leq 1$, we have $f(0) = 1 - 0 = 1$.

Since $1 \leq 1$, we have $f(1) = 1 - 1 = 0$.

Since $2 > 1$, we have $f(2) = 2^2 = 4$.

How do we draw the graph of f? We observe that if $x \leq 1$, then $f(x) = 1 - x$, so the part of the graph of f that lies to the left of the vertical line $x = 1$ must coincide with the line $y = 1 - x$, which has slope -1 and y-intercept 1. If $x > 1$, then $f(x) = x^2$, so the part of the graph of f that lies to the right of the line $x = 1$ must coincide with the graph of $y = x^2$, which is a parabola. This enables us to sketch the graph in Figure 11. The solid dot indicates that the point $(1, 0)$ is included on the graph; the open dot indicates that the point $(1, 1)$ is excluded from the graph. ■

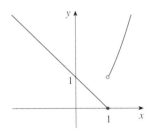

FIGURE 11

The next example of a piecewise defined function is the absolute value function. Recall that the **absolute value** of a number a, denoted by $|a|$, is the distance from a to 0 on the real number line. Distances are always positive or 0, so we have

$$|a| \geq 0 \qquad \text{for every number } a$$

■ www.stewartcalculus.com
For a more extensive review of absolute values, click on *Review of Algebra.*

For example,

$$|3| = 3 \qquad |-3| = 3 \qquad |0| = 0 \qquad |\sqrt{2} - 1| = \sqrt{2} - 1 \qquad |3 - \pi| = \pi - 3$$

In general, we have

$$|a| = a \qquad \text{if } a \geqslant 0$$
$$|a| = -a \quad \text{if } a < 0$$

(Remember that if a is negative, then $-a$ is positive.)

EXAMPLE 5 Sketch the graph of the absolute value function $f(x) = |x|$.

SOLUTION From the preceding discussion we know that

$$|x| = \begin{cases} x & \text{if } x \geqslant 0 \\ -x & \text{if } x < 0 \end{cases}$$

Using the same method as in Example 4, we see that the graph of f coincides with the line $y = x$ to the right of the y-axis and coincides with the line $y = -x$ to the left of the y-axis (see Figure 12). ■

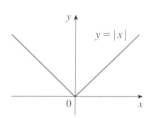

FIGURE 12

EXAMPLE 6 In Example C at the beginning of this section we considered the cost $C(w)$ of mailing a first-class letter with weight w. In effect, this is a piecewise defined function because, from the table of values, we have

$$C(w) = \begin{cases} 0.39 & \text{if } 0 < w \leqslant 1 \\ 0.63 & \text{if } 1 < w \leqslant 2 \\ 0.87 & \text{if } 2 < w \leqslant 3 \\ 1.11 & \text{if } 3 < w \leqslant 4 \end{cases}$$

The graph is shown in Figure 13. You can see why functions similar to this one are called **step functions**—they jump from one value to the next. ■

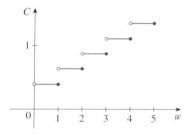

FIGURE 13

SYMMETRY

If a function f satisfies $f(-x) = f(x)$ for every number x in its domain, then f is called an **even function**. For instance, the function $f(x) = x^2$ is even because

$$f(-x) = (-x)^2 = x^2 = f(x)$$

The geometric significance of an even function is that its graph is symmetric with respect to the y-axis (see Figure 14). This means that if we have plotted the graph of

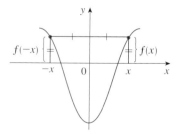

FIGURE 14 An even function

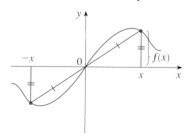

FIGURE 15 An odd function

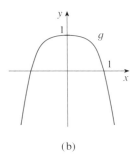

(a)

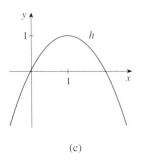

(b)

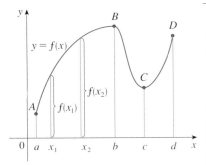

(c)

FIGURE 16

f for $x \geq 0$, we obtain the entire graph simply by reflecting this portion about the y-axis.

If f satisfies $f(-x) = -f(x)$ for every number x in its domain, then f is called an **odd function**. For example, the function $f(x) = x^3$ is odd because

$$f(-x) = (-x)^3 = -x^3 = -f(x)$$

The graph of an odd function is symmetric about the origin (see Figure 15 on page 6). If we already have the graph of f for $x \geq 0$, we can obtain the entire graph by rotating this portion through $180°$ about the origin.

▼ EXAMPLE 7 Determine whether each of the following functions is even, odd, or neither even nor odd.

(a) $f(x) = x^5 + x$ (b) $g(x) = 1 - x^4$ (c) $h(x) = 2x - x^2$

SOLUTION

(a)
$$f(-x) = (-x)^5 + (-x) = (-1)^5 x^5 + (-x)$$
$$= -x^5 - x = -(x^5 + x)$$
$$= -f(x)$$

Therefore, f is an odd function.

(b)
$$g(-x) = 1 - (-x)^4 = 1 - x^4 = g(x)$$

So g is even.

(c)
$$h(-x) = 2(-x) - (-x)^2 = -2x - x^2$$

Since $h(-x) \neq h(x)$ and $h(-x) \neq -h(x)$, we conclude that h is neither even nor odd. ■

The graphs of the functions in Example 7 are shown in Figure 16. Notice that the graph of h is symmetric neither about the y-axis nor about the origin.

INCREASING AND DECREASING FUNCTIONS

The graph shown in Figure 17 rises from A to B, falls from B to C, and rises again from C to D. The function f is said to be increasing on the interval $[a, b]$, decreasing on $[b, c]$, and increasing again on $[c, d]$. Notice that if x_1 and x_2 are any two numbers between a and b with $x_1 < x_2$, then $f(x_1) < f(x_2)$. We use this as the defining property of an increasing function.

A function f is called **increasing** on an interval I if

$$f(x_1) < f(x_2) \qquad \text{whenever } x_1 < x_2 \text{ in } I$$

It is called **decreasing** on I if

$$f(x_1) > f(x_2) \qquad \text{whenever } x_1 < x_2 \text{ in } I$$

FIGURE 17

In the definition of an increasing function it is important to realize that the inequality $f(x_1) < f(x_2)$ must be satisfied for *every* pair of numbers x_1 and x_2 in I with $x_1 < x_2$.

You can see from Figure 18 that the function $f(x) = x^2$ is decreasing on the interval $(-\infty, 0]$ and increasing on the interval $[0, \infty)$.

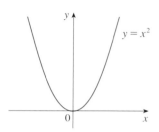

FIGURE 18

1.1 EXERCISES

1. The graph of a function f is given.
(a) State the value of $f(-1)$.
(b) Estimate the value of $f(2)$.
(c) For what values of x is $f(x) = 2$?
(d) Estimate the values of x such that $f(x) = 0$.
(e) State the domain and range of f.
(f) On what interval is f increasing?

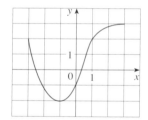

2. The graphs of f and g are given.
(a) State the values of $f(-4)$ and $g(3)$.
(b) For what values of x is $f(x) = g(x)$?
(c) Estimate the solution of the equation $f(x) = -1$.
(d) On what interval is f decreasing?
(e) State the domain and range of f.
(f) State the domain and range of g.

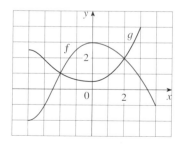

3–6 ■ Determine whether the curve is the graph of a function of x. If it is, state the domain and range of the function.

3.
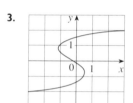

4.
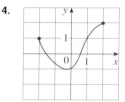

5.
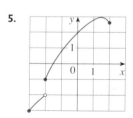

6.
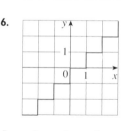

■ ■ ■ ■ ■ ■ ■ ■ ■ ■ ■ ■ ■

7. The graph shown gives the weight of a certain person as a function of age. Describe in words how this person's weight varies over time. What do you think happened when this person was 30 years old?

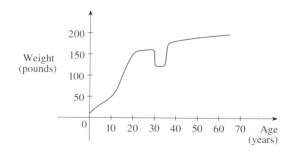

8. The graph shown gives a salesman's distance from his home as a function of time on a certain day. Describe in words what the graph indicates about his travels on this day.

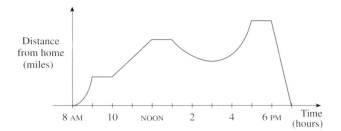

9. You put some ice cubes in a glass, fill the glass with cold water, and then let the glass sit on a table. Describe how the temperature of the water changes as time passes. Then sketch a rough graph of the temperature of the water as a function of the elapsed time.

10. Sketch a rough graph of the number of hours of daylight as a function of the time of year.

11. Sketch a rough graph of the outdoor temperature as a function of time during a typical spring day.

12. Sketch a rough graph of the market value of a new car as a function of time for a period of 20 years. Assume the car is well maintained.

13. Sketch the graph of the amount of a particular brand of coffee sold by a store as a function of the price of the coffee.

14. You place a frozen pie in an oven and bake it for an hour. Then you take it out and let it cool before eating it. Describe how the temperature of the pie changes as time passes. Then sketch a rough graph of the temperature of the pie as a function of time.

15. A homeowner mows the lawn every Wednesday afternoon. Sketch a rough graph of the height of the grass as a function of time over the course of a four-week period.

16. A jet takes off from an airport and lands an hour later at another airport, 400 miles away. If t represents the time in minutes since the plane has left the terminal, let $x(t)$ be the horizontal distance traveled and $y(t)$ be the altitude of the plane.
(a) Sketch a possible graph of $x(t)$.
(b) Sketch a possible graph of $y(t)$.
(c) Sketch a possible graph of the ground speed.
(d) Sketch a possible graph of the vertical velocity.

17. If $f(x) = 3x^2 - x + 2$, find $f(2)$, $f(-2)$, $f(a)$, $f(-a)$, $f(a + 1)$, $2f(a)$, $f(2a)$, $f(a^2)$, $[f(a)]^2$, and $f(a + h)$.

18. A spherical balloon with radius r inches has volume $V(r) = \frac{4}{3}\pi r^3$. Find a function that represents the amount of air required to inflate the balloon from a radius of r inches to a radius of $r + 1$ inches.

19–22 ▪ Evaluate the difference quotient for the given function. Simplify your answer.

19. $f(x) = 4 + 3x - x^2$, $\quad \dfrac{f(3 + h) - f(3)}{h}$

20. $f(x) = x^3$, $\quad \dfrac{f(a + h) - f(a)}{h}$

21. $f(x) = \dfrac{1}{x}$, $\quad \dfrac{f(x) - f(a)}{x - a}$

22. $f(x) = \dfrac{x + 3}{x + 1}$, $\quad \dfrac{f(x) - f(1)}{x - 1}$

23–27 ▪ Find the domain of the function.

23. $f(x) = \dfrac{x}{3x - 1}$

24. $f(x) = \dfrac{5x + 4}{x^2 + 3x + 2}$

25. $f(t) = \sqrt{t} + \sqrt[3]{t}$

26. $g(u) = \sqrt{u} + \sqrt{4 - u}$

27. $h(x) = \dfrac{1}{\sqrt[4]{x^2 - 5x}}$

28. Find the domain and range and sketch the graph of the function $h(x) = \sqrt{4 - x^2}$.

29–40 ▪ Find the domain and sketch the graph of the function.

29. $f(x) = 5$

30. $F(x) = \frac{1}{2}(x + 3)$

31. $f(t) = t^2 - 6t$

32. $H(t) = \dfrac{4 - t^2}{2 - t}$

33. $g(x) = \sqrt{x - 5}$

34. $F(x) = |2x + 1|$

35. $G(x) = \dfrac{3x + |x|}{x}$

36. $g(x) = \dfrac{|x|}{x^2}$

37. $f(x) = \begin{cases} x + 2 & \text{if } x < 0 \\ 1 - x & \text{if } x \geq 0 \end{cases}$

38. $f(x) = \begin{cases} 3 - \frac{1}{2}x & \text{if } x \leq 2 \\ 2x - 5 & \text{if } x > 2 \end{cases}$

39. $f(x) = \begin{cases} x + 2 & \text{if } x \leq -1 \\ x^2 & \text{if } x > -1 \end{cases}$

40. $f(x) = \begin{cases} -1 & \text{if } x \leq -1 \\ 3x + 2 & \text{if } |x| < 1 \\ 7 - 2x & \text{if } x \geq 1 \end{cases}$

41–44 ▪ Find an expression for the function whose graph is the given curve.

41. The line segment joining the points $(-2, 1)$ and $(4, -6)$

42. The line segment joining the points $(-3, -2)$ and $(6, 3)$

43. The bottom half of the parabola $x + (y - 1)^2 = 0$

44. The top half of the circle $(x - 1)^2 + y^2 = 1$

▪ ▪ ▪ ▪ ▪ ▪ ▪ ▪ ▪ ▪ ▪

45–49 ▪ Find a formula for the described function and state its domain.

45. A rectangle has perimeter 20 m. Express the area of the rectangle as a function of the length of one of its sides.

46. A rectangle has area 16 m². Express the perimeter of the rectangle as a function of the length of one of its sides.

47. Express the area of an equilateral triangle as a function of the length of a side.

48. Express the surface area of a cube as a function of its volume.

49. An open rectangular box with volume 2 m³ has a square base. Express the surface area of the box as a function of the length of a side of the base.

▪ ▪ ▪ ▪ ▪ ▪ ▪ ▪ ▪ ▪ ▪

50. A taxi company charges two dollars for the first mile (or part of a mile) and 20 cents for each succeeding tenth of a mile (or part). Express the cost C (in dollars) of a ride as a function of the distance x traveled (in miles) for $0 < x < 2$, and sketch the graph of this function.

51. In a certain country, income tax is assessed as follows. There is no tax on income up to $10,000. Any income over $10,000 is taxed at a rate of 10%, up to an income of $20,000. Any income over $20,000 is taxed at 15%.
(a) Sketch the graph of the tax rate R as a function of the income I.
(b) How much tax is assessed on an income of $14,000? On $26,000?
(c) Sketch the graph of the total assessed tax T as a function of the income I.

52. The functions in Example 6 and Exercises 50 and 51(a) are called *step functions* because their graphs look like

stairs. Give two other examples of step functions that arise in everyday life.

53–54 ▪ Graphs of f and g are shown. Decide whether each function is even, odd, or neither. Explain your reasoning.

53. 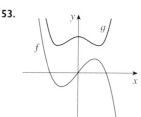 **54.**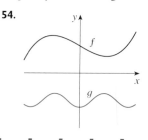

▪ ▪ ▪ ▪ ▪ ▪ ▪ ▪ ▪ ▪ ▪

55. (a) If the point $(5, 3)$ is on the graph of an even function, what other point must also be on the graph?
(b) If the point $(5, 3)$ is on the graph of an odd function, what other point must also be on the graph?

56. A function f has domain $[-5, 5]$ and a portion of its graph is shown.
(a) Complete the graph of f if it is known that f is even.
(b) Complete the graph of f if it is known that f is odd.

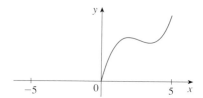

57–62 ▪ Determine whether f is even, odd, or neither. If you have a graphing calculator, use it to check your answer visually.

57. $f(x) = \dfrac{x}{x^2 + 1}$

58. $f(x) = \dfrac{x^2}{x^4 + 1}$

59. $f(x) = \dfrac{x}{x + 1}$

60. $f(x) = x|x|$

61. $f(x) = 1 + 3x^2 - x^4$

62. $f(x) = 1 + 3x^3 - x^5$

▪ ▪ ▪ ▪ ▪ ▪ ▪ ▪ ▪ ▪ ▪

1.2 | A CATALOG OF ESSENTIAL FUNCTIONS

In solving calculus problems you will find that it is helpful to be familiar with the graphs of some commonly occurring functions. These same basic functions are often used to model real-world phenomena, so we begin with a discussion of mathematical modeling. We also review briefly how to transform these functions by shifting, stretching, and reflecting their graphs as well as how to combine pairs of functions by the standard arithmetic operations and by composition.

MATHEMATICAL MODELING

A **mathematical model** is a mathematical description (often by means of a function or an equation) of a real-world phenomenon such as the size of a population, the demand for a product, the speed of a falling object, the concentration of a product in a chemical reaction, the life expectancy of a person at birth, or the cost of emission reductions. The purpose of the model is to understand the phenomenon and perhaps to make predictions about future behavior.

Figure 1 illustrates the process of mathematical modeling. Given a real-world problem, our first task is to formulate a mathematical model by identifying and naming the independent and dependent variables and making assumptions that simplify the phenomenon enough to make it mathematically tractable. We use our knowledge of the physical situation and our mathematical skills to obtain equations that relate the variables. In situations where there is no physical law to guide us, we may need to collect data (either from a library or the Internet or by conducting our own experiments) and examine the data in the form of a table in order to discern patterns. From this numerical representation of a function we may wish to obtain a graphical representation by plotting the data. The graph might even suggest a suitable algebraic formula in some cases.

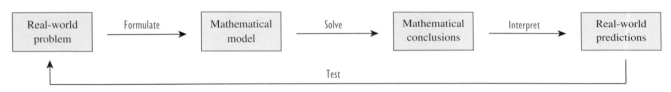

FIGURE 1 The modeling process

The second stage is to apply the mathematics that we know (such as the calculus that will be developed throughout this book) to the mathematical model that we have formulated in order to derive mathematical conclusions. Then, in the third stage, we take those mathematical conclusions and interpret them as information about the original real-world phenomenon by way of offering explanations or making predictions. The final step is to test our predictions by checking against new real data. If the predictions don't compare well with reality, we need to refine our model or to formulate a new model and start the cycle again.

A mathematical model is never a completely accurate representation of a physical situation—it is an *idealization*. A good model simplifies reality enough to permit mathematical calculations but is accurate enough to provide valuable conclusions. It is important to realize the limitations of the model. In the end, Mother Nature has the final say.

There are many different types of functions that can be used to model relationships observed in the real world. In what follows, we discuss the behavior and graphs of these functions and give examples of situations appropriately modeled by such functions.

▢ LINEAR MODELS

▪ www.stewartcalculus.com
To review the coordinate geometry of lines, click on *Review of Analytic Geometry.*

When we say that y is a **linear function** of x, we mean that the graph of the function is a line, so we can use the slope-intercept form of the equation of a line to write a formula for the function as

$$y = f(x) = mx + b$$

where m is the slope of the line and b is the y-intercept.

A characteristic feature of linear functions is that they grow at a constant rate. For instance, Figure 2 shows a graph of the linear function $f(x) = 3x - 2$ and a table of sample values. Notice that whenever x increases by 0.1, the value of $f(x)$ increases by 0.3. So $f(x)$ increases three times as fast as x. Thus the slope of the graph $y = 3x - 2$, namely 3, can be interpreted as the rate of change of y with respect to x.

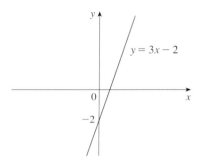

x	$f(x) = 3x - 2$
1.0	1.0
1.1	1.3
1.2	1.6
1.3	1.9
1.4	2.2
1.5	2.5

FIGURE 2

☑ **EXAMPLE 1**

(a) As dry air moves upward, it expands and cools. If the ground temperature is 20°C and the temperature at a height of 1 km is 10°C, express the temperature T (in °C) as a function of the height h (in kilometers), assuming that a linear model is appropriate.

(b) Draw the graph of the function in part (a). What does the slope represent?

(c) What is the temperature at a height of 2.5 km?

SOLUTION

(a) Because we are assuming that T is a linear function of h, we can write

$$T = mh + b$$

We are given that $T = 20$ when $h = 0$, so

$$20 = m \cdot 0 + b = b$$

In other words, the y-intercept is $b = 20$.

We are also given that $T = 10$ when $h = 1$, so

$$10 = m \cdot 1 + 20$$

The slope of the line is therefore $m = 10 - 20 = -10$ and the required linear function is

$$T = -10h + 20$$

(b) The graph is sketched in Figure 3. The slope is $m = -10$°C/km, and this represents the rate of change of temperature with respect to height.

(c) At a height of $h = 2.5$ km, the temperature is

$$T = -10(2.5) + 20 = -5°C$$

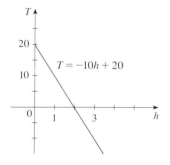

FIGURE 3

▫ **POLYNOMIALS**

A function P is called a **polynomial** if

$$P(x) = a_n x^n + a_{n-1} x^{n-1} + \cdots + a_2 x^2 + a_1 x + a_0$$

where n is a nonnegative integer and the numbers $a_0, a_1, a_2, \ldots, a_n$ are constants called the **coefficients** of the polynomial. The domain of any polynomial is $\mathbb{R} = (-\infty, \infty)$. If the leading coefficient $a_n \neq 0$, then the **degree** of the polynomial is n. For example, the function

$$P(x) = 2x^6 - x^4 + \tfrac{2}{5} x^3 + \sqrt{2}$$

is a polynomial of degree 6.

A polynomial of degree 1 is of the form $P(x) = mx + b$ and so it is a linear function. A polynomial of degree 2 is of the form $P(x) = ax^2 + bx + c$ and is called a **quadratic function**. Its graph is always a parabola obtained by shifting the parabola $y = ax^2$. The parabola opens upward if $a > 0$ and downward if $a < 0$. (See Figure 4.)

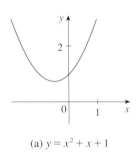
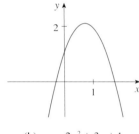

FIGURE 4
The graphs of quadratic
functions are parabolas.

(a) $y = x^2 + x + 1$

(b) $y = -2x^2 + 3x + 1$

A polynomial of degree 3 is of the form

$$P(x) = ax^3 + bx^2 + cx + d \qquad a \neq 0$$

and is called a **cubic function**. Figure 5 shows the graph of a cubic function in part (a) and graphs of polynomials of degrees 4 and 5 in parts (b) and (c). We will see later why the graphs have these shapes.

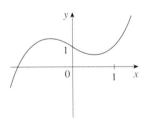
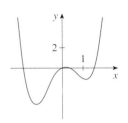
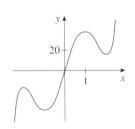

FIGURE 5

(a) $y = x^3 - x + 1$

(b) $y = x^4 - 3x^2 + x$

(c) $y = 3x^5 - 25x^3 + 60x$

Polynomials are commonly used to model various quantities that occur in the natural and social sciences. For instance, in Chapter 2 we will explain why economists often use a polynomial $P(x)$ to represent the cost of producing x units of a commodity.

□ POWER FUNCTIONS

A function of the form $f(x) = x^a$, where a is a constant, is called a **power function**. We consider several cases.

(i) $a = n$, where n is a positive integer

The graphs of $f(x) = x^n$ for $n = 1, 2, 3, 4$, and 5 are shown in Figure 6. (These are polynomials with only one term.) You are familiar with the shape of the graphs of $y = x$ (a line through the origin with slope 1) and $y = x^2$ (a parabola).

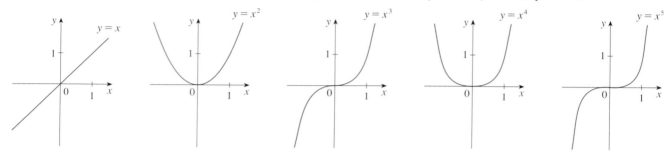

FIGURE 6 Graphs of $f(x) = x^n$ for $n = 1, 2, 3, 4, 5$

The general shape of the graph of $f(x) = x^n$ depends on whether n is even or odd. If n is even, then $f(x) = x^n$ is an even function and its graph is similar to the parabola $y = x^2$. If n is odd, then $f(x) = x^n$ is an odd function and its graph is similar to that of $y = x^3$. Notice from Figure 7, however, that as n increases, the graph of $y = x^n$ becomes flatter near 0 and steeper when $|x| \geqslant 1$. (If x is small, then x^2 is smaller, x^3 is even smaller, x^4 is smaller still, and so on.)

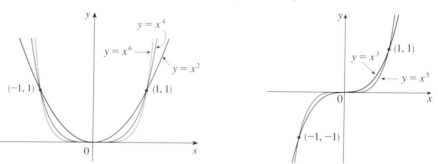

FIGURE 7
Families of power functions

(ii) $a = 1/n$, where n is a positive integer

The function $f(x) = x^{1/n} = \sqrt[n]{x}$ is a **root function**. For $n = 2$ it is the square root function $f(x) = \sqrt{x}$, whose domain is $[0, \infty)$ and whose graph is the upper half of the parabola $x = y^2$. [See Figure 8(a).] For other even values of n, the graph of $y = \sqrt[n]{x}$ is similar to that of $y = \sqrt{x}$. For $n = 3$ we have the cube root function

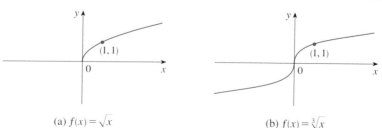

FIGURE 8
Graphs of root functions

(a) $f(x) = \sqrt{x}$

(b) $f(x) = \sqrt[3]{x}$

$f(x) = \sqrt[3]{x}$ whose domain is $\mathbb{R}$ (recall that every real number has a cube root) and whose graph is shown in Figure 8(b). The graph of $y = \sqrt[n]{x}$ for n odd $(n > 3)$ is similar to that of $y = \sqrt[3]{x}$.

(iii) $a = -1$

The graph of the **reciprocal function** $f(x) = x^{-1} = 1/x$ is shown in Figure 9. Its graph has the equation $y = 1/x$, or $xy = 1$, and is a hyperbola with the coordinate axes as its asymptotes. This function arises in physics and chemistry in connection with Boyle's Law, which says that, when the temperature is constant, the volume V of a gas is inversely proportional to the pressure P:

$$V = \frac{C}{P}$$

where C is a constant. Thus the graph of V as a function of P has the same general shape as the right half of Figure 9.

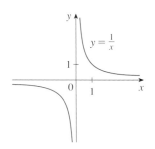

FIGURE 9
The reciprocal function

□ **RATIONAL FUNCTIONS**
A **rational function** f is a ratio of two polynomials:

$$f(x) = \frac{P(x)}{Q(x)}$$

where P and Q are polynomials. The domain consists of all values of x such that $Q(x) \neq 0$. A simple example of a rational function is the function $f(x) = 1/x$, whose domain is $\{x \mid x \neq 0\}$; this is the reciprocal function graphed in Figure 9. The function

$$f(x) = \frac{2x^4 - x^2 + 1}{x^2 - 4}$$

is a rational function with domain $\{x \mid x \neq \pm 2\}$. Its graph is shown in Figure 10.

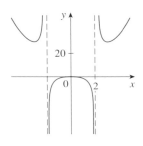

FIGURE 10
$f(x) = \dfrac{2x^4 - x^2 + 1}{x^2 - 4}$

□ **TRIGONOMETRIC FUNCTIONS**
Trigonometry and the trigonometric functions are reviewed on Reference Page 2 and also in Appendix A. In calculus the convention is that radian measure is always used (except when otherwise indicated). For example, when we use the function $f(x) = \sin x$, it is understood that $\sin x$ means the sine of the angle whose radian measure is x. Thus the graphs of the sine and cosine functions are as shown in Figure 11.

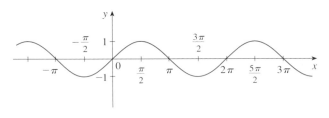

(a) $f(x) = \sin x$

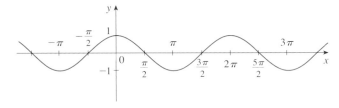

(b) $g(x) = \cos x$

FIGURE 11

Notice that for both the sine and cosine functions the domain is $(-\infty, \infty)$ and the range is the closed interval $[-1, 1]$. Thus, for all values of x, we have

$$-1 \leqslant \sin x \leqslant 1 \qquad -1 \leqslant \cos x \leqslant 1$$

or, in terms of absolute values,

$$|\sin x| \leq 1 \qquad |\cos x| \leq 1$$

Also, the zeros of the sine function occur at the integer multiples of π; that is,

$$\sin x = 0 \qquad \text{when} \qquad x = n\pi \quad n \text{ an integer}$$

An important property of the sine and cosine functions is that they are periodic functions and have period 2π. This means that, for all values of x,

$$\sin(x + 2\pi) = \sin x \qquad \cos(x + 2\pi) = \cos x$$

The periodic nature of these functions makes them suitable for modeling repetitive phenomena such as tides, vibrating springs, and sound waves.

The tangent function is related to the sine and cosine functions by the equation

$$\tan x = \frac{\sin x}{\cos x}$$

and its graph is shown in Figure 12. It is undefined whenever $\cos x = 0$, that is, when $x = \pm\pi/2, \pm 3\pi/2, \ldots$. Its range is $(-\infty, \infty)$. Notice that the tangent function has period π:

$$\tan(x + \pi) = \tan x \qquad \text{for all } x$$

The remaining three trigonometric functions (cosecant, secant, and cotangent) are the reciprocals of the sine, cosine, and tangent functions. Their graphs are shown in Appendix A.

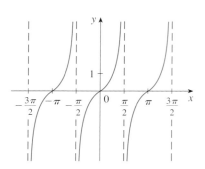

FIGURE 12
$y = \tan x$

□ **EXPONENTIAL FUNCTIONS AND LOGARITHMS**

The **exponential functions** are the functions of the form $f(x) = a^x$, where the base a is a positive constant. The graphs of $y = 2^x$ and $y = (0.5)^x$ are shown in Figure 13. In both cases the domain is $(-\infty, \infty)$ and the range is $(0, \infty)$.

Exponential functions will be studied in detail in Section 3.1, and we will see that they are useful for modeling many natural phenomena, such as population growth (if $a > 1$) and radioactive decay (if $a < 1$).

The **logarithmic functions** $f(x) = \log_a x$, where the base a is a positive constant, are the inverse functions of the exponential functions. They will be studied in Section 3.2. Figure 14 shows the graphs of four logarithmic functions with various bases. In each case the domain is $(0, \infty)$, the range is $(-\infty, \infty)$, and the function increases slowly when $x > 1$.

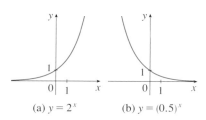

(a) $y = 2^x$ (b) $y = (0.5)^x$

FIGURE 13

TRANSFORMATIONS OF FUNCTIONS

By applying certain transformations to the graph of a given function we can obtain the graphs of certain related functions. This will give us the ability to sketch the graphs of many functions quickly by hand. It will also enable us to write equations for given

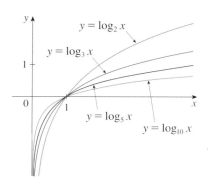

FIGURE 14

■ Figure 15 illustrates these shifts by showing how the graph of $y = (x + 3)^2 + 1$ is obtained from the graph of the parabola $y = x^2$: Shift 3 units to the left and 1 unit upward.

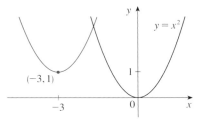

FIGURE 15
$y = (x + 3)^2 + 1$

graphs. Let's first consider **translations**. If c is a positive number, then the graph of $y = f(x) + c$ is just the graph of $y = f(x)$ shifted upward a distance of c units (because each y-coordinate is increased by the same number c). Likewise, if $g(x) = f(x - c)$, where $c > 0$, then the value of g at x is the same as the value of f at $x - c$ (c units to the left of x). Therefore, the graph of $y = f(x - c)$ is just the graph of $y = f(x)$ shifted c units to the right.

VERTICAL AND HORIZONTAL SHIFTS Suppose $c > 0$. To obtain the graph of
$y = f(x) + c$, shift the graph of $y = f(x)$ a distance c units upward
$y = f(x) - c$, shift the graph of $y = f(x)$ a distance c units downward
$y = f(x - c)$, shift the graph of $y = f(x)$ a distance c units to the right
$y = f(x + c)$, shift the graph of $y = f(x)$ a distance c units to the left

---

Now let's consider the **stretching** and **reflecting** transformations. If $c > 1$, then the graph of $y = cf(x)$ is the graph of $y = f(x)$ stretched by a factor of c in the vertical direction (because each y-coordinate is multiplied by the same number c). The graph of $y = -f(x)$ is the graph of $y = f(x)$ reflected about the x-axis because the point (x, y) is replaced by the point $(x, -y)$. The following chart also incorporates the results of other stretching, compressing, and reflecting transformations.

VERTICAL AND HORIZONTAL STRETCHING AND REFLECTING
Suppose $c > 1$. To obtain the graph of
$y = cf(x)$, stretch the graph of $y = f(x)$ vertically by a factor of c
$y = (1/c)f(x)$, compress the graph of $y = f(x)$ vertically by a factor of c
$y = f(cx)$, compress the graph of $y = f(x)$ horizontally by a factor of c
$y = f(x/c)$, stretch the graph of $y = f(x)$ horizontally by a factor of c
$y = -f(x)$, reflect the graph of $y = f(x)$ about the x-axis
$y = f(-x)$, reflect the graph of $y = f(x)$ about the y-axis

---

Figure 16 illustrates these stretching transformations when applied to the cosine function with $c = 2$. For instance, in order to get the graph of $y = 2 \cos x$ we multiply the y-coordinate of each point on the graph of $y = \cos x$ by 2. This means that the graph of $y = \cos x$ gets stretched vertically by a factor of 2.

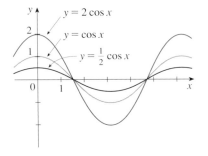
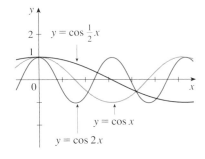

FIGURE 16

V EXAMPLE 2 Given the graph of $y = \sqrt{x}$, use transformations to graph $y = \sqrt{x} - 2$, $y = \sqrt{x-2}$, $y = -\sqrt{x}$, $y = 2\sqrt{x}$, and $y = \sqrt{-x}$.

SOLUTION The graph of the square root function $y = \sqrt{x}$, obtained from Figure 8(a), is shown in Figure 17(a). In the other parts of the figure we sketch $y = \sqrt{x} - 2$ by shifting 2 units downward, $y = \sqrt{x-2}$ by shifting 2 units to the right, $y = -\sqrt{x}$ by reflecting about the x-axis, $y = 2\sqrt{x}$ by stretching vertically by a factor of 2, and $y = \sqrt{-x}$ by reflecting about the y-axis.

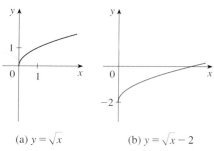 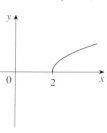 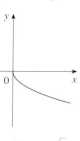 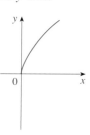 

(a) $y = \sqrt{x}$ (b) $y = \sqrt{x} - 2$ (c) $y = \sqrt{x-2}$ (d) $y = -\sqrt{x}$ (e) $y = 2\sqrt{x}$ (f) $y = \sqrt{-x}$

FIGURE 17   ■

EXAMPLE 3 Sketch the graph of the function $y = 1 - \sin x$.

SOLUTION To obtain the graph of $y = 1 - \sin x$, we start with $y = \sin x$. We reflect about the x-axis to get the graph $y = -\sin x$ and then we shift 1 unit upward to get $y = 1 - \sin x$. (See Figure 18.)

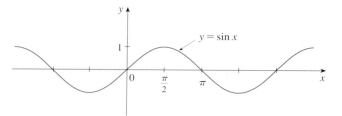 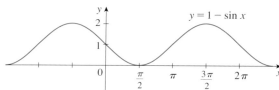

FIGURE 18   ■

COMBINATIONS OF FUNCTIONS

Two functions f and g can be combined to form new functions $f + g$, $f - g$, fg, and f/g in a manner similar to the way we add, subtract, multiply, and divide real numbers. The sum and difference functions are defined by

$$(f + g)(x) = f(x) + g(x) \qquad (f - g)(x) = f(x) - g(x)$$

If the domain of f is A and the domain of g is B, then the domain of $f + g$ is the intersection $A \cap B$ because both $f(x)$ and $g(x)$ have to be defined. For example, the domain of $f(x) = \sqrt{x}$ is $A = [0, \infty)$ and the domain of $g(x) = \sqrt{2 - x}$ is $B = (-\infty, 2]$, so the domain of $(f + g)(x) = \sqrt{x} + \sqrt{2 - x}$ is $A \cap B = [0, 2]$.

Similarly, the product and quotient functions are defined by

$$(fg)(x) = f(x)g(x) \qquad \left(\frac{f}{g}\right)(x) = \frac{f(x)}{g(x)}$$

The domain of fg is $A \cap B$, but we can't divide by 0 and so the domain of f/g is $\{x \in A \cap B \mid g(x) \neq 0\}$. For instance, if $f(x) = x^2$ and $g(x) = x - 1$, then the domain of the rational function $(f/g)(x) = x^2/(x - 1)$ is $\{x \mid x \neq 1\}$, or $(-\infty, 1) \cup (1, \infty)$.

There is another way of combining two functions to get a new function. For example, suppose that $y = f(u) = \sqrt{u}$ and $u = g(x) = x^2 + 1$. Since y is a function of u and u is, in turn, a function of x, it follows that y is ultimately a function of x. We compute this by substitution:

$$y = f(u) = f(g(x)) = f(x^2 + 1) = \sqrt{x^2 + 1}$$

The procedure is called *composition* because the new function is *composed* of the two given functions f and g.

In general, given any two functions f and g, we start with a number x in the domain of g and find its image $g(x)$. If this number $g(x)$ is in the domain of f, then we can calculate the value of $f(g(x))$. The result is a new function $h(x) = f(g(x))$ obtained by substituting g into f. It is called the *composition* (or *composite*) of f and g and is denoted by $f \circ g$ ("f circle g").

DEFINITION Given two functions f and g, the **composite function** $f \circ g$ (also called the **composition** of f and g) is defined by

$$(f \circ g)(x) = f(g(x))$$

The domain of $f \circ g$ is the set of all x in the domain of g such that $g(x)$ is in the domain of f. In other words, $(f \circ g)(x)$ is defined whenever both $g(x)$ and $f(g(x))$ are defined. Figure 19 shows how to picture $f \circ g$ in terms of machines.

FIGURE 19

The $f \circ g$ machine is composed of the g machine (first) and then the f machine.

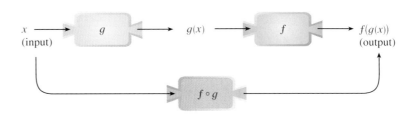

EXAMPLE 4 If $f(x) = x^2$ and $g(x) = x - 3$, find the composite functions $f \circ g$ and $g \circ f$.

SOLUTION We have

$$(f \circ g)(x) = f(g(x)) = f(x - 3) = (x - 3)^2$$

$$(g \circ f)(x) = g(f(x)) = g(x^2) = x^2 - 3 \qquad \blacksquare$$

⊘   **NOTE** You can see from Example 4 that, in general, $f \circ g \neq g \circ f$. Remember, the notation $f \circ g$ means that the function g is applied first and then f is applied second. In Example 4, $f \circ g$ is the function that *first* subtracts 3 and *then* squares; $g \circ f$ is the function that *first* squares and *then* subtracts 3.

▼ EXAMPLE 5 If $f(x) = \sqrt{x}$ and $g(x) = \sqrt{2 - x}$, find each function and its domain.

(a) $f \circ g$ (b) $g \circ f$ (c) $f \circ f$ (d) $g \circ g$

SOLUTION

(a)
$$(f \circ g)(x) = f(g(x)) = f(\sqrt{2 - x}) = \sqrt{\sqrt{2 - x}} = \sqrt[4]{2 - x}$$

The domain of $f \circ g$ is $\{x \mid 2 - x \geq 0\} = \{x \mid x \leq 2\} = (-\infty, 2]$.

(b)
$$(g \circ f)(x) = g(f(x)) = g(\sqrt{x}) = \sqrt{2 - \sqrt{x}}$$

If $0 \leq a \leq b$, then $a^2 \leq b^2$.

For $\sqrt{x}$ to be defined we must have $x \geq 0$. For $\sqrt{2 - \sqrt{x}}$ to be defined we must have $2 - \sqrt{x} \geq 0$, that is, $\sqrt{x} \leq 2$, or $x \leq 4$. Thus we have $0 \leq x \leq 4$, so the domain of $g \circ f$ is the closed interval $[0, 4]$.

(c)
$$(f \circ f)(x) = f(f(x)) = f(\sqrt{x}) = \sqrt{\sqrt{x}} = \sqrt[4]{x}$$

The domain of $f \circ f$ is $[0, \infty)$.

(d)
$$(g \circ g)(x) = g(g(x)) = g(\sqrt{2 - x}) = \sqrt{2 - \sqrt{2 - x}}$$

This expression is defined when both $2 - x \geq 0$ and $2 - \sqrt{2 - x} \geq 0$. The first inequality means $x \leq 2$, and the second is equivalent to $\sqrt{2 - x} \leq 2$, or $2 - x \leq 4$, or $x \geq -2$. Thus, $-2 \leq x \leq 2$, so the domain of $g \circ g$ is the closed interval $[-2, 2]$.   ■

It is possible to take the composition of three or more functions. For instance, the composite function $f \circ g \circ h$ is found by first applying h, then g, and then f as follows:

$$(f \circ g \circ h)(x) = f(g(h(x)))$$

So far we have used composition to build complicated functions from simpler ones. But in calculus it is often useful to be able to *decompose* a complicated function into simpler ones, as in the following example.

EXAMPLE 6 Given $F(x) = \cos^2(x + 9)$, find functions f, g, and h such that $F = f \circ g \circ h$.

SOLUTION Since $F(x) = [\cos(x + 9)]^2$, the formula for F says: First add 9, then take the cosine of the result, and finally square. So we let

$$h(x) = x + 9 \qquad g(x) = \cos x \qquad f(x) = x^2$$

Then

$$(f \circ g \circ h)(x) = f(g(h(x))) = f(g(x + 9)) = f(\cos(x + 9))$$
$$= [\cos(x + 9)]^2 = F(x)$$ ■

1.2   EXERCISES

1. (a) Find an equation for the family of linear functions with slope 2 and sketch several members of the family.
  (b) Find an equation for the family of linear functions such that $f(2) = 1$ and sketch several members of the family.
  (c) Which function belongs to both families?

2. What do all members of the family of linear functions $f(x) = 1 + m(x + 3)$ have in common? Sketch several members of the family.

3. What do all members of the family of linear functions $f(x) = c - x$ have in common? Sketch several members of the family.

4. Find expressions for the quadratic functions whose graphs are shown.

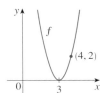
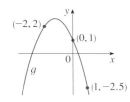

5. Find an expression for a cubic function f if $f(1) = 6$ and $f(-1) = f(0) = f(2) = 0$.

6. Some scientists believe that the average surface temperature of the world has been rising steadily. They have modeled the temperature by the linear function $T = 0.02t + 8.50$, where T is temperature in °C and t represents years since 1900.
  (a) What do the slope and T-intercept represent?
  (b) Use the equation to predict the average global surface temperature in 2100.

7. If the recommended adult dosage for a drug is D (in mg), then to determine the appropriate dosage c for a child of age a, pharmacists use the equation $c = 0.0417D(a + 1)$. Suppose the dosage for an adult is 200 mg.
  (a) Find the slope of the graph of c. What does it represent?
  (b) What is the dosage for a newborn?

8. The manager of a weekend flea market knows from past experience that if he charges x dollars for a rental space at the flea market, then the number y of spaces he can rent is given by the equation $y = 200 - 4x$.
  (a) Sketch a graph of this linear function. (Remember that the rental charge per space and the number of spaces rented can't be negative quantities.)
  (b) What do the slope, the y-intercept, and the x-intercept of the graph represent?

9. The relationship between the Fahrenheit (F) and Celsius (C) temperature scales is given by the linear function $F = \frac{9}{5}C + 32$.
  (a) Sketch a graph of this function.

  (b) What is the slope of the graph and what does it represent? What is the F-intercept and what does it represent?

10. Jason leaves Detroit at 2:00 PM and drives at a constant speed west along I-96. He passes Ann Arbor, 40 mi from Detroit, at 2:50 PM.
  (a) Express the distance traveled in terms of the time elapsed.
  (b) Draw the graph of the equation in part (a).
  (c) What is the slope of this line? What does it represent?

11. Biologists have noticed that the chirping rate of crickets of a certain species is related to temperature, and the relationship appears to be very nearly linear. A cricket produces 113 chirps per minute at 70°F and 173 chirps per minute at 80°F.
  (a) Find a linear equation that models the temperature T as a function of the number of chirps per minute N.
  (b) What is the slope of the graph? What does it represent?
  (c) If the crickets are chirping at 150 chirps per minute, estimate the temperature.

12. The manager of a furniture factory finds that it costs $2200 to manufacture 100 chairs in one day and $4800 to produce 300 chairs in one day.
  (a) Express the cost as a function of the number of chairs produced, assuming that it is linear. Then sketch the graph.
  (b) What is the slope of the graph and what does it represent?
  (c) What is the y-intercept of the graph and what does it represent?

13. At the surface of the ocean, the water pressure is the same as the air pressure above the water, 15 lb/in². Below the surface, the water pressure increases by 4.34 lb/in² for every 10 ft of descent.
  (a) Express the water pressure as a function of the depth below the ocean surface.
  (b) At what depth is the pressure 100 lb/in²?

14. The monthly cost of driving a car depends on the number of miles driven. Lynn found that in May it cost her $380 to drive 480 mi and in June it cost her $460 to drive 800 mi.
  (a) Express the monthly cost C as a function of the distance driven d, assuming that a linear relationship gives a suitable model.
  (b) Use part (a) to predict the cost of driving 1500 miles per month.
  (c) Draw the graph of the linear function. What does the slope represent?
  (d) What does the y-intercept represent?
  (e) Why does a linear function give a suitable model in this situation?

15. Suppose the graph of f is given. Write equations for the graphs that are obtained from the graph of f as follows.
(a) Shift 3 units upward.
(b) Shift 3 units downward.
(c) Shift 3 units to the right.
(d) Shift 3 units to the left.
(e) Reflect about the x-axis.
(f) Reflect about the y-axis.
(g) Stretch vertically by a factor of 3.
(h) Shrink vertically by a factor of 3.

16. Explain how the following graphs are obtained from the graph of $y = f(x)$.
(a) $y = 5f(x)$
(b) $y = f(x - 5)$
(c) $y = -f(x)$
(d) $y = -5f(x)$
(e) $y = f(5x)$
(f) $y = 5f(x) - 3$

17. The graph of $y = f(x)$ is given. Match each equation with its graph and give reasons for your choices.
(a) $y = f(x - 4)$
(b) $y = f(x) + 3$
(c) $y = \frac{1}{3}f(x)$
(d) $y = -f(x + 4)$
(e) $y = 2f(x + 6)$

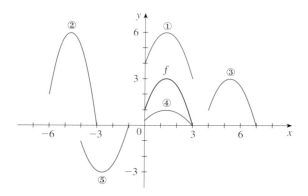

18. The graph of f is given. Draw the graphs of the following functions.
(a) $y = f(x + 4)$
(b) $y = f(x) + 4$
(c) $y = 2f(x)$
(d) $y = -\frac{1}{2}f(x) + 3$

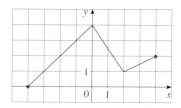

19. The graph of f is given. Use it to graph the following functions.
(a) $y = f(2x)$
(b) $y = f(\frac{1}{2}x)$
(c) $y = f(-x)$
(d) $y = -f(-x)$

20. (a) How is the graph of $y = 2\sin x$ related to the graph of $y = \sin x$? Use your answer and Figure 18(a) to sketch the graph of $y = 2\sin x$.
(b) How is the graph of $y = 1 + \sqrt{x}$ related to the graph of $y = \sqrt{x}$? Use your answer and Figure 17(a) to sketch the graph of $y = 1 + \sqrt{x}$.

21–34 ▪ Graph the function by hand, not by plotting points, but by starting with the graph of one of the standard functions and then applying the appropriate transformations.

21. $y = -x^3$

22. $y = 1 - x^2$

23. $y = (x + 1)^2$

24. $y = x^2 - 4x + 3$

25. $y = 1 + 2\cos x$

26. $y = 4\sin 3x$

27. $y = \sin(x/2)$

28. $y = \dfrac{1}{x - 4}$

29. $y = \sqrt{x + 3}$

30. $y = (x + 2)^4 + 3$

31. $y = \frac{1}{2}(x^2 + 8x)$

32. $y = 1 + \sqrt[3]{x - 1}$

33. $y = \dfrac{2}{x + 1}$

34. $y = \dfrac{1}{4}\tan\left(x - \dfrac{\pi}{4}\right)$

▪ ▪ ▪ ▪ ▪ ▪ ▪ ▪ ▪ ▪ ▪ ▪ ▪

35–36 ▪ Find $f + g$, $f - g$, fg, and f/g and state their domains.

35. $f(x) = x^3 + 2x^2$, $\quad g(x) = 3x^2 - 1$

36. $f(x) = \sqrt{1 + x}$, $\quad g(x) = \sqrt{1 - x}$

▪ ▪ ▪ ▪ ▪ ▪ ▪ ▪ ▪ ▪ ▪ ▪ ▪

37–42 ▪ Find the functions (a) $f \circ g$, (b) $g \circ f$, (c) $f \circ f$, and (d) $g \circ g$ and their domains.

37. $f(x) = x^2 - 1$, $\quad g(x) = 2x + 1$

38. $f(x) = 1 - x^3$, $\quad g(x) = 1/x$

39. $f(x) = \sin x$, $\quad g(x) = 1 - \sqrt{x}$

40. $f(x) = 1 - 3x$, $\quad g(x) = 5x^2 + 3x + 2$

41. $f(x) = x + \dfrac{1}{x}$, $\quad g(x) = \dfrac{x + 1}{x + 2}$

42. $f(x) = \sqrt{2x + 3}$, $\quad g(x) = x^2 + 1$

▪ ▪ ▪ ▪ ▪ ▪ ▪ ▪ ▪ ▪ ▪ ▪ ▪

43–44 ▪ Find $f \circ g \circ h$.

43. $f(x) = \sqrt{x - 1}, \quad g(x) = x^2 + 2, \quad h(x) = x + 3$

44. $f(x) = \dfrac{2}{x + 1}, \quad g(x) = \cos x, \quad h(x) = \sqrt{x + 3}$

▪ ▪ ▪ ▪ ▪ ▪ ▪ ▪ ▪ ▪ ▪

45–48 ▪ Express the function in the form $f \circ g$.

45. $F(x) = (x^2 + 1)^{10}$ **46.** $F(x) = \sin(\sqrt{x})$

47. $u(t) = \sqrt{\cos t}$ **48.** $u(t) = \dfrac{\tan t}{1 + \tan t}$

▪ ▪ ▪ ▪ ▪ ▪ ▪ ▪ ▪ ▪ ▪

49–51 ▪ Express the function in the form $f \circ g \circ h$.

49. $H(x) = 1 - 3^{x^2}$ **50.** $H(x) = \sqrt[8]{2 + |x|}$

51. $H(x) = \sec^4(\sqrt{x})$

▪ ▪ ▪ ▪ ▪ ▪ ▪ ▪ ▪ ▪ ▪

52. Use the table to evaluate each expression.
- (a) $f(g(1))$
- (b) $g(f(1))$
- (c) $f(f(1))$
- (d) $g(g(1))$
- (e) $(g \circ f)(3)$
- (f) $(f \circ g)(6)$

x	1	2	3	4	5	6
$f(x)$	3	1	4	2	2	5
$g(x)$	6	3	2	1	2	3

53. Use the given graphs of f and g to evaluate each expression, or explain why it is undefined.
- (a) $f(g(2))$
- (b) $g(f(0))$
- (c) $(f \circ g)(0)$
- (d) $(g \circ f)(6)$
- (e) $(g \circ g)(-2)$
- (f) $(f \circ f)(4)$

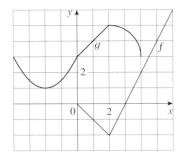

54. A spherical balloon is being inflated and the radius of the balloon is increasing at a rate of 2 cm/s.
- (a) Express the radius r of the balloon as a function of the time t (in seconds).
- (b) If V is the volume of the balloon as a function of the radius, find $V \circ r$ and interpret it.

55. A stone is dropped into a lake, creating a circular ripple that travels outward at a speed of 60 cm/s.
- (a) Express the radius r of this circle as a function of the time t (in seconds).
- (b) If A is the area of this circle as a function of the radius, find $A \circ r$ and interpret it.

56. An airplane is flying at a speed of 350 mi/h at an altitude of one mile and passes directly over a radar station at time $t = 0$.
- (a) Express the horizontal distance d (in miles) that the plane has flown as a function of t.
- (b) Express the distance s between the plane and the radar station as a function of d.
- (c) Use composition to express s as a function of t.

57. The **Heaviside function** H is defined by

$$H(t) = \begin{cases} 0 & \text{if } t < 0 \\ 1 & \text{if } t \geq 0 \end{cases}$$

It is used in the study of electric circuits to represent the sudden surge of electric current, or voltage, when a switch is instantaneously turned on.
- (a) Sketch the graph of the Heaviside function.
- (b) Sketch the graph of the voltage $V(t)$ in a circuit if the switch is turned on at time $t = 0$ and 120 volts are applied instantaneously to the circuit. Write a formula for $V(t)$ in terms of $H(t)$.
- (c) Sketch the graph of the voltage $V(t)$ in a circuit if the switch is turned on at time $t = 5$ seconds and 240 volts are applied instantaneously to the circuit. Write a formula for $V(t)$ in terms of $H(t)$. (Note that starting at $t = 5$ corresponds to a translation.)

58. The Heaviside function defined in Exercise 57 can also be used to define the **ramp function** $y = ctH(t)$, which represents a gradual increase in voltage or current in a circuit.
- (a) Sketch the graph of the ramp function $y = tH(t)$.
- (b) Sketch the graph of the voltage $V(t)$ in a circuit if the switch is turned on at time $t = 0$ and the voltage is gradually increased to 120 volts over a 60-second time interval. Write a formula for $V(t)$ in terms of $H(t)$ for $t \leq 60$.
- (c) Sketch the graph of the voltage $V(t)$ in a circuit if the switch is turned on at time $t = 7$ seconds and the voltage is gradually increased to 100 volts over a period of 25 seconds. Write a formula for $V(t)$ in terms of $H(t)$ for $t \leq 32$.

59. Let f and g be linear functions with equations $f(x) = m_1 x + b_1$ and $g(x) = m_2 x + b_2$. Is $f \circ g$ also a linear function? If so, what is the slope of its graph?

60. If you invest x dollars at 4% interest compounded annually, then the amount $A(x)$ of the investment after one year is $A(x) = 1.04x$. Find $A \circ A$, $A \circ A \circ A$, and $A \circ A \circ A \circ A$. What do these compositions represent? Find a formula for the composition of n copies of A.

61. (a) If $g(x) = 2x + 1$ and $h(x) = 4x^2 + 4x + 7$, find a function f such that $f \circ g = h$. (Think about what operations you would have to perform on the formula for g to end up with the formula for h.)

(b) If $f(x) = 3x + 5$ and $h(x) = 3x^2 + 3x + 2$, find a function g such that $f \circ g = h$.

62. If $f(x) = x + 4$ and $h(x) = 4x - 1$, find a function g such that $g \circ f = h$.

63. (a) Suppose f and g are even functions. What can you say about $f + g$ and fg?

(b) What if f and g are both odd?

64. Suppose f is even and g is odd. What can you say about fg?

65. Suppose g is an even function and let $h = f \circ g$. Is h always an even function?

66. Suppose g is an odd function and let $h = f \circ g$. Is h always an odd function? What if f is odd? What if f is even?

1.3	THE LIMIT OF A FUNCTION

Our aim in this section is to explore the meaning of the limit of a function. We begin by showing how the idea of a limit arises when we try to find the velocity of a falling ball.

▼ **EXAMPLE 1** Suppose that a ball is dropped from the upper observation deck of the CN Tower in Toronto, 450 m above the ground. Find the velocity of the ball after 5 seconds.

SOLUTION Through experiments carried out four centuries ago, Galileo discovered that the distance fallen by any freely falling body is proportional to the square of the time it has been falling. (This model for free fall neglects air resistance.) If the distance fallen after t seconds is denoted by $s(t)$ and measured in meters, then Galileo's law is expressed by the equation

$$s(t) = 4.9t^2$$

The difficulty in finding the velocity after 5 s is that we are dealing with a single instant of time ($t = 5$), so no time interval is involved. However, we can approximate the desired quantity by computing the average velocity over the brief time interval of a tenth of a second from $t = 5$ to $t = 5.1$:

$$\text{average velocity} = \frac{\text{change in position}}{\text{time elapsed}}$$

$$= \frac{s(5.1) - s(5)}{0.1}$$

$$= \frac{4.9(5.1)^2 - 4.9(5)^2}{0.1} = 49.49 \text{ m/s}$$

Time interval	Average velocity (m/s)
$5 \leqslant t \leqslant 6$	53.9
$5 \leqslant t \leqslant 5.1$	49.49
$5 \leqslant t \leqslant 5.05$	49.245
$5 \leqslant t \leqslant 5.01$	49.049
$5 \leqslant t \leqslant 5.001$	49.0049

The table shows the results of similar calculations of the average velocity over successively smaller time periods. It appears that as we shorten the time period, the average velocity is becoming closer to 49 m/s. The **instantaneous velocity** when $t = 5$ is defined to be the limiting value of these average velocities over shorter and shorter time periods that start at $t = 5$. Thus the (instantaneous) velocity after 5 s is

$$v = 49 \text{ m/s} \qquad ■$$

INTUITIVE DEFINITION OF A LIMIT

Let's investigate the behavior of the function f defined by $f(x) = x^2 - x + 2$ for values of x near 2. The following table gives values of $f(x)$ for values of x close to 2, but not equal to 2.

x	$f(x)$	x	$f(x)$
1.0	2.000000	3.0	8.000000
1.5	2.750000	2.5	5.750000
1.8	3.440000	2.2	4.640000
1.9	3.710000	2.1	4.310000
1.95	3.852500	2.05	4.152500
1.99	3.970100	2.01	4.030100
1.995	3.985025	2.005	4.015025
1.999	3.997001	2.001	4.003001

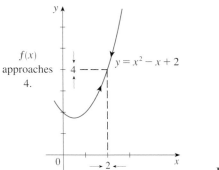

As x approaches 2,

FIGURE 1

From the table and the graph of f (a parabola) shown in Figure 1 we see that when x is close to 2 (on either side of 2), $f(x)$ is close to 4. In fact, it appears that we can make the values of $f(x)$ as close as we like to 4 by taking x sufficiently close to 2. We express this by saying "the limit of the function $f(x) = x^2 - x + 2$ as x approaches 2 is equal to 4." The notation for this is

$$\lim_{x \to 2} (x^2 - x + 2) = 4$$

In general, we use the following notation.

> **1 DEFINITION** We write
>
> $$\lim_{x \to a} f(x) = L$$
>
> and say   "the limit of $f(x)$, as x approaches a, equals L"
>
> if we can make the values of $f(x)$ arbitrarily close to L (as close to L as we like) by taking x to be sufficiently close to a (on either side of a) but not equal to a.

Roughly speaking, this says that the values of $f(x)$ tend to get closer and closer to the number L as x gets closer and closer to the number a (from either side of a) but $x \neq a$.

An alternative notation for

$$\lim_{x \to a} f(x) = L$$

is $f(x) \to L$ as $x \to a$

which is usually read "$f(x)$ approaches L as x approaches a."

Notice the phrase "but $x \neq a$" in the definition of limit. This means that in finding the limit of $f(x)$ as x approaches a, we never consider $x = a$. In fact, $f(x)$ need not even be defined when $x = a$. The only thing that matters is how f is defined *near* a.

Figure 2 shows the graphs of three functions. Note that in part (c), $f(a)$ is not defined and in part (b), $f(a) \neq L$. But in each case, regardless of what happens at a, it is true that $\lim_{x \to a} f(x) = L$.

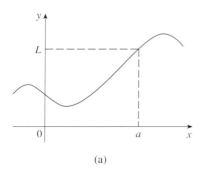

(a)

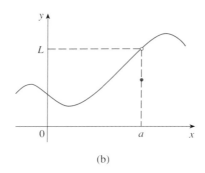

(b)

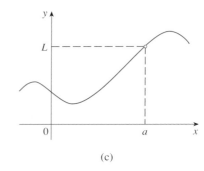

(c)

FIGURE 2 $\lim\limits_{x \to a} f(x) = L$ in all three cases

EXAMPLE 2 Guess the value of $\lim\limits_{x \to 1} \dfrac{x - 1}{x^2 - 1}$.

SOLUTION Notice that the function $f(x) = (x - 1)/(x^2 - 1)$ is not defined when $x = 1$, but that doesn't matter because the definition of $\lim_{x \to a} f(x)$ says that we consider values of x that are close to a but not equal to a.

The tables at the left give values of $f(x)$ (correct to six decimal places) for values of x that approach 1 (but are not equal to 1). On the basis of the values in the tables, we make the guess that

$$\lim_{x \to 1} \frac{x - 1}{x^2 - 1} = 0.5 \qquad \blacksquare$$

$x < 1$	$f(x)$
0.5	0.666667
0.9	0.526316
0.99	0.502513
0.999	0.500250
0.9999	0.500025

$x > 1$	$f(x)$
1.5	0.400000
1.1	0.476190
1.01	0.497512
1.001	0.499750
1.0001	0.499975

Example 2 is illustrated by the graph of f in Figure 3. Now let's change f slightly by giving it the value 2 when $x = 1$ and calling the resulting function g:

$$g(x) = \begin{cases} \dfrac{x - 1}{x^2 - 1} & \text{if } x \neq 1 \\ 2 & \text{if } x = 1 \end{cases}$$

This new function g still has the same limit as x approaches 1. (See Figure 4.)

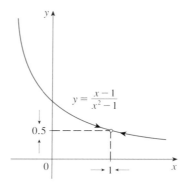

FIGURE 3

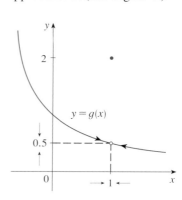

FIGURE 4

EXAMPLE 3 Estimate the value of $\lim\limits_{t \to 0} \dfrac{\sqrt{t^2 + 9} - 3}{t^2}$.

SOLUTION The table lists values of the function for several values of t near 0.

t	$\dfrac{\sqrt{t^2 + 9} - 3}{t^2}$
± 1.0	0.16228
± 0.5	0.16553
± 0.1	0.16662
± 0.05	0.16666
± 0.01	0.16667

As t approaches 0, the values of the function seem to approach $0.1666666\ldots$ and so we guess that

$$\lim_{t \to 0} \frac{\sqrt{t^2 + 9} - 3}{t^2} = \frac{1}{6}$$ ▪

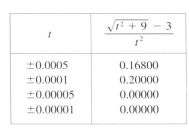

t	$\dfrac{\sqrt{t^2 + 9} - 3}{t^2}$
± 0.0005	0.16800
± 0.0001	0.20000
± 0.00005	0.00000
± 0.00001	0.00000

In Example 3 what would have happened if we had taken even smaller values of t? The table in the margin shows the results from one calculator; you can see that something strange seems to be happening.

If you try these calculations on your own calculator you might get different values, but eventually you will get the value 0 if you make t sufficiently small. Does this mean that the answer is really 0 instead of $\frac{1}{6}$? No, the value of the limit is $\frac{1}{6}$, as we will show in the next section. The problem is that the calculator gave false values because $\sqrt{t^2 + 9}$ is very close to 3 when t is small. (In fact, when t is sufficiently small, a calculator's value for $\sqrt{t^2 + 9}$ is $3.000\ldots$ to as many digits as the calculator is capable of carrying.)

Something similar happens when we try to graph the function

■ **www.stewartcalculus.com**
For a further explanation of why calculators sometimes give false values, click on *Lies My Calculator and Computer Told Me*. In particular, see the section called *The Perils of Subtraction*.

$$f(t) = \frac{\sqrt{t^2 + 9} - 3}{t^2}$$

of Example 3 on a graphing calculator or computer. Parts (a) and (b) of Figure 5 show quite accurate graphs of f, and when we use the trace mode (if available) we can estimate easily that the limit is about $\frac{1}{6}$. But if we zoom in too much, as in parts (c) and (d), then we get inaccurate graphs, again because of problems with subtraction.

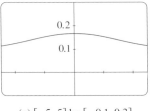

(a) $[-5, 5]$ by $[-0.1, 0.3]$

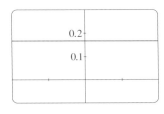

(b) $[-0.1, 0.1]$ by $[-0.1, 0.3]$

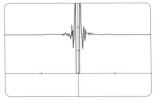

(c) $[-10^{-6}, 10^{-6}]$ by $[-0.1, 0.3]$

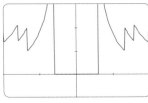

(d) $[-10^{-7}, 10^{-7}]$ by $[-0.1, 0.3]$

FIGURE 5

x	$\dfrac{\sin x}{x}$
± 1.0	0.84147098
± 0.5	0.95885108
± 0.4	0.97354586
± 0.3	0.98506736
± 0.2	0.99334665
± 0.1	0.99833417
± 0.05	0.99958339
± 0.01	0.99998333
± 0.005	0.99999583
± 0.001	0.99999983

▼ EXAMPLE 4 Guess the value of $\displaystyle\lim_{x \to 0} \frac{\sin x}{x}$.

SOLUTION The function $f(x) = (\sin x)/x$ is not defined when $x = 0$. Using a calculator (and remembering that, if $x \in \mathbb{R}$, $\sin x$ means the sine of the angle whose *radian* measure is x), we construct the table of values correct to eight decimal places. From the table at the left and the graph in Figure 6 we guess that

$$\lim_{x \to 0} \frac{\sin x}{x} = 1$$

This guess is in fact correct, as will be proved in the next section using a geometric argument.

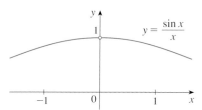

FIGURE 6

▼ EXAMPLE 5 Investigate $\displaystyle\lim_{x \to 0} \sin \frac{\pi}{x}$.

■ **COMPUTER ALGEBRA SYSTEMS**
Computer algebra systems (CAS) have commands that compute limits. In order to avoid the types of pitfalls demonstrated in Examples 3 and 5, they don't find limits by numerical experimentation. Instead, they use more sophisticated techniques such as computing infinite series. If you have access to a CAS, use the limit command to compute the limits in the examples of this section and to check your answers in the exercises of this chapter.

SOLUTION Again the function $f(x) = \sin(\pi/x)$ is undefined at 0. Evaluating the function for some small values of x, we get

$$f(1) = \sin \pi = 0 \qquad\qquad f\left(\tfrac{1}{2}\right) = \sin 2\pi = 0$$

$$f\left(\tfrac{1}{3}\right) = \sin 3\pi = 0 \qquad\qquad f\left(\tfrac{1}{4}\right) = \sin 4\pi = 0$$

$$f(0.1) = \sin 10\pi = 0 \qquad f(0.01) = \sin 100\pi = 0$$

Similarly, $f(0.001) = f(0.0001) = 0$. On the basis of this information we might be tempted to guess that

$$\lim_{x \to 0} \sin \frac{\pi}{x} = 0$$

⊘ but this time our guess is wrong. Note that although $f(1/n) = \sin n\pi = 0$ for any integer n, it is also true that $f(x) = 1$ for infinitely many values of x that approach 0. The graph of f is given in Figure 7.

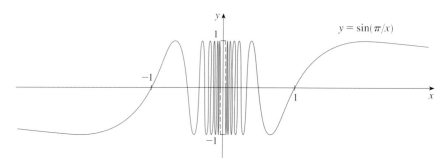

FIGURE 7

The dashed lines near the *y*-axis indicate that the values of $\sin(\pi/x)$ oscillate between 1 and −1 infinitely often as *x* approaches 0. (Use a graphing device to graph *f* and zoom in toward the origin several times. What do you observe?)

Since the values of $f(x)$ do not approach a fixed number as *x* approaches 0,

$$\lim_{x \to 0} \sin \frac{\pi}{x} \quad \text{does not exist}$$ ▪

⊘ Examples 3 and 5 illustrate some of the pitfalls in guessing the value of a limit. It is easy to guess the wrong value if we use inappropriate values of *x*, but it is difficult to know when to stop calculating values. And, as the discussion after Example 3 shows, sometimes calculators and computers give the wrong values. In the next section, however, we will develop foolproof methods for calculating limits.

☑ EXAMPLE 6 The Heaviside function *H* is defined by

$$H(t) = \begin{cases} 0 & \text{if } t < 0 \\ 1 & \text{if } t \geq 0 \end{cases}$$

[This function is named after the electrical engineer Oliver Heaviside (1850–1925) and can be used to describe an electric current that is switched on at time $t = 0$.] Its graph is shown in Figure 8.

As *t* approaches 0 from the left, $H(t)$ approaches 0. As *t* approaches 0 from the right, $H(t)$ approaches 1. There is no single number that $H(t)$ approaches as *t* approaches 0. Therefore, $\lim_{t \to 0} H(t)$ does not exist. ▪

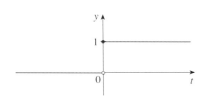

FIGURE 8

ONE-SIDED LIMITS

We noticed in Example 6 that $H(t)$ approaches 0 as *t* approaches 0 from the left and $H(t)$ approaches 1 as *t* approaches 0 from the right. We indicate this situation symbolically by writing

$$\lim_{t \to 0^-} H(t) = 0 \qquad \text{and} \qquad \lim_{t \to 0^+} H(t) = 1$$

The symbol "$t \to 0^-$" indicates that we consider only values of *t* that are less than 0. Likewise, "$t \to 0^+$" indicates that we consider only values of *t* that are greater than 0.

---

2 DEFINITION We write

$$\lim_{x \to a^-} f(x) = L$$

and say the **left-hand limit of $f(x)$ as x approaches a** [or the **limit of $f(x)$ as x approaches a from the left**] is equal to *L* if we can make the values of $f(x)$ arbitrarily close to *L* by taking *x* to be sufficiently close to *a* and *x* less than *a*.

Notice that Definition 2 differs from Definition 1 only in that we require x to be less than a. Similarly, if we require that x be greater than a, we get "the **right-hand limit of $f(x)$ as x approaches a** is equal to L" and we write

$$\lim_{x \to a^+} f(x) = L$$

Thus, the symbol "$x \to a^+$" means that we consider only $x > a$. These definitions are illustrated in Figure 9.

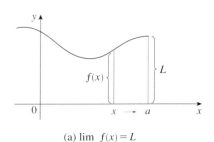

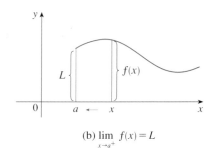

FIGURE 9

(a) $\lim_{x \to a^-} f(x) = L$

(b) $\lim_{x \to a^+} f(x) = L$

By comparing Definition 1 with the definitions of one-sided limits, we see that the following is true.

3 $\lim_{x \to a} f(x) = L$ if and only if $\lim_{x \to a^-} f(x) = L$ and $\lim_{x \to a^+} f(x) = L$

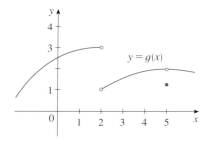

FIGURE 10

☑ **EXAMPLE 7** The graph of a function g is shown in Figure 10. Use it to state the values (if they exist) of the following:

(a) $\lim_{x \to 2^-} g(x)$ (b) $\lim_{x \to 2^+} g(x)$ (c) $\lim_{x \to 2} g(x)$

(d) $\lim_{x \to 5^-} g(x)$ (e) $\lim_{x \to 5^+} g(x)$ (f) $\lim_{x \to 5} g(x)$

SOLUTION From the graph we see that the values of $g(x)$ approach 3 as x approaches 2 from the left, but they approach 1 as x approaches 2 from the right. Therefore

(a) $\lim_{x \to 2^-} g(x) = 3$ and   (b) $\lim_{x \to 2^+} g(x) = 1$

(c) Since the left and right limits are different, we conclude from (3) that $\lim_{x \to 2} g(x)$ does not exist.

The graph also shows that

(d) $\lim_{x \to 5^-} g(x) = 2$ and   (e) $\lim_{x \to 5^+} g(x) = 2$

(f) This time the left and right limits are the same and so, by (3), we have

$$\lim_{x \to 5} g(x) = 2$$

Despite this fact, notice that $g(5) \neq 2$.   ▪

EXAMPLE 8   Find $\lim\limits_{x \to 0} \dfrac{1}{x^2}$ if it exists.

SOLUTION   As x becomes close to 0, x^2 also becomes close to 0, and $1/x^2$ becomes very large. (See the following table.) In fact, it appears from the graph of the function $f(x) = 1/x^2$ shown in Figure 11 that the values of $f(x)$ can be made arbitrarily large by taking x close enough to 0. Thus the values of $f(x)$ do not approach a number, so $\lim_{x \to 0} (1/x^2)$ does not exist.

x	$\dfrac{1}{x^2}$
± 1	1
± 0.5	4
± 0.2	25
± 0.1	100
± 0.05	400
± 0.01	10,000
± 0.001	1,000,000

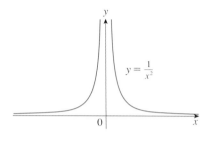

FIGURE 11   ▪

PRECISE DEFINITION OF A LIMIT

Definition 1 is appropriate for an intuitive understanding of limits, but for deeper understanding and rigorous proofs we need to be more precise.

We want to express, in a quantitative manner, that $f(x)$ can be made arbitrarily close to L by taking x to be sufficiently close to a (but $x \neq a$). This means that $f(x)$ can be made to lie within any preassigned distance from L (traditionally denoted by ε, the Greek letter epsilon) by requiring that x be within a specified distance δ (the Greek letter delta) from a. That is, $|f(x) - L| < \varepsilon$ when $|x - a| < \delta$ and $x \neq a$. Notice that we can stipulate that $x \neq a$ by writing $0 < |x - a|$. The resulting precise definition of a limit is as follows.

---

4   **DEFINITION**   Let f be a function defined on some open interval that contains the number a, except possibly at a itself. Then we say that the **limit of** $f(x)$ **as** x **approaches** a **is** L, and we write

$$\lim_{x \to a} f(x) = L$$

if for every number $\varepsilon > 0$ there is a corresponding number $\delta > 0$ such that

$$\text{if} \quad 0 < |x - a| < \delta \quad \text{then} \quad |f(x) - L| < \varepsilon$$

Definition 4 is illustrated in Figures 12–14. If a number $\varepsilon > 0$ is given, then we draw the horizontal lines $y = L + \varepsilon$ and $y = L - \varepsilon$ and the graph of f. (See Figure 12.) If $\lim_{x \to a} f(x) = L$, then we can find a number $\delta > 0$ such that if we restrict x to lie in the interval $(a - \delta, a + \delta)$ and take $x \neq a$, then the curve $y = f(x)$ lies

In Module 1.3/1.6 you can explore the precise definition of a limit both graphically and numerically.

between the lines $y = L - \varepsilon$ and $y = L + \varepsilon$. (See Figure 13.) You can see that if such a δ has been found, then any smaller δ will also work.

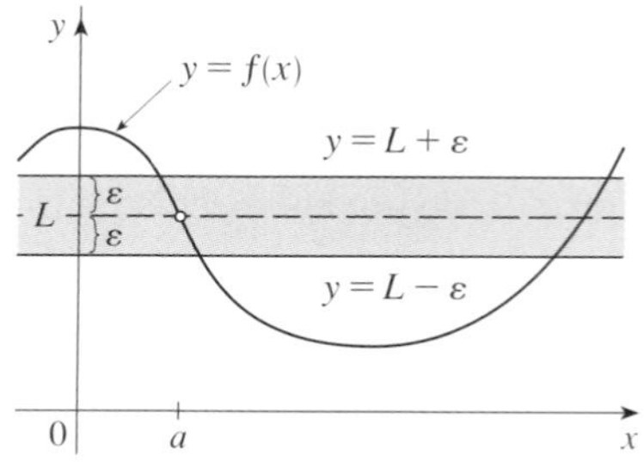

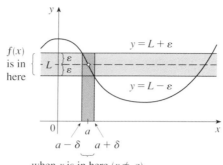

FIGURE 12

FIGURE 13

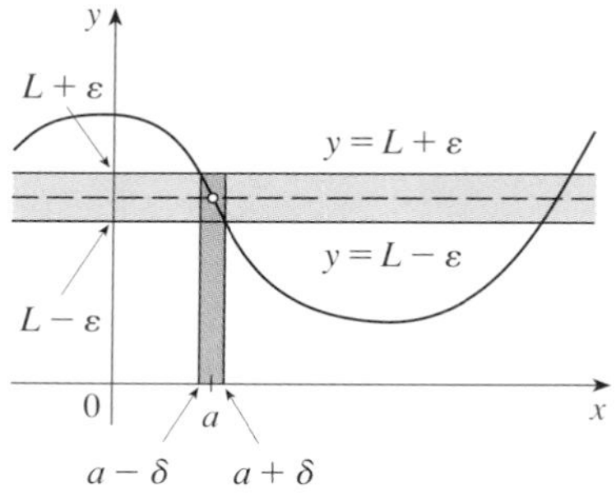

when x is in here $(x \neq a)$

FIGURE 14

It's important to realize that the process illustrated in Figures 12 and 13 must work for *every* positive number ε, no matter how small it is chosen. Figure 14 shows that if a smaller ε is chosen, then a smaller δ may be required.

In proving limit statements it may be helpful to think of the definition of limit as a challenge. First it challenges you with a number ε. Then you must be able to produce a suitable δ. You have to be able to do this for *every* $\varepsilon > 0$, not just a particular ε.

▼ EXAMPLE 9 Prove that $\lim_{x \to 3} (4x - 5) = 7$.

■ Figure 15 shows the geometry behind Example 9.

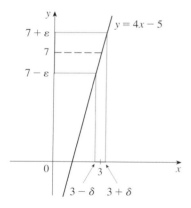

FIGURE 15

SOLUTION Let ε be a given positive number. According to Definition 4 with $a = 3$ and $L = 7$, we need to find a number δ such that

$$\text{if} \quad 0 < |x - 3| < \delta \quad \text{then} \quad |(4x - 5) - 7| < \varepsilon$$

But $|(4x - 5) - 7| = |4x - 12| = |4(x - 3)| = 4|x - 3|$. Therefore, we want:

$$\text{if} \quad 0 < |x - 3| < \delta \quad \text{then} \quad 4|x - 3| < \varepsilon$$

We can choose δ to be $\varepsilon/4$ because

$$\text{if} \quad 0 < |x - 3| < \delta = \frac{\varepsilon}{4} \quad \text{then} \quad 4|x - 3| < 4\left(\frac{\varepsilon}{4}\right) = \varepsilon$$

Therefore, by the definition of a limit,

$$\lim_{x \to 3} (4x - 5) = 7$$

For a left-hand limit we restrict x so that $x < a$, so in Definition 4 we replace $0 < |x - a| < \delta$ by $a - \delta < x < a$. Similarly, for a right-hand limit we use $a < x < a + \delta$.

▼ EXAMPLE 10 Prove that $\lim_{x \to 0^+} \sqrt{x} = 0$.

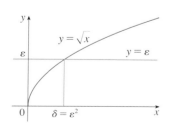

FIGURE 16

SOLUTION Let ε be a given positive number. We want to find a number δ such that

$$\text{if} \quad 0 < x < \delta \quad \text{then} \quad |\sqrt{x} - 0| < \varepsilon \quad \text{that is} \quad \sqrt{x} < \varepsilon$$

But $\sqrt{x} < \varepsilon \iff x < \varepsilon^2$. So if we choose $\delta = \varepsilon^2$ and $0 < x < \delta = \varepsilon^2$, then $\sqrt{x} < \varepsilon$. (See Figure 16.) This shows that $\sqrt{x} \to 0$ as $x \to 0^+$.

1.3 | EXERCISES

1. If a ball is thrown into the air with a velocity of 40 ft/s, its height in feet t seconds later is given by $y = 40t - 16t^2$.
  (a) Find the average velocity for the time period beginning when $t = 2$ and lasting
    (i) 0.5 second   (ii) 0.1 second
    (iii) 0.05 second   (iv) 0.01 second
  (b) Estimate the instantaneous velocity when $t = 2$.

2. If an arrow is shot upward on the moon with a velocity of 58 m/s, its height in meters t seconds later is given by $h = 58t - 0.83t^2$.
  (a) Find the average velocity over the given time intervals:
    (i) [1, 2]   (ii) [1, 1.5]   (iii) [1, 1.1]
    (iv) [1, 1.01]   (v) [1, 1.001]
  (b) Estimate the instantaneous velocity when $t = 1$.

3. Use the given graph of f to state the value of each quantity, if it exists. If it does not exist, explain why.
  (a) $\lim\limits_{x \to 1^-} f(x)$ (b) $\lim\limits_{x \to 1^+} f(x)$ (c) $\lim\limits_{x \to 1} f(x)$
  (d) $\lim\limits_{x \to 5} f(x)$ (e) $f(5)$

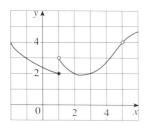

4. For the function f whose graph is given, state the value of each quantity, if it exists. If it does not exist, explain why.
  (a) $\lim\limits_{x \to 0} f(x)$ (b) $\lim\limits_{x \to 3^-} f(x)$ (c) $\lim\limits_{x \to 3^+} f(x)$
  (d) $\lim\limits_{x \to 3} f(x)$ (e) $f(3)$

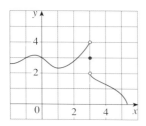

5. For the function g whose graph is given, state the value of each quantity, if it exists. If it does not exist, explain why.
  (a) $\lim\limits_{t \to 0^-} g(t)$ (b) $\lim\limits_{t \to 0^+} g(t)$ (c) $\lim\limits_{t \to 0} g(t)$
  (d) $\lim\limits_{t \to 2^-} g(t)$ (e) $\lim\limits_{t \to 2^+} g(t)$ (f) $\lim\limits_{t \to 2} g(t)$

  (g) $g(2)$ (h) $\lim\limits_{t \to 4} g(t)$

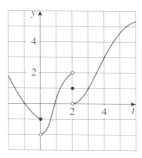

6. Sketch the graph of the following function and use it to determine the values of a for which $\lim\limits_{x \to a} f(x)$ exists:

$$f(x) = \begin{cases} 2 - x & \text{if } x < -1 \\ x & \text{if } -1 \leq x < 1 \\ (x - 1)^2 & \text{if } x \geq 1 \end{cases}$$

7–10 ▪ Sketch the graph of an example of a function f that satisfies all of the given conditions.

7. $\lim\limits_{x \to 1^-} f(x) = 2$, $\lim\limits_{x \to 1^+} f(x) = -2$, $f(1) = 2$

8. $\lim\limits_{x \to 0^-} f(x) = 1$, $\lim\limits_{x \to 0^+} f(x) = -1$, $\lim\limits_{x \to 2^-} f(x) = 0$,
  $\lim\limits_{x \to 2^+} f(x) = 1$, $f(2) = 1$, $f(0)$ is undefined

9. $\lim\limits_{x \to 3^+} f(x) = 4$, $\lim\limits_{x \to 3^-} f(x) = 2$, $\lim\limits_{x \to -2} f(x) = 2$,
  $f(3) = 3$, $f(-2) = 1$

10. $\lim\limits_{x \to 1} f(x) = 3$, $\lim\limits_{x \to 4^-} f(x) = 3$, $\lim\limits_{x \to 4^+} f(x) = -3$,
  $f(1) = 1$, $f(4) = -1$

▪ ▪ ▪ ▪ ▪ ▪ ▪ ▪ ▪ ▪ ▪ ▪

11–14 ▪ Guess the value of the limit (if it exists) by evaluating the function at the given numbers (correct to six decimal places).

11. $\lim\limits_{x \to 2} \dfrac{x^2 - 2x}{x^2 - x - 2}$
  $x = 2.5, 2.1, 2.05, 2.01, 2.005, 2.001$,
  $1.9, 1.95, 1.99, 1.995, 1.999$

12. $\lim\limits_{x \to -1} \dfrac{x^2 - 2x}{x^2 - x - 2}$
  $x = 0, -0.5, -0.9, -0.95, -0.99, -0.999$,
  $-2, -1.5, -1.1, -1.01, -1.001$

13. $\lim\limits_{x \to 0} \dfrac{\sin x}{x + \tan x}$
  $x = \pm 1, \pm 0.5, \pm 0.2, \pm 0.1, \pm 0.05, \pm 0.01$

14. $\lim_{x \to 16} \dfrac{\sqrt{x} - 4}{x - 16}$, $\quad x = 17, 16.5, 16.1, 16.05, 16.01,$

$\quad$ 15, 15.5, 15.9, 15.95, 15.99

■　■　■　■　■　■　■　■　■　■　■

15–18 ■ Use a table of values to estimate the value of the limit. If you have a graphing device, use it to confirm your result graphically.

15. $\lim_{x \to 0} \dfrac{\sqrt{x + 4} - 2}{x}$

16. $\lim_{x \to 0} \dfrac{\tan 3x}{\tan 5x}$

17. $\lim_{x \to 1} \dfrac{x^6 - 1}{x^{10} - 1}$

18. $\lim_{x \to 0} \dfrac{9^x - 5^x}{x}$

■　■　■　■　■　■　■　■　■　■　■

19. (a) By graphing the function $f(x) = (\tan 4x)/x$ and zooming in toward the point where the graph crosses the y-axis, estimate the value of $\lim_{x \to 0} f(x)$.

(b) Check your answer in part (a) by evaluating $f(x)$ for values of x that approach 0.

20. (a) Estimate the value of

$$\lim_{x \to 0} \frac{6^x - 2^x}{x}$$

by graphing the function $y = (6^x - 2^x)/x$. State your answer correct to two decimal places.

(b) Check your answer in part (a) by evaluating $f(x)$ for values of x that approach 0.

21. (a) Evaluate the function $f(x) = x^2 - (2^x/1000)$ for $x = 1$, 0.8, 0.6, 0.4, 0.2, 0.1, and 0.05, and guess the value of

$$\lim_{x \to 0} \left(x^2 - \frac{2^x}{1000} \right)$$

(b) Evaluate $f(x)$ for $x = 0.04, 0.02, 0.01, 0.005, 0.003$, and 0.001. Guess again.

22. (a) Evaluate $h(x) = (\tan x - x)/x^3$ for $x = 1, 0.5, 0.1, 0.05$, 0.01, and 0.005.

(b) Guess the value of $\lim_{x \to 0} \dfrac{\tan x - x}{x^3}$.

(c) Evaluate $h(x)$ for successively smaller values of x until you finally reach 0 values for $h(x)$. Are you still confident that your guess in part (b) is correct? Explain why you eventually obtained 0 values. (In Section 3.7 a method for evaluating the limit will be explained.)

(d) Graph the function h in the viewing rectangle $[-1, 1]$ by $[0, 1]$. Then zoom in toward the point where the graph crosses the y-axis to estimate the limit of $h(x)$ as x approaches 0. Continue to zoom in until you observe distortions in the graph of h. Compare with the results of part (c).

23. Use the given graph of $f(x) = 1/x$ to find a number δ such that

$$\text{if} \quad |x - 2| < \delta \quad \text{then} \quad \left| \frac{1}{x} - 0.5 \right| < 0.2$$

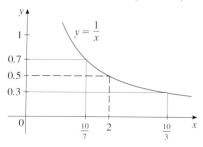

24. Use the given graph of $f(x) = x^2$ to find a number δ such that

$$\text{if} \quad |x - 1| < \delta \quad \text{then} \quad |x^2 - 1| < \tfrac{1}{2}$$

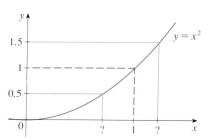

25. Use a graph to find a number δ such that

$$\text{if} \quad |x - 2| < \delta \quad \text{then} \quad |\sqrt{4x + 1} - 3| < 0.5$$

26. Use a graph to find a number δ such that

$$\text{if} \quad \left| x - \frac{\pi}{6} \right| < \delta \quad \text{then} \quad |\sin x - \tfrac{1}{2}| < 0.1$$

27. A machinist is required to manufacture a circular metal disk with area 1000 cm².

(a) What radius produces such a disk?

(b) If the machinist is allowed an error tolerance of ± 5 cm² in the area of the disk, how close to the ideal radius in part (a) must the machinist control the radius?

(c) In terms of the ε, δ definition of $\lim_{x \to a} f(x) = L$, what is x? What is $f(x)$? What is a? What is L? What value of ε is given? What is the corresponding value of δ?

28. A crystal growth furnace is used in research to determine how best to manufacture crystals used in electronic components for the space shuttle. For proper growth of the crystal, the temperature must be controlled accurately by adjusting the input power. Suppose the relationship is given by

$$T(w) = 0.1w^2 + 2.155w + 20$$

where T is the temperature in degrees Celsius and w is the power input in watts.

(a) How much power is needed to maintain the temperature at 200°C ?

(b) If the temperature is allowed to vary from 200°C by up to ±1°C , what range of wattage is allowed for the input power?

(c) In terms of the ε, δ definition of $\lim_{x \to a} f(x) = L$, what is x? What is $f(x)$? What is a? What is L? What value of ε is given? What is the corresponding value of δ?

29–32 ■ Prove the statement using the ε, δ definition of limit and illustrate with a diagram like Figure 15.

29. $\lim_{x \to 1} (2x + 3) = 5$

30. $\lim_{x \to -2} \left(\tfrac{1}{2}x + 3\right) = 2$

31. $\lim_{x \to -3} (1 - 4x) = 13$

32. $\lim_{x \to 4} (7 - 3x) = -5$

■ ■ ■ ■ ■ ■ ■ ■ ■ ■ ■

33–44 ■ Prove the statement using the ε, δ definition of limit.

33. $\lim_{x \to 3} \dfrac{x}{5} = \dfrac{3}{5}$

34. $\lim_{x \to 6} \left(\dfrac{x}{4} + 3\right) = \dfrac{9}{2}$

35. $\lim_{x \to -5} \left(4 - \dfrac{3x}{5}\right) = 7$

36. $\lim_{x \to 3} \dfrac{x^2 + x - 12}{x - 3} = 7$

37. $\lim_{x \to a} x = a$

38. $\lim_{x \to a} c = c$

39. $\lim_{x \to 0} x^2 = 0$

40. $\lim_{x \to 0} x^3 = 0$

41. $\lim_{x \to 0} |x| = 0$

42. $\lim_{x \to 9^-} \sqrt[4]{9 - x} = 0$

43. $\lim_{x \to 3} x^2 = 9$ [*Hint:* Write $|x^2 - 9| = |x + 3||x - 3|$. Show that if $|x - 3| < 1$, then $|x + 3| < 7$. If you let δ be the smaller of the numbers 1 and $\varepsilon/7$, show that this δ works.]

44. $\lim_{x \to 3} (x^2 + x - 4) = 8$ [*Hint:* If $|x - 3| < 1$, what can you say about $|x + 4|$?]

■ ■ ■ ■ ■ ■ ■ ■ ■ ■ ■ ■

[CAS] **45.** (a) For the limit $\lim_{x \to 1} (x^3 + x + 1) = 3$, use a graph to find a value of δ that corresponds to $\varepsilon = 0.4$.

(b) By using a computer algebra system to solve the cubic equation $x^3 + x + 1 = 3 + \varepsilon$, find the largest possible value of δ that works for any given $\varepsilon > 0$.

(c) Put $\varepsilon = 0.4$ in your answer to part (b) and compare with your answer to part (a).

46. If H is the Heaviside function defined in Example 6, prove, using Definition 4, that $\lim_{t \to 0} H(t)$ does not exist. [*Hint:* Use an indirect proof as follows. Suppose that the limit is L. Take $\varepsilon = \tfrac{1}{2}$ in the definition of a limit and try to arrive at a contradiction.]

| **1.4** | **CALCULATING LIMITS** |

In Section 1.3 we used calculators and graphs to guess the values of limits, but we saw that such methods don't always lead to the correct answer. In this section we use the following properties of limits, called the *Limit Laws*, to calculate limits.

LIMIT LAWS Suppose that c is a constant and the limits

$$\lim_{x \to a} f(x) \qquad \text{and} \qquad \lim_{x \to a} g(x)$$

exist. Then

1. $\lim_{x \to a} [f(x) + g(x)] = \lim_{x \to a} f(x) + \lim_{x \to a} g(x)$

2. $\lim_{x \to a} [f(x) - g(x)] = \lim_{x \to a} f(x) - \lim_{x \to a} g(x)$

3. $\lim_{x \to a} [cf(x)] = c \lim_{x \to a} f(x)$

4. $\lim_{x \to a} [f(x)g(x)] = \lim_{x \to a} f(x) \cdot \lim_{x \to a} g(x)$

5. $\lim_{x \to a} \dfrac{f(x)}{g(x)} = \dfrac{\lim_{x \to a} f(x)}{\lim_{x \to a} g(x)}$ if $\lim_{x \to a} g(x) \neq 0$

These five laws can be stated verbally as follows:

Sum Law

I. The limit of a sum is the sum of the limits.

Difference Law

2. The limit of a difference is the difference of the limits.

Constant Multiple Law

3. The limit of a constant times a function is the constant times the limit of the function.

Product Law

4. The limit of a product is the product of the limits.

Quotient Law

5. The limit of a quotient is the quotient of the limits (provided that the limit of the denominator is not 0).

It is easy to believe that these properties are true. For instance, if $f(x)$ is close to L and $g(x)$ is close to M, it is reasonable to conclude that $f(x) + g(x)$ is close to $L + M$. This gives us an intuitive basis for believing that Law 1 is true. All of these laws can be proved using the precise definition of a limit. (See Appendix B.)

If we use the Product Law repeatedly with $g(x) = f(x)$, we obtain the following law.

Power Law

6. $\displaystyle \lim_{x \to a} [f(x)]^n = \left[\lim_{x \to a} f(x) \right]^n$ where n is a positive integer

In applying these six limit laws, we need to use two special limits:

7. $\displaystyle \lim_{x \to a} c = c$ **8.** $\displaystyle \lim_{x \to a} x = a$

These limits are obvious from an intuitive point of view (state them in words or draw graphs of $y = c$ and $y = x$), but they can be proved from the precise definition. (See Exercises 37 and 38 in Section 1.3.)

If we now put $f(x) = x$ in Law 6 and use Law 8, we get another useful special limit.

9. $\displaystyle \lim_{x \to a} x^n = a^n$ where n is a positive integer

A similar limit holds for roots as follows.

10. $\displaystyle \lim_{x \to a} \sqrt[n]{x} = \sqrt[n]{a}$ where n is a positive integer

(If n is even, we assume that $a > 0$.)

More generally, we have the following law.

Root Law

II. $\displaystyle \lim_{x \to a} \sqrt[n]{f(x)} = \sqrt[n]{\lim_{x \to a} f(x)}$ where n is a positive integer

$\left[\text{If } n \text{ is even, we assume that } \lim_{x \to a} f(x) > 0. \right]$

EXAMPLE 1 Evaluate the following limits and justify each step.

(a) $\lim_{x \to 5} (2x^2 - 3x + 4)$ (b) $\lim_{x \to -2} \dfrac{x^3 + 2x^2 - 1}{5 - 3x}$

SOLUTION

(a)
$$\lim_{x \to 5} (2x^2 - 3x + 4) = \lim_{x \to 5} (2x^2) - \lim_{x \to 5} (3x) + \lim_{x \to 5} 4 \qquad \text{(by Laws 2 and 1)}$$

$$= 2 \lim_{x \to 5} x^2 - 3 \lim_{x \to 5} x + \lim_{x \to 5} 4 \qquad \text{(by 3)}$$

$$= 2(5^2) - 3(5) + 4 \qquad \text{(by 9, 8, and 7)}$$

$$= 39$$

(b) We start by using Law 5, but its use is fully justified only at the final stage when we see that the limits of the numerator and denominator exist and the limit of the denominator is not 0.

$$\lim_{x \to -2} \frac{x^3 + 2x^2 - 1}{5 - 3x} = \frac{\lim_{x \to -2} (x^3 + 2x^2 - 1)}{\lim_{x \to -2} (5 - 3x)} \qquad \text{(by Law 5)}$$

$$= \frac{\lim_{x \to -2} x^3 + 2 \lim_{x \to -2} x^2 - \lim_{x \to -2} 1}{\lim_{x \to -2} 5 - 3 \lim_{x \to -2} x} \qquad \text{(by 1, 2, and 3)}$$

$$= \frac{(-2)^3 + 2(-2)^2 - 1}{5 - 3(-2)} \qquad \text{(by 9, 8, and 7)}$$

$$= -\frac{1}{11}$$ ∎

NOTE If we let $f(x) = 2x^2 - 3x + 4$, then $f(5) = 39$. In other words, we would have gotten the correct answer in Example 1(a) by substituting 5 for x. Similarly, direct substitution provides the correct answer in part (b). The functions in Example 1 are a polynomial and a rational function, respectively, and similar use of the Limit Laws proves that direct substitution always works for such functions (see Exercises 49 and 50). We state this fact as follows.

> **DIRECT SUBSTITUTION PROPERTY** If f is a polynomial or a rational function and a is in the domain of f, then
>
> $$\lim_{x \to a} f(x) = f(a)$$

The trigonometric functions also enjoy the Direct Substitution Property. We know from the definitions of $\sin \theta$ and $\cos \theta$ that the coordinates of the point P in Figure 1 are $(\cos \theta, \sin \theta)$. As $\theta \to 0$, we see that P approaches the point $(1, 0)$ and so $\cos \theta \to 1$ and $\sin \theta \to 0$. Thus

$$\boxed{1} \qquad \lim_{\theta \to 0} \cos \theta = 1 \qquad \lim_{\theta \to 0} \sin \theta = 0$$

Since $\cos 0 = 1$ and $\sin 0 = 0$, the equations in (1) assert that the cosine and sine

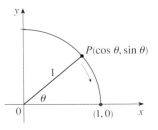

FIGURE 1

▪ Another way to establish the limits in (1) is to use the inequality $\sin\theta < \theta$ (for $\theta > 0$), which is proved on page 42.

functions satisfy the Direct Substitution Property at 0. The addition formulas for cosine and sine can then be used to deduce that these functions satisfy the Direct Substitution Property everywhere (see Exercises 51 and 52). In other words, for any real number a,

$$\lim_{\theta\to a}\sin\theta = \sin a \qquad \lim_{\theta\to a}\cos\theta = \cos a$$

This enables us to evaluate certain limits quite simply. For example,

$$\lim_{x\to\pi} x\cos x = \left(\lim_{x\to\pi} x\right)\left(\lim_{x\to\pi}\cos x\right) = \pi\cdot\cos\pi = -\pi$$

Functions with the Direct Substitution Property are called *continuous at a* and will be studied in Section 1.5. However, not all limits can be evaluated by direct substitution, as the following examples show.

EXAMPLE 2 Find $\lim\limits_{x\to 1}\dfrac{x^2 - 1}{x - 1}$.

SOLUTION Let $f(x) = (x^2 - 1)/(x - 1)$. We can't find the limit by substituting $x = 1$ because $f(1)$ isn't defined. Nor can we apply the Quotient Law, because the limit of the denominator is 0. Instead, we need to do some preliminary algebra. We factor the numerator as a difference of squares:

$$\frac{x^2 - 1}{x - 1} = \frac{(x - 1)(x + 1)}{x - 1}$$

The numerator and denominator have a common factor of $x - 1$. When we take the limit as x approaches 1, we have $x \neq 1$ and so $x - 1 \neq 0$. Therefore, we can cancel the common factor and compute the limit as follows:

$$\lim_{x\to 1}\frac{x^2 - 1}{x - 1} = \lim_{x\to 1}\frac{(x - 1)(x + 1)}{x - 1}$$
$$= \lim_{x\to 1}(x + 1)$$
$$= 1 + 1 = 2 \qquad\blacksquare$$

NOTE In Example 2 we were able to compute the limit by replacing the given function $f(x) = (x^2 - 1)/(x - 1)$ by a simpler function, $g(x) = x + 1$, with the same limit. This is valid because $f(x) = g(x)$ except when $x = 1$, and in computing a limit as x approaches 1 we don't consider what happens when x is actually *equal* to 1. In general, we have the following useful fact.

> If $f(x) = g(x)$ when $x \neq a$, then $\lim\limits_{x\to a} f(x) = \lim\limits_{x\to a} g(x)$, provided the limits exist.

EXAMPLE 3 Find $\lim\limits_{x\to 1} g(x)$ where

$$g(x) = \begin{cases} x + 1 & \text{if } x \neq 1 \\ \pi & \text{if } x = 1 \end{cases}$$

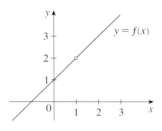

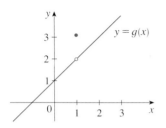

FIGURE 2

The graphs of the functions f (from Example 2) and g (from Example 3)

SOLUTION Here g is defined at $x = 1$ and $g(1) = \pi$, but the value of a limit as x approaches 1 does not depend on the value of the function at 1. Since $g(x) = x + 1$ for $x \neq 1$, we have

$$\lim_{x \to 1} g(x) = \lim_{x \to 1} (x + 1) = 2$$ ▪

Note that the values of the functions in Examples 2 and 3 are identical except when $x = 1$ (see Figure 2) and so they have the same limit as x approaches 1.

Ⅴ EXAMPLE 4 Evaluate $\lim\limits_{h \to 0} \dfrac{(3 + h)^2 - 9}{h}$.

SOLUTION If we define

$$F(h) = \frac{(3 + h)^2 - 9}{h}$$

then, as in Example 2, we can't compute $\lim_{h \to 0} F(h)$ by letting $h = 0$ since $F(0)$ is undefined. But if we simplify $F(h)$ algebraically, we find that

$$F(h) = \frac{(9 + 6h + h^2) - 9}{h} = \frac{6h + h^2}{h} = 6 + h$$

(Recall that we consider only $h \neq 0$ when letting h approach 0.) Thus

$$\lim_{h \to 0} \frac{(3 + h)^2 - 9}{h} = \lim_{h \to 0} (6 + h) = 6$$ ▪

EXAMPLE 5 Find $\lim\limits_{t \to 0} \dfrac{\sqrt{t^2 + 9} - 3}{t^2}$.

SOLUTION We can't apply the Quotient Law immediately, since the limit of the denominator is 0. Here the preliminary algebra consists of rationalizing the numerator:

$$\lim_{t \to 0} \frac{\sqrt{t^2 + 9} - 3}{t^2} = \lim_{t \to 0} \frac{\sqrt{t^2 + 9} - 3}{t^2} \cdot \frac{\sqrt{t^2 + 9} + 3}{\sqrt{t^2 + 9} + 3}$$

$$= \lim_{t \to 0} \frac{(t^2 + 9) - 9}{t^2 \left(\sqrt{t^2 + 9} + 3 \right)} = \lim_{t \to 0} \frac{t^2}{t^2 \left(\sqrt{t^2 + 9} + 3 \right)}$$

$$= \lim_{t \to 0} \frac{1}{\sqrt{t^2 + 9} + 3} = \frac{1}{\sqrt{\lim_{t \to 0} (t^2 + 9)} + 3} = \frac{1}{3 + 3} = \frac{1}{6}$$

This calculation confirms the guess that we made in Example 3 in Section 1.3. ▪

Some limits are best calculated by first finding the left- and right-hand limits. The following theorem is a reminder of what we discovered in Section 1.3. It says that a two-sided limit exists if and only if both of the one-sided limits exist and are equal.

2 THEOREM $\lim\limits_{x \to a} f(x) = L$ if and only if $\lim\limits_{x \to a^-} f(x) = L = \lim\limits_{x \to a^+} f(x)$

When computing one-sided limits, we use the fact that the Limit Laws also hold for one-sided limits.

EXAMPLE 6 Show that $\lim\limits_{x \to 0} |x| = 0$.

SOLUTION Recall that

$$|x| = \begin{cases} x & \text{if } x \geq 0 \\ -x & \text{if } x < 0 \end{cases}$$

Since $|x| = x$ for $x > 0$, we have

■ The result of Example 6 looks plausible from Figure 3.

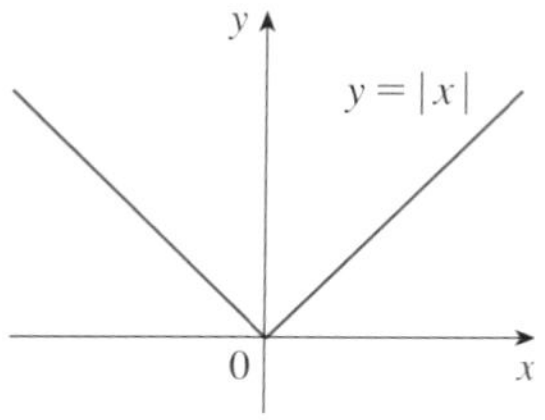

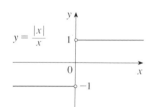

$$\lim_{x \to 0^+} |x| = \lim_{x \to 0^+} x = 0$$

For $x < 0$ we have $|x| = -x$ and so

$$\lim_{x \to 0^-} |x| = \lim_{x \to 0^-} (-x) = 0$$

Therefore, by Theorem 2,

$$\lim_{x \to 0} |x| = 0$$

FIGURE 3

■ **EXAMPLE 7** Prove that $\lim\limits_{x \to 0} \dfrac{|x|}{x}$ does not exist.

SOLUTION
$$\lim_{x \to 0^+} \frac{|x|}{x} = \lim_{x \to 0^+} \frac{x}{x} = \lim_{x \to 0^+} 1 = 1$$

$$\lim_{x \to 0^-} \frac{|x|}{x} = \lim_{x \to 0^-} \frac{-x}{x} = \lim_{x \to 0^-} (-1) = -1$$

Since the right- and left-hand limits are different, it follows from Theorem 2 that $\lim_{x \to 0} |x|/x$ does not exist. The graph of the function $f(x) = |x|/x$ is shown in Figure 4 and supports the one-sided limits that we found.

FIGURE 4

■ Other notations for $[\![x]\!]$ are $[x]$ and $\lfloor x \rfloor$. The greatest integer function is sometimes called the *floor function*.

EXAMPLE 8 The **greatest integer function** is defined by $[\![x]\!] = $ the largest integer that is less than or equal to x. (For instance, $[\![4]\!] = 4$, $[\![4.8]\!] = 4$, $[\![\pi]\!] = 3$, $[\![\sqrt{2}\,]\!] = 1$, $[\![-\frac{1}{2}]\!] = -1$.) Show that $\lim_{x \to 3} [\![x]\!]$ does not exist.

SOLUTION The graph of the greatest integer function is shown in Figure 5. Since $[\![x]\!] = 3$ for $3 \leq x < 4$, we have

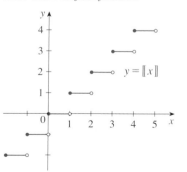

$$\lim_{x \to 3^+} [\![x]\!] = \lim_{x \to 3^+} 3 = 3$$

Since $[\![x]\!] = 2$ for $2 \leq x < 3$, we have

$$\lim_{x \to 3^-} [\![x]\!] = \lim_{x \to 3^-} 2 = 2$$

FIGURE 5
Greatest integer function

Because these one-sided limits are not equal, $\lim_{x \to 3} [\![x]\!]$ does not exist by Theorem 2.

The next two theorems give two additional properties of limits. Their proofs can be found in Appendix B.

---

3 THEOREM If $f(x) \leq g(x)$ when x is near a (except possibly at a) and the limits of f and g both exist as x approaches a, then

$$\lim_{x \to a} f(x) \leq \lim_{x \to a} g(x)$$

---

4 THE SQUEEZE THEOREM If $f(x) \leq g(x) \leq h(x)$ when x is near a (except possibly at a) and

$$\lim_{x \to a} f(x) = \lim_{x \to a} h(x) = L$$

then

$$\lim_{x \to a} g(x) = L$$

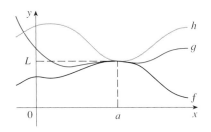

FIGURE 6

The Squeeze Theorem, which is sometimes called the Sandwich Theorem or the Pinching Theorem, is illustrated by Figure 6. It says that if $g(x)$ is squeezed between $f(x)$ and $h(x)$ near a, and if f and h have the same limit L at a, then g is forced to have the same limit L at a.

▼ EXAMPLE 9 Show that $\lim\limits_{x \to 0} x^2 \sin \dfrac{1}{x} = 0$.

SOLUTION First note that we **cannot** use

$$\lim_{x \to 0} x^2 \sin \frac{1}{x} = \lim_{x \to 0} x^2 \cdot \lim_{x \to 0} \sin \frac{1}{x}$$

because $\lim_{x \to 0} \sin(1/x)$ does not exist (see Example 5 in Section 1.3). However, since

$$-1 \leq \sin \frac{1}{x} \leq 1$$

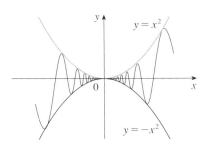

FIGURE 7
$y = x^2 \sin(1/x)$

we have, as illustrated by Figure 7,

$$-x^2 \leq x^2 \sin \frac{1}{x} \leq x^2$$

We know that

$$\lim_{x \to 0} x^2 = 0 \qquad \text{and} \qquad \lim_{x \to 0} (-x^2) = 0$$

Taking $f(x) = -x^2$, $g(x) = x^2 \sin(1/x)$, and $h(x) = x^2$ in the Squeeze Theorem, we obtain

$$\lim_{x \to 0} x^2 \sin \frac{1}{x} = 0$$

■

In Example 4 in Section 1.3 we made the guess, on the basis of numerical and graphical evidence, that

5

$$\lim_{\theta \to 0} \frac{\sin \theta}{\theta} = 1$$

We can prove Equation 5 with help from the Squeeze Theorem. Assume first that θ lies between 0 and $\pi/2$. Figure 8(a) shows a sector of a circle with center O, central angle θ, and radius 1. BC is drawn perpendicular to OA. By the definition of radian measure, we have arc $AB = \theta$. Also, $|BC| = |OB| \sin \theta = \sin \theta$. From the diagram we see that

$$|BC| < |AB| < \text{arc } AB$$

Therefore $\qquad \sin \theta < \theta \qquad$ so $\qquad \dfrac{\sin \theta}{\theta} < 1$

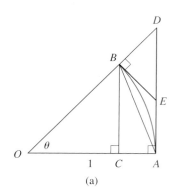

(a)

Let the tangent lines at A and B intersect at E. You can see from Figure 8(b) that the circumference of a circle is smaller than the length of a circumscribed polygon, and so arc $AB < |AE| + |EB|$. Thus

$$\theta = \text{arc } AB < |AE| + |EB| < |AE| + |ED|$$

$$= |AD| = |OA| \tan \theta = \tan \theta$$

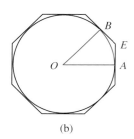

(b)

FIGURE 8

(In Appendix B the inequality $\theta \leqslant \tan \theta$ is proved directly from the definition of the length of an arc without resorting to geometric intuition as we did here.) Therefore, we have

$$\theta < \frac{\sin \theta}{\cos \theta} \qquad \text{and so} \qquad \cos \theta < \frac{\sin \theta}{\theta} < 1$$

We know that $\lim_{\theta \to 0} 1 = 1$ and $\lim_{\theta \to 0} \cos \theta = 1$, so by the Squeeze Theorem, we have

$$\lim_{\theta \to 0^+} \frac{\sin \theta}{\theta} = 1$$

But the function $(\sin \theta)/\theta$ is an even function, so its right and left limits must be equal. Hence, we have

$$\lim_{\theta \to 0} \frac{\sin \theta}{\theta} = 1$$

so we have proved Equation 5.

EXAMPLE 10 Find $\lim\limits_{x \to 0} \dfrac{\sin 7x}{4x}$.

SOLUTION In order to apply Equation 5, we first rewrite the function by multiplying and dividing by 7:

Note that $\sin 7x \neq 7 \sin x$.

$$\frac{\sin 7x}{4x} = \frac{7}{4}\left(\frac{\sin 7x}{7x}\right)$$

Notice that as $x \to 0$, we have $7x \to 0$, and so, by Equation 5 with $\theta = 7x$,

$$\lim_{x \to 0} \frac{\sin 7x}{7x} = \lim_{7x \to 0} \frac{\sin(7x)}{7x} = 1$$

Thus

$$\lim_{x \to 0} \frac{\sin 7x}{4x} = \lim_{x \to 0} \frac{7}{4}\left(\frac{\sin 7x}{7x}\right)$$

$$= \frac{7}{4} \lim_{x \to 0} \frac{\sin 7x}{7x} = \frac{7}{4} \cdot 1 = \frac{7}{4} \quad ∎$$

EXAMPLE 11 Evaluate $\displaystyle\lim_{\theta \to 0} \frac{\cos \theta - 1}{\theta}$.

SOLUTION

▪ We multiply numerator and denominator by $\cos \theta + 1$ in order to put the function in a form in which we can use the limits we know.

$$\lim_{\theta \to 0} \frac{\cos \theta - 1}{\theta} = \lim_{\theta \to 0}\left(\frac{\cos \theta - 1}{\theta} \cdot \frac{\cos \theta + 1}{\cos \theta + 1}\right) = \lim_{\theta \to 0} \frac{\cos^2\theta - 1}{\theta(\cos \theta + 1)}$$

$$= \lim_{\theta \to 0} \frac{-\sin^2\theta}{\theta(\cos \theta + 1)} = -\lim_{\theta \to 0}\left(\frac{\sin \theta}{\theta} \cdot \frac{\sin \theta}{\cos \theta + 1}\right)$$

$$= -\lim_{\theta \to 0} \frac{\sin \theta}{\theta} \cdot \lim_{\theta \to 0} \frac{\sin \theta}{\cos \theta + 1}$$

$$= -1 \cdot \left(\frac{0}{1 + 1}\right) = 0 \qquad \text{(by Equation 5)} \quad ∎$$

1.4 EXERCISES

1. Given that

$$\lim_{x \to a} f(x) = -3 \qquad \lim_{x \to a} g(x) = 0 \qquad \lim_{x \to a} h(x) = 8$$

find the limits that exist. If the limit does not exist, explain why.

(a) $\displaystyle\lim_{x \to a}\,[f(x) + h(x)]$

(b) $\displaystyle\lim_{x \to a}\,[f(x)]^2$

(c) $\displaystyle\lim_{x \to a} \sqrt[3]{h(x)}$

(d) $\displaystyle\lim_{x \to a} \frac{1}{f(x)}$

(e) $\displaystyle\lim_{x \to a} \frac{f(x)}{h(x)}$

(f) $\displaystyle\lim_{x \to a} \frac{g(x)}{f(x)}$

(g) $\displaystyle\lim_{x \to a} \frac{f(x)}{g(x)}$

(h) $\displaystyle\lim_{x \to a} \frac{2f(x)}{h(x) - f(x)}$

2. The graphs of f and g are given. Use them to evaluate each limit, if it exists. If the limit does not exist, explain why.

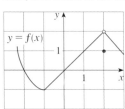
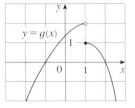

(a) $\displaystyle\lim_{x \to 2}\,[f(x) + g(x)]$

(b) $\displaystyle\lim_{x \to 1}\,[f(x) + g(x)]$

(c) $\displaystyle\lim_{x \to 0}\,[f(x)g(x)]$

(d) $\displaystyle\lim_{x \to -1} \frac{f(x)}{g(x)}$

(e) $\displaystyle\lim_{x \to 2}\,[x^3 f(x)]$

(f) $\displaystyle\lim_{x \to 1} \sqrt{3 + f(x)}$

3–9 ■ Evaluate the limit and justify each step by indicating the appropriate Limit Law(s).

3. $\lim\limits_{x \to -2} (3x^4 + 2x^2 - x + 1)$

4. $\lim\limits_{t \to -1} (t^2 + 1)^3(t + 3)^5$

5. $\lim\limits_{x \to 8} (1 + \sqrt[3]{x})(2 - 6x^2 + x^3)$

6. $\lim\limits_{u \to -2} \sqrt{u^4 + 3u + 6}$

7. $\lim\limits_{x \to 1} \left(\dfrac{1 + 3x}{1 + 4x^2 + 3x^4} \right)^3$

8. $\lim\limits_{x \to 0} \dfrac{\cos^4 x}{5 + 2x^3}$

9. $\lim\limits_{\theta \to (\pi/2)} \theta \sin \theta$

■ ■ ■ ■ ■ ■ ■ ■ ■ ■ ■ ■ ■

10. (a) What is wrong with the following equation?

$$\frac{x^2 + x - 6}{x - 2} = x + 3$$

(b) In view of part (a), explain why the equation

$$\lim_{x \to 2} \frac{x^2 + x - 6}{x - 2} = \lim_{x \to 2} (x + 3)$$

is correct.

11–24 ■ Evaluate the limit, if it exists.

11. $\lim\limits_{x \to 2} \dfrac{x^2 + x - 6}{x - 2}$

12. $\lim\limits_{x \to -4} \dfrac{x^2 + 5x + 4}{x^2 + 3x - 4}$

13. $\lim\limits_{x \to 2} \dfrac{x^2 - x + 6}{x - 2}$

14. $\lim\limits_{x \to 4} \dfrac{x^2 - 4x}{x^2 - 3x - 4}$

15. $\lim\limits_{t \to -3} \dfrac{t^2 - 9}{2t^2 + 7t + 3}$

16. $\lim\limits_{x \to -1} \dfrac{x^2 - 4x}{x^2 - 3x - 4}$

17. $\lim\limits_{h \to 0} \dfrac{(4 + h)^2 - 16}{h}$

18. $\lim\limits_{h \to 0} \dfrac{\sqrt{1 + h} - 1}{h}$

19. $\lim\limits_{x \to -2} \dfrac{x + 2}{x^3 + 8}$

20. $\lim\limits_{x \to -1} \dfrac{x^2 + 2x + 1}{x^4 - 1}$

21. $\lim\limits_{x \to 7} \dfrac{\sqrt{x + 2} - 3}{x - 7}$

22. $\lim\limits_{h \to 0} \dfrac{(3 + h)^{-1} - 3^{-1}}{h}$

23. $\lim\limits_{x \to -4} \dfrac{\dfrac{1}{4} + \dfrac{1}{x}}{4 + x}$

24. $\lim\limits_{t \to 0} \left(\dfrac{1}{t} - \dfrac{1}{t^2 + t} \right)$

■ ■ ■ ■ ■ ■ ■ ■ ■ ■ ■ ■ ■

25. (a) Estimate the value of

$$\lim_{x \to 0} \frac{x}{\sqrt{1 + 3x} - 1}$$

by graphing the function $f(x) = x/(\sqrt{1 + 3x} - 1)$.
(b) Make a table of values of $f(x)$ for x close to 0 and guess the value of the limit.
(c) Use the Limit Laws to prove that your guess is correct.

26. (a) Use a graph of

$$f(x) = \frac{\sqrt{3 + x} - \sqrt{3}}{x}$$

to estimate the value of $\lim_{x \to 0} f(x)$ to two decimal places.
(b) Use a table of values of $f(x)$ to estimate the limit to four decimal places.
(c) Use the Limit Laws to find the exact value of the limit.

27. Use the Squeeze Theorem to show that $\lim_{x \to 0} x^2 \cos 20\pi x = 0$. Illustrate by graphing the functions $f(x) = -x^2$, $g(x) = x^2 \cos 20\pi x$, and $h(x) = x^2$ on the same screen.

28. Use the Squeeze Theorem to show that

$$\lim_{x \to 0} \sqrt{x^3 + x^2} \, \sin \frac{\pi}{x} = 0$$

Illustrate by graphing the functions f, g, and h (in the notation of the Squeeze Theorem) on the same screen.

29. If $4x - 9 \leq f(x) \leq x^2 - 4x + 7$ for $x \geq 0$, find $\lim_{x \to 4} f(x)$.

30. If $2x \leq g(x) \leq x^4 - x^2 + 2$ for all x, evaluate $\lim_{x \to 1} g(x)$.

31. Prove that $\lim\limits_{x \to 0} x^4 \cos \dfrac{2}{x} = 0$.

32. Prove that $\lim\limits_{x \to 0^+} \sqrt{x} \, [1 + \sin^2(2\pi/x)] = 0$.

33–36 ■ Find the limit, if it exists. If the limit does not exist, explain why.

33. $\lim\limits_{x \to 3} (2x + |x - 3|)$

34. $\lim\limits_{x \to -6} \dfrac{2x + 12}{|x + 6|}$

35. $\lim\limits_{x \to 0^-} \left(\dfrac{1}{x} - \dfrac{1}{|x|} \right)$

36. $\lim\limits_{x \to 0^+} \left(\dfrac{1}{x} - \dfrac{1}{|x|} \right)$

■ ■ ■ ■ ■ ■ ■ ■ ■ ■ ■ ■ ■

37. Let

$$g(x) = \begin{cases} -x & \text{if } x \leq -1 \\ 1 - x^2 & \text{if } -1 < x < 1 \\ x - 1 & \text{if } x > 1 \end{cases}$$

(a) Evaluate each of the following limits, if it exists.

(i) $\lim\limits_{x \to 1^+} g(x)$ (ii) $\lim\limits_{x \to 1} g(x)$ (iii) $\lim\limits_{x \to 0} g(x)$

(iv) $\lim\limits_{x \to -1^-} g(x)$ (v) $\lim\limits_{x \to -1^+} g(x)$ (vi) $\lim\limits_{x \to -1} g(x)$

(b) Sketch the graph of g.

38. Let $F(x) = \dfrac{x^2 - 1}{|x - 1|}$.

(a) Find

(i) $\lim\limits_{x \to 1^+} F(x)$ (ii) $\lim\limits_{x \to 1^-} F(x)$

(b) Does $\lim_{x \to 1} F(x)$ exist?

(c) Sketch the graph of F.

39. (a) If the symbol $[\![\ ]\!]$ denotes the greatest integer function defined in Example 8, evaluate

(i) $\lim_{x \to -2^+} [\![x]\!]$ (ii) $\lim_{x \to -2} [\![x]\!]$ (iii) $\lim_{x \to -2.4} [\![x]\!]$

(b) If n is an integer, evaluate

(i) $\lim_{x \to n^-} [\![x]\!]$ (ii) $\lim_{x \to n^+} [\![x]\!]$

(c) For what values of a does $\lim_{x \to a} [\![x]\!]$ exist?

40. Let $f(x) = x - [\![x]\!]$.

(a) Sketch the graph of f.

(b) If n is an integer, evaluate

(i) $\lim_{x \to n^-} f(x)$ (ii) $\lim_{x \to n^+} f(x)$

(c) For what values of a does $\lim_{x \to a} f(x)$ exist?

41. If $f(x) = [\![x]\!] + [\![-x]\!]$, show that $\lim_{x \to 2} f(x)$ exists but is not equal to $f(2)$.

42. In the theory of relativity, the Lorentz contraction formula

$$L = L_0 \sqrt{1 - v^2/c^2}$$

expresses the length L of an object as a function of its velocity v with respect to an observer, where L_0 is the length of the object at rest and c is the speed of light. Find $\lim_{v \to c^-} L$ and interpret the result. Why is a left-hand limit necessary?

43–48 ▪ Find the limit.

43. $\lim_{x \to 0} \dfrac{\sin 3x}{x}$

44. $\lim_{x \to 0} \dfrac{\sin 4x}{\sin 6x}$

45. $\lim_{t \to 0} \dfrac{\tan 6t}{\sin 2t}$

46. $\lim_{t \to 0} \dfrac{\sin^2 3t}{t^2}$

47. $\lim_{\theta \to 0} \dfrac{\sin \theta}{\theta + \tan \theta}$

48. $\lim_{x \to 0} x \cot x$

▪ ▪ ▪ ▪ ▪ ▪ ▪ ▪ ▪ ▪ ▪ ▪ ▪ ▪ ▪

49. If p is a polynomial, show that $\lim_{x \to a} p(x) = p(a)$.

50. If r is a rational function, use Exercise 49 to show that $\lim_{x \to a} r(x) = r(a)$ for every number a in the domain of r.

51. To prove that sine has the Direct Substitution Property we need to show that $\lim_{x \to a} \sin x = \sin a$ for every real number a. If we let $h = x - a$, then $x = a + h$ and $x \to a \iff h \to 0$. So an equivalent statement is that

$$\lim_{h \to 0} \sin(a + h) = \sin a$$

Use (1) to show that this is true.

52. Prove that cosine has the Direct Substitution Property.

53. Show by means of an example that $\lim_{x \to a} [f(x) + g(x)]$ may exist even though neither $\lim_{x \to a} f(x)$ nor $\lim_{x \to a} g(x)$ exists.

54. Show by means of an example that $\lim_{x \to a} [f(x)g(x)]$ may exist even though neither $\lim_{x \to a} f(x)$ nor $\lim_{x \to a} g(x)$ exists.

55. Is there a number a such that

$$\lim_{x \to -2} \frac{3x^2 + ax + a + 3}{x^2 + x - 2}$$

exists? If so, find the value of a and the value of the limit.

56. The figure shows a fixed circle C_1 with equation $(x - 1)^2 + y^2 = 1$ and a shrinking circle C_2 with radius r and center the origin. P is the point $(0, r)$, Q is the upper point of intersection of the two circles, and R is the point of intersection of the line PQ and the x-axis. What happens to R as C_2 shrinks, that is, as $r \to 0^+$?

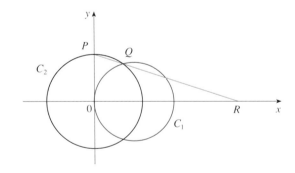

1.5	**CONTINUITY**

We noticed in Section 1.4 that the limit of a function as x approaches a can often be found simply by calculating the value of the function at a. Functions with this property are called *continuous at a*. We will see that the mathematical definition of continuity corresponds closely with the meaning of the word *continuity* in everyday language. (A continuous process is one that takes place gradually, without interruption or abrupt change.)

> **1 DEFINITION** A function f is **continuous at a number** a if
>
> $$\lim_{x \to a} f(x) = f(a)$$

■ As illustrated in Figure 1, if f is continuous, then the points $(x, f(x))$ on the graph of f approach the point $(a, f(a))$ on the graph. So there is no gap in the curve.

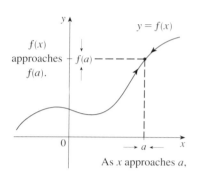

FIGURE 1

Notice that Definition 1 implicitly requires three things if f is continuous at a:

1. $f(a)$ is defined (that is, a is in the domain of f)

2. $\lim_{x \to a} f(x)$ exists

3. $\lim_{x \to a} f(x) = f(a)$

The definition says that f is continuous at a if $f(x)$ approaches $f(a)$ as x approaches a. Thus a continuous function f has the property that a small change in x produces only a small change in $f(x)$. In fact, the change in $f(x)$ can be kept as small as we please by keeping the change in x sufficiently small.

If f is defined near a (in other words, f is defined on an open interval containing a, except perhaps at a), we say that f is **discontinuous at a** (or f has a **discontinuity** at a) if f is not continuous at a.

Physical phenomena are usually continuous. For instance, the displacement or velocity of a vehicle varies continuously with time, as does a person's height. But discontinuities do occur in such situations as electric currents. [See Example 6 in Section 1.3, where the Heaviside function is discontinuous at 0 because $\lim_{t \to 0} H(t)$ does not exist.]

Geometrically, you can think of a function that is continuous at every number in an interval as a function whose graph has no break in it. The graph can be drawn without removing your pen from the paper.

EXAMPLE 1 Figure 2 shows the graph of a function f. At which numbers is f discontinuous? Why?

SOLUTION It looks as if there is a discontinuity when $a = 1$ because the graph has a break there. The official reason that f is discontinuous at 1 is that $f(1)$ is not defined.

The graph also has a break when $a = 3$, but the reason for the discontinuity is different. Here, $f(3)$ is defined, but $\lim_{x \to 3} f(x)$ does not exist (because the left and right limits are different). So f is discontinuous at 3.

What about $a = 5$? Here, $f(5)$ is defined and $\lim_{x \to 5} f(x)$ exists (because the left and right limits are the same). But

$$\lim_{x \to 5} f(x) \neq f(5)$$

So f is discontinuous at 5. ■

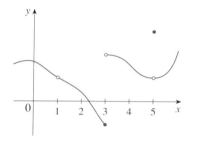

FIGURE 2

Now let's see how to detect discontinuities when a function is defined by a formula.

▼ EXAMPLE 2 Where are each of the following functions discontinuous?

(a) $f(x) = \dfrac{x^2 - x - 2}{x - 2}$

(b) $f(x) = \begin{cases} \dfrac{1}{x^2} & \text{if } x \neq 0 \\ 1 & \text{if } x = 0 \end{cases}$

(c) $f(x) = \begin{cases} \dfrac{x^2 - x - 2}{x - 2} & \text{if } x \neq 2 \\ 1 & \text{if } x = 2 \end{cases}$

(d) $f(x) = [\![x]\!]$

SOLUTION

(a) Notice that $f(2)$ is not defined, so f is discontinuous at 2. Later we'll see why f is continuous at all other numbers.

(b) Here $f(0) = 1$ is defined but

$$\lim_{x \to 0} f(x) = \lim_{x \to 0} \frac{1}{x^2}$$

does not exist. (See Example 8 in Section 1.3.) So f is discontinuous at 0.

(c) Here $f(2) = 1$ is defined and

$$\lim_{x \to 2} f(x) = \lim_{x \to 2} \frac{x^2 - x - 2}{x - 2} = \lim_{x \to 2} \frac{(x - 2)(x + 1)}{x - 2} = \lim_{x \to 2} (x + 1) = 3$$

exists. But

$$\lim_{x \to 2} f(x) \neq f(2)$$

so f is not continuous at 2.

(d) The greatest integer function $f(x) = [\![x]\!]$ has discontinuities at all of the integers because $\lim_{x \to n} [\![x]\!]$ does not exist if n is an integer. (See Example 8 and Exercise 39 in Section 1.4.) ■

Figure 3 shows the graphs of the functions in Example 2. In each case the graph can't be drawn without lifting the pen from the paper because a hole or break or jump occurs in the graph. The kind of discontinuity illustrated in parts (a) and (c) is called **removable** because we could remove the discontinuity by redefining f at just the single number 2. [The function $g(x) = x + 1$ is continuous.] The discontinuity in part (b) is called an **infinite discontinuity**. The discontinuities in part (d) are called **jump discontinuities** because the function "jumps" from one value to another.

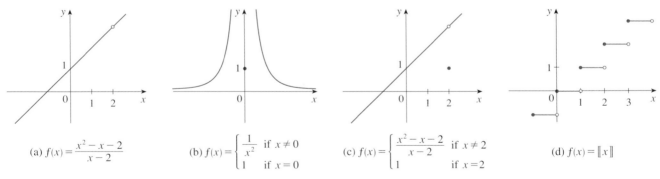

(a) $f(x) = \dfrac{x^2 - x - 2}{x - 2}$

(b) $f(x) = \begin{cases} \dfrac{1}{x^2} & \text{if } x \neq 0 \\ 1 & \text{if } x = 0 \end{cases}$

(c) $f(x) = \begin{cases} \dfrac{x^2 - x - 2}{x - 2} & \text{if } x \neq 2 \\ 1 & \text{if } x = 2 \end{cases}$

(d) $f(x) = [\![x]\!]$

FIGURE 3 Graphs of the functions in Example 2

2 DEFINITION A function f is **continuous from the right at a number** a if

$$\lim_{x \to a^+} f(x) = f(a)$$

and f is **continuous from the left at** a if

$$\lim_{x \to a^-} f(x) = f(a)$$

EXAMPLE 3 At each integer n, the function $f(x) = [\![x]\!]$ [see Figure 3(d)] is continuous from the right but discontinuous from the left because

$$\lim_{x \to n^+} f(x) = \lim_{x \to n^+} [\![x]\!] = n = f(n)$$

but

$$\lim_{x \to n^-} f(x) = \lim_{x \to n^-} [\![x]\!] = n - 1 \neq f(n)$$ ∎

---

3 DEFINITION A function f is **continuous on an interval** if it is continuous at every number in the interval. (If f is defined only on one side of an endpoint of the interval, we understand *continuous* at the endpoint to mean *continuous from the right* or *continuous from the left*.)

EXAMPLE 4 Show that the function $f(x) = 1 - \sqrt{1 - x^2}$ is continuous on the interval $[-1, 1]$.

SOLUTION If $-1 < a < 1$, then using the Limit Laws, we have

$$\lim_{x \to a} f(x) = \lim_{x \to a} \left(1 - \sqrt{1 - x^2}\right)$$

$$= 1 - \lim_{x \to a} \sqrt{1 - x^2} \qquad \text{(by Laws 2 and 7)}$$

$$= 1 - \sqrt{\lim_{x \to a} (1 - x^2)} \qquad \text{(by 11)}$$

$$= 1 - \sqrt{1 - a^2} \qquad \text{(by 2, 7, and 9)}$$

$$= f(a)$$

Thus, by Definition 1, f is continuous at a if $-1 < a < 1$. Similar calculations show that

$$\lim_{x \to -1^+} f(x) = 1 = f(-1) \qquad \text{and} \qquad \lim_{x \to 1^-} f(x) = 1 = f(1)$$

so f is continuous from the right at -1 and continuous from the left at 1. Therefore, according to Definition 3, f is continuous on $[-1, 1]$.

The graph of f is sketched in Figure 4. It is the lower half of the circle

$$x^2 + (y - 1)^2 = 1$$ ∎

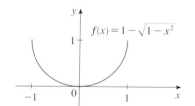

FIGURE 4

Instead of always using Definitions 1, 2, and 3 to verify the continuity of a function as we did in Example 4, it is often convenient to use the next theorem, which shows how to build up complicated continuous functions from simple ones.

---

4 THEOREM If f and g are continuous at a and c is a constant, then the following functions are also continuous at a:

1. $f + g$ **2.** $f - g$ **3.** cf

4. fg **5.** $\dfrac{f}{g}$ if $g(a) \neq 0$

PROOF Each of the five parts of this theorem follows from the corresponding Limit Law in Section 1.4. For instance, we give the proof of part 1. Since f and g are continuous at a, we have

$$\lim_{x \to a} f(x) = f(a) \qquad \text{and} \qquad \lim_{x \to a} g(x) = g(a)$$

Therefore

$$\lim_{x \to a} (f + g)(x) = \lim_{x \to a} [f(x) + g(x)]$$

$$= \lim_{x \to a} f(x) + \lim_{x \to a} g(x) \qquad \text{(by Law 1)}$$

$$= f(a) + g(a)$$

$$= (f + g)(a)$$

This shows that $f + g$ is continuous at a. ☐

It follows from Theorem 4 and Definition 3 that if f and g are continuous on an interval, then so are the functions $f + g$, $f - g$, cf, fg, and (if g is never 0) f/g. The following theorem was stated in Section 1.4 as the Direct Substitution Property.

---

5 THEOREM
(a) Any polynomial is continuous everywhere; that is, it is continuous on $\mathbb{R} = (-\infty, \infty)$.
(b) Any rational function is continuous wherever it is defined; that is, it is continuous on its domain.

PROOF
(a) A polynomial is a function of the form

$$P(x) = c_n x^n + c_{n-1} x^{n-1} + \cdots + c_1 x + c_0$$

where $c_0, c_1, \ldots, c_n$ are constants. We know that

$$\lim_{x \to a} c_0 = c_0 \qquad \text{(by Law 7)}$$

and

$$\lim_{x \to a} x^m = a^m \qquad m = 1, 2, \ldots, n \qquad \text{(by 9)}$$

This equation is precisely the statement that the function $f(x) = x^m$ is a continuous function. Thus, by part 3 of Theorem 4, the function $g(x) = cx^m$ is continuous. Since P is a sum of functions of this form and a constant function, it follows from part 1 of Theorem 4 that P is continuous.
(b) A rational function is a function of the form

$$f(x) = \frac{P(x)}{Q(x)}$$

where P and Q are polynomials. The domain of f is $D = \{x \in \mathbb{R} \mid Q(x) \neq 0\}$. We know from part (a) that P and Q are continuous everywhere. Thus, by part 5 of Theorem 4, f is continuous at every number in D. ☐

As an illustration of Theorem 5, observe that the volume of a sphere varies contin-uously with its radius because the formula $V(r) = \frac{4}{3}\pi r^3$ shows that V is a polynomial function of r. Likewise, if a ball is thrown vertically into the air with a velocity of 50 ft/s, then the height of the ball in feet t seconds later is given by the formula $h = 50t - 16t^2$. Again this is a polynomial function, so the height is a continuous function of the elapsed time.

Knowledge of which functions are continuous enables us to evaluate some limits very quickly, as the following example shows. Compare it with Example 1(b) in Sec-tion 1.4.

EXAMPLE 5 Find $\lim\limits_{x \to -2} \dfrac{x^3 + 2x^2 - 1}{5 - 3x}$.

SOLUTION The function

$$f(x) = \frac{x^3 + 2x^2 - 1}{5 - 3x}$$

is rational, so by Theorem 5 it is continuous on its domain, which is $\left\{ x \mid x \neq \frac{5}{3} \right\}$. Therefore

$$\lim_{x \to -2} \frac{x^3 + 2x^2 - 1}{5 - 3x} = \lim_{x \to -2} f(x) = f(-2)$$

$$= \frac{(-2)^3 + 2(-2)^2 - 1}{5 - 3(-2)} = -\frac{1}{11}$$
■

It turns out that most of the familiar functions are continuous at every number in their domains. For instance, Limit Law 10 (page 36) is exactly the statement that root functions are continuous.

From the appearance of the graphs of the sine and cosine functions (Figure 11 in Section 1.2), we would certainly guess that they are continuous. And in Section 1.4 we showed that

$$\lim_{\theta \to a} \sin \theta = \sin a \qquad \lim_{\theta \to a} \cos \theta = \cos a$$

In other words, the sine and cosine functions are continuous everywhere. It follows from part 5 of Theorem 4 that

$$\tan x = \frac{\sin x}{\cos x}$$

is continuous except where $\cos x = 0$. This happens when x is an odd integer mul-tiple of $\pi/2$, so $y = \tan x$ has infinite discontinuities when $x = \pm\pi/2, \pm3\pi/2, \pm5\pi/2$, and so on (see Figure 5).

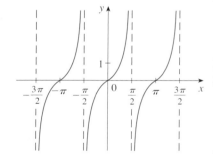

FIGURE 5
$y = \tan x$

> **6 THEOREM** The following types of functions are continuous at every number in their domains: polynomials, rational functions, root functions, trigonometric functions

EXAMPLE 6 On what intervals is each function continuous?

(a) $f(x) = x^{100} - 2x^{37} + 75$

(b) $g(x) = \dfrac{x^2 + 2x + 17}{x^2 - 1}$

(c) $h(x) = \sqrt{x} + \dfrac{x + 1}{x - 1} - \dfrac{x + 1}{x^2 + 1}$

SOLUTION

(a) f is a polynomial, so it is continuous on $(-\infty, \infty)$ by Theorem 5(a).

(b) g is a rational function, so by Theorem 5(b) it is continuous on its domain, which is $D = \{x \mid x^2 - 1 \neq 0\} = \{x \mid x \neq \pm 1\}$. Thus, g is continuous on the intervals $(-\infty, -1)$, $(-1, 1)$, and $(1, \infty)$.

(c) We can write $h(x) = F(x) + G(x) - H(x)$, where

$$F(x) = \sqrt{x} \qquad G(x) = \frac{x + 1}{x - 1} \qquad H(x) = \frac{x + 1}{x^2 + 1}$$

F is continuous on $[0, \infty)$ by Theorem 6. G is a rational function, so it is continuous everywhere except when $x - 1 = 0$, that is, $x = 1$. H is also a rational function, but its denominator is never 0, so H is continuous everywhere. Thus, by parts 1 and 2 of Theorem 4, h is continuous on the intervals $[0, 1)$ and $(1, \infty)$. ■

Another way of combining continuous functions f and g to get a new continuous function is to form the composite function $f \circ g$. This fact is a consequence of the following theorem.

■ This theorem says that a limit symbol can be moved through a function symbol if the function is continuous and the limit exists. In other words, the order of these two symbols can be reversed.

7 THEOREM If f is continuous at b and $\lim\limits_{x \to a} g(x) = b$, then $\lim\limits_{x \to a} f(g(x)) = f(b)$. In other words,

$$\lim_{x \to a} f(g(x)) = f\left(\lim_{x \to a} g(x)\right)$$

Intuitively, Theorem 7 is reasonable because if x is close to a, then $g(x)$ is close to b, and since f is continuous at b, if $g(x)$ is close to b, then $f(g(x))$ is close to $f(b)$. A proof of Theorem 7 is given in Appendix B.

8 THEOREM If g is continuous at a and f is continuous at $g(a)$, then the composite function $f \circ g$ given by $(f \circ g)(x) = f(g(x))$ is continuous at a.

This theorem is often expressed informally by saying "a continuous function of a continuous function is a continuous function."

PROOF Since g is continuous at a, we have

$$\lim_{x \to a} g(x) = g(a)$$

Since f is continuous at $b = g(a)$, we can apply Theorem 7 to obtain

$$\lim_{x \to a} f(g(x)) = f(g(a))$$

which is precisely the statement that the function $h(x) = f(g(x))$ is continuous at a; that is, $f \circ g$ is continuous at a. □

☑ **EXAMPLE 7** Where are the following functions continuous?

(a) $h(x) = \sin(x^2)$

(b) $F(x) = \dfrac{1}{\sqrt{x^2 + 7} - 4}$

SOLUTION

(a) We have $h(x) = f(g(x))$, where

$$g(x) = x^2 \qquad \text{and} \qquad f(x) = \sin x$$

Now g is continuous on $\mathbb{R}$ since it is a polynomial, and f is also continuous everywhere by Theorem 6. Thus, $h = f \circ g$ is continuous on $\mathbb{R}$ by Theorem 8.

(b) Notice that F can be broken up as the composition of four continuous functions:

$$F = f \circ g \circ h \circ k \qquad \text{or} \qquad F(x) = f(g(h(k(x))))$$

where $\quad f(x) = \dfrac{1}{x} \qquad g(x) = x - 4 \qquad h(x) = \sqrt{x} \qquad k(x) = x^2 + 7$

We know that each of these functions is continuous on its domain (by Theorems 5 and 6), so by Theorem 8, F is continuous on its domain, which is

$$\{x \in \mathbb{R} \mid \sqrt{x^2 + 7} \neq 4\} = \{x \mid x \neq \pm 3\} = (-\infty, -3) \cup (-3, 3) \cup (3, \infty) \quad \blacksquare$$

An important property of continuous functions is expressed by the following theorem, whose proof is found in more advanced books on calculus.

---

9 **THE INTERMEDIATE VALUE THEOREM** Suppose that f is continuous on the closed interval $[a, b]$ and let N be any number between $f(a)$ and $f(b)$, where $f(a) \neq f(b)$. Then there exists a number c in (a, b) such that $f(c) = N$.

The Intermediate Value Theorem states that a continuous function takes on every intermediate value between the function values $f(a)$ and $f(b)$. It is illustrated by Figure 6. Note that the value N can be taken on once [as in part (a)] or more than once [as in part (b)].

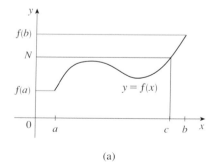

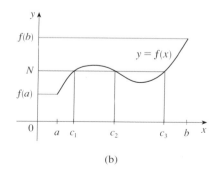

FIGURE 6　　　　　　(a)　　　　　　　　　　　　　　(b)

If we think of a continuous function as a function whose graph has no hole or break, then it is easy to believe that the Intermediate Value Theorem is true. In geometric terms it says that if any horizontal line $y = N$ is given between $y = f(a)$ and

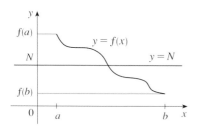

FIGURE 7

$y = f(b)$ as in Figure 7, then the graph of f can't jump over the line. It must intersect $y = N$ somewhere.

It is important that the function f in Theorem 9 be continuous. The Intermediate Value Theorem is not true in general for discontinuous functions (see Exercise 34).

One use of the Intermediate Value Theorem is in locating roots of equations as in the following example.

V EXAMPLE 8 Show that there is a root of the equation

$$4x^3 - 6x^2 + 3x - 2 = 0$$

between 1 and 2.

SOLUTION Let $f(x) = 4x^3 - 6x^2 + 3x - 2$. We are looking for a solution of the given equation, that is, a number c between 1 and 2 such that $f(c) = 0$. Therefore, we take $a = 1$, $b = 2$, and $N = 0$ in Theorem 9. We have

$$f(1) = 4 - 6 + 3 - 2 = -1 < 0$$

and
$$f(2) = 32 - 24 + 6 - 2 = 12 > 0$$

Thus $f(1) < 0 < f(2)$; that is, $N = 0$ is a number between $f(1)$ and $f(2)$. Now f is continuous since it is a polynomial, so the Intermediate Value Theorem says there is a number c between 1 and 2 such that $f(c) = 0$. In other words, the equation $4x^3 - 6x^2 + 3x - 2 = 0$ has at least one root c in the interval $(1, 2)$.

In fact, we can locate a root more precisely by using the Intermediate Value Theorem again. Since

$$f(1.2) = -0.128 < 0 \qquad \text{and} \qquad f(1.3) = 0.548 > 0$$

a root must lie between 1.2 and 1.3. A calculator gives, by trial and error,

$$f(1.22) = -0.007008 < 0 \qquad \text{and} \qquad f(1.23) = 0.056068 > 0$$

so a root lies in the interval $(1.22, 1.23)$. ■

We can use a graphing calculator or computer to illustrate the use of the Intermediate Value Theorem in Example 8. Figure 8 shows the graph of f in the viewing rectangle $[-1, 3]$ by $[-3, 3]$ and you can see that the graph crosses the x-axis between 1 and 2. Figure 9 shows the result of zooming in to the viewing rectangle $[1.2, 1.3]$ by $[-0.2, 0.2]$.

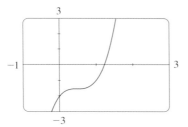

FIGURE 8   **FIGURE 9**

In fact, the Intermediate Value Theorem plays a role in the very way these graphing devices work. A computer calculates a finite number of points on the graph and turns on the pixels that contain these calculated points. It assumes that the function is continuous and takes on all the intermediate values between two consecutive points. The computer therefore connects the pixels by turning on the intermediate pixels.

1.5 EXERCISES

1. Write an equation that expresses the fact that a function f is continuous at the number 4.

2. If f is continuous on $(-\infty, \infty)$, what can you say about its graph?

3. (a) From the graph of f, state the numbers at which f is discontinuous and explain why.
(b) For each of the numbers stated in part (a), determine whether f is continuous from the right, or from the left, or neither.

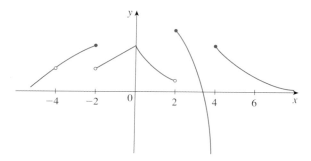

4. From the graph of g, state the intervals on which g is continuous.

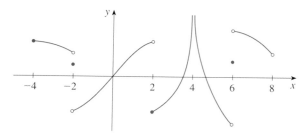

5. Sketch the graph of a function that is continuous everywhere except at $x = 3$ and is continuous from the left at 3.

6. Sketch the graph of a function that has a jump discontinuity at $x = 2$ and a removable discontinuity at $x = 4$, but is continuous elsewhere.

7. A parking lot charges \$3 for the first hour (or part of an hour) and \$2 for each succeeding hour (or part), up to a daily maximum of \$10.
(a) Sketch a graph of the cost of parking at this lot as a function of the time parked there.

(b) Discuss the discontinuities of this function and their significance to someone who parks in the lot.

8. Explain why each function is continuous or discontinuous.
(a) The temperature at a specific location as a function of time
(b) The temperature at a specific time as a function of the distance due west from New York City
(c) The altitude above sea level as a function of the distance due west from New York City
(d) The cost of a taxi ride as a function of the distance traveled
(e) The current in the circuit for the lights in a room as a function of time

9. If f and g are continuous functions with $f(3) = 5$ and $\lim_{x \to 3} [2f(x) - g(x)] = 4$, find $g(3)$.

10–11 ■ Use the definition of continuity and the properties of limits to show that the function is continuous at the given number a.

10. $f(x) = x^2 + \sqrt{7 - x}$, $a = 4$

11. $f(x) = (x + 2x^3)^4$, $a = -1$

■ ■ ■ ■ ■ ■ ■ ■ ■ ■ ■ ■ ■

12. Use the definition of continuity and the properties of limits to show that the function $f(x) = x\sqrt{16 - x^2}$ is continuous on the interval $[-4, 4]$.

13–16 ■ Explain why the function is discontinuous at $a = 1$. Sketch the graph of the function.

13. $f(x) = -\dfrac{1}{(x - 1)^2}$

14. $f(x) = \begin{cases} \dfrac{1}{x - 1} & \text{if } x \neq 1 \\ 2 & \text{if } x = 1 \end{cases}$

15. $f(x) = \begin{cases} 1 - x^2 & \text{if } x < 1 \\ 1/x & \text{if } x \geq 1 \end{cases}$

16. $f(x) = \begin{cases} \dfrac{x^2 - x}{x^2 - 1} & \text{if } x \neq 1 \\ 1 & \text{if } x = 1 \end{cases}$

■ ■ ■ ■ ■ ■ ■ ■ ■ ■ ■ ■ ■

17–22 ■ Explain, using Theorems 4, 5, 6, and 8, why the function is continuous at every number in its domain. State the domain.

17. $F(x) = \dfrac{x}{x^2 + 5x + 6}$

18. $G(x) = \sqrt[3]{x}\,(1 + x^3)$

19. $R(x) = x^2 + \sqrt{2x - 1}$

20. $h(x) = \dfrac{\sin x}{x + 1}$

21. $F(x) = \sqrt{x}\,\sin x$

22. $F(x) = \sin(\cos(\sin x))$

■ ■ ■ ■ ■ ■ ■ ■ ■ ■ ■ ■ ■

23–24 ■ Locate the discontinuities of the function and illustrate by graphing.

23. $y = \dfrac{1}{1 + \sin x}$

24. $y = \tan \sqrt{x}$

■ ■ ■ ■ ■ ■ ■ ■ ■ ■ ■ ■ ■

25–26 ■ Use continuity to evaluate the limit.

25. $\lim\limits_{x \to 4} \dfrac{5 + \sqrt{x}}{\sqrt{5 + x}}$

26. $\lim\limits_{x \to \pi} \sin(x + \sin x)$

■ ■ ■ ■ ■ ■ ■ ■ ■ ■ ■ ■ ■

27–28 ■ Show that f is continuous on $(-\infty, \infty)$.

27. $f(x) = \begin{cases} x^2 & \text{if } x < 1 \\ \sqrt{x} & \text{if } x \geq 1 \end{cases}$

28. $f(x) = \begin{cases} \sin x & \text{if } x < \pi/4 \\ \cos x & \text{if } x \geq \pi/4 \end{cases}$

■ ■ ■ ■ ■ ■ ■ ■ ■ ■ ■ ■ ■

29. Find the numbers at which the function

$$f(x) = \begin{cases} x + 2 & \text{if } x < 0 \\ 2x^2 & \text{if } 0 \leq x \leq 1 \\ 2 - x & \text{if } x > 1 \end{cases}$$

is discontinuous. At which of these points is f continuous from the right, from the left, or neither? Sketch the graph of f.

30. The gravitational force exerted by the Earth on a unit mass at a distance r from the center of the planet is

$$F(r) = \begin{cases} \dfrac{GMr}{R^3} & \text{if } r < R \\[2mm] \dfrac{GM}{r^2} & \text{if } r \geq R \end{cases}$$

where M is the mass of the Earth, R is its radius, and G is the gravitational constant. Is F a continuous function of r?

31. For what value of the constant c is the function f continuous on $(-\infty, \infty)$?

$$f(x) = \begin{cases} cx^2 + 2x & \text{if } x < 2 \\ x^3 - cx & \text{if } x \geq 2 \end{cases}$$

32. Find the constant c that makes g continuous on $(-\infty, \infty)$.

$$g(x) = \begin{cases} x^2 - c^2 & \text{if } x < 4 \\ cx + 20 & \text{if } x \geq 4 \end{cases}$$

33. Which of the following functions f has a removable discontinuity at a? If the discontinuity is removable, find a function g that agrees with f for $x \neq a$ and is continuous at a.

(a) $f(x) = \dfrac{x^2 - 2x - 8}{x + 2}$ $\qquad a = -2$

(b) $f(x) = \dfrac{x - 7}{|x - 7|}$ $\qquad a = 7$

(c) $f(x) = \dfrac{x^3 + 64}{x + 4}$ $\qquad a = -4$

(d) $f(x) = \dfrac{3 - \sqrt{x}}{9 - x}$ $\qquad a = 9$

34. Suppose that a function f is continuous on $[0, 1]$ except at 0.25 and that $f(0) = 1$ and $f(1) = 3$. Let $N = 2$. Sketch two possible graphs of f, one showing that f might not satisfy the conclusion of the Intermediate Value Theorem and one showing that f might still satisfy the conclusion of the Intermediate Value Theorem (even though it doesn't satisfy the hypothesis).

35. If $f(x) = x^2 + 10 \sin x$, show that there is a number c such that $f(c) = 1000$.

36. Use the Intermediate Value Theorem to prove that there is a positive number c such that $c^2 = 2$. (This proves the existence of the number $\sqrt{2}$.)

37–40 ■ Use the Intermediate Value Theorem to show that there is a root of the given equation in the specified interval.

37. $x^4 + x - 3 = 0$, $\quad (1, 2)$

38. $\sqrt[3]{x} = 1 - x$, $\quad (0, 1)$

39. $\cos x = x$, $\quad (0, 1)$

40. $\tan x = 2x$, $\quad (0, 1.4)$

■ ■ ■ ■ ■ ■ ■ ■ ■ ■ ■ ■ ■

41–42 ■ (a) Prove that the equation has at least one real root. (b) Use your calculator to find an interval of length 0.01 that contains a root.

41. $\cos x = x^3$

42. $x^5 - x^2 + 2x + 3 = 0$

■ ■ ■ ■ ■ ■ ■ ■ ■ ■ ■ ■ ■

43–44 ■ (a) Prove that the equation has at least one real root. (b) Use your graphing device to find the root correct to three decimal places.

43. $x^5 - x^2 - 4 = 0$

44. $\sqrt{x - 5} = \dfrac{1}{x + 3}$

■ ■ ■ ■ ■ ■ ■ ■ ■ ■ ■ ■ ■

45. Is there a number that is exactly 1 more than its cube?

46. (a) Show that the absolute value function $F(x) = |x|$ is continuous everywhere.
(b) Prove that if f is a continuous function on an interval, then so is $|f|$.
(c) Is the converse of the statement in part (b) also true? In other words, if $|f|$ is continuous, does it follow that f is continuous? If so, prove it. If not, find a counter-example.

47. A Tibetan monk leaves the monastery at 7:00 AM and takes his usual path to the top of the mountain, arriving at 7:00 PM. The following morning, he starts at 7:00 AM at the top and takes the same path back, arriving at the monastery at 7:00 PM. Use the Intermediate Value Theorem to show that there is a point on the path that the monk will cross at exactly the same time of day on both days.

1.6 | **LIMITS INVOLVING INFINITY**

In this section we investigate the global behavior of functions and, in particular, whether their graphs approach asymptotes, vertical or horizontal.

INFINITE LIMITS

In Example 8 in Section 1.3 we concluded that

$$\lim_{x \to 0} \frac{1}{x^2} \quad \text{does not exist}$$

x	$\dfrac{1}{x^2}$
± 1	1
± 0.5	4
± 0.2	25
± 0.1	100
± 0.05	400
± 0.01	10,000
± 0.001	1,000,000

by observing, from the table of values and the graph of $y = 1/x^2$ in Figure 1, that the values of $1/x^2$ can be made arbitrarily large by taking x close enough to 0. Thus the values of $f(x)$ do not approach a number, so $\lim_{x \to 0} (1/x^2)$ does not exist.

To indicate this kind of behavior we use the notation

$$\lim_{x \to 0} \frac{1}{x^2} = \infty$$

⊘ This does not mean that we are regarding ∞ as a number. Nor does it mean that the limit exists. It simply expresses the particular way in which the limit does not exist: $1/x^2$ can be made as large as we like by taking x close enough to 0.

In general, we write symbolically

$$\lim_{x \to a} f(x) = \infty$$

to indicate that the values of $f(x)$ become larger and larger (or "increase without bound") as x approaches a.

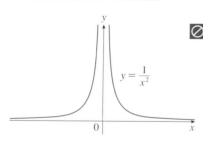

$y = \dfrac{1}{x^2}$

FIGURE 1

■ A more precise version of Definition 1 is given at the end of this section.

> **1 DEFINITION** The notation
>
> $$\lim_{x \to a} f(x) = \infty$$
>
> means that the values of $f(x)$ can be made arbitrarily large (as large as we please) by taking x sufficiently close to a (on either side of a) but not equal to a.

Another notation for $\lim_{x \to a} f(x) = \infty$ is

$$f(x) \to \infty \qquad \text{as} \qquad x \to a$$

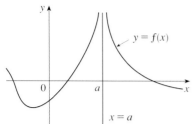

FIGURE 2
$\lim\limits_{x \to a} f(x) = \infty$

▪ When we say that a number is "large negative," we mean that it is negative but its magnitude (absolute value) is large.

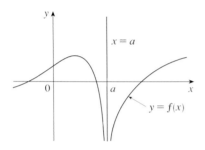

FIGURE 3
$\lim\limits_{x \to a} f(x) = -\infty$

Again, the symbol ∞ is not a number, but the expression $\lim_{x \to a} f(x) = \infty$ is often read as

"the limit of $f(x)$, as x approaches a, is infinity"

or "$f(x)$ becomes infinite as x approaches a"

or "$f(x)$ increases without bound as x approaches a"

This definition is illustrated graphically in Figure 2.
Similarly, as shown in Figure 3,

$$\lim\limits_{x \to a} f(x) = -\infty$$

means that the values of $f(x)$ are as large negative as we like for all values of x that are sufficiently close to a, but not equal to a.

The symbol $\lim_{x \to a} f(x) = -\infty$ can be read as "the limit of $f(x)$, as x approaches a, is negative infinity" or "$f(x)$ decreases without bound as x approaches a." As an example we have

$$\lim\limits_{x \to 0} \left(-\frac{1}{x^2} \right) = -\infty$$

Similar definitions can be given for the one-sided infinite limits

$$\lim\limits_{x \to a^-} f(x) = \infty \qquad\qquad \lim\limits_{x \to a^+} f(x) = \infty$$

$$\lim\limits_{x \to a^-} f(x) = -\infty \qquad\qquad \lim\limits_{x \to a^+} f(x) = -\infty$$

remembering that "$x \to a^-$" means that we consider only values of x that are less than a, and similarly "$x \to a^+$" means that we consider only $x > a$. Illustrations of these four cases are given in Figure 4.

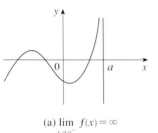

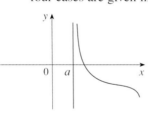

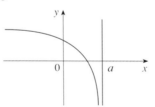

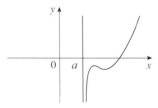

(a) $\lim\limits_{x \to a^-} f(x) = \infty$ (b) $\lim\limits_{x \to a^+} f(x) = \infty$ (c) $\lim\limits_{x \to a^-} f(x) = -\infty$ (d) $\lim\limits_{x \to a^+} f(x) = -\infty$

FIGURE 4

---

2 DEFINITION The line $x = a$ is called a **vertical asymptote** of the curve $y = f(x)$ if at least one of the following statements is true:

$$\lim\limits_{x \to a} f(x) = \infty \qquad \lim\limits_{x \to a^-} f(x) = \infty \qquad \lim\limits_{x \to a^+} f(x) = \infty$$

$$\lim\limits_{x \to a} f(x) = -\infty \qquad \lim\limits_{x \to a^-} f(x) = -\infty \qquad \lim\limits_{x \to a^+} f(x) = -\infty$$

For instance, the y-axis is a vertical asymptote of the curve $y = 1/x^2$ because $\lim_{x \to 0} (1/x^2) = \infty$. In Figure 4 the line $x = a$ is a vertical asymptote in each of the four cases shown.

EXAMPLE 1 Find $\lim\limits_{x \to 3^+} \dfrac{2x}{x-3}$ and $\lim\limits_{x \to 3^-} \dfrac{2x}{x-3}$.

SOLUTION If x is close to 3 but larger than 3, then the denominator $x - 3$ is a small positive number and $2x$ is close to 6. So the quotient $2x/(x - 3)$ is a large *positive* number. Thus, intuitively, we see that

$$\lim_{x \to 3^+} \frac{2x}{x-3} = \infty$$

Likewise, if x is close to 3 but smaller than 3, then $x - 3$ is a small negative number but $2x$ is still a positive number (close to 6). So $2x/(x - 3)$ is a numerically large *negative* number. Thus

$$\lim_{x \to 3^-} \frac{2x}{x-3} = -\infty$$

The graph of the curve $y = 2x/(x - 3)$ is given in Figure 5. The line $x = 3$ is a vertical asymptote. ■

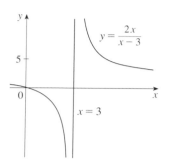

FIGURE 5

EXAMPLE 2 Find the vertical asymptotes of $f(x) = \tan x$.

SOLUTION Because

$$\tan x = \frac{\sin x}{\cos x}$$

there are potential vertical asymptotes where $\cos x = 0$. In fact, since $\cos x \to 0^+$ as $x \to (\pi/2)^-$ and $\cos x \to 0^-$ as $x \to (\pi/2)^+$, whereas $\sin x$ is positive (and not near 0) when x is near $\pi/2$, we have

$$\lim_{x \to (\pi/2)^-} \tan x = \infty \quad \text{and} \quad \lim_{x \to (\pi/2)^+} \tan x = -\infty$$

This shows that the line $x = \pi/2$ is a vertical asymptote. Similar reasoning shows that the lines $x = (2n + 1)\pi/2$, where n is an integer, are all vertical asymptotes of $f(x) = \tan x$. The graph in Figure 6 confirms this. ■

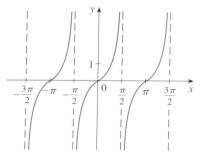

FIGURE 6
$y = \tan x$

LIMITS AT INFINITY

In computing infinite limits, we let x approach a number and the result was that the values of y became arbitrarily large (positive or negative). Here we let x become arbitrarily large (positive or negative) and see what happens to y.

Let's begin by investigating the behavior of the function f defined by

$$f(x) = \frac{x^2 - 1}{x^2 + 1}$$

as x becomes large. The table at the left gives values of this function correct to six decimal places, and the graph of f has been drawn by a computer in Figure 7.

x	$f(x)$
0	−1
±1	0
±2	0.600000
±3	0.800000
±4	0.882353
±5	0.923077
±10	0.980198
±50	0.999200
±100	0.999800
±1000	0.999998

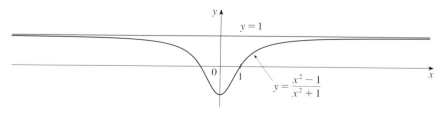

FIGURE 7

As x grows larger and larger you can see that the values of $f(x)$ get closer and closer to 1. In fact, it seems that we can make the values of $f(x)$ as close as we like to 1 by taking x sufficiently large. This situation is expressed symbolically by writing

$$\lim_{x \to \infty} \frac{x^2 - 1}{x^2 + 1} = 1$$

In general, we use the notation

$$\lim_{x \to \infty} f(x) = L$$

to indicate that the values of $f(x)$ approach L as x becomes larger and larger.

---

3 DEFINITION Let f be a function defined on some interval (a, ∞). Then

$$\lim_{x \to \infty} f(x) = L$$

means that the values of $f(x)$ can be made as close to L as we like by taking x sufficiently large.

Another notation for $\lim_{x \to \infty} f(x) = L$ is

$$f(x) \to L \quad \text{as} \quad x \to \infty$$

The symbol ∞ does not represent a number. Nonetheless, the expression $\lim_{x \to \infty} f(x) = L$ is often read as

"the limit of $f(x)$, as x approaches infinity, is L"

or "the limit of $f(x)$, as x becomes infinite, is L"

or "the limit of $f(x)$, as x increases without bound, is L"

The meaning of such phrases is given by Definition 3. A more precise definition, similar to the ε, δ definition of Section 1.3, is given at the end of this section.

Geometric illustrations of Definition 3 are shown in Figure 8. Notice that there are many ways for the graph of f to approach the line $y = L$ (which is called a *horizontal asymptote*) as we look to the far right of each graph.

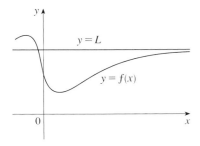

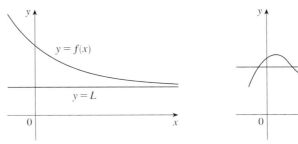

FIGURE 8
Examples illustrating $\lim_{x \to \infty} f(x) = L$

Referring back to Figure 7, we see that for numerically large negative values of x, the values of $f(x)$ are close to 1. By letting x decrease through negative values without bound, we can make $f(x)$ as close to 1 as we like. This is expressed by writing

$$\lim_{x \to -\infty} \frac{x^2 - 1}{x^2 + 1} = 1$$

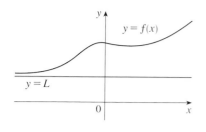

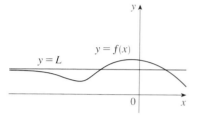

FIGURE 9

Examples illustrating $\lim_{x \to -\infty} f(x) = L$

In general, as shown in Figure 9, the notation

$$\lim_{x \to -\infty} f(x) = L$$

means that the values of $f(x)$ can be made arbitrarily close to L by taking x sufficiently large negative.

Again, the symbol $-\infty$ does not represent a number, but the expression $\lim_{x \to -\infty} f(x) = L$ is often read as

"the limit of $f(x)$, as x approaches negative infinity, is L"

---

4 DEFINITION The line $y = L$ is called a **horizontal asymptote** of the curve $y = f(x)$ if either

$$\lim_{x \to \infty} f(x) = L \qquad \text{or} \qquad \lim_{x \to -\infty} f(x) = L$$

For instance, the curve illustrated in Figure 7 has the line $y = 1$ as a horizontal asymptote because

$$\lim_{x \to \infty} \frac{x^2 - 1}{x^2 + 1} = 1$$

The curve $y = f(x)$ sketched in Figure 10 has both $y = -1$ and $y = 2$ as horizontal asymptotes because

$$\lim_{x \to \infty} f(x) = -1 \qquad \text{and} \qquad \lim_{x \to -\infty} f(x) = 2$$

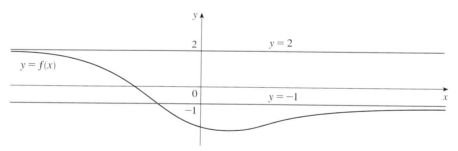

FIGURE 10

EXAMPLE 3 Find the infinite limits, limits at infinity, and asymptotes for the function f whose graph is shown in Figure 11.

SOLUTION We see that the values of $f(x)$ become large as $x \to -1$ from both sides, so

$$\lim_{x \to -1} f(x) = \infty$$

Notice that $f(x)$ becomes large negative as x approaches 2 from the left, but large positive as x approaches 2 from the right. So

$$\lim_{x \to 2^-} f(x) = -\infty \qquad \text{and} \qquad \lim_{x \to 2^+} f(x) = \infty$$

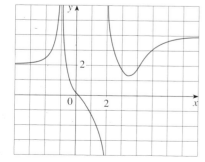

FIGURE 11

Thus, both of the lines $x = -1$ and $x = 2$ are vertical asymptotes.

As x becomes large, it appears that $f(x)$ approaches 4. But as x decreases through negative values, $f(x)$ approaches 2. So

$$\lim_{x \to \infty} f(x) = 4 \qquad \text{and} \qquad \lim_{x \to -\infty} f(x) = 2$$

This means that both $y = 4$ and $y = 2$ are horizontal asymptotes. ▪

EXAMPLE 4 Find $\displaystyle\lim_{x \to \infty} \frac{1}{x}$ and $\displaystyle\lim_{x \to -\infty} \frac{1}{x}$.

SOLUTION Observe that when x is large, $1/x$ is small. For instance,

$$\frac{1}{100} = 0.01 \qquad \frac{1}{10{,}000} = 0.0001 \qquad \frac{1}{1{,}000{,}000} = 0.000001$$

In fact, by taking x large enough, we can make $1/x$ as close to 0 as we please. Therefore, according to Definition 3, we have

$$\lim_{x \to \infty} \frac{1}{x} = 0$$

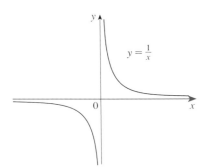

Similar reasoning shows that when x is large negative, $1/x$ is small negative, so we also have

$$\lim_{x \to -\infty} \frac{1}{x} = 0$$

It follows that the line $y = 0$ (the x-axis) is a horizontal asymptote of the curve $y = 1/x$. (This is an equilateral hyperbola; see Figure 12.) ▪

FIGURE 12

$\displaystyle\lim_{x \to \infty} \frac{1}{x} = 0, \quad \lim_{x \to -\infty} \frac{1}{x} = 0$

Most of the Limit Laws that were given in Section 1.4 also hold for limits at infinity. It can be proved that the *Limit Laws listed in Section 1.4 (with the exception of Laws 9 and 10) are also valid if "$x \to a$" is replaced by "$x \to \infty$" or "$x \to -\infty$."* In particular, if we combine Law 6 with the results of Example 4 we obtain the following important rule for calculating limits.

---

5 If n is a positive integer, then

$$\lim_{x \to \infty} \frac{1}{x^n} = 0 \qquad \lim_{x \to -\infty} \frac{1}{x^n} = 0$$

▼ EXAMPLE 5 Evaluate

$$\lim_{x \to \infty} \frac{3x^2 - x - 2}{5x^2 + 4x + 1}$$

SOLUTION As x becomes large, both numerator and denominator become large, so it isn't obvious what happens to their ratio. We need to do some preliminary algebra.

To evaluate the limit at infinity of any rational function, we first divide both the numerator and denominator by the highest power of x that occurs in the denominator. (We may assume that $x \neq 0$, since we are interested only in large values of x.) In this case the highest power of x is x^2, and so, using the Limit Laws, we have

$$\lim_{x \to \infty} \frac{3x^2 - x - 2}{5x^2 + 4x + 1} = \lim_{x \to \infty} \frac{\dfrac{3x^2 - x - 2}{x^2}}{\dfrac{5x^2 + 4x + 1}{x^2}} = \lim_{x \to \infty} \frac{3 - \dfrac{1}{x} - \dfrac{2}{x^2}}{5 + \dfrac{4}{x} + \dfrac{1}{x^2}}$$

▪ Figure 13 illustrates Example 5 by showing how the graph of the given rational function approaches the horizontal asymptote $y = \frac{3}{5}$.

$$= \frac{\lim\limits_{x \to \infty} \left(3 - \dfrac{1}{x} - \dfrac{2}{x^2} \right)}{\lim\limits_{x \to \infty} \left(5 + \dfrac{4}{x} + \dfrac{1}{x^2} \right)}$$

$$= \frac{\lim\limits_{x \to \infty} 3 - \lim\limits_{x \to \infty} \dfrac{1}{x} - 2 \lim\limits_{x \to \infty} \dfrac{1}{x^2}}{\lim\limits_{x \to \infty} 5 + 4 \lim\limits_{x \to \infty} \dfrac{1}{x} + \lim\limits_{x \to \infty} \dfrac{1}{x^2}}$$

$$= \frac{3 - 0 - 0}{5 + 0 + 0} \qquad \text{[by (5)]}$$

$$= \frac{3}{5}$$

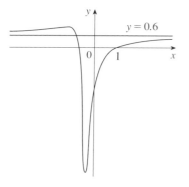

FIGURE 13
$$y = \frac{3x^2 - x - 2}{5x^2 + 4x + 1}$$

A similar calculation shows that the limit as $x \to -\infty$ is also $\frac{3}{5}$. ▪

EXAMPLE 6 Compute $\lim\limits_{x \to \infty} \left(\sqrt{x^2 + 1} - x \right)$.

SOLUTION Because both $\sqrt{x^2 + 1}$ and x are large when x is large, it's difficult to see what happens to their difference, so we use algebra to rewrite the function. We first multiply numerator and denominator by the conjugate radical:

▪ We can think of the given function as having a denominator of 1.

$$\lim_{x \to \infty} \left(\sqrt{x^2 + 1} - x \right) = \lim_{x \to \infty} \left(\sqrt{x^2 + 1} - x \right) \frac{\sqrt{x^2 + 1} + x}{\sqrt{x^2 + 1} + x}$$

$$= \lim_{x \to \infty} \frac{(x^2 + 1) - x^2}{\sqrt{x^2 + 1} + x} = \lim_{x \to \infty} \frac{1}{\sqrt{x^2 + 1} + x}$$

The Squeeze Theorem could be used to show that this limit is 0. But an easier method is to divide numerator and denominator by x. Doing this and remembering that $x = \sqrt{x^2}$ for $x > 0$, we obtain

$$\lim_{x \to \infty} \left(\sqrt{x^2 + 1} - x \right) = \lim_{x \to \infty} \frac{1}{\sqrt{x^2 + 1} + x} = \lim_{x \to \infty} \frac{\dfrac{1}{x}}{\dfrac{\sqrt{x^2 + 1} + x}{x}}$$

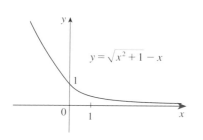

$$= \lim_{x \to \infty} \frac{\dfrac{1}{x}}{\sqrt{1 + \dfrac{1}{x^2}} + 1} = \frac{0}{\sqrt{1 + 0} + 1} = 0$$

FIGURE 14

Figure 14 illustrates this result. ▪

EXAMPLE 7 Evaluate $\lim\limits_{x \to \infty} \sin \dfrac{1}{x}$.

SOLUTION If we let $t = 1/x$, then $t \to 0^+$ as $x \to \infty$. Therefore

$$\lim_{x \to \infty} \sin \frac{1}{x} = \lim_{t \to 0^+} \sin t = 0$$

(See Exercise 55.) ▪

EXAMPLE 8 Evaluate $\lim\limits_{x \to \infty} \sin x$.

SOLUTION As x increases, the values of $\sin x$ oscillate between 1 and -1 infinitely often. Thus $\lim_{x \to \infty} \sin x$ does not exist. ▪

INFINITE LIMITS AT INFINITY

The notation
$$\lim_{x \to \infty} f(x) = \infty$$

is used to indicate that the values of $f(x)$ become large as x becomes large. Similar meanings are attached to the following symbols:

$$\lim_{x \to -\infty} f(x) = \infty \qquad \lim_{x \to \infty} f(x) = -\infty \qquad \lim_{x \to -\infty} f(x) = -\infty$$

EXAMPLE 9 Find $\lim\limits_{x \to \infty} x^3$ and $\lim\limits_{x \to -\infty} x^3$.

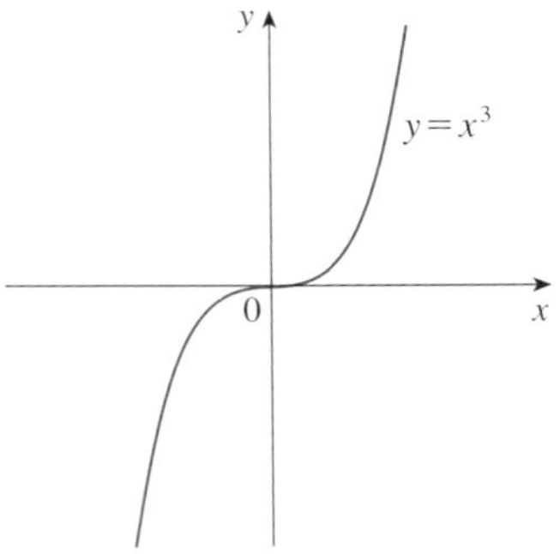

SOLUTION When x becomes large, x^3 also becomes large. For instance,

$$10^3 = 1000 \qquad 100^3 = 1,000,000 \qquad 1000^3 = 1,000,000,000$$

In fact, we can make x^3 as big as we like by taking x large enough. Therefore, we can write

$$\lim_{x \to \infty} x^3 = \infty$$

Similarly, when x is large negative, so is x^3. Thus

$$\lim_{x \to -\infty} x^3 = -\infty$$

FIGURE 15

$\lim\limits_{x \to \infty} x^3 = \infty, \ \lim\limits_{x \to -\infty} x^3 = -\infty$

These limit statements can also be seen from the graph of $y = x^3$ in Figure 15. ▪

EXAMPLE 10 Find $\lim\limits_{x \to \infty} (x^2 - x)$.

⊘ **SOLUTION** It would be **wrong** to write

$$\lim_{x \to \infty} (x^2 - x) = \lim_{x \to \infty} x^2 - \lim_{x \to \infty} x = \infty - \infty$$

The Limit Laws can't be applied to infinite limits because ∞ is not a number ($\infty - \infty$ can't be defined). However, we can write

$$\lim_{x \to \infty} (x^2 - x) = \lim_{x \to \infty} x(x - 1) = \infty$$

because both x and $x - 1$ become arbitrarily large. ▪

EXAMPLE 11 Find $\lim\limits_{x \to \infty} \dfrac{x^2 + x}{3 - x}$.

SOLUTION We divide numerator and denominator by x (the highest power of x that occurs in the denominator):

$$\lim_{x \to \infty} \frac{x^2 + x}{3 - x} = \lim_{x \to \infty} \frac{x + 1}{\dfrac{3}{x} - 1} = -\infty$$

because $x + 1 \to \infty$ and $3/x - 1 \to -1$ as $x \to \infty$. ∎

PRECISE DEFINITIONS

The following is a precise version of Definition 1.

> **6 DEFINITION** Let f be a function defined on some open interval that contains the number a, except possibly at a itself. Then
>
> $$\lim_{x \to a} f(x) = \infty$$
>
> means that for every positive number M there is a positive number δ such that
>
> if $\quad 0 < |x - a| < \delta \quad$ then $\quad f(x) > M$

This says that the values of $f(x)$ can be made arbitrarily large (larger than any given number M) by taking x close enough to a (within a distance δ, where δ depends on M, but with $x \neq a$). A geometric illustration is shown in Figure 16.

Given any horizontal line $y = M$, we can find a number $\delta > 0$ such that if we restrict x to lie in the interval $(a - \delta, a + \delta)$ but $x \neq a$, then the curve $y = f(x)$ lies above the line $y = M$. You can see that if a larger M is chosen, then a smaller δ may be required.

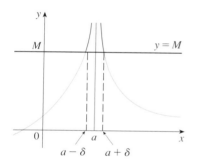

FIGURE 16

▼ EXAMPLE 12 Use Definition 6 to prove that $\lim\limits_{x \to 0} \dfrac{1}{x^2} = \infty$.

SOLUTION Let M be a given positive number. According to Definition 6, we need to find a number δ such that

if $\quad 0 < |x| < \delta \quad$ then $\quad \dfrac{1}{x^2} > M \quad$ that is $\quad x^2 < \dfrac{1}{M}$

But $x^2 < 1/M \iff |x| < 1/\sqrt{M}$. We can choose $\delta = 1/\sqrt{M}$ because

if $\quad 0 < |x| < \delta = \dfrac{1}{\sqrt{M}} \quad$ then $\quad \dfrac{1}{x^2} > \dfrac{1}{\delta^2} = M$

Therefore, by Definition 6,

$$\lim_{x \to 0} \frac{1}{x^2} = \infty$$

∎

Similarly, $\lim_{x \to a} f(x) = -\infty$ means that for every negative number N there is a positive number δ such that if $0 < |x - a| < \delta$, then $f(x) < N$.

Definition 3 can be stated precisely as follows.

---

7 DEFINITION Let f be a function defined on some interval (a, ∞). Then

$$\lim_{x \to \infty} f(x) = L$$

means that for every $\varepsilon > 0$ there is a corresponding number N such that

if $\quad x > N \quad$ then $\quad |f(x) - L| < \varepsilon$

In words, this says that the values of $f(x)$ can be made arbitrarily close to L (within a distance ε, where ε is any positive number) by taking x sufficiently large (larger than N, where N depends on ε). Graphically it says that by choosing x large enough (larger than some number N) we can make the graph of f lie between the given horizontal lines $y = L - \varepsilon$ and $y = L + \varepsilon$ as in Figure 17. This must be true no matter how small we choose ε. Figure 18 shows that if a smaller value of ε is chosen, then a larger value of N may be required.

Module 1.3/1.6 illustrates Definition 7 graphically and numerically.

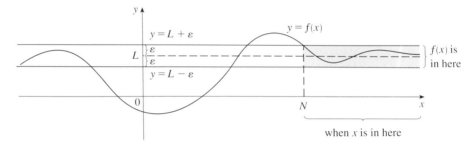

FIGURE 17
$\lim_{x \to \infty} f(x) = L$

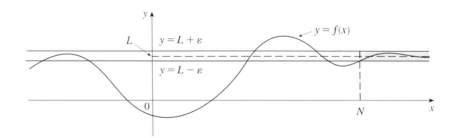

FIGURE 18
$\lim_{x \to \infty} f(x) = L$

Similarly, $\lim_{x \to -\infty} f(x) = L$ means that for every $\varepsilon > 0$ there is a corresponding number N such that if $x < N$, then $|f(x) - L| < \varepsilon$.

EXAMPLE 13 Use Definition 7 to prove that $\lim_{x \to \infty} \dfrac{1}{x} = 0$.

SOLUTION Given $\varepsilon > 0$, we want to find N such that

if $\quad x > N \quad$ then $\quad \left| \dfrac{1}{x} - 0 \right| < \varepsilon$

In computing the limit we may assume that $x > 0$. Then $1/x < \varepsilon \iff x > 1/\varepsilon$. Let's choose $N = 1/\varepsilon$. So

$$\text{if} \quad x > N = \frac{1}{\varepsilon} \quad \text{then} \quad \left| \frac{1}{x} - 0 \right| = \frac{1}{x} < \varepsilon$$

Therefore, by Definition 7,

$$\lim_{x \to \infty} \frac{1}{x} = 0$$

Figure 19 illustrates the proof by showing some values of ε and the corresponding values of N.

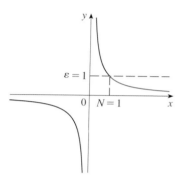 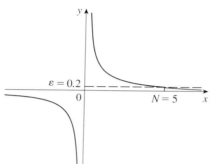 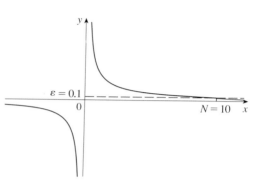

FIGURE 19

■

Finally we note that an infinite limit at infinity can be defined as follows. The geometric illustration is given in Figure 20.

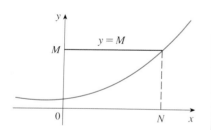

FIGURE 20
$\lim_{x \to \infty} f(x) = \infty$

8 DEFINITION Let f be a function defined on some interval (a, ∞). Then

$$\lim_{x \to \infty} f(x) = \infty$$

means that for every positive number M there is a corresponding positive number N such that

$$\text{if} \quad x > N \quad \text{then} \quad f(x) > M$$

Similar definitions apply when the symbol ∞ is replaced by $-\infty$.

1.6 EXERCISES

1. For the function f whose graph is given, state the following.

(a) $\lim_{x \to 2} f(x)$

(b) $\lim_{x \to -1^-} f(x)$

(c) $\lim_{x \to -1^+} f(x)$

(d) $\lim_{x \to \infty} f(x)$

(e) $\lim_{x \to -\infty} f(x)$

(f) The equations of the asymptotes

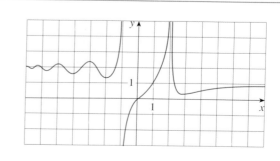

2. For the function g whose graph is given, state the following.

(a) $\lim\limits_{x \to \infty} g(x)$
(b) $\lim\limits_{x \to -\infty} g(x)$

(c) $\lim\limits_{x \to 3} g(x)$
(d) $\lim\limits_{x \to 0} g(x)$

(e) $\lim\limits_{x \to -2^+} g(x)$
(f) The equations of the asymptotes

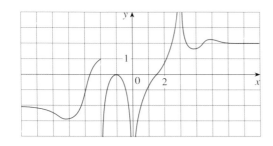

3–8 ▪ Sketch the graph of an example of a function f that satisfies all of the given conditions.

3. $f(0) = 0$, $f(1) = 1$, $\lim\limits_{x \to \infty} f(x) = 0$, f is odd

4. $\lim\limits_{x \to 0^+} f(x) = \infty$, $\lim\limits_{x \to 0^-} f(x) = -\infty$, $\lim\limits_{x \to \infty} f(x) = 1$,
$\lim\limits_{x \to -\infty} f(x) = 1$

5. $\lim\limits_{x \to 2} f(x) = -\infty$, $\lim\limits_{x \to \infty} f(x) = \infty$, $\lim\limits_{x \to -\infty} f(x) = 0$,
$\lim\limits_{x \to 0^+} f(x) = \infty$, $\lim\limits_{x \to 0^-} f(x) = -\infty$

6. $\lim\limits_{x \to -2} f(x) = \infty$, $\lim\limits_{x \to -\infty} f(x) = 3$, $\lim\limits_{x \to \infty} f(x) = -3$

7. $f(0) = 3$, $\lim\limits_{x \to 0^-} f(x) = 4$, $\lim\limits_{x \to 0^+} f(x) = 2$,
$\lim\limits_{x \to -\infty} f(x) = -\infty$, $\lim\limits_{x \to 4^-} f(x) = -\infty$, $\lim\limits_{x \to 4^+} f(x) = \infty$,
$\lim\limits_{x \to \infty} f(x) = 3$

8. $\lim\limits_{x \to 3} f(x) = -\infty$, $\lim\limits_{x \to \infty} f(x) = 2$, $f(0) = 0$, f is even

9. Guess the value of the limit

$$\lim\limits_{x \to \infty} \frac{x^2}{2^x}$$

by evaluating the function $f(x) = x^2/2^x$ for $x = 0, 1, 2, 3,$ 4, 5, 6, 7, 8, 9, 10, 20, 50, and 100. Then use a graph of f to support your guess.

10. Determine $\lim\limits_{x \to 1^-} \dfrac{1}{x^3 - 1}$ and $\lim\limits_{x \to 1^+} \dfrac{1}{x^3 - 1}$

(a) by evaluating $f(x) = 1/(x^3 - 1)$ for values of x that approach 1 from the left and from the right,
(b) by reasoning as in Example 1, and
(c) from a graph of f.

11. Use a graph to estimate all the vertical and horizontal asymptotes of the curve

$$y = \frac{x^3}{x^3 - 2x + 1}$$

12. (a) Use a graph of

$$f(x) = \left(1 - \frac{2}{x}\right)^x$$

to estimate the value of $\lim\limits_{x \to \infty} f(x)$ correct to two decimal places.
(b) Use a table of values of $f(x)$ to estimate the limit to four decimal places.

13–31 ▪ Find the limit.

13. $\lim\limits_{x \to -3^+} \dfrac{x + 2}{x + 3}$

14. $\lim\limits_{x \to 5^-} \dfrac{6}{x - 5}$

15. $\lim\limits_{x \to 1} \dfrac{2 - x}{(x - 1)^2}$

16. $\lim\limits_{x \to \pi^-} \cot x$

17. $\lim\limits_{x \to (-\pi/2)^-} \sec x$

18. $\lim\limits_{x \to \infty} \dfrac{3x + 5}{x - 4}$

19. $\lim\limits_{x \to \infty} \dfrac{x^3 + 5x}{2x^3 - x^2 + 4}$

20. $\lim\limits_{t \to -\infty} \dfrac{t^2 + 2}{t^3 + t^2 - 1}$

21. $\lim\limits_{u \to \infty} \dfrac{4u^4 + 5}{(u^2 - 2)(2u^2 - 1)}$

22. $\lim\limits_{x \to \infty} \dfrac{x + 2}{\sqrt{9x^2 + 1}}$

23. $\lim\limits_{x \to \infty} \left(\sqrt{9x^2 + x} - 3x\right)$

24. $\lim\limits_{x \to \infty} \left(\sqrt{x^2 + ax} - \sqrt{x^2 + bx}\right)$

25. $\lim\limits_{x \to \infty} \cos x$

26. $\lim\limits_{x \to \infty} \dfrac{\sin^2 x}{x^2}$

27. $\lim\limits_{x \to \infty} \left(x - \sqrt{x}\right)$

28. $\lim\limits_{x \to \infty} \dfrac{x^3 - 2x + 3}{5 - 2x^2}$

29. $\lim\limits_{x \to -\infty} (x^4 + x^5)$

30. $\lim\limits_{x \to \infty} (x^2 - x^4)$

31. $\lim\limits_{x \to \infty} \dfrac{x + x^3 + x^5}{1 - x^2 + x^4}$

32. (a) Graph the function

$$f(x) = \frac{\sqrt{2x^2 + 1}}{3x - 5}$$

How many horizontal and vertical asymptotes do you observe? Use the graph to estimate the values of the limits

$$\lim\limits_{x \to \infty} \frac{\sqrt{2x^2 + 1}}{3x - 5} \quad \text{and} \quad \lim\limits_{x \to -\infty} \frac{\sqrt{2x^2 + 1}}{3x - 5}$$

(b) By calculating values of $f(x)$, give numerical estimates of the limits in part (a).

(c) Calculate the exact values of the limits in part (a). Did you get the same value or different values for these two limits? [In view of your answer to part (a), you might have to check your calculation for the second limit.]

33–34 ▪ Find the horizontal and vertical asymptotes of each curve. Check your work by graphing the curve and estimating the asymptotes.

33. $y = \dfrac{2x^2 + x - 1}{x^2 + x - 2}$

34. $F(x) = \dfrac{x - 9}{\sqrt{4x^2 + 3x + 2}}$

▪ ▪ ▪ ▪ ▪ ▪ ▪ ▪ ▪ ▪ ▪ ▪ ▪

35. (a) Estimate the value of

$$\lim_{x \to -\infty} \left(\sqrt{x^2 + x + 1} + x \right)$$

by graphing the function $f(x) = \sqrt{x^2 + x + 1} + x$.
(b) Use a table of values of $f(x)$ to guess the value of the limit.
(c) Prove that your guess is correct.

36. (a) Use a graph of

$$f(x) = \sqrt{3x^2 + 8x + 6} - \sqrt{3x^2 + 3x + 1}$$

to estimate the value of $\lim_{x \to \infty} f(x)$ to one decimal place.
(b) Use a table of values of $f(x)$ to estimate the limit to four decimal places.
(c) Find the exact value of the limit.

37. Estimate the horizontal asymptote of the function

$$f(x) = \dfrac{3x^3 + 500x^2}{x^3 + 500x^2 + 100x + 2000}$$

by graphing f for $-10 \le x \le 10$. Then calculate the equation of the asymptote by evaluating the limit. How do you explain the discrepancy?

38. Find a formula for a function that has vertical asymptotes $x = 1$ and $x = 3$ and horizontal asymptote $y = 1$.

39. Find a formula for a function f that satisfies the following conditions:

$$\lim_{x \to \pm\infty} f(x) = 0, \quad \lim_{x \to 0} f(x) = -\infty, \quad f(2) = 0,$$

$$\lim_{x \to 3^-} f(x) = \infty, \quad \lim_{x \to 3^+} f(x) = -\infty$$

40. By the *end behavior* of a function we mean the behavior of its values as $x \to \infty$ and as $x \to -\infty$.
(a) Describe and compare the end behavior of the functions

$$P(x) = 3x^5 - 5x^3 + 2x \qquad Q(x) = 3x^5$$

by graphing both functions in the viewing rectangles $[-2, 2]$ by $[-2, 2]$ and $[-10, 10]$ by $[-10,000, 10,000]$.

(b) Two functions are said to have the *same end behavior* if their ratio approaches 1 as $x \to \infty$. Show that P and Q have the same end behavior.

41. Let P and Q be polynomials. Find

$$\lim_{x \to \infty} \dfrac{P(x)}{Q(x)}$$

if the degree of P is (a) less than the degree of Q and (b) greater than the degree of Q.

42. Make a rough sketch of the curve $y = x^n$ (n an integer) for the following five cases:
  (i) $n = 0$ (ii) $n > 0$, n odd
  (iii) $n > 0$, n even   (iv) $n < 0$, n odd
  (v) $n < 0$, n even
Then use these sketches to find the following limits.
(a) $\lim\limits_{x \to 0^+} x^n$ (b) $\lim\limits_{x \to 0^-} x^n$
(c) $\lim\limits_{x \to \infty} x^n$ (d) $\lim\limits_{x \to -\infty} x^n$

43. Find $\lim_{x \to \infty} f(x)$ if, for all $x > 5$,

$$\dfrac{4x - 1}{x} < f(x) < \dfrac{4x^2 + 3x}{x^2}$$

44. In the theory of relativity, the mass of a particle with velocity v is

$$m = \dfrac{m_0}{\sqrt{1 - v^2/c^2}}$$

where m_0 is the mass of the particle at rest and c is the speed of light. What happens as $v \to c^-$?

45. (a) A tank contains 5000 L of pure water. Brine that contains 30 g of salt per liter of water is pumped into the tank at a rate of 25 L/min. Show that the concentration of salt t minutes later (in grams per liter) is

$$C(t) = \dfrac{30t}{200 + t}$$

(b) What happens to the concentration as $t \to \infty$?

46. (a) Show that $\lim\limits_{x \to \infty} \dfrac{4x^2 - 5x}{2x^2 + 1} = 2$.

(b) By graphing the function in part (a) and the line $y = 1.9$ on a common screen, find a number N such that

$$\dfrac{4x^2 - 5x}{2x^2 + 1} > 1.9 \qquad \text{when} \qquad x > N$$

What if 1.9 is replaced by 1.99?

47. How close to -3 do we have to take x so that

$$\frac{1}{(x+3)^4} > 10{,}000$$

48. Prove, using Definition 6, that $\displaystyle\lim_{x\to-3}\frac{1}{(x+3)^4} = \infty$.

49. Prove that $\displaystyle\lim_{x\to-1^-}\frac{5}{(x+1)^3} = -\infty$.

50. For the limit

$$\lim_{x\to\infty}\frac{\sqrt{4x^2+1}}{x+1} = 2$$

illustrate Definition 7 by finding values of N that correspond to $\varepsilon = 0.5$ and $\varepsilon = 0.1$.

51. Use a graph to find a number N such that

$$\left|\frac{6x^2+5x-3}{2x^2-1} - 3\right| < 0.2 \qquad \text{whenever} \qquad x > N$$

52. For the limit

$$\lim_{x\to\infty}\frac{2x+1}{\sqrt{x+1}} = \infty$$

illustrate Definition 8 by finding a value of N that corresponds to $M = 100$.

53. (a) How large do we have to take x so that $1/x^2 < 0.0001$?
  (b) Taking $n = 2$ in (5), we have the statement

$$\lim_{x\to\infty}\frac{1}{x^2} = 0$$

  Prove this directly using Definition 7.

54. Prove, using Definition 8, that $\displaystyle\lim_{x\to\infty} x^3 = \infty$.

55. Prove that

$$\lim_{x\to\infty} f(x) = \lim_{t\to0^+} f(1/t)$$

and

$$\lim_{x\to-\infty} f(x) = \lim_{t\to0^-} f(1/t)$$

if these limits exist.

---

1 | REVIEW

CONCEPT CHECK

1. (a) What is a function? What are its domain and range?
  (b) What is the graph of a function?
  (c) How can you tell whether a given curve is the graph of a function?

2. Discuss four ways of representing a function. Illustrate your discussion with examples.

3. (a) What is an even function? How can you tell if a function is even by looking at its graph?
  (b) What is an odd function? How can you tell if a function is odd by looking at its graph?

4. What is a mathematical model?

5. Give an example of each type of function.
  (a) Linear function   (b) Power function
  (c) Exponential function   (d) Quadratic function
  (e) Polynomial of degree 5   (f) Rational function

6. Sketch by hand, on the same axes, the graphs of the following functions.
  (a) $f(x) = x$ (b) $g(x) = x^2$
  (c) $h(x) = x^3$ (d) $j(x) = x^4$

7. Draw, by hand, a rough sketch of the graph of each function.
  (a) $y = \sin x$ (b) $y = \tan x$
  (c) $y = 2^x$ (d) $y = 1/x$
  (e) $y = |x|$ (f) $y = \sqrt{x}$

8. Suppose that f has domain A and g has domain B.
  (a) What is the domain of $f + g$?
  (b) What is the domain of fg?
  (c) What is the domain of f/g?

9. How is the composite function $f \circ g$ defined? What is its domain?

10. Suppose the graph of f is given. Write an equation for each of the graphs that are obtained from the graph of f as follows.
  (a) Shift 2 units upward.
  (b) Shift 2 units downward.
  (c) Shift 2 units to the right.
  (d) Shift 2 units to the left.
  (e) Reflect about the x-axis.
  (f) Reflect about the y-axis.
  (g) Stretch vertically by a factor of 2.
  (h) Shrink vertically by a factor of 2.
  (i) Stretch horizontally by a factor of 2.
  (j) Shrink horizontally by a factor of 2.

11. Explain what each of the following means and illustrate with a sketch.
  (a) $\displaystyle\lim_{x\to a^-} f(x) = L$ (b) $\displaystyle\lim_{x\to a^+} f(x) = L$
  (c) $\displaystyle\lim_{x\to a} f(x) = L$ (d) $\displaystyle\lim_{x\to a} f(x) = \infty$
  (e) $\displaystyle\lim_{x\to\infty} f(x) = L$

12. Describe several ways in which a limit can fail to exist. Illustrate with sketches.

13. State the following Limit Laws.
(a) Sum Law
(b) Difference Law
(c) Constant Multiple Law
(d) Product Law
(e) Quotient Law
(f) Power Law
(g) Root Law

14. What does the Squeeze Theorem say?

15. (a) What does it mean for f to be continuous at a?

(b) What does it mean for f to be continuous on the interval $(-\infty, \infty)$? What can you say about the graph of such a function?

16. What does the Intermediate Value Theorem say?

17. (a) What does it mean to say that the line $x = a$ is a vertical asymptote of the curve $y = f(x)$? Draw curves to illustrate the various possibilities.

(b) What does it mean to say that the line $y = L$ is a horizontal asymptote of the curve $y = f(x)$? Draw curves to illustrate the various possibilities.

TRUE-FALSE QUIZ

Determine whether the statement is true or false. If it is true, explain why. If it is false, explain why or give an example that disproves the statement.

1. If f is a function, then $f(s + t) = f(s) + f(t)$.

2. If $f(s) = f(t)$, then $s = t$.

3. A vertical line intersects the graph of a function at most once.

4. If f and g are functions, then $f \circ g = g \circ f$.

5. $\lim\limits_{x \to 4} \left(\dfrac{2x}{x-4} - \dfrac{8}{x-4} \right) = \lim\limits_{x \to 4} \dfrac{2x}{x-4} - \lim\limits_{x \to 4} \dfrac{8}{x-4}$

6. $\lim\limits_{x \to 1} \dfrac{x^2 + 6x - 7}{x^2 + 5x - 6} = \dfrac{\lim\limits_{x \to 1} (x^2 + 6x - 7)}{\lim\limits_{x \to 1} (x^2 + 5x - 6)}$

7. $\lim\limits_{x \to 1} \dfrac{x - 3}{x^2 + 2x - 4} = \dfrac{\lim\limits_{x \to 1} (x - 3)}{\lim\limits_{x \to 1} (x^2 + 2x - 4)}$

8. If $\lim\limits_{x \to 5} f(x) = 2$ and $\lim\limits_{x \to 5} g(x) = 0$, then $\lim\limits_{x \to 5} [f(x)/g(x)]$ does not exist.

9. If $\lim\limits_{x \to 5} f(x) = 0$ and $\lim\limits_{x \to 5} g(x) = 0$, then $\lim\limits_{x \to 5} [f(x)/g(x)]$ does not exist.

10. If $\lim\limits_{x \to 6} f(x)g(x)$ exists, then the limit must be $f(6)g(6)$.

11. If p is a polynomial, then $\lim\limits_{x \to b} p(x) = p(b)$.

12. If $\lim\limits_{x \to 0} f(x) = \infty$ and $\lim\limits_{x \to 0} g(x) = \infty$, then $\lim\limits_{x \to 0} [f(x) - g(x)] = 0$.

13. A function can have two different horizontal asymptotes.

14. If f has domain $[0, \infty)$ and has no horizontal asymptote, then $\lim\limits_{x \to \infty} f(x) = \infty$ or $\lim\limits_{x \to \infty} f(x) = -\infty$.

15. If the line $x = 1$ is a vertical asymptote of $y = f(x)$, then f is not defined at 1.

16. If $f(1) > 0$ and $f(3) < 0$, then there exists a number c between 1 and 3 such that $f(c) = 0$.

17. If f is continuous at 5 and $f(5) = 2$ and $f(4) = 3$, then $\lim\limits_{x \to 2} f(4x^2 - 11) = 2$.

18. If f is continuous on $[-1, 1]$ and $f(-1) = 4$ and $f(1) = 3$, then there exists a number r such that $|r| < 1$ and $f(r) = \pi$.

19. Let f be a function such that $\lim\limits_{x \to 0} f(x) = 6$. Then there exists a number δ such that if $0 < |x| < \delta$, then $|f(x) - 6| < 1$.

20. If $f(x) > 1$ for all x and $\lim\limits_{x \to 0} f(x)$ exists, then $\lim\limits_{x \to 0} f(x) > 1$.

EXERCISES

1. Let f be the function whose graph is given.
(a) Estimate the value of $f(2)$.
(b) Estimate the values of x such that $f(x) = 3$.
(c) State the domain of f.
(d) State the range of f.
(e) On what interval is f increasing?
(f) Is f even, odd, or neither even nor odd? Explain.

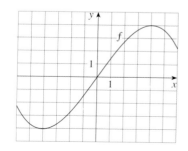

2. Determine whether each curve is the graph of a function of x. If it is, state the domain and range of the function.

(a)

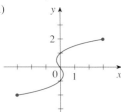

(b)

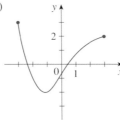

3–6 ■ Find the domain and range of the function.

3. $f(x) = \sqrt{4 - 3x^2}$

4. $g(x) = 1/(x + 1)$

5. $y = 1 + \sin x$

6. $y = \tan 2x$

■ ■ ■ ■ ■ ■ ■ ■ ■ ■ ■ ■ ■

7. Suppose that the graph of f is given. Describe how the graphs of the following functions can be obtained from the graph of f.

(a) $y = f(x) + 8$
(b) $y = f(x + 8)$
(c) $y = 1 + 2f(x)$
(d) $y = f(x - 2) - 2$
(e) $y = -f(x)$
(f) $y = 3 - f(x)$

8. The graph of f is given. Draw the graphs of the following functions.

(a) $y = f(x - 8)$
(b) $y = -f(x)$
(c) $y = 2 - f(x)$
(d) $y = \frac{1}{2}f(x) - 1$

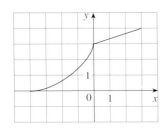

9–14 ■ Use transformations to sketch the graph of the function.

9. $y = -\sin 2x$

10. $y = (x - 2)^2$

11. $y = 1 + \frac{1}{2}x^3$

12. $y = 2 - \sqrt{x}$

13. $f(x) = \dfrac{1}{x + 2}$

14. $f(x) = \begin{cases} 1 + x & \text{if } x < 0 \\ 1 + x^2 & \text{if } x \geq 0 \end{cases}$

■ ■ ■ ■ ■ ■ ■ ■ ■ ■ ■ ■ ■

15. Determine whether f is even, odd, or neither even nor odd.

(a) $f(x) = 2x^5 - 3x^2 + 2$
(b) $f(x) = x^3 - x^7$
(c) $f(x) = \cos(x^2)$
(d) $f(x) = 1 + \sin x$

16. Find an expression for the function whose graph consists of the line segment from the point $(-2, 2)$ to the point $(-1, 0)$ together with the top half of the circle with center the origin and radius 1.

17. If $f(x) = \sqrt{x}$ and $g(x) = \sin x$, find the functions (a) $f \circ g$, (b) $g \circ f$, (c) $f \circ f$, (d) $g \circ g$, and their domains.

18. Express the function $F(x) = 1/\sqrt{x + \sqrt{x}}$ as a composition of three functions.

19. Use graphs to discover what members of the family of functions $f(x) = \sin^n x$ have in common, where n is a positive integer. How do they differ? What happens to the graphs as n becomes large?

20. A small-appliance manufacturer finds that it costs \$9000 to produce 1000 toaster ovens a week and \$12,000 to produce 1500 toaster ovens a week.

(a) Express the cost as a function of the number of toaster ovens produced, assuming that it is linear. Then sketch the graph.
(b) What is the slope of the graph and what does it represent?
(c) What is the y-intercept of the graph and what does it represent?

21. The graph of f is given.

(a) Find each limit, or explain why it does not exist.

(i) $\lim\limits_{x \to 2^+} f(x)$

(ii) $\lim\limits_{x \to -3^+} f(x)$

(iii) $\lim\limits_{x \to -3} f(x)$

(iv) $\lim\limits_{x \to 4} f(x)$

(v) $\lim\limits_{x \to 0} f(x)$

(vi) $\lim\limits_{x \to 2^-} f(x)$

(vii) $\lim\limits_{x \to \infty} f(x)$

(viii) $\lim\limits_{x \to -\infty} f(x)$

(b) State the equations of the horizontal asymptotes.
(c) State the equations of the vertical asymptotes.
(d) At what numbers is f discontinuous? Explain.

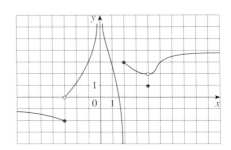

22. Sketch the graph of an example of a function f that satisfies all of the following conditions:

$$\lim\limits_{x \to -\infty} f(x) = -2, \quad \lim\limits_{x \to \infty} f(x) = 0, \quad \lim\limits_{x \to -3} f(x) = \infty,$$

$$\lim\limits_{x \to 3^-} f(x) = -\infty, \quad \lim\limits_{x \to 3^+} f(x) = 2,$$

f is continuous from the right at 3

23–38 ▪ Find the limit.

23. $\lim\limits_{x \to 0} \cos(x + \sin x)$

24. $\lim\limits_{x \to 3} \dfrac{x^2 - 9}{x^2 + 2x - 3}$

25. $\lim\limits_{x \to -3} \dfrac{x^2 - 9}{x^2 + 2x - 3}$

26. $\lim\limits_{x \to 1^+} \dfrac{x^2 - 9}{x^2 + 2x - 3}$

27. $\lim\limits_{h \to 0} \dfrac{(h - 1)^3 + 1}{h}$

28. $\lim\limits_{t \to 2} \dfrac{t^2 - 4}{t^3 - 8}$

29. $\lim\limits_{r \to 9} \dfrac{\sqrt{r}}{(r - 9)^4}$

30. $\lim\limits_{v \to 4^+} \dfrac{4 - v}{|4 - v|}$

31. $\lim\limits_{s \to 16} \dfrac{4 - \sqrt{s}}{s - 16}$

32. $\lim\limits_{v \to 2} \dfrac{v^2 + 2v - 8}{v^4 - 16}$

33. $\lim\limits_{x \to \infty} \dfrac{1 + 2x - x^2}{1 - x + 2x^2}$

34. $\lim\limits_{x \to -\infty} \dfrac{1 - 2x^2 - x^4}{5 + x - 3x^4}$

35. $\lim\limits_{x \to \infty} \left(\sqrt{x^2 + 4x + 1} - x \right)$

36. $\lim\limits_{x \to 1} \left(\dfrac{1}{x - 1} + \dfrac{1}{x^2 - 3x + 2} \right)$

37. $\lim\limits_{x \to 0} \dfrac{\cot 2x}{\csc x}$

38. $\lim\limits_{t \to 0} \dfrac{t^3}{\tan^3 2t}$

▪ ▪ ▪ ▪ ▪ ▪ ▪ ▪ ▪ ▪ ▪ ▪

39–40 ▪ Use graphs to discover the asymptotes of the curve. Then prove what you have discovered.

39. $y = \dfrac{\cos^2 x}{x^2}$

40. $y = \sqrt{x^2 + x + 1} - \sqrt{x^2 - x}$

▪ ▪ ▪ ▪ ▪ ▪ ▪ ▪ ▪ ▪ ▪ ▪ ▪

41. If $2x - 1 \le f(x) \le x^2$ for $0 < x < 3$, find $\lim\limits_{x \to 1} f(x)$.

42. Prove that $\lim\limits_{x \to 0} x^2 \cos(1/x^2) = 0$.

43–46 ▪ Prove the statement using the precise definition of a limit.

43. $\lim\limits_{x \to 5} (7x - 27) = 8$

44. $\lim\limits_{x \to 0} \sqrt[3]{x} = 0$

45. $\lim\limits_{x \to \infty} \dfrac{1}{x^4} = 0$

46. $\lim\limits_{x \to 4^+} \dfrac{2}{\sqrt{x - 4}} = \infty$

▪ ▪ ▪ ▪ ▪ ▪ ▪ ▪ ▪ ▪ ▪ ▪ ▪

47. Let

$$f(x) = \begin{cases} \sqrt{-x} & \text{if } x < 0 \\ 3 - x & \text{if } 0 \le x < 3 \\ (x - 3)^2 & \text{if } x > 3 \end{cases}$$

(a) Evaluate each limit, if it exists.

(i) $\lim\limits_{x \to 0^+} f(x)$ (ii) $\lim\limits_{x \to 0^-} f(x)$ (iii) $\lim\limits_{x \to 0} f(x)$

(iv) $\lim\limits_{x \to 3^-} f(x)$ (v) $\lim\limits_{x \to 3^+} f(x)$ (vi) $\lim\limits_{x \to 3} f(x)$

(b) Where is f discontinuous?

(c) Sketch the graph of f.

48. Show that each function is continuous on its domain. State the domain.

(a) $g(x) = \dfrac{\sqrt{x^2 - 9}}{x^2 - 2}$

(b) $h(x) = \sqrt[4]{x} + x^3 \cos x$

49–50 ▪ Use the Intermediate Value Theorem to show that there is a root of the equation in the given interval.

49. $2x^3 + x^2 + 2 = 0$, $(-2, -1)$

50. $2 \sin x = 3 - 2x$, $(0, 1)$

▪ ▪ ▪ ▪ ▪ ▪ ▪ ▪ ▪ ▪ ▪ ▪ ▪

2 DERIVATIVES

In this chapter we study a special type of limit, called a derivative, that occurs when we want to find the slope of a tangent line, or a velocity, or any instantaneous rate of change.

2.1 DERIVATIVES AND RATES OF CHANGE

The problem of finding the tangent line to a curve and the problem of finding the velocity of an object involve finding the same type of limit, which we call a *derivative*.

THE TANGENT PROBLEM

The word *tangent* is derived from the Latin word *tangens*, which means "touching." Thus a tangent to a curve is a line that touches the curve. In other words, a tangent line should have the same direction as the curve at the point of contact. How can this idea be made precise?

For a circle we could simply follow Euclid and say that a tangent is a line that intersects the circle once and only once as in Figure 1(a). For more complicated curves this definition is inadequate. Figure 1(b) shows two lines L and T passing through a point P on a curve C. The line L intersects C only once, but it certainly does not look like what we think of as a tangent. The line T, on the other hand, looks like a tangent but it intersects C twice.

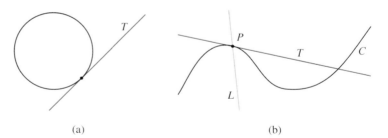

FIGURE 1   (a)   (b)

To be specific, let's look at the problem of trying to find a tangent line T to the parabola $y = x^2$ in the following example.

▼ **EXAMPLE 1** Find an equation of the tangent line to the parabola $y = x^2$ at the point $P(1, 1)$.

SOLUTION We will be able to find an equation of the tangent line T as soon as we know its slope m. The difficulty is that we know only one point, P, on T, whereas we need two points to compute the slope. But observe that we can compute an approximation to m by choosing a nearby point $Q(x, x^2)$ on the parabola (as in Figure 2) and computing the slope m_{PQ} of the secant line PQ.

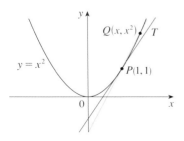

FIGURE 2

We choose $x \neq 1$ so that $Q \neq P$. Then

$$m_{PQ} = \frac{x^2 - 1}{x - 1}$$

What happens as x approaches 1? From Figure 3 we see that Q approaches P along the parabola and the secant lines PQ rotate about P and approach the tangent line T.

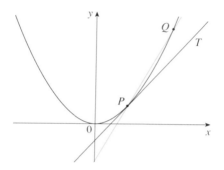

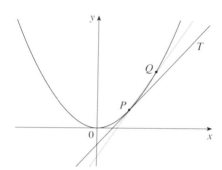

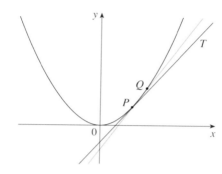

Q approaches P from the right

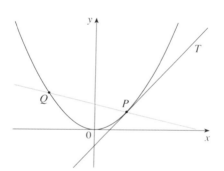

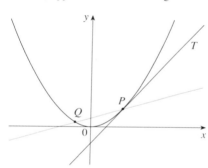

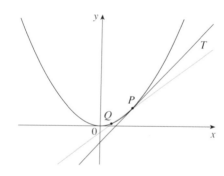

Q approaches P from the left

FIGURE 3

It appears that the slope m of the tangent line is the limit of the slopes of the secant lines as x approaches 1:

 In Visual 2.1A you can see how the process in Figure 3 works for additional functions.

$$m = \lim_{x \to 1} \frac{x^2 - 1}{x - 1} = \lim_{x \to 1} \frac{(x - 1)(x + 1)}{x - 1}$$

$$= \lim_{x \to 1} (x + 1) = 1 + 1 = 2$$

▪ Point-slope form for a line through the point (x_1, y_1) with slope m:

$$y - y_1 = m(x - x_1)$$

Using the point-slope form of the equation of a line, we find that an equation of the tangent line at $(1, 1)$ is

$$y - 1 = 2(x - 1) \qquad \text{or} \qquad y = 2x - 1 \qquad ▪$$

We sometimes refer to the slope of the tangent line to a curve at a point as the **slope of the curve** at the point. The idea is that if we zoom in far enough toward the point, the curve looks almost like a straight line. Figure 4 illustrates this procedure for the curve $y = x^2$ in Example 1. The more we zoom in, the more the parabola looks like a line. In other words, the curve becomes almost indistinguishable from its tangent line.

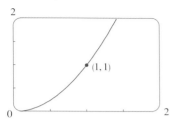 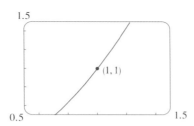 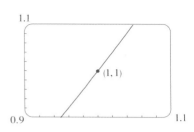

FIGURE 4   Zooming in toward the point $(1, 1)$ on the parabola $y = x^2$

 Visual 2.1B shows an animation of Figure 4.

In general, if a curve C has equation $y = f(x)$ and we want to find the tangent line to C at the point $P(a, f(a))$, then we consider a nearby point $Q(x, f(x))$, where $x \neq a$, and compute the slope of the secant line PQ:

$$m_{PQ} = \frac{f(x) - f(a)}{x - a}$$

Then we let Q approach P along the curve C by letting x approach a. If m_{PQ} approaches a number m, then we define the *tangent T* to be the line through P with slope m. (This amounts to saying that the tangent line is the limiting position of the secant line PQ as Q approaches P. See Figure 5.)

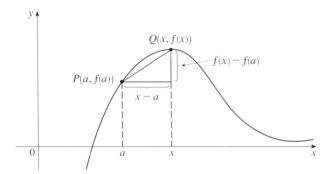 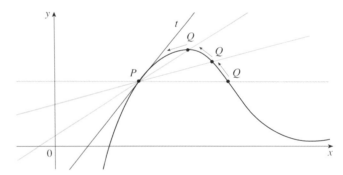

FIGURE 5

1   DEFINITION   The **tangent line** to the curve $y = f(x)$ at the point $P(a, f(a))$ is the line through P with slope

$$m = \lim_{x \to a} \frac{f(x) - f(a)}{x - a}$$

provided that this limit exists.

There is another expression for the slope of a tangent line that is sometimes easier to use. If $h = x - a$, then $x = a + h$ and so the slope of the secant line PQ is

$$m_{PQ} = \frac{f(a + h) - f(a)}{h}$$

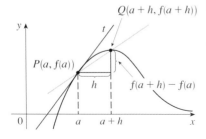

FIGURE 6

(See Figure 6 where the case $h > 0$ is illustrated and Q is to the right of P. If it happened that $h < 0$, however, Q would be to the left of P.) Notice that as x approaches a, h approaches 0 (because $h = x - a$) and so the expression for the slope of the tangent line in Definition 1 becomes

2
$$m = \lim_{h \to 0} \frac{f(a + h) - f(a)}{h}$$

EXAMPLE 2 Find an equation of the tangent line to the hyperbola $y = 3/x$ at the point $(3, 1)$.

SOLUTION Let $f(x) = 3/x$. Then the slope of the tangent at $(3, 1)$ is

$$m = \lim_{h \to 0} \frac{f(3 + h) - f(3)}{h}$$

$$= \lim_{h \to 0} \frac{\dfrac{3}{3 + h} - 1}{h} = \lim_{h \to 0} \frac{\dfrac{3 - (3 + h)}{3 + h}}{h}$$

$$= \lim_{h \to 0} \frac{-h}{h(3 + h)} = \lim_{h \to 0} -\frac{1}{3 + h} = -\frac{1}{3}$$

Therefore, an equation of the tangent at the point $(3, 1)$ is

$$y - 1 = -\tfrac{1}{3}(x - 3)$$

which simplifies to
$$x + 3y - 6 = 0$$

The hyperbola and its tangent are shown in Figure 7. ■

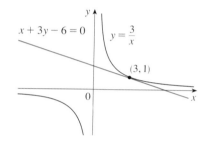

FIGURE 7

THE VELOCITY PROBLEM

In Section 1.3 we investigated the motion of a ball dropped from the CN Tower and defined its velocity to be the limiting value of average velocities over shorter and shorter time periods.

In general, suppose an object moves along a straight line according to an equation of motion $s = f(t)$, where s is the displacement (directed distance) of the object from the origin at time t. The function f that describes the motion is called the **position function** of the object. In the time interval from $t = a$ to $t = a + h$ the change in position is $f(a + h) - f(a)$. (See Figure 8.) The average velocity over this time interval is

$$\text{average velocity} = \frac{\text{displacement}}{\text{time}} = \frac{f(a + h) - f(a)}{h}$$

which is the same as the slope of the secant line PQ in Figure 9.

Now suppose we compute the average velocities over shorter and shorter time intervals $[a, a + h]$. In other words, we let h approach 0. As in the example of the falling ball, we define the **velocity** (or **instantaneous velocity**) $v(a)$ at time $t = a$ to be the limit of these average velocities:

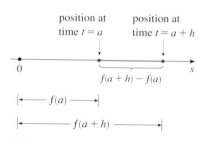

FIGURE 8

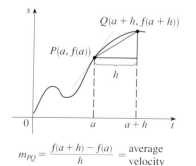

FIGURE 9

3
$$v(a) = \lim_{h \to 0} \frac{f(a + h) - f(a)}{h}$$

This means that the velocity at time $t = a$ is equal to the slope of the tangent line at P (compare Equations 2 and 3).

Now that we know how to compute limits, let's reconsider the problem of the falling ball.

▼ EXAMPLE 3 Suppose that a ball is dropped from the upper observation deck of the CN Tower, 450 m above the ground.
(a) What is the velocity of the ball after 5 seconds?
(b) How fast is the ball traveling when it hits the ground?

▪ Recall from Section 1.3: The distance (in meters) fallen after t seconds is $4.9t^2$.

SOLUTION We first use the equation of motion $s = f(t) = 4.9t^2$ to find the velocity $v(a)$ after a seconds:

$$v(a) = \lim_{h \to 0} \frac{f(a + h) - f(a)}{h} = \lim_{h \to 0} \frac{4.9(a + h)^2 - 4.9a^2}{h}$$

$$= \lim_{h \to 0} \frac{4.9(a^2 + 2ah + h^2 - a^2)}{h} = \lim_{h \to 0} \frac{4.9(2ah + h^2)}{h}$$

$$= \lim_{h \to 0} 4.9(2a + h) = 9.8a$$

(a) The velocity after 5 s is $v(5) = (9.8)(5) = 49$ m/s.

(b) Since the observation deck is 450 m above the ground, the ball will hit the ground at the time t_1 when $s(t_1) = 450$, that is,

$$4.9t_1^2 = 450$$

This gives

$$t_1^2 = \frac{450}{4.9} \quad \text{and} \quad t_1 = \sqrt{\frac{450}{4.9}} \approx 9.6 \text{ s}$$

The velocity of the ball as it hits the ground is therefore

$$v(t_1) = 9.8t_1 = 9.8\sqrt{\frac{450}{4.9}} \approx 94 \text{ m/s}$$ ▪

DERIVATIVES

We have seen that the same type of limit arises in finding the slope of a tangent line (Equation 2) or the velocity of an object (Equation 3). In fact, limits of the form

$$\lim_{h \to 0} \frac{f(a + h) - f(a)}{h}$$

arise whenever we calculate a rate of change in any of the sciences or engineering, such as a rate of reaction in chemistry or a marginal cost in economics. Since this type of limit occurs so widely, it is given a special name and notation.

---

4 DEFINITION   The **derivative of a function f at a number a**, denoted by $f'(a)$, is

▪ $f'(a)$ is read "f prime of a."

$$f'(a) = \lim_{h \to 0} \frac{f(a + h) - f(a)}{h}$$

if this limit exists.

If we write $x = a + h$, then $h = x - a$ and h approaches 0 if and only if x approaches a. Therefore, an equivalent way of stating the definition of the derivative, as we saw in finding tangent lines, is

5

$$f'(a) = \lim_{x \to a} \frac{f(x) - f(a)}{x - a}$$

✔ EXAMPLE 4 Find the derivative of the function $f(x) = x^2 - 8x + 9$ at the number a.

SOLUTION From Definition 4 we have

$$f'(a) = \lim_{h \to 0} \frac{f(a + h) - f(a)}{h}$$

$$= \lim_{h \to 0} \frac{[(a + h)^2 - 8(a + h) + 9] - [a^2 - 8a + 9]}{h}$$

$$= \lim_{h \to 0} \frac{a^2 + 2ah + h^2 - 8a - 8h + 9 - a^2 + 8a - 9}{h}$$

$$= \lim_{h \to 0} \frac{2ah + h^2 - 8h}{h} = \lim_{h \to 0} (2a + h - 8)$$

$$= 2a - 8 \qquad\blacksquare$$

We defined the tangent line to the curve $y = f(x)$ at the point $P(a, f(a))$ to be the line that passes through P and has slope m given by Equation 1 or 2. Since, by Definition 4, this is the same as the derivative $f'(a)$, we can now say the following.

> The tangent line to $y = f(x)$ at $(a, f(a))$ is the line through $(a, f(a))$ whose slope is equal to $f'(a)$, the derivative of f at a.

If we use the point-slope form of the equation of a line, we can write an equation of the tangent line to the curve $y = f(x)$ at the point $(a, f(a))$:

$$y - f(a) = f'(a)(x - a)$$

✔ EXAMPLE 5 Find an equation of the tangent line to the parabola $y = x^2 - 8x + 9$ at the point $(3, -6)$.

SOLUTION From Example 4 we know that the derivative of $f(x) = x^2 - 8x + 9$ at the number a is $f'(a) = 2a - 8$. Therefore, the slope of the tangent line at $(3, -6)$ is $f'(3) = 2(3) - 8 = -2$. Thus, an equation of the tangent line, shown in Figure 10, is

$$y - (-6) = (-2)(x - 3) \qquad \text{or} \qquad y = -2x \qquad\blacksquare$$

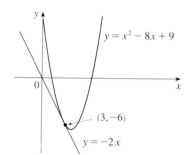

$y = x^2 - 8x + 9$

$(3, -6)$

$y = -2x$

FIGURE 10

RATES OF CHANGE

Suppose y is a quantity that depends on another quantity x. Thus y is a function of x and we write $y = f(x)$. If x changes from x_1 to x_2, then the change in x (also called the **increment** of x) is

$$\Delta x = x_2 - x_1$$

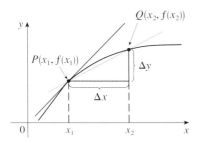

average rate of change = m_{PQ}

instantaneous rate of change =
  slope of tangent at P

FIGURE 11

and the corresponding change in y is

$$\Delta y = f(x_2) - f(x_1)$$

The difference quotient

$$\frac{\Delta y}{\Delta x} = \frac{f(x_2) - f(x_1)}{x_2 - x_1}$$

is called the **average rate of change of y with respect to x** over the interval $[x_1, x_2]$ and can be interpreted as the slope of the secant line PQ in Figure 11.

By analogy with velocity, we consider the average rate of change over smaller and smaller intervals by letting x_2 approach x_1 and therefore letting Δx approach 0. The limit of these average rates of change is called the (**instantaneous**) **rate of change of y with respect to x** at $x = x_1$, which is interpreted as the slope of the tangent to the curve $y = f(x)$ at $P(x_1, f(x_1))$:

> **6**   instantaneous rate of change $= \displaystyle\lim_{\Delta x \to 0} \frac{\Delta y}{\Delta x} = \lim_{x_2 \to x_1} \frac{f(x_2) - f(x_1)}{x_2 - x_1}$

We recognize this limit as being the derivative $f'(x_1)$.

We know that one interpretation of the derivative $f'(a)$ is as the slope of the tangent line to the curve $y = f(x)$ when $x = a$. We now have a second interpretation:

> The derivative $f'(a)$ is the instantaneous rate of change of $y = f(x)$ with respect to x when $x = a$.

The connection with the first interpretation is that if we sketch the curve $y = f(x)$, then the instantaneous rate of change is the slope of the tangent to this curve at the point where $x = a$. This means that when the derivative is large (and therefore the curve is steep, as at the point P in Figure 12), the y-values change rapidly. When the derivative is small, the curve is relatively flat and the y-values change slowly.

In particular, if $s = f(t)$ is the position function of a particle that moves along a straight line, then $f'(a)$ is the rate of change of the displacement s with respect to the time t. In other words, $f'(a)$ *is the velocity of the particle at time $t = a$.* The **speed** of the particle is the absolute value of the velocity, that is, $|f'(a)|$.

In the following example we estimate the rate of change of the national debt with respect to time. Here the function is defined not by a formula but by a table of values.

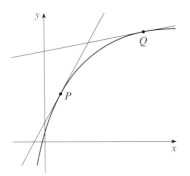

FIGURE 12
The y-values are changing rapidly at P and slowly at Q.

t	$D(t)$
1980	930.2
1985	1945.9
1990	3233.3
1995	4974.0
2000	5674.2

▼ EXAMPLE 6 Let $D(t)$ be the US national debt at time t. The table in the margin gives approximate values of this function by providing end of year estimates, in billions of dollars, from 1980 to 2000. Interpret and estimate the value of $D'(1990)$.

SOLUTION The derivative $D'(1990)$ means the rate of change of D with respect to t when $t = 1990$, that is, the rate of increase of the national debt in 1990.

According to Equation 5,

$$D'(1990) = \lim_{t \to 1990} \frac{D(t) - D(1990)}{t - 1990}$$

So we compute and tabulate values of the difference quotient (the average rates of change) as follows.

t	$\dfrac{D(t) - D(1990)}{t - 1990}$
1980	230.31
1985	257.48
1995	348.14
2000	244.09

■ **A NOTE ON UNITS**

The units for the average rate of change $\Delta D / \Delta t$ are the units for ΔD divided by the units for Δt, namely, billions of dollars per year. The instantaneous rate of change is the limit of the average rates of change, so it is measured in the same units: billions of dollars per year.

From this table we see that $D'(1990)$ lies somewhere between 257.48 and 348.14 billion dollars per year. [Here we are making the reasonable assumption that the debt didn't fluctuate wildly between 1980 and 2000.] We estimate that the rate of increase of the national debt of the United States in 1990 was the average of these two numbers, namely

$$D'(1990) \approx 303 \text{ billion dollars per year}$$

Another method would be to plot the debt function and estimate the slope of the tangent line when $t = 1990$. ■

The rate of change of the debt with respect to time in Example 6 is just one example of a rate of change. Here are a few of the many others:

The velocity of a particle is the rate of change of displacement with respect to time. Physicists are interested in other rates of change as well—for instance, the rate of change of work with respect to time (which is called *power*). Chemists who study a chemical reaction are interested in the rate of change in the concentration of a reactant with respect to time (called the *rate of reaction*). A steel manufacturer is interested in the rate of change of the cost of producing x tons of steel per day with respect to x (called the *marginal cost*). A biologist is interested in the rate of change of the population of a colony of bacteria with respect to time. In fact, the computation of rates of change is important in all of the natural sciences, in engineering, and even in the social sciences.

All these rates of change can be interpreted as slopes of tangents. This gives added significance to the solution of the tangent problem. Whenever we solve a problem involving tangent lines, we are not just solving a problem in geometry. We are also implicitly solving a great variety of problems involving rates of change in science and engineering.

2.1 EXERCISES

1. (a) Find the slope of the tangent line to the parabola
$y = x^2 + 2x$ at the point $(-3, 3)$
  (i) using Definition 1
  (ii) using Equation 2
(b) Find an equation of the tangent line in part (a).
(c) Graph the parabola and the tangent line. As a check on your work, zoom in toward the point $(-3, 3)$ until the parabola and the tangent line are indistinguishable.

2. (a) Find the slope of the tangent line to the curve $y = x^3$ at the point $(-1, -1)$
  (i) using Definition 1
  (ii) using Equation 2
(b) Find an equation of the tangent line in part (a).
(c) Graph the curve and the tangent line in successively smaller viewing rectangles centered at $(-1, -1)$ until the curve and the line appear to coincide.

3–6 ▪ Find an equation of the tangent line to the curve at the given point.

3. $y = (x - 1)/(x - 2)$, $(3, 2)$

4. $y = 2x^3 - 5x$, $(-1, 3)$

5. $y = \sqrt{x}$, $(1, 1)$

6. $y = 2x/(x + 1)^2$, $(0, 0)$

▪ ▪ ▪ ▪ ▪ ▪ ▪ ▪ ▪ ▪ ▪ ▪ ▪

7. (a) Find the slope of the tangent to the curve
  $y = 3 + 4x^2 - 2x^3$ at the point where $x = a$.
  (b) Find equations of the tangent lines at the points $(1, 5)$
  and $(2, 3)$.
  (c) Graph the curve and both tangents on a common screen.

8. (a) Find the slope of the tangent to the curve $y = 1/\sqrt{x}$ at
  the point where $x = a$.
  (b) Find equations of the tangent lines at the points $(1, 1)$
  and $\left(4, \frac{1}{2}\right)$.
  (c) Graph the curve and both tangents on a common screen.

9. The graph shows the position function of a car. Use the
  shape of the graph to explain your answers to the following
  questions.
  (a) What was the initial velocity of the car?
  (b) Was the car going faster at B or at C?
  (c) Was the car slowing down or speeding up at A, B, and C?
  (d) What happened between D and E?

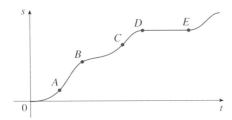

10. Shown are graphs of the position functions of two runners,
  A and B, who run a 100-m race and finish in a tie.

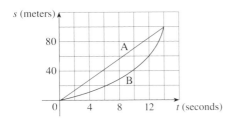

  (a) Describe and compare how the runners run the race.
  (b) At what time is the distance between the runners the
  greatest?
  (c) At what time do they have the same velocity?

11. If a ball is thrown into the air with a velocity of 40 ft/s, its
  height (in feet) after t seconds is given by $y = 40t - 16t^2$.
  Find the velocity when $t = 2$.

12. If an arrow is shot upward on the moon with a velocity of
  58 m/s, its height (in meters) after t seconds is given by
  $H = 58t - 0.83t^2$.
  (a) Find the velocity of the arrow after one second.
  (b) Find the velocity of the arrow when $t = a$.
  (c) When will the arrow hit the moon?
  (d) With what velocity will the arrow hit the moon?

13. The displacement (in meters) of a particle moving in a
  straight line is given by the equation of motion $s = 1/t^2$,
  where t is measured in seconds. Find the velocity of the
  particle at times $t = a$, $t = 1$, $t = 2$, and $t = 3$.

14. The displacement (in meters) of a particle moving in a
  straight line is given by $s = t^2 - 8t + 18$, where t is measured in seconds.
  (a) Find the average velocity over each time interval:
      (i) $[3, 4]$ (ii) $[3.5, 4]$
      (iii) $[4, 5]$ (iv) $[4, 4.5]$
  (b) Find the instantaneous velocity when $t = 4$.
  (c) Draw the graph of s as a function of t and draw the
  secant lines whose slopes are the average velocities in
  part (a) and the tangent line whose slope is the instantaneous velocity in part (b).

15. For the function g whose graph is given, arrange the following numbers in increasing order and explain your reasoning:

$$0 \qquad g'(-2) \qquad g'(0) \qquad g'(2) \qquad g'(4)$$

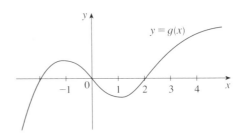

16. (a) Find an equation of the tangent line to the graph of
  $y = g(x)$ at $x = 5$ if $g(5) = -3$ and $g'(5) = 4$.
  (b) If the tangent line to $y = f(x)$ at $(4, 3)$ passes through
  the point $(0, 2)$, find $f(4)$ and $f'(4)$.

17. Sketch the graph of a function f for which $f(0) = 0$,
  $f'(0) = 3$, $f'(1) = 0$, and $f'(2) = -1$.

18. Sketch the graph of a function g for which $g(0) = g'(0) = 0$,
  $g'(-1) = -1$, $g'(1) = 3$, and $g'(2) = 1$.

19. If $f(x) = 3x^2 - 5x$, find $f'(2)$ and use it to find an equation of the tangent line to the parabola $y = 3x^2 - 5x$ at the
  point $(2, 2)$.

20. If $g(x) = 1 - x^3$, find $g'(0)$ and use it to find an equation of
  the tangent line to the curve $y = 1 - x^3$ at the point $(0, 1)$.

21. (a) If $F(x) = 5x/(1 + x^2)$, find $F'(2)$ and use it to find an equation of the tangent line to the curve $y = 5x/(1 + x^2)$ at the point $(2, 2)$.

(b) Illustrate part (a) by graphing the curve and the tangent line on the same screen.

22. (a) If $G(x) = 4x^2 - x^3$, find $G'(a)$ and use it to find equations of the tangent lines to the curve $y = 4x^2 - x^3$ at the points $(2, 8)$ and $(3, 9)$.

(b) Illustrate part (a) by graphing the curve and the tangent lines on the same screen.

23–28 ▪ Find $f'(a)$.

23. $f(x) = 3 - 2x + 4x^2$

24. $f(t) = t^4 - 5t$

25. $f(t) = \dfrac{2t + 1}{t + 3}$

26. $f(x) = \dfrac{x^2 + 1}{x - 2}$

27. $f(x) = \dfrac{1}{\sqrt{x + 2}}$

28. $f(x) = \sqrt{3x + 1}$

▪ ▪ ▪ ▪ ▪ ▪ ▪ ▪ ▪ ▪ ▪ ▪ ▪ ▪ ▪

29–34 ▪ Each limit represents the derivative of some function f at some number a. State such an f and a in each case.

29. $\displaystyle\lim_{h \to 0} \frac{(1 + h)^{10} - 1}{h}$

30. $\displaystyle\lim_{h \to 0} \frac{\sqrt[4]{16 + h} - 2}{h}$

31. $\displaystyle\lim_{x \to 5} \frac{2^x - 32}{x - 5}$

32. $\displaystyle\lim_{x \to \pi/4} \frac{\tan x - 1}{x - \pi/4}$

33. $\displaystyle\lim_{h \to 0} \frac{\cos(\pi + h) + 1}{h}$

34. $\displaystyle\lim_{t \to 1} \frac{t^4 + t - 2}{t - 1}$

▪ ▪ ▪ ▪ ▪ ▪ ▪ ▪ ▪ ▪ ▪ ▪ ▪ ▪ ▪

35. A warm can of soda is placed in a cold refrigerator. Sketch the graph of the temperature of the soda as a function of time. Is the initial rate of change of temperature greater or less than the rate of change after an hour?

36. A roast turkey is taken from an oven when its temperature has reached 185°F and is placed on a table in a room where the temperature is 75°F. The graph shows how the temperature of the turkey decreases and eventually approaches room temperature. By measuring the slope of the tangent, estimate the rate of change of the temperature after an hour.

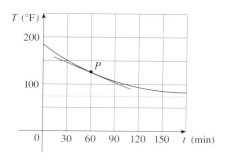

37. The table shows the estimated percentage P of the population of Europe that use cell phones. (Midyear estimates are given.)

Year	1998	1999	2000	2001	2002	2003
P	28	39	55	68	77	83

(a) Find the average rate of cell phone growth
  (i) from 2000 to 2002   (ii) from 2000 to 2001
  (iii) from 1999 to 2000
  In each case, include the units.

(b) Estimate the instantaneous rate of growth in 2000 by taking the average of two average rates of change. What are its units?

(c) Estimate the instantaneous rate of growth in 2000 by measuring the slope of a tangent.

38. The number N of locations of a popular coffeehouse chain is given in the table. (The numbers of locations as of June 30 are given.)

Year	1998	1999	2000	2001	2002
N	1886	2135	3501	4709	5886

(a) Find the average rate of growth
  (i) from 2000 to 2002   (ii) from 2000 to 2001
  (iii) from 1999 to 2000
  In each case, include the units.

(b) Estimate the instantaneous rate of growth in 2000 by taking the average of two average rates of change. What are its units?

(c) Estimate the instantaneous rate of growth in 2000 by measuring the slope of a tangent.

39. The cost (in dollars) of producing x units of a certain commodity is $C(x) = 5000 + 10x + 0.05x^2$.

(a) Find the average rate of change of C with respect to x when the production level is changed
  (i) from $x = 100$ to $x = 105$
  (ii) from $x = 100$ to $x = 101$

(b) Find the instantaneous rate of change of C with respect to x when $x = 100$. (This is called the *marginal cost*. Its significance will be explained in Section 2.3.)

40. If a cylindrical tank holds 100,000 gallons of water, which can be drained from the bottom of the tank in an hour, then Torricelli's Law gives the volume V of water remaining in the tank after t minutes as

$$V(t) = 100{,}000\left(1 - \tfrac{1}{60}t\right)^2 \qquad 0 \le t \le 60$$

Find the rate at which the water is flowing out of the tank (the instantaneous rate of change of V with respect to t) as a function of t. What are its units? For times $t = 0, 10, 20, 30, 40, 50,$ and 60 min, find the flow rate and the amount of water remaining in the tank. Summarize your findings in a sentence or two. At what time is the flow rate the greatest? The least?

41. The cost of producing x ounces of gold from a new gold mine is $C = f(x)$ dollars.
   (a) What is the meaning of the derivative $f'(x)$? What are its units?
   (b) What does the statement $f'(800) = 17$ mean?
   (c) Do you think the values of $f'(x)$ will increase or decrease in the short term? What about the long term? Explain.

42. The number of bacteria after t hours in a controlled laboratory experiment is $n = f(t)$.
   (a) What is the meaning of the derivative $f'(5)$? What are its units?
   (b) Suppose there is an unlimited amount of space and nutrients for the bacteria. Which do you think is larger, $f'(5)$ or $f'(10)$? If the supply of nutrients is limited, would that affect your conclusion? Explain.

43. Let $T(t)$ be the temperature (in °F) in Dallas t hours after midnight on June 2, 2001. The table shows values of this function recorded every two hours. What is the meaning of $T'(10)$? Estimate its value.

t	0	2	4	6	8	10	12	14
T	73	73	70	69	72	81	88	91

44. The quantity (in pounds) of a gourmet ground coffee that is sold by a coffee company at a price of p dollars per pound is $Q = f(p)$.
   (a) What is the meaning of the derivative $f'(8)$? What are its units?
   (b) Is $f'(8)$ positive or negative? Explain.

45. The quantity of oxygen that can dissolve in water depends on the temperature of the water. (So thermal pollution influences the oxygen content of water.) The graph shows how oxygen solubility S varies as a function of the water temperature T.
   (a) What is the meaning of the derivative $S'(T)$? What are its units?

   (b) Estimate the value of $S'(16)$ and interpret it.

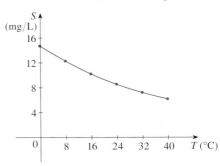

46. The graph shows the influence of the temperature T on the maximum sustainable swimming speed S of Coho salmon.
   (a) What is the meaning of the derivative $S'(T)$? What are its units?
   (b) Estimate the values of $S'(15)$ and $S'(25)$ and interpret them.

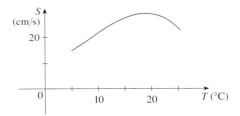

47–48 ▪ Determine whether $f'(0)$ exists.

47. $f(x) = \begin{cases} x \sin \dfrac{1}{x} & \text{if } x \neq 0 \\ 0 & \text{if } x = 0 \end{cases}$

48. $f(x) = \begin{cases} x^2 \sin \dfrac{1}{x} & \text{if } x \neq 0 \\ 0 & \text{if } x = 0 \end{cases}$

▪   ▪   ▪   ▪   ▪   ▪   ▪   ▪   ▪   ▪   ▪   ▪   ▪   ▪

2.2   THE DERIVATIVE AS A FUNCTION

In Section 2.1 we considered the derivative of a function f at a fixed number a:

1
$$f'(a) = \lim_{h \to 0} \frac{f(a + h) - f(a)}{h}$$

Here we change our point of view and let the number a vary. If we replace a in Equation 1 by a variable x, we obtain

2
$$f'(x) = \lim_{h \to 0} \frac{f(x + h) - f(x)}{h}$$

Given any number x for which this limit exists, we assign to x the number $f'(x)$. So we can regard f' as a new function, called the **derivative of f** and defined by Equation 2. We know that the value of f' at x, $f'(x)$, can be interpreted geometrically as the slope of the tangent line to the graph of f at the point $(x, f(x))$.

The function f' is called the derivative of f because it has been "derived" from f by the limiting operation in Equation 2. The domain of f' is the set $\{x \mid f'(x) \text{ exists}\}$ and may be smaller than the domain of f.

☑ EXAMPLE 1 The graph of a function f is given in Figure 1. Use it to sketch the graph of the derivative f'.

SOLUTION We can estimate the value of the derivative at any value of x by drawing the tangent at the point $(x, f(x))$ and estimating its slope. For instance, for $x = 5$ we draw the tangent at P in Figure 2(a) and estimate its slope to be about $\frac{3}{2}$, so $f'(5) \approx 1.5$. This allows us to plot the point $P'(5, 1.5)$ on the graph of f' directly beneath P. Repeating this procedure at several points, we get the graph shown in Figure 2(b). Notice that the tangents at A, B, and C are horizontal, so the derivative is 0 there and the graph of f' crosses the x-axis at the points A', B', and C', directly

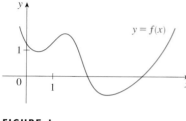

FIGURE 1

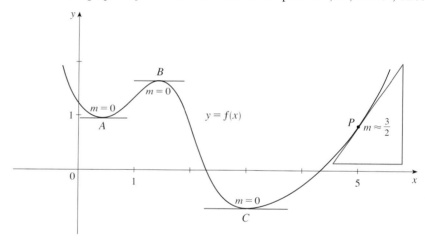

(a)

Visual 2.2 shows an animation of Figure 2 for several functions.

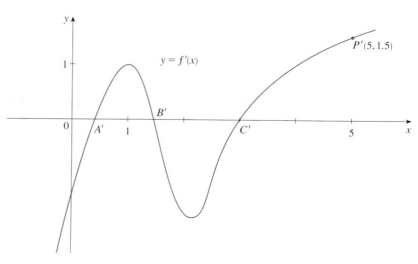

FIGURE 2

(b)

beneath A, B, and C. Between A and B the tangents have positive slope, so $f'(x)$ is positive there. But between B and C the tangents have negative slope, so $f'(x)$ is negative there.   ■

▼ EXAMPLE 2
(a) If $f(x) = x^3 - x$, find a formula for $f'(x)$.
(b) Illustrate by comparing the graphs of f and f'.

SOLUTION
(a) When using Equation 2 to compute a derivative, we must remember that the variable is h and that x is temporarily regarded as a constant during the calculation of the limit.

$$f'(x) = \lim_{h \to 0} \frac{f(x + h) - f(x)}{h} = \lim_{h \to 0} \frac{[(x + h)^3 - (x + h)] - [x^3 - x]}{h}$$

$$= \lim_{h \to 0} \frac{x^3 + 3x^2h + 3xh^2 + h^3 - x - h - x^3 + x}{h}$$

$$= \lim_{h \to 0} \frac{3x^2h + 3xh^2 + h^3 - h}{h}$$

$$= \lim_{h \to 0} (3x^2 + 3xh + h^2 - 1) = 3x^2 - 1$$

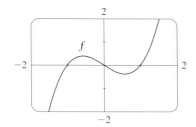

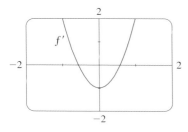

FIGURE 3

(b) We use a graphing device to graph f and f' in Figure 3. Notice that $f'(x) = 0$ when f has horizontal tangents and $f'(x)$ is positive when the tangents have positive slope. So these graphs serve as a check on our work in part (a).   ■

EXAMPLE 3 If $f(x) = \sqrt{x}$, find the derivative of f. State the domain of f'.

SOLUTION

$$f'(x) = \lim_{h \to 0} \frac{f(x + h) - f(x)}{h}$$

$$= \lim_{h \to 0} \frac{\sqrt{x + h} - \sqrt{x}}{h}$$

Here we rationalize the numerator.

$$= \lim_{h \to 0} \left(\frac{\sqrt{x + h} - \sqrt{x}}{h} \cdot \frac{\sqrt{x + h} + \sqrt{x}}{\sqrt{x + h} + \sqrt{x}} \right)$$

$$= \lim_{h \to 0} \frac{(x + h) - x}{h(\sqrt{x + h} + \sqrt{x})} = \lim_{h \to 0} \frac{1}{\sqrt{x + h} + \sqrt{x}}$$

$$= \frac{1}{\sqrt{x} + \sqrt{x}} = \frac{1}{2\sqrt{x}}$$

We see that $f'(x)$ exists if $x > 0$, so the domain of f' is $(0, \infty)$. This is smaller than the domain of f, which is $[0, \infty)$.   ■

Let's check to see that the result of Example 3 is reasonable by looking at the graphs of f and f' in Figure 4. When x is close to 0, $\sqrt{x}$ is also close to 0, so $f'(x) = 1/(2\sqrt{x})$ is very large and this corresponds to the steep tangent lines near $(0, 0)$ in Figure 4(a) and the large values of $f'(x)$ just to the right of 0 in Figure 4(b).

When x is large, $f'(x)$ is very small and this corresponds to the flatter tangent lines at the far right of the graph of f and the horizontal asymptote of the graph of f'.

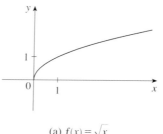

FIGURE 4

(a) $f(x) = \sqrt{x}$ (b) $f'(x) = \dfrac{1}{2\sqrt{x}}$

EXAMPLE 4 Find f' if $f(x) = \dfrac{1-x}{2+x}$.

$\dfrac{\dfrac{a}{b} - \dfrac{c}{d}}{e} = \dfrac{ad - bc}{bd} \cdot \dfrac{1}{e}$

SOLUTION

$$f'(x) = \lim_{h \to 0} \frac{f(x+h) - f(x)}{h} = \lim_{h \to 0} \frac{\dfrac{1-(x+h)}{2+(x+h)} - \dfrac{1-x}{2+x}}{h}$$

$$= \lim_{h \to 0} \frac{(1-x-h)(2+x) - (1-x)(2+x+h)}{h(2+x+h)(2+x)}$$

$$= \lim_{h \to 0} \frac{(2-x-2h-x^2-xh) - (2-x+h-x^2-xh)}{h(2+x+h)(2+x)}$$

$$= \lim_{h \to 0} \frac{-3h}{h(2+x+h)(2+x)}$$

$$= \lim_{h \to 0} \frac{-3}{(2+x+h)(2+x)} = -\frac{3}{(2+x)^2} \qquad ■$$

OTHER NOTATIONS

If we use the traditional notation $y = f(x)$ to indicate that the independent variable is x and the dependent variable is y, then some common alternative notations for the derivative are as follows:

$$f'(x) = y' = \frac{dy}{dx} = \frac{df}{dx} = \frac{d}{dx} f(x) = Df(x) = D_x f(x)$$

The symbols D and d/dx are called **differentiation operators** because they indicate the operation of **differentiation**, which is the process of calculating a derivative.

The symbol dy/dx, which was introduced by Leibniz, should not be regarded as a ratio (for the time being); it is simply a synonym for $f'(x)$. Nonetheless, it is a very useful and suggestive notation, especially when used in conjunction with increment notation. Referring to Equation 2.1.6, we can rewrite the definition of derivative in Leibniz notation in the form

$$\frac{dy}{dx} = \lim_{\Delta x \to 0} \frac{\Delta y}{\Delta x}$$

If we want to indicate the value of a derivative dy/dx in Leibniz notation at a specific number a, we use the notation

$$\frac{dy}{dx}\bigg|_{x=a} \qquad \text{or} \qquad \frac{dy}{dx}\bigg]_{x=a}$$

which is a synonym for $f'(a)$.

DIFFERENTIABLE FUNCTIONS

> **3 DEFINITION** A function f is **differentiable at a** if $f'(a)$ exists. It is **differentiable on an open interval** (a, b) [or (a, ∞) or $(-\infty, a)$ or $(-\infty, \infty)$] if it is differentiable at every number in the interval.

▼ EXAMPLE 5 Where is the function $f(x) = |x|$ differentiable?

SOLUTION If $x > 0$, then $|x| = x$ and we can choose h small enough that $x + h > 0$ and hence $|x + h| = x + h$. Therefore, for $x > 0$ we have

$$f'(x) = \lim_{h \to 0} \frac{|x + h| - |x|}{h}$$

$$= \lim_{h \to 0} \frac{(x + h) - x}{h} = \lim_{h \to 0} \frac{h}{h} = \lim_{h \to 0} 1 = 1$$

and so f is differentiable for any $x > 0$.

Similarly, for $x < 0$ we have $|x| = -x$ and h can be chosen small enough that $x + h < 0$ and so $|x + h| = -(x + h)$. Therefore, for $x < 0$,

$$f'(x) = \lim_{h \to 0} \frac{|x + h| - |x|}{h}$$

$$= \lim_{h \to 0} \frac{-(x + h) - (-x)}{h} = \lim_{h \to 0} \frac{-h}{h} = \lim_{h \to 0} (-1) = -1$$

and so f is differentiable for any $x < 0$.

For $x = 0$ we have to investigate

$$f'(0) = \lim_{h \to 0} \frac{f(0 + h) - f(0)}{h}$$

$$= \lim_{h \to 0} \frac{|0 + h| - |0|}{h} \qquad \text{(if it exists)}$$

Let's compute the left and right limits separately:

$$\lim_{h \to 0^+} \frac{|0 + h| - |0|}{h} = \lim_{h \to 0^+} \frac{|h|}{h} = \lim_{h \to 0^+} \frac{h}{h} = \lim_{h \to 0^+} 1 = 1$$

and $\qquad \lim_{h \to 0^-} \frac{|0 + h| - |0|}{h} = \lim_{h \to 0^-} \frac{|h|}{h} = \lim_{h \to 0^-} \frac{-h}{h} = \lim_{h \to 0^-} (-1) = -1$

Since these limits are different, $f'(0)$ does not exist. Thus f is differentiable at all x except 0.

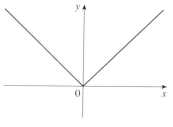

(a) $y = f(x) = |x|$

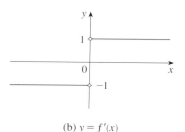

(b) $y = f'(x)$

FIGURE 5

A formula for f' is given by

$$f'(x) = \begin{cases} 1 & \text{if } x > 0 \\ -1 & \text{if } x < 0 \end{cases}$$

and its graph is shown in Figure 5(b). The fact that $f'(0)$ does not exist is reflected geometrically in the fact that the curve $y = |x|$ does not have a tangent line at $(0, 0)$. [See Figure 5(a).] ▪

Both continuity and differentiability are desirable properties for a function to have. The following theorem shows how these properties are related.

> **4 THEOREM** If f is differentiable at a, then f is continuous at a.

PROOF To prove that f is continuous at a, we have to show that $\lim_{x \to a} f(x) = f(a)$. We do this by showing that the difference $f(x) - f(a)$ approaches 0.

The given information is that f is differentiable at a, that is,

$$f'(a) = \lim_{x \to a} \frac{f(x) - f(a)}{x - a}$$

exists (see Equation 2.1.5). To connect the given and the unknown, we divide and multiply $f(x) - f(a)$ by $x - a$ (which we can do when $x \neq a$):

$$f(x) - f(a) = \frac{f(x) - f(a)}{x - a}(x - a)$$

Thus, using the Product Law and (2.1.5), we can write

$$\lim_{x \to a} [f(x) - f(a)] = \lim_{x \to a} \frac{f(x) - f(a)}{x - a}(x - a)$$

$$= \lim_{x \to a} \frac{f(x) - f(a)}{x - a} \cdot \lim_{x \to a} (x - a)$$

$$= f'(a) \cdot 0 = 0$$

To use what we have just proved, we start with $f(x)$ and add and subtract $f(a)$:

$$\lim_{x \to a} f(x) = \lim_{x \to a} [f(a) + (f(x) - f(a))]$$

$$= \lim_{x \to a} f(a) + \lim_{x \to a} [f(x) - f(a)]$$

$$= f(a) + 0 = f(a)$$

Therefore, f is continuous at a. ☐

⊘ **NOTE** The converse of Theorem 4 is false; that is, there are functions that are continuous but not differentiable. For instance, the function $f(x) = |x|$ is continuous at 0 because

$$\lim_{x \to 0} f(x) = \lim_{x \to 0} |x| = 0 = f(0)$$

(See Example 6 in Section 1.4.) But in Example 5 we showed that f is not differentiable at 0.

HOW CAN A FUNCTION FAIL TO BE DIFFERENTIABLE?

We saw that the function $y = |x|$ in Example 5 is not differentiable at 0 and Figure 5(a) shows that its graph changes direction abruptly when $x = 0$. In general, if the graph of a function f has a "corner" or "kink" in it, then the graph of f has no tangent at this point and f is not differentiable there. [In trying to compute $f'(a)$, we find that the left and right limits are different.]

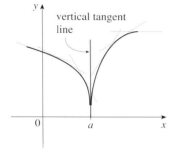

FIGURE 6

Theorem 4 gives another way for a function not to have a derivative. It says that if f is not continuous at a, then f is not differentiable at a. So at any discontinuity (for instance, a jump discontinuity) f fails to be differentiable.

A third possibility is that the curve has a **vertical tangent line** when $x = a$; that is, f is continuous at a and

$$\lim_{x \to a} |f'(x)| = \infty$$

This means that the tangent lines become steeper and steeper as $x \to a$. Figure 6 shows one way that this can happen; Figure 7(c) shows another. Figure 7 illustrates the three possibilities that we have discussed.

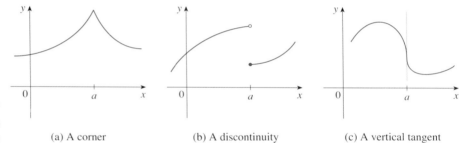

FIGURE 7
Three ways for f not to be differentiable at a

(a) A corner   (b) A discontinuity   (c) A vertical tangent

A graphing calculator or computer provides another way of looking at differentiability. If f is differentiable at a, then when we zoom in toward the point $(a, f(a))$ the graph straightens out and appears more and more like a line. (See Figure 8. We saw a specific example of this in Figure 4 in Section 2.1.) But no matter how much we zoom in toward a point like the ones in Figures 6 and 7(a), we can't eliminate the sharp point or corner (see Figure 9).

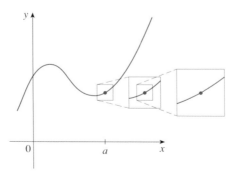

FIGURE 8
f is differentiable at a.

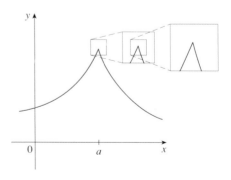

FIGURE 9
f is not differentiable at a.

HIGHER DERIVATIVES

If f is a differentiable function, then its derivative f' is also a function, so f' may have a derivative of its own, denoted by $(f')' = f''$. This new function f'' is called the **second derivative** of f because it is the derivative of the derivative of f. Using Leibniz notation, we write the second derivative of $y = f(x)$ as

$$\frac{d}{dx}\left(\frac{dy}{dx}\right) = \frac{d^2y}{dx^2}$$

EXAMPLE 6 If $f(x) = x^3 - x$, find and interpret $f''(x)$.

SOLUTION In Example 2 we found that the first derivative is $f'(x) = 3x^2 - 1$. So the second derivative is

$$f''(x) = \lim_{h \to 0} \frac{f'(x + h) - f'(x)}{h}$$

$$= \lim_{h \to 0} \frac{[3(x + h)^2 - 1] - [3x^2 - 1]}{h}$$

$$= \lim_{h \to 0} \frac{3x^2 + 6xh + 3h^2 - 1 - 3x^2 + 1}{h}$$

$$= \lim_{h \to 0} (6x + 3h) = 6x$$

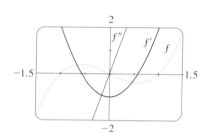

FIGURE 10

In Module 2.2 you can see how changing the coefficients of a polynomial f affects the appearance of the graphs of f, f', and f''.

The graphs of f, f', f'' are shown in Figure 10.

We can interpret $f''(x)$ as the slope of the curve $y = f'(x)$ at the point $(x, f'(x))$. In other words, it is the rate of change of the slope of the original curve $y = f(x)$.

Notice from Figure 10 that $f''(x)$ is negative when $y = f'(x)$ has negative slope and positive when $y = f'(x)$ has positive slope. So the graphs serve as a check on our calculations. ■

In general, we can interpret a second derivative as a rate of change of a rate of change. The most familiar example of this is *acceleration*, which we define as follows.

If $s = s(t)$ is the position function of an object that moves in a straight line, we know that its first derivative represents the velocity $v(t)$ of the object as a function of time:

$$v(t) = s'(t) = \frac{ds}{dt}$$

The instantaneous rate of change of velocity with respect to time is called the **acceleration** $a(t)$ of the object. Thus the acceleration function is the derivative of the velocity function and is therefore the second derivative of the position function:

$$a(t) = v'(t) = s''(t)$$

or, in Leibniz notation,

$$a = \frac{dv}{dt} = \frac{d^2s}{dt^2}$$

The **third derivative** f''' is the derivative of the second derivative: $f''' = (f'')'$. So $f'''(x)$ can be interpreted as the slope of the curve $y = f''(x)$ or as the rate of change of $f''(x)$. If $y = f(x)$, then alternative notations for the third derivative are

$$y''' = f'''(x) = \frac{d}{dx}\left(\frac{d^2y}{dx^2}\right) = \frac{d^3y}{dx^3}$$

The process can be continued. The fourth derivative f'''' is usually denoted by $f^{(4)}$. In general, the nth derivative of f is denoted by $f^{(n)}$ and is obtained from f by differentiating n times. If $y = f(x)$, we write

$$y^{(n)} = f^{(n)}(x) = \frac{d^ny}{dx^n}$$

EXAMPLE 7 If $f(x) = x^3 - x$, find $f'''(x)$ and $f^{(4)}(x)$.

SOLUTION In Example 6 we found that $f''(x) = 6x$. The graph of the second derivative has equation $y = 6x$ and so it is a straight line with slope 6. Since the derivative $f'''(x)$ is the slope of $f''(x)$, we have

$$f'''(x) = 6$$

for all values of x. So f''' is a constant function and its graph is a horizontal line. Therefore, for all values of x,

$$f^{(4)}(x) = 0 \qquad\qquad ■$$

We have seen that one application of second derivatives occurs in analyzing the motion of objects using acceleration. We will investigate another application of second derivatives in Section 4.3, where we show how knowledge of f'' gives us information about the shape of the graph of f. In Section 8.7 we will see how second and higher derivatives enable us to represent functions as sums of infinite series.

2.2 | EXERCISES

1–2 ▪ Use the given graph to estimate the value of each derivative. Then sketch the graph of f'.

1. (a) $f'(-3)$ (b) $f'(-2)$ (c) $f'(-1)$
   (d) $f'(0)$ (e) $f'(1)$ (f) $f'(2)$
   (g) $f'(3)$

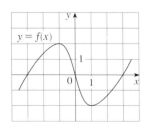

2. (a) $f'(0)$ (b) $f'(1)$
   (c) $f'(2)$ (d) $f'(3)$
   (e) $f'(4)$ (f) $f'(5)$

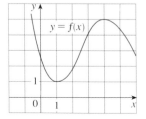

▪   ▪   ▪   ▪   ▪   ▪   ▪   ▪   ▪   ▪   ▪   ▪   ▪

3. Match the graph of each function in (a)–(d) with the graph of its derivative in I–IV. Give reasons for your choices.

(a)

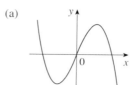

(b)

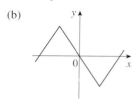

(c)

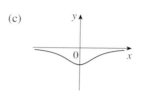

(d)

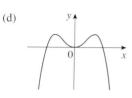

I

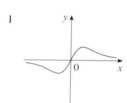

II

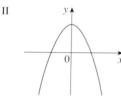

III

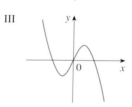

IV

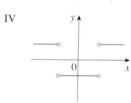

4–11 ■ Trace or copy the graph of the given function f. (Assume that the axes have equal scales.) Then use the method of Example 1 to sketch the graph of f' below it.

4.

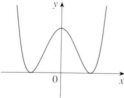

5.

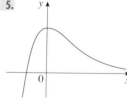

6.

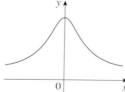

7.

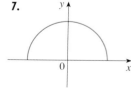

8.

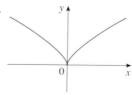

9.

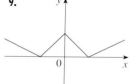

10.

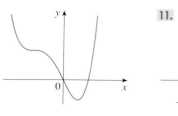

11.

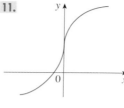

■ ■ ■ ■ ■ ■ ■ ■ ■ ■ ■ ■ ■ ■ ■

12. Shown is the graph of the population function $P(t)$ for yeast cells in a laboratory culture. Use the method of Example 1 to graph the derivative $P'(t)$. What does the graph of P' tell us about the yeast population?

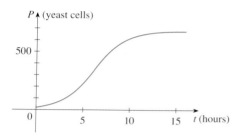

13. The graph shows how the average age of first marriage of Japanese men has varied in the last half of the 20th century. Sketch the graph of the derivative function $M'(t)$. During which years was the derivative negative?

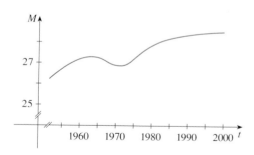

14. Make a careful sketch of the graph of the sine function and below it sketch the graph of its derivative in the same manner as in Exercises 4–11. Can you guess what the derivative of the sine function is from its graph?

15. Let $f(x) = x^2$.
(a) Estimate the values of $f'(0)$, $f'(\frac{1}{2})$, $f'(1)$, and $f'(2)$ by using a graphing device to zoom in on the graph of f.
(b) Use symmetry to deduce the values of $f'(-\frac{1}{2})$, $f'(-1)$, and $f'(-2)$.
(c) Use the results from parts (a) and (b) to guess a formula for $f'(x)$.

(d) Use the definition of a derivative to prove that your guess in part (c) is correct.

16. Let $f(x) = x^3$.

(a) Estimate the values of $f'(0)$, $f'(\frac{1}{2})$, $f'(1)$, $f'(2)$, and $f'(3)$ by using a graphing device to zoom in on the graph of f.

(b) Use symmetry to deduce the values of $f'(-\frac{1}{2})$, $f'(-1)$, $f'(-2)$, and $f'(-3)$.

(c) Use the values from parts (a) and (b) to graph f'.

(d) Guess a formula for $f'(x)$.

(e) Use the definition of a derivative to prove that your guess in part (d) is correct.

17–23 ▪ Find the derivative of the function using the definition of derivative. State the domain of the function and the domain of its derivative.

17. $f(x) = \frac{1}{2}x - \frac{1}{3}$ **18.** $f(x) = 1.5x^2 - x + 3.7$

19. $f(x) = x^3 - 3x + 5$ **20.** $f(x) = x + \sqrt{x}$

21. $g(x) = \sqrt{1 + 2x}$ **22.** $f(x) = \dfrac{3 + x}{1 - 3x}$

23. $G(t) = \dfrac{4t}{t + 1}$

▪ ▪ ▪ ▪ ▪ ▪ ▪ ▪ ▪ ▪ ▪ ▪

24. (a) Sketch the graph of $f(x) = \sqrt{6 - x}$ by starting with the graph of $y = \sqrt{x}$ and using the transformations of Section 1.2.

(b) Use the graph from part (a) to sketch the graph of f'.

(c) Use the definition of a derivative to find $f'(x)$. What are the domains of f and f'?

(d) Use a graphing device to graph f' and compare with your sketch in part (b).

25. (a) If $f(x) = x^4 + 2x$, find $f'(x)$.

(b) Check to see that your answer to part (a) is reasonable by comparing the graphs of f and f'.

26. (a) If $f(t) = t^2 - \sqrt{t}$, find $f'(t)$.

(b) Check to see that your answer to part (a) is reasonable by comparing the graphs of f and f'.

27–30 ▪ The graph of f is given. State, with reasons, the numbers at which f is not differentiable.

27. 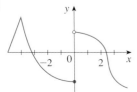   **28.**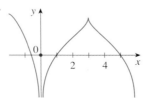

29.

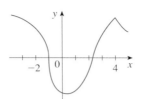

30.

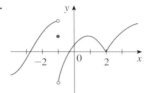

▪ ▪ ▪ ▪ ▪ ▪ ▪ ▪ ▪ ▪ ▪ ▪ ▪

31. Graph the function $f(x) = x + \sqrt{|x|}$. Zoom in repeatedly, first toward the point $(-1, 0)$ and then toward the origin. What is different about the behavior of f in the vicinity of these two points? What do you conclude about the differentiability of f?

32. Zoom in toward the points $(1, 0)$, $(0, 1)$, and $(-1, 0)$ on the graph of the function $g(x) = (x^2 - 1)^{2/3}$. What do you notice? Account for what you see in terms of the differentiability of g.

33. The figure shows the graphs of f, f', and f''. Identify each curve, and explain your choices.

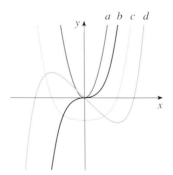

34. The figure shows graphs of f, f', f'', and f'''. Identify each curve, and explain your choices.

35. The figure shows the graphs of three functions. One is the position function of a car, one is the velocity of the car, and one is its acceleration. Identify each curve, and explain your choices.

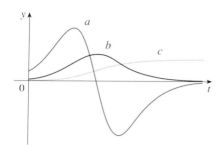

36–37 ▪ Use the definition of a derivative to find $f'(x)$ and $f''(x)$. Then graph f, f', and f'' on a common screen and check to see if your answers are reasonable.

36. $f(x) = 1/x$ **37.** $f(x) = 1 + 4x - x^2$

▪ ▪ ▪ ▪ ▪ ▪ ▪ ▪ ▪ ▪ ▪

38. If $f(x) = 2x^2 - x^3$, find $f'(x)$, $f''(x)$, $f'''(x)$, and $f^{(4)}(x)$. Graph f, f', f'', and f''' on a common screen. Are the graphs consistent with the geometric interpretations of these derivatives?

39. Let $f(x) = \sqrt[3]{x}$.
(a) If $a \neq 0$, use Equation 2.1.5 to find $f'(a)$.
(b) Show that $f'(0)$ does not exist.

(c) Show that $y = \sqrt[3]{x}$ has a vertical tangent line at $(0, 0)$. (Recall the shape of the graph of f. See Figure 8 in Section 1.2.)

40. (a) If $g(x) = x^{2/3}$, show that $g'(0)$ does not exist.
(b) If $a \neq 0$, find $g'(a)$.
(c) Show that $y = x^{2/3}$ has a vertical tangent line at $(0, 0)$.
(d) Illustrate part (c) by graphing $y = x^{2/3}$.

41. Show that the function $f(x) = |x - 6|$ is not differentiable at 6. Find a formula for f' and sketch its graph.

42. Where is the greatest integer function $f(x) = [\![x]\!]$ not differentiable? Find a formula for f' and sketch its graph.

43. Recall that a function f is called *even* if $f(-x) = f(x)$ for all x in its domain and *odd* if $f(-x) = -f(x)$ for all such x. Prove each of the following.
(a) The derivative of an even function is an odd function.
(b) The derivative of an odd function is an even function.

44. When you turn on a hot-water faucet, the temperature T of the water depends on how long the water has been running.
(a) Sketch a possible graph of T as a function of the time t that has elapsed since the faucet was turned on.
(b) Describe how the rate of change of T with respect to t varies as t increases.
(c) Sketch a graph of the derivative of T.

45. Let ℓ be the tangent line to the parabola $y = x^2$ at the point $(1, 1)$. The *angle of inclination* of ℓ is the angle ϕ that ℓ makes with the positive direction of the x-axis. Calculate ϕ correct to the nearest degree.

| 2.3 | **BASIC DIFFERENTIATION FORMULAS** |

If it were always necessary to compute derivatives directly from the definition, as we did in the preceding section, such computations would be tedious and the evaluation of some limits would require ingenuity. Fortunately, several rules have been developed for finding derivatives without having to use the definition directly. These formulas greatly simplify the task of differentiation.

In this section we learn how to differentiate constant functions, power functions, polynomials, and the sine and cosine functions. Then we use this knowledge to compute rates of change.

Let's start with the simplest of all functions, the *constant function* $f(x) = c$. The graph of this function is the horizontal line $y = c$, which has slope 0, so we must have $f'(x) = 0$. (See Figure 1.) A formal proof, from the definition of a derivative, is also easy:

$$f'(x) = \lim_{h \to 0} \frac{f(x + h) - f(x)}{h} = \lim_{h \to 0} \frac{c - c}{h}$$

$$= \lim_{h \to 0} 0 = 0$$

FIGURE 1
The graph of $f(x) = c$ is the line $y = c$, so $f'(x) = 0$.

In Leibniz notation, we write this rule as follows.

DERIVATIVE OF A CONSTANT FUNCTION

$$\frac{d}{dx}(c) = 0$$

POWER FUNCTIONS

We next look at the functions $f(x) = x^n$, where n is a positive integer. If $n = 1$, the graph of $f(x) = x$ is the line $y = x$, which has slope 1. (See Figure 2.) So

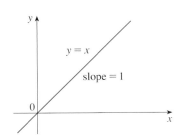

1

$$\frac{d}{dx}(x) = 1$$

FIGURE 2
The graph of $f(x) = x$ is the line $y = x$, so $f'(x) = 1$.

(You can also verify Equation 1 from the definition of a derivative.) We have already investigated the cases $n = 2$ and $n = 3$. In fact, in Section 2.2 (Exercises 15 and 16) we found that

2

$$\frac{d}{dx}(x^2) = 2x \qquad \frac{d}{dx}(x^3) = 3x^2$$

For $n = 4$ we find the derivative of $f(x) = x^4$ as follows:

$$f'(x) = \lim_{h \to 0} \frac{f(x + h) - f(x)}{h} = \lim_{h \to 0} \frac{(x + h)^4 - x^4}{h}$$

$$= \lim_{h \to 0} \frac{x^4 + 4x^3h + 6x^2h^2 + 4xh^3 + h^4 - x^4}{h}$$

$$= \lim_{h \to 0} \frac{4x^3h + 6x^2h^2 + 4xh^3 + h^4}{h}$$

$$= \lim_{h \to 0} (4x^3 + 6x^2h + 4xh^2 + h^3) = 4x^3$$

Thus

3

$$\frac{d}{dx}(x^4) = 4x^3$$

Comparing the equations in (1), (2), and (3), we see a pattern emerging. It seems to be a reasonable guess that, when n is a positive integer, $(d/dx)(x^n) = nx^{n-1}$. This turns out to be true.

THE POWER RULE If n is a positive integer, then

$$\frac{d}{dx}(x^n) = nx^{n-1}$$

PROOF If $f(x) = x^n$, then

$$f'(x) = \lim_{h \to 0} \frac{f(x+h) - f(x)}{h} = \lim_{h \to 0} \frac{(x+h)^n - x^n}{h}$$

■ The Binomial Theorem is given on Reference Page 1.

In finding the derivative of x^4 we had to expand $(x+h)^4$. Here we need to expand $(x+h)^n$ and we use the Binomial Theorem to do so:

$$f'(x) = \lim_{h \to 0} \frac{\left[x^n + nx^{n-1}h + \frac{n(n-1)}{2}x^{n-2}h^2 + \cdots + nxh^{n-1} + h^n \right] - x^n}{h}$$

$$= \lim_{h \to 0} \frac{nx^{n-1}h + \frac{n(n-1)}{2}x^{n-2}h^2 + \cdots + nxh^{n-1} + h^n}{h}$$

$$= \lim_{h \to 0} \left[nx^{n-1} + \frac{n(n-1)}{2}x^{n-2}h + \cdots + nxh^{n-2} + h^{n-1} \right]$$

$$= nx^{n-1}$$

because every term except the first has h as a factor and therefore approaches 0. ☐

We illustrate the Power Rule using various notations in Example 1.

EXAMPLE 1
(a) If $f(x) = x^6$, then $f'(x) = 6x^5$. (b) If $y = x^{1000}$, then $y' = 1000x^{999}$.

(c) If $y = t^4$, then $\dfrac{dy}{dt} = 4t^3$. (d) $\dfrac{d}{dr}(r^3) = 3r^2$ ■

What about power functions with negative integer exponents? In Exercise 55 we ask you to verify from the definition of a derivative that

$$\frac{d}{dx}\left(\frac{1}{x}\right) = -\frac{1}{x^2}$$

We can rewrite this equation as

$$\frac{d}{dx}(x^{-1}) = (-1)x^{-2}$$

and so the Power Rule is true when $n = -1$. In fact, we will show in the next section [Exercise 55(c)] that it holds for all negative integers.

What if the exponent is a fraction? In Example 3 in Section 2.2 we found that

$$\frac{d}{dx}\sqrt{x} = \frac{1}{2\sqrt{x}}$$

which can be written as

$$\frac{d}{dx}(x^{1/2}) = \tfrac{1}{2}x^{-1/2}$$

This shows that the Power Rule is true even when $n = \frac{1}{2}$. In fact, we will show in Section 3.3 that it is true for all real numbers n.

THE POWER RULE (GENERAL VERSION) If n is any real number, then

$$\frac{d}{dx}(x^n) = nx^{n-1}$$

EXAMPLE 2 Differentiate:

(a) $f(x) = \dfrac{1}{x^2}$ (b) $y = \sqrt[3]{x^2}$

SOLUTION In each case we rewrite the function as a power of x.

(a) Since $f(x) = x^{-2}$, we use the Power Rule with $n = -2$:

$$f'(x) = \frac{d}{dx}(x^{-2}) = -2x^{-2-1} = -2x^{-3} = -\frac{2}{x^3}$$

(b)

$$\frac{dy}{dx} = \frac{d}{dx}\left(\sqrt[3]{x^2}\right) = \frac{d}{dx}(x^{2/3}) = \tfrac{2}{3}x^{(2/3)-1} = \tfrac{2}{3}x^{-1/3}$$ ▪

The Power Rule enables us to find tangent lines without having to resort to the definition of a derivative. It also enables us to find *normal lines*. The **normal line** to a curve C at a point P is the line through P that is perpendicular to the tangent line at P. (In the study of optics, one needs to consider the angle between a light ray and the normal line to a lens.)

▪ Figure 3 shows the function y in Example 2(b) and its derivative y'. Notice that y is not differentiable at 0 (y' is not defined there). Observe that y' is positive when y increases and is negative when y decreases.

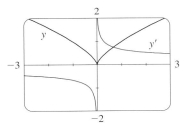

FIGURE 3
$y = \sqrt[3]{x^2}$

◥ EXAMPLE 3 Find equations of the tangent line and normal line to the curve $y = x\sqrt{x}$ at the point $(1, 1)$. Illustrate by graphing the curve and these lines.

SOLUTION The derivative of $f(x) = x\sqrt{x} = xx^{1/2} = x^{3/2}$ is

$$f'(x) = \tfrac{3}{2}x^{(3/2)-1} = \tfrac{3}{2}x^{1/2} = \tfrac{3}{2}\sqrt{x}$$

So the slope of the tangent line at $(1, 1)$ is $f'(1) = \frac{3}{2}$. Therefore, an equation of the tangent line is

$$y - 1 = \tfrac{3}{2}(x - 1) \qquad \text{or} \qquad y = \tfrac{3}{2}x - \tfrac{1}{2}$$

The normal line is perpendicular to the tangent line, so its slope is the negative reciprocal of $\frac{3}{2}$, that is, $-\frac{2}{3}$. Thus an equation of the normal line is

$$y - 1 = -\tfrac{2}{3}(x - 1) \qquad \text{or} \qquad y = -\tfrac{2}{3}x + \tfrac{5}{3}$$

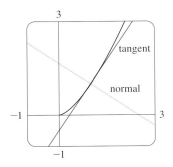

FIGURE 4

We graph the curve and its tangent line and normal line in Figure 4. ▪

NEW DERIVATIVES FROM OLD

When new functions are formed from old functions by addition, subtraction, or multiplication by a constant, their derivatives can be calculated in terms of derivatives of the old functions. In particular, the following formula says that *the derivative of a constant times a function is the constant times the derivative of the function.*

> **THE CONSTANT MULTIPLE RULE** If c is a constant and f is a differentiable function, then
>
> $$\frac{d}{dx}[cf(x)] = c\frac{d}{dx}f(x)$$

■ **GEOMETRIC INTERPRETATION OF THE CONSTANT MULTIPLE RULE**

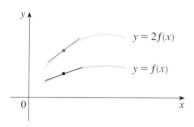

Multiplying by $c = 2$ stretches the graph vertically by a factor of 2. All the rises have been doubled but the runs stay the same. So the slopes are doubled, too.

PROOF Let $g(x) = cf(x)$. Then

$$g'(x) = \lim_{h \to 0} \frac{g(x + h) - g(x)}{h} = \lim_{h \to 0} \frac{cf(x + h) - cf(x)}{h}$$

$$= \lim_{h \to 0} c\left[\frac{f(x + h) - f(x)}{h}\right]$$

$$= c \lim_{h \to 0} \frac{f(x + h) - f(x)}{h} \qquad \text{(by Law 3 of limits)}$$

$$= cf'(x) \qquad \qquad \square$$

EXAMPLE 4

(a) $\dfrac{d}{dx}(3x^4) = 3\dfrac{d}{dx}(x^4) = 3(4x^3) = 12x^3$

(b) $\dfrac{d}{dx}(-x) = \dfrac{d}{dx}[(-1)x] = (-1)\dfrac{d}{dx}(x) = -1(1) = -1$ ■

The next rule tells us that *the derivative of a sum of functions is the sum of the derivatives.*

> **THE SUM RULE** If f and g are both differentiable, then
>
> $$\frac{d}{dx}[f(x) + g(x)] = \frac{d}{dx}f(x) + \frac{d}{dx}g(x)$$

■ Using prime notation, we can write the Sum Rule as

$$(f + g)' = f' + g'$$

PROOF Let $F(x) = f(x) + g(x)$. Then

$$F'(x) = \lim_{h \to 0} \frac{F(x + h) - F(x)}{h}$$

$$= \lim_{h \to 0} \frac{[f(x + h) + g(x + h)] - [f(x) + g(x)]}{h}$$

$$= \lim_{h \to 0} \left[\frac{f(x + h) - f(x)}{h} + \frac{g(x + h) - g(x)}{h}\right]$$

$$= \lim_{h \to 0} \frac{f(x + h) - f(x)}{h} + \lim_{h \to 0} \frac{g(x + h) - g(x)}{h} \qquad \text{(by Law 1)}$$

$$= f'(x) + g'(x) \qquad \qquad \square$$

The Sum Rule can be extended to the sum of any number of functions. For instance, using this theorem twice, we get

$$(f + g + h)' = [(f + g) + h]' = (f + g)' + h' = f' + g' + h'$$

By writing $f - g$ as $f + (-1)g$ and applying the Sum Rule and the Constant Multiple Rule, we get the following formula.

THE DIFFERENCE RULE If f and g are both differentiable, then

$$\frac{d}{dx}[f(x) - g(x)] = \frac{d}{dx}f(x) - \frac{d}{dx}g(x)$$

The Constant Multiple Rule, the Sum Rule, and the Difference Rule can be combined with the Power Rule to differentiate any polynomial, as the following examples demonstrate.

EXAMPLE 5

$$\frac{d}{dx}(x^8 + 12x^5 - 4x^4 + 10x^3 - 6x + 5)$$

$$= \frac{d}{dx}(x^8) + 12\frac{d}{dx}(x^5) - 4\frac{d}{dx}(x^4) + 10\frac{d}{dx}(x^3) - 6\frac{d}{dx}(x) + \frac{d}{dx}(5)$$

$$= 8x^7 + 12(5x^4) - 4(4x^3) + 10(3x^2) - 6(1) + 0$$

$$= 8x^7 + 60x^4 - 16x^3 + 30x^2 - 6 \qquad\blacksquare$$

▼ EXAMPLE 6 Find the points on the curve $y = x^4 - 6x^2 + 4$ where the tangent line is horizontal.

SOLUTION Horizontal tangents occur where the derivative is zero. We have

$$\frac{dy}{dx} = \frac{d}{dx}(x^4) - 6\frac{d}{dx}(x^2) + \frac{d}{dx}(4)$$

$$= 4x^3 - 12x + 0 = 4x(x^2 - 3)$$

Thus $dy/dx = 0$ if $x = 0$ or $x^2 - 3 = 0$, that is, $x = \pm\sqrt{3}$. So the given curve has horizontal tangents when $x = 0$, $\sqrt{3}$, and $-\sqrt{3}$. The corresponding points are $(0, 4)$, $(\sqrt{3}, -5)$, and $(-\sqrt{3}, -5)$. (See Figure 5.)

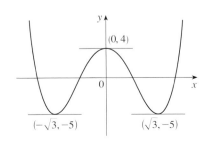

FIGURE 5

The curve $y = x^4 - 6x^2 + 4$ and its horizontal tangents

$\blacksquare$

THE SINE AND COSINE FUNCTIONS

If we sketch the graph of the function $f(x) = \sin x$ and use the interpretation of $f'(x)$ as the slope of the tangent to the sine curve in order to sketch the graph of f' (see Exercise 14 in Section 2.2), then it looks as if the graph of f' may be the same as the cosine curve (see Figure 6).

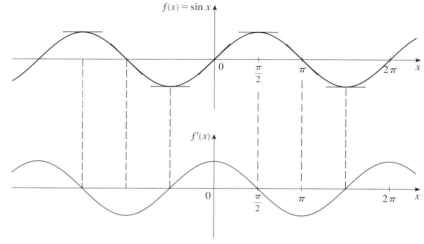

TEC Visual 2.3 shows an animation of Figure 6.

FIGURE 6

To prove that this is true we need to use two limits from Section 1.4 (see Equation 5 and Example 11 in that section):

$$\lim_{\theta \to 0} \frac{\sin \theta}{\theta} = 1 \qquad \lim_{\theta \to 0} \frac{\cos \theta - 1}{\theta} = 0$$

4
$$\frac{d}{dx}(\sin x) = \cos x$$

PROOF If $f(x) = \sin x$, then

$$f'(x) = \lim_{h \to 0} \frac{f(x+h) - f(x)}{h} = \lim_{h \to 0} \frac{\sin(x+h) - \sin x}{h}$$

■ We have used the addition formula for sine. See Appendix A.

$$= \lim_{h \to 0} \frac{\sin x \cos h + \cos x \sin h - \sin x}{h}$$

$$= \lim_{h \to 0} \left[\frac{\sin x \cos h - \sin x}{h} + \frac{\cos x \sin h}{h} \right]$$

$$= \lim_{h \to 0} \left[\sin x \left(\frac{\cos h - 1}{h} \right) + \cos x \left(\frac{\sin h}{h} \right) \right]$$

■ Note that we regard x as a constant when computing a limit as $h \to 0$, so $\sin x$ and $\cos x$ are also constants.

$$= \lim_{h \to 0} \sin x \cdot \lim_{h \to 0} \frac{\cos h - 1}{h} + \lim_{h \to 0} \cos x \cdot \lim_{h \to 0} \frac{\sin h}{h}$$

$$= (\sin x) \cdot 0 + (\cos x) \cdot 1 = \cos x \qquad \square$$

Using the same methods as in the proof of Formula 4, one can prove (see Exercise 56) that

5

$$\frac{d}{dx}(\cos x) = -\sin x$$

EXAMPLE 7 Differentiate $y = 3 \sin \theta + 4 \cos \theta$.

SOLUTION

$$\frac{dy}{d\theta} = 3\frac{d}{d\theta}(\sin \theta) + 4\frac{d}{d\theta}(\cos \theta) = 3\cos \theta - 4\sin \theta$$ ∎

EXAMPLE 8 Find the 27th derivative of $\cos x$.

SOLUTION The first few derivatives of $f(x) = \cos x$ are as follows:

$$f'(x) = -\sin x$$
$$f''(x) = -\cos x$$
$$f'''(x) = \sin x$$
$$f^{(4)}(x) = \cos x$$
$$f^{(5)}(x) = -\sin x$$

Looking for a pattern, we see that the successive derivatives occur in a cycle of length 4 and, in particular, $f^{(n)}(x) = \cos x$ whenever n is a multiple of 4. Therefore

$$f^{(24)}(x) = \cos x$$

and, differentiating three more times, we have

$$f^{(27)}(x) = \sin x$$ ∎

APPLICATIONS TO RATES OF CHANGE

We discussed velocity and other rates of change in Section 2.1, but now that we know some differentiation formulas we can solve problems involving rates of change more easily.

▼ **EXAMPLE 9** The position of a particle is given by the equation

$$s = f(t) = t^3 - 6t^2 + 9t$$

where t is measured in seconds and s in meters.
(a) Find the velocity at time t.
(b) What is the velocity after 2 s? After 4 s?
(c) When is the particle at rest?
(d) When is the particle moving forward (that is, in the positive direction)?
(e) Draw a diagram to represent the motion of the particle.
(f) Find the total distance traveled by the particle during the first five seconds.
(g) Find the acceleration at time t and after 4 s.

(h) Graph the position, velocity, and acceleration functions for $0 \leqslant t \leqslant 5$.

(i) When is the particle speeding up? When is it slowing down?

SOLUTION

(a) The velocity function is the derivative of the position function.

$$s = f(t) = t^3 - 6t^2 + 9t$$

$$v(t) = \frac{ds}{dt} = 3t^2 - 12t + 9$$

(b) The velocity after 2 s means the instantaneous velocity when $t = 2$, that is,

$$v(2) = \frac{ds}{dt}\bigg|_{t=2} = 3(2)^2 - 12(2) + 9 = -3 \text{ m/s}$$

The velocity after 4 s is

$$v(4) = 3(4)^2 - 12(4) + 9 = 9 \text{ m/s}$$

(c) The particle is at rest when $v(t) = 0$, that is,

$$3t^2 - 12t + 9 = 3(t^2 - 4t + 3) = 3(t - 1)(t - 3) = 0$$

and this is true when $t = 1$ or $t = 3$. Thus the particle is at rest after 1 s and after 3 s.

(d) The particle moves in the positive direction when $v(t) > 0$, that is,

$$3t^2 - 12t + 9 = 3(t - 1)(t - 3) > 0$$

This inequality is true when both factors are positive $(t > 3)$ or when both factors are negative $(t < 1)$. Thus the particle moves in the positive direction in the time intervals $t < 1$ and $t > 3$. It moves backward (in the negative direction) when $1 < t < 3$.

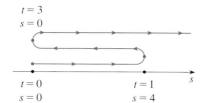

$t = 3$
$s = 0$

$t = 0$
$s = 0$

$t = 1$
$s = 4$

s

FIGURE 7

(e) Using the information from part (d) we make a schematic sketch in Figure 7 of the motion of the particle back and forth along a line (the s-axis).

(f) Because of what we learned in parts (d) and (e), we need to calculate the distances traveled during the time intervals [0, 1], [1, 3], and [3, 5] separately.

The distance traveled in the first second is

$$|f(1) - f(0)| = |4 - 0| = 4 \text{ m}$$

From $t = 1$ to $t = 3$ the distance traveled is

$$|f(3) - f(1)| = |0 - 4| = 4 \text{ m}$$

From $t = 3$ to $t = 5$ the distance traveled is

$$|f(5) - f(3)| = |20 - 0| = 20 \text{ m}$$

The total distance is $4 + 4 + 20 = 28$ m.

(g) The acceleration is the derivative of the velocity function:

$$a(t) = \frac{d^2s}{dt^2} = \frac{dv}{dt} = 6t - 12$$

$$a(4) = 6(4) - 12 = 12 \text{ m/s}^2$$

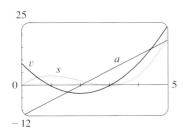

25

v s a

0 ——————— 5

−12

FIGURE 8

(h) Figure 8 shows the graphs of s, v, and a.

(i) The particle speeds up when the velocity is positive and increasing (v and a are both positive) and also when the velocity is negative and decreasing (v and a are both negative). In other words, the particle speeds up when the velocity and acceleration have the same sign. (The particle is pushed in the same direction it is moving.) From Figure 8 we see that this happens when $1 < t < 2$ and when $t > 3$. The particle slows down when v and a have opposite signs, that is, when $0 \leq t < 1$ and when $2 < t < 3$. Figure 9 summarizes the motion of the particle.

In Module 2.3 you can see an animation of Figure 9 with an expression for s that you can choose yourself.

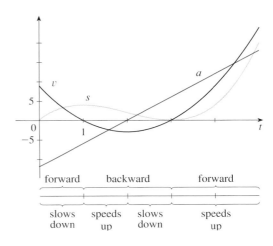

FIGURE 9

▪

■ **EXAMPLE 10** Suppose $C(x)$ is the total cost that a company incurs in producing x units of a certain commodity. The function C is called a **cost function**. If the number of items produced is increased from x_1 to x_2, then the additional cost is $\Delta C = C(x_2) - C(x_1)$, and the average rate of change of the cost is

$$\frac{\Delta C}{\Delta x} = \frac{C(x_2) - C(x_1)}{x_2 - x_1} = \frac{C(x_1 + \Delta x) - C(x_1)}{\Delta x}$$

The limit of this quantity as $\Delta x \to 0$, that is, the instantaneous rate of change of cost with respect to the number of items produced, is called the **marginal cost** by economists:

$$\text{marginal cost} = \lim_{\Delta x \to 0} \frac{\Delta C}{\Delta x} = \frac{dC}{dx}$$

[Since x often takes on only integer values, it may not make literal sense to let Δx approach 0, but we can always replace $C(x)$ by a smooth approximating function.]

Taking $\Delta x = 1$ and n large (so that Δx is small compared to n), we have

$$C'(n) \approx C(n + 1) - C(n)$$

Thus the marginal cost of producing n units is approximately equal to the cost of producing one more unit [the $(n + 1)$st unit].

It is often appropriate to represent a total cost function by a polynomial

$$C(x) = a + bx + cx^2 + dx^3$$

where a represents the overhead cost (rent, heat, maintenance) and the other terms represent the cost of raw materials, labor, and so on. (The cost of raw materials may be proportional to x, but labor costs might depend partly on higher powers of x because of overtime costs and inefficiencies involved in large-scale operations.)

For instance, suppose a company has estimated that the cost (in dollars) of producing x items is

$$C(x) = 10{,}000 + 5x + 0.01x^2$$

Then the marginal cost function is

$$C'(x) = 5 + 0.02x$$

The marginal cost at the production level of 500 items is

$$C'(500) = 5 + 0.02(500) = \$15/\text{item}$$

This gives the rate at which costs are increasing with respect to the production level when $x = 500$ and predicts the cost of the 501st item.

The actual cost of producing the 501st item is

$$C(501) - C(500) = [10{,}000 + 5(501) + 0.01(501)^2]$$
$$- [10{,}000 + 5(500) + 0.01(500)^2]$$
$$= \$15.01$$

Notice that $C'(500) \approx C(501) - C(500)$. ■

2.3 EXERCISES

1–24 ■ Differentiate the function.

1. $f(x) = 186.5$

2. $f(x) = \sqrt{30}$

3. $f(x) = 5x - 1$

4. $F(x) = -4x^{10}$

5. $f(x) = x^3 - 4x + 6$

6. $f(t) = \frac{1}{2}t^6 - 3t^4 + t$

7. $f(x) = x - 3 \sin x$

8. $y = \sin t + \pi \cos t$

9. $f(t) = \frac{1}{4}(t^4 + 8)$

10. $h(x) = (x - 2)(2x + 3)$

11. $y = x^{-2/5}$

12. $R(t) = 5t^{-3/5}$

13. $V(r) = \frac{4}{3}\pi r^3$

14. $R(x) = \dfrac{\sqrt{10}}{x^7}$

15. $F(x) = \left(\frac{1}{2}x\right)^5$

16. $y = \sqrt{x}\,(x - 1)$

17. $y = 4\pi^2$

18. $g(u) = \sqrt{2}\,u + \sqrt{3u}$

19. $y = \dfrac{x^2 + 4x + 3}{\sqrt{x}}$

20. $y = \dfrac{x^2 - 2\sqrt{x}}{x}$

21. $v = t^2 - \dfrac{1}{\sqrt[4]{t^3}}$

22. $y = \dfrac{\sin\theta}{2} + \dfrac{c}{\theta}$

23. $z = \dfrac{A}{y^{10}} + B \cos y$

24. $u = \sqrt[3]{t^2} + 2\sqrt{t^3}$

■   ■   ■   ■   ■   ■   ■   ■   ■   ■   ■   ■

25–26 ■ Find equations of the tangent line and normal line to the curve at the given point.

25. $y = 6 \cos x$, $(\pi/3, 3)$

26. $y = (1 + 2x)^2$, $(1, 9)$

■   ■   ■   ■   ■   ■   ■   ■   ■   ■   ■   ■

27–28 ■ Find an equation of the tangent line to the curve at the given point. Illustrate by graphing the curve and the tangent line on the same screen.

27. $y = x + \sqrt{x}$, $(1, 2)$

28. $y = 3x^2 - x^3$, $(1, 2)$

■   ■   ■   ■   ■   ■   ■   ■   ■   ■   ■   ■

29–32 ■ Find the first and second derivatives of the function.

29. $f(x) = x^4 - 3x^3 + 16x$

30. $G(r) = \sqrt{r} + \sqrt[3]{r}$

31. $g(t) = 2 \cos t - 3 \sin t$

32. $h(t) = \sqrt{t} + 5 \sin t$

■   ■   ■   ■   ■   ■   ■   ■   ■   ■   ■   ■

33. Find $\dfrac{d^{99}}{dx^{99}}(\sin x)$.

34. Find the nth derivative of each function by calculating the first few derivatives and observing the pattern that occurs.
(a) $f(x) = x^n$ (b) $f(x) = 1/x$

35. For what values of x does the graph of $f(x) = x + 2 \sin x$ have a horizontal tangent?

36. For what values of x does the graph of $f(x) = x^3 + 3x^2 + x + 3$ have a horizontal tangent?

37. Show that the curve $y = 6x^3 + 5x - 3$ has no tangent line with slope 4.

38. Find an equation of the tangent line to the curve $y = x\sqrt{x}$ that is parallel to the line $y = 1 + 3x$.

39. Find an equation of the normal line to the parabola $y = x^2 - 5x + 4$ that is parallel to the line $x - 3y = 5$.

40. Where does the normal line to the parabola $y = x - x^2$ at the point $(1, 0)$ intersect the parabola a second time? Illustrate with a sketch.

41. The equation of motion of a particle is $s = t^3 - 3t$, where s is in meters and t is in seconds. Find
(a) the velocity and acceleration as functions of t,
(b) the acceleration after 2 s, and
(c) the acceleration when the velocity is 0.

42. The equation of motion of a particle is $s = 2t^3 - 7t^2 + 4t + 1$, where s is in meters and t is in seconds.
(a) Find the velocity and acceleration as functions of t.
(b) Find the acceleration after 1 s.
(c) Graph the position, velocity, and acceleration functions on the same screen.

43–44 ■ A particle moves according to a law of motion $s = f(t)$, $t \geq 0$, where t is measured in seconds and s in feet.
(a) Find the velocity at time t.
(b) What is the velocity after 3 s?
(c) When is the particle at rest?
(d) When is the particle moving in the positive direction?
(e) Find the total distance traveled during the first 8 s.
(f) Draw a diagram like Figure 7 to illustrate the motion of the particle.

43. $f(t) = t^3 - 12t^2 + 36t$

44. $f(t) = t^3 - 9t^2 + 15t + 10$

■   ■   ■   ■   ■   ■   ■   ■   ■   ■   ■   ■

45. The position function of a particle is given by $s = t^3 - 4.5t^2 - 7t$, $t \geq 0$.
(a) When does the particle reach a velocity of 5 m/s?
(b) When is the acceleration 0? What is the significance of this value of t?

46. If a ball is given a push so that it has an initial velocity of 5 m/s down a certain inclined plane, then the distance it has rolled after t seconds is $s = 5t + 3t^2$.
(a) Find the velocity after 2 s.
(b) How long does it take for the velocity to reach 35 m/s?

47. If a stone is thrown vertically upward from the surface of the moon with a velocity of 10 m/s, its height (in meters) after t seconds is $h = 10t - 0.83t^2$.
(a) What is the velocity of the stone after 3 s?
(b) What is the velocity of the stone after it has risen 25 m?

48. If a ball is thrown vertically upward with a velocity of 80 ft/s, then its height after t seconds is $s = 80t - 16t^2$.
(a) What is the maximum height reached by the ball?
(b) What is the velocity of the ball when it is 96 ft above the ground on its way up? On its way down?

49. Suppose that the cost (in dollars) for a company to produce x pairs of a new line of jeans is
$$C(x) = 2000 + 3x + 0.01x^2 + 0.0002x^3$$
(a) Find the marginal cost function.
(b) Find $C'(100)$ and explain its meaning. What does it predict?
(c) Compare $C'(100)$ with the cost of manufacturing the 101st pair of jeans.

50. The cost function for a certain commodity is
$$C(x) = 84 + 0.16x - 0.0006x^2 + 0.000003x^3$$
(a) Find and interpret $C'(100)$.
(b) Compare $C'(100)$ with the cost of producing the 101st item.

51. A spherical balloon is being inflated. Find the rate of increase of the surface area ($S = 4\pi r^2$) with respect to the radius r when r is (a) 1 ft, (b) 2 ft, and (c) 3 ft. What conclusion can you make?

52. If a tank holds 5000 gallons of water, which drains from the bottom of the tank in 40 minutes, then Torricelli's Law gives the volume V of water remaining in the tank after t minutes as
$$V = 5000\left(1 - \tfrac{1}{40}t\right)^2 \qquad 0 \leq t \leq 40$$
Find the rate at which water is draining from the tank after (a) 5 min, (b) 10 min, (c) 20 min, and (d) 40 min. At what time is the water flowing out the fastest? The slowest? Summarize your findings.

53. Boyle's Law states that when a sample of gas is compressed at a constant temperature, the product of the pressure and the volume remains constant: $PV = C$.
(a) Find the rate of change of volume with respect to pressure.
(b) A sample of gas is in a container at low pressure and is steadily compressed at constant temperature for 10 minutes. Is the volume decreasing more rapidly at the beginning or the end of the 10 minutes? Explain.

54. Newton's Law of Gravitation says that the magnitude F of the force exerted by a body of mass m on a body of mass M is

$$F = \frac{GmM}{r^2}$$

where G is the gravitational constant and r is the distance between the bodies.
(a) Find dF/dr and explain its meaning. What does the minus sign indicate?
(b) Suppose it is known that the Earth attracts an object with a force that decreases at the rate of 2 N/km when $r = 20{,}000$ km. How fast does this force change when $r = 10{,}000$ km?

55. Use the definition of a derivative to show that if $f(x) = 1/x$, then $f'(x) = -1/x^2$. (This proves the Power Rule for the case $n = -1$.)

56. Prove, using the definition of derivative, that if $f(x) = \cos x$, then $f'(x) = -\sin x$.

57. The equation $y'' + y' - 2y = \sin x$ is called a **differential equation** because it involves an unknown function y and its derivatives y' and y''. Find constants A and B such that the function $y = A \sin x + B \cos x$ satisfies this equation. (Differential equations will be studied in detail in Section 7.6.)

58. Find constants A, B, and C such that the function $y = Ax^2 + Bx + C$ satisfies the differential equation $y'' + y' - 2y = x^2$.

59. Draw a diagram to show that there are two tangent lines to the parabola $y = x^2$ that pass through the point $(0, -4)$. Find the coordinates of the points where these tangent lines intersect the parabola.

60. (a) Find equations of both lines through the point $(2, -3)$ that are tangent to the parabola $y = x^2 + x$.
(b) Show that there is no line through the point $(2, 7)$ that is tangent to the parabola. Then draw a diagram to see why.

61. For what values of a and b is the line $2x + y = b$ tangent to the parabola $y = ax^2$ when $x = 2$?

62. Find a parabola with equation $y = ax^2 + bx + c$ that has slope 4 at $x = 1$, slope -8 at $x = -1$, and passes through the point $(2, 15)$.

63. Find a cubic function $y = ax^3 + bx^2 + cx + d$ whose graph has horizontal tangents at the points $(-2, 6)$ and $(2, 0)$.

64. A tangent line is drawn to the hyperbola $xy = c$ at a point P.
(a) Show that the midpoint of the line segment cut from this tangent line by the coordinate axes is P.
(b) Show that the triangle formed by the tangent line and the coordinate axes always has the same area, no matter where P is located on the hyperbola.

65. Evaluate $\lim\limits_{x \to 1} \dfrac{x^{1000} - 1}{x - 1}$.

66. Draw a diagram showing two perpendicular lines that intersect on the y-axis and are both tangent to the parabola $y = x^2$. Where do these lines intersect?

67. If $c > \frac{1}{2}$, how many lines through the point $(0, c)$ are normal lines to the parabola $y = x^2$? What if $c \leqslant \frac{1}{2}$?

68. Sketch the parabolas $y = x^2$ and $y = x^2 - 2x + 2$. Do you think there is a line that is tangent to both curves? If so, find its equation. If not, why not?

2.4	**THE PRODUCT AND QUOTIENT RULES**

The formulas of this section enable us to differentiate new functions formed from old functions by multiplication or division.

THE PRODUCT RULE

⊘ By analogy with the Sum and Difference Rules, one might be tempted to guess, as Leibniz did three centuries ago, that the derivative of a product is the product of the derivatives. We can see, however, that this guess is wrong by looking at a particular example. Let $f(x) = x$ and $g(x) = x^2$. Then the Power Rule gives $f'(x) = 1$ and $g'(x) = 2x$. But $(fg)(x) = x^3$, so $(fg)'(x) = 3x^2$. Thus $(fg)' \neq f'g'$. The correct formula was discovered by Leibniz (soon after his false start) and is called the Product Rule.

■ We can write the Product Rule in prime notation as
$$(fg)' = fg' + gf'$$

THE PRODUCT RULE If f and g are both differentiable, then

$$\frac{d}{dx}[f(x)g(x)] = f(x)\frac{d}{dx}[g(x)] + g(x)\frac{d}{dx}[f(x)]$$

PROOF Let $F(x) = f(x)g(x)$. Then

$$F'(x) = \lim_{h \to 0} \frac{F(x + h) - F(x)}{h}$$

$$= \lim_{h \to 0} \frac{f(x + h)g(x + h) - f(x)g(x)}{h}$$

In order to evaluate this limit, we would like to separate the functions f and g as in the proof of the Sum Rule. We can achieve this separation by subtracting and adding the term $f(x + h)g(x)$ in the numerator:

$$F'(x) = \lim_{h \to 0} \frac{f(x + h)g(x + h) - f(x + h)g(x) + f(x + h)g(x) - f(x)g(x)}{h}$$

$$= \lim_{h \to 0} \left[f(x + h) \frac{g(x + h) - g(x)}{h} + g(x) \frac{f(x + h) - f(x)}{h} \right]$$

$$= \lim_{h \to 0} f(x + h) \cdot \lim_{h \to 0} \frac{g(x + h) - g(x)}{h} + \lim_{h \to 0} g(x) \cdot \lim_{h \to 0} \frac{f(x + h) - f(x)}{h}$$

$$= f(x)g'(x) + g(x)f'(x)$$

Note that $\lim_{h \to 0} g(x) = g(x)$ because $g(x)$ is a constant with respect to the variable h. Also, since f is differentiable at x, it is continuous at x by Theorem 2.2.4, and so $\lim_{h \to 0} f(x + h) = f(x)$. □

In words, the Product Rule says that *the derivative of a product of two functions is the first function times the derivative of the second function plus the second function times the derivative of the first function.*

▪ Figure 1 shows the graphs of the function of Example 1 and its derivative. Notice that $y' = 0$ whenever y has a horizontal tangent.

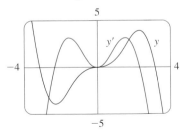

FIGURE 1

☑ EXAMPLE 1 Differentiate $y = x^2 \sin x$.

SOLUTION Using the Product Rule, we have

$$\frac{dy}{dx} = x^2 \frac{d}{dx} (\sin x) + \sin x \frac{d}{dx} (x^2)$$

$$= x^2 \cos x + 2x \sin x$$ ▪

EXAMPLE 2 Differentiate the function $f(t) = \sqrt{t} \, (a + bt)$.

▪ In Example 2, a and b are constants. It is customary in mathematics to use letters near the beginning of the alphabet to represent constants and letters near the end of the alphabet to represent variables.

SOLUTION 1 Using the Product Rule, we have

$$f'(t) = \sqrt{t} \, \frac{d}{dt} (a + bt) + (a + bt) \frac{d}{dt} (\sqrt{t})$$

$$= \sqrt{t} \cdot b + (a + bt) \cdot \tfrac{1}{2} t^{-1/2}$$

$$= b\sqrt{t} + \frac{a + bt}{2\sqrt{t}} = \frac{a + 3bt}{2\sqrt{t}}$$

SOLUTION 2 If we first use the laws of exponents to rewrite $f(t)$, then we can proceed directly without using the Product Rule.

$$f(t) = a\sqrt{t} + bt\sqrt{t} = at^{1/2} + bt^{3/2}$$

$$f'(t) = \tfrac{1}{2}at^{-1/2} + \tfrac{3}{2}bt^{1/2}$$

which is equivalent to the answer given in Solution 1. ▪

Example 2 shows that it is sometimes easier to simplify a product of functions than to use the Product Rule. In Example 1, however, the Product Rule is the only possible method.

EXAMPLE 3 If $h(x) = xg(x)$ and it is known that $g(3) = 5$ and $g'(3) = 2$, find $h'(3)$.

SOLUTION Applying the Product Rule, we get

$$h'(x) = \frac{d}{dx}[xg(x)] = x\frac{d}{dx}[g(x)] + g(x)\frac{d}{dx}[x]$$

$$= xg'(x) + g(x)$$

Therefore $\qquad h'(3) = 3g'(3) + g(3) = 3 \cdot 2 + 5 = 11$ ▪

THE QUOTIENT RULE

The following rule enables us to differentiate the quotient of two differentiable functions.

▪ In prime notation we can write the Quotient Rule as

$$\left(\frac{f}{g}\right)' = \frac{gf' - fg'}{g^2}$$

THE QUOTIENT RULE If f and g are differentiable, then

$$\frac{d}{dx}\left[\frac{f(x)}{g(x)}\right] = \frac{g(x)\dfrac{d}{dx}[f(x)] - f(x)\dfrac{d}{dx}[g(x)]}{[g(x)]^2}$$

PROOF Let $F(x) = f(x)/g(x)$. Then

$$F'(x) = \lim_{h \to 0} \frac{F(x + h) - F(x)}{h} = \lim_{h \to 0} \frac{\dfrac{f(x + h)}{g(x + h)} - \dfrac{f(x)}{g(x)}}{h}$$

$$= \lim_{h \to 0} \frac{f(x + h)g(x) - f(x)g(x + h)}{hg(x + h)g(x)}$$

We can separate f and g in this expression by subtracting and adding the term $f(x)g(x)$ in the numerator:

$$F'(x) = \lim_{h \to 0} \frac{f(x + h)g(x) - f(x)g(x) + f(x)g(x) - f(x)g(x + h)}{hg(x + h)g(x)}$$

$$= \lim_{h \to 0} \frac{g(x)\dfrac{f(x + h) - f(x)}{h} - f(x)\dfrac{g(x + h) - g(x)}{h}}{g(x + h)g(x)}$$

$$= \frac{\lim\limits_{h \to 0} g(x) \cdot \lim\limits_{h \to 0} \dfrac{f(x+h) - f(x)}{h} - \lim\limits_{h \to 0} f(x) \cdot \lim\limits_{h \to 0} \dfrac{g(x+h) - g(x)}{h}}{\lim\limits_{h \to 0} g(x+h) \cdot \lim\limits_{h \to 0} g(x)}$$

$$= \frac{g(x)f'(x) - f(x)g'(x)}{[g(x)]^2}$$

Again g is continuous by Theorem 2.2.4, so $\lim_{h \to 0} g(x+h) = g(x)$. ☐

In words, the Quotient Rule says that the *derivative of a quotient is the denominator times the derivative of the numerator minus the numerator times the derivative of the denominator, all divided by the square of the denominator.*

The Quotient Rule and the other differentiation formulas enable us to compute the derivative of any rational function, as the next example illustrates.

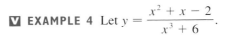 **EXAMPLE 4** Let $y = \dfrac{x^2 + x - 2}{x^3 + 6}$.

Then

$$y' = \frac{(x^3 + 6) \dfrac{d}{dx}(x^2 + x - 2) - (x^2 + x - 2) \dfrac{d}{dx}(x^3 + 6)}{(x^3 + 6)^2}$$

$$= \frac{(x^3 + 6)(2x + 1) - (x^2 + x - 2)(3x^2)}{(x^3 + 6)^2}$$

$$= \frac{(2x^4 + x^3 + 12x + 6) - (3x^4 + 3x^3 - 6x^2)}{(x^3 + 6)^2}$$

$$= \frac{-x^4 - 2x^3 + 6x^2 + 12x + 6}{(x^3 + 6)^2}$$ ■

▪ We can use a graphing device to check that the answer to Example 4 is plausible. Figure 2 shows the graphs of the function of Example 4 and its derivative. Notice that when y grows rapidly (near -2), y' is large. And when y grows slowly, y' is near 0.

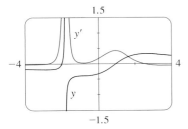

FIGURE 2

EXAMPLE 5 Find an equation of the tangent line to the curve $y = \sqrt{x}/(1 + x^2)$ at the point $\left(1, \frac{1}{2}\right)$.

SOLUTION According to the Quotient Rule, we have

$$\frac{dy}{dx} = \frac{(1 + x^2) \dfrac{d}{dx}\left(\sqrt{x}\right) - \sqrt{x} \dfrac{d}{dx}(1 + x^2)}{(1 + x^2)^2}$$

$$= \frac{(1 + x^2) \dfrac{1}{2\sqrt{x}} - \sqrt{x}\,(2x)}{(1 + x^2)^2}$$

$$= \frac{(1 + x^2) - 4x^2}{2\sqrt{x}\,(1 + x^2)^2} = \frac{1 - 3x^2}{2\sqrt{x}\,(1 + x^2)^2}$$

So the slope of the tangent line at $\left(1, \frac{1}{2}\right)$ is

$$\left.\frac{dy}{dx}\right|_{x=1} = \frac{1 - 3 \cdot 1^2}{2\sqrt{1}\,(1 + 1^2)^2} = -\frac{1}{4}$$

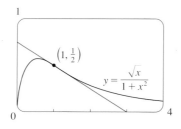

FIGURE 3

We use the point-slope form to write an equation of the tangent line at $\left(1, \frac{1}{2}\right)$:

$$y - \tfrac{1}{2} = -\tfrac{1}{4}(x - 1) \qquad \text{or} \qquad y = -\tfrac{1}{4}x + \tfrac{3}{4}$$

The curve and its tangent line are graphed in Figure 3. ■

NOTE Don't use the Quotient Rule *every* time you see a quotient. Sometimes it's easier to rewrite a quotient first to put it in a form that is simpler for the purpose of differentiation. For instance, although it is possible to differentiate the function

$$F(x) = \frac{3x^2 + 2\sqrt{x}}{x}$$

using the Quotient Rule, it is much easier to perform the division first and write the function as

$$F(x) = 3x + 2x^{-1/2}$$

before differentiating.

TRIGONOMETRIC FUNCTIONS

Knowing the derivatives of the sine and cosine functions, we can use the Quotient Rule to find the derivative of the tangent function:

$$\frac{d}{dx}(\tan x) = \frac{d}{dx}\left(\frac{\sin x}{\cos x}\right)$$

$$= \frac{\cos x \dfrac{d}{dx}(\sin x) - \sin x \dfrac{d}{dx}(\cos x)}{\cos^2 x}$$

$$= \frac{\cos x \cdot \cos x - \sin x\,(-\sin x)}{\cos^2 x}$$

$$= \frac{\cos^2 x + \sin^2 x}{\cos^2 x}$$

$$= \frac{1}{\cos^2 x} = \sec^2 x$$

$$\boxed{\frac{d}{dx}(\tan x) = \sec^2 x}$$

The derivatives of the remaining trigonometric functions, csc, sec, and cot, can also be found easily using the Quotient Rule (see Exercises 37–39). We collect all the differentiation formulas for trigonometric functions in the following table. Remember that they are valid only when x is measured in radians.

DERIVATIVES OF TRIGONOMETRIC FUNCTIONS

$$\frac{d}{dx}(\sin x) = \cos x \qquad\qquad \frac{d}{dx}(\csc x) = -\csc x \cot x$$

$$\frac{d}{dx}(\cos x) = -\sin x \qquad\qquad \frac{d}{dx}(\sec x) = \sec x \tan x$$

$$\frac{d}{dx}(\tan x) = \sec^2 x \qquad\qquad \frac{d}{dx}(\cot x) = -\csc^2 x$$

▪ When you memorize this table, it is helpful to notice that the minus signs go with the derivatives of the "cofunctions," that is, cosine, cosecant, and cotangent.

EXAMPLE 6 Differentiate $f(x) = \dfrac{\sec x}{1 + \tan x}$. For what values of x does the graph of f have a horizontal tangent?

SOLUTION The Quotient Rule gives

$$f'(x) = \frac{(1 + \tan x)\dfrac{d}{dx}(\sec x) - \sec x \dfrac{d}{dx}(1 + \tan x)}{(1 + \tan x)^2}$$

$$= \frac{(1 + \tan x)\sec x \tan x - \sec x \cdot \sec^2 x}{(1 + \tan x)^2}$$

$$= \frac{\sec x (\tan x + \tan^2 x - \sec^2 x)}{(1 + \tan x)^2}$$

$$= \frac{\sec x (\tan x - 1)}{(1 + \tan x)^2}$$

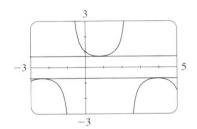

FIGURE 4
The horizontal tangents in Example 6

In simplifying the answer we have used the identity $\tan^2 x + 1 = \sec^2 x$.
Since $\sec x$ is never 0, we see that $f'(x) = 0$ when $\tan x = 1$, and this occurs when $x = n\pi + \pi/4$, where n is an integer (see Figure 4). ▪

2.4 EXERCISES

1. Find the derivative of $y = (x^2 + 1)(x^3 + 1)$ in two ways: by using the Product Rule and by performing the multiplication first. Do your answers agree?

2. Find the derivative of the function

$$F(x) = \frac{x - 3x\sqrt{x}}{\sqrt{x}}$$

in two ways: by using the Quotient Rule and by simplifying first. Show that your answers are equivalent. Which method do you prefer?

3–26 ▪ Differentiate.

3. $g(t) = t^3 \cos t$

4. $f(x) = \sqrt{x} \sin x$

5. $F(y) = \left(\dfrac{1}{y^2} - \dfrac{3}{y^4}\right)(y + 5y^3)$

6. $Y(u) = (u^{-2} + u^{-3})(u^5 - 2u^2)$

7. $f(x) = \sin x + \frac{1}{2}\cot x$

8. $y = 2\csc x + 5\cos x$

9. $h(\theta) = \theta \csc \theta - \cot \theta$

10. $y = u(a \cos u + b \cot u)$

11. $g(x) = \dfrac{3x - 1}{2x + 1}$

12. $f(t) = \dfrac{2t}{4 + t^2}$

13. $y = \dfrac{t^2}{3t^2 - 2t + 1}$

14. $y = \dfrac{t^3 + t}{t^4 - 2}$

15. $y = \dfrac{v^3 - 2v\sqrt{v}}{v}$

16. $y = \dfrac{\sqrt{x} - 1}{\sqrt{x} + 1}$

17. $y = \dfrac{r^2}{1 + \sqrt{r}}$

18. $y = \dfrac{cx}{1 + cx}$

19. $y = \dfrac{x}{\cos x}$

20. $y = \dfrac{1 + \sin x}{x + \cos x}$

21. $f(\theta) = \dfrac{\sec \theta}{1 + \sec \theta}$

22. $y = \dfrac{1 - \sec x}{\tan x}$

23. $y = \dfrac{\sin x}{x^2}$

24. $y = \dfrac{u^6 - 2u^3 + 5}{u^2}$

25. $f(x) = \dfrac{x}{x + \dfrac{c}{x}}$

26. $f(x) = \dfrac{ax + b}{cx + d}$

■ ■ ■ ■ ■ ■ ■ ■ ■ ■ ■ ■ ■ ■

27–30 ■ Find an equation of the tangent line to the curve at the given point.

27. $y = \dfrac{2x}{x + 1}$, (1, 1)

28. $y = \dfrac{\sqrt{x}}{x + 1}$, (4, 0.4)

29. $y = \tan x$, $(\pi/4, 1)$

30. $y = (1 + x)\cos x$, (0, 1)

■ ■ ■ ■ ■ ■ ■ ■ ■ ■ ■ ■ ■ ■

31. (a) The curve $y = 1/(1 + x^2)$ is called a **witch of Maria Agnesi**. Find an equation of the tangent line to this curve at the point $\left(-1, \frac{1}{2}\right)$.

 (b) Illustrate part (a) by graphing the curve and the tangent line on the same screen.

32. (a) The curve $y = x/(1 + x^2)$ is called a **serpentine**. Find an equation of the tangent line to this curve at the point (3, 0.3).

(b) Illustrate part (a) by graphing the curve and the tangent line on the same screen.

33. If $f(x) = x^2/(1 + x)$, find $f''(1)$.

34. If $f(x) = \sec x$, find $f''(\pi/4)$.

35. If $H(\theta) = \theta \sin \theta$, find $H'(\theta)$ and $H''(\theta)$.

36. Find $\dfrac{d^{35}}{dx^{35}}(x \sin x)$.

37. Prove that $\dfrac{d}{dx}(\csc x) = -\csc x \cot x$.

38. Prove that $\dfrac{d}{dx}(\sec x) = \sec x \tan x$.

39. Prove that $\dfrac{d}{dx}(\cot x) = -\csc^2 x$.

40. Suppose $f(\pi/3) = 4$ and $f'(\pi/3) = -2$, and let $g(x) = f(x) \sin x$ and $h(x) = (\cos x)/f(x)$. Find
(a) $g'(\pi/3)$
(b) $h'(\pi/3)$

41. Suppose that $f(5) = 1$, $f'(5) = 6$, $g(5) = -3$, and $g'(5) = 2$. Find the following values.
(a) $(fg)'(5)$
(b) $(f/g)'(5)$
(c) $(g/f)'(5)$

42. If $f(3) = 4$, $g(3) = 2$, $f'(3) = -6$, and $g'(3) = 5$, find the following numbers.
(a) $(f + g)'(3)$
(b) $(fg)'(3)$
(c) $(f/g)'(3)$

43. If f and g are the functions whose graphs are shown, let $u(x) = f(x)g(x)$ and $v(x) = f(x)/g(x)$.
(a) Find $u'(1)$.
(b) Find $v'(5)$.

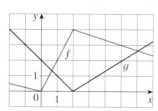

44. Let $P(x) = F(x)G(x)$ and $Q(x) = F(x)/G(x)$, where F and G are the functions whose graphs are shown.
(a) Find $P'(2)$.
(b) Find $Q'(7)$.

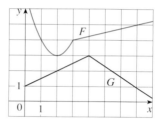

45. If g is a differentiable function, find an expression for the derivative of each of the following functions.
(a) $y = xg(x)$
(b) $y = \dfrac{x}{g(x)}$
(c) $y = \dfrac{g(x)}{x}$

46. If f is a differentiable function, find an expression for the derivative of each of the following functions.
(a) $y = x^2 f(x)$
(b) $y = \dfrac{f(x)}{x^2}$
(c) $y = \dfrac{x^2}{f(x)}$
(d) $y = \dfrac{1 + xf(x)}{\sqrt{x}}$

47. A mass on a spring vibrates horizontally on a smooth level surface (see the figure). Its equation of motion is $x(t) = 8 \sin t$, where t is in seconds and x in centimeters.
(a) Find the velocity and acceleration at time t.
(b) Find the position, velocity, and acceleration of the mass at time $t = 2\pi/3$. In what direction is it moving at that time? Is it speeding up or slowing down?

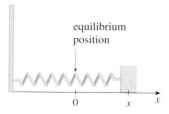

48. An object with weight W is dragged along a horizontal plane by a force acting along a rope attached to the object. If the rope makes an angle θ with the plane, then the magnitude of the force is

$$F = \frac{\mu W}{\mu \sin\theta + \cos\theta}$$

where μ is a constant called the *coefficient of friction*.
(a) Find the rate of change of F with respect to θ.
(b) When is this rate of change equal to 0?
(c) If $W = 50$ lb and $\mu = 0.6$, draw the graph of F as a function of θ and use it to locate the value of θ for which $dF/d\theta = 0$. Is the value consistent with your answer to part (b)?

49. The gas law for an ideal gas at absolute temperature T (in kelvins), pressure P (in atmospheres), and volume V (in liters) is $PV = nRT$, where n is the number of moles of the gas and $R = 0.0821$ is the gas constant. Suppose that, at a certain instant, $P = 8.0$ atm and is increasing at a rate of 0.10 atm/min and $V = 10$ L and is decreasing at a rate of 0.15 L/min. Find the rate of change of T with respect to time at that instant if $n = 10$ mol.

50. If R denotes the reaction of the body to some stimulus of strength x, the *sensitivity* S is defined to be the rate of change of the reaction with respect to x. A particular example is that when the brightness x of a light source is increased, the eye reacts by decreasing the area R of the pupil. The experimental formula

$$R = \frac{40 + 24x^{0.4}}{1 + 4x^{0.4}}$$

has been used to model the dependence of R on x when R is measured in square millimeters and x is measured in appropriate units of brightness.
(a) Find the sensitivity.
(b) Illustrate part (a) by graphing both R and S as functions of x. Comment on the values of R and S at low levels of brightness. Is this what you would expect?

51. How many tangent lines to the curve $y = x/(x + 1)$ pass through the point $(1, 2)$? At which points do these tangent lines touch the curve?

52. Find the points on the curve $y = (\cos x)/(2 + \sin x)$ at which the tangent is horizontal.

53. (a) Use the Product Rule twice to prove that if f, g, and h are differentiable, then $(fgh)' = f'gh + fg'h + fgh'$.
(b) Use part (a) to differentiate $y = x \sin x \cos x$.

54. (a) If $F(x) = f(x)g(x)$, where f and g have derivatives of all orders, show that $F'' = f''g + 2f'g' + fg''$.
(b) Find similar formulas for F''' and $F^{(4)}$.
(c) Guess a formula for $F^{(n)}$.

55. (a) If g is differentiable, the **Reciprocal Rule** says that

$$\frac{d}{dx}\left[\frac{1}{g(x)}\right] = -\frac{g'(x)}{[g(x)]^2}$$

Use the Quotient Rule to prove the Reciprocal Rule.
(b) Use the Reciprocal Rule to differentiate the function $y = 1/(x^4 + x^2 + 1)$.
(c) Use the Reciprocal Rule to verify that the Power Rule is valid for negative integers, that is,

$$\frac{d}{dx}(x^{-n}) = -nx^{-n-1}$$

for all positive integers n.

2.5	**THE CHAIN RULE**

Suppose you are asked to differentiate the function

$$F(x) = \sqrt{x^2 + 1}$$

The differentiation formulas you learned in the previous sections of this chapter do not enable you to calculate $F'(x)$.

▪ See Section 1.2 for a review of composite functions.

Observe that F is a composite function. In fact, if we let $y = f(u) = \sqrt{u}$ and let $u = g(x) = x^2 + 1$, then we can write $y = F(x) = f(g(x))$, that is, $F = f \circ g$. We know how to differentiate both f and g, so it would be useful to have a rule that tells us how to find the derivative of $F = f \circ g$ in terms of the derivatives of f and g.

It turns out that the derivative of the composite function $f \circ g$ is the product of the derivatives of f and g. This fact is one of the most important of the differentiation rules and is called the *Chain Rule*. It seems plausible if we interpret derivatives as rates of change. Regard du/dx as the rate of change of u with respect to x, dy/du as the rate of change of y with respect to u, and dy/dx as the rate of change of y with respect to x. If u changes twice as fast as x and y changes three times as fast as u, then it seems reasonable that y changes six times as fast as x, and so we expect that

$$\frac{dy}{dx} = \frac{dy}{du}\frac{du}{dx}$$

THE CHAIN RULE If f and g are both differentiable and $F = f \circ g$ is the composite function defined by $F(x) = f(g(x))$, then F is differentiable and F' is given by the product

$$F'(x) = f'(g(x)) \cdot g'(x)$$

In Leibniz notation, if $y = f(u)$ and $u = g(x)$ are both differentiable functions, then

$$\frac{dy}{dx} = \frac{dy}{du}\frac{du}{dx}$$

COMMENTS ON THE PROOF OF THE CHAIN RULE Let Δu be the change in u corresponding to a change of Δx in x, that is,

$$\Delta u = g(x + \Delta x) - g(x)$$

Then the corresponding change in y is

$$\Delta y = f(u + \Delta u) - f(u)$$

It is tempting to write

$$\frac{dy}{dx} = \lim_{\Delta x \to 0} \frac{\Delta y}{\Delta x}$$

1

$$= \lim_{\Delta x \to 0} \frac{\Delta y}{\Delta u} \cdot \frac{\Delta u}{\Delta x}$$

$$= \lim_{\Delta x \to 0} \frac{\Delta y}{\Delta u} \cdot \lim_{\Delta x \to 0} \frac{\Delta u}{\Delta x}$$

$$= \lim_{\Delta u \to 0} \frac{\Delta y}{\Delta u} \cdot \lim_{\Delta x \to 0} \frac{\Delta u}{\Delta x} \qquad \text{(Note that } \Delta u \to 0 \text{ as } \Delta x \to 0 \\ \text{since } g \text{ is continuous.)}$$

$$= \frac{dy}{du}\frac{du}{dx}$$

The only flaw in this reasoning is that in (1) it might happen that $\Delta u = 0$ (even when $\Delta x \neq 0$) and, of course, we can't divide by 0.

Nonetheless, this reasoning does at least *suggest* that the Chain Rule is true. A full proof of the Chain Rule is given at the end of this section.   □

The Chain Rule can be written either in the prime notation

$$[2] \qquad (f \circ g)'(x) = f'(g(x)) \cdot g'(x)$$

or, if $y = f(u)$ and $u = g(x)$, in Leibniz notation:

$$[3] \qquad \frac{dy}{dx} = \frac{dy}{du}\frac{du}{dx}$$

Equation 3 is easy to remember because if dy/du and du/dx were quotients, then we could cancel du. Remember, however, that du has not been defined and du/dx should not be thought of as an actual quotient.

EXAMPLE 1 Find $F'(x)$ if $F(x) = \sqrt{x^2 + 1}$.

SOLUTION 1 (using Equation 2):   At the beginning of this section we expressed F as $F(x) = (f \circ g)(x) = f(g(x))$ where $f(u) = \sqrt{u}$ and $g(x) = x^2 + 1$. Since

$$f'(u) = \tfrac{1}{2}u^{-1/2} = \frac{1}{2\sqrt{u}} \qquad \text{and} \qquad g'(x) = 2x$$

we have
$$F'(x) = f'(g(x)) \cdot g'(x)$$

$$= \frac{1}{2\sqrt{x^2 + 1}} \cdot 2x = \frac{x}{\sqrt{x^2 + 1}}$$

SOLUTION 2 (using Equation 3):   If we let $u = x^2 + 1$ and $y = \sqrt{u}$, then

$$F'(x) = \frac{dy}{du}\frac{du}{dx} = \frac{1}{2\sqrt{u}}(2x)$$

$$= \frac{1}{2\sqrt{x^2 + 1}}(2x) = \frac{x}{\sqrt{x^2 + 1}} \qquad \blacksquare$$

When using Formula 3 we should bear in mind that dy/dx refers to the derivative of y when y is considered as a function of x (called the *derivative of y with respect to x*), whereas dy/du refers to the derivative of y when considered as a function of u (the derivative of y with respect to u). For instance, in Example 1, y can be considered as a function of x $(y = \sqrt{x^2 + 1})$ and also as a function of u $(y = \sqrt{u})$. Note that

$$\frac{dy}{dx} = F'(x) = \frac{x}{\sqrt{x^2 + 1}} \qquad \text{whereas} \qquad \frac{dy}{du} = f'(u) = \frac{1}{2\sqrt{u}}$$

NOTE In using the Chain Rule we work from the outside to the inside. Formula 2 says that *we differentiate the outer function f [at the inner function $g(x)$] and then we multiply by the derivative of the inner function.*

$$\frac{d}{dx} \underbrace{f}_{\substack{\text{outer} \\ \text{function}}} \underbrace{(g(x))}_{\substack{\text{evaluated} \\ \text{at inner} \\ \text{function}}} = \underbrace{f'}_{\substack{\text{derivative} \\ \text{of outer} \\ \text{function}}} \underbrace{(g(x))}_{\substack{\text{evaluated} \\ \text{at inner} \\ \text{function}}} \cdot \underbrace{g'(x)}_{\substack{\text{derivative} \\ \text{of inner} \\ \text{function}}}$$

☑ EXAMPLE 2 Differentiate (a) $y = \sin(x^2)$ and (b) $y = \sin^2 x$.

SOLUTION

(a) If $y = \sin(x^2)$, then the outer function is the sine function and the inner function is the squaring function, so the Chain Rule gives

$$\frac{dy}{dx} = \frac{d}{dx} \underbrace{\sin}_{\substack{\text{outer} \\ \text{function}}} \underbrace{(x^2)}_{\substack{\text{evaluated} \\ \text{at inner} \\ \text{function}}} = \underbrace{\cos}_{\substack{\text{derivative} \\ \text{of outer} \\ \text{function}}} \underbrace{(x^2)}_{\substack{\text{evaluated} \\ \text{at inner} \\ \text{function}}} \cdot \underbrace{2x}_{\substack{\text{derivative} \\ \text{of inner} \\ \text{function}}}$$

$$= 2x \cos(x^2)$$

(b) Note that $\sin^2 x = (\sin x)^2$. Here the outer function is the squaring function and the inner function is the sine function. So

$$\frac{dy}{dx} = \frac{d}{dx} \underbrace{(\sin x)^2}_{\substack{\text{inner} \\ \text{function}}} = \underbrace{2}_{\substack{\text{derivative} \\ \text{of outer} \\ \text{function}}} \cdot \underbrace{(\sin x)}_{\substack{\text{evaluated} \\ \text{at inner} \\ \text{function}}} \cdot \underbrace{\cos x}_{\substack{\text{derivative} \\ \text{of inner} \\ \text{function}}}$$

■ See Reference Page 2 or Appendix A.

The answer can be left as $2 \sin x \cos x$ or written as $\sin 2x$ (by a trigonometric identity known as the double-angle formula). ■

In Example 2(a) we combined the Chain Rule with the rule for differentiating the sine function. In general, if $y = \sin u$, where u is a differentiable function of x, then, by the Chain Rule,

$$\frac{dy}{dx} = \frac{dy}{du} \frac{du}{dx} = \cos u \frac{du}{dx}$$

Thus

$$\frac{d}{dx} (\sin u) = \cos u \frac{du}{dx}$$

In a similar fashion, all of the formulas for differentiating trigonometric functions can be combined with the Chain Rule.

Let's make explicit the special case of the Chain Rule where the outer function f is a power function. If $y = [g(x)]^n$, then we can write $y = f(u) = u^n$ where $u = g(x)$. By using the Chain Rule and then the Power Rule, we get

$$\frac{dy}{dx} = \frac{dy}{du} \frac{du}{dx} = nu^{n-1} \frac{du}{dx} = n[g(x)]^{n-1} g'(x)$$

---

4 THE POWER RULE COMBINED WITH THE CHAIN RULE If n is any real number and $u = g(x)$ is differentiable, then

$$\frac{d}{dx} (u^n) = nu^{n-1} \frac{du}{dx}$$

Alternatively,

$$\frac{d}{dx} [g(x)]^n = n[g(x)]^{n-1} \cdot g'(x)$$

Notice that the derivative in Example 1 could be calculated by taking $n = \frac{1}{2}$ in Rule 4.

EXAMPLE 3 Differentiate $y = (x^3 - 1)^{100}$.

SOLUTION Taking $u = g(x) = x^3 - 1$ and $n = 100$ in (4), we have

$$\frac{dy}{dx} = \frac{d}{dx}(x^3 - 1)^{100} = 100(x^3 - 1)^{99}\frac{d}{dx}(x^3 - 1)$$

$$= 100(x^3 - 1)^{99} \cdot 3x^2 = 300x^2(x^3 - 1)^{99} \qquad ▪$$

▼ EXAMPLE 4 Find $f'(x)$ if $f(x) = \dfrac{1}{\sqrt[3]{x^2 + x + 1}}$.

SOLUTION First rewrite f: $f(x) = (x^2 + x + 1)^{-1/3}$. Thus

$$f'(x) = -\tfrac{1}{3}(x^2 + x + 1)^{-4/3}\frac{d}{dx}(x^2 + x + 1)$$

$$= -\tfrac{1}{3}(x^2 + x + 1)^{-4/3}(2x + 1) \qquad ▪$$

EXAMPLE 5 Find the derivative of the function

$$g(t) = \left(\frac{t - 2}{2t + 1}\right)^9$$

SOLUTION Combining the Power Rule, Chain Rule, and Quotient Rule, we get

$$g'(t) = 9\left(\frac{t - 2}{2t + 1}\right)^8 \frac{d}{dt}\left(\frac{t - 2}{2t + 1}\right)$$

$$= 9\left(\frac{t - 2}{2t + 1}\right)^8 \frac{(2t + 1) \cdot 1 - 2(t - 2)}{(2t + 1)^2} = \frac{45(t - 2)^8}{(2t + 1)^{10}} \qquad ▪$$

EXAMPLE 6 Differentiate $y = (2x + 1)^5(x^3 - x + 1)^4$.

SOLUTION In this example we must use the Product Rule before using the Chain Rule:

$$\frac{dy}{dx} = (2x + 1)^5 \frac{d}{dx}(x^3 - x + 1)^4 + (x^3 - x + 1)^4\frac{d}{dx}(2x + 1)^5$$

$$= (2x + 1)^5 \cdot 4(x^3 - x + 1)^3 \frac{d}{dx}(x^3 - x + 1)$$

$$+ (x^3 - x + 1)^4 \cdot 5(2x + 1)^4 \frac{d}{dx}(2x + 1)$$

$$= 4(2x + 1)^5(x^3 - x + 1)^3(3x^2 - 1) + 5(x^3 - x + 1)^4(2x + 1)^4 \cdot 2$$

Noticing that each term has the common factor $2(2x + 1)^4(x^3 - x + 1)^3$, we could factor it out and write the answer as

$$\frac{dy}{dx} = 2(2x + 1)^4(x^3 - x + 1)^3(17x^3 + 6x^2 - 9x + 3) \qquad ▪$$

▪ The graphs of the functions y and y' in Example 6 are shown in Figure 1. Notice that y' is large when y increases rapidly and $y' = 0$ when y has a horizontal tangent. So our answer appears to be reasonable.

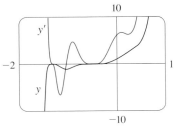

FIGURE 1

The reason for the name "Chain Rule" becomes clear when we make a longer chain by adding another link. Suppose that $y = f(u)$, $u = g(x)$, and $x = h(t)$, where f, g, and

h are differentiable functions. Then, to compute the derivative of y with respect to t, we use the Chain Rule twice:

$$\frac{dy}{dt} = \frac{dy}{dx}\frac{dx}{dt} = \frac{dy}{du}\frac{du}{dx}\frac{dx}{dt}$$

▼ EXAMPLE 7 If $f(x) = \sin(\cos(\tan x))$, then

$$f'(x) = \cos(\cos(\tan x))\frac{d}{dx}\cos(\tan x)$$

$$= \cos(\cos(\tan x))[-\sin(\tan x)]\frac{d}{dx}(\tan x)$$

$$= -\cos(\cos(\tan x))\sin(\tan x)\sec^2 x$$

Notice that we used the Chain Rule twice. ■

EXAMPLE 8 Differentiate $y = \sqrt{\sec x^3}$.

SOLUTION Here the outer function is the square root function, the middle function is the secant function, and the inner function is the cubing function. So we have

$$\frac{dy}{dx} = \frac{1}{2\sqrt{\sec x^3}}\frac{d}{dx}(\sec x^3)$$

$$= \frac{1}{2\sqrt{\sec x^3}}\sec x^3 \tan x^3\frac{d}{dx}(x^3)$$

$$= \frac{3x^2 \sec x^3 \tan x^3}{2\sqrt{\sec x^3}}$$

■

HOW TO PROVE THE CHAIN RULE

Recall that if $y = f(x)$ and x changes from a to $a + \Delta x$, we defined the increment of y as

$$\Delta y = f(a + \Delta x) - f(a)$$

According to the definition of a derivative, we have

$$\lim_{\Delta x \to 0}\frac{\Delta y}{\Delta x} = f'(a)$$

So if we denote by ε the difference between the difference quotient and the derivative, we obtain

$$\lim_{\Delta x \to 0}\varepsilon = \lim_{\Delta x \to 0}\left(\frac{\Delta y}{\Delta x} - f'(a)\right) = f'(a) - f'(a) = 0$$

But

$$\varepsilon = \frac{\Delta y}{\Delta x} - f'(a) \qquad \Rightarrow \qquad \Delta y = f'(a)\,\Delta x + \varepsilon\,\Delta x$$

If we define ε to be 0 when $\Delta x = 0$, then ε becomes a continuous function of Δx.

Thus, for a differentiable function f, we can write

$$\boxed{5} \qquad \Delta y = f'(a)\, \Delta x + \varepsilon\, \Delta x \qquad \text{where} \quad \varepsilon \to 0 \text{ as } \Delta x \to 0$$

and ε is a continuous function of Δx. This property of differentiable functions is what enables us to prove the Chain Rule.

PROOF OF THE CHAIN RULE Suppose $u = g(x)$ is differentiable at a and $y = f(u)$ is differentiable at $b = g(a)$. If Δx is an increment in x and Δu and Δy are the corresponding increments in u and y, then we can use Equation 5 to write

$$\boxed{6} \qquad \Delta u = g'(a)\, \Delta x + \varepsilon_1\, \Delta x = [g'(a) + \varepsilon_1]\, \Delta x$$

where $\varepsilon_1 \to 0$ as $\Delta x \to 0$. Similarly

$$\boxed{7} \qquad \Delta y = f'(b)\, \Delta u + \varepsilon_2\, \Delta u = [f'(b) + \varepsilon_2]\, \Delta u$$

where $\varepsilon_2 \to 0$ as $\Delta u \to 0$. If we now substitute the expression for Δu from Equation 6 into Equation 7, we get

$$\Delta y = [f'(b) + \varepsilon_2][g'(a) + \varepsilon_1]\, \Delta x$$

so

$$\frac{\Delta y}{\Delta x} = [f'(b) + \varepsilon_2][g'(a) + \varepsilon_1]$$

As $\Delta x \to 0$, Equation 6 shows that $\Delta u \to 0$. So both $\varepsilon_1 \to 0$ and $\varepsilon_2 \to 0$ as $\Delta x \to 0$. Therefore

$$\frac{dy}{dx} = \lim_{\Delta x \to 0} \frac{\Delta y}{\Delta x} = \lim_{\Delta x \to 0} [f'(b) + \varepsilon_2][g'(a) + \varepsilon_1]$$

$$= f'(b)g'(a) = f'(g(a))g'(a)$$

This proves the Chain Rule. ☐

2.5   EXERCISES

1–6 ▪ Write the composite function in the form $f(g(x))$. [Identify the inner function $u = g(x)$ and the outer function $y = f(u)$.] Then find the derivative dy/dx.

1. $y = \sin 4x$

2. $y = \sqrt{4 + 3x}$

3. $y = (1 - x^2)^{10}$

4. $y = \tan(\sin x)$

5. $y = \sqrt{\sin x}$

6. $y = \sin \sqrt{x}$

▪ ▪ ▪ ▪ ▪ ▪ ▪ ▪ ▪ ▪ ▪

7–38 ▪ Find the derivative of the function.

7. $F(x) = \sqrt[4]{1 + 2x + x^3}$

8. $F(x) = (x^2 - x + 1)^3$

9. $g(t) = \dfrac{1}{(t^4 + 1)^3}$

10. $f(t) = \sqrt[3]{1 + \tan t}$

11. $y = \cos(a^3 + x^3)$

12. $y = a^3 + \cos^3 x$

13. $y = \cot(x/2)$

14. $y = 4 \sec 5x$

15. $g(x) = (1 + 4x)^5 (3 + x - x^2)^8$

16. $h(t) = (t^4 - 1)^3 (t^3 + 1)^4$

17. $y = (2x - 5)^4 (8x^2 - 5)^{-3}$

18. $y = (x^2 + 1)\sqrt[3]{x^2 + 2}$

19. $y = x^3 \cos nx$

20. $y = x \sin \sqrt{x}$

21. $y = \sin(x \cos x)$

22. $f(x) = \dfrac{x}{\sqrt{7 - 3x}}$

23. $F(z) = \sqrt{\dfrac{z - 1}{z + 1}}$

24. $G(y) = \left(\dfrac{y^2}{y + 1}\right)^5$

25. $y = \dfrac{r}{\sqrt{r^2 + 1}}$

26. $y = \dfrac{\sin^2 x}{\cos x}$

27. $y = \tan(\cos x)$

28. $y = \tan^2(3\theta)$

29. $y = \sin\sqrt{1 + x^2}$

30. $y = x \sin \dfrac{1}{x}$

31. $y = (1 + \cos^2 x)^6$

32. $y = \cot(x^2) + \cot^2 x$

33. $y = \sec^2 x + \tan^2 x$

34. $y = \sin(\sin(\sin x))$

35. $y = \cot^2(\sin \theta)$

36. $y = \sqrt{x + \sqrt{x + \sqrt{x}}}$

37. $y = \sin(\tan \sqrt{\sin x})$

38. $y = \sqrt{\cos(\sin^2 x)}$

■ ■ ■ ■ ■ ■ ■ ■ ■ ■ ■ ■ ■ ■ ■

39–40 ■ Find an equation of the tangent line to the curve at the given point.

39. $y = (1 + 2x)^{10}$, $\quad$ (0, 1)

40. $y = \sin x + \sin^2 x$, $\quad$ (0, 0)

■ ■ ■ ■ ■ ■ ■ ■ ■ ■ ■ ■ ■ ■

41. (a) Find an equation of the tangent line to the curve $y = \tan(\pi x^2/4)$ at the point (1, 1).

 (b) Illustrate part (a) by graphing the curve and the tangent line on the same screen.

42. (a) The curve $y = |x|/\sqrt{2 - x^2}$ is called a *bullet-nose curve*. Find an equation of the tangent line to this curve at the point (1, 1).

 (b) Illustrate part (a) by graphing the curve and the tangent line on the same screen.

43–46 ■ Find the first and second derivatives of the function.

43. $F(t) = (1 - 7t)^6$

44. $h(x) = \sqrt{x^2 + 1}$

45. $y = (x^3 + 1)^{2/3}$

46. $H(t) = \tan 3t$

■ ■ ■ ■ ■ ■ ■ ■ ■ ■ ■ ■ ■ ■

47. If $F(x) = f(g(x))$, where $f(-2) = 8$, $f'(-2) = 4$, $f'(5) = 3$, $g(5) = -2$, and $g'(5) = 6$, find $F'(5)$.

48. If $h(x) = \sqrt{4 + 3f(x)}$, where $f(1) = 7$ and $f'(1) = 4$, find $h'(1)$.

49. A table of values for f, g, f', and g' is given.

x	$f(x)$	$g(x)$	$f'(x)$	$g'(x)$
1	3	2	4	6
2	1	8	5	7
3	7	2	7	9

(a) If $h(x) = f(g(x))$, find $h'(1)$.
(b) If $H(x) = g(f(x))$, find $H'(1)$.

50. Let f and g be the functions in Exercise 49.
(a) If $F(x) = f(f(x))$, find $F'(2)$.
(b) If $G(x) = g(g(x))$, find $G'(3)$.

51. If f and g are the functions whose graphs are shown, let $u(x) = f(g(x))$, $v(x) = g(f(x))$, and $w(x) = g(g(x))$. Find

each derivative, if it exists. If it does not exist, explain why.
(a) $u'(1)$ $\qquad$ (b) $v'(1)$ $\qquad$ (c) $w'(1)$

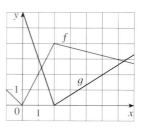

52. If f is the function whose graph is shown, let $h(x) = f(f(x))$ and $g(x) = f(x^2)$. Use the graph of f to estimate the value of each derivative.
(a) $h'(2)$ $\qquad$ (b) $g'(2)$

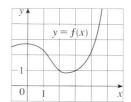

53. Suppose f is differentiable on $\mathbb{R}$. Let $F(x) = f(\cos x)$ and $G(x) = \cos(f(x))$. Find expressions for (a) $F'(x)$ and (b) $G'(x)$.

54. Suppose f is differentiable on $\mathbb{R}$ and α is a real number. Let $F(x) = f(x^\alpha)$ and $G(x) = [f(x)]^\alpha$. Find expressions for (a) $F'(x)$ and (b) $G'(x)$.

55. Let $r(x) = f(g(h(x)))$, where $h(1) = 2$, $g(2) = 3$, $h'(1) = 4$, $g'(2) = 5$, and $f'(3) = 6$. Find $r'(1)$.

56. If g is a twice differentiable function and $f(x) = xg(x^2)$, find f'' in terms of g, g', and g''.

57. Find all points on the graph of the function $f(x) = 2 \sin x + \sin^2 x$ at which the tangent line is horizontal.

58. Find the 50th derivative of $y = \cos 2x$.

59. The displacement of a particle on a vibrating string is given by the equation

$$s(t) = 10 + \tfrac{1}{4} \sin(10\pi t)$$

where s is measured in centimeters and t in seconds. Find the velocity of the particle after t seconds.

60. If the equation of motion of a particle is given by $s = A \cos(\omega t + \delta)$, the particle is said to undergo *simple harmonic motion*.
(a) Find the velocity of the particle at time t.
(b) When is the velocity 0?

61. A Cepheid variable star is a star whose brightness alternately increases and decreases. The most easily visible such star is Delta Cephei, for which the interval between times of maximum brightness is 5.4 days. The average brightness of this star is 4.0 and its brightness changes by ±0.35. In view of these data, the brightness of Delta Cephei at time t, where t is measured in days, has been modeled by the function

$$B(t) = 4.0 + 0.35 \sin(2\pi t/5.4)$$

(a) Find the rate of change of the brightness after t days.
(b) Find, correct to two decimal places, the rate of increase after one day.

62. A model for the length of daylight (in hours) in Philadelphia on the tth day of the year is given by the function

$$L(t) = 12 + 2.8 \sin\left[\frac{2\pi}{365}(t - 80)\right]$$

Use this model to compare how the number of hours of daylight is increasing in Philadelphia on March 21 and May 21.

63. A particle moves along a straight line with displacement $s(t)$, velocity $v(t)$, and acceleration $a(t)$. Show that

$$a(t) = v(t)\frac{dv}{ds}$$

Explain the difference between the meanings of the derivatives dv/dt and dv/ds.

64. Air is being pumped into a spherical weather balloon. At any time t, the volume of the balloon is $V(t)$ and its radius is $r(t)$.
(a) What do the derivatives dV/dr and dV/dt represent?
(b) Express dV/dt in terms of dr/dt.

65. (a) If n is a positive integer, prove that

$$\frac{d}{dx}(\sin^n x \cos nx) = n \sin^{n-1} x \cos(n + 1)x$$

(b) Find a formula for the derivative of $y = \cos^n x \cos nx$ that is similar to the one in part (a).

66. Use the Chain Rule to prove the following.
(a) The derivative of an even function is an odd function.
(b) The derivative of an odd function is an even function.

67. Use the Chain Rule to show that if θ is measured in degrees, then

$$\frac{d}{d\theta}(\sin \theta) = \frac{\pi}{180}\cos \theta$$

(This gives one reason for the convention that radian measure is always used when dealing with trigonometric functions in calculus: The differentiation formulas would not be as simple if we used degree measure.)

68. Suppose $y = f(x)$ is a curve that always lies above the x-axis and never has a horizontal tangent, where f is differentiable everywhere. For what value of y is the rate of change of y^5 with respect to x eighty times the rate of change of y with respect to x?

69. If $y = f(u)$ and $u = g(x)$, where f and g are twice differentiable functions, show that

$$\frac{d^2y}{dx^2} = \frac{dy}{du}\frac{d^2u}{dx^2} + \frac{d^2y}{du^2}\left(\frac{du}{dx}\right)^2$$

70. (a) Write $|x| = \sqrt{x^2}$ and use the Chain Rule to show that

$$\frac{d}{dx}|x| = \frac{x}{|x|}$$

(b) If $f(x) = |\sin x|$, find $f'(x)$ and sketch the graphs of f and f'. Where is f not differentiable?
(c) If $g(x) = \sin|x|$, find $g'(x)$ and sketch the graphs of g and g'. Where is g not differentiable?

2.6 | IMPLICIT DIFFERENTIATION

The functions that we have met so far can be described by expressing one variable explicitly in terms of another variable—for example,

$$y = \sqrt{x^3 + 1} \qquad \text{or} \qquad y = x \sin x$$

or, in general, $y = f(x)$. Some functions, however, are defined implicitly by a relation between x and y such as

1 $$x^2 + y^2 = 25$$

or

2 $$x^3 + y^3 = 6xy$$

In some cases it is possible to solve such an equation for y as an explicit function (or several functions) of x. For instance, if we solve Equation 1 for y, we obtain $y = \pm\sqrt{25 - x^2}$, so two of the functions determined by the implicit Equation 1 are $f(x) = \sqrt{25 - x^2}$ and $g(x) = -\sqrt{25 - x^2}$. The graphs of f and g are the upper and lower semicircles of the circle $x^2 + y^2 = 25$. (See Figure 1.)

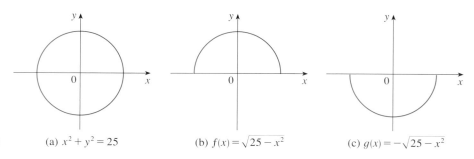

FIGURE 1   (a) $x^2 + y^2 = 25$ (b) $f(x) = \sqrt{25 - x^2}$ (c) $g(x) = -\sqrt{25 - x^2}$

It's not easy to solve Equation 2 for y explicitly as a function of x by hand. (A computer algebra system has no trouble, but the expressions it obtains are very complicated.) Nonetheless, (2) is the equation of a curve called the **folium of Descartes** shown in Figure 2 and it implicitly defines y as several functions of x. The graphs of three such functions are shown in Figure 3. When we say that f is a function defined implicitly by Equation 2, we mean that the equation

$$x^3 + [f(x)]^3 = 6xf(x)$$

is true for all values of x in the domain of f.

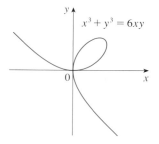

FIGURE 2 The folium of Descartes

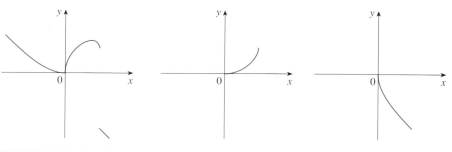

FIGURE 3 Graphs of three functions defined by the folium of Descartes

Fortunately, we don't need to solve an equation for y in terms of x in order to find the derivative of y. Instead we can use the method of **implicit differentiation**: This consists of differentiating both sides of the equation with respect to x and then solving the resulting equation for y'. In the examples and exercises of this section it is always assumed that the given equation determines y implicitly as a differentiable function of x so that the method of implicit differentiation can be applied.

▼ **EXAMPLE 1**

(a) If $x^2 + y^2 = 25$, find $\dfrac{dy}{dx}$.

(b) Find an equation of the tangent to the circle $x^2 + y^2 = 25$ at the point $(3, 4)$.

SOLUTION 1

(a) Differentiate both sides of the equation $x^2 + y^2 = 25$:

$$\frac{d}{dx}(x^2 + y^2) = \frac{d}{dx}(25)$$

$$\frac{d}{dx}(x^2) + \frac{d}{dx}(y^2) = 0$$

Remembering that y is a function of x and using the Chain Rule, we have

$$\frac{d}{dx}(y^2) = \frac{d}{dy}(y^2)\frac{dy}{dx} = 2y\frac{dy}{dx}$$

Thus

$$2x + 2y\frac{dy}{dx} = 0$$

Now we solve this equation for dy/dx:

$$\frac{dy}{dx} = -\frac{x}{y}$$

(b) At the point $(3, 4)$ we have $x = 3$ and $y = 4$, so

$$\frac{dy}{dx} = -\frac{3}{4}$$

An equation of the tangent to the circle at $(3, 4)$ is therefore

$$y - 4 = -\tfrac{3}{4}(x - 3) \qquad \text{or} \qquad 3x + 4y = 25$$

SOLUTION 2

(b) Solving the equation $x^2 + y^2 = 25$, we get $y = \pm\sqrt{25 - x^2}$. The point $(3, 4)$ lies on the upper semicircle $y = \sqrt{25 - x^2}$ and so we consider the function $f(x) = \sqrt{25 - x^2}$. Differentiating f using the Chain Rule, we have

$$f'(x) = \tfrac{1}{2}(25 - x^2)^{-1/2}\frac{d}{dx}(25 - x^2)$$

$$= \tfrac{1}{2}(25 - x^2)^{-1/2}(-2x) = -\frac{x}{\sqrt{25 - x^2}}$$

▪ Example 1 illustrates that even when it is possible to solve an equation explicitly for y in terms of x, it may be easier to use implicit differentiation.

So

$$f'(3) = -\frac{3}{\sqrt{25 - 3^2}} = -\frac{3}{4}$$

and, as in Solution 1, an equation of the tangent is $3x + 4y = 25$. ▪

▼ EXAMPLE 2

(a) Find y' if $x^3 + y^3 = 6xy$.

(b) Find the tangent to the folium of Descartes $x^3 + y^3 = 6xy$ at the point $(3, 3)$.

(c) At what point in the first quadrant is the tangent line horizontal?

SOLUTION

(a) Differentiating both sides of $x^3 + y^3 = 6xy$ with respect to x, regarding y as a function of x, and using the Chain Rule on the y^3 term and the Product Rule on the $6xy$ term, we get

$$3x^2 + 3y^2 y' = 6y + 6xy'$$

or

$$x^2 + y^2 y' = 2y + 2xy'$$

We now solve for y':

$$y^2 y' - 2xy' = 2y - x^2$$

$$(y^2 - 2x)y' = 2y - x^2$$

$$y' = \frac{2y - x^2}{y^2 - 2x}$$

(b) When $x = y = 3$,

$$y' = \frac{2 \cdot 3 - 3^2}{3^2 - 2 \cdot 3} = -1$$

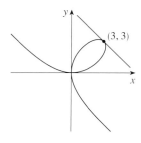

FIGURE 4

and a glance at Figure 4 confirms that this is a reasonable value for the slope at $(3, 3)$. So an equation of the tangent to the folium at $(3, 3)$ is

$$y - 3 = -1(x - 3) \qquad \text{or} \qquad x + y = 6$$

(c) The tangent line is horizontal if $y' = 0$. Using the expression for y' from part (a), we see that $y' = 0$ when $2y - x^2 = 0$ (provided that $y^2 - 2x \neq 0$). Substituting $y = \frac{1}{2}x^2$ in the equation of the curve, we get

$$x^3 + \left(\tfrac{1}{2}x^2\right)^3 = 6x\left(\tfrac{1}{2}x^2\right)$$

which simplifies to $x^6 = 16x^3$. Since $x \neq 0$ in the first quadrant, we have $x^3 = 16$. If $x = 16^{1/3} = 2^{4/3}$, then $y = \frac{1}{2}(2^{8/3}) = 2^{5/3}$. Thus the tangent is horizontal at $(2^{4/3}, 2^{5/3})$, which is approximately $(2.5198, 3.1748)$. Looking at Figure 5, we see that our answer is reasonable.

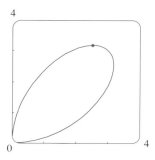

FIGURE 5

EXAMPLE 3 Find y' if $\sin(x + y) = y^2 \cos x$.

SOLUTION Differentiating implicitly with respect to x and remembering that y is a function of x, we get

$$\cos(x + y) \cdot (1 + y') = 2yy' \cos x + y^2(-\sin x)$$

(Note that we have used the Chain Rule on the left side and the Product Rule and Chain Rule on the right side.) If we collect the terms that involve y', we get

$$\cos(x + y) + y^2 \sin x = (2y \cos x)y' - \cos(x + y) \cdot y'$$

So

$$y' = \frac{y^2 \sin x + \cos(x + y)}{2y \cos x - \cos(x + y)}$$

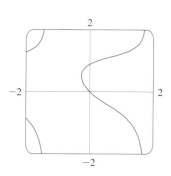

FIGURE 6

Figure 6, drawn with the implicit-plotting command of a computer algebra system, shows part of the curve $\sin(x + y) = y^2 \cos x$. As a check on our calculation, notice that $y' = -1$ when $x = y = 0$ and it appears from the graph that the slope is approximately -1 at the origin.

EXAMPLE 4 Find y'' if $x^4 + y^4 = 16$.

SOLUTION Differentiating the equation implicitly with respect to x, we get

$$4x^3 + 4y^3y' = 0$$

Solving for y' gives

3
$$y' = -\frac{x^3}{y^3}$$

To find y'' we differentiate this expression for y' using the Quotient Rule and remembering that y is a function of x:

$$y'' = \frac{d}{dx}\left(-\frac{x^3}{y^3}\right) = -\frac{y^3\,(d/dx)(x^3) - x^3\,(d/dx)(y^3)}{(y^3)^2}$$

$$= -\frac{y^3 \cdot 3x^2 - x^3(3y^2y')}{y^6}$$

■ Figure 7 shows the graph of the curve $x^4 + y^4 = 16$ of Example 4. Notice that it's a stretched and flattened version of the circle $x^2 + y^2 = 4$. For this reason it's sometimes called a *fat circle*. It starts out very steep on the left but quickly becomes very flat. This can be seen from the expression

$$y' = -\frac{x^3}{y^3} = -\left(\frac{x}{y}\right)^3$$

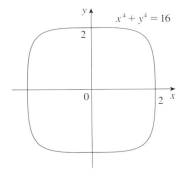

FIGURE 7

If we now substitute Equation 3 into this expression, we get

$$y'' = -\frac{3x^2y^3 - 3x^3y^2\left(-\dfrac{x^3}{y^3}\right)}{y^6}$$

$$= -\frac{3(x^2y^4 + x^6)}{y^7} = -\frac{3x^2(y^4 + x^4)}{y^7}$$

But the values of x and y must satisfy the original equation $x^4 + y^4 = 16$. So the answer simplifies to

$$y'' = -\frac{3x^2(16)}{y^7} = -48\frac{x^2}{y^7}$$

2.6 EXERCISES

1–2 ■
(a) Find y' by implicit differentiation.
(b) Solve the equation explicitly for y and differentiate to get y' in terms of x.
(c) Check that your solutions to parts (a) and (b) are consistent by substituting the expression for y into your solution for part (a).

1. $xy + 2x + 3x^2 = 4$ **2.** $4x^2 + 9y^2 = 36$

3–14 ■ Find dy/dx by implicit differentiation.

3. $x^3 + x^2y + 4y^2 = 6$ **4.** $x^2 - 2xy + y^3 = c$

5. $x^2y + xy^2 = 3x$ **6.** $y^5 + x^2y^3 = 1 + x^4y$

7. $x^2y^2 + x\sin y = 4$ **8.** $1 + x = \sin(xy^2)$

9. $4\cos x \sin y = 1$ **10.** $y\sin(x^2) = x\sin(y^2)$

11. $\tan(x/y) = x + y$ **12.** $\sqrt{x+y} = 1 + x^2y^2$

13. $\sqrt{xy} = 1 + x^2y$ **14.** $\sin x + \cos y = \sin x \cos y$

15. If $f(x) + x^2[f(x)]^3 = 10$ and $f(1) = 2$, find $f'(1)$.

16. If $g(x) + x\sin g(x) = x^2$, find $g'(0)$.

17–22 ■ Use implicit differentiation to find an equation of the tangent line to the curve at the given point.

17. $x^2 + xy + y^2 = 3$,   (1, 1)   (ellipse)

18. $x^2 + 2xy - y^2 + x = 2$,   (1, 2)   (hyperbola)

19. $x^2 + y^2 = (2x^2 + 2y^2 - x)^2$
$(0, \frac{1}{2})$
(cardioid)

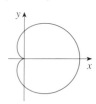

20. $x^{2/3} + y^{2/3} = 4$
$(-3\sqrt{3}, 1)$
(astroid)

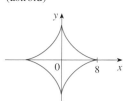

21. $2(x^2 + y^2)^2 = 25(x^2 - y^2)$
$(3, 1)$
(lemniscate)

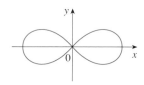

22. $y^2(y^2 - 4) = x^2(x^2 - 5)$
$(0, -2)$
(devil's curve)

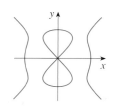

23–26 ■ Find y'' by implicit differentiation.

23. $9x^2 + y^2 = 9$

24. $\sqrt{x} + \sqrt{y} = 1$

25. $x^3 + y^3 = 1$

26. $x^4 + y^4 = a^4$

27. (a) The curve with equation $y^2 = 5x^4 - x^2$ is called a **kampyle of Eudoxus**. Find an equation of the tangent line to this curve at the point $(1, 2)$.

   (b) Illustrate part (a) by graphing the curve and the tangent line on a common screen. (If your graphing device will graph implicitly defined curves, then use that capability. If not, you can still graph this curve by graphing its upper and lower halves separately.)

28. (a) The curve with equation $y^2 = x^3 + 3x^2$ is called the **Tschirnhausen cubic**. Find an equation of the tangent line to this curve at the point $(1, -2)$.
   (b) At what points does this curve have a horizontal tangent?

   (c) Illustrate parts (a) and (b) by graphing the curve and the tangent lines on a common screen.

CAS 29. Fanciful shapes can be created by using the implicit plotting capabilities of computer algebra systems.
   (a) Graph the curve with equation
$$y(y^2 - 1)(y - 2) = x(x - 1)(x - 2)$$
   At how many points does this curve have horizontal tangents? Estimate the x-coordinates of these points.
   (b) Find equations of the tangent lines at the points $(0, 1)$ and $(0, 2)$.

(c) Find the exact x-coordinates of the points in part (a).
(d) Create even more fanciful curves by modifying the equation in part (a).

CAS 30. (a) The curve with equation
$$2y^3 + y^2 - y^5 = x^4 - 2x^3 + x^2$$
   has been likened to a bouncing wagon. Use a computer algebra system to graph this curve and discover why.
   (b) At how many points does this curve have horizontal tangent lines? Find the x-coordinates of these points.

31. Find the points on the lemniscate in Exercise 21 where the tangent is horizontal.

32. Show by implicit differentiation that the tangent to the ellipse
$$\frac{x^2}{a^2} + \frac{y^2}{b^2} = 1$$
at the point (x_0, y_0) is
$$\frac{x_0 x}{a^2} + \frac{y_0 y}{b^2} = 1$$

33–36 ■ Two curves are **orthogonal** if their tangent lines are perpendicular at each point of intersection. Show that the given families of curves are **orthogonal trajectories** of each other, that is, every curve in one family is orthogonal to every curve in the other family. Sketch both families of curves on the same axes.

33. $x^2 + y^2 = r^2$, $\quad ax + by = 0$

34. $x^2 + y^2 = ax$, $\quad x^2 + y^2 = by$

35. $y = cx^2$, $\quad x^2 + 2y^2 = k$

36. $y = ax^3$, $\quad x^2 + 3y^2 = b$

37. Show, using implicit differentiation, that any tangent line at a point P to a circle with center O is perpendicular to the radius OP.

38. Show that the sum of the x- and y-intercepts of any tangent line to the curve $\sqrt{x} + \sqrt{y} = \sqrt{c}$ is equal to c.

39. The equation $x^2 - xy + y^2 = 3$ represents a "rotated ellipse," that is, an ellipse whose axes are not parallel to the coordinate axes. Find the points at which this ellipse crosses the x-axis and show that the tangent lines at these points are parallel.

40. (a) Where does the normal line to the ellipse $x^2 - xy + y^2 = 3$ at the point $(-1, 1)$ intersect the ellipse a second time?

   (b) Illustrate part (a) by graphing the ellipse and the normal line.

41. Find all points on the curve $x^2 y^2 + xy = 2$ where the slope of the tangent line is -1.

42. Find equations of both the tangent lines to the ellipse $x^2 + 4y^2 = 36$ that pass through the point $(12, 3)$.

43. The **Bessel function** of order 0, $y = J(x)$, satisfies the differential equation $xy'' + y' + xy = 0$ for all values of x and its value at 0 is $J(0) = 1$.
(a) Find $J'(0)$.
(b) Use implicit differentiation to find $J''(0)$.

44. The figure shows a lamp located three units to the right of the y-axis and a shadow created by the elliptical region $x^2 + 4y^2 \leqslant 5$. If the point $(-5, 0)$ is on the edge of the shadow, how far above the x-axis is the lamp located?

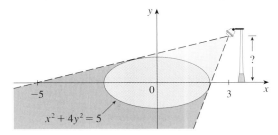

| **2.7** | **RELATED RATES** |

If we are pumping air into a balloon, both the volume and the radius of the balloon are increasing and their rates of increase are related to each other. But it is much easier to measure directly the rate of increase of the volume than the rate of increase of the radius.

In a related rates problem the idea is to compute the rate of change of one quantity in terms of the rate of change of another quantity (which may be more easily measured). The procedure is to find an equation that relates the two quantities and then use the Chain Rule to differentiate both sides with respect to time.

☑ EXAMPLE I Air is being pumped into a spherical balloon so that its volume increases at a rate of 100 cm³/s. How fast is the radius of the balloon increasing when the diameter is 50 cm?

SOLUTION We start by identifying two things:

the *given information:*

the rate of increase of the volume of air is 100 cm³/s

and the *unknown:*

the rate of increase of the radius when the diameter is 50 cm

In order to express these quantities mathematically, we introduce some suggestive *notation:*

Let V be the volume of the balloon and let r be its radius.

The key thing to remember is that rates of change are derivatives. In this problem, the volume and the radius are both functions of the time t. The rate of increase of the volume with respect to time is the derivative dV/dt, and the rate of increase of the radius is dr/dt. We can therefore restate the given and the unknown as follows:

$$\text{Given:} \qquad \frac{dV}{dt} = 100 \text{ cm}^3/\text{s}$$

$$\text{Unknown:} \qquad \frac{dr}{dt} \quad \text{when } r = 25 \text{ cm}$$

In order to connect dV/dt and dr/dt, we first relate V and r by the formula for the volume of a sphere:

$$V = \tfrac{4}{3}\pi r^3$$

In order to use the given information, we differentiate each side of this equation with respect to t. To differentiate the right side, we need to use the Chain Rule:

$$\frac{dV}{dt} = \frac{dV}{dr}\frac{dr}{dt} = 4\pi r^2 \frac{dr}{dt}$$

Now we solve for the unknown quantity:

$$\frac{dr}{dt} = \frac{1}{4\pi r^2}\frac{dV}{dt}$$

▪ Notice that, although dV/dt is constant, dr/dt is *not* constant.

If we put $r = 25$ and $dV/dt = 100$ in this equation, we obtain

$$\frac{dr}{dt} = \frac{1}{4\pi(25)^2}100 = \frac{1}{25\pi}$$

The radius of the balloon is increasing at the rate of $1/(25\pi)$ cm/s. ▪

EXAMPLE 2 A ladder 10 ft long rests against a vertical wall. If the bottom of the ladder slides away from the wall at a rate of 1 ft/s, how fast is the top of the ladder sliding down the wall when the bottom of the ladder is 6 ft from the wall?

SOLUTION We first draw a diagram and label it as in Figure 1. Let x feet be the distance from the bottom of the ladder to the wall and y feet the distance from the top of the ladder to the ground. Note that x and y are both functions of t (time, measured in seconds).

We are given that $dx/dt = 1$ ft/s and we are asked to find dy/dt when $x = 6$ ft. (See Figure 2.) In this problem, the relationship between x and y is given by the Pythagorean Theorem:

$$x^2 + y^2 = 100$$

Differentiating each side with respect to t using the Chain Rule, we have

$$2x\frac{dx}{dt} + 2y\frac{dy}{dt} = 0$$

and solving this equation for the desired rate, we obtain

$$\frac{dy}{dt} = -\frac{x}{y}\frac{dx}{dt}$$

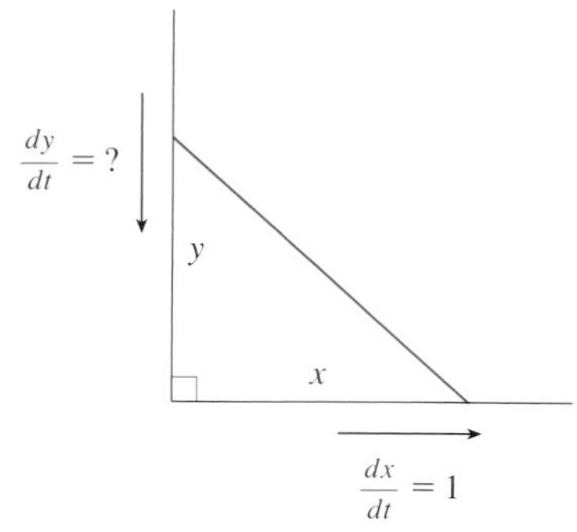

When $x = 6$, the Pythagorean Theorem gives $y = 8$ and so, substituting these values and $dx/dt = 1$, we have

$$\frac{dy}{dt} = -\frac{6}{8}(1) = -\frac{3}{4}\text{ ft/s}$$

The fact that dy/dt is negative means that the distance from the top of the ladder to the ground is *decreasing* at a rate of $\frac{3}{4}$ ft/s. In other words, the top of the ladder is sliding down the wall at a rate of $\frac{3}{4}$ ft/s. ▪

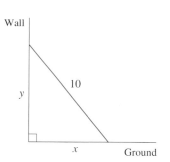

Wall · 10 · y · x · Ground

FIGURE 1

$\dfrac{dy}{dt} = ?$ · y · x · $\dfrac{dx}{dt} = 1$

FIGURE 2

EXAMPLE 3 A water tank has the shape of an inverted circular cone with base radius 2 m and height 4 m. If water is being pumped into the tank at a rate of 2 m³/min, find the rate at which the water level is rising when the water is 3 m deep.

SOLUTION We first sketch the cone and label it as in Figure 3. Let V, r, and h be the volume of the water, the radius of the surface, and the height at time t, where t is measured in minutes.

We are given that $dV/dt = 2$ m³/min and we are asked to find dh/dt when h is 3 m. The quantities V and h are related by the equation

$$V = \tfrac{1}{3} \pi r^2 h$$

but it is very useful to express V as a function of h alone. In order to eliminate r, we use the similar triangles in Figure 3 to write

$$\frac{r}{h} = \frac{2}{4} \qquad r = \frac{h}{2}$$

and the expression for V becomes

$$V = \frac{1}{3} \pi \left(\frac{h}{2} \right)^2 h = \frac{\pi}{12} h^3$$

Now we can differentiate each side with respect to t:

$$\frac{dV}{dt} = \frac{\pi}{4} h^2 \frac{dh}{dt}$$

so

$$\frac{dh}{dt} = \frac{4}{\pi h^2} \frac{dV}{dt}$$

Substituting $h = 3$ m and $dV/dt = 2$ m³/min, we have

$$\frac{dh}{dt} = \frac{4}{\pi (3)^2} \cdot 2 = \frac{8}{9\pi}$$

The water level is rising at a rate of $8/(9\pi) \approx 0.28$ m/min. ▪

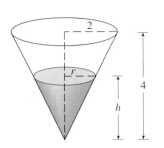

FIGURE 3

STRATEGY   Examples 1–3 suggest the following steps in solving related rates problems:

1. Read the problem carefully.

2. Draw a diagram if possible.

3. Introduce notation. Assign symbols to all quantities that are functions of time.

4. Express the given information and the required rate in terms of derivatives.

5. Write an equation that relates the various quantities of the problem. If necessary, use the geometry of the situation to eliminate one of the variables by substitution (as in Example 3).

6. Use the Chain Rule to differentiate both sides of the equation with respect to t.

7. Substitute the given information into the resulting equation and solve for the unknown rate.

The following examples are further illustrations of the strategy.

⊘ **WARNING** A common error is to substitute the given numerical information (for quantities that vary with time) too early. This should be done only *after* the differentiation. (Step 7 follows Step 6.) For instance, in Example 3 we dealt with general values of h until we finally substituted $h = 3$ at the last stage. (If we had put $h = 3$ earlier, we would have gotten $dV/dt = 0$, which is clearly wrong.)

V EXAMPLE 4 Car A is traveling west at 50 mi/h and car B is traveling north at 60 mi/h. Both are headed for the intersection of the two roads. At what rate are the cars approaching each other when car A is 0.3 mi and car B is 0.4 mi from the intersection?

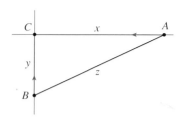

FIGURE 4

SOLUTION We draw Figure 4, where C is the intersection of the roads. At a given time t, let x be the distance from car A to C, let y be the distance from car B to C, and let z be the distance between the cars, where x, y, and z are measured in miles.

We are given that $dx/dt = -50$ mi/h and $dy/dt = -60$ mi/h. (The derivatives are negative because x and y are decreasing.) We are asked to find dz/dt. The equation that relates x, y, and z is given by the Pythagorean Theorem:

$$z^2 = x^2 + y^2$$

Differentiating each side with respect to t, we have

$$2z \frac{dz}{dt} = 2x \frac{dx}{dt} + 2y \frac{dy}{dt}$$

$$\frac{dz}{dt} = \frac{1}{z}\left(x \frac{dx}{dt} + y \frac{dy}{dt} \right)$$

When $x = 0.3$ mi and $y = 0.4$ mi, the Pythagorean Theorem gives $z = 0.5$ mi, so

$$\frac{dz}{dt} = \frac{1}{0.5} [0.3(-50) + 0.4(-60)]$$

$$= -78 \text{ mi/h}$$

The cars are approaching each other at a rate of 78 mi/h. ▪

V EXAMPLE 5 A man walks along a straight path at a speed of 4 ft/s. A searchlight is located on the ground 20 ft from the path and is kept focused on the man. At what rate is the searchlight rotating when the man is 15 ft from the point on the path closest to the searchlight?

SOLUTION We draw Figure 5 and let x be the distance from the man to the point on the path closest to the searchlight. We let θ be the angle between the beam of the searchlight and the perpendicular to the path.

We are given that $dx/dt = 4$ ft/s and are asked to find $d\theta/dt$ when $x = 15$. The equation that relates x and θ can be written from Figure 5:

$$\frac{x}{20} = \tan \theta \qquad x = 20 \tan \theta$$

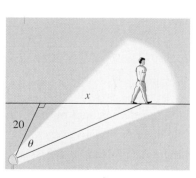

FIGURE 5

Differentiating each side with respect to t, we get

$$\frac{dx}{dt} = 20 \sec^2\theta \frac{d\theta}{dt}$$

so

$$\frac{d\theta}{dt} = \tfrac{1}{20} \cos^2\theta \frac{dx}{dt} = \tfrac{1}{20} \cos^2\theta \,(4) = \tfrac{1}{5} \cos^2\theta$$

When $x = 15$ ft, the length of the beam is 25 ft, so $\cos \theta = \frac{4}{5}$ and

$$\frac{d\theta}{dt} = \frac{1}{5} \left(\frac{4}{5} \right)^2 = \frac{16}{125} = 0.128$$

The searchlight is rotating at a rate of 0.128 rad/s. ▪

| **2.7** | **EXERCISES** |

1. If V is the volume of a cube with edge length x and the cube expands as time passes, find dV/dt in terms of dx/dt.

2. (a) If A is the area of a circle with radius r and the circle expands as time passes, find dA/dt in terms of dr/dt.
(b) Suppose oil spills from a ruptured tanker and spreads in a circular pattern. If the radius of the oil spill increases at a constant rate of 1 m/s, how fast is the area of the spill increasing when the radius is 30 m?

3. Each side of a square is increasing at a rate of 6 cm/s. At what rate is the area of the square increasing when the area of the square is 16 cm²?

4. The length of a rectangle is increasing at a rate of 8 cm/s and its width is increasing at a rate of 3 cm/s. When the length is 20 cm and the width is 10 cm, how fast is the area of the rectangle increasing?

5. If $y = x^3 + 2x$ and $dx/dt = 5$, find dy/dt when $x = 2$.

6. If $x^2 + y^2 = 25$ and $dy/dt = 6$, find dx/dt when $y = 4$.

7. If $z^2 = x^2 + y^2$, $dx/dt = 2$, and $dy/dt = 3$, find dz/dt when $x = 5$ and $y = 12$.

8. A particle moves along the curve $y = \sqrt{1 + x^3}$. As it reaches the point $(2, 3)$, the y-coordinate is increasing at a rate of 4 cm/s. How fast is the x-coordinate of the point changing at that instant?

9–12 ▪
(a) What quantities are given in the problem?
(b) What is the unknown?
(c) Draw a picture of the situation for any time t.
(d) Write an equation that relates the quantities.
(e) Finish solving the problem.

9. If a snowball melts so that its surface area decreases at a rate of 1 cm²/min, find the rate at which the diameter decreases when the diameter is 10 cm.

10. At noon, ship A is 150 km west of ship B. Ship A is sailing east at 35 km/h and ship B is sailing north at 25 km/h. How fast is the distance between the ships changing at 4:00 PM?

11. A plane flying horizontally at an altitude of 1 mi and a speed of 500 mi/h passes directly over a radar station. Find the rate at which the distance from the plane to the station is increasing when it is 2 mi away from the station.

12. A street light is mounted at the top of a 15-ft-tall pole. A man 6 ft tall walks away from the pole with a speed of 5 ft/s along a straight path. How fast is the tip of his shadow moving when he is 40 ft from the pole?

▪ ▪ ▪ ▪ ▪ ▪ ▪ ▪ ▪ ▪ ▪ ▪

13. Two cars start moving from the same point. One travels south at 60 mi/h and the other travels west at 25 mi/h. At what rate is the distance between the cars increasing two hours later?

14. A spotlight on the ground shines on a wall 12 m away. If a man 2 m tall walks from the spotlight toward the building at a speed of 1.6 m/s, how fast is the length of his shadow on the building decreasing when he is 4 m from the building?

15. A man starts walking north at 4 ft/s from a point P. Five minutes later a woman starts walking south at 5 ft/s from a point 500 ft due east of P. At what rate are the people moving apart 15 min after the woman starts walking?

16. A baseball diamond is a square with side 90 ft. A batter hits the ball and runs toward first base with a speed of 24 ft/s.
(a) At what rate is his distance from second base decreasing when he is halfway to first base?
(b) At what rate is his distance from third base increasing at the same moment?

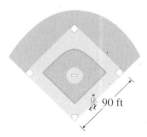

90 ft

17. The altitude of a triangle is increasing at a rate of 1 cm/min while the area of the triangle is increasing at a rate of 2 cm²/min. At what rate is the base of the triangle changing when the altitude is 10 cm and the area is 100 cm²?

18. A boat is pulled into a dock by a rope attached to the bow of the boat and passing through a pulley on the dock that is 1 m higher than the bow of the boat. If the rope is pulled in at a rate of 1 m/s, how fast is the boat approaching the dock when it is 8 m from the dock?

19. At noon, ship A is 100 km west of ship B. Ship A is sailing south at 35 km/h and ship B is sailing north at 25 km/h. How fast is the distance between the ships changing at 4:00 PM?

20. A particle is moving along the curve $y = \sqrt{x}$. As the particle passes through the point $(4, 2)$, its x-coordinate increases at a rate of 3 cm/s. How fast is the distance from the particle to the origin changing at this instant?

21. Two carts, A and B, are connected by a rope 39 ft long that passes over a pulley P. The point Q is on the floor 12 ft directly beneath P and between the carts. Cart A is being pulled away from Q at a speed of 2 ft/s. How fast is cart B moving toward Q at the instant when cart A is 5 ft from Q?

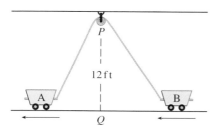

22. Water is leaking out of an inverted conical tank at a rate of 10,000 cm³/min at the same time that water is being pumped into the tank at a constant rate. The tank has height 6 m and the diameter at the top is 4 m. If the water level is rising at a rate of 20 cm/min when the height of the water is 2 m, find the rate at which water is being pumped into the tank.

23. A trough is 10 ft long and its ends have the shape of isosceles triangles that are 3 ft across at the top and have a height of 1 ft. If the trough is being filled with water at a rate of 12 ft³/min, how fast is the water level rising when the water is 6 inches deep?

24. A swimming pool is 20 ft wide, 40 ft long, 3 ft deep at the shallow end, and 9 ft deep at its deepest point. A cross-section is shown in the figure. If the pool is being filled at a rate of 0.8 ft³/min, how fast is the water level rising when the depth at the deepest point is 5 ft?

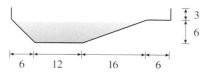

25. Gravel is being dumped from a conveyor belt at a rate of 30 ft³/min, and its coarseness is such that it forms a pile in the shape of a cone whose base diameter and height are

always equal. How fast is the height of the pile increasing when the pile is 10 ft high?

26. A kite 100 ft above the ground moves horizontally at a speed of 8 ft/s. At what rate is the angle between the string and the horizontal decreasing when 200 ft of string has been let out?

27. Two sides of a triangle are 4 m and 5 m in length and the angle between them is increasing at a rate of 0.06 rad/s. Find the rate at which the area of the triangle is increasing when the angle between the sides of fixed length is $\pi/3$.

28. Two sides of a triangle have lengths 12 m and 15 m. The angle between them is increasing at a rate of 2°/min. How fast is the length of the third side increasing when the angle between the sides of fixed length is 60°?

29. Boyle's Law states that when a sample of gas is compressed at a constant temperature, the pressure P and volume V satisfy the equation $PV = C$, where C is a constant. Suppose that at a certain instant the volume is 600 cm³, the pressure is 150 kPa, and the pressure is increasing at a rate of 20 kPa/min. At what rate is the volume decreasing at this instant?

30. When air expands adiabatically (without gaining or losing heat), its pressure P and volume V are related by the equation $PV^{1.4} = C$, where C is a constant. Suppose that at a certain instant the volume is 400 cm³ and the pressure is 80 kPa and is decreasing at a rate of 10 kPa/min. At what rate is the volume increasing at this instant?

31. If two resistors with resistances R_1 and R_2 are connected in parallel, as in the figure, then the total resistance R, measured in ohms (Ω), is given by

$$\frac{1}{R} = \frac{1}{R_1} + \frac{1}{R_2}$$

If R_1 and R_2 are increasing at rates of 0.3 Ω/s and 0.2 Ω/s, respectively, how fast is R changing when $R_1 = 80\ \Omega$ and $R_2 = 100\ \Omega$?

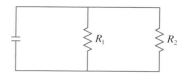

32. Brain weight B as a function of body weight W in fish has been modeled by the power function $B = 0.007W^{2/3}$, where B and W are measured in grams. A model for body weight as a function of body length L (measured in centimeters) is $W = 0.12L^{2.53}$. If, over 10 million years, the average length of a certain species of fish evolved from 15 cm to 20 cm at a constant rate, how fast was this species' brain growing when the average length was 18 cm?

33. A television camera is positioned 4000 ft from the base of a rocket launching pad. The angle of elevation of the camera has to change at the correct rate in order to keep the rocket in sight. Also, the mechanism for focusing the camera has to take into account the increasing distance from the camera to the rising rocket. Let's assume the rocket rises vertically and its speed is 600 ft/s when it has risen 3000 ft.
(a) How fast is the distance from the television camera to the rocket changing at that moment?
(b) If the television camera is always kept aimed at the rocket, how fast is the camera's angle of elevation changing at that same moment?

34. A lighthouse is located on a small island 3 km away from the nearest point P on a straight shoreline and its light makes four revolutions per minute. How fast is the beam of light moving along the shoreline when it is 1 km from P?

35. A plane flying with a constant speed of 300 km/h passes over a ground radar station at an altitude of 1 km and climbs at an angle of 30°. At what rate is the distance from the plane to the radar station increasing a minute later?

36. Two people start from the same point. One walks east at 3 mi/h and the other walks northeast at 2 mi/h. How fast is the distance between the people changing after 15 minutes?

37. A runner sprints around a circular track of radius 100 m at a constant speed of 7 m/s. The runner's friend is standing at a distance 200 m from the center of the track. How fast is the distance between the friends changing when the distance between them is 200 m?

38. The minute hand on a watch is 8 mm long and the hour hand is 4 mm long. How fast is the distance between the tips of the hands changing at one o'clock?

2.8   LINEAR APPROXIMATIONS AND DIFFERENTIALS

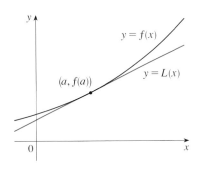

FIGURE 1

We have seen that a curve lies very close to its tangent line near the point of tangency. In fact, by zooming in toward a point on the graph of a differentiable function, we noticed that the graph looks more and more like its tangent line. (See Figure 4 in Section 2.1.) This observation is the basis for a method of finding approximate values of functions.

The idea is that it might be easy to calculate a value $f(a)$ of a function, but difficult (or even impossible) to compute nearby values of f. So we settle for the easily computed values of the linear function L whose graph is the tangent line of f at $(a, f(a))$. (See Figure 1.)

In other words, we use the tangent line at $(a, f(a))$ as an approximation to the curve $y = f(x)$ when x is near a. An equation of this tangent line is

$$y = f(a) + f'(a)(x - a)$$

and the approximation

1 $$f(x) \approx f(a) + f'(a)(x - a)$$

is called the **linear approximation** or **tangent line approximation** of f at a. The linear function whose graph is this tangent line, that is,

2 $$L(x) = f(a) + f'(a)(x - a)$$

is called the **linearization** of f at a.

▼ EXAMPLE 1 Find the linearization of the function $f(x) = \sqrt{x + 3}$ at $a = 1$ and use it to approximate the numbers $\sqrt{3.98}$ and $\sqrt{4.05}$. Are these approximations overestimates or underestimates?

SOLUTION The derivative of $f(x) = (x + 3)^{1/2}$ is

$$f'(x) = \tfrac{1}{2}(x + 3)^{-1/2} = \frac{1}{2\sqrt{x + 3}}$$

and so we have $f(1) = 2$ and $f'(1) = \frac{1}{4}$. Putting these values into Equation 2, we see that the linearization is

$$L(x) = f(1) + f'(1)(x - 1) = 2 + \frac{1}{4}(x - 1) = \frac{7}{4} + \frac{x}{4}$$

The corresponding linear approximation (1) is

$$\sqrt{x + 3} \approx \frac{7}{4} + \frac{x}{4} \qquad \text{(when } x \text{ is near 1)}$$

In particular, we have

$$\sqrt{3.98} \approx \tfrac{7}{4} + \tfrac{0.98}{4} = 1.995 \qquad \text{and} \qquad \sqrt{4.05} \approx \tfrac{7}{4} + \tfrac{1.05}{4} = 2.0125$$

The linear approximation is illustrated in Figure 2. We see that, indeed, the tangent line approximation is a good approximation to the given function when x is near 1. We also see that our approximations are overestimates because the tangent line lies above the curve.

Of course, a calculator could give us approximations for $\sqrt{3.98}$ and $\sqrt{4.05}$, but the linear approximation gives an approximation *over an entire interval.* ■

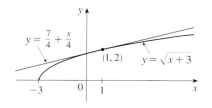

FIGURE 2

In the following table we compare the estimates from the linear approximation in Example 1 with the true values. Notice from this table, and also from Figure 2, that the tangent line approximation gives good estimates when x is close to 1 but the accuracy of the approximation deteriorates when x is farther away from 1.

	x	From $L(x)$	Actual value
$\sqrt{3.9}$	0.9	1.975	1.97484176 . . .
$\sqrt{3.98}$	0.98	1.995	1.99499373 . . .
$\sqrt{4}$	1	2	2.00000000 . . .
$\sqrt{4.05}$	1.05	2.0125	2.01246117 . . .
$\sqrt{4.1}$	1.1	2.025	2.02484567 . . .
$\sqrt{5}$	2	2.25	2.23606797 . . .
$\sqrt{6}$	3	2.5	2.44948974 . . .

How good is the approximation that we obtained in Example 1? The next example shows that by using a graphing calculator or computer we can determine an interval throughout which a linear approximation provides a specified accuracy.

EXAMPLE 2 For what values of x is the linear approximation

$$\sqrt{x + 3} \approx \frac{7}{4} + \frac{x}{4}$$

accurate to within 0.5? What about accuracy to within 0.1?

SOLUTION Accuracy to within 0.5 means that the functions should differ by less than 0.5:

$$\left| \sqrt{x + 3} - \left(\frac{7}{4} + \frac{x}{4} \right) \right| < 0.5$$

Equivalently, we could write

$$\sqrt{x + 3} - 0.5 < \frac{7}{4} + \frac{x}{4} < \sqrt{x + 3} + 0.5$$

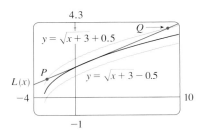

FIGURE 3

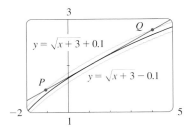

FIGURE 4

This says that the linear approximation should lie between the curves obtained by shifting the curve $y = \sqrt{x+3}$ upward and downward by an amount 0.5. Figure 3 shows the tangent line $y = (7 + x)/4$ intersecting the upper curve $y = \sqrt{x+3} + 0.5$ at P and Q. Zooming in and using the cursor, we estimate that the x-coordinate of P is about -2.66 and the x-coordinate of Q is about 8.66. Thus we see from the graph that the approximation

$$\sqrt{x+3} \approx \frac{7}{4} + \frac{x}{4}$$

is accurate to within 0.5 when $-2.6 < x < 8.6$. (We have rounded to be safe.)

Similarly, from Figure 4 we see that the approximation is accurate to within 0.1 when $-1.1 < x < 3.9$. ▪

APPLICATIONS TO PHYSICS

Linear approximations are often used in physics. In analyzing the consequences of an equation, a physicist sometimes needs to simplify a function by replacing it with its linear approximation. For instance, in deriving a formula for the period of a pendulum, physics textbooks obtain the expression $a_T = -g \sin \theta$ for tangential acceleration and then replace $\sin \theta$ by θ with the remark that $\sin \theta$ is very close to θ if θ is not too large. [See, for example, *Physics: Calculus,* 2d ed., by Eugene Hecht (Pacific Grove, CA: Brooks/Cole, 2000), p. 431.] You can verify that the linearization of the function $f(x) = \sin x$ at $a = 0$ is $L(x) = x$ and so the linear approximation at 0 is

$$\sin x \approx x$$

(see Exercise 26). So, in effect, the derivation of the formula for the period of a pendulum uses the tangent line approximation for the sine function.

Another example occurs in the theory of optics, where light rays that arrive at shallow angles relative to the optical axis are called *paraxial rays*. In paraxial (or Gaussian) optics, both $\sin \theta$ and $\cos \theta$ are replaced by their linearizations. In other words, the linear approximations

$$\sin \theta \approx \theta \qquad \text{and} \qquad \cos \theta \approx 1$$

are used because θ is close to 0. The results of calculations made with these approximations became the basic theoretical tool used to design lenses. [See *Optics,* 4th ed., by Eugene Hecht (San Francisco: Addison Wesley, 2002), p. 154.]

In Section 8.8 we will present several other applications of the idea of linear approximations to physics.

DIFFERENTIALS

The ideas behind linear approximations are sometimes formulated in the terminology and notation of *differentials*. If $y = f(x)$, where f is a differentiable function, then the **differential** dx is an independent variable; that is, dx can be given the value of any real number. The **differential** dy is then defined in terms of dx by the equation

▪ If $dx \neq 0$, we can divide both sides of Equation 3 by dx to obtain

$$\frac{dy}{dx} = f'(x)$$

We have seen similar equations before, but now the left side can genuinely be interpreted as a ratio of differentials.

3 $$dy = f'(x)\, dx$$

So dy is a dependent variable; it depends on the values of x and dx. If dx is given a specific value and x is taken to be some specific number in the domain of f, then the numerical value of dy is determined.

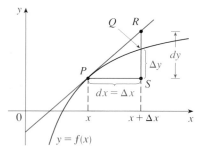

FIGURE 5

The geometric meaning of differentials is shown in Figure 5. Let $P(x, f(x))$ and $Q(x + \Delta x, f(x + \Delta x))$ be points on the graph of f and let $dx = \Delta x$. The corresponding change in y is

$$\Delta y = f(x + \Delta x) - f(x)$$

The slope of the tangent line PR is the derivative $f'(x)$. Thus the directed distance from S to R is $f'(x) \, dx = dy$. Therefore, dy represents the amount that the tangent line rises or falls (the change in the linearization), whereas Δy represents the amount that the curve $y = f(x)$ rises or falls when x changes by an amount dx. Notice from Figure 5 that the approximation $\Delta y \approx dy$ becomes better as Δx becomes smaller.

If we let $dx = x - a$, then $x = a + dx$ and we can rewrite the linear approximation (1) in the notation of differentials:

$$f(a + dx) \approx f(a) + dy$$

For instance, for the function $f(x) = \sqrt{x + 3}$ in Example 1, we have

$$dy = f'(x) \, dx = \frac{dx}{2\sqrt{x + 3}}$$

If $a = 1$ and $dx = \Delta x = 0.05$, then

$$dy = \frac{0.05}{2\sqrt{1 + 3}} = 0.0125$$

and

$$\sqrt{4.05} = f(1.05) \approx f(1) + dy = 2.0125$$

just as we found in Example 1.

Our final example illustrates the use of differentials in estimating the errors that occur because of approximate measurements.

▼ EXAMPLE 3 The radius of a sphere was measured and found to be 21 cm with a possible error in measurement of at most 0.05 cm. What is the maximum error in using this value of the radius to compute the volume of the sphere?

SOLUTION If the radius of the sphere is r, then its volume is $V = \frac{4}{3}\pi r^3$. If the error in the measured value of r is denoted by $dr = \Delta r$, then the corresponding error in the calculated value of V is ΔV, which can be approximated by the differential

$$dV = 4\pi r^2 \, dr$$

When $r = 21$ and $dr = 0.05$, this becomes

$$dV = 4\pi(21)^2 0.05 \approx 277$$

The maximum error in the calculated volume is about 277 cm^3. ■

NOTE Although the possible error in Example 3 may appear to be rather large, a better picture of the error is given by the **relative error**, which is computed by dividing the error by the total volume:

$$\frac{\Delta V}{V} \approx \frac{dV}{V} = \frac{4\pi r^2 \, dr}{\frac{4}{3}\pi r^3} = 3 \frac{dr}{r}$$

Therefore, the relative error in the volume is approximately three times the relative error in the radius. In Example 3 the relative error in the radius is approximately $dr/r = 0.05/21 \approx 0.0024$ and it produces a relative error of about 0.007 in the volume. The errors could also be expressed as **percentage errors** of 0.24% in the radius and 0.7% in the volume.

2.8 EXERCISES

1–4 ▪ Find the linearization $L(x)$ of the function at a.

1. $f(x) = x^4 + 3x^2, \quad a = -1$

2. $f(x) = 1/\sqrt{2 + x}, \quad a = 0$

3. $f(x) = \cos x, \quad a = \pi/2$ **4.** $f(x) = x^{3/4}, \quad a = 16$

▪ ▪ ▪ ▪ ▪ ▪ ▪ ▪ ▪ ▪ ▪ ▪ ▪

5. Find the linear approximation of the function $f(x) = \sqrt{1 - x}$ at $a = 0$ and use it to approximate the numbers $\sqrt{0.9}$ and $\sqrt{0.99}$. Illustrate by graphing f and the tangent line.

6. Find the linear approximation of the function $g(x) = \sqrt[3]{1 + x}$ at $a = 0$ and use it to approximate the numbers $\sqrt[3]{0.95}$ and $\sqrt[3]{1.1}$. Illustrate by graphing g and the tangent line.

7–10 ▪ Verify the given linear approximation at $a = 0$. Then determine the values of x for which the linear approximation is accurate to within 0.1.

7. $\sqrt[3]{1 - x} \approx 1 - \frac{1}{3}x$ **8.** $\tan x \approx x$

9. $1/(1 + 2x)^4 \approx 1 - 8x$ **10.** $1/\sqrt{4 - x} \approx \frac{1}{2} + \frac{1}{16}x$

▪ ▪ ▪ ▪ ▪ ▪ ▪ ▪ ▪ ▪ ▪ ▪ ▪

11–14 ▪ Use a linear approximation (or differentials) to estimate the given number.

11. $(2.001)^5$ **12.** $\sqrt{99.8}$

13. $(8.06)^{2/3}$ **14.** $1/1002$

▪ ▪ ▪ ▪ ▪ ▪ ▪ ▪ ▪ ▪ ▪ ▪ ▪

15–16 ▪ Explain, in terms of linear approximations or differentials, why the approximation is reasonable.

15. $\sec 0.08 \approx 1$ **16.** $(1.01)^6 \approx 1.06$

▪ ▪ ▪ ▪ ▪ ▪ ▪ ▪ ▪ ▪ ▪ ▪ ▪

17–18 ▪ Find the differential of each function.

17. (a) $y = x^2 \sin 2x$ (b) $y = \sqrt{4 + 5x}$

18. (a) $y = s/(1 + 2s)$ (b) $y = 1/(x + 1)$

▪ ▪ ▪ ▪ ▪ ▪ ▪ ▪ ▪ ▪ ▪ ▪ ▪

19. Let $y = \tan x$.
(a) Find the differential dy.
(b) Evaluate dy and Δy if $x = \pi/4$ and $dx = -0.1$.

20. Let $y = \sqrt{x}$.
(a) Find the differential dy.
(b) Evaluate dy and Δy if $x = 1$ and $dx = \Delta x = 1$.
(c) Sketch a diagram like Figure 5 showing the line segments with lengths dx, dy, and Δy.

21. The edge of a cube was found to be 30 cm with a possible error in measurement of 0.1 cm. Use differentials to estimate the maximum possible error, relative error, and percentage error in computing (a) the volume of the cube and (b) the surface area of the cube.

22. The radius of a circular disk is given as 24 cm with a maximum error in measurement of 0.2 cm.
(a) Use differentials to estimate the maximum error in the calculated area of the disk.
(b) What is the relative error? What is the percentage error?

23. The circumference of a sphere was measured to be 84 cm with a possible error of 0.5 cm.
(a) Use differentials to estimate the maximum error in the calculated surface area. What is the relative error?
(b) Use differentials to estimate the maximum error in the calculated volume. What is the relative error?

24. Use differentials to estimate the amount of paint needed to apply a coat of paint 0.05 cm thick to a hemispherical dome with diameter 50 m.

25. When blood flows along a blood vessel, the flux F (the volume of blood per unit time that flows past a given point) is proportional to the fourth power of the radius R of the blood vessel:

$$F = kR^4$$

(This is known as Poiseuille's Law.) A partially clogged artery can be expanded by an operation called angioplasty, in which a balloon-tipped catheter is inflated inside the artery in order to widen it and restore the normal blood flow.
    Show that the relative change in F is about four times the relative change in R. How will a 5% increase in the radius affect the flow of blood?

26. On page 431 of *Physics: Calculus,* 2d ed., by Eugene Hecht (Pacific Grove, CA: Brooks/Cole, 2000), in the course of deriving the formula $T = 2\pi\sqrt{L/g}$ for the period of a pendulum of length L, the author obtains the equation $a_T = -g\sin\theta$ for the tangential acceleration of the bob of the pendulum. He then says, "for small angles, the value of θ in radians is very nearly the value of $\sin\theta$; they differ by less than 2% out to about 20°."

(a) Verify the linear approximation at 0 for the sine function:

$$\sin x \approx x$$

(b) Use a graphing device to determine the values of x for which $\sin x$ and x differ by less than 2%. Then verify Hecht's statement by converting from radians to degrees.

27. Suppose that the only information we have about a function f is that $f(1) = 5$ and the graph of its *derivative* is as shown.
(a) Use a linear approximation to estimate $f(0.9)$ and $f(1.1)$.

(b) Are your estimates in part (a) too large or too small? Explain.

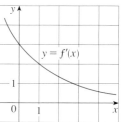

28. Suppose that we don't have a formula for $g(x)$ but we know that $g(2) = -4$ and $g'(x) = \sqrt{x^2 + 5}$ for all x.
(a) Use a linear approximation to estimate $g(1.95)$ and $g(2.05)$.
(b) Are your estimates in part (a) too large or too small? Explain.

---

2 REVIEW

CONCEPT CHECK

1. Write an expression for the slope of the tangent line to the curve $y = f(x)$ at the point $(a, f(a))$.

2. Suppose an object moves along a straight line with position $f(t)$ at time t. Write an expression for the instantaneous velocity of the object at time $t = a$. How can you interpret this velocity in terms of the graph of f?

3. Define the derivative $f'(a)$. Discuss two ways of interpreting this number.

4. If $y = f(x)$ and x changes from x_1 to x_2, write expressions for the following.
(a) The average rate of change of y with respect to x over the interval $[x_1, x_2]$.
(b) The instantaneous rate of change of y with respect to x at $x = x_1$.

5. Define the second derivative of f. If $f(t)$ is the position function of a particle, how can you interpret the second derivative?

6. (a) What does it mean for f to be differentiable at a?
(b) What is the relation between the differentiability and continuity of a function?

(c) Sketch the graph of a function that is continuous but not differentiable at $a = 2$.

7. Describe several ways in which a function can fail to be differentiable. Illustrate with sketches.

8. State each differentiation rule both in symbols and in words.
(a) The Power Rule   (b) The Constant Multiple Rule
(c) The Sum Rule   (d) The Difference Rule
(e) The Product Rule   (f) The Quotient Rule
(g) The Chain Rule

9. State the derivative of each function.
(a) $y = x^n$ (b) $y = \sin x$ (c) $y = \cos x$
(d) $y = \tan x$ (e) $y = \csc x$ (f) $y = \sec x$
(g) $y = \cot x$

10. Explain how implicit differentiation works.

11. (a) Write an expression for the linearization of f at a.
(b) If $y = f(x)$, write an expression for the differential dy.
(c) If $dx = \Delta x$, draw a picture showing the geometric meanings of Δy and dy.

TRUE-FALSE QUIZ

Determine whether the statement is true or false. If it is true, explain why. If it is false, explain why or give an example that disproves the statement.

1. If f is continuous at a, then f is differentiable at a.

2. If f and g are differentiable, then

$$\frac{d}{dx}[f(x) + g(x)] = f'(x) + g'(x)$$

3. If f and g are differentiable, then

$$\frac{d}{dx}[f(x)g(x)] = f'(x)g'(x)$$

4. If f and g are differentiable, then

$$\frac{d}{dx}[f(g(x))] = f'(g(x))g'(x)$$

5. If f is differentiable, then

$$\frac{d}{dx}\sqrt{f(x)} = \frac{f'(x)}{2\sqrt{f(x)}}$$

6. If f is differentiable, then

$$\frac{d}{dx}f(\sqrt{x}) = \frac{f'(x)}{2\sqrt{x}}$$

7. $\dfrac{d}{dx}\left|x^2 + x\right| = \left|2x + 1\right|$

8. If $f'(r)$ exists, then $\lim_{x \to r} f(x) = f(r)$.

9. If $g(x) = x^5$, then

$$\lim_{x \to 2}\frac{g(x) - g(2)}{x - 2} = 80$$

10. $\dfrac{d^2 y}{dx^2} = \left(\dfrac{dy}{dx}\right)^2$

11. An equation of the tangent line to the parabola $y = x^2$ at $(-2, 4)$ is $y - 4 = 2x(x + 2)$.

12. $\dfrac{d}{dx}(\tan^2 x) = \dfrac{d}{dx}(\sec^2 x)$

EXERCISES

---

1. For the function f whose graph is shown, arrange the following numbers in increasing order:

$$0 \qquad 1 \qquad f'(2) \qquad f'(3) \qquad f'(5) \qquad f''(5)$$

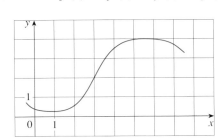

2. Find a function f and a number a such that

$$\lim_{h \to 0}\frac{(2 + h)^6 - 64}{h} = f'(a)$$

3. The total cost of repaying a student loan at an interest rate of $r\%$ per year is $C = f(r)$.
(a) What is the meaning of the derivative $f'(r)$? What are its units?
(b) What does the statement $f'(10) = 1200$ mean?
(c) Is $f'(r)$ always positive or does it change sign?

4–6 ▪ Trace or copy the graph of the function. Then sketch a graph of its derivative directly beneath.

4.

5.

6.

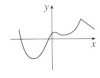

7. The figure shows the graphs of f, f', and f''. Identify each curve, and explain your choices.

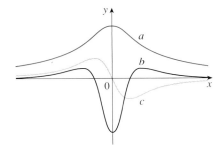

8. The *total fertility rate* at time t, denoted by $F(t)$, is an estimate of the average number of children born to each woman (assuming that current birth rates remain constant). The graph of the total fertility rate in the United States shows the fluctuations from 1940 to 1990.
(a) Estimate the values of $F'(1950)$, $F'(1965)$, and $F'(1987)$.
(b) What are the meanings of these derivatives?
(c) Can you suggest reasons for the values of these derivatives?

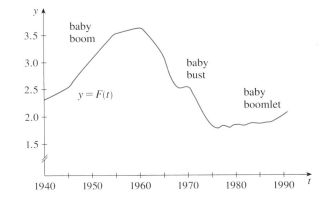

9. Let $C(t)$ be the total value of US currency (coins and banknotes) in circulation at time t. The table gives values of this function from 1980 to 2000, as of September 30, in billions of dollars. Interpret and estimate the value of $C'(1990)$.

t	1980	1985	1990	1995	2000
$C(t)$	129.9	187.3	271.9	409.3	568.6

10–11 ▪ Find $f'(x)$ from first principles, that is, directly from the definition of a derivative.

10. $f(x) = \dfrac{4 - x}{3 + x}$

11. $f(x) = x^3 + 5x + 4$

▪ ▪ ▪ ▪ ▪ ▪ ▪ ▪ ▪ ▪ ▪ ▪ ▪

12. (a) If $f(x) = \sqrt{3 - 5x}$, use the definition of a derivative to find $f'(x)$.
(b) Find the domains of f and f'.
(c) Graph f and f' on a common screen. Compare the graphs to see whether your answer to part (a) is reasonable.

13–38 ▪ Calculate y'.

13. $y = (x^4 - 3x^2 + 5)^3$

14. $y = \cos(\tan x)$

15. $y = \sqrt{x} + \dfrac{1}{\sqrt[3]{x^4}}$

16. $y = \dfrac{3x - 2}{\sqrt{2x + 1}}$

17. $y = 2x\sqrt{x^2 + 1}$

18. $y = \left(x + \dfrac{1}{x^2}\right)^{\sqrt{7}}$

19. $y = \dfrac{t}{1 - t^2}$

20. $y = \sin(\cos x)$

21. $y = \tan \sqrt{1 - x}$

22. $y = \dfrac{1}{\sin(x - \sin x)}$

23. $xy^4 + x^2 y = x + 3y$

24. $y = \sec(1 + x^2)$

25. $y = \dfrac{\sec 2\theta}{1 + \tan 2\theta}$

26. $x^2 \cos y + \sin 2y = xy$

27. $y = (1 - x^{-1})^{-1}$

28. $y = 1/\sqrt[3]{x + \sqrt{x}}$

29. $\sin(xy) = x^2 - y$

30. $y = \sqrt{\sin \sqrt{x}}$

31. $y = \cot(3x^2 + 5)$

32. $y = \dfrac{(x + \lambda)^4}{x^4 + \lambda^4}$

33. $y = \sin(\tan \sqrt{1 + x^3})$

34. $y = \dfrac{\sin mx}{x}$

35. $y = \tan^2(\sin \theta)$

36. $x \tan y = y - 1$

37. $y = \sqrt[5]{x \tan x}$

38. $y = \dfrac{(x - 1)(x - 4)}{(x - 2)(x - 3)}$

▪ ▪ ▪ ▪ ▪ ▪ ▪ ▪ ▪ ▪ ▪ ▪ ▪

39. If $f(t) = \sqrt{4t + 1}$, find $f''(2)$.

40. If $g(\theta) = \theta \sin \theta$, find $g''(\pi/6)$.

41. Find y'' if $x^6 + y^6 = 1$.

42. Find $f^{(n)}(x)$ if $f(x) = 1/(2 - x)$.

43–46 ▪ Find an equation of the tangent to the curve at the given point.

43. $y = 4 \sin^2 x$, $(\pi/6, 1)$

44. $y = \dfrac{x^2 - 1}{x^2 + 1}$, $(0, -1)$

45. $y = \sqrt{1 + 4 \sin x}$, $(0, 1)$

46. $x^2 + 4xy + y^2 = 13$, $(2, 1)$

▪ ▪ ▪ ▪ ▪ ▪ ▪ ▪ ▪ ▪ ▪ ▪ ▪

47. At what points on the curve $y = \sin x + \cos x$, $0 \le x \le 2\pi$, is the tangent line horizontal?

48. Find the points on the ellipse $x^2 + 2y^2 = 1$ where the tangent line has slope 1.

49. Suppose that $h(x) = f(x)g(x)$ and $F(x) = f(g(x))$, where $f(2) = 3$, $g(2) = 5$, $g'(2) = 4$, $f'(2) = -2$, and $f'(5) = 11$. Find (a) $h'(2)$ and (b) $F'(2)$.

50. If f and g are the functions whose graphs are shown, let $P(x) = f(x)g(x)$, $Q(x) = f(x)/g(x)$, and $C(x) = f(g(x))$. Find (a) $P'(2)$, (b) $Q'(2)$, and (c) $C'(2)$.

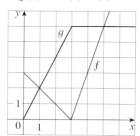

51–58 ▪ Find f' in terms of g'.

51. $f(x) = x^2 g(x)$

52. $f(x) = g(x^2)$

53. $f(x) = [g(x)]^2$

54. $f(x) = x^a g(x^b)$

55. $f(x) = g(g(x))$

56. $f(x) = \sin(g(x))$

57. $f(x) = g(\sin x)$

58. $f(x) = g(\tan \sqrt{x})$

▪ ▪ ▪ ▪ ▪ ▪ ▪ ▪ ▪ ▪ ▪ ▪ ▪

59–60 ▪ Find h' in terms of f' and g'.

59. $h(x) = \dfrac{f(x)g(x)}{f(x) + g(x)}$

60. $h(x) = f(g(\sin 4x))$

▪ ▪ ▪ ▪ ▪ ▪ ▪ ▪ ▪ ▪ ▪ ▪ ▪

61. The graph of f is shown. State, with reasons, the numbers at which f is not differentiable.

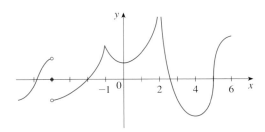

62. The volume of a right circular cone is $V = \pi r^2 h / 3$, where r is the radius of the base and h is the height.
(a) Find the rate of change of the volume with respect to the height if the radius is constant.
(b) Find the rate of change of the volume with respect to the radius if the height is constant.

63. A particle moves on a vertical line so that its coordinate at time t is $y = t^3 - 12t + 3$, $t \geq 0$.
(a) Find the velocity and acceleration functions.
(b) When is the particle moving upward and when is it moving downward?
(c) Find the distance that the particle travels in the time interval $0 \leq t \leq 3$.

64. The cost, in dollars, of producing x units of a certain commodity is

$$C(x) = 920 + 2x - 0.02x^2 + 0.00007x^3$$

(a) Find the marginal cost function.
(b) Find $C'(100)$ and explain its meaning.
(c) Compare $C'(100)$ with the cost of producing the 101st item.

65. The volume of a cube is increasing at a rate of 10 cm³/min. How fast is the surface area increasing when the length of an edge is 30 cm?

66. A paper cup has the shape of a cone with height 10 cm and radius 3 cm (at the top). If water is poured into the cup at a rate of 2 cm³/s, how fast is the water level rising when the water is 5 cm deep?

67. A balloon is rising at a constant speed of 5 ft/s. A boy is cycling along a straight road at a speed of 15 ft/s. When he passes under the balloon, it is 45 ft above him. How fast is the distance between the boy and the balloon increasing 3 s later?

68. A waterskier skis over the ramp shown in the figure at a speed of 30 ft/s. How fast is she rising as she leaves the ramp?

69. The angle of elevation of the Sun is decreasing at a rate of 0.25 rad/h. How fast is the shadow cast by a 400-ft-tall building increasing when the angle of elevation of the Sun is $\pi/6$?

70. (a) Find the linear approximation to $f(x) = \sqrt{25 - x^2}$ near 3.
(b) Illustrate part (a) by graphing f and the linear approximation.
(c) For what values of x is the linear approximation accurate to within 0.1?

71. (a) Find the linearization of $f(x) = \sqrt[3]{1 + 3x}$ at $a = 0$. State the corresponding linear approximation and use it to give an approximate value for $\sqrt[3]{1.03}$.
(b) Determine the values of x for which the linear approximation given in part (a) is accurate to within 0.1.

72. Evaluate dy if $y = x^3 - 2x^2 + 1$, $x = 2$, and $dx = 0.2$.

73. A window has the shape of a square surmounted by a semicircle. The base of the window is measured as having width 60 cm with a possible error in measurement of 0.1 cm. Use differentials to estimate the maximum error possible in computing the area of the window.

74–76 ▪ Express the limit as a derivative and evaluate.

74. $\displaystyle \lim_{x \to 1} \frac{x^{17} - 1}{x - 1}$

75. $\displaystyle \lim_{h \to 0} \frac{\sqrt[4]{16 + h} - 2}{h}$

76. $\displaystyle \lim_{\theta \to \pi/3} \frac{\cos \theta - 0.5}{\theta - \pi/3}$

▪ ▪ ▪ ▪ ▪ ▪ ▪ ▪ ▪ ▪ ▪ ▪

77. Evaluate $\displaystyle \lim_{x \to 0} \frac{\sqrt{1 + \tan x} - \sqrt{1 + \sin x}}{x^3}$.

78. Show that the length of the portion of any tangent line to the astroid $x^{2/3} + y^{2/3} = a^{2/3}$ cut off by the coordinate axes is constant.

INVERSE FUNCTIONS

EXPONENTIAL, LOGARITHMIC, AND INVERSE TRIGONOMETRIC FUNCTIONS

The common theme that links the functions of this chapter is that they occur as pairs of inverse functions. In particular, two of the most important functions that occur in mathematics and its applications are the exponential function $f(x) = a^x$ and its inverse function, the logarithmic function $g(x) = \log_a x$. Here we investigate their properties, compute their derivatives, and use them to describe exponential growth and decay in biology, physics, chemistry, and other sciences. We also study the inverses of the trigonometric and hyperbolic functions. Finally we look at a method (l'Hospital's Rule) for computing limits of such functions.

3.1 | EXPONENTIAL FUNCTIONS

The function $f(x) = 2^x$ is called an *exponential function* because the variable, x, is the exponent. It should not be confused with the power function $g(x) = x^2$, in which the variable is the base.

In general, an **exponential function** is a function of the form

$$f(x) = a^x$$

where a is a positive constant. Let's recall what this means.

If $x = n$, a positive integer, then

$$a^n = \underbrace{a \cdot a \cdot \cdots \cdot a}_{n \text{ factors}}$$

If $x = 0$, then $a^0 = 1$, and if $x = -n$, where n is a positive integer, then

$$a^{-n} = \frac{1}{a^n}$$

If x is a rational number, $x = p/q$, where p and q are integers and $q > 0$, then

$$a^x = a^{p/q} = \sqrt[q]{a^p} = \left(\sqrt[q]{a}\right)^p$$

But what is the meaning of a^x if x is an irrational number? For instance, what is meant by $2^{\sqrt{3}}$ or 5^π?

To help us answer this question we first look at the graph of the function $y = 2^x$, where x is rational. A representation of this graph is shown in Figure 1. We want to enlarge the domain of $y = 2^x$ to include both rational and irrational numbers.

There are holes in the graph in Figure 1 corresponding to irrational values of x. We want to fill in the holes by defining $f(x) = 2^x$, where $x \in \mathbb{R}$, so that f is an increasing continuous function. In particular, since the irrational number $\sqrt{3}$ satisfies

$$1.7 < \sqrt{3} < 1.8$$

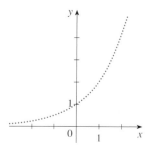

FIGURE 1

Representation of $y = 2^x$, x rational

we must have

$$2^{1.7} < 2^{\sqrt{3}} < 2^{1.8}$$

and we know what $2^{1.7}$ and $2^{1.8}$ mean because 1.7 and 1.8 are rational numbers. Similarly, if we use better approximations for $\sqrt{3}$, we obtain better approximations for $2^{\sqrt{3}}$:

$$1.73 < \sqrt{3} < 1.74 \qquad \Rightarrow \qquad 2^{1.73} < 2^{\sqrt{3}} < 2^{1.74}$$

$$1.732 < \sqrt{3} < 1.733 \qquad \Rightarrow \qquad 2^{1.732} < 2^{\sqrt{3}} < 2^{1.733}$$

$$1.7320 < \sqrt{3} < 1.7321 \qquad \Rightarrow \qquad 2^{1.7320} < 2^{\sqrt{3}} < 2^{1.7321}$$

$$1.73205 < \sqrt{3} < 1.73206 \qquad \Rightarrow \qquad 2^{1.73205} < 2^{\sqrt{3}} < 2^{1.73206}$$

$$\vdots \qquad\qquad \vdots \qquad\qquad\qquad \vdots \qquad\qquad \vdots$$

■ A proof of this fact is given in J. Marsden and A. Weinstein, *Calculus Unlimited* (Menlo Park, CA: Benjamin/Cummings, 1981). For an online version, see

www.cds.caltech.edu/~marsden/
volume/cu/CU.pdf

It can be shown that there is exactly one number that is greater than all of the numbers

$$2^{1.7}, \quad 2^{1.73}, \quad 2^{1.732}, \quad 2^{1.7320}, \quad 2^{1.73205}, \quad \ldots$$

and less than all of the numbers

$$2^{1.8}, \quad 2^{1.74}, \quad 2^{1.733}, \quad 2^{1.7321}, \quad 2^{1.73206}, \quad \ldots$$

We define $2^{\sqrt{3}}$ to be this number. Using the preceding approximation process we can compute it correct to six decimal places:

$$2^{\sqrt{3}} \approx 3.321997$$

Similarly, we can define 2^x (or a^x, if $a > 0$) where x is any irrational number. Figure 2 shows how all the holes in Figure 1 have been filled to complete the graph of the function $f(x) = 2^x$, $x \in \mathbb{R}$.

In general, if a is any positive number, we define

1
$$a^x = \lim_{r \to x} a^r \qquad r \text{ rational}$$

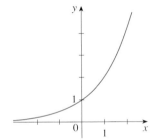

FIGURE 2
$y = 2^x$, x real

This definition makes sense because any irrational number can be approximated as closely as we like by a rational number. For instance, because $\sqrt{3}$ has the decimal representation $\sqrt{3} = 1.7320508 \ldots$, Definition 1 says that $2^{\sqrt{3}}$ is the limit of the sequence of numbers

$$2^{1.7}, \quad 2^{1.73}, \quad 2^{1.732}, \quad 2^{1.7320}, \quad 2^{1.73205}, \quad 2^{1.732050}, \quad 2^{1.7320508}, \quad \ldots$$

Similarly, 5^π is the limit of the sequence of numbers

$$5^{3.1}, \quad 5^{3.14}, \quad 5^{3.141}, \quad 5^{3.1415}, \quad 5^{3.14159}, \quad 5^{3.141592}, \quad 5^{3.1415926}, \quad \ldots$$

It can be shown that Definition 1 uniquely specifies a^x and makes the function $f(x) = a^x$ continuous.

The graphs of members of the family of functions $y = a^x$ are shown in Figure 3 for various values of the base a. Notice that all of these graphs pass through the same point $(0, 1)$ because $a^0 = 1$ for $a \neq 0$. Notice also that as the base a gets larger, the exponential function grows more rapidly (for $x > 0$).

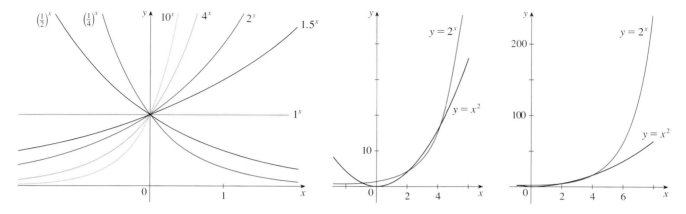

FIGURE 3 Members of the family of exponential functions   FIGURE 4   FIGURE 5

Figure 4 shows how the exponential function $y = 2^x$ compares with the power function $y = x^2$. The graphs intersect three times, but ultimately the exponential curve $y = 2^x$ grows far more rapidly than the parabola $y = x^2$. (See also Figure 5.)

You can see from Figure 3 that there are basically three kinds of exponential functions $y = a^x$. If $0 < a < 1$, the exponential function decreases; if $a = 1$, it is a constant; and if $a > 1$, it increases. These three cases are illustrated in Figure 6. Since $(1/a)^x = 1/a^x = a^{-x}$, the graph of $y = (1/a)^x$ is just the reflection of the graph of $y = a^x$ about the y-axis.

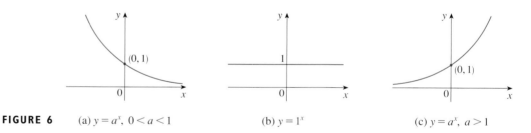

FIGURE 6   (a) $y = a^x$, $0 < a < 1$ (b) $y = 1^x$ (c) $y = a^x$, $a > 1$

The properties of the exponential function are summarized in the following theorem.

---

2 THEOREM If $a > 0$ and $a \neq 1$, then $f(x) = a^x$ is a continuous function with domain $\mathbb{R}$ and range $(0, \infty)$. In particular, $a^x > 0$ for all x. If $a, b > 0$ and $x, y \in \mathbb{R}$, then

1. $a^{x+y} = a^x a^y$ **2.** $a^{x-y} = \dfrac{a^x}{a^y}$ **3.** $(a^x)^y = a^{xy}$ **4.** $(ab)^x = a^x b^x$

■ In Appendix D we present a definition of the exponential function that enables us to give an easy proof of the Laws of Exponents.

The reason for the importance of the exponential function lies in properties 1–4, which are called the **Laws of Exponents**. If x and y are rational numbers, then these laws are well known from elementary algebra. For arbitrary real numbers x and y these laws can be deduced from the special case where the exponents are rational by using Equation 1.

The following limits can be read from the graphs shown in Figure 6 or proved from the definition of a limit at infinity. (See Exercise 77 in Section 3.2.)

3   If $a > 1$, then $\displaystyle\lim_{x \to \infty} a^x = \infty$ and $\displaystyle\lim_{x \to -\infty} a^x = 0$

If $0 < a < 1$, then $\displaystyle\lim_{x \to \infty} a^x = 0$ and $\displaystyle\lim_{x \to -\infty} a^x = \infty$

In particular, if $a \neq 1$, then the x-axis is a horizontal asymptote of the graph of the exponential function $y = a^x$.

EXAMPLE 1
(a) Find $\lim_{x \to \infty} (2^{-x} - 1)$.
(b) Sketch the graph of the function $y = 2^{-x} - 1$.

SOLUTION

(a)
$$\lim_{x \to \infty} (2^{-x} - 1) = \lim_{x \to \infty} \left[\left(\tfrac{1}{2}\right)^x - 1\right]$$
$$= 0 - 1 \qquad \left[\text{by (3) with } a = \tfrac{1}{2} < 1\right]$$
$$= -1$$

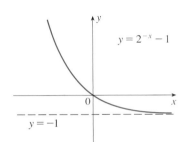

FIGURE 7

(b) We write $y = \left(\tfrac{1}{2}\right)^x - 1$ as in part (a). The graph of $y = \left(\tfrac{1}{2}\right)^x$ is shown in Figure 3, so we shift it down one unit to obtain the graph of $y = \left(\tfrac{1}{2}\right)^x - 1$ shown in Figure 7. (For a review of shifting graphs, see Section 1.2.) Part (a) shows that the line $y = -1$ is a horizontal asymptote. ▪

THE NUMBER e AND THE NATURAL EXPONENTIAL FUNCTION

Of all possible bases for an exponential function, there is one that is most convenient for the purposes of calculus. We will see in Section 3.3 that the differentiation formula for an exponential function is simplest when the base is chosen to be the number e, which is defined as follows:

4
$$e = \lim_{x \to 0} (1 + x)^{1/x}$$

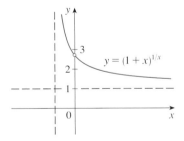

FIGURE 8

x	$(1 + x)^{1/x}$
0.1	2.59374246
0.01	2.70481383
0.001	2.71692393
0.0001	2.71814593
0.00001	2.71826824
0.000001	2.71828047
0.0000001	2.71828169
0.00000001	2.71828181

The graph of the function $y = (1 + x)^{1/x}$ is shown in Figure 8. It is not defined when $x = 0$, but its behavior when x is near 0 is indicated by the table of values correct to eight decimal places. These values suggest (but don't prove) that the limit in Definition 4 exists and that $e \approx 2.71828$. The existence of the limit is proved in Appendix B. The approximate value to 20 decimal places is

$$e \approx 2.71828182845904523536$$

The decimal expansion of e is nonrepeating because e is an irrational number. (See Exercise 30 in Section 8.8.) The notation e for this number was chosen by the Swiss mathematician Leonhard Euler in 1727, probably because it's the first letter of the word *exponential*.

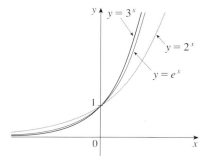

FIGURE 9

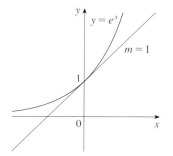

FIGURE 10

The natural exponential function
crosses the y-axis with a slope of 1.

The exponential function $y = e^x$ with base e is called the **natural exponential function.** Because e lies between 2 and 3, the graph of $y = e^x$ lies between the graphs of $y = 2^x$ and $y = 3^x$, as shown in Figure 9.

We will see in Section 3.3 that the natural exponential function is the exponential function whose graph crosses the y-axis with a slope of 1. (See Figure 10.) In fact, we can see why this might be true if we look at the limit in Definition 4. The slope of the tangent line to the graph of $f(x) = e^x$ at the point $(0, 1)$ is

$$f'(0) = \lim_{h \to 0} \frac{f(0 + h) - f(0)}{h} = \lim_{h \to 0} \frac{e^h - 1}{h}$$

Replacing x by h in Definition 4, we see that, for small values of h,

$$e \approx (1 + h)^{1/h} \quad \text{so} \quad e^h \approx 1 + h \quad \text{and} \quad e^h - 1 \approx h$$

Thus if h is near 0, we have

$$\frac{e^h - 1}{h} \approx 1$$

and so it seems plausible that $f'(0) = 1$.

The exponential function $f(x) = e^x$ is one of the most frequently occurring functions in calculus and its applications, so it is important to be familiar with its graph (Figure 10) and properties. We summarize these properties as follows, using the fact that this function is just a special case of the exponential functions considered before but with base $a = e > 1$.

> **5 PROPERTIES OF THE NATURAL EXPONENTIAL FUNCTION** The exponential function $f(x) = e^x$ is a continuous function with domain $\mathbb{R}$ and range $(0, \infty)$. Thus $e^x > 0$ for all x. Also
>
> $$\lim_{x \to -\infty} e^x = 0 \qquad \lim_{x \to \infty} e^x = \infty$$
>
> So the x-axis is a horizontal asymptote of $f(x) = e^x$.

V EXAMPLE 2 Evaluate $\lim_{x \to 0^-} e^{1/x}$.

SOLUTION If we let $t = 1/x$, we know from Section 1.6 that $t \to -\infty$ as $x \to 0^-$. Therefore, by (5),

$$\lim_{x \to 0^-} e^{1/x} = \lim_{t \to -\infty} e^t = 0$$ ■

EXAMPLE 3 Find $\lim_{x \to \infty} \frac{e^{2x}}{e^{2x} + 1}$.

SOLUTION We divide numerator and denominator by e^{2x}:

$$\lim_{x \to \infty} \frac{e^{2x}}{e^{2x} + 1} = \lim_{x \to \infty} \frac{1}{1 + e^{-2x}} = \frac{1}{1 + \lim_{x \to \infty} e^{-2x}} = \frac{1}{1 + 0} = 1$$

We have used the fact that $t = -2x \to -\infty$ as $x \to \infty$ and so

$$\lim_{x \to \infty} e^{-2x} = \lim_{t \to -\infty} e^t = 0$$ ■

3.1 | EXERCISES

1. (a) Write an equation that defines the exponential function with base $a > 0$.
(b) What is the domain of this function?
(c) If $a \neq 1$, what is the range of this function?
(d) Sketch the general shape of the graph of the exponential function for each of the following cases.
(i) $a > 1$ (ii) $a = 1$ (iii) $0 < a < 1$

2. (a) How is the number e defined?
(b) What is an approximate value for e?
(c) What is the natural exponential function?

3–6 ▪ Graph the given functions on a common screen. How are these graphs related?

3. $y = 2^x$, $y = e^x$, $y = 5^x$, $y = 20^x$

4. $y = e^x$, $y = e^{-x}$, $y = 8^x$, $y = 8^{-x}$

5. $y = 3^x$, $y = 10^x$, $y = \left(\frac{1}{3}\right)^x$, $y = \left(\frac{1}{10}\right)^x$

6. $y = 0.9^x$, $y = 0.6^x$, $y = 0.3^x$, $y = 0.1^x$

7–12 ▪ Make a rough sketch of the graph of the function. Do not use a calculator. Just use the graphs given in Figures 3 and 9 and, if necessary, the transformations of Section 1.2.

7. $y = 4^x - 3$

8. $y = 4^{x-3}$

9. $y = -2^{-x}$

10. $y = 1 + 2e^x$

11. $y = 1 - \frac{1}{2}e^{-x}$

12. $y = 2(1 - e^x)$

13. Starting with the graph of $y = e^x$, write the equation of the graph that results from
(a) shifting 2 units downward
(b) shifting 2 units to the right
(c) reflecting about the x-axis
(d) reflecting about the y-axis
(e) reflecting about the x-axis and then about the y-axis

14. Starting with the graph of $y = e^x$, find the equation of the graph that results from
(a) reflecting about the line $y = 4$
(b) reflecting about the line $x = 2$

15–16 ▪ Find the domain of each function.

15. (a) $f(x) = \dfrac{1}{1 + e^x}$ (b) $f(x) = \dfrac{1}{1 - e^x}$

16. (a) $g(t) = \sin(e^{-t})$ (b) $g(t) = \sqrt{1 - 2^t}$

17–18 ▪ Find the exponential function $f(x) = Ca^x$ whose graph is given.

17.

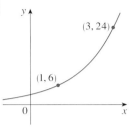

$(3, 24)$
$(1, 6)$

18.

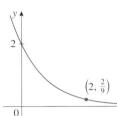

$\left(2, \frac{2}{9}\right)$

19. Suppose the graphs of $f(x) = x^2$ and $g(x) = 2^x$ are drawn on a coordinate grid where the unit of measurement is 1 inch. Show that, at a distance 2 ft to the right of the origin, the height of the graph of f is 48 ft but the height of the graph of g is about 265 mi.

20. Compare the rates of growth of the functions $f(x) = x^5$ and $g(x) = 5^x$ by graphing both functions in several viewing rectangles. Find all points of intersection of the graphs correct to one decimal place.

21. Compare the functions $f(x) = x^{10}$ and $g(x) = e^x$ by graphing both f and g in several viewing rectangles. When does the graph of g finally surpass the graph of f?

22. Use a graph to estimate the values of x such that $e^x > 1{,}000{,}000{,}000$.

23–30 ▪ Find the limit.

23. $\displaystyle\lim_{x \to \infty} (1.001)^x$

24. $\displaystyle\lim_{x \to \infty} e^{-x^2}$

25. $\displaystyle\lim_{x \to \infty} \frac{e^{3x} - e^{-3x}}{e^{3x} + e^{-3x}}$

26. $\displaystyle\lim_{x \to \infty} \frac{2 + 10^x}{3 - 10^x}$

27. $\displaystyle\lim_{x \to 2^+} e^{3/(2-x)}$

28. $\displaystyle\lim_{x \to 2^-} e^{3/(2-x)}$

29. $\displaystyle\lim_{x \to \infty} (e^{-2x} \cos x)$

30. $\displaystyle\lim_{x \to (\pi/2)^+} e^{\tan x}$

31. If you graph the function

$$f(x) = \frac{1 - e^{1/x}}{1 + e^{1/x}}$$

you'll see that f appears to be an odd function. Prove it.

32. Graph several members of the family of functions

$$f(x) = \frac{1}{1 + ae^{bx}}$$

where $a > 0$. How does the graph change when b changes? How does it change when a changes?

3.2 | INVERSE FUNCTIONS AND LOGARITHMS

Table 1 gives data from an experiment in which a bacteria culture started with 100 bacteria in a limited nutrient medium; the size of the bacteria population was recorded at hourly intervals. The number of bacteria N is a function of the time t: $N = f(t)$.

Suppose, however, that the biologist changes her point of view and becomes interested in the time required for the population to reach various levels. In other words, she is thinking of t as a function of N. This function is called the *inverse function* of f, denoted by f^{-1}, and read "f inverse." Thus $t = f^{-1}(N)$ is the time required for the population level to reach N. The values of f^{-1} can be found by reading Table 1 from right to left or by consulting Table 2. For instance, $f^{-1}(550) = 6$ because $f(6) = 550$.

TABLE 1 N as a function of t

t (hours)	$N = f(t)$ = population at time t
0	100
1	168
2	259
3	358
4	445
5	509
6	550
7	573
8	586

TABLE 2 t as a function of N

N	$t = f^{-1}(N)$ = time to reach N bacteria
100	0
168	1
259	2
358	3
445	4
509	5
550	6
573	7
586	8

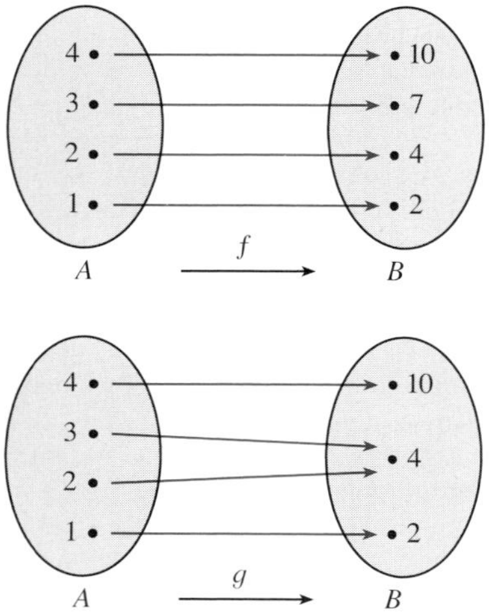

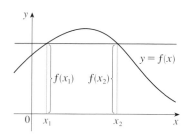

FIGURE 1

f is one-to-one; g is not

Not all functions possess inverses. Let's compare the functions f and g whose arrow diagrams are shown in Figure 1. Note that f never takes on the same value twice (any two inputs in A have different outputs), whereas g does take on the same value twice (both 2 and 3 have the same output, 4). In symbols,

$$g(2) = g(3)$$

but

$$f(x_1) \neq f(x_2) \qquad \text{whenever } x_1 \neq x_2$$

Functions that share this property with f are called *one-to-one functions*.

▪ In the language of inputs and outputs, Definition 1 says that f is one-to-one if each output corresponds to only one input.

> **1 DEFINITION** A function f is called a **one-to-one function** if it never takes on the same value twice; that is,
>
> $$f(x_1) \neq f(x_2) \qquad \text{whenever } x_1 \neq x_2$$

If a horizontal line intersects the graph of f in more than one point, then we see from Figure 2 that there are numbers x_1 and x_2 such that $f(x_1) = f(x_2)$. This means that f is not one-to-one. Therefore, we have the following geometric method for determining whether a function is one-to-one.

FIGURE 2

This function is not one-to-one because $f(x_1) = f(x_2)$.

> **HORIZONTAL LINE TEST** A function is one-to-one if and only if no horizontal line intersects its graph more than once.

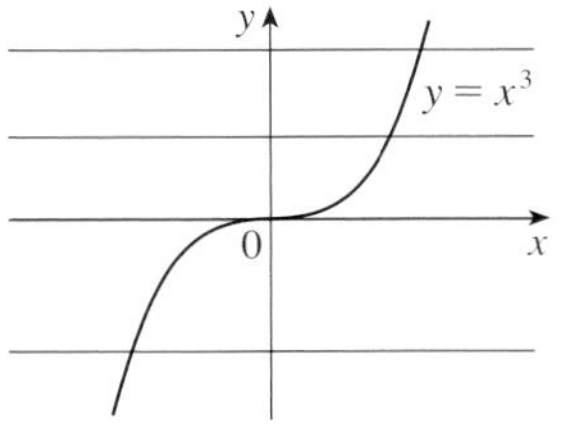

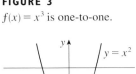

FIGURE 3

$f(x) = x^3$ is one-to-one.

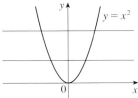

FIGURE 4

$g(x) = x^2$ is not one-to-one.

☑ **EXAMPLE 1**   Is the function $f(x) = x^3$ one-to-one?

SOLUTION 1   If $x_1 \neq x_2$, then $x_1^3 \neq x_2^3$ (two different numbers can't have the same cube). Therefore, by Definition 1, $f(x) = x^3$ is one-to-one.

SOLUTION 2   From Figure 3 we see that no horizontal line intersects the graph of $f(x) = x^3$ more than once. Therefore, by the Horizontal Line Test, f is one-to-one. ■

☑ **EXAMPLE 2**   Is the function $g(x) = x^2$ one-to-one?

SOLUTION 1   This function is not one-to-one because, for instance,

$$g(1) = 1 = g(-1)$$

and so 1 and -1 have the same output.

SOLUTION 2   From Figure 4 we see that there are horizontal lines that intersect the graph of g more than once. Therefore, by the Horizontal Line Test, g is not one-to-one. ■

One-to-one functions are important because they are precisely the functions that possess inverse functions according to the following definition.

> **2   DEFINITION**   Let f be a one-to-one function with domain A and range B. Then its **inverse function** f^{-1} has domain B and range A and is defined by
>
> $$f^{-1}(y) = x \quad \Longleftrightarrow \quad f(x) = y$$
>
> for any y in B.

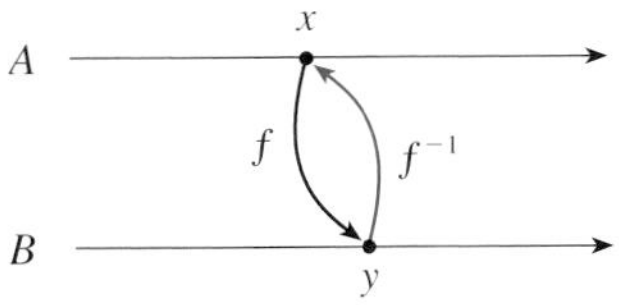

FIGURE 5

This definition says that if f maps x into y, then f^{-1} maps y back into x. (If f were not one-to-one, then f^{-1} would not be uniquely defined.) The arrow diagram in Figure 5 indicates that f^{-1} reverses the effect of f. Note that

> domain of f^{-1} = range of f
>
> range of f^{-1} = domain of f

For example, the inverse function of $f(x) = x^3$ is $f^{-1}(x) = x^{1/3}$ because if $y = x^3$, then

$$f^{-1}(y) = f^{-1}(x^3) = (x^3)^{1/3} = x$$

⊘ **CAUTION**   Do not mistake the -1 in f^{-1} for an exponent. Thus

$$f^{-1}(x) \quad \text{does } not \text{ mean} \quad \frac{1}{f(x)}$$

The reciprocal $1/f(x)$ could, however, be written as $[f(x)]^{-1}$.

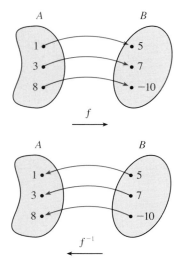

FIGURE 6

The inverse function reverses
inputs and outputs.

☑ EXAMPLE 3 If $f(1) = 5$, $f(3) = 7$, and $f(8) = -10$, find $f^{-1}(7)$, $f^{-1}(5)$, and $f^{-1}(-10)$.

SOLUTION From the definition of f^{-1} we have

$$f^{-1}(7) = 3 \qquad \text{because} \qquad f(3) = 7$$

$$f^{-1}(5) = 1 \qquad \text{because} \qquad f(1) = 5$$

$$f^{-1}(-10) = 8 \qquad \text{because} \qquad f(8) = -10$$

The diagram in Figure 6 makes it clear how f^{-1} reverses the effect of f in this case. ▪

The letter x is traditionally used as the independent variable, so when we concentrate on f^{-1} rather than on f, we usually reverse the roles of x and y in Definition 2 and write

3
$$f^{-1}(x) = y \quad \Longleftrightarrow \quad f(y) = x$$

By substituting for y in Definition 2 and substituting for x in (3), we get the following **cancellation equations**:

4
$$f^{-1}(f(x)) = x \quad \text{for every } x \text{ in } A$$
$$f(f^{-1}(x)) = x \quad \text{for every } x \text{ in } B$$

The first cancellation equation says that if we start with x, apply f, and then apply f^{-1}, we arrive back at x, where we started (see the machine diagram in Figure 7). Thus f^{-1} undoes what f does. The second equation says that f undoes what f^{-1} does.

FIGURE 7

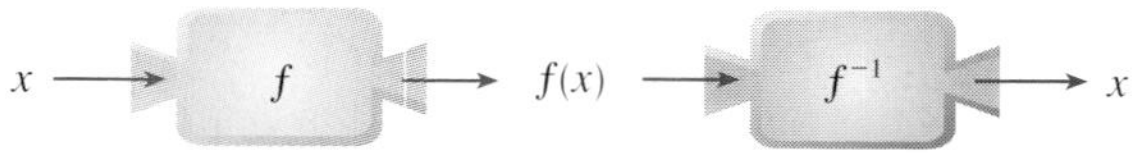

$$x \longrightarrow \boxed{f} \longrightarrow f(x) \longrightarrow \boxed{f^{-1}} \longrightarrow x$$

For example, if $f(x) = x^3$, then $f^{-1}(x) = x^{1/3}$ and so the cancellation equations become

$$f^{-1}(f(x)) = (x^3)^{1/3} = x$$

$$f(f^{-1}(x)) = (x^{1/3})^3 = x$$

These equations simply say that the cube function and the cube root function cancel each other when applied in succession.

Now let's see how to compute inverse functions. If we have a function $y = f(x)$ and are able to solve this equation for x in terms of y, then according to Definition 2 we must have $x = f^{-1}(y)$. If we want to call the independent variable x, we then interchange x and y and arrive at the equation $y = f^{-1}(x)$.

5 **HOW TO FIND THE INVERSE FUNCTION OF A ONE-TO-ONE FUNCTION** f

STEP 1 Write $y = f(x)$.

STEP 2 Solve this equation for x in terms of y (if possible).

STEP 3 To express f^{-1} as a function of x, interchange x and y. The resulting equation is $y = f^{-1}(x)$.

☑ EXAMPLE 4 Find the inverse function of $f(x) = x^3 + 2$.

SOLUTION According to (5) we first write

$$y = x^3 + 2$$

Then we solve this equation for x:

$$x^3 = y - 2$$

$$x = \sqrt[3]{y - 2}$$

Finally, we interchange x and y:

$$y = \sqrt[3]{x - 2}$$

▪ In Example 4, notice how f^{-1} reverses the effect of f. The function f is the rule "Cube, then add 2"; f^{-1} is the rule "Subtract 2, then take the cube root."

Therefore, the inverse function is $f^{-1}(x) = \sqrt[3]{x - 2}$. ▪

The principle of interchanging x and y to find the inverse function also gives us the method for obtaining the graph of f^{-1} from the graph of f. Since $f(a) = b$ if and only if $f^{-1}(b) = a$, the point (a, b) is on the graph of f if and only if the point (b, a) is on the graph of f^{-1}. But we get the point (b, a) from (a, b) by reflecting about the line $y = x$. (See Figure 8.)

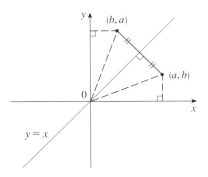

FIGURE 8

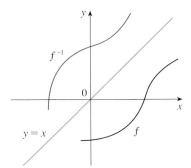

FIGURE 9

Therefore, as illustrated by Figure 9:

The graph of f^{-1} is obtained by reflecting the graph of f about the line $y = x$.

EXAMPLE 5 Sketch the graphs of $f(x) = \sqrt{-1 - x}$ and its inverse function using the same coordinate axes.

SOLUTION First we sketch the curve $y = \sqrt{-1 - x}$ (the top half of the parabola $y^2 = -1 - x$, or $x = -y^2 - 1$) and then we reflect about the line $y = x$ to get the graph of f^{-1}. (See Figure 10.) As a check on our graph, notice that the expression for f^{-1} is $f^{-1}(x) = -x^2 - 1$, $x \geq 0$. So the graph of f^{-1} is the right half of the parabola $y = -x^2 - 1$ and this seems reasonable from Figure 10.

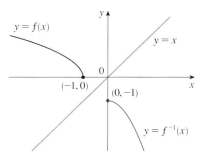

FIGURE 10

THE CALCULUS OF INVERSE FUNCTIONS

Now let's look at inverse functions from the point of view of calculus. Suppose that f is both one-to-one and continuous. We think of a continuous function as one whose graph has no break in it. (It consists of just one piece.) Since the graph of f^{-1} is obtained from the graph of f by reflecting about the line $y = x$, the graph of f^{-1} has no break in it either (see Figure 9). Thus we might expect that f^{-1} is also a continuous function.

This geometrical argument does not prove the following theorem but at least it makes the theorem plausible. A proof can be found in Appendix B.

> **6** **THEOREM** If f is a one-to-one continuous function defined on an interval, then its inverse function f^{-1} is also continuous.

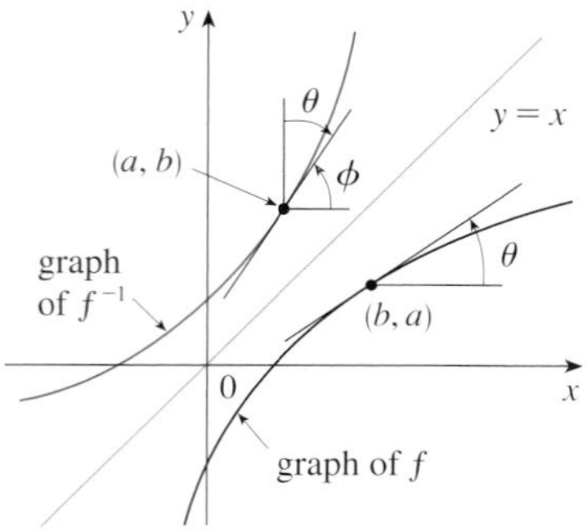

Now suppose that f is a one-to-one differentiable function. Geometrically we can think of a differentiable function as one whose graph has no corner or kink in it. We get the graph of f^{-1} by reflecting the graph of f about the line $y = x$, so the graph of f^{-1} has no corner or kink in it either. We therefore expect that f^{-1} is also differentiable (except where its tangents are vertical). In fact, we can predict the value of the derivative of f^{-1} at a given point by a geometric argument. In Figure 11 the graphs of f and its inverse f^{-1} are shown. If $f(b) = a$, then $f^{-1}(a) = b$ and $(f^{-1})'(a)$ is the slope of the tangent to the graph of f^{-1} at (a, b), which is $\tan \phi$. Likewise, $f'(b) = \tan \theta$. From Figure 11 we see that $\theta + \phi = \pi/2$, so

$$(f^{-1})'(a) = \tan \phi = \tan\left(\frac{\pi}{2} - \theta\right) = \cot \theta = \frac{1}{\tan \theta} = \frac{1}{f'(b)}$$

FIGURE 11

that is,

$$(f^{-1})'(a) = \frac{1}{f'(f^{-1}(a))}$$

> **7 THEOREM** If f is a one-to-one differentiable function with inverse function f^{-1} and $f'(f^{-1}(a)) \neq 0$, then the inverse function is differentiable at a and
> $$(f^{-1})'(a) = \frac{1}{f'(f^{-1}(a))}$$

PROOF Write the definition of derivative as in Equation 2.1.5:

$$(f^{-1})'(a) = \lim_{x \to a} \frac{f^{-1}(x) - f^{-1}(a)}{x - a}$$

If $f(b) = a$, then $f^{-1}(a) = b$. And if we let $y = f^{-1}(x)$, then $f(y) = x$. Since f is differentiable, it is continuous, so f^{-1} is continuous by Theorem 6. Thus if $x \to a$, then $f^{-1}(x) \to f^{-1}(a)$, that is, $y \to b$. Therefore

▪ Note that $x \neq a \Rightarrow f(y) \neq f(b)$ because f is one-to-one.

$$(f^{-1})'(a) = \lim_{x \to a} \frac{f^{-1}(x) - f^{-1}(a)}{x - a} = \lim_{y \to b} \frac{y - b}{f(y) - f(b)}$$

$$= \lim_{y \to b} \frac{1}{\dfrac{f(y) - f(b)}{y - b}} = \frac{1}{\displaystyle\lim_{y \to b} \frac{f(y) - f(b)}{y - b}}$$

$$= \frac{1}{f'(b)} = \frac{1}{f'(f^{-1}(a))} \qquad \square$$

NOTE 1 Replacing a by the general number x in the formula of Theorem 7, we get

8
$$(f^{-1})'(x) = \frac{1}{f'(f^{-1}(x))}$$

If we write $y = f^{-1}(x)$, then $f(y) = x$, so Equation 8, when expressed in Leibniz notation, becomes

$$\frac{dy}{dx} = \frac{1}{\dfrac{dx}{dy}}$$

NOTE 2 If it is known in advance that f^{-1} is differentiable, then its derivative can be computed more easily than in the proof of Theorem 7 by using implicit differentiation. If $y = f^{-1}(x)$, then $f(y) = x$. Differentiating the equation $f(y) = x$ implicitly with respect to x, remembering that y is a function of x, and using the Chain Rule, we get

$$f'(y) \frac{dy}{dx} = 1$$

Therefore
$$\frac{dy}{dx} = \frac{1}{f'(y)} = \frac{1}{\dfrac{dx}{dy}}$$

▼ EXAMPLE 6 If $f(x) = 2x + \cos x$, find $(f^{-1})'(1)$.

SOLUTION Notice that f is differentiable and one-to-one. (Its graph is shown in Figure 12.) To use Theorem 7 we need to know $f^{-1}(1)$ and we can find it by inspection:

$$f(0) = 1 \quad \Rightarrow \quad f^{-1}(1) = 0$$

Therefore $\quad (f^{-1})'(1) = \dfrac{1}{f'(f^{-1}(1))} = \dfrac{1}{f'(0)} = \dfrac{1}{2 - \sin 0} = \dfrac{1}{2}$

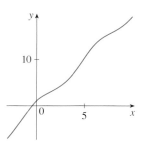

FIGURE 12 ■

LOGARITHMIC FUNCTIONS

If $a > 0$ and $a \neq 1$, the exponential function $f(x) = a^x$ is either increasing or decreasing and so it is one-to-one by the Horizontal Line Test. It therefore has an inverse function f^{-1}, which is called the **logarithmic function with base a** and is denoted by $\log_a$. If we use the formulation of an inverse function given by (3),

$$f^{-1}(x) = y \quad \Longleftrightarrow \quad f(y) = x$$

then we have

$$\boxed{\log_a x = y \quad \Longleftrightarrow \quad a^y = x}$$

Thus if $x > 0$, then $\log_a x$ is the exponent to which the base a must be raised to give x. For example, $\log_{10} 0.001 = -3$ because $10^{-3} = 0.001$.

The cancellation equations (4), when applied to the functions $f(x) = a^x$ and $f^{-1}(x) = \log_a x$, become

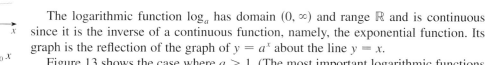

$$\boxed{\begin{aligned} \log_a(a^x) &= x \quad \text{for every } x \in \mathbb{R} \\ a^{\log_a x} &= x \quad \text{for every } x > 0 \end{aligned}}$$

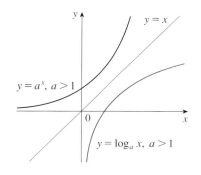

FIGURE 13

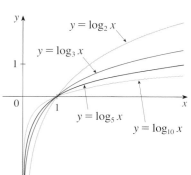

FIGURE 14

The logarithmic function $\log_a$ has domain $(0, \infty)$ and range $\mathbb{R}$ and is continuous since it is the inverse of a continuous function, namely, the exponential function. Its graph is the reflection of the graph of $y = a^x$ about the line $y = x$.

Figure 13 shows the case where $a > 1$. (The most important logarithmic functions have base $a > 1$.) The fact that $y = a^x$ is a very rapidly increasing function for $x > 0$ is reflected in the fact that $y = \log_a x$ is a very slowly increasing function for $x > 1$.

Figure 14 shows the graphs of $y = \log_a x$ with various values of the base $a > 1$. Since $\log_a 1 = 0$, the graphs of all logarithmic functions pass through the point $(1, 0)$.

The following properties of logarithmic functions follow from the corresponding properties of exponential functions given in Section 3.1.

LAWS OF LOGARITHMS   If x and y are positive numbers, then

1. $\log_a(xy) = \log_a x + \log_a y$

2. $\log_a\left(\dfrac{x}{y}\right) = \log_a x - \log_a y$

3. $\log_a(x^r) = r \log_a x$ (where r is any real number)

EXAMPLE 7 Use the laws of logarithms to evaluate $\log_2 80 - \log_2 5$.

SOLUTION Using Law 2, we have

$$\log_2 80 - \log_2 5 = \log_2\left(\frac{80}{5}\right) = \log_2 16 = 4$$

because $2^4 = 16$.   ■

The limits of exponential functions given in Section 3.1 are reflected in the following limits of logarithmic functions. (Compare with Figure 13.)

---

11   If $a > 1$, then

$$\lim_{x \to \infty} \log_a x = \infty \qquad \text{and} \qquad \lim_{x \to 0^+} \log_a x = -\infty$$

In particular, the y-axis is a vertical asymptote of the curve $y = \log_a x$.

EXAMPLE 8 Find $\lim_{x \to 0} \log_{10}(\tan^2 x)$.

SOLUTION As $x \to 0$, we know that $t = \tan^2 x \to \tan^2 0 = 0$ and the values of t are positive. So by (11) with $a = 10 > 1$, we have

$$\lim_{x \to 0} \log_{10}(\tan^2 x) = \lim_{t \to 0^+} \log_{10} t = -\infty$$ ■

NATURAL LOGARITHMS

■ **NOTATION FOR LOGARITHMS**
Most textbooks in calculus and the sciences, as well as calculators, use the notation $\ln x$ for the natural logarithm and $\log x$ for the "common logarithm," $\log_{10} x$. In the more advanced mathematical and scientific literature and in computer languages, however, the notation $\log x$ usually denotes the natural logarithm.

Of all possible bases a for logarithms, we will see in the next section that the most convenient choice of a base is the number e, which was defined in Section 3.1. The logarithm with base e is called the **natural logarithm** and has a special notation:

$$\log_e x = \ln x$$

If we put $a = e$ and replace $\log_e$ with "ln" in (9) and (10), then the defining properties of the natural logarithm function become

12

$$\ln x = y \iff e^y = x$$

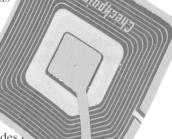

13

$$\ln(e^x) = x \qquad x \in \mathbb{R}$$
$$e^{\ln x} = x \qquad x > 0$$

In particular, if we set $x = 1$, we get

$$\ln e = 1$$

EXAMPLE 9 Find x if $\ln x = 5$.

SOLUTION 1 From (12) we see that

$$\ln x = 5 \qquad \text{means}$$

Therefore, $x = e^5$.

(If you have trouble working with the "ln the equation becomes $\log_e x = 5$; so, by th

SOLUTION 2 Start with the equation

$$\ln x$$

and apply the exponential function to both sides

$$e^{\ln x} = e^5$$

But the second cancellation equation in (13) says that $e^{\ln x} = x$. Therefore, $x = e^5$. ∎

⊽ EXAMPLE 10 Solve the equation $e^{5-3x} = 10$.

SOLUTION We take natural logarithms of both sides of the equation and use (13):

$$\ln(e^{5-3x}) = \ln 10$$
$$5 - 3x = \ln 10$$
$$3x = 5 - \ln 10$$
$$x = \tfrac{1}{3}(5 - \ln 10)$$

Since the natural logarithm is found on scientific calculators, we can approximate the solution to four decimal places: $x \approx 0.8991$. ∎

⊽ EXAMPLE 11 Express $\ln a + \tfrac{1}{2}\ln b$ as a single logarithm.

SOLUTION Using Laws 3 and 1 of logarithms, we have

$$\ln a + \tfrac{1}{2}\ln b = \ln a + \ln b^{1/2} = \ln a + \ln \sqrt{b} = \ln(a\sqrt{b})$$ ∎

The following formula shows that logarithms with any base can be expressed in terms of the natural logarithm.

14 CHANGE OF BASE FORMULA For any positive number a $(a \neq 1)$, we have

$$\log_a x = \frac{\ln x}{\ln a}$$

PROOF Let $y = \log_a x$. Then, from (9), we have $a^y = x$. Taking natural logarithms of both sides of this equation, we get $y \ln a = \ln x$. Therefore

$$y = \frac{\ln x}{\ln a} \qquad \square$$

Scientific calculators have a key for natural logarithms, so Formula 14 enables us to use a calculator to compute a logarithm with any base (as shown in the following example). Similarly, Formula 14 allows us to graph any logarithmic function on a graphing calculator or computer (see Exercises 55 and 56).

EXAMPLE 12 Evaluate $\log_8 5$ correct to six decimal places.

SOLUTION Formula 14 gives

$$\log_8 5 = \frac{\ln 5}{\ln 8} \approx 0.773976 \qquad \blacksquare$$

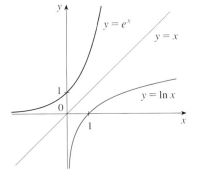

FIGURE 15

The graphs of the exponential function $y = e^x$ and its inverse function, the natural logarithm function, are shown in Figure 15. Because the curve $y = e^x$ crosses the y-axis with a slope of 1, it follows that the reflected curve $y = \ln x$ crosses the x-axis with a slope of 1.

In common with all other logarithmic functions with base greater than 1, the natural logarithm is a continuous, increasing function defined on $(0, \infty)$ and the y-axis is a vertical asymptote.

If we put $a = e$ in (11), then we have the following limits:

15

$$\lim_{x \to \infty} \ln x = \infty \qquad \lim_{x \to 0^+} \ln x = -\infty$$

▼ EXAMPLE 13 Sketch the graph of the function $y = \ln(x - 2) - 1$.

SOLUTION We start with the graph of $y = \ln x$ as given in Figure 15. Using the transformations of Section 1.2, we shift it 2 units to the right to get the graph of $y = \ln(x - 2)$ and then we shift it 1 unit downward to get the graph of $y = \ln(x - 2) - 1$. (See Figure 16 on page 158.) Notice that the line $x = 2$ is a vertical asymptote since

$$\lim_{x \to 2^+} [\ln(x - 2) - 1] = -\infty$$

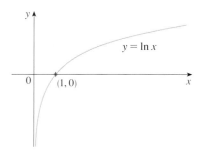
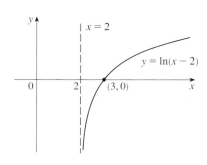
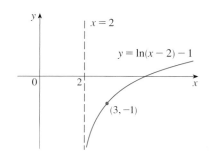

FIGURE 16

| **3.2** | **EXERCISES** |

1. (a) What is a one-to-one function?
(b) How can you tell from the graph of a function whether it is one-to-one?

2. (a) Suppose f is a one-to-one function with domain A and range B. How is the inverse function f^{-1} defined? What is the domain of f^{-1}? What is the range of f^{-1}?
(b) If you are given a formula for f, how do you find a formula for f^{-1}?
(c) If you are given the graph of f, how do you find the graph of f^{-1}?

3–14 ■ A function is given by a table of values, a graph, a formula, or a verbal description. Determine whether it is one-to-one.

3.

x	1	2	3	4	5	6
$f(x)$	1.5	2.0	3.6	5.3	2.8	2.0

4.

x	1	2	3	4	5	6
$f(x)$	1	2	4	8	16	32

5.
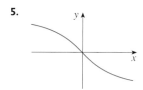

6.
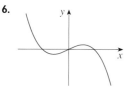

7.
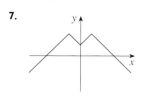

8.
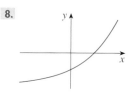

9. $f(x) = x^2 - 2x$

10. $f(x) = 10 - 3x$

11. $g(x) = 1/x$

12. $g(x) = \cos x$

13. $f(t)$ is the height of a football t seconds after kickoff.

14. $f(t)$ is your height at age t.

■   ■   ■   ■   ■   ■   ■   ■   ■   ■   ■   ■

15. If f is a one-to-one function such that $f(2) = 9$, what is $f^{-1}(9)$?

16. If $f(x) = x + \cos x$, find $f^{-1}(1)$.

17. If $g(x) = 3 + x + e^x$, find $g^{-1}(4)$.

18. The graph of f is given.
(a) Why is f one-to-one?
(b) What are the domain and range of f^{-1}?
(c) What is the value of $f^{-1}(2)$?
(d) Estimate the value of $f^{-1}(0)$.

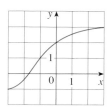

19. The formula $C = \frac{5}{9}(F - 32)$, where $F \geq -459.67$, expresses the Celsius temperature C as a function of the Fahrenheit temperature F. Find a formula for the inverse function and interpret it. What is the domain of the inverse function?

20. In the theory of relativity, the mass of a particle with speed v is

$$m = f(v) = \frac{m_0}{\sqrt{1 - v^2/c^2}}$$

where m_0 is the rest mass of the particle and c is the speed of light in a vacuum. Find the inverse function of f and explain its meaning.

21–26 ■ Find a formula for the inverse of the function.

21. $f(x) = \sqrt{10 - 3x}$

22. $f(x) = \dfrac{4x - 1}{2x + 3}$

23. $f(x) = e^{x^3}$

24. $y = 2x^3 + 3$

25. $y = \ln(x + 3)$

26. $y = \dfrac{1 + e^x}{1 - e^x}$

■　■　■　■　■　■　■　■　■　■　■　■

 27–28 ■ Find an explicit formula for f^{-1} and use it to graph f^{-1}, f, and the line $y = x$ on the same screen. To check your work, see whether the graphs of f and f^{-1} are reflections about the line.

27. $f(x) = x^4 + 1, \quad x \geq 0$

28. $f(x) = 2 - e^x$

■　■　■　■　■　■　■　■　■　■　■　■

29–30 ■ Use the given graph of f to sketch the graph of f^{-1}.

29.

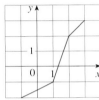

30.

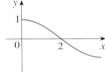

■　■　■　■　■　■　■　■　■　■　■　■

31–34 ■
(a) Show that f is one-to-one.
(b) Use Theorem 7 to find $(f^{-1})'(a)$.
(c) Calculate $f^{-1}(x)$ and state the domain and range of f^{-1}.
(d) Calculate $(f^{-1})'(a)$ from the formula in part (c) and check that it agrees with the result of part (b).
(e) Sketch the graphs of f and f^{-1} on the same axes.

31. $f(x) = x^3, \quad a = 8$

32. $f(x) = \sqrt{x - 2}, \quad a = 2$

33. $f(x) = 9 - x^2, \quad 0 \leq x \leq 3, \quad a = 8$

34. $f(x) = 1/(x - 1), \quad x > 1, \quad a = 2$

■　■　■　■　■　■　■　■　■　■　■

35–38 ■ Find $(f^{-1})'(a)$.

35. $f(x) = x^3 + x + 1, \quad a = 1$

36. $f(x) = x^5 - x^3 + 2x, \quad a = 2$

37. $f(x) = 3 + x^2 + \tan(\pi x/2), \quad -1 < x < 1, \quad a = 3$

38. $f(x) = \sqrt{x^3 + x^2 + x + 1}, \quad a = 2$

■　■　■　■　■　■　■　■　■　■　■

39. Suppose f^{-1} is the inverse function of a differentiable function f and $f(4) = 5$, $f'(4) = \frac{2}{3}$. Find $(f^{-1})'(5)$.

40. Suppose f^{-1} is the inverse function of a differentiable function f and let $G(x) = 1/f^{-1}(x)$. If $f(3) = 2$ and $f'(3) = \frac{1}{9}$, find $G'(2)$.

41. (a) How is the logarithmic function $y = \log_a x$ defined?
(b) What is the domain of this function?
(c) What is the range of this function?
(d) Sketch the general shape of the graph of the function $y = \log_a x$ if $a > 1$.

42. (a) What is the natural logarithm?
(b) What is the common logarithm?
(c) Sketch the graphs of the natural logarithm function and the natural exponential function with a common set of axes.

43–46 ■ Find the exact value of each expression (without a calculator).

43. (a) $\log_2 64$　　　　(b) $\log_6 \frac{1}{36}$

44. (a) $\log_8 2$　　　　(b) $\ln e^{\sqrt{2}}$

45. (a) $\log_{10} 1.25 + \log_{10} 80$
(b) $\log_5 10 + \log_5 20 - 3 \log_5 2$

46. (a) $2^{(\log_2 3 + \log_2 5)}$　　　　(b) $e^{3 \ln 2}$

■　■　■　■　■　■　■　■　■　■　■　■　■

47–50 ■ Use the properties of logarithms to expand the quantity.

47. $\log_2\left(\dfrac{x^3 y}{z^2}\right)$

48. $\ln \sqrt{a(b^2 + c^2)}$

49. $\ln(uv)^{10}$

50. $\ln \dfrac{3x^2}{(x + 1)^5}$

■　■　■　■　■　■　■　■　■　■　■　■

51–53 ■ Express the given quantity as a single logarithm.

51. $2 \ln 4 - \ln 2$

52. $\ln x + a \ln y - b \ln z$

53. $\ln(1 + x^2) + \frac{1}{2} \ln x - \ln \sin x$

■　■　■　■　■　■　■　■　■　■　■　■

54. Use Formula 14 to evaluate each logarithm correct to six decimal places.
(a) $\log_{12} 10$　　　　(b) $\log_2 8.4$

55–56 ■ Use Formula 14 to graph the given functions on a common screen. How are these graphs related?

55. $y = \log_{1.5} x, \quad y = \ln x, \quad y = \log_{10} x, \quad y = \log_{50} x$

56. $y = \ln x, \quad y = \log_{10} x, \quad y = e^x, \quad y = 10^x$

■　■　■　■　■　■　■　■　■　■　■　■

57. Suppose that the graph of $y = \log_2 x$ is drawn on a coordinate grid where the unit of measurement is an inch. How many miles to the right of the origin do we have to move before the height of the curve reaches 3 ft?

58. Compare the functions $f(x) = x^{0.1}$ and $g(x) = \ln x$ by graphing both f and g in several viewing rectangles. When does the graph of f finally surpass the graph of g?

59–60 ■ Make a rough sketch of the graph of each function. Do not use a calculator. Just use the graphs given in Figures 14 and 15 and, if necessary, the transformations of Section 1.2.

59. (a) $y = \log_{10}(x + 5)$ (b) $y = -\ln x$

60. (a) $y = \ln(-x)$ (b) $y = \ln|x|$

■ ■ ■ ■ ■ ■ ■ ■ ■ ■ ■ ■

61–64 ■ Solve each equation for x.

61. (a) $2 \ln x = 1$ (b) $e^{-x} = 5$

62. (a) $e^{2x+3} - 7 = 0$ (b) $\ln(5 - 2x) = -3$

63. (a) $2^{x-5} = 3$ (b) $\ln x + \ln(x - 1) = 1$

64. (a) $\ln(\ln x) = 1$ (b) $e^{ax} = Ce^{bx}$, where $a \neq b$

■ ■ ■ ■ ■ ■ ■ ■ ■ ■ ■ ■

65–66 ■ Solve each inequality for x.

65. (a) $e^x < 10$ (b) $\ln x > -1$

66. (a) $2 < \ln x < 9$ (b) $e^{2-3x} > 4$

■ ■ ■ ■ ■ ■ ■ ■ ■ ■ ■ ■

67–68 ■ Find (a) the domain of f and (b) f^{-1} and its domain.

67. $f(x) = \sqrt{3 - e^{2x}}$ **68.** $f(x) = \ln(2 + \ln x)$

■ ■ ■ ■ ■ ■ ■ ■ ■ ■ ■ ■

69–74 ■ Find the limit.

69. $\lim_{x \to 2^-} \ln(2 - x)$ **70.** $\lim_{x \to 3^+} \log_{10}(x^2 - 5x + 6)$

71. $\lim_{x \to 0} \ln(\cos x)$ **72.** $\lim_{x \to 0^+} \ln(\sin x)$

73. $\lim_{x \to \infty} \left[\ln(1 + x^2) - \ln(1 + x)\right]$

74. $\lim_{x \to \infty} \left[\ln(2 + x) - \ln(1 + x)\right]$

■ ■ ■ ■ ■ ■ ■ ■ ■ ■ ■ ■

CAS **75.** Graph the function $f(x) = \sqrt{x^3 + x^2 + x + 1}$ and explain why it is one-to-one. Then use a computer algebra system to find an explicit expression for $f^{-1}(x)$. (Your CAS will produce three possible expressions. Explain why two of them are irrelevant in this context.)

76. When a camera flash goes off, the batteries immediately begin to recharge the flash's capacitor, which stores electric charge given by

$$Q(t) = Q_0(1 - e^{-t/a})$$

(The maximum charge capacity is Q_0 and t is measured in seconds.)
(a) Find the inverse of this function and explain its meaning.
(b) How long does it take to recharge the capacitor to 90% of capacity if $a = 2$?

77. Let $a > 1$. Prove, using precise definitions, that
(a) $\lim_{x \to -\infty} a^x = 0$ (b) $\lim_{x \to \infty} a^x = \infty$

78. (a) If we shift a curve to the left, what happens to its reflection about the line $y = x$? In view of this geometric principle, find an expression for the inverse of $g(x) = f(x + c)$, where f is a one-to-one function.
(b) Find an expression for the inverse of $h(x) = f(cx)$, where $c \neq 0$.

| **3.3** | **DERIVATIVES OF LOGARITHMIC AND EXPONENTIAL FUNCTIONS** |

In this section we find formulas for the derivatives of logarithmic functions and then use them to calculate the derivatives of exponential functions.

DERIVATIVES OF LOGARITHMIC FUNCTIONS

In using the definition of a derivative to differentiate the function $f(x) = \log_a x$, we use the fact that it is continuous, together with some of the laws of logarithms. We also need to recall the definition of e from Section 3.1:

$$e = \lim_{x \to 0} (1 + x)^{1/x}$$

---

1 **THEOREM** The function $f(x) = \log_a x$ is differentiable and

$$f'(x) = \frac{1}{x} \log_a e$$

PROOF

$$f'(x) = \lim_{h \to 0} \frac{f(x + h) - f(x)}{h} = \lim_{h \to 0} \frac{\log_a(x + h) - \log_a x}{h}$$

$$= \lim_{h \to 0} \frac{\log_a\left(\dfrac{x + h}{x}\right)}{h} = \lim_{h \to 0} \frac{1}{h} \log_a\left(1 + \frac{h}{x}\right)$$

$$= \lim_{h \to 0} \frac{1}{x} \cdot \frac{x}{h} \log_a\left(1 + \frac{h}{x}\right)$$

$$= \frac{1}{x} \lim_{h \to 0} \frac{x}{h} \log_a\left(1 + \frac{h}{x}\right) \qquad \text{(by Limit Law 3)}$$

$$= \frac{1}{x} \lim_{h \to 0} \log_a\left(1 + \frac{h}{x}\right)^{x/h} \qquad \text{(by Law 3 of Logarithms)}$$

$$= \frac{1}{x} \log_a\left[\lim_{h \to 0}\left(1 + \frac{h}{x}\right)^{x/h}\right] \qquad \text{(since } \log_a \text{ is continuous)}$$

$$= \frac{1}{x} \log_a\left[\lim_{h \to 0}\left(1 + \frac{h}{x}\right)^{1/(h/x)}\right] = \frac{1}{x} \log_a e$$

The final step may be seen more clearly by making the change of variable $t = h/x$. As $h \to 0$, we also have $t \to 0$, so

$$\lim_{h \to 0}\left(1 + \frac{h}{x}\right)^{1/(h/x)} = \lim_{t \to 0}(1 + t)^{1/t} = e$$

by the definition of e. Thus

$$f'(x) = \frac{1}{x} \log_a e$$

NOTE We know from the Change of Base Formula (3.2.14) that

$$\log_a e = \frac{\ln e}{\ln a} = \frac{1}{\ln a}$$

and so the formula in Theorem 1 can be rewritten as follows:

2

$$\frac{d}{dx}(\log_a x) = \frac{1}{x \ln a}$$

EXAMPLE 1 Differentiate $f(x) = \log_{10}(2 + \sin x)$.

SOLUTION Using Formula 2 with $a = 10$, together with the Chain Rule, we have

$$f'(x) = \frac{d}{dx} \log_{10}(2 + \sin x) = \frac{1}{(2 + \sin x) \ln 10} \frac{d}{dx}(2 + \sin x)$$

$$= \frac{\cos x}{(2 + \sin x) \ln 10}$$

If we put $a = e$ in Formula 2, then the factor $\ln a$ on the right side becomes $\ln e = 1$ and we get the formula for the derivative of the natural logarithmic function $\log_e x = \ln x$:

> **3** **DERIVATIVE OF THE NATURAL LOGARITHMIC FUNCTION**
>
> $$\frac{d}{dx}(\ln x) = \frac{1}{x}$$

By comparing Formulas 2 and 3, we see one of the main reasons that natural logarithms (logarithms with base e) are used in calculus: The differentiation formula is simplest when $a = e$ because $\ln e = 1$.

V EXAMPLE 2 Differentiate $y = \ln(x^3 + 1)$.

SOLUTION To use the Chain Rule, we let $u = x^3 + 1$. Then $y = \ln u$, so

$$\frac{dy}{dx} = \frac{dy}{du}\frac{du}{dx} = \frac{1}{u}\frac{du}{dx} = \frac{1}{x^3 + 1}(3x^2) = \frac{3x^2}{x^3 + 1} \qquad \blacksquare$$

In general, if we combine Formula 3 with the Chain Rule as in Example 2, we get

4
$$\frac{d}{dx}(\ln u) = \frac{1}{u}\frac{du}{dx} \qquad \text{or} \qquad \frac{d}{dx}[\ln g(x)] = \frac{g'(x)}{g(x)}$$

V EXAMPLE 3 Find $\dfrac{d}{dx}\ln(\sin x)$.

SOLUTION Using (4), we have

$$\frac{d}{dx}\ln(\sin x) = \frac{1}{\sin x}\frac{d}{dx}(\sin x) = \frac{1}{\sin x}\cos x = \cot x \qquad \blacksquare$$

EXAMPLE 4 Differentiate $f(x) = \sqrt{\ln x}$.

SOLUTION This time the logarithm is the inner function, so the Chain Rule gives

$$f'(x) = \tfrac{1}{2}(\ln x)^{-1/2}\frac{d}{dx}(\ln x) = \frac{1}{2\sqrt{\ln x}} \cdot \frac{1}{x} = \frac{1}{2x\sqrt{\ln x}} \qquad \blacksquare$$

EXAMPLE 5 Find $\dfrac{d}{dx}\ln\dfrac{x + 1}{\sqrt{x - 2}}$.

SOLUTION I

$$\frac{d}{dx}\ln\frac{x + 1}{\sqrt{x - 2}} = \frac{1}{\dfrac{x + 1}{\sqrt{x - 2}}}\frac{d}{dx}\frac{x + 1}{\sqrt{x - 2}}$$

$$= \frac{\sqrt{x - 2}}{x + 1}\frac{\sqrt{x - 2} \cdot 1 - (x + 1)(\tfrac{1}{2})(x - 2)^{-1/2}}{x - 2}$$

$$= \frac{x - 2 - \tfrac{1}{2}(x + 1)}{(x + 1)(x - 2)} = \frac{x - 5}{2(x + 1)(x - 2)}$$

▪ Figure 1 shows the graph of the function f of Example 5 together with the graph of its derivative. It gives a visual check on our calculation. Notice that $f'(x)$ is large negative when f is rapidly decreasing.

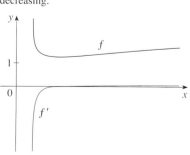

FIGURE I

SOLUTION 2 If we first simplify the given function using the laws of logarithms, then the differentiation becomes easier:

$$\frac{d}{dx} \ln \frac{x+1}{\sqrt{x-2}} = \frac{d}{dx} \left[\ln(x+1) - \tfrac{1}{2} \ln(x-2) \right]$$

$$= \frac{1}{x+1} - \frac{1}{2}\left(\frac{1}{x-2}\right)$$

(This answer can be left as written, but if we used a common denominator we would see that it gives the same answer as in Solution 1.) ▪

■ Figure 2 shows the graph of the function $f(x) = \ln|x|$ in Example 6 and its derivative $f'(x) = 1/x$. Notice that when x is small, the graph of $y = \ln|x|$ is steep and so $f'(x)$ is large (positive or negative).

Ⓥ EXAMPLE 6 Find $f'(x)$ if $f(x) = \ln|x|$.

SOLUTION Since

$$f(x) = \begin{cases} \ln x & \text{if } x > 0 \\ \ln(-x) & \text{if } x < 0 \end{cases}$$

it follows that

$$f'(x) = \begin{cases} \dfrac{1}{x} & \text{if } x > 0 \\ \dfrac{1}{-x}(-1) = \dfrac{1}{x} & \text{if } x < 0 \end{cases}$$

Thus $f'(x) = 1/x$ for all $x \neq 0$. ▪

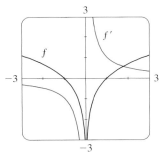

FIGURE 2

The result of Example 6 is worth remembering:

5

$$\frac{d}{dx} \ln|x| = \frac{1}{x}$$

LOGARITHMIC DIFFERENTIATION

The calculation of derivatives of complicated functions involving products, quotients, or powers can often be simplified by taking logarithms. The method used in the following example is called **logarithmic differentiation**.

Ⓥ EXAMPLE 7 Differentiate $y = \dfrac{x^{3/4}\sqrt{x^2+1}}{(3x+2)^5}$.

SOLUTION We take logarithms of both sides of the equation and use the Laws of Logarithms to simplify:

$$\ln y = \tfrac{3}{4} \ln x + \tfrac{1}{2} \ln(x^2 + 1) - 5 \ln(3x + 2)$$

Differentiating implicitly with respect to x gives

$$\frac{1}{y}\frac{dy}{dx} = \frac{3}{4} \cdot \frac{1}{x} + \frac{1}{2} \cdot \frac{2x}{x^2+1} - 5 \cdot \frac{3}{3x+2}$$

Solving for dy/dx, we get

$$\frac{dy}{dx} = y\left(\frac{3}{4x} + \frac{x}{x^2 + 1} - \frac{15}{3x + 2}\right)$$

Because we have an explicit expression for y, we can substitute and write

$$\frac{dy}{dx} = \frac{x^{3/4}\sqrt{x^2 + 1}}{(3x + 2)^5}\left(\frac{3}{4x} + \frac{x}{x^2 + 1} - \frac{15}{3x + 2}\right)$$ ■

■ If we hadn't used logarithmic differentiation in Example 7, we would have had to use both the Quotient Rule and the Product Rule. The resulting calculation would have been horrendous.

STEPS IN LOGARITHMIC DIFFERENTIATION

1. Take natural logarithms of both sides of an equation $y = f(x)$ and use the Laws of Logarithms to simplify.

2. Differentiate implicitly with respect to x.

3. Solve the resulting equation for y'.

If $f(x) < 0$ for some values of x, then $\ln f(x)$ is not defined, but we can write $|y| = |f(x)|$ and use Equation 5. We illustrate this procedure by proving the general version of the Power Rule, as promised in Section 2.3.

THE POWER RULE If n is any real number and $f(x) = x^n$, then

$$f'(x) = nx^{n-1}$$

PROOF Let $y = x^n$ and use logarithmic differentiation:

$$\ln|y| = \ln|x|^n = n\ln|x| \qquad x \neq 0$$

■ If $x = 0$, we can show that $f'(0) = 0$ for $n > 1$ directly from the definition of a derivative.

Therefore

$$\frac{y'}{y} = \frac{n}{x}$$

Hence

$$y' = n\frac{y}{x} = n\frac{x^n}{x} = nx^{n-1}$$ □

DERIVATIVES OF EXPONENTIAL FUNCTIONS

To compute the derivative of the exponential function $y = a^x$ we use the fact that exponential and logarithmic functions are inverse functions.

---

6 THEOREM The exponential function $f(x) = a^x$, $a > 0$, is differentiable and

$$\frac{d}{dx}(a^x) = a^x \ln a$$

PROOF We know that the logarithmic function $y = \log_a x$ is differentiable (and its derivative is nonzero) by Theorem 1. So its inverse function $y = a^x$ is differentiable by Theorem 3.2.7.

■ Another method for proving Theorem 6 is to use logarithmic differentiation.

If $y = a^x$, then $\log_a y = x$. Differentiating this equation implicitly with respect to x, we get

$$\frac{1}{y \ln a} \frac{dy}{dx} = 1$$

Thus

$$\frac{dy}{dx} = y \ln a = a^x \ln a$$

□

EXAMPLE 8 Combining Formula 6 with the Chain Rule, we have

$$\frac{d}{dx} \left(10^{x^2}\right) = 10^{x^2}(\ln 10) \frac{d}{dx} (x^2) = (2 \ln 10)x10^{x^2}$$

■

If we put $a = e$ in Theorem 6, the differentiation formula for exponential functions takes on a particularly simple form:

---

7 **DERIVATIVE OF THE NATURAL EXPONENTIAL FUNCTION**

$$\frac{d}{dx} (e^x) = e^x$$

Visual 3.3 uses the slope-a-scope to illustrate this formula.

This equation says that the exponential function $f(x) = e^x$ is its own derivative. Comparing Equations 6 and 7, we see that the simplest differentiation formula for an exponential function occurs when $a = e$. This is the reason that the natural exponential function is most often used in calculus.

The geometric significance of Equation 7 is that the slope of a tangent to the curve $y = e^x$ at any point is equal to the y-coordinate of the point. In particular, if $f(x) = e^x$, then $f'(0) = e^0 = 1$. This means that of all the possible exponential functions $y = a^x$, $y = e^x$ is the one that crosses the y-axis with a slope of 1. (See Figure 3.)

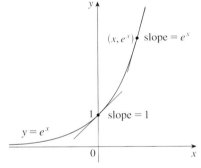

FIGURE 3

EXAMPLE 9 Differentiate the function $y = e^{\tan x}$.

SOLUTION To use the Chain Rule, we let $u = \tan x$. Then we have $y = e^u$, so

$$\frac{dy}{dx} = \frac{dy}{du} \frac{du}{dx} = e^u \frac{du}{dx} = e^{\tan x} \sec^2 x$$

■

In general if we combine Formula 7 with the Chain Rule, as in Example 9, we get

8
$$\frac{d}{dx} (e^u) = e^u \frac{du}{dx}$$

EXAMPLE 10 Find y' if $y = e^{-4x} \sin 5x$.

SOLUTION Using Formula 8 and the Product Rule, we have

$$y' = e^{-4x}(\cos 5x)(5) + (\sin 5x)e^{-4x}(-4) = e^{-4x}(5 \cos 5x - 4 \sin 5x)$$

■

To differentiate a function of the form $y = [f(x)]^{g(x)}$, where both the base and the exponent are functions, logarithmic differentiation can be used as in the following example.

▼ EXAMPLE 11 Differentiate $y = x^{\sqrt{x}}$.

SOLUTION 1 Using logarithmic differentiation, we have

$$\ln y = \ln x^{\sqrt{x}} = \sqrt{x}\,\ln x$$

$$\frac{y'}{y} = \sqrt{x} \cdot \frac{1}{x} + (\ln x)\frac{1}{2\sqrt{x}}$$

$$y' = y\left(\frac{1}{\sqrt{x}} + \frac{\ln x}{2\sqrt{x}}\right) = x^{\sqrt{x}}\left(\frac{2 + \ln x}{2\sqrt{x}}\right)$$

■ Figure 4 illustrates Example 11 by showing the graphs of $f(x) = x^{\sqrt{x}}$ and its derivative.

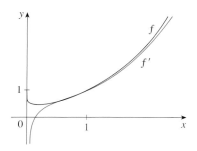

FIGURE 4

SOLUTION 2 Another method is to write $x^{\sqrt{x}} = (e^{\ln x})^{\sqrt{x}}$:

$$\frac{d}{dx}\left(x^{\sqrt{x}}\right) = \frac{d}{dx}\left(e^{\sqrt{x}\,\ln x}\right) = e^{\sqrt{x}\,\ln x}\frac{d}{dx}\left(\sqrt{x}\,\ln x\right)$$

$$= x^{\sqrt{x}}\left(\frac{2 + \ln x}{2\sqrt{x}}\right) \qquad \text{(as in Solution 1)}$$ ∎

3.3	**EXERCISES**

1–36 ■ Differentiate the function.

1. $f(x) = \log_2(1 - 3x)$

2. $f(x) = \ln(x^2 + 10)$

3. $f(\theta) = \ln(\cos \theta)$

4. $f(x) = \cos(\ln x)$

5. $f(x) = \sqrt[5]{\ln x}$

6. $f(x) = \ln \sqrt[5]{x}$

7. $f(x) = \sin x \ln(5x)$

8. $f(x) = \log_5(xe^x)$

9. $g(x) = \ln \dfrac{a - x}{a + x}$

10. $f(t) = \dfrac{1 + \ln t}{1 - \ln t}$

11. $F(t) = \ln \dfrac{(2t + 1)^3}{(3t - 1)^4}$

12. $f(x) = \log_{10}\left(\dfrac{x}{x - 1}\right)$

13. $f(u) = \dfrac{\ln u}{1 + \ln(2u)}$

14. $y = \ln(x^4 \sin^2 x)$

15. $y = \ln|2 - x - 5x^2|$

16. $G(u) = \ln \sqrt{\dfrac{3u + 2}{3u - 2}}$

17. $f(x) = x^2 e^x$

18. $g(x) = \sqrt{x}\, e^x$

19. $y = \dfrac{e^x}{x^2}$

20. $y = \dfrac{e^x}{1 + x}$

21. $y = xe^{-x^2}$

22. $y = e^{-5x}\cos 3x$

23. $y = e^{x\cos x}$

24. $y = 10^{1-x^2}$

25. $h(t) = t^3 - 3^t$

26. $y = \dfrac{1}{s + ke^s}$

27. $y = \dfrac{ae^x + b}{ce^x + d}$

28. $f(x) = \dfrac{1 - xe^x}{x + e^x}$

29. $y = 2^{\sin \pi x}$

30. $y = \dfrac{e^u - e^{-u}}{e^u + e^{-u}}$

31. $f(u) = e^{1/u}$

32. $y = e^{k\tan\sqrt{x}}$

33. $y = \ln(e^{-x} + xe^{-x})$

34. $y = [\ln(1 + e^x)]^2$

35. $F(t) = e^{t\sin 2t}$

36. $y = 2^{3^{x^2}}$

37–40 ■ Find y' and y''.

37. $y = e^{\alpha x}\sin \beta x$

38. $y = \dfrac{\ln x}{x^2}$

39. $y = x \ln x$

40. $y = \ln(\sec x + \tan x)$

41–42 ■ Find an equation of the tangent line to the curve at the given point.

41. $y = \ln \ln x$, $(e, 0)$

42. $y = e^x/x$, $(1, e)$

43–44 ■ Differentiate f and find the domain of f.

43. $f(x) = \dfrac{x}{1 - \ln(x - 1)}$

44. $f(x) = \ln \ln \ln x$

45–54 ▪ Use logarithmic differentiation or an alternative method to find the derivative of the function.

45. $y = (2x + 1)^5(x^4 - 3)^6$

46. $y = \sqrt{x}\, e^{x^2}(x^2 + 1)^{10}$

47. $y = \dfrac{\sin^2 x \tan^4 x}{(x^2 + 1)^2}$

48. $y = \sqrt[4]{\dfrac{x^2 + 1}{x^2 - 1}}$

49. $y = x^x$

50. $y = x^{\cos x}$

51. $y = (\cos x)^x$

52. $y = \sqrt{x}^{\,x}$

53. $y = (\tan x)^{1/x}$

54. $y = (\sin x)^{\ln x}$

▪ ▪ ▪ ▪ ▪ ▪ ▪ ▪ ▪ ▪ ▪ ▪ ▪

55. Find y' if $e^{x^2 y} = x + y$.

56. Find an equation of the tangent line to the curve $xe^y + ye^x = 1$ at the point $(0, 1)$.

57. Find y' if $y = \ln(x^2 + y^2)$.

58. Find y' if $x^y = y^x$.

59. The motion of a spring that is subject to a frictional force or a damping force (such as a shock absorber in a car) is often modeled by the product of an exponential function and a sine or cosine function. Suppose the equation of motion of a point on such a spring is

$$s(t) = 2e^{-1.5t} \sin 2\pi t$$

where s is measured in centimeters and t in seconds. Find the velocity after t seconds and graph both the position and velocity functions for $0 \leq t \leq 2$.

60. Under certain circumstances a rumor spreads according to the equation

$$p(t) = \frac{1}{1 + ae^{-kt}}$$

where $p(t)$ is the proportion of the population that knows the rumor at time t and a and k are positive constants.
(a) Find $\lim_{t \to \infty} p(t)$.
(b) Find the rate of spread of the rumor.
(c) Graph p for the case $a = 10$, $k = 0.5$ with t measured in hours. Use the graph to estimate how long it will take for 80% of the population to hear the rumor.

61. Show that the function $y = Ae^{-x} + Bxe^{-x}$ satisfies the differential equation $y'' + 2y' + y = 0$.

62. For what values of r does the function $y = e^{rx}$ satisfy the equation $y'' + 5y' - 6y = 0$?

63. If $f(x) = e^{2x}$, find a formula for $f^{(n)}(x)$.

64. Find the thousandth derivative of $f(x) = xe^{-x}$.

65. Find a formula for $f^{(n)}(x)$ if $f(x) = \ln(x - 1)$.

66. Find $\dfrac{d^9}{dx^9}(x^8 \ln x)$.

67. If $f(x) = 3 + x + e^x$, find $(f^{-1})'(4)$.

68. Evaluate $\lim\limits_{x \to \pi} \dfrac{e^{\sin x} - 1}{x - \pi}$.

3.4 EXPONENTIAL GROWTH AND DECAY

In many natural phenomena, quantities grow or decay at a rate proportional to their size. For instance, if $y = f(t)$ is the number of individuals in a population of animals or bacteria at time t, then it seems reasonable to expect that the rate of growth $f'(t)$ is proportional to the population $f(t)$; that is, $f'(t) = kf(t)$ for some constant k. Indeed, under ideal conditions (unlimited environment, adequate nutrition, immunity to disease) the mathematical model given by the equation $f'(t) = kf(t)$ predicts what actually happens fairly accurately. Another example occurs in nuclear physics where the mass of a radioactive substance decays at a rate proportional to the mass. In chemistry, the rate of a unimolecular first-order reaction is proportional to the concentration of the substance. In finance, the value of a savings account with continuously compounded interest increases at a rate proportional to that value.

In general, if $y(t)$ is the value of a quantity y at time t and if the rate of change of y with respect to t is proportional to its size $y(t)$ at any time, then

1

$$\frac{dy}{dt} = ky$$

where k is a constant. Equation 1 is sometimes called the **law of natural growth** (if $k > 0$) or the **law of natural decay** (if $k < 0$). It is called a **differential equation** because it involves an unknown function y and its derivative dy/dt.

It's not hard to think of a solution of Equation 1. This equation asks us to find a function whose derivative is a constant multiple of itself. We have met such functions in this chapter. Any exponential function of the form $y(t) = Ce^{kt}$, where C is a constant, satisfies

$$y'(t) = C(ke^{kt}) = k(Ce^{kt}) = ky(t)$$

We will see in Section 7.6 that *any* function that satsifies $dy/dt = ky$ must be of the form $y = Ce^{kt}$. To see the significance of the constant C, we observe that

$$y(0) = Ce^{k \cdot 0} = C$$

Therefore C is the initial value of the function.

> **2 THEOREM** The only solutions of the differential equation $dy/dt = ky$ are the exponential functions
>
> $$y(t) = y(0)e^{kt}$$

POPULATION GROWTH

What is the significance of the proportionality constant k? In the context of population growth, where $P(t)$ is the size of a population at time t, we can write

3
$$\frac{dP}{dt} = kP \qquad \text{or} \qquad \frac{1}{P}\frac{dP}{dt} = k$$

The quantity

$$\frac{1}{P}\frac{dP}{dt}$$

is the growth rate divided by the population size; it is called the **relative growth rate**. According to (3), instead of saying "the growth rate is proportional to population size" we could say "the relative growth rate is constant." Then (2) says that a population with constant relative growth rate must grow exponentially. Notice that the relative growth rate k appears as the coefficient of t in the exponential function Ce^{kt}. For instance, if

$$\frac{dP}{dt} = 0.02P$$

and t is measured in years, then the relative growth rate is $k = 0.02$ and the population grows at a relative rate of 2% per year. If the population at time 0 is P_0, then the expression for the population is

$$P(t) = P_0 e^{0.02t}$$

☑ EXAMPLE 1 Use the fact that the world population was 2560 million in 1950 and 3040 million in 1960 to model the population of the world in the second half of the 20th century. (Assume that the growth rate is proportional to the population size.)

What is the relative growth rate? Use the model to estimate the world population in 1993 and to predict the population in the year 2020.

SOLUTION We measure the time t in years and let $t = 0$ in the year 1950. We measure the population $P(t)$ in millions of people. Then $P(0) = 2560$ and $P(10) = 3040$. Since we are assuming that $dP/dt = kP$, Theorem 2 gives

$$P(t) = P(0)e^{kt} = 2560e^{kt}$$

$$P(10) = 2560e^{10k} = 3040$$

$$k = \frac{1}{10}\ln\frac{3040}{2560} \approx 0.017185$$

The relative growth rate is about 1.7% per year and the model is

$$P(t) = 2560e^{0.017185t}$$

We estimate that the world population in 1993 was

$$P(43) = 2560e^{0.017185(43)} \approx 5360 \text{ million}$$

The model predicts that the population in 2020 will be

$$P(70) = 2560e^{0.017185(70)} \approx 8524 \text{ million}$$

The graph in Figure 1 shows that the model is fairly accurate to date (the dots represent the actual population), so the estimate for 1993 is quite reliable. But the prediction for 2020 is riskier.

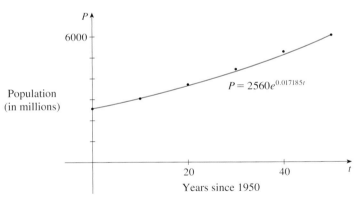

FIGURE 1
A model for world population growth in the second half of the 20th century

RADIOACTIVE DECAY

Radioactive substances decay by spontaneously emitting radiation. If $m(t)$ is the mass remaining from an initial mass m_0 of the substance after time t, then the relative decay rate

$$-\frac{1}{m}\frac{dm}{dt}$$

has been found experimentally to be constant. (Since dm/dt is negative, the relative decay rate is positive.) It follows that

$$\frac{dm}{dt} = km$$

where k is a negative constant. In other words, radioactive substances decay at a rate proportional to the remaining mass. This means that we can use (2) to show that the mass decays exponentially:

$$m(t) = m_0 e^{kt}$$

Physicists express the rate of decay in terms of **half-life**, the time required for half of any given quantity to decay.

◢ **EXAMPLE 2** The half-life of radium-226 ($^{226}_{88}$Ra) is 1590 years.
(a) A sample of radium-226 has a mass of 100 mg. Find a formula for the mass of $^{226}_{88}$Ra that remains after t years.
(b) Find the mass after 1000 years correct to the nearest milligram.
(c) When will the mass be reduced to 30 mg?

SOLUTION
(a) Let $m(t)$ be the mass of radium-226 (in milligrams) that remains after t years. Then $dm/dt = km$ and $y(0) = 100$, so (2) gives

$$m(t) = m(0)e^{kt} = 100e^{kt}$$

In order to determine the value of k, we use the fact that $y(1590) = \frac{1}{2}(100)$. Thus

$$100e^{1590k} = 50 \qquad \text{so} \qquad e^{1590k} = \frac{1}{2}$$

and
$$1590k = \ln \frac{1}{2} = -\ln 2$$

$$k = -\frac{\ln 2}{1590}$$

Therefore
$$m(t) = 100e^{-(\ln 2)t/1590}$$

We could use the fact that $e^{\ln 2} = 2$ to write the expression for $m(t)$ in the alternative form

$$m(t) = 100 \times 2^{-t/1590}$$

(b) The mass after 1000 years is

$$m(1000) = 100e^{-(\ln 2)1000/1590} \approx 65 \text{ mg}$$

(c) We want to find the value of t such that $m(t) = 30$, that is,

$$100e^{-(\ln 2)t/1590} = 30 \qquad \text{or} \qquad e^{-(\ln 2)t/1590} = 0.3$$

We solve this equation for t by taking the natural logarithm of both sides:

$$-\frac{\ln 2}{1590}t = \ln 0.3$$

Thus
$$t = -1590 \frac{\ln 0.3}{\ln 2} \approx 2762 \text{ years} \qquad \blacksquare$$

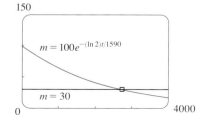

$m = 100e^{-(\ln 2)t/1590}$

$m = 30$

FIGURE 2

As a check on our work in Example 2, we use a graphing device to draw the graph of $m(t)$ in Figure 2 together with the horizontal line $m = 30$. These curves intersect when $t \approx 2800$, and this agrees with the answer to part (c).

NEWTON'S LAW OF COOLING

Newton's Law of Cooling states that the rate of cooling of an object is proportional to the temperature difference between the object and its surroundings, provided that this difference is not too large. (This law also applies to warming.) If we let $T(t)$ be the temperature of the object at time t and T_s be the temperature of the surroundings, then we can formulate Newton's Law of Cooling as a differential equation:

$$\frac{dT}{dt} = k(T - T_s)$$

where k is a constant. This equation is not quite the same as Equation 1, so we make the change of variable $y(t) = T(t) - T_s$. Because T_s is constant, we have $y'(t) = T'(t)$ and so the equation becomes

$$\frac{dy}{dt} = ky$$

We can then use (2) to find an expression for y, from which we can find T.

EXAMPLE 3 A bottle of soda pop at room temperature (72°F) is placed in a refrigerator where the temperature is 44°F. After half an hour the soda pop has cooled to 61°F.
(a) What is the temperature of the soda pop after another half hour?
(b) How long does it take for the soda pop to cool to 50°F?

SOLUTION
(a) Let $T(t)$ be the temperature of the soda after t minutes. The surrounding temperature is $T_s = 44°F$, so Newton's Law of Cooling states that

$$\frac{dT}{dt} = k(T - 44)$$

If we let $y = T - 44$, then $y(0) = T(0) - 44 = 72 - 44 = 28$, so y satisfies

$$\frac{dy}{dt} = ky \qquad y(0) = 28$$

and by (2) we have

$$y(t) = y(0)e^{kt} = 28e^{kt}$$

We are given that $T(30) = 61$, so $y(30) = 61 - 44 = 17$ and

$$28e^{30k} = 17 \qquad e^{30k} = \tfrac{17}{28}$$

Taking logarithms, we have

$$k = \frac{\ln\left(\tfrac{17}{28}\right)}{30} \approx -0.01663$$

Thus

$$y(t) = 28e^{-0.01663t}$$

$$T(t) = 44 + 28e^{-0.01663t}$$

$$T(60) = 44 + 28e^{-0.01663(60)} \approx 54.3$$

So after another half hour the pop has cooled to about 54°F.

(b) We have $T(t) = 50$ when

$$44 + 28e^{-0.01663t} = 50$$

$$e^{-0.01663t} = \tfrac{6}{28}$$

$$t = \frac{\ln\left(\tfrac{6}{28}\right)}{-0.01663} \approx 92.6$$

The pop cools to 50°F after about 1 hour 33 minutes. ∎

Notice that in Example 3, we have

$$\lim_{t \to \infty} T(t) = \lim_{t \to \infty} (44 + 28e^{-0.01663t}) = 44 + 28 \cdot 0 = 44$$

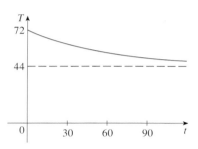

FIGURE 3

which is to be expected. The graph of the temperature function is shown in Figure 3.

CONTINUOUSLY COMPOUNDED INTEREST

EXAMPLE 4 If $1000 is invested at 6% interest, compounded annually, then after 1 year the investment is worth $1000(1.06) = $1060, after 2 years it's worth $[1000(1.06)]1.06 = $1123.60, and after t years it's worth $1000(1.06)^t$. In general, if an amount A_0 is invested at an interest rate r ($r = 0.06$ in this example), then after t years it's worth $A_0(1 + r)^t$. Usually, however, interest is compounded more frequently, say, n times a year. Then in each compounding period the interest rate is r/n and there are nt compounding periods in t years, so the value of the investment is

$$A_0\left(1 + \frac{r}{n}\right)^{nt}$$

For instance, after 3 years at 6% interest a $1000 investment will be worth

$$\$1000(1.06)^3 = \$1191.02 \quad \text{with annual compounding}$$

$$\$1000(1.03)^6 = \$1194.05 \quad \text{with semiannual compounding}$$

$$\$1000(1.015)^{12} = \$1195.62 \quad \text{with quarterly compounding}$$

$$\$1000(1.005)^{36} = \$1196.68 \quad \text{with monthly compounding}$$

$$\$1000\left(1 + \frac{0.06}{365}\right)^{365 \cdot 3} = \$1197.20 \quad \text{with daily compounding}$$

You can see that the interest paid increases as the number of compounding periods (n) increases. If we let $n \to \infty$, then we will be compounding the interest **continuously** and the value of the investment will be

$$A(t) = \lim_{n \to \infty} A_0 \left(1 + \frac{r}{n}\right)^{nt} = \lim_{n \to \infty} A_0 \left[\left(1 + \frac{r}{n}\right)^{n/r}\right]^{rt}$$

$$= A_0 \left[\lim_{n \to \infty} \left(1 + \frac{r}{n}\right)^{n/r}\right]^{rt}$$

$$= A_0 \left[\lim_{m \to \infty} \left(1 + \frac{1}{m}\right)^{m}\right]^{rt} \qquad \text{(where } m = n/r\text{)}$$

▪ Recall: $e = \lim\limits_{x \to 0} (1 + x)^{1/x}$

If we put $n = 1/x$, then $n \to \infty$ as $x \to 0^+$ and so an alternative expression for e is

$$e = \lim_{n \to \infty} \left(1 + \frac{1}{n}\right)^{n}$$

But the limit in this expression is equal to the number e. So with continuous compounding of interest at interest rate r, the amount after t years is

$$A(t) = A_0 e^{rt}$$

If we differentiate this equation, we get

$$\frac{dA}{dt} = rA_0 e^{rt} = rA(t)$$

which says that, with continuous compounding of interest, the rate of increase of an investment is proportional to its size.

Returning to the example of $1000 invested for 3 years at 6% interest, we see that with continuous compounding of interest the value of the investment will be

$$A(3) = \$1000 e^{(0.06)3} = \$1197.22$$

Notice how close this is to the amount we calculated for daily compounding, $1197.20. But the amount is easier to compute if we use continuous compounding. ▪

3.4 | **EXERCISES**

1. A population of protozoa develops with a constant relative growth rate of 0.7944 per member per day. On day zero the population consists of two members. Find the population size after six days.

2. A common inhabitant of human intestines is the bacterium *Escherichia coli*. A cell of this bacterium in a nutrient-broth medium divides into two cells every 20 minutes. The initial population of a culture is 60 cells.
   (a) Find the relative growth rate.
   (b) Find an expression for the number of cells after t hours.
   (c) Find the number of cells after 8 hours.
   (d) Find the rate of growth after 8 hours.
   (e) When will the population reach 20,000 cells?

3. A bacteria culture initially contains 100 cells and grows at a rate proportional to its size. After an hour the population has increased to 420.
   (a) Find an expression for the number of bacteria after t hours.
   (b) Find the number of bacteria after 3 hours.
   (c) Find the rate of growth after 3 hours.
   (d) When will the population reach 10,000?

4. A bacteria culture grows with constant relative growth rate. After 2 hours there are 600 bacteria and after 8 hours the count is 75,000.
   (a) Find the initial population.
   (b) Find an expression for the population after t hours.

(c) Find the number of cells after 5 hours.

(d) Find the rate of growth after 5 hours.

(e) When will the population reach 200,000?

5. The table gives estimates of the world population, in millions, from 1750 to 2000:

Year	Population	Year	Population
1750	790	1900	1650
1800	980	1950	2560
1850	1260	2000	6080

(a) Use the exponential model and the population figures for 1750 and 1800 to predict the world population in 1900 and 1950. Compare with the actual figures.

(b) Use the exponential model and the population figures for 1850 and 1900 to predict the world population in 1950. Compare with the actual population.

(c) Use the exponential model and the population figures for 1900 and 1950 to predict the world population in 2000. Compare with the actual population and try to explain the discrepancy.

6. The table gives the population of the United States, from census figures in millions, for the years 1900–2000.

Year	Population	Year	Population
1900	76	1960	179
1910	92	1970	203
1920	106	1980	227
1930	123	1990	250
1940	131	2000	275
1950	150		

(a) Use the exponential model and the census figures for 1900 and 1910 to predict the population in 2000. Compare with the actual figure and try to explain the discrepancy.

(b) Use the exponential model and the census figures for 1980 and 1990 to predict the population in 2000. Compare with the actual population. Then use this model to predict the population in the years 2010 and 2020.

 (c) Graph both of the exponential functions in parts (a) and (b) together with a plot of the actual population. Are these models reasonable ones?

7. Experiments show that if the chemical reaction

$$N_2O_5 \rightarrow 2NO_2 + \tfrac{1}{2}O_2$$

takes place at 45°C, the rate of reaction of dinitrogen pentoxide is proportional to its concentration as follows:

$$-\frac{d[N_2O_5]}{dt} = 0.0005[N_2O_5]$$

(a) Find an expression for the concentration $[N_2O_5]$ after t seconds if the initial concentration is C.

(b) How long will the reaction take to reduce the concentration of N_2O_5 to 90% of its original value?

8. Bismuth-210 has a half-life of 5.0 days.

(a) A sample originally has a mass of 800 mg. Find a formula for the mass remaining after t days.

(b) Find the mass remaining after 30 days.

(c) When is the mass reduced to 1 mg?

(d) Sketch the graph of the mass function.

9. The half-life of cesium-137 is 30 years. Suppose we have a 100-mg sample.

(a) Find the mass that remains after t years.

(b) How much of the sample remains after 100 years?

(c) After how long will only 1 mg remain?

10. A sample of tritium-3 decayed to 94.5% of its original amount after a year.

(a) What is the half-life of tritium-3?

(b) How long would it take the sample to decay to 20% of its original amount?

11. Scientists can determine the age of ancient objects by a method called *radiocarbon dating*. The bombardment of the upper atmosphere by cosmic rays converts nitrogen to a radioactive isotope of carbon, ^{14}C, with a half-life of about 5730 years. Vegetation absorbs carbon dioxide through the atmosphere and animal life assimilates ^{14}C through food chains. When a plant or animal dies, it stops replacing its carbon and the amount of ^{14}C begins to decrease through radioactive decay. Therefore, the level of radioactivity must also decay exponentially. A parchment fragment was discovered that had about 74% as much ^{14}C radioactivity as does plant material on Earth today. Estimate the age of the parchment.

12. A curve passes through the point $(0, 5)$ and has the property that the slope of the curve at every point P is twice the y-coordinate of P. What is the equation of the curve?

13. A roast turkey is taken from an oven when its temperature has reached 185°F and is placed on a table in a room where the temperature is 75°F.

(a) If the temperature of the turkey is 150°F after half an hour, what is the temperature after 45 minutes?

(b) When will the turkey have cooled to 100°F?

14. A thermometer is taken from a room where the temperature is 20°C to the outdoors, where the temperature is 5°C. After one minute the thermometer reads 12°C.

(a) What will the reading on the thermometer be after one more minute?

(b) When will the thermometer read 6°C?

15. When a cold drink is taken from a refrigerator, its temperature is 5°C. After 25 minutes in a 20°C room its temperature has increased to 10°C.

(a) What is the temperature of the drink after 50 minutes?

(b) When will its temperature be 15°C?

16. A freshly brewed cup of coffee has temperature 95°C in a 20°C room. When its temperature is 70°C, it is cooling at a rate of 1°C per minute. When does this occur?

17. The rate of change of atmospheric pressure P with respect to altitude h is proportional to P, provided that the temperature is constant. At 15°C the pressure is 101.3 kPa at sea level and 87.14 kPa at $h = 1000$ m.
(a) What is the pressure at an altitude of 3000 m?
(b) What is the pressure at the top of Mount McKinley, at an altitude of 6187 m?

18. (a) If $500 is borrowed at 14% interest, find the amounts due at the end of 2 years if the interest is compounded (i) annually, (ii) quarterly, (iii) monthly, (iv) daily, (v) hourly, and (vi) continuously.
(b) Suppose $500 is borrowed and the interest is compounded continuously. If $A(t)$ is the amount due after t years, where $0 \leq t \leq 2$, graph $A(t)$ for each of the interest rates 14%, 10%, and 6% on a common screen.

19. If $3000 is invested at 5% interest, find the value of the investment at the end of 5 years if the interest is compounded
(a) annually (b) semiannually
(c) monthly (d) weekly
(e) daily (f) continuously

20. (a) How long will it take an investment to double in value if the interest rate is 6% compounded continuously?
(b) What is the equivalent annual interest rate?

3.5 INVERSE TRIGONOMETRIC FUNCTIONS

In this section we apply the ideas of Section 3.2 to find the derivatives of the so-called inverse trigonometric functions. We have a slight difficulty in this task: Because the trigonometric functions are not one-to-one, they do not have inverse functions. The difficulty is overcome by restricting the domains of these functions so that they become one-to-one.

You can see from Figure 1 that the sine function $y = \sin x$ is not one-to-one (use the Horizontal Line Test). But the function $f(x) = \sin x$, $-\pi/2 \leq x \leq \pi/2$ (see Figure 2), *is* one-to-one. The inverse function of this restricted sine function f exists and is denoted by $\sin^{-1}$ or arcsin. It is called the **inverse sine function** or the **arcsine function**.

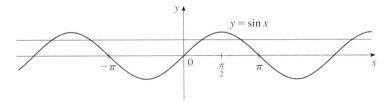

FIGURE 1

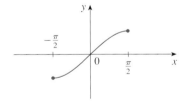

FIGURE 2 $y = \sin x, -\frac{\pi}{2} \leq x \leq \frac{\pi}{2}$

Since the definition of an inverse function says that

$$f^{-1}(x) = y \iff f(y) = x$$

we have

1 $\qquad \sin^{-1}x = y \iff \sin y = x \quad \text{and} \quad -\frac{\pi}{2} \leq y \leq \frac{\pi}{2}$

⊘ $\sin^{-1}x \neq \dfrac{1}{\sin x}$

Thus if $-1 \leq x \leq 1$, $\sin^{-1}x$ is the number between $-\pi/2$ and $\pi/2$ whose sine is x.

EXAMPLE I Evaluate (a) $\sin^{-1}\left(\frac{1}{2}\right)$ and (b) $\tan\left(\arcsin\frac{1}{3}\right)$.

SOLUTION

(a) We have

$$\sin^{-1}\left(\tfrac{1}{2}\right) = \frac{\pi}{6}$$

because $\sin(\pi/6) = \frac{1}{2}$ and $\pi/6$ lies between $-\pi/2$ and $\pi/2$.

(b) Let $\theta = \arcsin\frac{1}{3}$, so $\sin\theta = \frac{1}{3}$. Then we can draw a right triangle with angle θ as in Figure 3 and deduce from the Pythagorean Theorem that the third side has length $\sqrt{9 - 1} = 2\sqrt{2}$. This enables us to read from the triangle that

$$\tan\left(\arcsin\tfrac{1}{3}\right) = \tan\theta = \frac{1}{2\sqrt{2}}$$

■

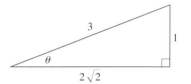

FIGURE 3

The cancellation equations for inverse functions become, in this case,

2

$$\sin^{-1}(\sin x) = x \quad \text{for} \ -\frac{\pi}{2} \leqslant x \leqslant \frac{\pi}{2}$$

$$\sin(\sin^{-1}x) = x \quad \text{for} \ -1 \leqslant x \leqslant 1$$

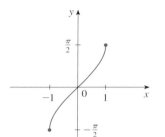

FIGURE 4 $y = \sin^{-1}x = \arcsin x$

The inverse sine function, $\sin^{-1}$, has domain $[-1, 1]$ and range $[-\pi/2, \pi/2]$, and its graph, shown in Figure 4, is obtained from that of the restricted sine function (Figure 2) by reflection about the line $y = x$.

We know that the sine function f is continuous, so the inverse sine function is also continuous. We also know from Section 2.3 that the sine function is differentiable, so the inverse sine function is also differentiable. We could calculate the derivative of $\sin^{-1}$ by the formula in Theorem 3.2.7, but since we know that $\sin^{-1}$ is differentiable, we can just as easily calculate it by implicit differentiation as follows.

Let $y = \sin^{-1}x$. Then $\sin y = x$ and $-\pi/2 \leqslant y \leqslant \pi/2$. Differentiating $\sin y = x$ implicitly with respect to x, we obtain

$$\cos y \, \frac{dy}{dx} = 1$$

and

$$\frac{dy}{dx} = \frac{1}{\cos y}$$

Now $\cos y \geqslant 0$ since $-\pi/2 \leqslant y \leqslant \pi/2$, so

$$\cos y = \sqrt{1 - \sin^2 y} = \sqrt{1 - x^2}$$

Therefore

$$\frac{dy}{dx} = \frac{1}{\cos y} = \frac{1}{\sqrt{1 - x^2}}$$

3

$$\frac{d}{dx}(\sin^{-1}x) = \frac{1}{\sqrt{1 - x^2}} \qquad -1 < x < 1$$

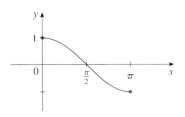

FIGURE 5

▪ The graphs of the function f of Example 2 and its derivative are shown in Figure 5. Notice that f is not differentiable at 0 and this is consistent with the fact that the graph of f' makes a sudden jump at $x = 0$.

▼ EXAMPLE 2 If $f(x) = \sin^{-1}(x^2 - 1)$, find (a) the domain of f, (b) $f'(x)$, and (c) the domain of f'.

SOLUTION

(a) Since the domain of the inverse sine function is $[-1, 1]$, the domain of f is

$$\{x \mid -1 \leqslant x^2 - 1 \leqslant 1\} = \{x \mid 0 \leqslant x^2 \leqslant 2\}$$
$$= \{x \mid |x| \leqslant \sqrt{2}\} = [-\sqrt{2}, \sqrt{2}\,]$$

(b) Combining Formula 3 with the Chain Rule, we have

$$f'(x) = \frac{1}{\sqrt{1 - (x^2 - 1)^2}} \frac{d}{dx}(x^2 - 1)$$
$$= \frac{1}{\sqrt{1 - (x^4 - 2x^2 + 1)}}\, 2x = \frac{2x}{\sqrt{2x^2 - x^4}}$$

(c) The domain of f' is

$$\{x \mid -1 < x^2 - 1 < 1\} = \{x \mid 0 < x^2 < 2\}$$
$$= \{x \mid 0 < |x| < \sqrt{2}\} = (-\sqrt{2}, 0) \cup (0, \sqrt{2}) \quad ■$$

The **inverse cosine function** is handled similarly. The restricted cosine function $f(x) = \cos x$, $0 \leqslant x \leqslant \pi$, is one-to-one (see Figure 6) and so it has an inverse function denoted by $\cos^{-1}$ or arccos.

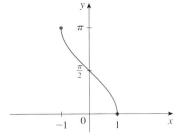

FIGURE 6 $y = \cos x, 0 \leqslant x \leqslant \pi$

4
$$\cos^{-1}x = y \quad \Longleftrightarrow \quad \cos y = x \quad \text{and} \quad 0 \leqslant y \leqslant \pi$$

The cancellation equations are

5
$$\cos^{-1}(\cos x) = x \quad \text{for } 0 \leqslant x \leqslant \pi$$
$$\cos(\cos^{-1}x) = x \quad \text{for } -1 \leqslant x \leqslant 1$$

The inverse cosine function, $\cos^{-1}$, has domain $[-1, 1]$ and range $[0, \pi]$ and is a continuous function whose graph is shown in Figure 7. Its derivative is given by

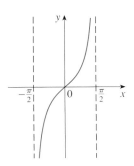

FIGURE 7 $y = \cos^{-1}x = \arccos x$

6
$$\frac{d}{dx}(\cos^{-1}x) = -\frac{1}{\sqrt{1 - x^2}} \qquad -1 < x < 1$$

Formula 6 can be proved by the same method as for Formula 3 and is left as Exercise 11.

The tangent function can be made one-to-one by restricting it to the interval $(-\pi/2, \pi/2)$. Thus the **inverse tangent function** is defined as the inverse of the function $f(x) = \tan x$, $-\pi/2 < x < \pi/2$. (See Figure 8.) It is denoted by $\tan^{-1}$ or arctan.

FIGURE 8

$y = \tan x, -\frac{\pi}{2} < x < \frac{\pi}{2}$

7
$$\tan^{-1}x = y \quad \Longleftrightarrow \quad \tan y = x \quad \text{and} \quad -\frac{\pi}{2} < y < \frac{\pi}{2}$$

EXAMPLE 3 Simplify the expression $\cos(\tan^{-1}x)$.

SOLUTION 1 Let $y = \tan^{-1}x$. Then $\tan y = x$ and $-\pi/2 < y < \pi/2$. We want to find $\cos y$ but, since $\tan y$ is known, it's easier to find $\sec y$ first:

$$\sec^2 y = 1 + \tan^2 y = 1 + x^2$$

$$\sec y = \sqrt{1 + x^2} \qquad \text{(since } \sec y > 0 \text{ for } -\pi/2 < y < \pi/2\text{)}$$

Thus
$$\cos(\tan^{-1}x) = \cos y = \frac{1}{\sec y} = \frac{1}{\sqrt{1 + x^2}}$$

SOLUTION 2 Instead of using trigonometric identities as in Solution 1, it is perhaps easier to use a diagram. If $y = \tan^{-1}x$, then $\tan y = x$, and we can read from Figure 9 (which illustrates the case $y > 0$) that

$$\cos(\tan^{-1}x) = \cos y = \frac{1}{\sqrt{1 + x^2}}$$

∎

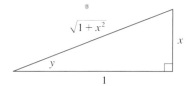

FIGURE 9

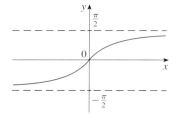

FIGURE 10
$y = \tan^{-1}x = \arctan x$

The inverse tangent function, $\tan^{-1} = \arctan$, has domain $\mathbb{R}$ and its range is $(-\pi/2, \pi/2)$. Its graph is shown in Figure 10.

We know that

$$\lim_{x \to (\pi/2)^-} \tan x = \infty \qquad \text{and} \qquad \lim_{x \to -(\pi/2)^+} \tan x = -\infty$$

and so the lines $x = \pm\pi/2$ are vertical asymptotes of the graph of tan. Since the graph of $\tan^{-1}$ is obtained by reflecting the graph of the restricted tangent function about the line $y = x$, it follows that the lines $y = \pi/2$ and $y = -\pi/2$ are horizontal asymptotes of the graph of $\tan^{-1}$. This fact is expressed by the following limits:

8
$$\lim_{x \to \infty} \tan^{-1}x = \frac{\pi}{2} \qquad \lim_{x \to -\infty} \tan^{-1}x = -\frac{\pi}{2}$$

EXAMPLE 4 Evaluate $\displaystyle\lim_{x \to 2^+} \arctan\left(\frac{1}{x - 2}\right)$.

SOLUTION Since
$$\frac{1}{x - 2} \to \infty \qquad \text{as } x \to 2^+$$

the first equation in (8) gives

$$\lim_{x \to 2^+} \arctan\left(\frac{1}{x - 2}\right) = \frac{\pi}{2}$$

∎

Since tan is differentiable, $\tan^{-1}$ is also differentiable. To find its derivative, let $y = \tan^{-1}x$. Then $\tan y = x$. Differentiating this last equation implicitly with respect to x, we have

$$\sec^2 y \frac{dy}{dx} = 1$$

and so
$$\frac{dy}{dx} = \frac{1}{\sec^2 y} = \frac{1}{1 + \tan^2 y} = \frac{1}{1 + x^2}$$

9
$$\frac{d}{dx}(\tan^{-1}x) = \frac{1}{1 + x^2}$$

The remaining inverse trigonometric functions are not used as frequently and are summarized here.

10
$$y = \csc^{-1}x \ (|x| \geq 1) \iff \csc y = x \quad \text{and} \quad y \in (0, \pi/2] \cup (\pi, 3\pi/2]$$

$$y = \sec^{-1}x \ (|x| \geq 1) \iff \sec y = x \quad \text{and} \quad y \in [0, \pi/2) \cup [\pi, 3\pi/2)$$

$$y = \cot^{-1}x \ (x \in \mathbb{R}) \iff \cot y = x \quad \text{and} \quad y \in (0, \pi)$$

The choice of intervals for y in the definitions of $\csc^{-1}$ and $\sec^{-1}$ is not universally agreed upon. For instance, some authors use $y \in [0, \pi/2) \cup (\pi/2, \pi]$ in the definition of $\sec^{-1}$. [You can see from the graph of the secant function in Figure 11 that both this choice and the one in (10) will work.] The reason for the choice in (10) is that the differentiation formulas are simpler (see Exercise 41).

We collect in Table 11 the differentiation formulas for all of the inverse trigonometric functions. The proofs of the formulas for the derivatives of $\csc^{-1}$, $\sec^{-1}$, and $\cot^{-1}$ are left as Exercises 13–15.

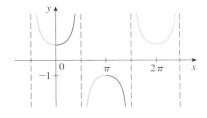

FIGURE 11
$y = \sec x$

11 TABLE OF DERIVATIVES OF INVERSE TRIGONOMETRIC FUNCTIONS

$$\frac{d}{dx}(\sin^{-1}x) = \frac{1}{\sqrt{1 - x^2}} \qquad \frac{d}{dx}(\csc^{-1}x) = -\frac{1}{x\sqrt{x^2 - 1}}$$

$$\frac{d}{dx}(\cos^{-1}x) = -\frac{1}{\sqrt{1 - x^2}} \qquad \frac{d}{dx}(\sec^{-1}x) = \frac{1}{x\sqrt{x^2 - 1}}$$

$$\frac{d}{dx}(\tan^{-1}x) = \frac{1}{1 + x^2} \qquad \frac{d}{dx}(\cot^{-1}x) = -\frac{1}{1 + x^2}$$

Each of these formulas can be combined with the Chain Rule. For instance, if u is a differentiable function of x, then

$$\frac{d}{dx}(\sin^{-1}u) = \frac{1}{\sqrt{1 - u^2}}\frac{du}{dx} \qquad \text{and} \qquad \frac{d}{dx}(\tan^{-1}u) = \frac{1}{1 + u^2}\frac{du}{dx}$$

EXAMPLE 5 Differentiate $f(x) = x\tan^{-1}\sqrt{x}$.

SOLUTION

$$f'(x) = x\frac{1}{1 + (\sqrt{x})^2}\frac{1}{2}x^{-1/2} + \tan^{-1}\sqrt{x} = \frac{\sqrt{x}}{2(1 + x)} + \tan^{-1}\sqrt{x} \qquad \blacksquare$$

| 3.5 | **EXERCISES** |

1–6 ▪ Find the exact value of each expression.

1. (a) $\sin^{-1}(\sqrt{3}/2)$ (b) $\cos^{-1}(-1)$

2. (a) $\arctan(-1)$ (b) $\csc^{-1} 2$

3. (a) $\tan^{-1}\sqrt{3}$ (b) $\arcsin(-1/\sqrt{2})$

4. (a) $\sec^{-1}\sqrt{2}$ (b) $\arcsin 1$

5. (a) $\sin(\sin^{-1}(0.7))$ (b) $\tan^{-1}\left(\tan\dfrac{4\pi}{3}\right)$

6. (a) $\sec(\arctan 2)$ (b) $\cos\left(2\sin^{-1}\left(\frac{5}{13}\right)\right)$

7. Prove that $\cos(\sin^{-1}x) = \sqrt{1 - x^2}$.

8–10 ▪ Simplify the expression.

8. $\tan(\sin^{-1}x)$

9. $\sin(\tan^{-1}x)$ **10.** $\csc(\arctan 2x)$

11. Prove Formula 6 for the derivative of $\cos^{-1}$ by the same method as for Formula 3.

12. (a) Prove that $\sin^{-1}x + \cos^{-1}x = \pi/2$.
(b) Use part (a) to prove Formula 6.

13. Prove that $\dfrac{d}{dx}(\cot^{-1}x) = -\dfrac{1}{1 + x^2}$.

14. Prove that $\dfrac{d}{dx}(\sec^{-1}x) = \dfrac{1}{x\sqrt{x^2 - 1}}$.

15. Prove that $\dfrac{d}{dx}(\csc^{-1}x) = -\dfrac{1}{x\sqrt{x^2 - 1}}$.

16–29 ▪ Find the derivative of the function. Simplify where possible.

16. $y = \sqrt{\tan^{-1}x}$

17. $y = \tan^{-1}\sqrt{x}$ **18.** $h(x) = \sqrt{1 - x^2}\arcsin x$

19. $y = \sin^{-1}(2x + 1)$ **20.** $f(x) = x\ln(\arctan x)$

21. $H(x) = (1 + x^2)\arctan x$

22. $h(t) = e^{\sec^{-1}t}$

23. $y = \cos^{-1}(e^{2x})$

24. $y = x\cos^{-1}x - \sqrt{1 - x^2}$

25. $y = \arctan(\cos\theta)$

26. $y = \tan^{-1}(x - \sqrt{1 + x^2})$

27. $h(t) = \cot^{-1}(t) + \cot^{-1}(1/t)$

28. $y = \tan^{-1}\left(\dfrac{x}{a}\right) + \ln\sqrt{\dfrac{x - a}{x + a}}$

29. $y = \arccos\left(\dfrac{b + a\cos x}{a + b\cos x}\right), \quad 0 \leqslant x \leqslant \pi, \ a > b > 0$

30–31 ▪ Find the derivative of the function. Find the domains of the function and its derivative.

30. $f(x) = \arcsin(e^x)$ **31.** $g(x) = \cos^{-1}(3 - 2x)$

32. Find y' if $\tan^{-1}(xy) = 1 + x^2y$.

33. If $g(x) = x\sin^{-1}(x/4) + \sqrt{16 - x^2}$, find $g'(2)$.

34. Find an equation of the tangent line to the curve $y = 3\arccos(x/2)$ at the point $(1, \pi)$.

35–38 ▪ Find the limit.

35. $\lim\limits_{x \to -1^+} \sin^{-1}x$ **36.** $\lim\limits_{x \to \infty} \arccos\left(\dfrac{1 + x^2}{1 + 2x^2}\right)$

37. $\lim\limits_{x \to \infty} \arctan(e^x)$ **38.** $\lim\limits_{x \to 0^+} \tan^{-1}(\ln x)$

39. A ladder 10 ft long leans against a vertical wall. If the bottom of the ladder slides away from the base of the wall at a speed of 2 ft/s, how fast is the angle between the ladder and the wall changing when the bottom of the ladder is 6 ft from the base of the wall?

40. A lighthouse is located on a small island, 3 km away from the nearest point P on a straight shoreline, and its light makes four revolutions per minute. How fast is the beam of light moving along the shoreline when it is 1 km from P?

41. Some authors define $y = \sec^{-1}x \iff \sec y = x$ and $y \in [0, \pi/2) \cup (\pi/2, \pi]$. Show that with this definition, we have (instead of the formula given in Exercise 14)

$$\frac{d}{dx}(\sec^{-1}x) = \frac{1}{|x|\sqrt{x^2 - 1}} \qquad |x| > 1$$

42. (a) Sketch the graph of the function $f(x) = \sin(\sin^{-1}x)$.
(b) Sketch the graph of the function $g(x) = \sin^{-1}(\sin x)$, $x \in \mathbb{R}$.
(c) Show that $g'(x) = \dfrac{\cos x}{|\cos x|}$.
(d) Sketch the graph of $h(x) = \cos^{-1}(\sin x)$, $x \in \mathbb{R}$, and find its derivative.

3.6 | HYPERBOLIC FUNCTIONS

Certain combinations of the exponential functions e^x and e^{-x} arise so frequently in mathematics and its applications that they deserve to be given special names. In many ways they are analogous to the trigonometric functions, and they have the same relationship to the hyperbola that the trigonometric functions have to the circle. For this reason they are collectively called **hyperbolic functions** and individually called **hyperbolic sine**, **hyperbolic cosine**, and so on.

DEFINITION OF THE HYPERBOLIC FUNCTIONS

$$\sinh x = \frac{e^x - e^{-x}}{2} \qquad\qquad \operatorname{csch} x = \frac{1}{\sinh x}$$

$$\cosh x = \frac{e^x + e^{-x}}{2} \qquad\qquad \operatorname{sech} x = \frac{1}{\cosh x}$$

$$\tanh x = \frac{\sinh x}{\cosh x} \qquad\qquad \coth x = \frac{\cosh x}{\sinh x}$$

The graphs of hyperbolic sine and cosine can be sketched using graphical addition as in Figures 1 and 2.

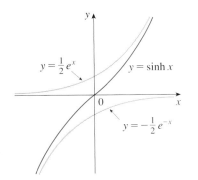

FIGURE 1
$y = \sinh x = \frac{1}{2}e^x - \frac{1}{2}e^{-x}$

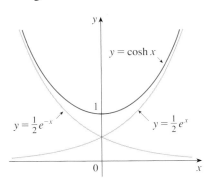

FIGURE 2
$y = \cosh x = \frac{1}{2}e^x + \frac{1}{2}e^{-x}$

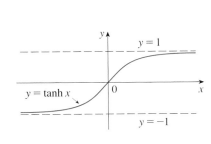

FIGURE 3

Note that sinh has domain $\mathbb{R}$ and range $\mathbb{R}$, while cosh has domain $\mathbb{R}$ and range $[1, \infty)$. The graph of tanh is shown in Figure 3. It has the horizontal asymptotes $y = \pm 1$. (See Exercise 19.)

Applications of hyperbolic functions to science and engineering occur whenever an entity such as light, velocity, electricity, or radioactivity is gradually absorbed or extinguished, for the decay can be represented by hyperbolic functions. The most famous application is the use of hyperbolic cosine to describe the shape of a hanging wire. It can be proved that if a heavy flexible cable (such as a telephone or power line) is suspended between two points at the same height, then it takes the shape of a curve with equation $y = c + a \cosh(x/a)$ called a *catenary* (see Figure 4). (The Latin word *catena* means "chain.")

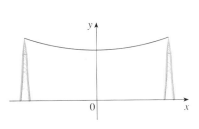

FIGURE 4
A catenary $y = c + a \cosh(x/a)$

The hyperbolic functions satisfy a number of identities that are similar to well-known trigonometric identities. We list some of them here and leave most of the proofs to the exercises.

HYPERBOLIC IDENTITIES

$$\sinh(-x) = -\sinh x \qquad\qquad \cosh(-x) = \cosh x$$

$$\cosh^2 x - \sinh^2 x = 1 \qquad\qquad 1 - \tanh^2 x = \operatorname{sech}^2 x$$

$$\sinh(x + y) = \sinh x \cosh y + \cosh x \sinh y$$

$$\cosh(x + y) = \cosh x \cosh y + \sinh x \sinh y$$

☑ EXAMPLE 1 Prove (a) $\cosh^2 x - \sinh^2 x = 1$ and (b) $1 - \tanh^2 x = \operatorname{sech}^2 x$.

SOLUTION

(a)
$$\cosh^2 x - \sinh^2 x = \left(\frac{e^x + e^{-x}}{2}\right)^2 - \left(\frac{e^x - e^{-x}}{2}\right)^2$$

$$= \frac{e^{2x} + 2 + e^{-2x}}{4} - \frac{e^{2x} - 2 + e^{-2x}}{4}$$

$$= \tfrac{4}{4} = 1$$

(b) We start with the identity proved in part (a):

$$\cosh^2 x - \sinh^2 x = 1$$

If we divide both sides by $\cosh^2 x$, we get

$$1 - \frac{\sinh^2 x}{\cosh^2 x} = \frac{1}{\cosh^2 x}$$

or
$$1 - \tanh^2 x = \operatorname{sech}^2 x \qquad\blacksquare$$

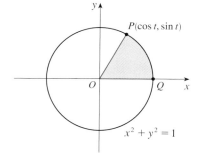

FIGURE 5

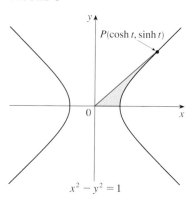

FIGURE 6

The identity proved in Example 1(a) gives a clue to the reason for the name "hyperbolic" functions:

If t is any real number, the point $P(\cos t, \sin t)$ lies on the unit circle $x^2 + y^2 = 1$ because $\cos^2 t + \sin^2 t = 1$. In fact, t can be interpreted as the radian measure of $\angle POQ$ in Figure 5. For this reason the trigonometric functions are sometimes called *circular* functions.

Likewise, if t is any real number, then the point $P(\cosh t, \sinh t)$ lies on the right branch of the hyperbola $x^2 - y^2 = 1$ because $\cosh^2 t - \sinh^2 t = 1$ and $\cosh t \geqslant 1$. This time, t does not represent the measure of an angle. However, it turns out that t represents twice the area of the shaded hyperbolic sector in Figure 6, just as in the trigonometric case t represents twice the area of the shaded circular sector in Figure 5.

The derivatives of the hyperbolic functions are easily computed. For example,

$$\frac{d}{dx}(\sinh x) = \frac{d}{dx}\left(\frac{e^x - e^{-x}}{2}\right) = \frac{e^x + e^{-x}}{2} = \cosh x$$

We list the differentiation formulas for the hyperbolic functions as Table 1. The remaining proofs are left as exercises. Note the analogy with the differentiation formulas for trigonometric functions, but beware that the signs are different in some cases.

---

1 **DERIVATIVES OF HYPERBOLIC FUNCTIONS**

$$\frac{d}{dx}(\sinh x) = \cosh x \qquad \frac{d}{dx}(\operatorname{csch} x) = -\operatorname{csch} x \coth x$$

$$\frac{d}{dx}(\cosh x) = \sinh x \qquad \frac{d}{dx}(\operatorname{sech} x) = -\operatorname{sech} x \tanh x$$

$$\frac{d}{dx}(\tanh x) = \operatorname{sech}^2 x \qquad \frac{d}{dx}(\coth x) = -\operatorname{csch}^2 x$$

▼ EXAMPLE 2 Any of these differentiation rules can be combined with the Chain Rule. For instance,

$$\frac{d}{dx}\left(\cosh \sqrt{x}\right) = \sinh \sqrt{x} \cdot \frac{d}{dx}\sqrt{x} = \frac{\sinh \sqrt{x}}{2\sqrt{x}}$$ ∎

INVERSE HYPERBOLIC FUNCTIONS

You can see from Figures 1 and 3 that sinh and tanh are one-to-one functions and so they have inverse functions denoted by $\sinh^{-1}$ and $\tanh^{-1}$. Figure 2 shows that cosh is not one-to-one, but when restricted to the domain $[0, \infty)$ it becomes one-to-one. The inverse hyperbolic cosine function is defined as the inverse of this restricted function.

2

$$y = \sinh^{-1}x \iff \sinh y = x$$

$$y = \cosh^{-1}x \iff \cosh y = x \quad \text{and} \quad y \geqslant 0$$

$$y = \tanh^{-1}x \iff \tanh y = x$$

The remaining inverse hyperbolic functions are defined similarly (see Exercise 24).

We can sketch the graphs of $\sinh^{-1}$, $\cosh^{-1}$, and $\tanh^{-1}$ in Figures 7, 8, and 9 by using Figures 1, 2, and 3.

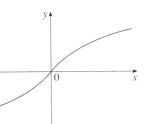

FIGURE 7
$y = \sinh^{-1}x$
domain $= \mathbb{R}$ range $= \mathbb{R}$

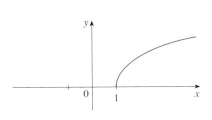

FIGURE 8
$y = \cosh^{-1}x$
domain $= [1, \infty)$ range $= [0, \infty)$

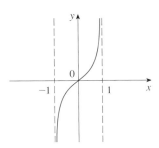

FIGURE 9
$y = \tanh^{-1}x$
domain $= (-1, 1)$ range $= \mathbb{R}$

Since the hyperbolic functions are defined in terms of exponential functions, it's not surprising to learn that the inverse hyperbolic functions can be expressed in terms of logarithms. In particular, we have:

3 $$\sinh^{-1}x = \ln\left(x + \sqrt{x^2 + 1}\right) \qquad x \in \mathbb{R}$$

4 $$\cosh^{-1}x = \ln\left(x + \sqrt{x^2 - 1}\right) \qquad x \geqslant 1$$

5 $$\tanh^{-1}x = \tfrac{1}{2}\ln\left(\frac{1 + x}{1 - x}\right) \qquad -1 < x < 1$$

▪ Formula 3 is proved in Example 3. The proofs of Formulas 4 and 5 are requested in Exercises 22 and 23.

EXAMPLE 3 Show that $\sinh^{-1}x = \ln\left(x + \sqrt{x^2 + 1}\right)$.

SOLUTION Let $y = \sinh^{-1}x$. Then

$$x = \sinh y = \frac{e^y - e^{-y}}{2}$$

so

$$e^y - 2x - e^{-y} = 0$$

or, multiplying by e^y,

$$e^{2y} - 2xe^y - 1 = 0$$

This is really a quadratic equation in e^y:

$$(e^y)^2 - 2x(e^y) - 1 = 0$$

Solving by the quadratic formula, we get

$$e^y = \frac{2x \pm \sqrt{4x^2 + 4}}{2} = x \pm \sqrt{x^2 + 1}$$

Note that $e^y > 0$, but $x - \sqrt{x^2 + 1} < 0$ $\left(\text{because } x < \sqrt{x^2 + 1}\right)$. Thus the minus sign is inadmissible and we have

$$e^y = x + \sqrt{x^2 + 1}$$

Therefore

$$y = \ln(e^y) = \ln\left(x + \sqrt{x^2 + 1}\right)$$

(See Exercise 21 for another method.) ▪

6 DERIVATIVES OF INVERSE HYPERBOLIC FUNCTIONS

$$\frac{d}{dx}\left(\sinh^{-1}x\right) = \frac{1}{\sqrt{1 + x^2}} \qquad\qquad \frac{d}{dx}\left(\operatorname{csch}^{-1}x\right) = -\frac{1}{|x|\sqrt{x^2 + 1}}$$

$$\frac{d}{dx}\left(\cosh^{-1}x\right) = \frac{1}{\sqrt{x^2 - 1}} \qquad\qquad \frac{d}{dx}\left(\operatorname{sech}^{-1}x\right) = -\frac{1}{x\sqrt{1 - x^2}}$$

$$\frac{d}{dx}\left(\tanh^{-1}x\right) = \frac{1}{1 - x^2} \qquad\qquad \frac{d}{dx}\left(\coth^{-1}x\right) = \frac{1}{1 - x^2}$$

▪ Notice that the formulas for the derivatives of $\tanh^{-1}x$ and $\coth^{-1}x$ appear to be identical. But the domains of these functions have no numbers in common: $\tanh^{-1}x$ is defined for $|x| < 1$, whereas $\coth^{-1}x$ is defined for $|x| > 1$.

The inverse hyperbolic functions are all differentiable because the hyperbolic functions are differentiable. The formulas in Table 6 can be proved either by the method for inverse functions or by differentiating Formulas 3, 4, and 5.

▼ **EXAMPLE 4** Prove that $\dfrac{d}{dx}(\sinh^{-1}x) = \dfrac{1}{\sqrt{1+x^2}}$.

SOLUTION Let $y = \sinh^{-1}x$. Then $\sinh y = x$. If we differentiate this equation implicitly with respect to x, we get

$$\cosh y \, \frac{dy}{dx} = 1$$

▪ Another method for solving Example 4 is to differentiate Formula 3.

Since $\cosh^2 y - \sinh^2 y = 1$ and $\cosh y \geq 0$, we have $\cosh y = \sqrt{1 + \sinh^2 y}$, so

$$\frac{dy}{dx} = \frac{1}{\cosh y} = \frac{1}{\sqrt{1 + \sinh^2 y}} = \frac{1}{\sqrt{1+x^2}}$$

■

▼ **EXAMPLE 5** Find $\dfrac{d}{dx}[\tanh^{-1}(\sin x)]$.

SOLUTION Using Table 6 and the Chain Rule, we have

$$\frac{d}{dx}[\tanh^{-1}(\sin x)] = \frac{1}{1-(\sin x)^2}\frac{d}{dx}(\sin x)$$

$$= \frac{1}{1-\sin^2 x}\cos x = \frac{\cos x}{\cos^2 x} = \sec x$$

■

3.6 EXERCISES

1–6 ▪ Find the numerical value of each expression.

1. (a) $\sinh 0$ (b) $\cosh 0$

2. (a) $\tanh 0$ (b) $\tanh 1$

3. (a) $\sinh(\ln 2)$ (b) $\sinh 2$

4. (a) $\cosh 3$ (b) $\cosh(\ln 3)$

5. (a) $\operatorname{sech} 0$ (b) $\cosh^{-1}1$

6. (a) $\sinh 1$ (b) $\sinh^{-1}1$

7–15 ▪ Prove the identity.

7. $\sinh(-x) = -\sinh x$
(This shows that sinh is an odd function.)

8. $\cosh(-x) = \cosh x$
(This shows that cosh is an even function.)

9. $\cosh x + \sinh x = e^x$

10. $\cosh x - \sinh x = e^{-x}$

11. $\sinh(x+y) = \sinh x \cosh y + \cosh x \sinh y$

12. $\cosh(x+y) = \cosh x \cosh y + \sinh x \sinh y$

13. $\sinh 2x = 2 \sinh x \cosh x$

14. $\dfrac{1+\tanh x}{1-\tanh x} = e^{2x}$

15. $(\cosh x + \sinh x)^n = \cosh nx + \sinh nx$
(n any real number)

16. If $\sinh x = \tfrac{3}{4}$, find the values of the other hyperbolic functions at x.

17. If $\tanh x = \tfrac{4}{5}$, find the values of the other hyperbolic functions at x.

18. (a) Use the graphs of sinh, cosh, and tanh in Figures 1–3 to draw the graphs of csch, sech, and coth.
(b) Check the graphs that you sketched in part (a) by using a graphing device to produce them.

19. Use the definitions of the hyperbolic functions to find each of the following limits.

(a) $\lim\limits_{x \to \infty} \tanh x$ (b) $\lim\limits_{x \to -\infty} \tanh x$

(c) $\lim\limits_{x \to \infty} \sinh x$ (d) $\lim\limits_{x \to -\infty} \sinh x$

(e) $\lim\limits_{x \to \infty} \operatorname{sech} x$ (f) $\lim\limits_{x \to \infty} \coth x$

(g) $\lim\limits_{x \to 0^+} \coth x$ (h) $\lim\limits_{x \to 0^-} \coth x$

(i) $\lim\limits_{x \to -\infty} \operatorname{csch} x$

20. Prove the formulas given in Table 1 for the derivatives of the functions (a) cosh, (b) tanh, (c) csch, (d) sech, and (e) coth.

21. Give an alternative solution to Example 3 by letting $y = \sinh^{-1}x$ and then using Exercise 9 and Example 1(a) with x replaced by y.

22. Prove Equation 4.

23. Prove Formula 5 using (a) the method of Example 3 and (b) Exercise 14 with x replaced by y.

24. For each of the following functions (i) give a definition like those in (2), (ii) sketch the graph, and (iii) find a formula similar to Formula 3.

(a) csch^{-1} (b) sech^{-1} (c) $\coth^{-1}$

25. Prove the formulas given in Table 6 for the derivatives of the following functions.

(a) $\cosh^{-1}$ (b) $\tanh^{-1}$ (c) sech^{-1}

26–41 ■ Find the derivative.

26. $g(x) = \sinh^2 x$

27. $f(x) = x \cosh x$

28. $F(x) = \sinh x \tanh x$

29. $h(x) = \sinh(x^2)$

30. $f(t) = e^t \operatorname{sech} t$

31. $h(t) = \coth \sqrt{1 + t^2}$

32. $f(t) = \ln(\sinh t)$

33. $H(t) = \tanh(e^t)$

34. $y = \sinh(\cosh x)$

35. $y = e^{\cosh 3x}$

36. $y = x^2 \sinh^{-1}(2x)$

37. $y = \tanh^{-1}\sqrt{x}$

38. $y = x \tanh^{-1}x + \ln \sqrt{1 - x^2}$

39. $y = x \sinh^{-1}(x/3) - \sqrt{9 + x^2}$

40. $y = \operatorname{sech}^{-1}\sqrt{1 - x^2}, \quad x > 0$

41. $y = \coth^{-1}\sqrt{x^2 + 1}$

■   ■   ■   ■   ■   ■   ■   ■   ■   ■   ■   ■   ■   ■

42. A flexible cable always hangs in the shape of a catenary $y = c + a \cosh(x/a)$, where c and a are constants and $a > 0$ (see Figure 4 and Exercise 44). Graph several members of the family of functions $y = a \cosh(x/a)$. How does the graph change as a varies?

43. A telephone line hangs between two poles 14 m apart in the shape of the catenary $y = 20 \cosh(x/20) - 15$, where x and y are measured in meters.

(a) Find the slope of this curve where it meets the right pole.

(b) Find the angle θ between the line and the pole.

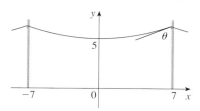

44. Using principles from physics it can be shown that when a cable is hung between two poles, it takes the shape of a curve $y = f(x)$ that satisfies the differential equation

$$\frac{d^2y}{dx^2} = \frac{\rho g}{T} \sqrt{1 + \left(\frac{dy}{dx}\right)^2}$$

where ρ is the linear density of the cable, g is the acceleration due to gravity, and T is the tension in the cable at its lowest point, and the coordinate system is chosen appropriately. Verify that the function

$$y = f(x) = \frac{T}{\rho g} \cosh\left(\frac{\rho g x}{T}\right)$$

is a solution of this differential equation.

45. (a) Show that any function of the form

$$y = A \sinh mx + B \cosh mx$$

satisfies the differential equation $y'' = m^2 y$.

(b) Find $y = y(x)$ such that $y'' = 9y$, $y(0) = -4$, and $y'(0) = 6$.

46. Evaluate $\lim\limits_{x \to \infty} \dfrac{\sinh x}{e^x}$.

47. At what point of the curve $y = \cosh x$ does the tangent have slope 1?

48. If $x = \ln(\sec \theta + \tan \theta)$, show that $\sec \theta = \cosh x$.

49. Show that if $a \neq 0$ and $b \neq 0$, then there exist numbers α and β such that $ae^x + be^{-x}$ equals either $\alpha \sinh(x + \beta)$ or $\alpha \cosh(x + \beta)$. In other words, almost every function of the form $f(x) = ae^x + be^{-x}$ is a shifted and stretched hyperbolic sine or cosine function.

3.7 | INDETERMINATE FORMS AND L'HOSPITAL'S RULE

Suppose we are trying to analyze the behavior of the function

$$F(x) = \frac{\ln x}{x - 1}$$

Although F is not defined when $x = 1$, we need to know how F behaves *near* 1. In particular, we would like to know the value of the limit

1
$$\lim_{x \to 1} \frac{\ln x}{x - 1}$$

In computing this limit we can't apply Law 5 of limits (the limit of a quotient is the quotient of the limits, see Section 1.4) because the limit of the denominator is 0. In fact, although the limit in (1) exists, its value is not obvious because both numerator and denominator approach 0 and $\frac{0}{0}$ is not defined.

In general, if we have a limit of the form

$$\lim_{x \to a} \frac{f(x)}{g(x)}$$

where both $f(x) \to 0$ and $g(x) \to 0$ as $x \to a$, then this limit may or may not exist and is called an **indeterminate form of type $\frac{0}{0}$**. We met some limits of this type in Chapter 1. For rational functions, we can cancel common factors:

$$\lim_{x \to 1} \frac{x^2 - x}{x^2 - 1} = \lim_{x \to 1} \frac{x(x - 1)}{(x + 1)(x - 1)} = \lim_{x \to 1} \frac{x}{x + 1} = \frac{1}{2}$$

We used a geometric argument to show that

$$\lim_{x \to 0} \frac{\sin x}{x} = 1$$

But these methods do not work for limits such as (1), so in this section we introduce a systematic method, known as *l'Hospital's Rule,* for the evaluation of indeterminate forms.

Another situation in which a limit is not obvious occurs when we look for a horizontal asymptote of F and need to evaluate the limit

2
$$\lim_{x \to \infty} \frac{\ln x}{x - 1}$$

It isn't obvious how to evaluate this limit because both numerator and denominator become large as $x \to \infty$. There is a struggle between numerator and denominator. If the numerator wins, the limit will be ∞; if the denominator wins, the answer will be 0. Or there may be some compromise, in which case the answer may be some finite positive number.

In general, if we have a limit of the form

$$\lim_{x \to a} \frac{f(x)}{g(x)}$$

where both $f(x) \to \infty$ (or $-\infty$) and $g(x) \to \infty$ (or $-\infty$), then the limit may or may not exist and is called an **indeterminate form of type** ∞/∞. We saw in Section 1.6 that this type of limit can be evaluated for certain functions, including rational functions, by dividing numerator and denominator by the highest power of x that occurs in the denominator. For instance,

$$\lim_{x \to \infty} \frac{x^2 - 1}{2x^2 + 1} = \lim_{x \to \infty} \frac{1 - \dfrac{1}{x^2}}{2 + \dfrac{1}{x^2}} = \frac{1 - 0}{2 + 0} = \frac{1}{2}$$

This method does not work for limits such as (2), but l'Hospital's Rule also applies to this type of indeterminate form.

■ L'Hospital's Rule is named after a French nobleman, the Marquis de l'Hospital (1661–1704), but was discovered by a Swiss mathematician, John Bernoulli (1667–1748). See Exercise 45 for the example that the Marquis used to illustrate his rule.

L'HOSPITAL'S RULE Suppose f and g are differentiable and $g'(x) \neq 0$ near a (except possibly at a). Suppose that

$$\lim_{x \to a} f(x) = 0 \qquad \text{and} \qquad \lim_{x \to a} g(x) = 0$$

or that

$$\lim_{x \to a} f(x) = \pm\infty \qquad \text{and} \qquad \lim_{x \to a} g(x) = \pm\infty$$

(In other words, we have an indeterminate form of type $\frac{0}{0}$ or ∞/∞.) Then

$$\lim_{x \to a} \frac{f(x)}{g(x)} = \lim_{x \to a} \frac{f'(x)}{g'(x)}$$

if the limit on the right side exists (or is ∞ or $-\infty$).

NOTE 1 L'Hospital's Rule says that the limit of a quotient of functions is equal to the limit of the quotient of their derivatives, provided that the given conditions are satisfied. It is especially important to verify the conditions regarding the limits of f and g before using l'Hospital's Rule.

NOTE 2 L'Hospital's Rule is also valid for one-sided limits and for limits at infinity or negative infinity; that is, "$x \to a$" can be replaced by any of the symbols $x \to a^+$, $x \to a^-$, $x \to \infty$, or $x \to -\infty$.

NOTE 3 For the special case in which $f(a) = g(a) = 0$, f' and g' are continuous, and $g'(a) \neq 0$, it is easy to see why l'Hospital's Rule is true. In fact, using the alternative form of the definition of a derivative, we have

FIGURE 1

■ Figure 1 suggests visually why l'Hospital's Rule might be true. The first graph shows two differentiable functions f and g, each of which approaches 0 as $x \to a$. If we were to zoom in toward the point $(a, 0)$, the graphs would start to look almost linear. But if the functions actually *were* linear, as in the second graph, then their ratio would be

$$\frac{m_1(x - a)}{m_2(x - a)} = \frac{m_1}{m_2}$$

which is the ratio of their derivatives. This suggests that

$$\lim_{x \to a} \frac{f(x)}{g(x)} = \lim_{x \to a} \frac{f'(x)}{g'(x)}$$

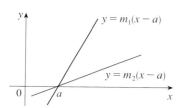

$$\lim_{x \to a} \frac{f'(x)}{g'(x)} = \frac{f'(a)}{g'(a)} = \frac{\displaystyle\lim_{x \to a} \frac{f(x) - f(a)}{x - a}}{\displaystyle\lim_{x \to a} \frac{g(x) - g(a)}{x - a}} = \lim_{x \to a} \frac{\dfrac{f(x) - f(a)}{x - a}}{\dfrac{g(x) - g(a)}{x - a}}$$

$$= \lim_{x \to a} \frac{f(x) - f(a)}{g(x) - g(a)} = \lim_{x \to a} \frac{f(x)}{g(x)}$$

The general version of l'Hospital's Rule is more difficult; its proof can be found in Appendix B.

V EXAMPLE 1 Find $\lim\limits_{x \to 1} \dfrac{\ln x}{x - 1}$.

SOLUTION Since

$$\lim_{x \to 1} \ln x = \ln 1 = 0 \qquad \text{and} \qquad \lim_{x \to 1} (x - 1) = 0$$

we can apply l'Hospital's Rule:

⊘ Notice that when using l'Hospital's Rule we differentiate the numerator and denominator *separately*. We do *not* use the Quotient Rule.

$$\lim_{x \to 1} \frac{\ln x}{x - 1} = \lim_{x \to 1} \frac{\dfrac{d}{dx}(\ln x)}{\dfrac{d}{dx}(x - 1)} = \lim_{x \to 1} \frac{1/x}{1} = \lim_{x \to 1} \frac{1}{x} = 1$$

■

V EXAMPLE 2 Calculate $\lim\limits_{x \to \infty} \dfrac{e^x}{x^2}$.

SOLUTION We have $\lim_{x \to \infty} e^x = \infty$ and $\lim_{x \to \infty} x^2 = \infty$, so l'Hospital's Rule gives

■ The graph of the function of Example 2 is shown in Figure 2. We have noticed previously that exponential functions grow far more rapidly than power functions, so the result of Example 2 is not unexpected. See also Exercise 39.

$$\lim_{x \to \infty} \frac{e^x}{x^2} = \lim_{x \to \infty} \frac{\dfrac{d}{dx}(e^x)}{\dfrac{d}{dx}(x^2)} = \lim_{x \to \infty} \frac{e^x}{2x}$$

Since $e^x \to \infty$ and $2x \to \infty$ as $x \to \infty$, the limit on the right side is also indeterminate, but a second application of l'Hospital's Rule gives

$$\lim_{x \to \infty} \frac{e^x}{x^2} = \lim_{x \to \infty} \frac{e^x}{2x} = \lim_{x \to \infty} \frac{e^x}{2} = \infty$$

■

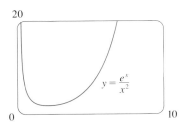

20

$y = \dfrac{e^x}{x^2}$

0   10

FIGURE 2

V EXAMPLE 3 Calculate $\lim\limits_{x \to \infty} \dfrac{\ln x}{\sqrt[3]{x}}$.

SOLUTION Since $\ln x \to \infty$ and $\sqrt[3]{x} \to \infty$ as $x \to \infty$, l'Hospital's Rule applies:

$$\lim_{x \to \infty} \frac{\ln x}{\sqrt[3]{x}} = \lim_{x \to \infty} \frac{1/x}{\frac{1}{3} x^{-2/3}}$$

■ The graph of the function of Example 3 is shown in Figure 3. We have discussed previously the slow growth of logarithms, so it isn't surprising that this ratio approaches 0 as $x \to \infty$. See also Exercise 40.

Notice that the limit on the right side is now an indeterminate of type $\frac{0}{0}$. But instead of applying l'Hospital's Rule a second time as we did in Example 2, we simplify the expression and see that a second application is unnecessary:

$$\lim_{x \to \infty} \frac{\ln x}{\sqrt[3]{x}} = \lim_{x \to \infty} \frac{1/x}{\frac{1}{3} x^{-2/3}} = \lim_{x \to \infty} \frac{3}{\sqrt[3]{x}} = 0$$

■

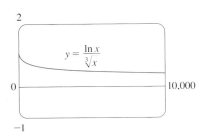

2

$y = \dfrac{\ln x}{\sqrt[3]{x}}$

0   10,000

−1

FIGURE 3

EXAMPLE 4 Find $\lim\limits_{x \to 0} \dfrac{\tan x - x}{x^3}$. [See Exercise 22 in Section 1.3]

SOLUTION Noting that both $\tan x - x \to 0$ and $x^3 \to 0$ as $x \to 0$, we use l'Hospital's Rule:

$$\lim_{x \to 0} \frac{\tan x - x}{x^3} = \lim_{x \to 0} \frac{\sec^2 x - 1}{3x^2}$$

■ The graph in Figure 4 gives visual confirmation of the result of Example 4. If we were to zoom in too far, however, we would get an inaccurate graph because $\tan x$ is close to x when x is small. See Exercise 22(d) in Section 1.3.

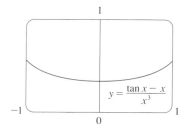

$$y = \frac{\tan x - x}{x^3}$$

FIGURE 4

Since the limit on the right side is still indeterminate of type $\frac{0}{0}$, we apply l'Hospital's Rule again:

$$\lim_{x \to 0} \frac{\sec^2 x - 1}{3x^2} = \lim_{x \to 0} \frac{2 \sec^2 x \tan x}{6x}$$

Because $\lim_{x \to 0} \sec^2 x = 1$, we simplify the calculation by writing

$$\lim_{x \to 0} \frac{2 \sec^2 x \tan x}{6x} = \frac{1}{3} \lim_{x \to 0} \sec^2 x \cdot \lim_{x \to 0} \frac{\tan x}{x} = \frac{1}{3} \lim_{x \to 0} \frac{\tan x}{x}$$

We can evaluate this last limit either by using l'Hospital's Rule a third time or by writing $\tan x$ as $(\sin x)/(\cos x)$ and making use of our knowledge of trigonometric limits. Putting together all the steps, we get

$$\lim_{x \to 0} \frac{\tan x - x}{x^3} = \lim_{x \to 0} \frac{\sec^2 x - 1}{3x^2} = \lim_{x \to 0} \frac{2 \sec^2 x \tan x}{6x}$$

$$= \frac{1}{3} \lim_{x \to 0} \frac{\tan x}{x} = \frac{1}{3} \lim_{x \to 0} \frac{\sec^2 x}{1} = \frac{1}{3}$$ ■

▼ EXAMPLE 5 Find $\lim_{x \to \pi^-} \dfrac{\sin x}{1 - \cos x}$.

SOLUTION If we blindly attempted to use l'Hospital's Rule, we would get

$$\lim_{x \to \pi^-} \frac{\sin x}{1 - \cos x} = \lim_{x \to \pi^-} \frac{\cos x}{\sin x} = -\infty$$

This is **wrong!** Although the numerator $\sin x \to 0$ as $x \to \pi^-$, notice that the denominator $(1 - \cos x)$ does not approach 0, so l'Hospital's Rule can't be applied here.

The required limit is, in fact, easy to find because the function is continuous at π and the denominator is nonzero there:

$$\lim_{x \to \pi^-} \frac{\sin x}{1 - \cos x} = \frac{\sin \pi}{1 - \cos \pi} = \frac{0}{1 - (-1)} = 0$$ ■

Example 5 shows what can go wrong if you use l'Hospital's Rule without thinking. Other limits *can* be found using l'Hospital's Rule but are more easily found by other methods. (See Examples 2 and 4 in Section 1.4, Example 5 in Section 1.6, and the discussion at the beginning of this section.) So when evaluating any limit, you should consider other methods before using l'Hospital's Rule.

INDETERMINATE PRODUCTS

If $\lim_{x \to a} f(x) = 0$ and $\lim_{x \to a} g(x) = \infty$ (or $-\infty$), then it isn't clear what the value of $\lim_{x \to a} f(x)g(x)$, if any, will be. There is a struggle between f and g. If f wins, the answer will be 0; if g wins, the answer will be ∞ (or $-\infty$). Or there may be a compromise where the answer is a finite nonzero number. This kind of limit is called an **indeterminate form of type $0 \cdot \infty$**. We can deal with it by writing the product fg as a quotient:

$$fg = \frac{f}{1/g} \qquad \text{or} \qquad fg = \frac{g}{1/f}$$

This converts the given limit into an indeterminate form of type $\frac{0}{0}$ or ∞/∞ so that we can use l'Hospital's Rule.

▼ EXAMPLE 6 Evaluate $\lim\limits_{x \to 0^+} x \ln x$.

SOLUTION The given limit is indeterminate because, as $x \to 0^+$, the first factor (x) approaches 0 while the second factor $(\ln x)$ approaches $-\infty$. Writing $x = 1/(1/x)$, we have $1/x \to \infty$ as $x \to 0^+$, so l'Hospital's Rule gives

$$\lim_{x \to 0^+} x \ln x = \lim_{x \to 0^+} \frac{\ln x}{1/x} = \lim_{x \to 0^+} \frac{1/x}{-1/x^2} = \lim_{x \to 0^+} (-x) = 0 \qquad ▪$$

NOTE In solving Example 6 another possible option would have been to write

$$\lim_{x \to 0^+} x \ln x = \lim_{x \to 0^+} \frac{x}{1/\ln x}$$

This gives an indeterminate form of the type $0/0$, but if we apply l'Hospital's Rule we get a more complicated expression than the one we started with. In general, when we rewrite an indeterminate product, we try to choose the option that leads to the simpler limit.

■ Figure 5 shows the graph of the function in Example 6. Notice that the function is undefined at $x = 0$; the graph approaches the origin but never quite reaches it.

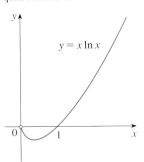

$y = x \ln x$

FIGURE 5

INDETERMINATE DIFFERENCES

If $\lim_{x \to a} f(x) = \infty$ and $\lim_{x \to a} g(x) = \infty$, then the limit

$$\lim_{x \to a} [f(x) - g(x)]$$

is called an **indeterminate form of type $\infty - \infty$**. Again there is a contest between f and g. Will the answer be ∞ (f wins) or will it be $-\infty$ (g wins) or will they compromise on a finite number? To find out, we try to convert the difference into a quotient (for instance, by using a common denominator, or rationalization, or factoring out a common factor) so that we have an indeterminate form of type $\frac{0}{0}$ or ∞/∞.

EXAMPLE 7 Compute $\lim\limits_{x \to (\pi/2)^-} (\sec x - \tan x)$.

SOLUTION First notice that $\sec x \to \infty$ and $\tan x \to \infty$ as $x \to (\pi/2)^-$, so the limit is indeterminate. Here we use a common denominator:

$$\lim_{x \to (\pi/2)^-} (\sec x - \tan x) = \lim_{x \to (\pi/2)^-} \left(\frac{1}{\cos x} - \frac{\sin x}{\cos x} \right)$$

$$= \lim_{x \to (\pi/2)^-} \frac{1 - \sin x}{\cos x} = \lim_{x \to (\pi/2)^-} \frac{-\cos x}{-\sin x} = 0$$

Note that the use of l'Hospital's Rule is justified because $1 - \sin x \to 0$ and $\cos x \to 0$ as $x \to (\pi/2)^-$. ▪

INDETERMINATE POWERS

Several indeterminate forms arise from the limit

$$\lim_{x \to a} [f(x)]^{g(x)}$$

1. $\lim_{x \to a} f(x) = 0$ and $\lim_{x \to a} g(x) = 0$ type 0^0

2. $\lim_{x \to a} f(x) = \infty$ and $\lim_{x \to a} g(x) = 0$ type ∞^0

3. $\lim_{x \to a} f(x) = 1$ and $\lim_{x \to a} g(x) = \pm\infty$ type 1^∞

Each of these three cases can be treated either by taking the natural logarithm:

$$\text{let} \quad y = [f(x)]^{g(x)}, \quad \text{then} \quad \ln y = g(x) \ln f(x)$$

or by writing the function as an exponential:

$$[f(x)]^{g(x)} = e^{g(x) \ln f(x)}$$

(Recall that both of these methods were used in differentiating such functions.) In either method we are led to the indeterminate product $g(x) \ln f(x)$, which is of type $0 \cdot \infty$.

EXAMPLE 8 Calculate $\lim_{x \to 0^+} (1 + \sin 4x)^{\cot x}$.

SOLUTION First notice that as $x \to 0^+$, we have $1 + \sin 4x \to 1$ and $\cot x \to \infty$, so the given limit is indeterminate. Let

$$y = (1 + \sin 4x)^{\cot x}$$

Then $\ln y = \ln[(1 + \sin 4x)^{\cot x}] = \cot x \ln(1 + \sin 4x)$

so l'Hospital's Rule gives

$$\lim_{x \to 0^+} \ln y = \lim_{x \to 0^+} \frac{\ln(1 + \sin 4x)}{\tan x} = \lim_{x \to 0^+} \frac{\dfrac{4 \cos 4x}{1 + \sin 4x}}{\sec^2 x} = 4$$

■ The graph of the function $y = x^x$, $x > 0$, is shown in Figure 6. Notice that although 0^0 is not defined, the values of the function approach 1 as $x \to 0^+$. This confirms the result of Example 9.

So far we have computed the limit of $\ln y$, but what we want is the limit of y. To find this we use the fact that $y = e^{\ln y}$:

$$\lim_{x \to 0^+} (1 + \sin 4x)^{\cot x} = \lim_{x \to 0^+} y = \lim_{x \to 0^+} e^{\ln y} = e^4$$ ■

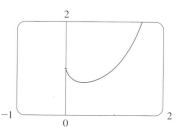

FIGURE 6

✓ EXAMPLE 9 Find $\lim_{x \to 0^+} x^x$.

SOLUTION Notice that this limit is indeterminate since $0^x = 0$ for any $x > 0$ but $x^0 = 1$ for any $x \neq 0$. We could proceed as in Example 8 or by writing the function as an exponential:

$$x^x = (e^{\ln x})^x = e^{x \ln x}$$

In Example 6 we used l'Hospital's Rule to show that

$$\lim_{x \to 0^+} x \ln x = 0$$

Therefore $$\lim_{x \to 0^+} x^x = \lim_{x \to 0^+} e^{x \ln x} = e^0 = 1$$ ▪

3.7   EXERCISES

1–36 ▪ Find the limit. Use l'Hospital's Rule where appropriate. If there is a more elementary method, consider using it. If l'Hospital's Rule doesn't apply, explain why.

1. $\displaystyle \lim_{x \to -1} \frac{x^2 - 1}{x + 1}$

2. $\displaystyle \lim_{x \to 1} \frac{x^a - 1}{x^b - 1}$

3. $\displaystyle \lim_{x \to (\pi/2)^+} \frac{\cos x}{1 - \sin x}$

4. $\displaystyle \lim_{x \to 0} \frac{x + \tan x}{\sin x}$

5. $\displaystyle \lim_{t \to 0} \frac{e^t - 1}{t^3}$

6. $\displaystyle \lim_{t \to 0} \frac{e^{3t} - 1}{t}$

7. $\displaystyle \lim_{x \to 0} \frac{\tan px}{\tan qx}$

8. $\displaystyle \lim_{\theta \to \pi/2} \frac{1 - \sin \theta}{\csc \theta}$

9. $\displaystyle \lim_{x \to 0^+} \frac{\ln x}{x}$

10. $\displaystyle \lim_{x \to \infty} \frac{\ln \ln x}{x}$

11. $\displaystyle \lim_{t \to 0} \frac{5^t - 3^t}{t}$

12. $\displaystyle \lim_{x \to 1} \frac{\ln x}{\sin \pi x}$

13. $\displaystyle \lim_{x \to 0} \frac{e^x - 1 - x}{x^2}$

14. $\displaystyle \lim_{x \to \infty} \frac{e^x}{x^3}$

15. $\displaystyle \lim_{x \to \infty} \frac{x}{\ln(1 + 2e^x)}$

16. $\displaystyle \lim_{x \to 0} \frac{\cos mx - \cos nx}{x^2}$

17. $\displaystyle \lim_{x \to 1} \frac{1 - x + \ln x}{1 + \cos \pi x}$

18. $\displaystyle \lim_{x \to 0} \frac{x}{\tan^{-1}(4x)}$

19. $\displaystyle \lim_{x \to 1} \frac{x^a - ax + a - 1}{(x - 1)^2}$

20. $\displaystyle \lim_{x \to 0} \frac{1 - e^{-2x}}{\sec x}$

21. $\displaystyle \lim_{x \to 0^+} \sqrt{x} \, \ln x$

22. $\displaystyle \lim_{x \to -\infty} x^2 e^x$

23. $\displaystyle \lim_{x \to 0} \cot 2x \, \sin 6x$

24. $\displaystyle \lim_{x \to 0^+} \sin x \, \ln x$

25. $\displaystyle \lim_{x \to \infty} x^3 e^{-x^2}$

26. $\displaystyle \lim_{x \to \infty} x \tan(1/x)$

27. $\displaystyle \lim_{x \to \infty} (xe^{1/x} - x)$

28. $\displaystyle \lim_{x \to 0} (\csc x - \cot x)$

29. $\displaystyle \lim_{x \to \infty} (x - \ln x)$

30. $\displaystyle \lim_{x \to 1} \left(\frac{1}{\ln x} - \frac{1}{x - 1} \right)$

31. $\displaystyle \lim_{x \to 0^+} x^{x^2}$

32. $\displaystyle \lim_{x \to 0^+} (\tan 2x)^x$

33. $\displaystyle \lim_{x \to 0} (1 - 2x)^{1/x}$

34. $\displaystyle \lim_{x \to \infty} \left(1 + \frac{a}{x} \right)^{bx}$

35. $\displaystyle \lim_{x \to 0^+} (\cos x)^{1/x^2}$

36. $\displaystyle \lim_{x \to \infty} x^{(\ln 2)/(1 + \ln x)}$

▪ ▪ ▪ ▪ ▪ ▪ ▪ ▪ ▪ ▪ ▪ ▪ ▪

37–38 ▪ Use a graph to estimate the value of the limit. Then use l'Hospital's Rule to find the exact value.

37. $\displaystyle \lim_{x \to \infty} x [\ln(x + 5) - \ln x]$

38. $\displaystyle \lim_{x \to \pi/4} (\tan x)^{\tan 2x}$

▪ ▪ ▪ ▪ ▪ ▪ ▪ ▪ ▪ ▪ ▪ ▪ ▪

39. Prove that

$$\lim_{x \to \infty} \frac{e^x}{x^n} = \infty$$

for any positive integer n. This shows that the exponential function approaches infinity faster than any power of x.

40. Prove that

$$\lim_{x \to \infty} \frac{\ln x}{x^p} = 0$$

for any number $p > 0$. This shows that the logarithmic function approaches ∞ more slowly than any power of x.

41. If an initial amount A_0 of money is invested at an interest rate r compounded n times a year, the value of the investment after t years is

$$A = A_0 \left(1 + \frac{r}{n} \right)^{nt}$$

If we let $n \to \infty$, we refer to the *continuous compounding* of interest. Use l'Hospital's Rule to show that if interest is compounded continuously, then the amount after t years is

$$A = A_0 e^{rt}$$

42. If an object with mass m is dropped from rest, one model for its speed v after t seconds, taking air resistance into account, is

$$v = \frac{mg}{c} (1 - e^{-ct/m})$$

where g is the acceleration due to gravity and c is a positive constant.
(a) Calculate $\lim_{t \to \infty} v$. What is the meaning of this limit?
(b) For fixed t, use l'Hospital's Rule to calculate $\lim_{c \to 0^+} v$. What can you conclude about the velocity of a falling object in a vacuum?

43. If an electrostatic field E acts on a liquid or a gaseous polar dielectric, the net dipole moment P per unit volume is

$$P(E) = \frac{e^E + e^{-E}}{e^E - e^{-E}} - \frac{1}{E}$$

Show that $\lim_{E \to 0^+} P(E) = 0$.

44. A metal cable has radius r and is covered by insulation, so that the distance from the center of the cable to the exterior of the insulation is R. The velocity v of an electrical impulse in the cable is

$$v = -c\left(\frac{r}{R}\right)^2 \ln\left(\frac{r}{R}\right)$$

where c is a positive constant. Find the following limits and interpret your answers.

(a) $\displaystyle \lim_{R \to r^+} v$ (b) $\displaystyle \lim_{r \to 0^+} v$

45. The first appearance in print of l'Hospital's Rule was in the book *Analyse des Infiniment Petits* published by the Marquis de l'Hospital in 1696. This was the first calculus *textbook* ever published and the example that the Marquis used in that book to illustrate his rule was to find the limit of the function

$$y = \frac{\sqrt{2a^3x - x^4} - a\sqrt[3]{aax}}{a - \sqrt[4]{ax^3}}$$

as x approaches a, where $a > 0$. (At that time it was common to write aa instead of a^2.) Solve this problem.

46. The figure shows a sector of a circle with central angle θ. Let $A(\theta)$ be the area of the segment between the chord PR and the arc PR. Let $B(\theta)$ be the area of the triangle PQR. Find $\lim_{\theta \to 0^+} A(\theta)/B(\theta)$.

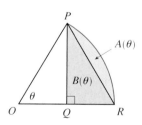

47. If f' is continuous, $f(2) = 0$, and $f'(2) = 7$, evaluate

$$\lim_{x \to 0} \frac{f(2 + 3x) + f(2 + 5x)}{x}$$

48. For what values of a and b is the following equation true?

$$\lim_{x \to 0}\left(\frac{\sin 2x}{x^3} + a + \frac{b}{x^2}\right) = 0$$

49. If f' is continuous, use l'Hospital's Rule to show that

$$\lim_{h \to 0} \frac{f(x + h) - f(x - h)}{2h} = f'(x)$$

Explain the meaning of this equation with the aid of a diagram.

50. If f'' is continuous, show that

$$\lim_{h \to 0} \frac{f(x + h) - 2f(x) + f(x - h)}{h^2} = f''(x)$$

51. Let

$$f(x) = \begin{cases} e^{-1/x^2} & \text{if } x \neq 0 \\ 0 & \text{if } x = 0 \end{cases}$$

(a) Use the definition of derivative to compute $f'(0)$.
(b) Show that f has derivatives of all orders that are defined on $\mathbb{R}$. [*Hint:* First show by induction that there is a polynomial $p_n(x)$ and a nonnegative integer k_n such that $f^{(n)}(x) = p_n(x)f(x)/x^{k_n}$ for $x \neq 0$.]

52. Let

$$f(x) = \begin{cases} |x|^x & \text{if } x \neq 0 \\ 1 & \text{if } x = 0 \end{cases}$$

(a) Show that f is continuous at 0.
(b) Investigate graphically whether f is differentiable at 0 by zooming in several times toward the point $(0, 1)$ on the graph of f.
(c) Show that f is not differentiable at 0. How can you reconcile this fact with the appearance of the graphs in part (b)?

3 REVIEW

1. (a) What is a one-to-one function? How can you tell if a function is one-to-one by looking at its graph?
   (b) If f is a one-to-one function, how is its inverse function f^{-1} defined? How do you obtain the graph of f^{-1} from the graph of f?
   (c) Suppose f is a one-to-one function. If $f'(f^{-1}(a)) \neq 0$, write a formula for $(f^{-1})'(a)$.

2. (a) Express e as a limit.
   (b) What is the value of e correct to five decimal places?
   (c) Why is the natural exponential function $y = e^x$ used more often in calculus than the other exponential functions $y = a^x$?
   (d) Why is the natural logarithmic function $y = \ln x$ used more often in calculus than the other logarithmic functions $y = \log_a x$?

3. (a) What are the domain and range of the natural exponential function $f(x) = e^x$?
   (b) What are the domain and range of the natural logarithmic function $f(x) = \ln x$?
   (c) How are the graphs of these functions related? Sketch these graphs, by hand, using the same axes.
   (d) If a is a positive number, $a \neq 1$, write an equation that expresses $\log_a x$ in terms of $\ln x$.

4. (a) How is the inverse sine function $f(x) = \sin^{-1} x$ defined? What are its domain and range?
   (b) How is the inverse cosine function $f(x) = \cos^{-1} x$ defined? What are its domain and range?

(c) How is the inverse tangent function $f(x) = \tan^{-1} x$ defined? What are its domain and range? Sketch its graph.

5. Write the definitions of the hyperbolic functions $\sinh x$, $\cosh x$, and $\tanh x$.

6. State the derivative of each function.
   (a) $y = e^x$ (b) $y = a^x$ (c) $y = \ln x$
   (d) $y = \log_a x$ (e) $y = \sin^{-1} x$ (f) $y = \cos^{-1} x$
   (g) $y = \tan^{-1} x$ (h) $y = \sinh x$ (i) $y = \cosh x$
   (j) $y = \tanh x$ (k) $y = \sinh^{-1} x$ (l) $y = \cosh^{-1} x$
   (m) $y = \tanh^{-1} x$

7. (a) Write a differential equation that expresses the law of natural growth. What does it say in terms of relative growth rate?
   (b) Under what circumstances is this an appropriate model for population growth?
   (c) What are the solutions of this equation?

8. (a) What does l'Hospital's Rule say?
   (b) How can you use l'Hospital's Rule if you have a product $f(x)g(x)$ where $f(x) \to 0$ and $g(x) \to \infty$ as $x \to a$?
   (c) How can you use l'Hospital's Rule if you have a difference $f(x) - g(x)$ where $f(x) \to \infty$ and $g(x) \to \infty$ as $x \to a$?
   (d) How can you use l'Hospital's Rule if you have a power $[f(x)]^{g(x)}$ where $f(x) \to 0$ and $g(x) \to 0$ as $x \to a$?

Determine whether the statement is true or false. If it is true, explain why. If it is false, explain why or give an example that disproves the statement.

1. If f is one-to-one, with domain $\mathbb{R}$, then $f^{-1}(f(6)) = 6$.

2. If f is one-to-one and differentiable, with domain $\mathbb{R}$, then $(f^{-1})'(6) = 1/f'(6)$.

3. The function $f(x) = \cos x$, $-\pi/2 \leqslant x \leqslant \pi/2$, is one-to-one.

4. $\tan^{-1}(-1) = 3\pi/4$

5. If $0 < a < b$, then $\ln a < \ln b$.

6. $\pi^{\sqrt{5}} = e^{\sqrt{5} \ln \pi}$

7. You can always divide by e^x.

8. If $a > 0$ and $b > 0$, then $\ln(a + b) = \ln a + \ln b$.

9. If $x > 0$, then $(\ln x)^6 = 6 \ln x$.

10. $\dfrac{d}{dx}(10^x) = x10^{x-1}$

11. $\dfrac{d}{dx}(\ln 10) = \dfrac{1}{10}$

12. The inverse function of $y = e^{3x}$ is $y = \frac{1}{3} \ln x$.

13. $\cos^{-1} x = \dfrac{1}{\cos x}$

14. $\tan^{-1} x = \dfrac{\sin^{-1} x}{\cos^{-1} x}$

15. $\cosh x \geqslant 1$ for all x

16. $\displaystyle\lim_{x \to \pi^-} \dfrac{\tan x}{1 - \cos x} = \lim_{x \to \pi^-} \dfrac{\sec^2 x}{\sin x} = \infty$

$$\boxed{\text{EXERCISES}}$$

1. The graph of f is shown. Is f one-to-one? Explain.

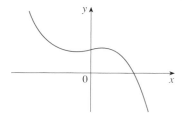

2. The graph of g is given.
 (a) Why is g one-to-one?
 (b) Estimate the value of $g^{-1}(2)$.
 (c) Estimate the domain of g^{-1}.
 (d) Sketch the graph of g^{-1}.

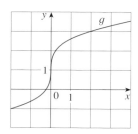

3. Suppose f is one-to-one, $f(7) = 3$, and $f'(7) = 8$. Find
 (a) $f^{-1}(3)$ and (b) $(f^{-1})'(3)$.

4. Find the inverse function of $f(x) = \dfrac{x + 1}{2x + 1}$.

5–9 ■ Sketch a rough graph of the function without using a calculator.

5. $y = 5^x - 1$

6. $y = -e^{-x}$

7. $y = -\ln x$

8. $y = \ln(x - 1)$

9. $y = 2 \arctan x$

■ ■ ■ ■ ■ ■ ■ ■ ■ ■ ■ ■ ■

10. Let $a > 1$. For large values of x, which of the functions $y = x^a$, $y = a^x$, and $y = \log_a x$ has the largest values and which has the smallest values?

11–12 ■ Find the exact value of each expression.

11. (a) $e^{2 \ln 3}$
 (b) $\log_{10} 25 + \log_{10} 4$

12. (a) $\ln e^{\pi}$
 (b) $\tan\left(\arcsin \frac{1}{2}\right)$

■ ■ ■ ■ ■ ■ ■ ■ ■ ■ ■ ■ ■

13–20 ■ Solve the equation for x.

13. $\ln x = \frac{1}{3}$

14. $e^x = \frac{1}{3}$

15. $e^{e^x} = 17$

16. $\ln(1 + e^{-x}) = 3$

17. $\ln(x + 1) + \ln(x - 1) = 1$

18. $\log_5(c^x) = d$

19. $\tan^{-1}x = 1$

20. $\sin x = 0.3$

■ ■ ■ ■ ■ ■ ■ ■ ■ ■ ■ ■ ■

21–47 ■ Differentiate.

21. $f(t) = t^2 \ln t$

22. $g(t) = \dfrac{e^t}{1 + e^t}$

23. $h(\theta) = e^{\tan 2\theta}$

24. $h(u) = 10^{\sqrt{u}}$

25. $y = \ln|\sec 5x + \tan 5x|$

26. $y = e^{-t}(t^2 - 2t + 2)$

27. $y = e^{cx}(c \sin x - \cos x)$

28. $y = \sin^{-1}(e^x)$

29. $y = \ln(\sec^2 x)$

30. $y = \ln(x^2 e^x)$

31. $y = xe^{-1/x}$

32. $y = x^r e^{sx}$

33. $y = 2^{-t^2}$

34. $y = e^{\cos x} + \cos(e^x)$

35. $H(v) = v \tan^{-1}v$

36. $F(z) = \log_{10}(1 + z^2)$

37. $y = x \sinh(x^2)$

38. $y = (\cos x)^x$

39. $y = \ln \sin x - \frac{1}{2} \sin^2 x$

40. $y = \arctan(\arcsin \sqrt{x}\,)$

41. $y = \ln\left(\dfrac{1}{x}\right) + \dfrac{1}{\ln x}$

42. $xe^y = y - 1$

43. $y = \ln(\cosh 3x)$

44. $y = \dfrac{(x^2 + 1)^4}{(2x + 1)^3(3x - 1)^5}$

45. $y = \cosh^{-1}(\sinh x)$

46. $y = x \tanh^{-1}\sqrt{x}$

47. $f(x) = e^{\sin^3(\ln(x^2 + 1))}$

■ ■ ■ ■ ■ ■ ■ ■ ■ ■ ■ ■ ■

48. Show that

$$\frac{d}{dx}\left(\tfrac{1}{2} \tan^{-1}x + \tfrac{1}{4} \ln \frac{(x + 1)^2}{x^2 + 1}\right) = \frac{1}{(1 + x)(1 + x^2)}$$

49–52 ■ Find f' in terms of g'.

49. $f(x) = e^{g(x)}$

50. $f(x) = g(e^x)$

51. $f(x) = \ln|g(x)|$

52. $f(x) = g(\ln x)$

■ ■ ■ ■ ■ ■ ■ ■ ■ ■ ■ ■ ■

53–54 ■ Find $f^{(n)}(x)$.

53. $f(x) = 2^x$

54. $f(x) = \ln(2x)$

■ ■ ■ ■ ■ ■ ■ ■ ■ ■ ■ ■ ■

55. Use mathematical induction to show that if $f(x) = xe^x$, then $f^{(n)}(x) = (x + n)e^x$.

56. Find y' if $y = x + \arctan y$.

57–58 ■ Find an equation of the tangent to the curve at the given point.

57. $y = (2 + x)e^{-x}$, $(0, 2)$

58. $y = x \ln x$, (e, e)

■ ■ ■ ■ ■ ■ ■ ■ ■ ■ ■ ■ ■

59. At what point on the curve $y = [\ln(x + 4)]^2$ is the tangent horizontal?

60. If $f(x) = xe^{\sin x}$, find $f'(x)$. Graph f and f' on the same screen and comment.

61. (a) Find an equation of the tangent to the curve $y = e^x$ that is parallel to the line $x - 4y = 1$.
(b) Find an equation of the tangent to the curve $y = e^x$ that passes through the origin.

62. The function $C(t) = K(e^{-at} - e^{-bt})$, where a, b, and K are positive constants and $b > a$, is used to model the concentration at time t of a drug injected into the bloodstream.
(a) Show that $\lim_{t \to \infty} C(t) = 0$.
(b) Find $C'(t)$, the rate at which the drug is cleared from circulation.
(c) When is this rate equal to 0?

63. A bacteria culture contains 200 cells initially and grows at a rate proportional to its size. After half an hour the population has increased to 360 cells.
(a) Find the number of bacteria after t hours.
(b) Find the number of bacteria after 4 hours.
(c) Find the rate of growth after 4 hours.
(d) When will the population reach 10,000?

64. Cobalt-60 has a half-life of 5.24 years.
(a) Find the mass that remains from a 100-mg sample after 20 years.
(b) How long would it take for the mass to decay to 1 mg?

65. Let $C(t)$ be the concentration of a drug in the bloodstream. As the body eliminates the drug, $C(t)$ decreases at a rate that is proportional to the amount of the drug that is present at the time. Thus $C'(t) = -kC(t)$, where k is a positive number called the *elimination constant* of the drug.
(a) If C_0 is the concentration at time $t = 0$, find the concentration at time t.

(b) If the body eliminates half the drug in 30 hours, how long does it take to eliminate 90% of the drug?

66. A cup of hot chocolate has temperature 80°C in a room kept at 20°C. After half an hour the hot chocolate cools to 60°C.
(a) What is the temperature of the chocolate after another half hour?
(b) When will the chocolate have cooled to 40°C?

67–82 ▪ Evaluate the limit.

67. $\lim\limits_{x \to \infty} e^{-3x}$

68. $\lim\limits_{x \to 10^-} \ln(100 - x^2)$

69. $\lim\limits_{x \to 3^-} e^{2/(x-3)}$

70. $\lim\limits_{x \to \infty} \arctan(x^3 - x)$

71. $\lim\limits_{x \to 0^+} \ln(\sinh x)$

72. $\lim\limits_{x \to \infty} e^{-x} \sin x$

73. $\lim\limits_{x \to \infty} \dfrac{1 + 2^x}{1 - 2^x}$

74. $\lim\limits_{x \to \infty} \left(1 + \dfrac{4}{x}\right)^x$

75. $\lim\limits_{x \to 0} \dfrac{\tan \pi x}{\ln(1 + x)}$

76. $\lim\limits_{x \to 0} \dfrac{1 - \cos x}{x^2 + x}$

77. $\lim\limits_{x \to 0} \dfrac{e^{4x} - 1 - 4x}{x^2}$

78. $\lim\limits_{x \to \infty} \dfrac{e^{4x} - 1 - 4x}{x^2}$

79. $\lim\limits_{x \to \infty} x^3 e^{-x}$

80. $\lim\limits_{x \to 0^+} x^2 \ln x$

81. $\lim\limits_{x \to 1^+} \left(\dfrac{x}{x - 1} - \dfrac{1}{\ln x}\right)$

82. $\lim\limits_{x \to (\pi/2)^-} (\tan x)^{\cos x}$

83. If $f(x) = \ln x + \tan^{-1}x$, find $(f^{-1})'(\pi/4)$.

84. Show that

$$\cos\{\arctan[\sin(\text{arccot } x)]\} = \sqrt{\dfrac{x^2 + 1}{x^2 + 2}}$$

4 APPLICATIONS OF DIFFERENTIATION

We have already investigated some of the applications of derivatives, but now that we know the differentiation rules we are in a better position to pursue the applications of differentiation in greater depth. Here we learn how derivatives affect the shape of a graph of a function and, in particular, how they help us locate maximum and minimum values of functions. Many practical problems require us to minimize a cost or maximize an area or somehow find the best possible outcome of a situation. In particular, we will be able to investigate the optimal shape of a can and to explain the shape of cells in beehives.

4.1 MAXIMUM AND MINIMUM VALUES

Some of the most important applications of differential calculus are *optimization problems*, in which we are required to find the optimal (best) way of doing something. Here are examples of such problems that we will solve in this chapter:

- What is the shape of a can that minimizes manufacturing costs?

- What is the maximum acceleration of a space shuttle? (This is an important question to the astronauts who have to withstand the effects of acceleration.)

- What is the radius of a contracted windpipe that expels air most rapidly during a cough?

- How far should you stand from a painting in an art gallery to get the best view of the painting?

These problems can be reduced to finding the maximum or minimum values of a function. Let's first explain exactly what we mean by maximum and minimum values.

> **1 DEFINITION** A function f has an **absolute maximum** (or **global maximum**) at c if $f(c) \geq f(x)$ for all x in D, where D is the domain of f. The number $f(c)$ is called the **maximum value** of f on D. Similarly, f has an **absolute minimum** at c if $f(c) \leq f(x)$ for all x in D and the number $f(c)$ is called the **minimum value** of f on D. The maximum and minimum values of f are called the **extreme values** of f.

Figure 1 shows the graph of a function f with absolute maximum at d and absolute minimum at a. Note that $(d, f(d))$ is the highest point on the graph and $(a, f(a))$ is the lowest point.

In Figure 1, if we consider only values of x near b [for instance, if we restrict our attention to the interval (a, c)], then $f(b)$ is the largest of those values of $f(x)$ and is called a *local maximum value* of f. Likewise, $f(c)$ is called a *local minimum value* of f because $f(c) \leq f(x)$ for x near c [in the interval (b, d), for instance]. The function f also has a local minimum at e. In general, we have the following definition.

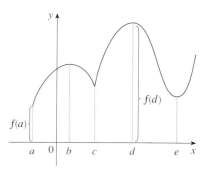

FIGURE 1
Minimum value $f(a)$,
maximum value $f(d)$

> **2 DEFINITION** A function f has a **local maximum** (or **relative maximum**)
> at c if $f(c) \geqslant f(x)$ when x is near c. [This means that $f(c) \geqslant f(x)$ for all x in
> some open interval containing c.] Similarly, f has a **local minimum** at c if
> $f(c) \leqslant f(x)$ when x is near c.

EXAMPLE 1 The function $f(x) = \cos x$ takes on its (local and absolute) maximum
value of 1 infinitely many times, since $\cos 2n\pi = 1$ for any integer n and
$-1 \leqslant \cos x \leqslant 1$ for all x. Likewise, $\cos(2n + 1)\pi = -1$ is its minimum value,
where n is any integer. ▪

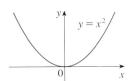

FIGURE 2
Minimum value 0, no maximum

EXAMPLE 2 If $f(x) = x^2$, then $f(x) \geqslant f(0)$ because $x^2 \geqslant 0$ for all x. Therefore,
$f(0) = 0$ is the absolute (and local) minimum value of f. This corresponds to the
fact that the origin is the lowest point on the parabola $y = x^2$. (See Figure 2.) However, there is no highest point on the parabola and so this function has no maximum
value. ▪

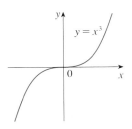

FIGURE 3
No minimum, no maximum

EXAMPLE 3 From the graph of the function $f(x) = x^3$, shown in Figure 3, we see
that this function has neither an absolute maximum value nor an absolute minimum
value. In fact, it has no local extreme values either. ▪

▼ EXAMPLE 4 The graph of the function

$$f(x) = 3x^4 - 16x^3 + 18x^2 \qquad -1 \leqslant x \leqslant 4$$

is shown in Figure 4. You can see that $f(1) = 5$ is a local maximum, whereas the
absolute maximum is $f(-1) = 37$. (This absolute maximum is not a local maximum because it occurs at an endpoint.) Also, $f(0) = 0$ is a local minimum and
$f(3) = -27$ is both a local and an absolute minimum. Note that f has neither a
local nor an absolute maximum at $x = 4$. ▪

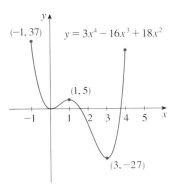

FIGURE 4

We have seen that some functions have extreme values, whereas others do not. The
following theorem gives conditions under which a function is guaranteed to possess
extreme values.

> **3 THE EXTREME VALUE THEOREM** If f is continuous on a closed interval
> $[a, b]$, then f attains an absolute maximum value $f(c)$ and an absolute mini-
> mum value $f(d)$ at some numbers c and d in $[a, b]$.

The Extreme Value Theorem is illustrated in Figure 5. Note that an extreme value
can be taken on more than once. Although the Extreme Value Theorem is intuitively
very plausible, it is difficult to prove and so we omit the proof.

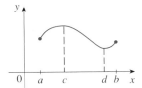 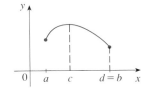 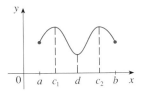

FIGURE 5

Figures 6 and 7 show that a function need not possess extreme values if either hypothesis (continuity or closed interval) is omitted from the Extreme Value Theorem.

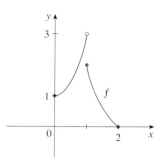

FIGURE 6
This function has minimum value
$f(2) = 0$, but no maximum value.

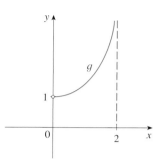

FIGURE 7
This continuous function g has
no maximum or minimum.

The function f whose graph is shown in Figure 6 is defined on the closed interval [0, 2] but has no maximum value. [Notice that the range of f is [0, 3). The function takes on values arbitrarily close to 3, but never actually attains the value 3.] This does not contradict the Extreme Value Theorem because f is not continuous. [Nonetheless, a discontinuous function *could* have maximum and minimum values. See Exercise 13(b).]

The function g shown in Figure 7 is continuous on the open interval (0, 2) but has neither a maximum nor a minimum value. [The range of g is (1, ∞). The function takes on arbitrarily large values.] This does not contradict the Extreme Value Theorem because the interval (0, 2) is not closed.

The Extreme Value Theorem says that a continuous function on a closed interval has a maximum value and a minimum value, but it does not tell us how to find these extreme values. We start by looking for local extreme values.

Figure 8 shows the graph of a function f with a local maximum at c and a local minimum at d. It appears that at the maximum and minimum points the tangent lines are horizontal and therefore each has slope 0. We know that the derivative is the slope of the tangent line, so it appears that $f'(c) = 0$ and $f'(d) = 0$. The following theorem says that this is always true for differentiable functions.

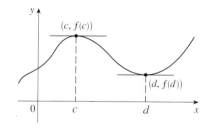

FIGURE 8

■ Fermat's Theorem is named after Pierre Fermat (1601–1665), a French lawyer who took up mathematics as a hobby. Despite his amateur status, Fermat was one of the two inventors of analytic geometry (Descartes was the other). His methods for finding tangents to curves and maximum and minimum values (before the invention of limits and derivatives) made him a forerunner of Newton in the creation of differential calculus.

4 FERMAT'S THEOREM If f has a local maximum or minimum at c, and if $f'(c)$ exists, then $f'(c) = 0$.

PROOF Suppose, for the sake of definiteness, that f has a local maximum at c. Then, according to Definition 2, $f(c) \geq f(x)$ if x is sufficiently close to c. This implies that if h is sufficiently close to 0, with h being positive or negative, then

$$f(c) \geq f(c + h)$$

and therefore

5

$$f(c + h) - f(c) \leq 0$$

We can divide both sides of an inequality by a positive number. Thus if $h > 0$ and h is sufficiently small, we have

$$\frac{f(c + h) - f(c)}{h} \leqslant 0$$

Taking the right-hand limit of both sides of this inequality (using Theorem 1.4.3), we get

$$\lim_{h \to 0^+} \frac{f(c + h) - f(c)}{h} \leqslant \lim_{h \to 0^+} 0 = 0$$

But since $f'(c)$ exists, we have

$$f'(c) = \lim_{h \to 0} \frac{f(c + h) - f(c)}{h} = \lim_{h \to 0^+} \frac{f(c + h) - f(c)}{h}$$

and so we have shown that $f'(c) \leqslant 0$.

If $h < 0$, then the direction of the inequality (5) is reversed when we divide by h:

$$\frac{f(c + h) - f(c)}{h} \geqslant 0 \qquad h < 0$$

So, taking the left-hand limit, we have

$$f'(c) = \lim_{h \to 0} \frac{f(c + h) - f(c)}{h} = \lim_{h \to 0^-} \frac{f(c + h) - f(c)}{h} \geqslant 0$$

We have shown that $f'(c) \geqslant 0$ and also that $f'(c) \leqslant 0$. Since both of these inequalities must be true, the only possibility is that $f'(c) = 0$.

We have proved Fermat's Theorem for the case of a local maximum. The case of a local minimum can be proved in a similar manner, or we could use Exercise 62 to deduce it from the case we have just proved (see Exercise 63).   ☐

Although Fermat's Theorem is very useful, we have to guard against reading too much into it. If $f(x) = x^3$, then $f'(x) = 3x^2$, so $f'(0) = 0$. But f has no maximum or minimum at 0, as you can see from its graph in Figure 9. The fact that $f'(0) = 0$ simply means that the curve $y = x^3$ has a horizontal tangent at $(0, 0)$. Instead of having a maximum or minimum at $(0, 0)$, the curve crosses its horizontal tangent there.

⊘   Thus, when $f'(c) = 0$, f doesn't necessarily have a maximum or minimum at c. (In other words, the converse of Fermat's Theorem is false in general.)

We should bear in mind that there may be an extreme value where $f'(c)$ does not exist. For instance, the function $f(x) = |x|$ has its (local and absolute) minimum value at 0 (see Figure 10), but that value cannot be found by setting $f'(x) = 0$ because, as was shown in Example 5 in Section 2.2, $f'(0)$ does not exist.

Fermat's Theorem does suggest that we should at least *start* looking for extreme values of f at the numbers c where $f'(c) = 0$ or where $f'(c)$ does not exist. Such numbers are given a special name.

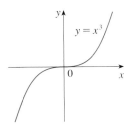

FIGURE 9
If $f(x) = x^3$, then $f'(0) = 0$ but f has no maximum or minimum.

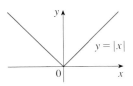

FIGURE 10
If $f(x) = |x|$, then $f(0) = 0$ is a minimum value, but $f'(0)$ does not exist.

> **6 DEFINITION** A **critical number** of a function f is a number c in the domain of f such that either $f'(c) = 0$ or $f'(c)$ does not exist.

▪ Figure 11 shows a graph of the function f in Example 5. It supports our answer because there is a horizontal tangent when $x = 1.5$ and a vertical tangent when $x = 0$.

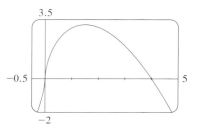

FIGURE 11

☑ EXAMPLE 5 Find the critical numbers of $f(x) = x^{3/5}(4 - x)$.

SOLUTION The Product Rule gives

$$f'(x) = x^{3/5}(-1) + \tfrac{3}{5}x^{-2/5}(4 - x) = -x^{3/5} + \frac{3(4 - x)}{5x^{2/5}}$$

$$= \frac{-5x + 3(4 - x)}{5x^{2/5}} = \frac{12 - 8x}{5x^{2/5}}$$

[The same result could be obtained by first writing $f(x) = 4x^{3/5} - x^{8/5}$.] Therefore, $f'(x) = 0$ if $12 - 8x = 0$, that is, $x = \tfrac{3}{2}$, and $f'(x)$ does not exist when $x = 0$. Thus the critical numbers are $\tfrac{3}{2}$ and 0. ▪

In terms of critical numbers, Fermat's Theorem can be rephrased as follows (compare Definition 6 with Theorem 4):

> **7** If f has a local maximum or minimum at c, then c is a critical number of f.

To find an absolute maximum or minimum of a continuous function on a closed interval, we note that either it is local [in which case it occurs at a critical number by (7)] or it occurs at an endpoint of the interval. Thus the following three-step procedure always works.

> **THE CLOSED INTERVAL METHOD** To find the *absolute* maximum and minimum values of a continuous function f on a closed interval $[a, b]$:
>
> **1.** Find the values of f at the critical numbers of f in (a, b).
> **2.** Find the values of f at the endpoints of the interval.
> **3.** The largest of the values from Steps 1 and 2 is the absolute maximum value; the smallest of these values is the absolute minimum value.

☑ EXAMPLE 6 Find the absolute maximum and minimum values of the function

$$f(x) = x^3 - 3x^2 + 1 \qquad -\tfrac{1}{2} \leqslant x \leqslant 4$$

SOLUTION Since f is continuous on $\left[-\tfrac{1}{2}, 4\right]$, we can use the Closed Interval Method:

$$f(x) = x^3 - 3x^2 + 1$$

$$f'(x) = 3x^2 - 6x = 3x(x - 2)$$

Since $f'(x)$ exists for all x, the only critical numbers of f occur when $f'(x) = 0$, that is, $x = 0$ or $x = 2$. Notice that each of these critical numbers lies in the interval

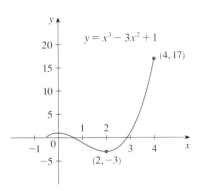

FIGURE 12

$\left(-\frac{1}{2}, 4\right)$. The values of f at these critical numbers are

$$f(0) = 1 \qquad f(2) = -3$$

The values of f at the endpoints of the interval are

$$f\left(-\tfrac{1}{2}\right) = \tfrac{1}{8} \qquad f(4) = 17$$

Comparing these four numbers, we see that the absolute maximum value is $f(4) = 17$ and the absolute minimum value is $f(2) = -3$.

Note that in this example the absolute maximum occurs at an endpoint, whereas the absolute minimum occurs at a critical number. The graph of f is sketched in Figure 12. ∎

4.1 EXERCISES

1. Explain the difference between an absolute minimum and a local minimum.

2. Suppose f is a continuous function defined on a closed interval $[a, b]$.
  (a) What theorem guarantees the existence of an absolute maximum value and an absolute minimum value for f?
  (b) What steps would you take to find those maximum and minimum values?

3–4 ▪ For each of the numbers a, b, c, d, e, r, s, and t, state whether the function whose graph is shown has an absolute maximum or minimum, a local maximum or minimum, or neither a maximum nor a minimum.

3.

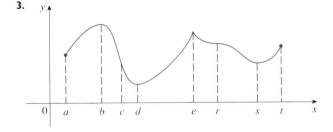

4.

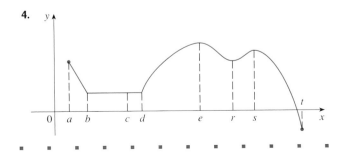

5–6 ▪ Use the graph to state the absolute and local maximum and minimum values of the function.

5.

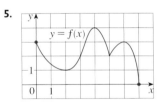

6.

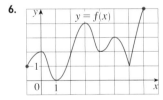

▪ ▪ ▪ ▪ ▪ ▪ ▪ ▪ ▪ ▪ ▪ ▪ ▪ ▪

7–10 ▪ Sketch the graph of a function f that is continuous on [1, 5] and has the given properties.

7. Absolute minimum at 2, absolute maximum at 3, local minimum at 4

8. Absolute minimum at 1, absolute maximum at 5, local maximum at 2, local minimum at 4

9. Absolute maximum at 5, absolute minimum at 2, local maximum at 3, local minima at 2 and 4

10. f has no local maximum or minimum, but 2 and 4 are critical numbers

▪ ▪ ▪ ▪ ▪ ▪ ▪ ▪ ▪ ▪ ▪ ▪ ▪ ▪

11. (a) Sketch the graph of a function that has a local maximum at 2 and is differentiable at 2.
  (b) Sketch the graph of a function that has a local maximum at 2 and is continuous but not differentiable at 2.

(c) Sketch the graph of a function that has a local maximum at 2 and is not continuous at 2.

12. (a) Sketch the graph of a function on $[-1, 2]$ that has an absolute maximum but no local maximum.
   (b) Sketch the graph of a function on $[-1, 2]$ that has a local maximum but no absolute maximum.

13. (a) Sketch the graph of a function on $[-1, 2]$ that has an absolute maximum but no absolute minimum.
   (b) Sketch the graph of a function on $[-1, 2]$ that is discontinuous but has both an absolute maximum and an absolute minimum.

14. (a) Sketch the graph of a function that has two local maxima, one local minimum, and no absolute minimum.
   (b) Sketch the graph of a function that has three local minima, two local maxima, and seven critical numbers.

15–22 ▪ Sketch the graph of f by hand and use your sketch to find the absolute and local maximum and minimum values of f. (Use the graphs and transformations of Section 1.2.)

15. $f(x) = 8 - 3x, \quad x \geqslant 1$

16. $f(x) = 3 - 2x, \quad x \leqslant 5$

17. $f(x) = x^2, \quad 0 < x < 2$

18. $f(x) = e^x$

19. $f(\theta) = \sin \theta, \quad -2\pi \leqslant \theta \leqslant 2\pi$

20. $f(\theta) = \tan \theta, \quad -\pi/4 \leqslant \theta < \pi/2$

21. $f(x) = 1 - \sqrt{x}$

22. $f(x) = \begin{cases} 4 - x^2 & \text{if } -2 \leqslant x < 0 \\ 2x - 1 & \text{if } 0 \leqslant x \leqslant 2 \end{cases}$

▪ ▪ ▪ ▪ ▪ ▪ ▪ ▪ ▪ ▪ ▪ ▪ ▪ ▪

23–36 ▪ Find the critical numbers of the function.

23. $f(x) = 5x^2 + 4x$

24. $f(x) = x^3 + x^2 - x$

25. $f(x) = x^3 + 3x^2 - 24x$

26. $f(x) = x^3 + x^2 + x$

27. $s(t) = 3t^4 + 4t^3 - 6t^2$

28. $g(t) = |3t - 4|$

29. $g(y) = \dfrac{y - 1}{y^2 - y + 1}$

30. $h(p) = \dfrac{p - 1}{p^2 + 4}$

31. $F(x) = x^{4/5}(x - 4)^2$

32. $G(x) = \sqrt[3]{x^2 - x}$

33. $f(\theta) = 2 \cos \theta + \sin^2\theta$

34. $g(\theta) = 4\theta - \tan \theta$

35. $f(x) = x \ln x$

36. $f(x) = xe^{2x}$

▪ ▪ ▪ ▪ ▪ ▪ ▪ ▪ ▪ ▪ ▪ ▪ ▪ ▪

37–48 ▪ Find the absolute maximum and absolute minimum values of f on the given interval.

37. $f(x) = 3x^2 - 12x + 5, \quad [0, 3]$

38. $f(x) = x^3 - 3x + 1, \quad [0, 3]$

39. $f(x) = 2x^3 - 3x^2 - 12x + 1, \quad [-2, 3]$

40. $f(x) = x^3 - 6x^2 + 9x + 2, \quad [-1, 4]$

41. $f(x) = x^4 - 2x^2 + 3, \quad [-2, 3]$

42. $f(x) = (x^2 - 1)^3, \quad [-1, 2]$

43. $f(t) = t\sqrt{4 - t^2}, \quad [-1, 2]$

44. $f(x) = \dfrac{x}{x^2 + 4}, \quad [0, 3]$

45. $f(x) = \sin x + \cos x, \quad [0, \pi/3]$

46. $f(x) = x - 2 \cos x, \quad [-\pi, \pi]$

47. $f(x) = xe^{-x^2/8}, \quad [-1, 4]$

48. $f(x) = x - \ln x, \quad \left[\frac{1}{2}, 2\right]$

▪ ▪ ▪ ▪ ▪ ▪ ▪ ▪ ▪ ▪ ▪ ▪ ▪ ▪

49. If a and b are positive numbers, find the maximum value of $f(x) = x^a(1 - x)^b, 0 \leqslant x \leqslant 1$.

50. Use a graph to estimate the critical numbers of $f(x) = |x^3 - 3x^2 + 2|$ correct to one decimal place.

51–54 ▪
(a) Use a graph to estimate the absolute maximum and minimum values of the function to two decimal places.
(b) Use calculus to find the exact maximum and minimum values.

51. $f(x) = x^5 - x^3 + 2, \quad -1 \leqslant x \leqslant 1$

52. $f(x) = e^{x^3 - x}, \quad -1 \leqslant x \leqslant 0$

53. $f(x) = x\sqrt{x - x^2}$

54. $f(x) = x - 2 \cos x, \quad -2 \leqslant x \leqslant 0$

▪ ▪ ▪ ▪ ▪ ▪ ▪ ▪ ▪ ▪ ▪ ▪ ▪ ▪

55. Between 0°C and 30°C, the volume V (in cubic centimeters) of 1 kg of water at a temperature T is given approximately by the formula

$$V = 999.87 - 0.06426T + 0.0085043T^2 - 0.0000679T^3$$

Find the temperature at which water has its maximum density.

56. An object with weight W is dragged along a horizontal plane by a force acting along a rope attached to the object. If the rope makes an angle θ with the plane, then the magnitude of the force is

$$F = \frac{\mu W}{\mu \sin \theta + \cos \theta}$$

where μ is a positive constant called the *coefficient of friction* and where $0 \leqslant \theta \leqslant \pi/2$. Show that F is minimized when $\tan \theta = \mu$.

57. A model for the food-price index (the price of a representative "basket" of foods) between 1984 and 1994 is given by the function

$$I(t) = 0.00009045t^5 + 0.001438t^4 - 0.06561t^3$$
$$+ 0.4598t^2 - 0.6270t + 99.33$$

where t is measured in years since midyear 1984, so $0 \leq t \leq 10$, and $I(t)$ is measured in 1987 dollars and scaled such that $I(3) = 100$. Estimate the times when food was cheapest and most expensive during the period 1984–1994.

58. The Hubble Space Telescope was deployed April 24, 1990, by the space shuttle *Discovery*. A model for the velocity of the shuttle during this mission, from liftoff at $t = 0$ until the solid rocket boosters were jettisoned at $t = 126$ s, is given by

$$v(t) = 0.001302t^3 - 0.09029t^2 + 23.61t - 3.083$$

(in feet per second). Using this model, estimate the absolute maximum and minimum values of the *acceleration* of the shuttle between liftoff and the jettisoning of the boosters.

59. When a foreign object lodged in the trachea (windpipe) forces a person to cough, the diaphragm thrusts upward causing an increase in pressure in the lungs. This is accompanied by a contraction of the trachea, making a narrower channel for the expelled air to flow through. For a given amount of air to escape in a fixed time, it must move faster through the narrower channel than the wider one. The greater the velocity of the airstream, the greater the force on the foreign object. X rays show that the radius of the circular tracheal tube contracts to about two-thirds of its normal radius during a cough. According to a mathematical model

of coughing, the velocity v of the airstream is related to the radius r of the trachea by the equation

$$v(r) = k(r_0 - r)r^2 \qquad \tfrac{1}{2}r_0 \leq r \leq r_0$$

where k is a constant and r_0 is the normal radius of the trachea. The restriction on r is due to the fact that the tracheal wall stiffens under pressure and a contraction greater than $\tfrac{1}{2}r_0$ is prevented (otherwise the person would suffocate).
(a) Determine the value of r in the interval $\left[\tfrac{1}{2}r_0, r_0\right]$ at which v has an absolute maximum. How does this compare with experimental evidence?
(b) What is the absolute maximum value of v on the interval?
(c) Sketch the graph of v on the interval $[0, r_0]$.

60. Show that 5 is a critical number of the function $g(x) = 2 + (x - 5)^3$ but g does not have a local extreme value at 5.

61. Prove that the function $f(x) = x^{101} + x^{51} + x + 1$ has neither a local maximum nor a local minimum.

62. If f has a minimum value at c, show that the function $g(x) = -f(x)$ has a maximum value at c.

63. Prove Fermat's Theorem for the case in which f has a local minimum at c.

64. A cubic function is a polynomial of degree 3; that is, it has the form $f(x) = ax^3 + bx^2 + cx + d$, where $a \neq 0$.
(a) Show that a cubic function can have two, one, or no critical number(s). Give examples and sketches to illustrate the three possibilities.
(b) How many local extreme values can a cubic function have?

| **4.2** | **THE MEAN VALUE THEOREM** |

We will see that many of the results of this chapter depend on one central fact, which is called the Mean Value Theorem. But to arrive at the Mean Value Theorem we first need the following result.

■ Rolle's Theorem was first published in 1691 by the French mathematician Michel Rolle (1652–1719) in a book entitled *Méthode pour résoudre les égalitéz*. Later, however, he became a vocal critic of the methods of his day and attacked calculus as being a "collection of ingenious fallacies."

> **ROLLE'S THEOREM**   Let f be a function that satisfies the following three hypotheses:
>
> **1.** f is continuous on the closed interval $[a, b]$.
>
> **2.** f is differentiable on the open interval (a, b).
>
> **3.** $f(a) = f(b)$
>
> Then there is a number c in (a, b) such that $f'(c) = 0$.

Before giving the proof let's take a look at the graphs of some typical functions that satisfy the three hypotheses. Figure 1 shows the graphs of four such functions. In each case it appears that there is at least one point $(c, f(c))$ on the graph where the tangent is horizontal and therefore $f'(c) = 0$. Thus Rolle's Theorem is plausible.

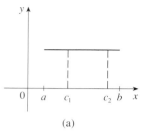

(a)

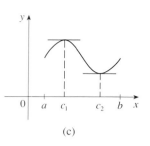

(b)

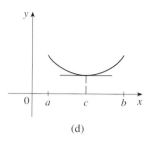

(c)

(d)

FIGURE 1

PROOF There are three cases:

CASE I $f(x) = k$, **a constant**
Then $f'(x) = 0$, so the number c can be taken to be *any* number in (a, b).

CASE II $f(x) > f(a)$ **for some x in (a, b)** [as in Figure 1(b) or (c)]
By the Extreme Value Theorem (which we can apply by hypothesis 1), f has a maximum value somewhere in $[a, b]$. Since $f(a) = f(b)$, it must attain this maximum value at a number c in the open interval (a, b). Then f has a *local* maximum at c and, by hypothesis 2, f is differentiable at c. Therefore, $f'(c) = 0$ by Fermat's Theorem.

CASE III $f(x) < f(a)$ **for some x in (a, b)** [as in Figure 1(c) or (d)]
By the Extreme Value Theorem, f has a minimum value in $[a, b]$ and, since $f(a) = f(b)$, it attains this minimum value at a number c in (a, b). Again $f'(c) = 0$ by Fermat's Theorem. ☐

EXAMPLE 1 Let's apply Rolle's Theorem to the position function $s = f(t)$ of a moving object. If the object is in the same place at two different instants $t = a$ and $t = b$, then $f(a) = f(b)$. Rolle's Theorem says that there is some instant of time $t = c$ between a and b when $f'(c) = 0$; that is, the velocity is 0. (In particular, you can see that this is true when a ball is thrown directly upward.) ■

EXAMPLE 2 Prove that the equation $x^3 + x - 1 = 0$ has exactly one real root.

■ Figure 2 shows a graph of the function $f(x) = x^3 + x - 1$ discussed in Example 2. Rolle's Theorem shows that, no matter how much we enlarge the viewing rectangle, we can never find a second x-intercept.

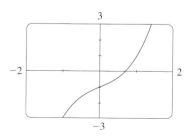

FIGURE 2

SOLUTION First we use the Intermediate Value Theorem (1.5.9) to show that a root exists. Let $f(x) = x^3 + x - 1$. Then $f(0) = -1 < 0$ and $f(1) = 1 > 0$. Since f is a polynomial, it is continuous, so the Intermediate Value Theorem states that there is a number c between 0 and 1 such that $f(c) = 0$. Thus the given equation has a root.

To show that the equation has no other real root, we use Rolle's Theorem and argue by contradiction. Suppose that it had two roots a and b. Then $f(a) = 0 = f(b)$ and, since f is a polynomial, it is differentiable on (a, b) and continuous on $[a, b]$. Thus by Rolle's Theorem there is a number c between a and b such that $f'(c) = 0$. But

$$f'(x) = 3x^2 + 1 \geq 1 \qquad \text{for all } x$$

(since $x^2 \geq 0$) so $f'(x)$ can never be 0. This gives a contradiction. Therefore, the equation can't have two real roots. ■

Our main use of Rolle's Theorem is in proving the following important theorem, which was first stated by another French mathematician, Joseph-Louis Lagrange.

■ The Mean Value Theorem is an example of what is called an existence theorem. Like the Intermediate Value Theorem, the Extreme Value Theorem, and Rolle's Theorem, it guarantees that there *exists* a number with a certain property, but it doesn't tell us how to find the number.

THE MEAN VALUE THEOREM Let f be a function that satisfies the following hypotheses:

1. f is continuous on the closed interval $[a, b]$.

2. f is differentiable on the open interval (a, b).

Then there is a number c in (a, b) such that

1
$$f'(c) = \frac{f(b) - f(a)}{b - a}$$

or, equivalently,

2
$$f(b) - f(a) = f'(c)(b - a)$$

Before proving this theorem, we can see that it is reasonable by interpreting it geometrically. Figures 3 and 4 show the points $A(a, f(a))$ and $B(b, f(b))$ on the graphs of two differentiable functions. The slope of the secant line AB is

3
$$m_{AB} = \frac{f(b) - f(a)}{b - a}$$

which is the same expression as on the right side of Equation 1. Since $f'(c)$ is the slope of the tangent line at the point $(c, f(c))$, the Mean Value Theorem, in the form given by Equation 1, says that there is at least one point $P(c, f(c))$ on the graph where the slope of the tangent line is the same as the slope of the secant line AB. In other words, there is a point P where the tangent line is parallel to the secant line AB.

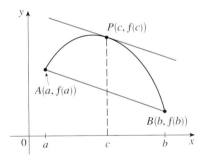

FIGURE 3

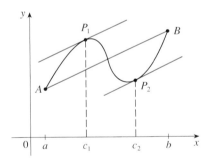

FIGURE 4

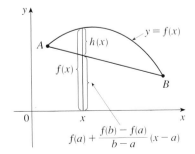

FIGURE 5

PROOF We apply Rolle's Theorem to a new function h defined as the difference between f and the function whose graph is the secant line AB. Using Equation 3, we see that the equation of the line AB can be written as

$$y - f(a) = \frac{f(b) - f(a)}{b - a}(x - a)$$

or as

$$y = f(a) + \frac{f(b) - f(a)}{b - a}(x - a)$$

So, as shown in Figure 5,

4
$$h(x) = f(x) - f(a) - \frac{f(b) - f(a)}{b - a}(x - a)$$

First we must verify that h satisfies the three hypotheses of Rolle's Theorem.

1. The function h is continuous on $[a, b]$ because it is the sum of f and a first-degree polynomial, both of which are continuous.

2. The function h is differentiable on (a, b) because both f and the first-degree polynomial are differentiable. In fact, we can compute h' directly from Equation 4:

$$h'(x) = f'(x) - \frac{f(b) - f(a)}{b - a}$$

(Note that $f(a)$ and $[f(b) - f(a)]/(b - a)$ are constants.)

3.
$$h(a) = f(a) - f(a) - \frac{f(b) - f(a)}{b - a}(a - a) = 0$$

$$h(b) = f(b) - f(a) - \frac{f(b) - f(a)}{b - a}(b - a)$$

$$= f(b) - f(a) - [f(b) - f(a)] = 0$$

Therefore, $h(a) = h(b)$.

Since h satisfies the hypotheses of Rolle's Theorem, that theorem says there is a number c in (a, b) such that $h'(c) = 0$. Therefore

$$0 = h'(c) = f'(c) - \frac{f(b) - f(a)}{b - a}$$

and so
$$f'(c) = \frac{f(b) - f(a)}{b - a}$$

▼ EXAMPLE 3 To illustrate the Mean Value Theorem with a specific function, let's consider $f(x) = x^3 - x$, $a = 0$, $b = 2$. Since f is a polynomial, it is continuous and differentiable for all x, so it is certainly continuous on $[0, 2]$ and differentiable on $(0, 2)$. Therefore, by the Mean Value Theorem, there is a number c in $(0, 2)$ such that

$$f(2) - f(0) = f'(c)(2 - 0)$$

Now $f(2) = 6$, $f(0) = 0$, and $f'(x) = 3x^2 - 1$, so this equation becomes

$$6 = (3c^2 - 1)2 = 6c^2 - 2$$

which gives $c^2 = \frac{4}{3}$, that is, $c = \pm 2/\sqrt{3}$. But c must lie in $(0, 2)$, so $c = 2/\sqrt{3}$. Figure 6 illustrates this calculation: The tangent line at this value of c is parallel to the secant line OB.

▼ EXAMPLE 4 If an object moves in a straight line with position function $s = f(t)$, then the average velocity between $t = a$ and $t = b$ is

$$\frac{f(b) - f(a)}{b - a}$$

■ The Mean Value Theorem was first formulated by Joseph-Louis Lagrange (1736–1813), born in Italy of a French father and an Italian mother. He was a child prodigy and became a professor in Turin at the tender age of 19. Lagrange made great contributions to number theory, theory of functions, theory of equations, and analytical and celestial mechanics. In particular, he applied calculus to the analysis of the stability of the solar system. At the invitation of Frederick the Great, he succeeded Euler at the Berlin Academy and, when Frederick died, Lagrange accepted King Louis XVI's invitation to Paris, where he was given apartments in the Louvre. Despite all the trappings of luxury and fame, he was a kind and quiet man, living only for science.

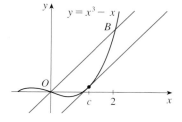

FIGURE 6

and the velocity at $t = c$ is $f'(c)$. Thus the Mean Value Theorem (in the form of Equation 1) tells us that at some time $t = c$ between a and b the instantaneous velocity $f'(c)$ is equal to that average velocity. For instance, if a car traveled 180 km in 2 hours, then the speedometer must have read 90 km/h at least once.

In general, the Mean Value Theorem can be interpreted as saying that there is a number at which the instantaneous rate of change is equal to the average rate of change over an interval. ▪

The main significance of the Mean Value Theorem is that it enables us to obtain information about a function from information about its derivative. The next example provides an instance of this principle.

☑ **EXAMPLE 5** Suppose that $f(0) = -3$ and $f'(x) \leq 5$ for all values of x. How large can $f(2)$ possibly be?

SOLUTION We are given that f is differentiable (and therefore continuous) every-where. In particular, we can apply the Mean Value Theorem on the interval $[0, 2]$. There exists a number c such that

$$f(2) - f(0) = f'(c)(2 - 0)$$

so $$f(2) = f(0) + 2f'(c) = -3 + 2f'(c)$$

We are given that $f'(x) \leq 5$ for all x, so in particular we know that $f'(c) \leq 5$. Multiplying both sides of this inequality by 2, we have $2f'(c) \leq 10$, so

$$f(2) = -3 + 2f'(c) \leq -3 + 10 = 7$$

The largest possible value for $f(2)$ is 7. ▪

The Mean Value Theorem can be used to establish some of the basic facts of differential calculus. One of these basic facts is the following theorem. Others will be found in the following sections.

---

5 THEOREM If $f'(x) = 0$ for all x in an interval (a, b), then f is constant on (a, b).

PROOF Let x_1 and x_2 be any two numbers in (a, b) with $x_1 < x_2$. Since f is differentiable on (a, b), it must be differentiable on (x_1, x_2) and continuous on $[x_1, x_2]$. By applying the Mean Value Theorem to f on the interval $[x_1, x_2]$, we get a number c such that $x_1 < c < x_2$ and

6 $$f(x_2) - f(x_1) = f'(c)(x_2 - x_1)$$

Since $f'(x) = 0$ for all x, we have $f'(c) = 0$, and so Equation 6 becomes

$$f(x_2) - f(x_1) = 0 \qquad \text{or} \qquad f(x_2) = f(x_1)$$

Therefore, f has the same value at *any* two numbers x_1 and x_2 in (a, b). This means that f is constant on (a, b). ☐

> **7 COROLLARY** If $f'(x) = g'(x)$ for all x in an interval (a, b), then $f - g$ is constant on (a, b); that is, $f(x) = g(x) + c$ where c is a constant.

PROOF Let $F(x) = f(x) - g(x)$. Then

$$F'(x) = f'(x) - g'(x) = 0$$

for all x in (a, b). Thus, by Theorem 5, F is constant; that is, $f - g$ is constant. □

NOTE Care must be taken in applying Theorem 5. Let

$$f(x) = \frac{x}{|x|} = \begin{cases} 1 & \text{if } x > 0 \\ -1 & \text{if } x < 0 \end{cases}$$

The domain of f is $D = \{x \mid x \neq 0\}$ and $f'(x) = 0$ for all x in D. But f is obviously not a constant function. This does not contradict Theorem 5 because D is not an interval. Notice that f is constant on the interval $(0, \infty)$ and also on the interval $(-\infty, 0)$.

We will make extensive use of Theorem 5 and Corollary 7 when we study antiderivatives in Section 4.7.

4.2 EXERCISES

1–4 ■ Verify that the function satisfies the three hypotheses of Rolle's Theorem on the given interval. Then find all numbers c that satisfy the conclusion of Rolle's Theorem.

1. $f(x) = x^2 - 4x + 1$, $[0, 4]$

2. $f(x) = x^3 - 3x^2 + 2x + 5$, $[0, 2]$

3. $f(x) = \sin 2\pi x$, $[-1, 1]$

4. $f(x) = x\sqrt{x + 6}$, $[-6, 0]$

■ ■ ■ ■ ■ ■ ■ ■ ■ ■ ■ ■ ■ ■

5. Let $f(x) = 1 - x^{2/3}$. Show that $f(-1) = f(1)$ but there is no number c in $(-1, 1)$ such that $f'(c) = 0$. Why does this not contradict Rolle's Theorem?

6. Let $f(x) = (x - 1)^{-2}$. Show that $f(0) = f(2)$ but there is no number c in $(0, 2)$ such that $f'(c) = 0$. Why does this not contradict Rolle's Theorem?

7. Use the graph of f to estimate the values of c that satisfy the conclusion of the Mean Value Theorem for the interval $[0, 8]$.

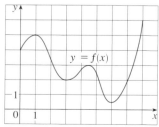

8. Use the graph of f given in Exercise 7 to estimate the values of c that satisfy the conclusion of the Mean Value Theorem for the interval $[1, 7]$.

9. (a) Graph the function $f(x) = x + 4/x$ in the viewing rectangle $[0, 10]$ by $[0, 10]$.
   (b) Graph the secant line that passes through the points $(1, 5)$ and $(8, 8.5)$ on the same screen with f.
   (c) Find the number c that satisfies the conclusion of the Mean Value Theorem for this function f and the interval $[1, 8]$. Then graph the tangent line at the point $(c, f(c))$ and notice that it is parallel to the secant line.

10. (a) In the viewing rectangle $[-3, 3]$ by $[-5, 5]$, graph the function $f(x) = x^3 - 2x$ and its secant line through the points $(-2, -4)$ and $(2, 4)$. Use the graph to estimate the x-coordinates of the points where the tangent line is parallel to the secant line.
   (b) Find the exact values of the numbers c that satisfy the conclusion of the Mean Value Theorem for the interval $[-2, 2]$ and compare with your answers to part (a).

11–14 ■ Verify that the function satisfies the hypotheses of the Mean Value Theorem on the given interval. Then find all numbers c that satisfy the conclusion of the Mean Value Theorem.

11. $f(x) = 3x^2 + 2x + 5$, $[-1, 1]$

12. $f(x) = x^3 + x - 1$, $[0, 2]$

13. $f(x) = e^{-2x}$, $[0, 3]$

14. $f(x) = \dfrac{x}{x + 2}$, $[1, 4]$

▪ ▪ ▪ ▪ ▪ ▪ ▪ ▪ ▪ ▪ ▪ ▪

15. Let $f(x) = |x - 1|$. Show that there is no value of c such that $f(3) - f(0) = f'(c)(3 - 0)$. Why does this not contradict the Mean Value Theorem?

16. Let $f(x) = (x + 1)/(x - 1)$. Show that there is no value of c such that $f(2) - f(0) = f'(c)(2 - 0)$. Why does this not contradict the Mean Value Theorem?

17. Show that the equation $1 + 2x + x^3 + 4x^5 = 0$ has exactly one real root.

18. Show that the equation $2x - 1 - \sin x = 0$ has exactly one real root.

19. Show that the equation $x^3 - 15x + c = 0$ has at most one root in the interval $[-2, 2]$.

20. Show that the equation $x^4 + 4x + c = 0$ has at most two real roots.

21. (a) Show that a polynomial of degree 3 has at most three real roots.
    (b) Show that a polynomial of degree n has at most n real roots.

22. (a) Suppose that f is differentiable on $\mathbb{R}$ and has two roots. Show that f' has at least one root.
    (b) Suppose f is twice differentiable on $\mathbb{R}$ and has three roots. Show that f'' has at least one real root.
    (c) Can you generalize parts (a) and (b)?

23. If $f(1) = 10$ and $f'(x) \geq 2$ for $1 \leq x \leq 4$, how small can $f(4)$ possibly be?

24. Suppose that $3 \leq f'(x) \leq 5$ for all values of x. Show that $18 \leq f(8) - f(2) \leq 30$.

25. Does there exist a function f such that $f(0) = -1$, $f(2) = 4$, and $f'(x) \leq 2$ for all x?

26. Suppose that f and g are continuous on $[a, b]$ and differentiable on (a, b). Suppose also that $f(a) = g(a)$ and $f'(x) < g'(x)$ for $a < x < b$. Prove that $f(b) < g(b)$. [Hint: Apply the Mean Value Theorem to the function $h = f - g$.]

27. Show that $\sqrt{1 + x} < 1 + \frac{1}{2}x$ if $x > 0$.

28. Suppose f is an odd function and is differentiable everywhere. Prove that for every positive number b, there exists a number c in $(-b, b)$ such that $f'(c) = f(b)/b$.

29. Use the Mean Value Theorem to prove the inequality
$$| \sin a - \sin b | \leq |a - b| \qquad \text{for all } a \text{ and } b$$

30. If $f'(x) = c$ (c a constant) for all x, use Corollary 7 to show that $f(x) = cx + d$ for some constant d.

31. Let $f(x) = 1/x$ and
$$g(x) = \begin{cases} \dfrac{1}{x} & \text{if } x > 0 \\[2mm] 1 + \dfrac{1}{x} & \text{if } x < 0 \end{cases}$$

Show that $f'(x) = g'(x)$ for all x in their domains. Can we conclude from Corollary 7 that $f - g$ is constant?

32. Use Theorem 5 to prove the identity
$$2 \sin^{-1}x = \cos^{-1}(1 - 2x^2) \qquad x \geq 0$$

33. Prove the identity
$$\arcsin \frac{x - 1}{x + 1} = 2 \arctan \sqrt{x} - \frac{\pi}{2}$$

34. At 2:00 PM a car's speedometer reads 30 mi/h. At 2:10 PM it reads 50 mi/h. Show that at some time between 2:00 and 2:10 the acceleration is exactly 120 mi/h².

35. Two runners start a race at the same time and finish in a tie. Prove that at some time during the race they have the same speed. [Hint: Consider $f(t) = g(t) - h(t)$, where g and h are the position functions of the two runners.]

36. A number a is called a **fixed point** of a function f if $f(a) = a$. Prove that if $f'(x) \neq 1$ for all real numbers x, then f has at most one fixed point.

4.3	**DERIVATIVES AND THE SHAPES OF GRAPHS**

Many of the applications of calculus depend on our ability to deduce facts about a function f from information concerning its derivatives. Because $f'(x)$ represents the slope of the curve $y = f(x)$ at the point $(x, f(x))$, it tells us the direction in which the curve proceeds at each point. So it is reasonable to expect that information about $f'(x)$ will provide us with information about $f(x)$.

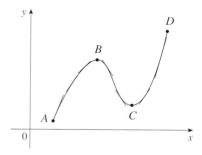

FIGURE 1

▪ Let's abbreviate the name of this test to the I/D Test.

WHAT DOES f' SAY ABOUT f?

To see how the derivative of f can tell us where a function is increasing or decreasing, look at Figure 1. (Increasing functions and decreasing functions were defined in Section 1.1.) Between A and B and between C and D, the tangent lines have positive slope and so $f'(x) > 0$. Between B and C, the tangent lines have negative slope and so $f'(x) < 0$. Thus it appears that f increases when $f'(x)$ is positive and decreases when $f'(x)$ is negative. To prove that this is always the case, we use the Mean Value Theorem.

INCREASING/DECREASING TEST

(a) If $f'(x) > 0$ on an interval, then f is increasing on that interval.

(b) If $f'(x) < 0$ on an interval, then f is decreasing on that interval.

PROOF

(a) Let x_1 and x_2 be any two numbers in the interval with $x_1 < x_2$. According to the definition of an increasing function (page 7) we have to show that $f(x_1) < f(x_2)$.

Because we are given that $f'(x) > 0$, we know that f is differentiable on $[x_1, x_2]$. So, by the Mean Value Theorem there is a number c between x_1 and x_2 such that

$$\boxed{1} \qquad f(x_2) - f(x_1) = f'(c)(x_2 - x_1)$$

Now $f'(c) > 0$ by assumption and $x_2 - x_1 > 0$ because $x_1 < x_2$. Thus the right side of Equation 1 is positive, and so

$$f(x_2) - f(x_1) > 0 \qquad \text{or} \qquad f(x_1) < f(x_2)$$

This shows that f is increasing.

Part (b) is proved similarly. ☐

▼ **EXAMPLE 1** Find where the function $f(x) = 3x^4 - 4x^3 - 12x^2 + 5$ is increasing and where it is decreasing.

SOLUTION $\qquad f'(x) = 12x^3 - 12x^2 - 24x = 12x(x - 2)(x + 1)$

To use the I/D Test we have to know where $f'(x) > 0$ and where $f'(x) < 0$. This depends on the signs of the three factors of $f'(x)$, namely, $12x$, $x - 2$, and $x + 1$. We divide the real line into intervals whose endpoints are the critical numbers -1, 0, and 2 and arrange our work in a chart. A plus sign indicates that the given expression is positive, and a minus sign indicates that it is negative. The last column of the chart gives the conclusion based on the I/D Test. For instance, $f'(x) < 0$ for $0 < x < 2$, so f is decreasing on $(0, 2)$. (It would also be true to say that f is decreasing on the closed interval $[0, 2]$.)

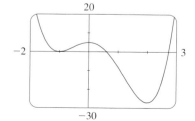

FIGURE 2

Interval	$12x$	$x - 2$	$x + 1$	$f'(x)$	f
$x < -1$	$-$	$-$	$-$	$-$	decreasing on $(-\infty, -1)$
$-1 < x < 0$	$-$	$-$	$+$	$+$	increasing on $(-1, 0)$
$0 < x < 2$	$+$	$-$	$+$	$-$	decreasing on $(0, 2)$
$x > 2$	$+$	$+$	$+$	$+$	increasing on $(2, \infty)$

The graph of f shown in Figure 2 confirms the information in the chart. ▪

Recall from Section 4.1 that if f has a local maximum or minimum at c, then c must be a critical number of f (by Fermat's Theorem), but not every critical number gives rise to a maximum or a minimum. We therefore need a test that will tell us whether or not f has a local maximum or minimum at a critical number.

You can see from Figure 2 that $f(0) = 5$ is a local maximum value of f because f increases on $(-1, 0)$ and decreases on $(0, 2)$. Or, in terms of derivatives, $f'(x) > 0$ for $-1 < x < 0$ and $f'(x) < 0$ for $0 < x < 2$. In other words, the sign of $f'(x)$ changes from positive to negative at 0. This observation is the basis of the following test.

> **THE FIRST DERIVATIVE TEST** Suppose that c is a critical number of a continuous function f.
> (a) If f' changes from positive to negative at c, then f has a local maximum at c.
> (b) If f' changes from negative to positive at c, then f has a local minimum at c.
> (c) If f' does not change sign at c (that is, f' is positive on both sides of c or negative on both sides), then f has no local maximum or minimum at c.

The First Derivative Test is a consequence of the I/D Test. In part (a), for instance, since the sign of $f'(x)$ changes from positive to negative at c, f is increasing to the left of c and decreasing to the right of c. It follows that f has a local maximum at c.

It is easy to remember the First Derivative Test by visualizing diagrams such as those in Figure 3.

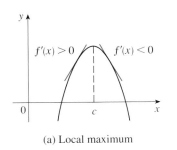
(a) Local maximum

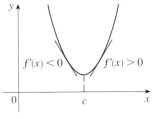
(b) Local minimum

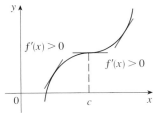
(c) No maximum or minimum

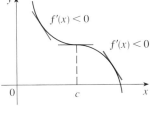
(d) No maximum or minimum

FIGURE 3

▼ EXAMPLE 2 Find the local minimum and maximum values of the function f in Example 1.

SOLUTION From the chart in the solution to Example 1 we see that $f'(x)$ changes from negative to positive at -1, so $f(-1) = 0$ is a local minimum value by the First Derivative Test. Similarly, f' changes from negative to positive at 2, so $f(2) = -27$ is also a local minimum value. As previously noted, $f(0) = 5$ is a local maximum value because $f'(x)$ changes from positive to negative at 0. ▪

EXAMPLE 3 Find the local maximum and minimum values of the function

$$g(x) = x + 2 \sin x \qquad 0 \le x \le 2\pi$$

SOLUTION To find the critical numbers of g, we differentiate:

$$g'(x) = 1 + 2 \cos x$$

So $g'(x) = 0$ when $\cos x = -\frac{1}{2}$. The solutions of this equation are $2\pi/3$ and $4\pi/3$. Because g is differentiable everywhere, the only critical numbers are $2\pi/3$ and $4\pi/3$ and so we analyze g in the following table.

■ The + signs in the table come from the fact that $g'(x) > 0$ when $\cos x > -\frac{1}{2}$. From the graph of $y = \cos x$, this is true in the indicated intervals.

Interval	$g'(x) = 1 + 2 \cos x$	g
$0 < x < 2\pi/3$	+	increasing on $(0, 2\pi/3)$
$2\pi/3 < x < 4\pi/3$	−	decreasing on $(2\pi/3, 4\pi/3)$
$4\pi/3 < x < 2\pi$	+	increasing on $(4\pi/3, 2\pi)$

Because $g'(x)$ changes from positive to negative at $2\pi/3$, the First Derivative Test tells us that there is a local maximum at $2\pi/3$ and the local maximum value is

$$g(2\pi/3) = \frac{2\pi}{3} + 2 \sin \frac{2\pi}{3} = \frac{2\pi}{3} + 2\left(\frac{\sqrt{3}}{2}\right) = \frac{2\pi}{3} + \sqrt{3} \approx 3.83$$

Likewise, $g'(x)$ changes from negative to positive at $4\pi/3$ and so

$$g(4\pi/3) = \frac{4\pi}{3} + 2 \sin \frac{4\pi}{3} = \frac{4\pi}{3} + 2\left(-\frac{\sqrt{3}}{2}\right) = \frac{4\pi}{3} - \sqrt{3} \approx 2.46$$

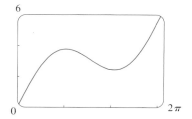

FIGURE 4
$y = x + 2 \sin x$

is a local minimum value. The graph of g in Figure 4 supports our conclusion. ■

WHAT DOES f'' SAY ABOUT f?

Figure 5 shows the graphs of two increasing functions on (a, b). Both graphs join point A to point B but they look different because they bend in different directions. How can we distinguish between these two types of behavior? In Figure 6 tangents to these curves have been drawn at several points. In (a) the curve lies above the tangents and f is called *concave upward* on (a, b). In (b) the curve lies below the tangents and g is called *concave downward* on (a, b).

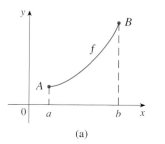

(a)

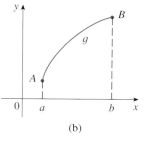

(b)

FIGURE 5

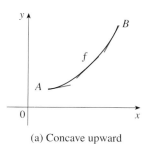

(a) Concave upward

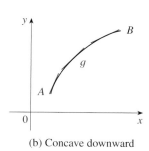

(b) Concave downward

FIGURE 6

DEFINITION If the graph of f lies above all of its tangents on an interval I, then it is called **concave upward** on I. If the graph of f lies below all of its tangents on I, it is called **concave downward** on I.

Figure 7 shows the graph of a function that is concave upward (abbreviated CU) on the intervals (b, c), (d, e), and (e, p) and concave downward (CD) on the intervals (a, b), (c, d), and (p, q).

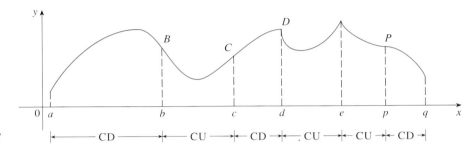

FIGURE 7

> **DEFINITION**   A point P on a curve $y = f(x)$ is called an **inflection point** if f is continuous there and the curve changes from concave upward to concave downward or from concave downward to concave upward at P.

For instance, in Figure 7, B, C, D, and P are the points of inflection. Notice that if a curve has a tangent at a point of inflection, then the curve crosses its tangent there.

Let's see how the second derivative helps determine the intervals of concavity. Looking at Figure 6(a), you can see that, going from left to right, the slope of the tangent increases. This means that the derivative f' is an increasing function and therefore its derivative f'' is positive. Likewise, in Figure 6(b) the slope of the tangent decreases from left to right, so f' decreases and therefore f'' is negative. This reasoning can be reversed and suggests that the following theorem is true. A proof is given in Appendix B with the help of the Mean Value Theorem.

> **CONCAVITY TEST**
>
> (a) If $f''(x) > 0$ for all x in I, then the graph of f is concave upward on I.
>
> (b) If $f''(x) < 0$ for all x in I, then the graph of f is concave downward on I.

In view of the Concavity Test, there is a point of inflection at any point where the second derivative changes sign.

☑ **EXAMPLE 4**   Sketch a possible graph of a function f that satisfies the following conditions:

   (i) $f'(x) > 0$ on $(-\infty, 1)$, $f'(x) < 0$ on $(1, \infty)$

   (ii) $f''(x) > 0$ on $(-\infty, -2)$ and $(2, \infty)$, $f''(x) < 0$ on $(-2, 2)$

   (iii) $\lim_{x \to -\infty} f(x) = -2$, $\lim_{x \to \infty} f(x) = 0$

SOLUTION   Condition (i) tells us that f is increasing on $(-\infty, 1)$ and decreasing on $(1, \infty)$. Condition (ii) says that f is concave upward on $(-\infty, -2)$ and $(2, \infty)$, and concave downward on $(-2, 2)$. From condition (iii) we know that the graph of f has two horizontal asymptotes: $y = -2$ and $y = 0$.

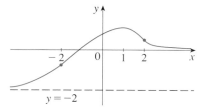

FIGURE 8

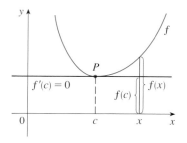

FIGURE 9
$f''(c) > 0$, f is concave upward

We first draw the horizontal asymptote $y = -2$ as a dashed line (see Figure 8). We then draw the graph of f approaching this asymptote at the far left, increasing to its maximum point at $x = 1$ and decreasing toward the x-axis at the far right. We also make sure that the graph has inflection points when $x = -2$ and 2. Notice that we made the curve bend upward for $x < -2$ and $x > 2$, and bend downward when x is between -2 and 2. ■

Another application of the second derivative is the following test for maximum and minimum values. It is a consequence of the Concavity Test.

THE SECOND DERIVATIVE TEST Suppose f'' is continuous near c.
(a) If $f'(c) = 0$ and $f''(c) > 0$, then f has a local minimum at c.
(b) If $f'(c) = 0$ and $f''(c) < 0$, then f has a local maximum at c.

For instance, part (a) is true because $f''(x) > 0$ near c and so f is concave upward near c. This means that the graph of f lies *above* its horizontal tangent at c and so f has a local minimum at c. (See Figure 9.)

▼ EXAMPLE 5 Discuss the curve $y = x^4 - 4x^3$ with respect to concavity, points of inflection, and local maxima and minima. Use this information to sketch the curve.

SOLUTION If $f(x) = x^4 - 4x^3$, then

$$f'(x) = 4x^3 - 12x^2 = 4x^2(x - 3)$$
$$f''(x) = 12x^2 - 24x = 12x(x - 2)$$

To find the critical numbers we set $f'(x) = 0$ and obtain $x = 0$ and $x = 3$. To use the Second Derivative Test we evaluate f'' at these critical numbers:

$$f''(0) = 0 \qquad f''(3) = 36 > 0$$

Since $f'(3) = 0$ and $f''(3) > 0$, $f(3) = -27$ is a local minimum. Since $f''(0) = 0$, the Second Derivative Test gives no information about the critical number 0. But since $f'(x) < 0$ for $x < 0$ and also for $0 < x < 3$, the First Derivative Test tells us that f does not have a local maximum or minimum at 0. [In fact, the expression for $f'(x)$ shows that f decreases to the left of 3 and increases to the right of 3.]

Since $f''(x) = 0$ when $x = 0$ or 2, we divide the real line into intervals with these numbers as endpoints and complete the following chart.

Interval	$f''(x) = 12x(x - 2)$	Concavity
$(-\infty, 0)$	$+$	upward
$(0, 2)$	$-$	downward
$(2, \infty)$	$+$	upward

The point $(0, 0)$ is an inflection point since the curve changes from concave upward to concave downward there. Also $(2, -16)$ is an inflection point since the curve changes from concave downward to concave upward there.

Using the local minimum, the intervals of concavity, and the inflection points, we sketch the curve in Figure 10. ■

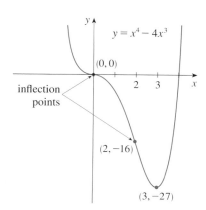

FIGURE 10

NOTE The Second Derivative Test is inconclusive when $f''(c) = 0$. In other words, at such a point there might be a maximum, there might be a minimum, or there might be neither (as in Example 5). This test also fails when $f''(c)$ does not exist. In such cases the First Derivative Test must be used. In fact, even when both tests apply, the First Derivative Test is often the easier one to use.

EXAMPLE 6 Sketch the graph of the function $f(x) = x^{2/3}(6 - x)^{1/3}$.

SOLUTION You can use the differentiation rules to check that the first two derivatives are

$$f'(x) = \frac{4 - x}{x^{1/3}(6 - x)^{2/3}} \qquad f''(x) = \frac{-8}{x^{4/3}(6 - x)^{5/3}}$$

Since $f'(x) = 0$ when $x = 4$ and $f'(x)$ does not exist when $x = 0$ or $x = 6$, the critical numbers are 0, 4, and 6.

■ Try reproducing the graph in Figure 11 with a graphing calculator or computer. Some machines produce the complete graph, some produce only the portion to the right of the *y*-axis, and some produce only the portion between $x = 0$ and $x = 6$. An equivalent expression that gives the correct graph is

$$y = (x^2)^{1/3} \cdot \frac{6 - x}{|6 - x|} |6 - x|^{1/3}$$

Interval	$4 - x$	$x^{1/3}$	$(6 - x)^{2/3}$	$f'(x)$	f
$x < 0$	$+$	$-$	$+$	$-$	decreasing on $(-\infty, 0)$
$0 < x < 4$	$+$	$+$	$+$	$+$	increasing on $(0, 4)$
$4 < x < 6$	$-$	$+$	$+$	$-$	decreasing on $(4, 6)$
$x > 6$	$-$	$+$	$+$	$-$	decreasing on $(6, \infty)$

To find the local extreme values we use the First Derivative Test. Since f' changes from negative to positive at 0, $f(0) = 0$ is a local minimum. Since f' changes from positive to negative at 4, $f(4) = 2^{5/3}$ is a local maximum. The sign of f' does not change at 6, so there is no minimum or maximum there. (The Second Derivative Test could be used at 4 but not at 0 or 6 since f'' does not exist at either of these numbers.)

Looking at the expression for $f''(x)$ and noting that $x^{4/3} \geqslant 0$ for all x, we have $f''(x) < 0$ for $x < 0$ and for $0 < x < 6$ and $f''(x) > 0$ for $x > 6$. So f is concave downward on $(-\infty, 0)$ and $(0, 6)$ and concave upward on $(6, \infty)$, and the only inflection point is $(6, 0)$. The graph is sketched in Figure 11. Note that the curve has vertical tangents at $(0, 0)$ and $(6, 0)$ because $|f'(x)| \to \infty$ as $x \to 0$ and as $x \to 6$. ■

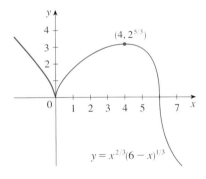

FIGURE 11

1–8 ■

(a) Find the intervals on which f is increasing or decreasing.

(b) Find the local maximum and minimum values of f.

(c) Find the intervals of concavity and the inflection points.

1. $f(x) = x^3 - 12x + 1$

2. $f(x) = x^4 - 4x - 1$

3. $f(x) = x - 2 \sin x, \quad 0 < x < 3\pi$

4. $f(x) = \dfrac{x^2}{x^2 + 3}$

5. $f(x) = xe^x$

6. $f(x) = x^2 e^x$

7. $f(x) = (\ln x)/\sqrt{x}$

8. $f(x) = x \ln x$

■ ■ ■ ■ ■ ■ ■ ■ ■ ■ ■ ■ ■

9–10 ■ Find the local maximum and minimum values of f using both the First and Second Derivative Tests. Which method do you prefer?

9. $f(x) = x + \sqrt{1 - x}$

10. $f(x) = \dfrac{x}{x^2 + 4}$

■ ■ ■ ■ ■ ■ ■ ■ ■ ■ ■ ■ ■

11. Suppose f'' is continuous on $(-\infty, \infty)$.

(a) If $f'(2) = 0$ and $f''(2) = -5$, what can you say about f?

(b) If $f'(6) = 0$ and $f''(6) = 0$, what can you say about f?

12. (a) Find the critical numbers of $f(x) = x^4(x - 1)^3$.

(b) What does the Second Derivative Test tell you about the behavior of f at these critical numbers?

(c) What does the First Derivative Test tell you?

13. In each part state the x-coordinates of the inflection points of f. Give reasons for your answers.
(a) The curve is the graph of f.
(b) The curve is the graph of f'.
(c) The curve is the graph of f''.

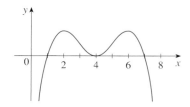

14. The graph of the first derivative f' of a function f is shown.
(a) On what intervals is f increasing? Explain.
(b) At what values of x does f have a local maximum or minimum? Explain.
(c) On what intervals is f concave upward or concave downward? Explain.
(d) What are the x-coordinates of the inflection points of f? Why?

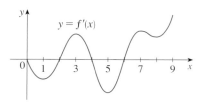

15–20 ■ Sketch the graph of a function that satisfies all of the given conditions.

15. $f'(x)$ and $f''(x)$ are always negative

16. $f'(x) > 0$ for all $x \neq 1$, vertical asymptote $x = 1$,
$f''(x) > 0$ if $x < 1$ or $x > 3$, $f''(x) < 0$ if $1 < x < 3$

17. $f'(0) = f'(2) = f'(4) = 0$,
$f'(x) > 0$ if $x < 0$ or $2 < x < 4$,
$f'(x) < 0$ if $0 < x < 2$ or $x > 4$,
$f''(x) > 0$ if $1 < x < 3$, $f''(x) < 0$ if $x < 1$ or $x > 3$

18. $f'(1) = f'(-1) = 0$, $f'(x) < 0$ if $|x| < 1$,
$f'(x) > 0$ if $1 < |x| < 2$, $f'(x) = -1$ if $|x| > 2$,
$f''(x) < 0$ if $-2 < x < 0$, inflection point $(0, 1)$

19. $f'(x) > 0$ if $|x| < 2$, $f'(x) < 0$ if $|x| > 2$,
$f'(-2) = 0$, $\lim_{x \to 2} |f'(x)| = \infty$, $f''(x) > 0$ if $x \neq 2$

20. $f'(x) > 0$ if $|x| < 2$, $f'(x) < 0$ if $|x| > 2$,
$f'(2) = 0$, $\lim_{x \to \infty} f(x) = 1$, $f(-x) = -f(x)$,
$f''(x) < 0$ if $0 < x < 3$, $f''(x) > 0$ if $x > 3$

21–22 ■ The graph of the derivative f' of a continuous function f is shown.
(a) On what intervals is f increasing or decreasing?
(b) At what values of x does f have a local maximum or minimum?
(c) On what intervals is f concave upward or downward?
(d) State the x-coordinate(s) of the point(s) of inflection.
(e) Assuming that $f(0) = 0$, sketch a graph of f.

21.

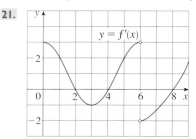

22.

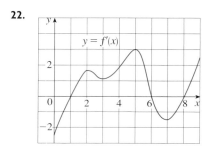

23–34 ■
(a) Find the intervals of increase or decrease.
(b) Find the local maximum and minimum values.
(c) Find the intervals of concavity and the inflection points.
(d) Use the information from parts (a)–(c) to sketch the graph. Check your work with a graphing device if you have one.

23. $f(x) = 2x^3 - 3x^2 - 12x$ **24.** $f(x) = 2 + 3x - x^3$

25. $f(x) = x^4 - 6x^2$

26. $g(x) = 200 + 8x^3 + x^4$

27. $h(x) = 3x^5 - 5x^3 + 3$ **28.** $h(x) = (x^2 - 1)^3$

29. $A(x) = x\sqrt{x + 3}$ **30.** $B(x) = 3x^{2/3} - x$

31. $C(x) = x^{1/3}(x + 4)$

32. $f(x) = \ln(x^4 + 27)$

33. $f(\theta) = 2 \cos \theta - \cos 2\theta$, $0 \leq \theta \leq 2\pi$

34. $f(t) = t + \cos t$, $-2\pi \leq t \leq 2\pi$

35–42 ■
(a) Find the vertical and horizontal asymptotes.
(b) Find the intervals of increase or decrease.
(c) Find the local maximum and minimum values.

(d) Find the intervals of concavity and the inflection points.
(e) Use the information from parts (a)–(d) to sketch the graph of f.

35. $f(x) = \dfrac{x^2}{x^2 - 1}$

36. $f(x) = \dfrac{x^2}{(x - 2)^2}$

37. $f(x) = \sqrt{x^2 + 1} - x$

38. $f(x) = x \tan x, \quad -\pi/2 < x < \pi/2$

39. $f(x) = \ln(1 - \ln x)$ **40.** $f(x) = \dfrac{e^x}{1 + e^x}$

41. $f(x) = e^{-1/(x+1)}$ **42.** $f(x) = \ln(\tan^2 x)$

▪   ▪   ▪   ▪   ▪   ▪   ▪   ▪   ▪   ▪   ▪   ▪

43. Suppose the derivative of a function f is
$f'(x) = (x + 1)^2(x - 3)^5(x - 6)^4$. On what interval is f increasing?

44. Use the methods of this section to sketch the curve
$y = x^3 - 3a^2x + 2a^3$, where a is a positive constant. What do the members of this family of curves have in common? How do they differ from each other?

45–46 ▪
(a) Use a graph of f to estimate the maximum and minimum values. Then find the exact values.
(b) Estimate the value of x at which f increases most rapidly. Then find the exact value.

45. $f(x) = \dfrac{x + 1}{\sqrt{x^2 + 1}}$ **46.** $f(x) = x^2 e^{-x}$

▪   ▪   ▪   ▪   ▪   ▪   ▪   ▪   ▪   ▪   ▪   ▪

47. For the period from 1980 to 2000, the percentage of households in the United States with at least one VCR has been modeled by the function

$$V(t) = \frac{85}{1 + 53e^{-0.5t}}$$

where the time t is measured in years since midyear 1980, so $0 \le t \le 20$. Use a graph to estimate the time at which the number of VCRs was increasing most rapidly. Then use derivatives to give a more accurate estimate.

48. The family of bell-shaped curves

$$y = \frac{1}{\sigma\sqrt{2\pi}} e^{-(x-\mu)^2/(2\sigma^2)}$$

occurs in probability and statistics, where it is called the *normal density function*. The constant μ is called the *mean*

and the positive constant σ is called the *standard deviation*. For simplicity, let's scale the function so as to remove the factor $1/(\sigma\sqrt{2\pi})$ and let's analyze the special case where $\mu = 0$. So we study the function

$$f(x) = e^{-x^2/(2\sigma^2)}$$

(a) Find the asymptote, maximum value, and inflection points of f.
(b) What role does σ play in the shape of the curve?
(c) Illustrate by graphing four members of this family on the same screen.

49. Find a cubic function $f(x) = ax^3 + bx^2 + cx + d$ that has a local maximum value of 3 at -2 and a local minimum value of 0 at 1.

50. For what values of the numbers a and b does the function

$$f(x) = axe^{bx^2}$$

have the maximum value $f(2) = 1$?

51. Show that $\tan x > x$ for $0 < x < \pi/2$. [*Hint:* Show that $f(x) = \tan x - x$ is increasing on $(0, \pi/2)$.]

52. (a) Show that $e^x \ge 1 + x$ for $x \ge 0$.
(b) Deduce that $e^x \ge 1 + x + \frac{1}{2}x^2$ for $x \ge 0$.
(c) Use mathematical induction to prove that for $x \ge 0$ and any positive integer n,

$$e^x \ge 1 + x + \frac{x^2}{2!} + \cdots + \frac{x^n}{n!}$$

53. Show that a cubic function (a third-degree polynomial) always has exactly one point of inflection. If its graph has three x-intercepts x_1, x_2, and x_3, show that the x-coordinate of the inflection point is $(x_1 + x_2 + x_3)/3$.

54. For what values of c does the polynomial
$P(x) = x^4 + cx^3 + x^2$ have two inflection points? One inflection point? None? Illustrate by graphing P for several values of c. How does the graph change as c decreases?

55. Prove that if $(c, f(c))$ is a point of inflection of the graph of f and f'' exists in an open interval that contains c, then $f''(c) = 0$. [*Hint:* Apply the First Derivative Test and Fermat's Theorem to the function $g = f'$.]

56. Show that if $f(x) = x^4$, then $f''(0) = 0$, but $(0, 0)$ is not an inflection point of the graph of f.

57. Show that the function $g(x) = x|x|$ has an inflection point at $(0, 0)$ but $g''(0)$ does not exist.

58. Suppose that f''' is continuous and $f'(c) = f''(c) = 0$, but $f'''(c) > 0$. Does f have a local maximum or minimum at c? Does f have a point of inflection at c?

4.4 CURVE SKETCHING

So far we have been concerned with some particular aspects of curve sketching: domain, range, symmetry, limits, continuity, and asymptotes in Chapter 1; derivatives and tangents in Chapters 2 and 3; l'Hospital's Rule in Chapter 3; and extreme values, intervals of increase and decrease, concavity, and points of inflection in this chapter. It's now time to put all of this information together to sketch graphs that reveal the important features of functions.

You may ask: Why don't we just use a graphing calculator or computer to graph a curve? Why do we need to use calculus?

It's true that modern technology is capable of producing very accurate graphs. But even the best graphing devices have to be used intelligently. The use of calculus enables us to discover the most interesting aspects of curves and to detect behavior that we might otherwise overlook. We will see in Example 4 how calculus helps us to avoid the pitfalls of technology.

GUIDELINES FOR SKETCHING A CURVE

The following checklist is intended as a guide to sketching a curve $y = f(x)$ by hand. Not every item is relevant to every function. (For instance, a given curve might not have an asymptote or possess symmetry.) But the guidelines provide all the information you need to make a sketch that displays the most important aspects of the function.

A. Domain It's often useful to start by determining the domain D of f, that is, the set of values of x for which $f(x)$ is defined.

B. Intercepts The y-intercept is $f(0)$ and this tells us where the curve intersects the y-axis. To find the x-intercepts, we set $y = 0$ and solve for x. (You can omit this step if the equation is difficult to solve.)

C. Symmetry

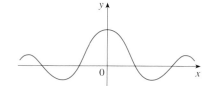

(a) Even function: reflectional symmetry

(i) If $f(-x) = f(x)$ for all x in D, that is, the equation of the curve is unchanged when x is replaced by $-x$, then f is an **even function** and the curve is symmetric about the y-axis. This means that our work is cut in half. If we know what the curve looks like for $x \geq 0$, then we need only reflect about the y-axis to obtain the complete curve [see Figure 1(a)]. Here are some examples: $y = x^2$, $y = x^4$, $y = |x|$, and $y = \cos x$.

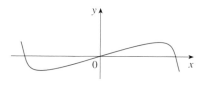

(b) Odd function: rotational symmetry

FIGURE 1

(ii) If $f(-x) = -f(x)$ for all x in D, then f is an **odd function** and the curve is symmetric about the origin. Again we can obtain the complete curve if we know what it looks like for $x \geq 0$. [Rotate 180° about the origin; see Figure 1(b).] Some simple examples of odd functions are $y = x$, $y = x^3$, $y = x^5$, and $y = \sin x$.

(iii) If $f(x + p) = f(x)$ for all x in D, where p is a positive constant, then f is called a **periodic function** and the smallest such number p is called the **period**. For instance, $y = \sin x$ has period 2π and $y = \tan x$ has period π. If we know what the graph looks like in an interval of length p, then we can use translation to sketch the entire graph (see Figure 2).

FIGURE 2

Periodic function: translational symmetry

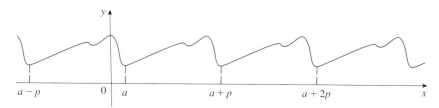

D. Asymptotes

(i) *Horizontal Asymptotes.* Recall from Section 1.6 that if $\lim_{x \to \infty} f(x) = L$ or $\lim_{x \to -\infty} f(x) = L$, then the line $y = L$ is a horizontal asymptote of the curve $y = f(x)$. If it turns out that $\lim_{x \to \infty} f(x) = \infty$ (or $-\infty$), then we do not have an asymptote to the right, but that is still useful information for sketching the curve.

(ii) *Vertical Asymptotes.* Recall from Section 1.6 that the line $x = a$ is a vertical asymptote if at least one of the following statements is true:

1
$$\lim_{x \to a^+} f(x) = \infty \qquad \lim_{x \to a^-} f(x) = \infty$$

$$\lim_{x \to a^+} f(x) = -\infty \qquad \lim_{x \to a^-} f(x) = -\infty$$

(For rational functions you can locate the vertical asymptotes by equating the denominator to 0 after canceling any common factors. But for other functions this method does not apply.) Furthermore, in sketching the curve it is very useful to know exactly which of the statements in (1) is true. If $f(a)$ is not defined but a is an endpoint of the domain of f, then you should compute $\lim_{x \to a^-} f(x)$ or $\lim_{x \to a^+} f(x)$, whether or not this limit is infinite.

E. Intervals of Increase or Decrease
Use the I/D Test. Compute $f'(x)$ and find the intervals on which $f'(x)$ is positive (f is increasing) and the intervals on which $f'(x)$ is negative (f is decreasing).

F. Local Maximum and Minimum Values
Find the critical numbers of f [the numbers c where $f'(c) = 0$ or $f'(c)$ does not exist]. Then use the First Derivative Test. If f' changes from positive to negative at a critical number c, then $f(c)$ is a local maximum. If f' changes from negative to positive at c, then $f(c)$ is a local minimum. Although it is usually preferable to use the First Derivative Test, you can use the Second Derivative Test if $f'(c) = 0$ and $f''(c) \neq 0$. Then $f''(c) > 0$ implies that $f(c)$ is a local minimum, whereas $f''(c) < 0$ implies that $f(c)$ is a local maximum.

G. Concavity and Points of Inflection
Compute $f''(x)$ and use the Concavity Test. The curve is concave upward where $f''(x) > 0$ and concave downward where $f''(x) < 0$. Inflection points occur where the direction of concavity changes.

H. Sketch the Curve
Using the information in items A–G, draw the graph. Sketch the asymptotes as dashed lines. Plot the intercepts, maximum and minimum points, and inflection points. Then make the curve pass through these points, rising and falling according to E, with concavity according to G, and approaching the asymptotes. If additional accuracy is desired near any point, you can compute the value of the derivative there. The tangent indicates the direction in which the curve proceeds.

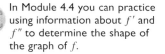

In Module 4.4 you can practice using information about f' and f'' to determine the shape of the graph of f.

▼ **EXAMPLE 1** Use the guidelines to sketch the curve $y = \dfrac{2x^2}{x^2 - 1}$.

A. The domain is

$$\{x \mid x^2 - 1 \neq 0\} = \{x \mid x \neq \pm 1\} = (-\infty, -1) \cup (-1, 1) \cup (1, \infty)$$

B. The x- and y-intercepts are both 0.

C. Since $f(-x) = f(x)$, the function f is even. The curve is symmetric about the y-axis.

D.
$$\lim_{x\to\pm\infty}\frac{2x^2}{x^2-1}=\lim_{x\to\pm\infty}\frac{2}{1-1/x^2}=2$$

Therefore, the line $y=2$ is a horizontal asymptote.
Since the denominator is 0 when $x=\pm1$, we compute the following limits:

$$\lim_{x\to1^+}\frac{2x^2}{x^2-1}=\infty \qquad \lim_{x\to1^-}\frac{2x^2}{x^2-1}=-\infty$$

$$\lim_{x\to-1^+}\frac{2x^2}{x^2-1}=-\infty \qquad \lim_{x\to-1^-}\frac{2x^2}{x^2-1}=\infty$$

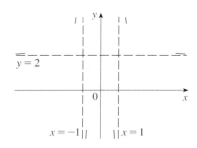

FIGURE 3
Preliminary sketch

Therefore, the lines $x=1$ and $x=-1$ are vertical asymptotes. This information about limits and asymptotes enables us to draw the preliminary sketch in Figure 3, showing the parts of the curve near the asymptotes.

E.
$$f'(x)=\frac{4x(x^2-1)-2x^2\cdot2x}{(x^2-1)^2}=\frac{-4x}{(x^2-1)^2}$$

■ We have shown the curve approaching its horizontal asymptote from above in Figure 3. This is confirmed by the intervals of increase and decrease.

Since $f'(x)>0$ when $x<0$ ($x\neq-1$) and $f'(x)<0$ when $x>0$ ($x\neq1$), f is increasing on $(-\infty,-1)$ and $(-1,0)$ and decreasing on $(0,1)$ and $(1,\infty)$.

F. The only critical number is $x=0$. Since f' changes from positive to negative at 0, $f(0)=0$ is a local maximum by the First Derivative Test.

G.
$$f''(x)=\frac{-4(x^2-1)^2+4x\cdot2(x^2-1)2x}{(x^2-1)^4}=\frac{12x^2+4}{(x^2-1)^3}$$

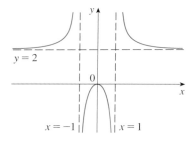

FIGURE 4
Finished sketch of $y=\dfrac{2x^2}{x^2-1}$

Since $12x^2+4>0$ for all x, we have

$$f''(x)>0 \iff x^2-1>0 \iff |x|>1$$

and $f''(x)<0 \iff |x|<1$. Thus the curve is concave upward on the intervals $(-\infty,-1)$ and $(1,\infty)$ and concave downward on $(-1,1)$. It has no point of inflection since 1 and -1 are not in the domain of f.

H. Using the information in E–G, we finish the sketch in Figure 4. ∎

☑ EXAMPLE 2 Sketch the graph of $f(x)=xe^x$.

A. The domain is $\mathbb{R}$.

B. The x- and y-intercepts are both 0.

C. Symmetry: None

D. Because both x and e^x become large as $x\to\infty$, we have $\lim_{x\to\infty}xe^x=\infty$. As $x\to-\infty$, however, $e^x\to0$ and so we have an indeterminate product that requires the use of l'Hospital's Rule:

$$\lim_{x\to-\infty}xe^x=\lim_{x\to-\infty}\frac{x}{e^{-x}}=\lim_{x\to-\infty}\frac{1}{-e^{-x}}=\lim_{x\to-\infty}(-e^x)=0$$

Thus the x-axis is a horizontal asymptote.

E.
$$f'(x)=xe^x+e^x=(x+1)e^x$$

Since e^x is always positive, we see that $f'(x)>0$ when $x+1>0$, and $f'(x)<0$ when $x+1<0$. So f is increasing on $(-1,\infty)$ and decreasing on $(-\infty,-1)$.

F. Because $f'(-1)=0$ and f' changes from negative to positive at $x=-1$, $f(-1)=-e^{-1}$ is a local (and absolute) minimum.

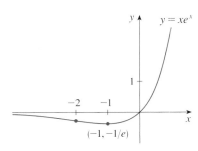

FIGURE 5

G.
$$f''(x) = (x + 1)e^x + e^x = (x + 2)e^x$$

Since $f''(x) > 0$ if $x > -2$ and $f''(x) < 0$ if $x < -2$, f is concave upward on $(-2, \infty)$ and concave downward on $(-\infty, -2)$. The inflection point is $(-2, -2e^{-2})$.

H. We use this information to sketch the curve in Figure 5. ■

EXAMPLE 3 Sketch the graph of $f(x) = \dfrac{\cos x}{2 + \sin x}$.

A. The domain is $\mathbb{R}$.

B. The y-intercept is $f(0) = \frac{1}{2}$. The x-intercepts occur when $\cos x = 0$, that is, $x = (2n + 1)\pi/2$, where n is an integer.

C. f is neither even nor odd, but $f(x + 2\pi) = f(x)$ for all x and so f is periodic and has period 2π. Thus in what follows we need to consider only $0 \le x \le 2\pi$ and then extend the curve by translation in part H.

D. Asymptotes: None

E.
$$f'(x) = \frac{(2 + \sin x)(-\sin x) - \cos x\,(\cos x)}{(2 + \sin x)^2} = -\frac{2 \sin x + 1}{(2 + \sin x)^2}$$

Thus $f'(x) > 0$ when $2 \sin x + 1 < 0 \iff \sin x < -\frac{1}{2} \iff$ $7\pi/6 < x < 11\pi/6$. So f is increasing on $(7\pi/6, 11\pi/6)$ and decreasing on $(0, 7\pi/6)$ and $(11\pi/6, 2\pi)$.

F. From part E and the First Derivative Test, we see that the local minimum value is $f(7\pi/6) = -1/\sqrt{3}$ and the local maximum value is $f(11\pi/6) = 1/\sqrt{3}$.

G. If we use the Quotient Rule again and simplify, we get
$$f''(x) = -\frac{2 \cos x\,(1 - \sin x)}{(2 + \sin x)^3}$$

Because $(2 + \sin x)^3 > 0$ and $1 - \sin x \ge 0$ for all x, we know that $f''(x) > 0$ when $\cos x < 0$, that is, $\pi/2 < x < 3\pi/2$. So f is concave upward on $(\pi/2, 3\pi/2)$ and concave downward on $(0, \pi/2)$ and $(3\pi/2, 2\pi)$. The inflection points are $(\pi/2, 0)$ and $(3\pi/2, 0)$.

H. The graph of the function restricted to $0 \le x \le 2\pi$ is shown in Figure 6. Then we extend it, using periodicity, to the complete graph in Figure 7.

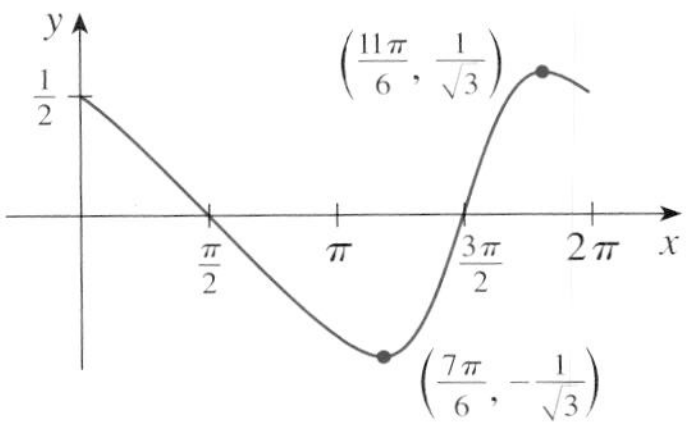

FIGURE 6

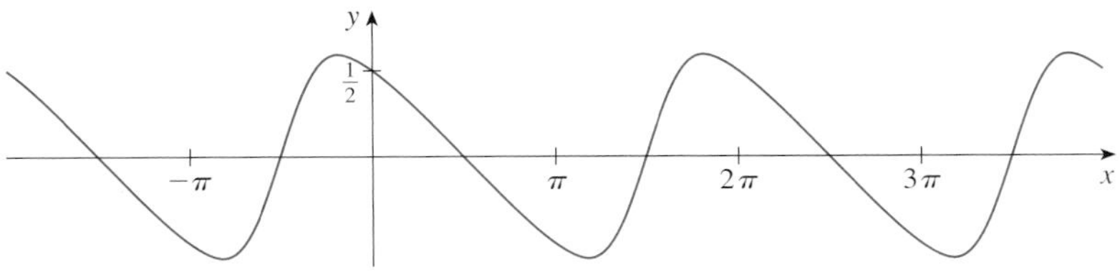

FIGURE 7 ■

GRAPHING WITH TECHNOLOGY

When we use technology to graph a curve, our strategy is different from that in Examples 1–3. Here we *start* with a graph produced by a graphing calculator or computer and then we refine it. We use calculus to make sure that we reveal all the important features of the curve. And with the use of graphing devices we can tackle curves that would be far too complicated to consider without technology.

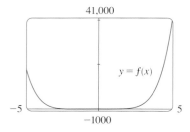

FIGURE 8

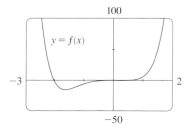

FIGURE 9

EXAMPLE 4 Graph the polynomial $f(x) = 2x^6 + 3x^5 + 3x^3 - 2x^2$. Use the graphs of f' and f'' to estimate all maximum and minimum points and intervals of concavity.

SOLUTION If we specify a domain but not a range, many graphing devices will deduce a suitable range from the values computed. Figure 8 shows the plot from one such device if we specify that $-5 \leq x \leq 5$. Although this viewing rectangle is useful for showing that the asymptotic behavior (or end behavior) is the same as for $y = 2x^6$, it is obviously hiding some finer detail. So we change to the viewing rectangle $[-3, 2]$ by $[-50, 100]$ shown in Figure 9.

From this graph it appears that there is an absolute minimum value of about -15.33 when $x \approx -1.62$ (by using the cursor) and f is decreasing on $(-\infty, -1.62)$ and increasing on $(-1.62, \infty)$. Also there appears to be a horizontal tangent at the origin and inflection points when $x = 0$ and when x is somewhere between -2 and -1.

Now let's try to confirm these impressions using calculus. We differentiate and get

$$f'(x) = 12x^5 + 15x^4 + 9x^2 - 4x$$

$$f''(x) = 60x^4 + 60x^3 + 18x - 4$$

When we graph f' in Figure 10 we see that $f'(x)$ changes from negative to positive when $x \approx -1.62$; this confirms (by the First Derivative Test) the minimum value that we found earlier. But, perhaps to our surprise, we also notice that $f'(x)$ changes from positive to negative when $x = 0$ and from negative to positive when $x \approx 0.35$. This means that f has a local maximum at 0 and a local minimum when $x \approx 0.35$, but these were hidden in Figure 9. Indeed, if we now zoom in toward the origin in Figure 11, we see what we missed before: a local maximum value of 0 when $x = 0$ and a local minimum value of about -0.1 when $x \approx 0.35$.

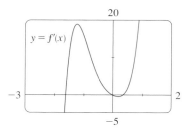

FIGURE 10

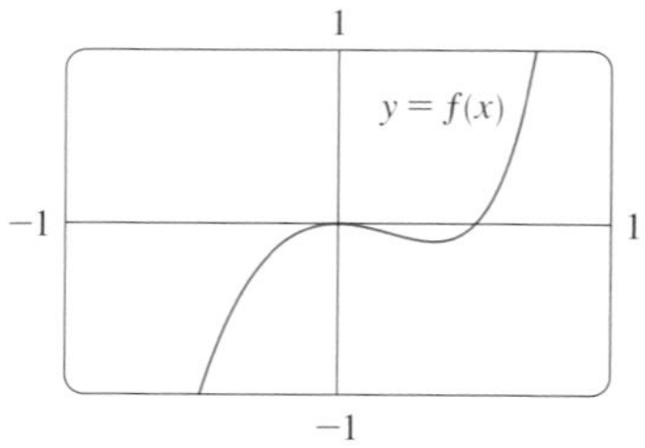

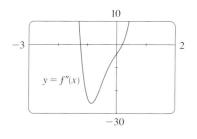

FIGURE II

What about concavity and inflection points? From Figures 9 and 11 there appear to be inflection points when x is a little to the left of -1 and when x is a little to the right of 0. But it's difficult to determine inflection points from the graph of f, so we graph the second derivative f'' in Figure 12. We see that f'' changes from positive to negative when $x \approx -1.23$ and from negative to positive when $x \approx 0.19$. So, correct to two decimal places, f is concave upward on $(-\infty, -1.23)$ and $(0.19, \infty)$ and concave downward on $(-1.23, 0.19)$. The inflection points are $(-1.23, -10.18)$ and $(0.19, -0.05)$.

We have discovered that no single graph reveals all the important features of this polynomial. But Figures 9 and 11, when taken together, do provide an accurate picture. ■

FIGURE 12

4.4 | EXERCISES

1–44 ▪ Use the guidelines of this section to sketch the curve.

1. $y = x^3 + x$

2. $y = x^3 + 6x^2 + 9x$

3. $y = 2 - 15x + 9x^2 - x^3$

4. $y = 8x^2 - x^4$

5. $y = x^4 + 4x^3$

6. $y = x(x + 2)^3$

7. $y = 2x^5 - 5x^2 + 1$

8. $y = 20x^3 - 3x^5$

9. $y = \dfrac{x}{x - 1}$

10. $y = \dfrac{x}{(x - 1)^2}$

11. $y = \dfrac{1}{x^2 - 9}$

12. $y = \dfrac{x}{x^2 - 9}$

13. $y = \dfrac{x}{x^2 + 9}$

14. $y = \dfrac{x^2}{x^2 + 9}$

15. $y = \dfrac{x - 1}{x^2}$

16. $y = \dfrac{x^3 - 1}{x^3 + 1}$

17. $y = x\sqrt{5 - x}$

18. $y = 2\sqrt{x} - x$

19. $y = \dfrac{x}{\sqrt{x^2 + 1}}$

20. $y = \sqrt{\dfrac{x}{x - 5}}$

21. $y = \dfrac{\sqrt{1 - x^2}}{x}$

22. $y = x\sqrt{2 - x^2}$

23. $y = x - 3x^{1/3}$

24. $y = x^{5/3} - 5x^{2/3}$

25. $y = x + \sqrt{|x|}$

26. $y = \sqrt[3]{(x^2 - 1)^2}$

27. $y = 3\sin x - \sin^3 x$

28. $y = \sin x - \tan x$

29. $y = x\tan x, \quad -\pi/2 < x < \pi/2$

30. $y = 2x - \tan x, \quad -\pi/2 < x < \pi/2$

31. $y = \frac{1}{2}x - \sin x, \quad 0 < x < 3\pi$

32. $y = \cos^2 x - 2\sin x$

33. $y = \dfrac{\sin x}{1 + \cos x}$

34. $y = \sin x - x$

35. $y = 1/(1 + e^{-x})$

36. $y = e^{2x} - e^x$

37. $y = x\ln x$

38. $y = e^x/x$

39. $y = xe^{-x}$

40. $y = x(\ln x)^2$

41. $y = \ln(\sin x)$

42. $y = e^x - 3e^{-x} - 4x$

43. $y = xe^{-x^2}$

44. $y = \tan^{-1}\left(\dfrac{x - 1}{x + 1}\right)$

▪ ▪ ▪ ▪ ▪ ▪ ▪ ▪ ▪ ▪ ▪ ▪ ▪ ▪

45. The figure shows a beam of length L embedded in concrete walls. If a constant load W is distributed evenly along its length, the beam takes the shape of the deflection curve

$$y = -\frac{W}{24EI}x^4 + \frac{WL}{12EI}x^3 - \frac{WL^2}{24EI}x^2$$

where E and I are positive constants. (E is Young's modulus of elasticity and I is the moment of inertia of a cross-section of the beam.) Sketch the graph of the deflection curve.

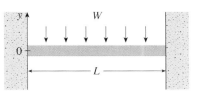

46. Coulomb's Law states that the force of attraction between two charged particles is directly proportional to the product of the charges and inversely proportional to the square of the distance between them. The figure shows particles with charge 1 located at positions 0 and 2 on a coordinate line and a particle with charge -1 at a position x between them. It follows from Coulomb's Law that the net force acting on the middle particle is

$$F(x) = -\frac{k}{x^2} + \frac{k}{(x - 2)^2} \qquad 0 < x < 2$$

where k is a positive constant. Sketch the graph of the net force function. What does the graph say about the force?

47–50 ▪ The line $y = mx + b$ is called a **slant asymptote** if $f(x) - (mx + b) \to 0$ as $x \to \infty$ or $x \to -\infty$ because the vertical distance between the curve $y = f(x)$ and the line $y = mx + b$ approaches 0 as x becomes large. Find an equation of the slant asymptote of the function and use it to help sketch the graph. [For rational functions, a slant asymptote occurs when the degree of the numerator is one more than the degree of the denominator. To find it, use long division to write $f(x) = mx + b + R(x)/Q(x)$.]

47. $y = \dfrac{-2x^2 + 5x - 1}{2x - 1}$

48. $y = \dfrac{x^2 + 12}{x - 2}$

49. $xy = x^2 + 4$

50. $y = e^x - x$

▪ ▪ ▪ ▪ ▪ ▪ ▪ ▪ ▪ ▪ ▪ ▪ ▪ ▪

51. Show that the curve $y = x - \tan^{-1}x$ has two slant asymptotes: $y = x + \pi/2$ and $y = x - \pi/2$. Use this fact to help sketch the curve.

52. Show that the curve $y = \sqrt{x^2 + 4x}$ has two slant asymptotes: $y = x + 2$ and $y = -x - 2$. Use this fact to help sketch the curve.

53–56 ▪ Produce graphs of f that reveal all the important aspects of the curve. In particular, you should use graphs of f' and f'' to estimate the intervals of increase and decrease, extreme values, intervals of concavity, and inflection points.

53. $f(x) = 4x^4 - 32x^3 + 89x^2 - 95x + 29$

54. $f(x) = x^6 - 15x^5 + 75x^4 - 125x^3 - x$

55. $f(x) = x^2 - 4x + 7 \cos x, \quad -4 \le x \le 4$

56. $f(x) = \tan x + 5 \cos x$

▪ ▪ ▪ ▪ ▪ ▪ ▪ ▪ ▪ ▪ ▪ ▪ ▪

57–58 ▪ Produce graphs of f that reveal all the important aspects of the curve. Estimate the intervals of increase and decrease and intervals of concavity, and use calculus to find these intervals exactly.

57. $f(x) = 1 + \dfrac{1}{x} + \dfrac{8}{x^2} + \dfrac{1}{x^3}$

58. $f(x) = \dfrac{1}{x^8} - \dfrac{2 \times 10^8}{x^4}$

▪ ▪ ▪ ▪ ▪ ▪ ▪ ▪ ▪ ▪ ▪ ▪ ▪

59–63 ▪ Describe how the graph of f varies as c varies. Graph several members of the family to illustrate the trends that you discover. In particular, you should investigate how maximum and minimum points and inflection points move when c changes. You should also identify any transitional values of c at which the basic shape of the curve changes.

59. $f(x) = x^4 + cx^2$ **60.** $f(x) = x^3 + cx$

61. $f(x) = e^{-c/x^2}$

62. $f(x) = \ln(x^2 + c)$

63. $f(x) = cx + \sin x$

▪ ▪ ▪ ▪ ▪ ▪ ▪ ▪ ▪ ▪ ▪ ▪ ▪

64. Investigate the family of curves given by the equation $f(x) = x^4 + cx^2 + x$. Start by determining the transitional value of c at which the number of inflection points changes. Then graph several members of the family to see what shapes are possible. There is another transitional value of c at which the number of critical numbers changes. Try to discover it graphically. Then prove what you have discovered.

4.5 OPTIMIZATION PROBLEMS

The methods we have learned in this chapter for finding extreme values have practical applications in many areas of life. A businessperson wants to minimize costs and maximize profits. A traveler wants to minimize transportation time. Fermat's Principle in optics states that light follows the path that takes the least time. In this section and the next we solve such problems as maximizing areas, volumes, and profits and minimizing distances, times, and costs.

In solving such practical problems the greatest challenge is often to convert the word problem into a mathematical optimization problem by setting up the function that is to be maximized or minimized. The following steps may be useful.

STEPS IN SOLVING OPTIMIZATION PROBLEMS

1. **Understand the Problem** The first step is to read the problem carefully until it is clearly understood. Ask yourself: What is the unknown? What are the given quantities? What are the given conditions?

2. **Draw a Diagram** In most problems it is useful to draw a diagram and identify the given and required quantities on the diagram.

3. **Introduce Notation** Assign a symbol to the quantity that is to be maximized or minimized (let's call it Q for now). Also select symbols $(a, b, c, \ldots, x, y)$ for other unknown quantities and label the diagram with these symbols. It may help to use initials as suggestive symbols—for example, A for area, h for height, t for time.

4. Express Q in terms of some of the other symbols from Step 3.

5. If Q has been expressed as a function of more than one variable in Step 4, use the given information to find relationships (in the form of equations) among these

variables. Then use these equations to eliminate all but one of the variables in the expression for Q. Thus Q will be expressed as a function of *one* variable x, say, $Q = f(x)$. Write the domain of this function.

6. Use the methods of Sections 4.1 and 4.3 to find the *absolute* maximum or minimum value of f. In particular, if the domain of f is a closed interval, then the Closed Interval Method in Section 4.1 can be used.

EXAMPLE I A farmer has 2400 ft of fencing and wants to fence off a rectangular field that borders a straight river. He needs no fence along the river. What are the dimensions of the field that has the largest area?

SOLUTION In order to get a feeling for what is happening in this problem, let's experiment with some special cases. Figure 1 (not to scale) shows three possible ways of laying out the 2400 ft of fencing. We see that when we try shallow, wide fields or deep, narrow fields, we get relatively small areas. It seems plausible that there is some intermediate configuration that produces the largest area.

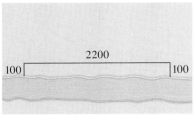

Area = 100 · 2200 = 220,000 ft²

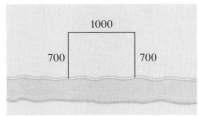

Area = 700 · 1000 = 700,000 ft²

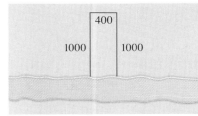

Area = 1000 · 400 = 400,000 ft²

FIGURE I

Figure 2 illustrates the general case. We wish to maximize the area A of the rectangle. Let x and y be the depth and width of the rectangle (in feet). Then we express A in terms of x and y:

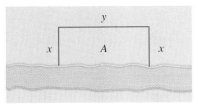

FIGURE 2

$$A = xy$$

We want to express A as a function of just one variable, so we eliminate y by expressing it in terms of x. To do this we use the given information that the total length of the fencing is 2400 ft. Thus

$$2x + y = 2400$$

From this equation we have $y = 2400 - 2x$, which gives

$$A = x(2400 - 2x) = 2400x - 2x^2$$

Note that $x \geqslant 0$ and $x \leqslant 1200$ (otherwise $A < 0$). So the function that we wish to maximize is

$$A(x) = 2400x - 2x^2 \qquad 0 \leqslant x \leqslant 1200$$

The derivative is $A'(x) = 2400 - 4x$, so to find the critical numbers we solve the equation

$$2400 - 4x = 0$$

which gives $x = 600$. The maximum value of A must occur either at this critical number or at an endpoint of the interval. Since $A(0) = 0$, $A(600) = 720{,}000$, and $A(1200) = 0$, the Closed Interval Method gives the maximum value as $A(600) = 720{,}000$.

[Alternatively, we could have observed that $A''(x) = -4 < 0$ for all x, so A is always concave downward and the local maximum at $x = 600$ must be an absolute maximum.]

Thus the rectangular field should be 600 ft deep and 1200 ft wide. ■

V EXAMPLE 2 A cylindrical can is to be made to hold 1 L of oil. Find the dimensions that will minimize the cost of the metal to manufacture the can.

SOLUTION Draw the diagram as in Figure 3, where r is the radius and h the height (both in centimeters). In order to minimize the cost of the metal, we minimize the total surface area of the cylinder (top, bottom, and sides). From Figure 4 we see that the sides are made from a rectangular sheet with dimensions $2\pi r$ and h. So the surface area is

$$A = 2\pi r^2 + 2\pi r h$$

To eliminate h we use the fact that the volume is given as 1 L, which we take to be 1000 cm³. Thus

$$\pi r^2 h = 1000$$

which gives $h = 1000/(\pi r^2)$. Substitution of this into the expression for A gives

$$A = 2\pi r^2 + 2\pi r \left(\frac{1000}{\pi r^2}\right) = 2\pi r^2 + \frac{2000}{r}$$

Therefore, the function that we want to minimize is

$$A(r) = 2\pi r^2 + \frac{2000}{r} \qquad r > 0$$

To find the critical numbers, we differentiate:

$$A'(r) = 4\pi r - \frac{2000}{r^2} = \frac{4(\pi r^3 - 500)}{r^2}$$

Then $A'(r) = 0$ when $\pi r^3 = 500$, so the only critical number is $r = \sqrt[3]{500/\pi}$.

Since the domain of A is $(0, \infty)$, we can't use the argument of Example 1 concerning endpoints. But we can observe that $A'(r) < 0$ for $r < \sqrt[3]{500/\pi}$ and $A'(r) > 0$ for $r > \sqrt[3]{500/\pi}$, so A is decreasing for *all* r to the left of the critical number and increasing for *all* r to the right. Thus $r = \sqrt[3]{500/\pi}$ must give rise to an *absolute* minimum.

[Alternatively, we could argue that $A(r) \to \infty$ as $r \to 0^+$ and $A(r) \to \infty$ as $r \to \infty$, so there must be a minimum value of $A(r)$, which must occur at the critical number. See Figure 5.]

The value of h corresponding to $r = \sqrt[3]{500/\pi}$ is

$$h = \frac{1000}{\pi r^2} = \frac{1000}{\pi (500/\pi)^{2/3}} = 2\sqrt[3]{\frac{500}{\pi}} = 2r$$

Thus to minimize the cost of the can, the radius should be $\sqrt[3]{500/\pi}$ cm and the height should be equal to twice the radius, namely, the diameter. ■

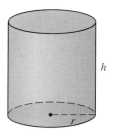

FIGURE 3

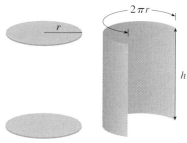

Area $2(\pi r^2)$ Area $(2\pi r)h$

FIGURE 4

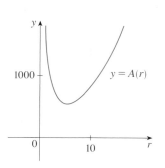

FIGURE 5

NOTE 1 The argument used in Example 2 to justify the absolute minimum is a variant of the First Derivative Test (which applies only to *local* maximum or minimum values) and is stated here for future reference.

Module 4.5 takes you through six additional optimization problems, including animations of the physical situations.

> **FIRST DERIVATIVE TEST FOR ABSOLUTE EXTREME VALUES** Suppose that c is a critical number of a continuous function f defined on an interval.
>
> (a) If $f'(x) > 0$ for all $x < c$ and $f'(x) < 0$ for all $x > c$, then $f(c)$ is the absolute maximum value of f.
>
> (b) If $f'(x) < 0$ for all $x < c$ and $f'(x) > 0$ for all $x > c$, then $f(c)$ is the absolute minimum value of f.

NOTE 2 An alternative method for solving optimization problems is to use implicit differentiation. Let's look at Example 2 again to illustrate the method. We work with the same equations

$$A = 2\pi r^2 + 2\pi rh \qquad \pi r^2 h = 100$$

but instead of eliminating h, we differentiate both equations implicitly with respect to r:

$$A' = 4\pi r + 2\pi rh' + 2\pi h \qquad \pi r^2 h' + 2\pi rh = 0$$

The minimum occurs at a critical number, so we set $A' = 0$, simplify, and arrive at the equations

$$2r + h + rh' = 0 \qquad 2h + rh' = 0$$

and subtraction gives $2r - h = 0$, or $h = 2r$.

▼ EXAMPLE 3 Find the point on the parabola $y^2 = 2x$ that is closest to the point $(1, 4)$.

SOLUTION The distance between the point $(1, 4)$ and the point (x, y) is

$$d = \sqrt{(x - 1)^2 + (y - 4)^2}$$

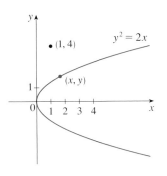

FIGURE 6

(See Figure 6.) But if (x, y) lies on the parabola, then $x = y^2/2$, so the expression for d becomes

$$d = \sqrt{\left(\tfrac{1}{2} y^2 - 1\right)^2 + (y - 4)^2}$$

(Alternatively, we could have substituted $y = \sqrt{2x}$ to get d in terms of x alone.) Instead of minimizing d, we minimize its square:

$$d^2 = f(y) = \left(\tfrac{1}{2} y^2 - 1\right)^2 + (y - 4)^2$$

(You should convince yourself that the minimum of d occurs at the same point as the minimum of d^2, but d^2 is easier to work with.) Differentiating, we obtain

$$f'(y) = 2\left(\tfrac{1}{2} y^2 - 1\right)y + 2(y - 4) = y^3 - 8$$

so $f'(y) = 0$ when $y = 2$. Observe that $f'(y) < 0$ when $y < 2$ and $f'(y) > 0$ when $y > 2$, so by the First Derivative Test for Absolute Extreme Values, the absolute minimum occurs when $y = 2$. (Or we could simply say that because of the geometric nature of the problem, it's obvious that there is a closest point but not a farthest point.) The corresponding value of x is $x = y^2/2 = 2$. Thus the point on $y^2 = 2x$ closest to $(1, 4)$ is $(2, 2)$.

EXAMPLE 4 A man launches his boat from point A on a bank of a straight river, 3 km wide, and wants to reach point B, 8 km downstream on the opposite bank, as quickly as possible (see Figure 7). He could row his boat directly across the river to point C and then run to B, or he could row directly to B, or he could row to some point D between C and B and then run to B. If he can row 6 km/h and run 8 km/h, where should he land to reach B as soon as possible? (We assume that the speed of the water is negligible compared with the speed at which the man rows.)

SOLUTION If we let x be the distance from C to D, then the running distance is $|DB| = 8 - x$ and the Pythagorean Theorem gives the rowing distance as $|AD| = \sqrt{x^2 + 9}$. We use the equation

$$\text{time} = \frac{\text{distance}}{\text{rate}}$$

Then the rowing time is $\sqrt{x^2 + 9}/6$ and the running time is $(8 - x)/8$, so the total time T as a function of x is

$$T(x) = \frac{\sqrt{x^2 + 9}}{6} + \frac{8 - x}{8}$$

The domain of this function T is $[0, 8]$. Notice that if $x = 0$ he rows to C and if $x = 8$ he rows directly to B. The derivative of T is

$$T'(x) = \frac{x}{6\sqrt{x^2 + 9}} - \frac{1}{8}$$

Thus, using the fact that $x \geqslant 0$, we have

$$T'(x) = 0 \iff \frac{x}{6\sqrt{x^2 + 9}} = \frac{1}{8} \iff 4x = 3\sqrt{x^2 + 9}$$

$$\iff 16x^2 = 9(x^2 + 9) \iff 7x^2 = 81$$

$$\iff x = \frac{9}{\sqrt{7}}$$

The only critical number is $x = 9/\sqrt{7}$. To see whether the minimum occurs at this critical number or at an endpoint of the domain $[0, 8]$, we evaluate T at all three points:

$$T(0) = 1.5 \qquad T\left(\frac{9}{\sqrt{7}}\right) = 1 + \frac{\sqrt{7}}{8} \approx 1.33 \qquad T(8) = \frac{\sqrt{73}}{6} \approx 1.42$$

Since the smallest of these values of T occurs when $x = 9/\sqrt{7}$, the absolute minimum value of T must occur there. Figure 8 illustrates this calculation by showing the graph of T.

Thus the man should land the boat at a point $9/\sqrt{7}$ km (≈ 3.4 km) downstream from his starting point.

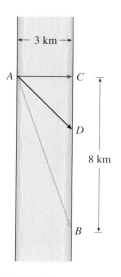

FIGURE 7

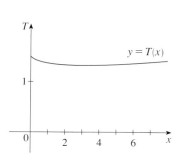

FIGURE 8

V EXAMPLE 5 Find the area of the largest rectangle that can be inscribed in a semicircle of radius r.

SOLUTION I Let's take the semicircle to be the upper half of the circle $x^2 + y^2 = r^2$ with center the origin. Then the word *inscribed* means that the rectangle has two vertices on the semicircle and two vertices on the x-axis as shown in Figure 9.

Let (x, y) be the vertex that lies in the first quadrant. Then the rectangle has sides of lengths $2x$ and y, so its area is

$$A = 2xy$$

To eliminate y we use the fact that (x, y) lies on the circle $x^2 + y^2 = r^2$ and so $y = \sqrt{r^2 - x^2}$. Thus

$$A = 2x\sqrt{r^2 - x^2}$$

The domain of this function is $0 \leq x \leq r$. Its derivative is

$$A' = -\frac{2x^2}{\sqrt{r^2 - x^2}} + 2\sqrt{r^2 - x^2} = \frac{2(r^2 - 2x^2)}{\sqrt{r^2 - x^2}}$$

which is 0 when $2x^2 = r^2$, that is, $x = r/\sqrt{2}$ (since $x \geq 0$). This value of x gives a maximum value of A since $A(0) = 0$ and $A(r) = 0$. Therefore, the area of the largest inscribed rectangle is

$$A\left(\frac{r}{\sqrt{2}}\right) = 2\frac{r}{\sqrt{2}}\sqrt{r^2 - \frac{r^2}{2}} = r^2$$

SOLUTION 2 A simpler solution is possible if we think of using an angle as a variable. Let θ be the angle shown in Figure 10. Then the area of the rectangle is

$$A(\theta) = (2r\cos\theta)(r\sin\theta) = r^2(2\sin\theta\,\cos\theta) = r^2\sin 2\theta$$

We know that $\sin 2\theta$ has a maximum value of 1 and it occurs when $2\theta = \pi/2$. So $A(\theta)$ has a maximum value of r^2 and it occurs when $\theta = \pi/4$.

Notice that this trigonometric solution doesn't involve differentiation. In fact, we didn't need to use calculus at all. ▪

APPLICATIONS TO BUSINESS AND ECONOMICS

In Example 10 in Section 2.3 we introduced the idea of marginal cost. Recall that if $C(x)$, the **cost function**, is the cost of producing x units of a certain product, then the **marginal cost** is the rate of change of C with respect to x. In other words, the marginal cost function is the derivative, $C'(x)$, of the cost function.

Now let's consider marketing. Let $p(x)$ be the price per unit that the company can charge if it sells x units. Then p is called the **demand function** (or **price function**) and we would expect it to be a decreasing function of x. If x units are sold and the price per unit is $p(x)$, then the total revenue is

$$R(x) = xp(x)$$

and R is called the **revenue function**. The derivative R' of the revenue function is called the **marginal revenue function** and is the rate of change of revenue with respect to the number of units sold.

FIGURE 9

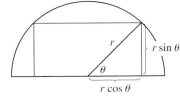

FIGURE 10

If x units are sold, then the total profit is

$$P(x) = R(x) - C(x)$$

and P is called the **profit function**. The **marginal profit function** is P', the derivative of the profit function. In Exercises 35–40 you are asked to use the marginal cost, revenue, and profit functions to minimize costs and maximize revenues and profits.

▼ EXAMPLE 6 A store has been selling 200 DVD burners a week at $350 each. A market survey indicates that for each $10 rebate offered to buyers, the number of units sold will increase by 20 a week. Find the demand function and the revenue function. How large a rebate should the store offer to maximize its revenue?

SOLUTION If x is the number of DVD burners sold per week, then the weekly increase in sales is $x - 200$. For each increase of 20 units sold, the price is decreased by $10. So for each additional unit sold, the decrease in price will be $\frac{1}{20} \times 10$ and the demand function is

$$p(x) = 350 - \tfrac{10}{20}(x - 200) = 450 - \tfrac{1}{2}x$$

The revenue function is

$$R(x) = xp(x) = 450x - \tfrac{1}{2}x^2$$

Since $R'(x) = 450 - x$, we see that $R'(x) = 0$ when $x = 450$. This value of x gives an absolute maximum by the First Derivative Test (or simply by observing that the graph of R is a parabola that opens downward). The corresponding price is

$$p(450) = 450 - \tfrac{1}{2}(450) = 225$$

and the rebate is $350 - 225 = 125$. Therefore, to maximize revenue the store should offer a rebate of $125. ■

4.5 EXERCISES

1. Consider the following problem: Find two numbers whose sum is 23 and whose product is a maximum.
   (a) Make a table of values, like the following one, so that the sum of the numbers in the first two columns is always 23. On the basis of the evidence in your table, estimate the answer to the problem.

First number	Second number	Product
1	22	22
2	21	42
3	20	60
⋮	⋮	⋮

   (b) Use calculus to solve the problem and compare with your answer to part (a).

2. Find two numbers whose difference is 100 and whose product is a minimum.

3. Find two positive numbers whose product is 100 and whose sum is a minimum.

4. Find a positive number such that the sum of the number and its reciprocal is as small as possible.

5. Find the dimensions of a rectangle with perimeter 100 m whose area is as large as possible.

6. Find the dimensions of a rectangle with area 1000 m² whose perimeter is as small as possible.

7. Consider the following problem: A farmer with 750 ft of fencing wants to enclose a rectangular area and then divide it into four pens with fencing parallel to one side of the rectangle. What is the largest possible total area of the four pens?
   (a) Draw several diagrams illustrating the situation, some with shallow, wide pens and some with deep, narrow pens. Find the total areas of these configurations. Does it appear that there is a maximum area? If so, estimate it.

(b) Draw a diagram illustrating the general situation. Introduce notation and label the diagram with your symbols.
(c) Write an expression for the total area.
(d) Use the given information to write an equation that relates the variables.
(e) Use part (d) to write the total area as a function of one variable.
(f) Finish solving the problem and compare the answer with your estimate in part (a).

8. Consider the following problem: A box with an open top is to be constructed from a square piece of cardboard, 3 ft wide, by cutting out a square from each of the four corners and bending up the sides. Find the largest volume that such a box can have.
(a) Draw several diagrams to illustrate the situation, some short boxes with large bases and some tall boxes with small bases. Find the volumes of several such boxes. Does it appear that there is a maximum volume? If so, estimate it.
(b) Draw a diagram illustrating the general situation. Introduce notation and label the diagram with your symbols.
(c) Write an expression for the volume.
(d) Use the given information to write an equation that relates the variables.
(e) Use part (d) to write the volume as a function of one variable.
(f) Finish solving the problem and compare the answer with your estimate in part (a).

9. If 1200 cm² of material is available to make a box with a square base and an open top, find the largest possible volume of the box.

10. A box with a square base and open top must have a volume of 32,000 cm³. Find the dimensions of the box that minimize the amount of material used.

11. (a) Show that of all the rectangles with a given area, the one with smallest perimeter is a square.
(b) Show that of all the rectangles with a given perimeter, the one with greatest area is a square.

12. A rectangular storage container with an open top is to have a volume of 10 m³. The length of its base is twice the width. Material for the base costs $10 per square meter. Material for the sides costs $6 per square meter. Find the cost of materials for the cheapest such container.

13. Find the points on the ellipse $4x^2 + y^2 = 4$ that are farthest away from the point $(1, 0)$.

14. Find, correct to two decimal places, the coordinates of the point on the curve $y = \tan x$ that is closest to the point $(1, 1)$.

15. Find the dimensions of the rectangle of largest area that can be inscribed in an equilateral triangle of side L if one side of the rectangle lies on the base of the triangle.

16. Find the dimensions of the rectangle of largest area that has its base on the x-axis and its other two vertices above the x-axis and lying on the parabola $y = 8 - x^2$.

17. A right circular cylinder is inscribed in a sphere of radius r. Find the largest possible volume of such a cylinder.

18. Find the area of the largest rectangle that can be inscribed in the ellipse $x^2/a^2 + y^2/b^2 = 1$.

19. A Norman window has the shape of a rectangle surmounted by a semicircle. (Thus the diameter of the semicircle is equal to the width of the rectangle.) If the perimeter of the window is 30 ft, find the dimensions of the window so that the greatest possible amount of light is admitted.

20. A right circular cylinder is inscribed in a cone with height h and base radius r. Find the largest possible volume of such a cylinder.

21. A piece of wire 10 m long is cut into two pieces. One piece is bent into a square and the other is bent into an equilateral triangle. How should the wire be cut so that the total area enclosed is (a) a maximum? (b) A minimum?

22. A fence 8 ft tall runs parallel to a tall building at a distance of 4 ft from the building. What is the length of the shortest ladder that will reach from the ground over the fence to the wall of the building?

23. A cone-shaped drinking cup is made from a circular piece of paper of radius R by cutting out a sector and joining the edges CA and CB. Find the maximum capacity of such a cup.

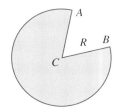

24. A cone-shaped paper drinking cup is to be made to hold 27 cm³ of water. Find the height and radius of the cup that will use the smallest amount of paper.

25. A cone with height h is inscribed in a larger cone with height H so that its vertex is at the center of the base of the larger cone. Show that the inner cone has maximum volume when $h = \frac{1}{3}H$.

26. The graph (on page 234) shows the fuel consumption c of a car (measured in gallons per hour) as a function of the speed v of the car. At very low speeds the engine runs inefficiently, so initially c decreases as the speed increases. But at high speeds the fuel consumption increases. You can see that $c(v)$ is minimized for this car when $v \approx 30$ mi/h. However, for fuel efficiency, what must be minimized is not the consumption in gallons per hour but rather the fuel consumption in gallons *per mile*. Let's call this consumption G. Using the graph, estimate the speed at which G has its minimum value.

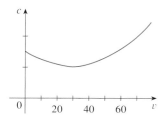

27. If a resistor of R ohms is connected across a battery of E volts with internal resistance r ohms, then the power (in watts) in the external resistor is

$$P = \frac{E^2 R}{(R + r)^2}$$

If E and r are fixed but R varies, what is the maximum value of the power?

28. For a fish swimming at a speed v relative to the water, the energy expenditure per unit time is proportional to v^3. It is believed that migrating fish try to minimize the total energy required to swim a fixed distance. If the fish are swimming against a current u ($u < v$), then the time required to swim a distance L is $L/(v - u)$ and the total energy E required to swim the distance is given by

$$E(v) = av^3 \cdot \frac{L}{v - u}$$

where a is the proportionality constant.
(a) Determine the value of v that minimizes E.
(b) Sketch the graph of E.

Note: This result has been verified experimentally; migrating fish swim against a current at a speed 50% greater than the current speed.

29. In a beehive, each cell is a regular hexagonal prism, open at one end with a trihedral angle at the other end as in the figure. It is believed that bees form their cells in such a way as to minimize the surface area for a given volume, thus using the least amount of wax in cell construction. Examination of these cells has shown that the measure of the apex angle θ is amazingly consistent. Based on the geometry of the cell, it can be shown that the surface area S is given by

$$S = 6sh - \tfrac{3}{2}s^2 \cot \theta + \left(3s^2\sqrt{3}/2\right) \csc \theta$$

where s, the length of the sides of the hexagon, and h, the height, are constants.
(a) Calculate $dS/d\theta$.
(b) What angle should the bees prefer?
(c) Determine the minimum surface area of the cell (in terms of s and h).

Note: Actual measurements of the angle θ in beehives have been made, and the measures of these angles seldom differ from the calculated value by more than $2°$.

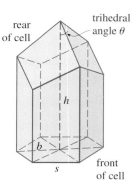

30. A boat leaves a dock at 2:00 PM and travels due south at a speed of 20 km/h. Another boat has been heading due east at 15 km/h and reaches the same dock at 3:00 PM. At what time were the two boats closest together?

31. The illumination of an object by a light source is directly proportional to the strength of the source and inversely proportional to the square of the distance from the source. If two light sources, one three times as strong as the other, are placed 10 ft apart, where should an object be placed on the line between the sources so as to receive the least illumination?

32. A woman at a point A on the shore of a circular lake with radius 2 mi wants to arrive at the point C diametrically opposite A on the other side of the lake in the shortest possible time. She can walk at the rate of 4 mi/h and row a boat at 2 mi/h. How should she proceed?

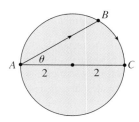

33. Find an equation of the line through the point $(3, 5)$ that cuts off the least area from the first quadrant.

34. At which points on the curve $y = 1 + 40x^3 - 3x^5$ does the tangent line have the largest slope?

35. (a) If $C(x)$ is the cost of producing x units of a commodity, then the **average cost** per unit is $c(x) = C(x)/x$. Show that if the average cost is a minimum, then the marginal cost equals the average cost.
(b) If $C(x) = 16,000 + 200x + 4x^{3/2}$, in dollars, find
(i) the cost, average cost, and marginal cost at a productional level of 1000 units; (ii) the production

level that will minimize the average cost; and (iii) the minimum average cost.

36. (a) Show that if the profit $P(x)$ is a maximum, then the marginal revenue equals the marginal cost.
(b) If $C(x) = 16{,}000 + 500x - 1.6x^2 + 0.004x^3$ is the cost function and $p(x) = 1700 - 7x$ is the demand function, find the production level that will maximize profit.

37. A baseball team plays in a stadium that holds 55,000 spectators. With ticket prices at $10, the average attendance had been 27,000. When ticket prices were lowered to $8, the average attendance rose to 33,000.
(a) Find the demand function, assuming that it is linear.
(b) How should ticket prices be set to maximize revenue?

38. During the summer months Terry makes and sells necklaces on the beach. Last summer he sold the necklaces for $10 each and his sales averaged 20 per day. When he increased the price by $1, he found that he lost two sales per day.
(a) Find the demand function, assuming that it is linear.
(b) If the material for each necklace costs Terry $6, what should the selling price be to maximize his profit?

39. A manufacturer has been selling 1000 television sets a week at $450 each. A market survey indicates that for each $10 rebate offered to the buyer, the number of sets sold will increase by 100 per week.
(a) Find the demand function.
(b) How large a rebate should the company offer the buyer in order to maximize its revenue?
(c) If its weekly cost function is $C(x) = 68{,}000 + 150x$, how should the manufacturer set the size of the rebate in order to maximize its profit?

40. The manager of a 100-unit apartment complex knows from experience that all units will be occupied if the rent is $800 per month. A market survey suggests that, on average, one additional unit will remain vacant for each $10 increase in rent. What rent should the manager charge to maximize revenue?

41. Let a and b be positive numbers. Find the length of the shortest line segment that is cut off by the first quadrant and passes through the point (a, b).

CAS 42. The frame for a kite is to be made from six pieces of wood. The four exterior pieces have been cut with the lengths indicated in the figure. To maximize the area of the kite, how long should the diagonal pieces be?

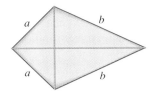

43. Let v_1 be the velocity of light in air and v_2 the velocity of light in water. According to Fermat's Principle, a ray of light will travel from a point A in the air to a point B in the water by a path ACB that minimizes the time taken. Show that

$$\frac{\sin \theta_1}{\sin \theta_2} = \frac{v_1}{v_2}$$

where θ_1 (the angle of incidence) and θ_2 (the angle of refraction) are as shown. This equation is known as Snell's Law.

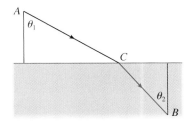

44. Two vertical poles PQ and ST are secured by a rope PRS going from the top of the first pole to a point R on the ground between the poles and then to the top of the second pole as in the figure. Show that the shortest length of such a rope occurs when $\theta_1 = \theta_2$.

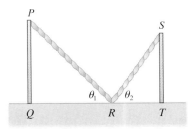

45. The upper right-hand corner of a piece of paper, 12 in. by 8 in., as in the figure, is folded over to the bottom edge. How would you fold it so as to minimize the length of the fold? In other words, how would you choose x to minimize y?

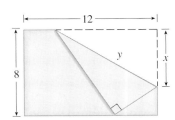

46. A steel pipe is being carried down a hallway 9 ft wide. At the end of the hall there is a right-angled turn into a narrower hallway 6 ft wide. What is the length of the longest pipe that can be carried horizontally around the corner?

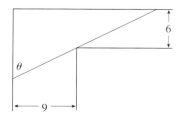

47. Find the maximum area of a rectangle that can be circumscribed about a given rectangle with length L and width W. [*Hint:* Express the area as a function of an angle θ.]

48. A rain gutter is to be constructed from a metal sheet of width 30 cm by bending up one-third of the sheet on each side through an angle θ. How should θ be chosen so that the gutter will carry the maximum amount of water?

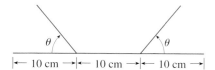

49. Where should the point P be chosen on the line segment AB so as to maximize the angle θ?

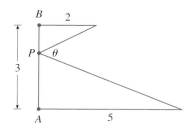

50. A painting in an art gallery has height h and is hung so that its lower edge is a distance d above the eye of an observer (as in the figure). How far from the wall should the observer stand to get the best view? (In other words, where should the observer stand so as to maximize the angle θ subtended at his eye by the painting?)

4.6	**NEWTON'S METHOD**

Suppose that a car dealer offers to sell you a car for $18,000 or for payments of $375 per month for five years. You would like to know what monthly interest rate the dealer is, in effect, charging you. To find the answer, you have to solve the equation

1 $$48x(1 + x)^{60} - (1 + x)^{60} + 1 = 0$$

(The details are explained in Exercise 29.) How would you solve such an equation?

For a quadratic equation $ax^2 + bx + c = 0$ there is a well-known formula for the roots. For third- and fourth-degree equations there are also formulas for the roots, but they are extremely complicated. If f is a polynomial of degree 5 or higher, there is no such formula. Likewise, there is no formula that will enable us to find the exact roots of a transcendental equation such as $\cos x = x$.

We can find an *approximate* solution to Equation 1 by plotting the left side of the equation. Using a graphing device, and after experimenting with viewing rectangles, we produce the graph in Figure 1.

We see that in addition to the solution $x = 0$, which doesn't interest us, there is a solution between 0.007 and 0.008. Zooming in shows that the root is approximately 0.0076. If we need more accuracy we could zoom in repeatedly, but that becomes tiresome. A faster alternative is to use a numerical rootfinder on a calculator or computer algebra system. If we do so, we find that the root, correct to nine decimal places, is 0.007628603.

How do those numerical rootfinders work? They use a variety of methods, but most of them make some use of **Newton's method**, which is also called the **Newton-**

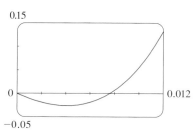

FIGURE 1

■ Try to solve Equation 1 using the numerical rootfinder on your calculator or computer. Some machines are not able to solve it. Others are successful but require you to specify a starting point for the search.

Raphson method. We will explain how this method works, partly to show what happens inside a calculator or computer, and partly as an application of the idea of linear approximation.

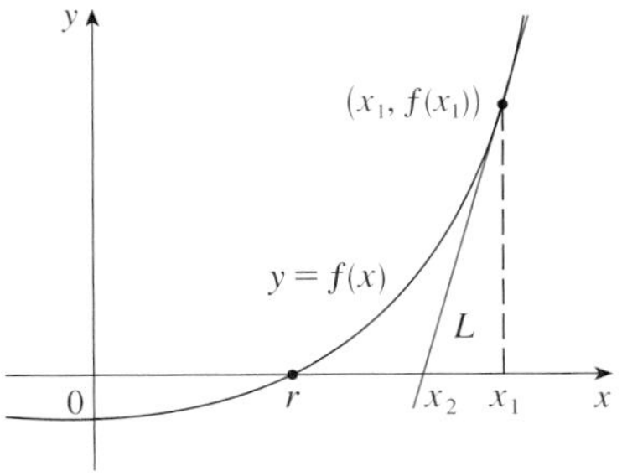

The geometry behind Newton's method is shown in Figure 2, where the root that we are trying to find is labeled r. We start with a first approximation x_1, which is obtained by guessing, or from a rough sketch of the graph of f, or from a computer-generated graph of f. Consider the tangent line L to the curve $y = f(x)$ at the point $(x_1, f(x_1))$ and look at the x-intercept of L, labeled x_2. The idea behind Newton's method is that the tangent line is close to the curve and so its x-intercept, x_2, is close to the x-intercept of the curve (namely, the root r that we are seeking). Because the tangent is a line, we can easily find its x-intercept.

To find a formula for x_2 in terms of x_1 we use the fact that the slope of L is $f'(x_1)$, so its equation is

$$y - f(x_1) = f'(x_1)(x - x_1)$$

Since the x-intercept of L is x_2, we set $y = 0$ and obtain

$$0 - f(x_1) = f'(x_1)(x_2 - x_1)$$

If $f'(x_1) \neq 0$, we can solve this equation for x_2:

$$x_2 = x_1 - \frac{f(x_1)}{f'(x_1)}$$

We use x_2 as a second approximation to r.

Next we repeat this procedure with x_1 replaced by x_2, using the tangent line at $(x_2, f(x_2))$. This gives a third approximation:

$$x_3 = x_2 - \frac{f(x_2)}{f'(x_2)}$$

If we keep repeating this process, we obtain a sequence of approximations x_1, x_2, x_3, x_4, ... as shown in Figure 3. In general, if the nth approximation is x_n and $f'(x_n) \neq 0$, then the next approximation is given by

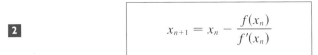

2
$$x_{n+1} = x_n - \frac{f(x_n)}{f'(x_n)}$$

If the numbers x_n become closer and closer to r as n becomes large, then we say that the sequence *converges* to r and we write

$$\lim_{n \to \infty} x_n = r$$

⊘ Although the sequence of successive approximations converges to the desired root for functions of the type illustrated in Figure 3, in certain circumstances the sequence may not converge. For example, consider the situation shown in Figure 4. You can see that x_2 is a worse approximation than x_1. This is likely to be the case when $f'(x_1)$ is close to 0. It might even happen that an approximation (such as x_3 in Figure 4) falls outside the domain of f. Then Newton's method fails and a better initial approximation x_1 should be chosen. See Exercises 23–25 for specific examples in which Newton's method works very slowly or does not work at all.

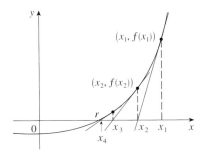

FIGURE 2

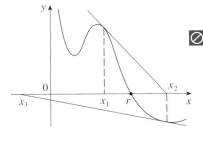

FIGURE 3

▪ The convergence of infinite sequences is discussed in detail in Section 8.1.

FIGURE 4

▼ EXAMPLE 1 Starting with $x_1 = 2$, find the third approximation x_3 to the root of the equation $x^3 - 2x - 5 = 0$.

SOLUTION We apply Newton's method with

$$f(x) = x^3 - 2x - 5 \qquad \text{and} \qquad f'(x) = 3x^2 - 2$$

In Module 4.6 you can investigate how Newton's method works for several functions and what happens when you change x_1.

Newton himself used this equation to illustrate his method and he chose $x_1 = 2$ after some experimentation because $f(1) = -6$, $f(2) = -1$, and $f(3) = 16$. Equation 2 becomes

$$x_{n+1} = x_n - \frac{x_n^3 - 2x_n - 5}{3x_n^2 - 2}$$

With $n = 1$ we have

$$x_2 = x_1 - \frac{x_1^3 - 2x_1 - 5}{3x_1^2 - 2}$$

■ Figure 5 shows the geometry behind the first step in Newton's method in Example 1. Since $f'(2) = 10$, the tangent line to $y = x^3 - 2x - 5$ at $(2, -1)$ has equation $y = 10x - 21$ and so its x-intercept is $x_2 = 2.1$.

$$= 2 - \frac{2^3 - 2(2) - 5}{3(2)^2 - 2} = 2.1$$

Then with $n = 2$ we obtain

$$x_3 = x_2 - \frac{x_2^3 - 2x_2 - 5}{3x_2^2 - 2}$$

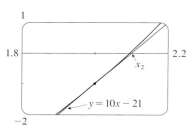

$$= 2.1 - \frac{(2.1)^3 - 2(2.1) - 5}{3(2.1)^2 - 2} \approx 2.0946$$

It turns out that this third approximation $x_3 \approx 2.0946$ is accurate to four decimal places. ∎

FIGURE 5

Suppose that we want to achieve a given accuracy, say to eight decimal places, using Newton's method. How do we know when to stop? The rule of thumb that is generally used is that we can stop when successive approximations x_n and x_{n+1} agree to eight decimal places. (A precise statement concerning accuracy in Newton's method will be given in Exercise 29 in Section 8.8.)

Notice that the procedure in going from n to $n + 1$ is the same for all values of n. (It is called an *iterative* process.) This means that Newton's method is particularly convenient for use with a programmable calculator or a computer.

▼ EXAMPLE 2 Use Newton's method to find $\sqrt[6]{2}$ correct to eight decimal places.

SOLUTION First we observe that finding $\sqrt[6]{2}$ is equivalent to finding the positive root of the equation

$$x^6 - 2 = 0$$

so we take $f(x) = x^6 - 2$. Then $f'(x) = 6x^5$ and Formula 2 (Newton's method) becomes

$$x_{n+1} = x_n - \frac{x_n^6 - 2}{6x_n^5}$$

If we choose $x_1 = 1$ as the initial approximation, then we obtain

$$x_2 \approx 1.16666667$$

$$x_3 \approx 1.12644368$$

$$x_4 \approx 1.12249707$$

$$x_5 \approx 1.12246205$$

$$x_6 \approx 1.12246205$$

Since x_5 and x_6 agree to eight decimal places, we conclude that

$$\sqrt[6]{2} \approx 1.12246205$$

to eight decimal places.   ■

■ **EXAMPLE 3** Find, correct to six decimal places, the root of the equation $\cos x = x$.

SOLUTION We first rewrite the equation in standard form:

$$\cos x - x = 0$$

Therefore, we let $f(x) = \cos x - x$. Then $f'(x) = -\sin x - 1$, so Formula 2 becomes

$$x_{n+1} = x_n - \frac{\cos x_n - x_n}{-\sin x_n - 1} = x_n + \frac{\cos x_n - x_n}{\sin x_n + 1}$$

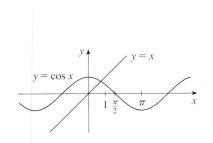

FIGURE 6

In order to guess a suitable value for x_1 we sketch the graphs of $y = \cos x$ and $y = x$ in Figure 6. It appears that they intersect at a point whose x-coordinate is somewhat less than 1, so let's take $x_1 = 1$ as a convenient first approximation. Then, remembering to put our calculator in radian mode, we get

$$x_2 \approx 0.75036387$$

$$x_3 \approx 0.73911289$$

$$x_4 \approx 0.73908513$$

$$x_5 \approx 0.73908513$$

Since x_4 and x_5 agree to six decimal places (eight, in fact), we conclude that the root of the equation, correct to six decimal places, is 0.739085.   ■

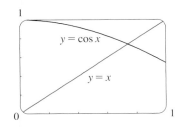

FIGURE 7

Instead of using the rough sketch in Figure 6 to get a starting approximation for Newton's method in Example 3, we could have used the more accurate graph that a calculator or computer provides. Figure 7 suggests that we use $x_1 = 0.75$ as the initial approximation. Then Newton's method gives

$$x_2 \approx 0.73911114 \qquad x_3 \approx 0.73908513 \qquad x_4 \approx 0.73908513$$

and so we obtain the same answer as before, but with one fewer step.

4.6	**EXERCISES**

1. The figure shows the graph of a function f. Suppose that Newton's method is used to approximate the root r of the equation $f(x) = 0$ with initial approximation $x_1 = 1$.
   (a) Draw the tangent lines that are used to find x_2 and x_3, and estimate the numerical values of x_2 and x_3.
   (b) Would $x_1 = 5$ be a better first approximation? Explain.

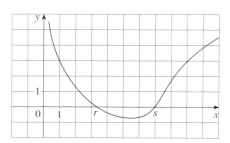

2. Follow the instructions for Exercise 1(a) but use $x_1 = 9$ as the starting approximation for finding the root s.

3. Suppose the line $y = 5x - 4$ is tangent to the curve $y = f(x)$ when $x = 3$. If Newton's method is used to locate a root of the equation $f(x) = 0$ and the initial approximation is $x_1 = 3$, find the second approximation x_2.

4. For each initial approximation, determine graphically what happens if Newton's method is used for the function whose graph is shown.
   (a) $x_1 = 0$ (b) $x_1 = 1$ (c) $x_1 = 3$
   (d) $x_1 = 4$ (e) $x_1 = 5$

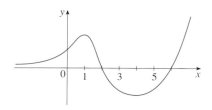

5–6 ▪ Use Newton's method with the specified initial approximation x_1 to find x_3, the third approximation to the root of the given equation. (Give your answer to four decimal places.)

5. $x^3 + 2x - 4 = 0$, $x_1 = 1$

6. $x^5 + 2 = 0$, $x_1 = -1$

▪ ▪ ▪ ▪ ▪ ▪ ▪ ▪ ▪ ▪ ▪ ▪ ▪

 7. Use Newton's method with initial approximation $x_1 = -1$ to find x_2, the second approximation to the root of the equation $x^3 + x + 3 = 0$. Explain how the method works by first graphing the function and its tangent line at $(-1, 1)$.

 8. Use Newton's method with initial approximation $x_1 = 1$ to find x_2, the second approximation to the root of the equation $x^4 - x - 1 = 0$. Explain how the method works by first graphing the function and its tangent line at $(1, -1)$.

9–10 ▪ Use Newton's method to approximate the given number correct to eight decimal places.

9. $\sqrt[3]{30}$ 10. $\sqrt[7]{1000}$

▪ ▪ ▪ ▪ ▪ ▪ ▪ ▪ ▪ ▪ ▪ ▪ ▪

11–12 ▪ Use Newton's method to approximate the indicated root of the equation correct to six decimal places.

11. The positive root of $\sin x = x^2$

12. The positive root of $2 \cos x = x^4$

▪ ▪ ▪ ▪ ▪ ▪ ▪ ▪ ▪ ▪ ▪ ▪ ▪

13–20 ▪ Use Newton's method to find all the roots of the equation correct to eight decimal places. Start by drawing a graph to find initial approximations.

13. $x^5 - x^4 - 5x^3 - x^2 + 4x + 3 = 0$

14. $x^2(4 - x^2) = \dfrac{4}{x^2 + 1}$

15. $e^{-x} = 2 + x$ 16. $\ln(4 - x^2) = x$

17. $x^2\sqrt{2 - x - x^2} = 1$ 18. $3 \sin(x^2) = 2x$

19. $\tan^{-1}x = 1 - x$ 20. $\tan x = \sqrt{9 - x^2}$

▪ ▪ ▪ ▪ ▪ ▪ ▪ ▪ ▪ ▪ ▪ ▪ ▪

21. (a) Apply Newton's method to the equation $x^2 - a = 0$ to derive the following square-root algorithm (used by the ancient Babylonians to compute $\sqrt{a}$):
$$x_{n+1} = \frac{1}{2}\left(x_n + \frac{a}{x_n}\right)$$
   (b) Use part (a) to compute $\sqrt{1000}$ correct to six decimal places.

22. (a) Apply Newton's method to the equation $1/x - a = 0$ to derive the following reciprocal algorithm:
$$x_{n+1} = 2x_n - ax_n^2$$
   (This algorithm enables a computer to find reciprocals without actually dividing.)
   (b) Use part (a) to compute $1/1.6984$ correct to six decimal places.

23. Explain why Newton's method doesn't work for finding the root of the equation $x^3 - 3x + 6 = 0$ if the initial approximation is chosen to be $x_1 = 1$.

24. (a) Use Newton's method with $x_1 = 1$ to find the root of the equation $x^3 - x = 1$ correct to six decimal places.
   (b) Solve the equation in part (a) using $x_1 = 0.6$ as the initial approximation.
   (c) Solve the equation in part (a) using $x_1 = 0.57$. (You definitely need a programmable calculator for this part.)

(d) Graph $f(x) = x^3 - x - 1$ and its tangent lines at $x_1 = 1, 0.6$, and 0.57 to explain why Newton's method is so sensitive to the value of the initial approximation.

25. Explain why Newton's method fails when applied to the equation $\sqrt[3]{x} = 0$ with any initial approximation $x_1 \neq 0$. Illustrate your explanation with a sketch.

26. Use Newton's method to find the absolute minimum value of the function $f(x) = x^2 + \sin x$ correct to six decimal places.

27. Use Newton's method to find the coordinates of the inflection point of the curve $y = e^{\cos x}$, $0 \leqslant x \leqslant \pi$, correct to six decimal places.

28. Of the infinitely many lines that are tangent to the curve $y = -\sin x$ and pass through the origin, there is one that has the largest slope. Use Newton's method to find the slope of that line correct to six decimal places.

29. A car dealer sells a new car for $18,000. He also offers to sell the same car for payments of $375 per month for five years. What monthly interest rate is this dealer charging?
  To solve this problem you will need to use the formula for the present value A of an annuity consisting of n equal payments of size R with interest rate i per time period:

$$A = \frac{R}{i} \left[1 - (1 + i)^{-n} \right]$$

Replacing i by x, show that

$$48x(1 + x)^{60} - (1 + x)^{60} + 1 = 0$$

Use Newton's method to solve this equation.

30. The figure shows the Sun located at the origin and the Earth at the point $(1, 0)$. (The unit here is the distance between the centers of the Earth and the Sun, called an *astronomical unit:* 1 AU $\approx 1.496 \times 10^8$ km.) There are five locations L_1, L_2, L_3, L_4, and L_5 in this plane of rotation of the Earth about the Sun where a satellite remains motionless with respect to the Earth because the forces acting on the satellite (including the gravitational attractions of the Earth and the Sun) balance each other. These locations are called *libration points.* (A solar research satellite has been placed at one of these libration points.) If m_1 is the mass of the Sun, m_2 is the mass of the Earth, and $r = m_2/(m_1 + m_2)$, it turns out that the x-coordinate of L_1 is the unique root of the fifth-degree equation

$$\begin{aligned} p(x) = x^5 &- (2 + r)x^4 + (1 + 2r)x^3 - (1 - r)x^2 \\ &+ 2(1 - r)x + r - 1 = 0 \end{aligned}$$

and the x-coordinate of L_2 is the root of the equation

$$p(x) - 2rx^2 = 0$$

Using the value $r \approx 3.04042 \times 10^{-6}$, find the locations of the libration points (a) L_1 and (b) L_2.

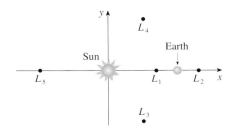

4.7 ANTIDERIVATIVES

A physicist who knows the velocity of a particle might wish to know its position at a given time. An engineer who can measure the variable rate at which water is leaking from a tank wants to know the amount leaked over a certain time period. A biologist who knows the rate at which a bacteria population is increasing might want to deduce what the size of the population will be at some future time. In each case, the problem is to find a function F whose derivative is a known function f. If such a function F exists, it is called an *antiderivative* of f.

> **DEFINITION** A function F is called an **antiderivative** of f on an interval I if $F'(x) = f(x)$ for all x in I.

For instance, let $f(x) = x^2$. It isn't difficult to discover an antiderivative of f if we keep the Power Rule in mind. In fact, if $F(x) = \frac{1}{3}x^3$, then $F'(x) = x^2 = f(x)$. But the function $G(x) = \frac{1}{3}x^3 + 100$ also satisfies $G'(x) = x^2$. Therefore, both F and G are antiderivatives of f. Indeed, any function of the form $H(x) = \frac{1}{3}x^3 + C$, where C is a constant, is an antiderivative of f. The question arises: Are there any others?

To answer this question, recall that in Section 4.2 we used the Mean Value Theorem to prove that if two functions have identical derivatives on an interval, then they must differ by a constant (Corollary 4.2.7). Thus, if F and G are any two antiderivatives of f, then

$$F'(x) = f(x) = G'(x)$$

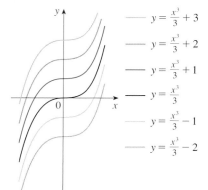

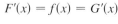
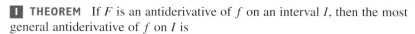

so $G(x) - F(x) = C$, where C is a constant. We can write this as $G(x) = F(x) + C$, so we have the following result.

---
1 THEOREM If F is an antiderivative of f on an interval I, then the most general antiderivative of f on I is

$$F(x) + C$$

where C is an arbitrary constant.

FIGURE 1
Members of the family of
antiderivatives of $f(x) = x^2$

Going back to the function $f(x) = x^2$, we see that the general antiderivative of f is $\frac{1}{3}x^3 + C$. By assigning specific values to the constant C, we obtain a family of functions whose graphs are vertical translates of one another (see Figure 1). This makes sense because each curve must have the same slope at any given value of x.

EXAMPLE 1 Find the most general antiderivative of each of the following functions.
(a) $f(x) = \sin x$ (b) $f(x) = 1/x$ (c) $f(x) = x^n$, $n \neq -1$

SOLUTION
(a) If $F(x) = -\cos x$, then $F'(x) = \sin x$, so an antiderivative of $\sin x$ is $-\cos x$. By Theorem 1, the most general antiderivative is $G(x) = -\cos x + C$.

(b) Recall from Section 3.3 that

$$\frac{d}{dx}(\ln x) = \frac{1}{x}$$

So on the interval $(0, \infty)$ the general antiderivative of $1/x$ is $\ln x + C$. We also learned that

$$\frac{d}{dx}(\ln |x|) = \frac{1}{x}$$

for all $x \neq 0$. Theorem 1 then tells us that the general antiderivative of $f(x) = 1/x$ is $\ln |x| + C$ on any interval that doesn't contain 0. In particular, this is true on each of the intervals $(-\infty, 0)$ and $(0, \infty)$. So the general antiderivative of f is

$$F(x) = \begin{cases} \ln x + C_1 & \text{if } x > 0 \\ \ln(-x) + C_2 & \text{if } x < 0 \end{cases}$$

(c) We use the Power Rule to discover an antiderivative of x^n. In fact, if $n \neq -1$, then

$$\frac{d}{dx}\left(\frac{x^{n+1}}{n+1}\right) = \frac{(n+1)x^n}{n+1} = x^n$$

Thus the general antiderivative of $f(x) = x^n$ is

$$F(x) = \frac{x^{n+1}}{n+1} + C$$

This is valid for $n \geq 0$ since then $f(x) = x^n$ is defined on an interval. If n is negative (but $n \neq -1$), it is valid on any interval that doesn't contain 0. ◼

As in Example 1, every differentiation formula, when read from right to left, gives rise to an antidifferentiation formula. In Table 2 we list some particular antiderivatives. Each formula in the table is true because the derivative of the function in the right column appears in the left column. In particular, the first formula says that the antiderivative of a constant times a function is the constant times the antiderivative of the function. The second formula says that the antiderivative of a sum is the sum of the antiderivatives. (We use the notation $F' = f$, $G' = g$.)

2 TABLE OF ANTIDIFFERENTIATION FORMULAS

▪ To obtain the most general antiderivative from the particular ones in Table 2, we have to add a constant (or constants), as in Example 1.

Function	Particular antiderivative	Function	Particular antiderivative
$cf(x)$	$cF(x)$	$\sin x$	$-\cos x$
$f(x) + g(x)$	$F(x) + G(x)$	$\sec^2 x$	$\tan x$
$x^n \ \ (n \neq -1)$	$\dfrac{x^{n+1}}{n+1}$	$\sec x \tan x$	$\sec x$
$1/x$	$\ln \lvert x \rvert$	$\dfrac{1}{\sqrt{1-x^2}}$	$\sin^{-1} x$
e^x	e^x	$\dfrac{1}{1+x^2}$	$\tan^{-1} x$
$\cos x$	$\sin x$		

EXAMPLE 2 Find all functions g such that

$$g'(x) = 4 \sin x + \frac{2x^5 - \sqrt{x}}{x}$$

SOLUTION We first rewrite the given function as follows:

$$g'(x) = 4 \sin x + \frac{2x^5}{x} - \frac{\sqrt{x}}{x} = 4 \sin x + 2x^4 - \frac{1}{\sqrt{x}}$$

Thus we want to find an antiderivative of

$$g'(x) = 4 \sin x + 2x^4 - x^{-1/2}$$

Using the formulas in Table 2 together with Theorem 1, we obtain

$$g(x) = 4(-\cos x) + 2\frac{x^5}{5} - \frac{x^{1/2}}{\frac{1}{2}} + C$$

$$= -4 \cos x + \tfrac{2}{5}x^5 - 2\sqrt{x} + C \qquad ◼$$

In applications of calculus it is very common to have a situation as in Example 2, where it is required to find a function, given knowledge about its derivatives. An equation that involves the derivatives of a function is called a **differential equation**. These will be studied in some detail in Section 7.6, but for the present we can solve some elementary differential equations. The general solution of a differential equation involves an arbitrary constant (or constants) as in Example 2. However, there may be some extra conditions given that will determine the constants and therefore uniquely specify the solution.

■ Figure 2 shows the graphs of the function f' in Example 3 and its antiderivative f. Notice that $f'(x) > 0$, so f is always increasing. Also notice that when f' has a maximum or minimum, f appears to have an inflection point. So the graph serves as a check on our calculation.

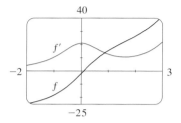

FIGURE 2

EXAMPLE 3 Find f if $f'(x) = e^x + 20(1 + x^2)^{-1}$ and $f(0) = -2$.

SOLUTION The general antiderivative of

$$f'(x) = e^x + \frac{20}{1 + x^2}$$

is

$$f(x) = e^x + 20 \tan^{-1}x + C$$

To determine C we use the fact that $f(0) = -2$:

$$f(0) = e^0 + 20 \tan^{-1} 0 + C = -2$$

Thus we have $C = -2 - 1 = -3$, so the particular solution is

$$f(x) = e^x + 20 \tan^{-1}x - 3 \qquad ■$$

EXAMPLE 4 Find f if $f''(x) = 12x^2 + 6x - 4$, $f(0) = 4$, and $f(1) = 1$.

SOLUTION The general antiderivative of $f''(x) = 12x^2 + 6x - 4$ is

$$f'(x) = 12 \frac{x^3}{3} + 6 \frac{x^2}{2} - 4x + C = 4x^3 + 3x^2 - 4x + C$$

Using the antidifferentiation rules once more, we find that

$$f(x) = 4 \frac{x^4}{4} + 3 \frac{x^3}{3} - 4 \frac{x^2}{2} + Cx + D = x^4 + x^3 - 2x^2 + Cx + D$$

To determine C and D we use the given conditions that $f(0) = 4$ and $f(1) = 1$. Since $f(0) = 0 + D = 4$, we have $D = 4$. Since

$$f(1) = 1 + 1 - 2 + C + 4 = 1$$

we have $C = -3$. Therefore, the required function is

$$f(x) = x^4 + x^3 - 2x^2 - 3x + 4 \qquad ■$$

RECTILINEAR MOTION

Antidifferentiation is particularly useful in analyzing the motion of an object moving in a straight line. Recall that if the object has position function $s = f(t)$, then the velocity function is $v(t) = s'(t)$. This means that the position function is an antiderivative of the velocity function. Likewise, the acceleration function is $a(t) = v'(t)$, so the velocity function is an antiderivative of the acceleration. If the acceleration and the initial values $s(0)$ and $v(0)$ are known, then the position function can be found by antidifferentiating twice.

EXAMPLE 5 A particle moves in a straight line and has acceleration given by $a(t) = 6t + 4$. Its initial velocity is $v(0) = -6$ cm/s and its initial displacement is $s(0) = 9$ cm. Find its position function $s(t)$.

SOLUTION Since $v'(t) = a(t) = 6t + 4$, antidifferentiation gives

$$v(t) = 6 \frac{t^2}{2} + 4t + C = 3t^2 + 4t + C$$

Note that $v(0) = C$. But we are given that $v(0) = -6$, so $C = -6$ and

$$v(t) = 3t^2 + 4t - 6$$

Since $v(t) = s'(t)$, s is the antiderivative of v:

$$s(t) = 3\frac{t^3}{3} + 4\frac{t^2}{2} - 6t + D = t^3 + 2t^2 - 6t + D$$

This gives $s(0) = D$. We are given that $s(0) = 9$, so $D = 9$ and the required position function is

$$s(t) = t^3 + 2t^2 - 6t + 9$$

  ▪

An object near the surface of the Earth is subject to a gravitational force that produces a downward acceleration denoted by g. For motion close to the ground we may assume that g is constant, its value being about 9.8 m/s² (or 32 ft/s²).

EXAMPLE 6 A ball is thrown upward with a speed of 48 ft/s from the edge of a cliff 432 ft above the ground. Find its height above the ground t seconds later. When does it reach its maximum height? When does it hit the ground?

SOLUTION The motion is vertical and we choose the positive direction to be upward. At time t the distance above the ground is $s(t)$ and the velocity $v(t)$ is decreasing. Therefore, the acceleration must be negative and we have

$$a(t) = \frac{dv}{dt} = -32$$

Taking antiderivatives, we have

$$v(t) = -32t + C$$

To determine C we use the given information that $v(0) = 48$. This gives $48 = 0 + C$, so

$$v(t) = -32t + 48$$

The maximum height is reached when $v(t) = 0$, that is, after 1.5 s. Since $s'(t) = v(t)$, we antidifferentiate again and obtain

$$s(t) = -16t^2 + 48t + D$$

Using the fact that $s(0) = 432$, we have $432 = 0 + D$ and so

$$s(t) = -16t^2 + 48t + 432$$

The expression for $s(t)$ is valid until the ball hits the ground. This happens when $s(t) = 0$, that is, when

$$-16t^2 + 48t + 432 = 0$$

or, equivalently,

$$t^2 - 3t - 27 = 0$$

▪ Figure 3 shows the position function of the ball in Example 6. The graph corroborates the conclusions we reached: The ball reaches its maximum height after 1.5 s and hits the ground after 6.9 s.

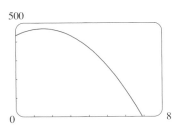

500

0   8

FIGURE 3

Using the quadratic formula to solve this equation, we get

$$t = \frac{3 \pm 3\sqrt{13}}{2}$$

We reject the solution with the minus sign since it gives a negative value for t. Therefore, the ball hits the ground after $3(1 + \sqrt{13})/2 \approx 6.9$ s. ■

4.7 EXERCISES

1–12 ■ Find the most general antiderivative of the function. (Check your answer by differentiation.)

1. $f(x) = 6x^2 - 8x + 3$ **2.** $f(x) = 1 - x^3 + 12x^5$

3. $f(x) = 5x^{1/4} - 7x^{3/4}$ **4.** $f(x) = 2x + 3x^{1.7}$

5. $f(x) = \sqrt[3]{x} + \dfrac{5}{x^6}$ **6.** $f(x) = \sqrt[4]{x^3} + \sqrt[3]{x^4}$

7. $f(u) = \dfrac{u^4 + 3\sqrt{u}}{u^2}$ **8.** $g(x) = \dfrac{5 - 4x^3 + 2x^6}{x^6}$

9. $g(\theta) = \cos\theta - 5\sin\theta$ **10.** $f(x) = 3e^x + 7\sec^2 x$

11. $f(x) = 2x + 5(1 - x^2)^{-1/2}$

12. $f(x) = \dfrac{x^2 + x + 1}{x}$

13–14 ■ Find the antiderivative F of f that satisfies the given condition. Check your answer by comparing the graphs of f and F.

13. $f(x) = 5x^4 - 2x^5$, $F(0) = 4$

14. $f(x) = 4 - 3(1 + x^2)^{-1}$, $F(1) = 0$

15–28 ■ Find f.

15. $f''(x) = 6x + 12x^2$ **16.** $f''(x) = 2 + x^3 + x^6$

17. $f''(x) = 1 + x^{4/5}$ **18.** $f''(x) = \cos x$

19. $f'(x) = \sqrt{x}\,(6 + 5x)$, $f(1) = 10$

20. $f'(x) = 2x - 3/x^4$, $x > 0$, $f(1) = 3$

21. $f'(t) = 2\cos t + \sec^2 t$, $-\pi/2 < t < \pi/2$, $f(\pi/3) = 4$

22. $f'(x) = 4/\sqrt{1 - x^2}$, $f(\tfrac{1}{2}) = 1$

23. $f''(x) = 24x^2 + 2x + 10$, $f(1) = 5$, $f'(1) = -3$

24. $f''(x) = 4 - 6x - 40x^3$, $f(0) = 2$, $f'(0) = 1$

25. $f''(\theta) = \sin\theta + \cos\theta$, $f(0) = 3$, $f'(0) = 4$

26. $f''(t) = 3/\sqrt{t}$, $f(4) = 20$, $f'(4) = 7$

27. $f''(x) = x^{-2}$, $x > 0$, $f(1) = 0$, $f(2) = 0$

28. $f''(t) = 2e^t + 3\sin t$, $f(0) = 0$, $f(\pi) = 0$

■   ■   ■   ■   ■   ■   ■   ■   ■   ■   ■   ■

29. Given that the graph of f passes through the point $(1, 6)$ and that the slope of its tangent line at $(x, f(x))$ is $2x + 1$, find $f(2)$.

30. Find a function f such that $f'(x) = x^3$ and the line $x + y = 0$ is tangent to the graph of f.

31–32 ■ The graph of a function f is shown. Which graph is an antiderivative of f and why?

31.

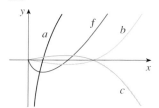

32.

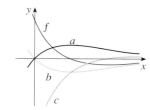

■   ■   ■   ■   ■   ■   ■   ■   ■   ■   ■   ■

33–36 ■ A particle is moving with the given data. Find the position of the particle.

33. $v(t) = \sin t - \cos t$, $s(0) = 0$

34. $v(t) = 1.5\sqrt{t}$, $s(4) = 10$

35. $a(t) = 10\sin t + 3\cos t$, $s(0) = 0$, $s(2\pi) = 12$

36. $a(t) = 10 + 3t - 3t^2$, $s(0) = 0$, $s(2) = 10$

■   ■   ■   ■   ■   ■   ■   ■   ■   ■   ■   ■

37. A stone is dropped from the upper observation deck (the Space Deck) of the CN Tower, 450 m above the ground.
   (a) Find the distance of the stone above ground level at time t.
   (b) How long does it take the stone to reach the ground?
   (c) With what velocity does it strike the ground?
   (d) If the stone is thrown downward with a speed of 5 m/s, how long does it take to reach the ground?

38. Show that for motion in a straight line with constant acceleration a, initial velocity v_0, and initial displacement s_0, the displacement after time t is

$$s = \tfrac{1}{2}at^2 + v_0 t + s_0$$

39. An object is projected upward with initial velocity v_0 meters per second from a point s_0 meters above the ground. Show that

$$[v(t)]^2 = v_0^2 - 19.6[s(t) - s_0]$$

40. Two balls are thrown upward from the edge of the cliff in Example 6. The first is thrown with a speed of 48 ft/s and the other is thrown a second later with a speed of 24 ft/s. Do the balls ever pass each other?

41. A stone was dropped off a cliff and hit the ground with a speed of 120 ft/s. What is the height of the cliff?

42. If a diver of mass m stands at the end of a diving board with length L and linear density ρ, then the board takes on the shape of a curve $y = f(x)$, where

$$EIy'' = mg(L - x) + \tfrac{1}{2}\rho g(L - x)^2$$

E and I are positive constants that depend on the material of the board and g (< 0) is the acceleration due to gravity.
(a) Find an expression for the shape of the curve.
(b) Use $f(L)$ to estimate the distance below the horizontal at the end of the board.

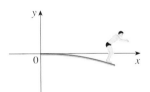

43. Since raindrops grow as they fall, their surface area increases and therefore the resistance to their falling increases. A raindrop has an initial downward velocity of 10 m/s and its downward acceleration is

$$a = \begin{cases} 9 - 0.9t & \text{if } 0 \leq t \leq 10 \\ 0 & \text{if } t > 10 \end{cases}$$

If the raindrop is initially 500 m above the ground, how long does it take to fall?

44. A car is traveling at 50 mi/h when the brakes are fully applied, producing a constant deceleration of 22 ft/s². What is the distance traveled before the car comes to a stop?

45. What constant acceleration is required to increase the speed of a car from 30 mi/h to 50 mi/h in 5 s?

46. A car braked with a constant deceleration of 16 ft/s², producing skid marks measuring 200 ft before coming to a stop. How fast was the car traveling when the brakes were first applied?

47. A car is traveling at 100 km/h when the driver sees an accident 80 m ahead and slams on the brakes. What constant deceleration is required to stop the car in time to avoid a pileup?

48. A model rocket is fired vertically upward from rest. Its acceleration for the first three seconds is $a(t) = 60t$, at which time the fuel is exhausted and it becomes a freely "falling" body. Fourteen seconds later, the rocket's parachute opens, and the (downward) velocity slows linearly to -18 ft/s in 5 s. The rocket then "floats" to the ground at that rate.
(a) Determine the position function s and the velocity function v (for all times t). Sketch the graphs of s and v.
(b) At what time does the rocket reach its maximum height, and what is that height?
(c) At what time does the rocket land?

49. A high-speed bullet train accelerates and decelerates at the rate of 4 ft/s². Its maximum cruising speed is 90 mi/h.
(a) What is the maximum distance the train can travel if it accelerates from rest until it reaches its cruising speed and then runs at that speed for 15 minutes?
(b) Suppose that the train starts from rest and must come to a complete stop in 15 minutes. What is the maximum distance it can travel under these conditions?
(c) Find the minimum time that the train takes to travel between two consecutive stations that are 45 miles apart.
(d) The trip from one station to the next takes 37.5 minutes. How far apart are the stations?

4	**REVIEW**

CONCEPT CHECK

1. Explain the difference between an absolute maximum and a local maximum. Illustrate with a sketch.

2. (a) What does the Extreme Value Theorem say?
(b) Explain how the Closed Interval Method works.

3. (a) State Fermat's Theorem.
(b) Define a critical number of f.

4. (a) State Rolle's Theorem.
(b) State the Mean Value Theorem and give a geometric interpretation.

5. (a) State the Increasing/Decreasing Test.
(b) What does it mean to say that f is concave upward on an interval I?
(c) State the Concavity Test.
(d) What are inflection points? How do you find them?

6. (a) State the First Derivative Test.
(b) State the Second Derivative Test.
(c) What are the relative advantages and disadvantages of these tests?

7. If you have a graphing calculator or computer, why do you need calculus to graph a function?

8. (a) Given an initial approximation x_1 to a root of the equation $f(x) = 0$, explain geometrically, with a diagram, how the second approximation x_2 in Newton's method is obtained.

(b) Write an expression for x_2 in terms of x_1, $f(x_1)$, and $f'(x_1)$.
(c) Write an expression for x_{n+1} in terms of x_n, $f(x_n)$, and $f'(x_n)$.
(d) Under what circumstances is Newton's method likely to fail or to work very slowly?

9. (a) What is an antiderivative of a function f?
(b) Suppose F_1 and F_2 are both antiderivatives of f on an interval I. How are F_1 and F_2 related?

TRUE-FALSE QUIZ

Determine whether the statement is true or false. If it is true, explain why. If it is false, explain why or give an example that disproves the statement.

1. If $f'(c) = 0$, then f has a local maximum or minimum at c.

2. If f has an absolute minimum value at c, then $f'(c) = 0$.

3. If f is continuous on (a, b), then f attains an absolute maximum value $f(c)$ and an absolute minimum value $f(d)$ at some numbers c and d in (a, b).

4. If f is differentiable and $f(-1) = f(1)$, then there is a number c such that $|c| < 1$ and $f'(c) = 0$.

5. If $f'(x) < 0$ for $1 < x < 6$, then f is decreasing on $(1, 6)$.

6. If $f''(2) = 0$, then $(2, f(2))$ is an inflection point of the curve $y = f(x)$.

7. If $f'(x) = g'(x)$ for $0 < x < 1$, then $f(x) = g(x)$ for $0 < x < 1$.

8. There exists a function f such that $f(1) = -2$, $f(3) = 0$, and $f'(x) > 1$ for all x.

9. There exists a function f such that $f(x) > 0$, $f'(x) < 0$, and $f''(x) > 0$ for all x.

10. There exists a function f such that $f(x) < 0$, $f'(x) < 0$, and $f''(x) > 0$ for all x.

11. If f and g are increasing on an interval I, then $f + g$ is increasing on I.

12. If f and g are increasing on an interval I, then $f - g$ is increasing on I.

13. If f and g are increasing on an interval I, then fg is increasing on I.

14. If f and g are positive increasing functions on an interval I, then fg is increasing on I.

15. If f is increasing and $f(x) > 0$ on I, then $g(x) = 1/f(x)$ is decreasing on I.

16. The most general antiderivative of $f(x) = x^{-2}$ is

$$F(x) = -\frac{1}{x} + C$$

17. If $f'(x)$ exists and is nonzero for all x, then $f(1) \neq f(0)$.

EXERCISES

1–4 ■ Find the local and absolute extreme values of the function on the given interval.

1. $f(x) = 10 + 27x - x^3$, $[0, 4]$

2. $f(x) = x - \sqrt{x}$, $[0, 4]$

3. $f(x) = \dfrac{x}{x^2 + x + 1}$, $[-2, 0]$

4. $f(x) = (\ln x)/x^2$, $[1, 3]$

5–7 ■ Sketch the graph of a function that satisfies the given conditions.

5. $f(0) = 0$, $f'(-2) = f'(1) = f'(9) = 0$,
$\lim_{x \to \infty} f(x) = 0$, $\lim_{x \to 6} f(x) = -\infty$,
$f'(x) < 0$ on $(-\infty, -2)$, $(1, 6)$, and $(9, \infty)$,
$f'(x) > 0$ on $(-2, 1)$ and $(6, 9)$,
$f''(x) > 0$ on $(-\infty, 0)$ and $(12, \infty)$,
$f''(x) < 0$ on $(0, 6)$ and $(6, 12)$

6. $f(0) = 0$, f is continuous and even,
$f'(x) = 2x$ if $0 < x < 1$, $f'(x) = -1$ if $1 < x < 3$,
$f'(x) = 1$ if $x > 3$

7. f is odd, $f'(x) < 0$ for $0 < x < 2$,
$f'(x) > 0$ for $x > 2$, $f''(x) > 0$ for $0 < x < 3$,
$f''(x) < 0$ for $x > 3$, $\lim_{x \to \infty} f(x) = -2$

8. The figure shows the graph of the *derivative* f' of a function f.
(a) On what intervals is f increasing or decreasing?
(b) For what values of x does f have a local maximum or minimum?
(c) Sketch the graph of f''.
(d) Sketch a possible graph of f.

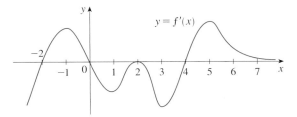

9–14 ▪
(a) Find the vertical and horizontal asymptotes, if any.
(b) Find the intervals of increase or decrease.
(c) Find the local maximum and minimum values.
(d) Find the intervals of concavity and the inflection points.
(e) Use the information from parts (a)–(d) to sketch the graph of f. Check your work with a graphing device.

9. $f(x) = 2 - 2x - x^3$ **10.** $f(x) = \dfrac{1}{1 - x^2}$

11. $y = \sin^2 x - 2\cos x$ **12.** $y = e^{2x - x^2}$

13. $y = e^x + e^{-3x}$ **14.** $y = \ln(x^2 - 1)$

15–22 ▪ Use the guidelines of Section 4.4 to sketch the curve.

15. $y = x^4 - 3x^3 + 3x^2 - x$ **16.** $y = x^3 - 6x^2 - 15x + 4$

17. $y = \dfrac{1}{x(x - 3)^2}$ **18.** $y = \dfrac{1}{x} + \dfrac{1}{x + 1}$

19. $y = x\sqrt{2 + x}$ **20.** $y = \sqrt{x} - \sqrt[3]{x}$

21. $y = \sin^{-1}(1/x)$

22. $y = 4x - \tan x$, $-\pi/2 < x < \pi/2$

23–26 ▪ Produce graphs of f that reveal all the important aspects of the curve. Use graphs of f' and f'' to estimate the intervals of increase and decrease, extreme values, intervals of concavity, and inflection points. In Exercise 23 use calculus to find these quantities exactly.

23. $f(x) = \dfrac{x^2 - 1}{x^3}$ **24.** $f(x) = \dfrac{\sqrt[3]{x}}{1 - x}$

25. $f(x) = 3x^6 - 5x^5 + x^4 - 5x^3 - 2x^2 + 2$

26. $f(x) = \sin x \cos^2 x$, $0 \le x \le 2\pi$

27. Graph $f(x) = e^{-1/x^2}$ in a viewing rectangle that shows all the main aspects of this function. Estimate the inflection points. Then use calculus to find them exactly.

CAS 28. (a) Graph the function $f(x) = 1/(1 + e^{1/x})$.
(b) Explain the shape of the graph by computing the limits of $f(x)$ as x approaches ∞, $-\infty$, 0^+, and 0^-.
(c) Use the graph of f to estimate the coordinates of the inflection points.
(d) Use your CAS to compute and graph f''.
(e) Use the graph in part (d) to estimate the inflection points more accurately.

CAS 29. If $f(x) = \arctan(\cos(3 \arcsin x))$, use the graphs of f, f', and f'' to estimate the x-coordinates of the maximum and minimum points and inflection points of f.

CAS 30. If $f(x) = \ln(2x + x \sin x)$, use the graphs of f, f', and f'' to estimate the intervals of increase and the inflection points of f on the interval $(0, 15]$.

31. Investigate the family of functions $f(x) = \ln(\sin x + C)$. What features do the members of this family have in common? How do they differ? For which values of C is f continuous on $(-\infty, \infty)$? For which values of C does f have no graph at all? What happens as $C \to \infty$?

32. Investigate the family of functions $f(x) = cxe^{-cx^2}$. What happens to the maximum and minimum points and the inflection points as c changes? Illustrate your conclusions by graphing several members of the family.

33. Show that the equation $x^{101} + x^{51} + x - 1 = 0$ has exactly one real root.

34. Suppose that f is continuous on $[0, 4]$, $f(0) = 1$, and $2 \le f'(x) \le 5$ for all x in $(0, 4)$. Show that $9 \le f(4) \le 21$.

35. By applying the Mean Value Theorem to the function $f(x) = x^{1/5}$ on the interval $[32, 33]$, show that

$$2 < \sqrt[5]{33} < 2.0125$$

36. For what values of the constants a and b is $(1, 6)$ a point of inflection of the curve $y = x^3 + ax^2 + bx + 1$?

37. Find two positive integers such that the sum of the first number and four times the second number is 1000 and the product of the numbers is as large as possible.

38. Find the point on the hyperbola $xy = 8$ that is closest to the point $(3, 0)$.

39. Find the smallest possible area of an isosceles triangle that is circumscribed about a circle of radius r.

40. Find the volume of the largest circular cone that can be inscribed in a sphere of radius r.

41. In $\triangle ABC$, D lies on AB, $|CD| = 5$ cm, $|AD| = 4$ cm, $|BD| = 4$ cm, and $CD \perp AB$. Where should a point P be chosen on CD so that the sum $|PA| + |PB| + |PC|$ is a minimum? What if $|CD| = 2$ cm?

42. An observer stands at a point P, one unit away from a track. Two runners start at the point S in the figure and run along the track. One runner runs three times as fast as the other. Find the maximum value of the observer's angle of sight θ between the runners. [*Hint:* Maximize $\tan \theta$.]

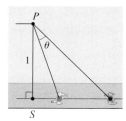

43. The velocity of a wave of length L in deep water is

$$v = K\sqrt{\frac{L}{C} + \frac{C}{L}}$$

where K and C are known positive constants. What is the length of the wave that gives the minimum velocity?

44. A metal storage tank with volume V is to be constructed in the shape of a right circular cylinder surmounted by a hemisphere. What dimensions will require the least amount of metal?

45. A hockey team plays in an arena with a seating capacity of 15,000 spectators. With the ticket price set at $12, average attendance at a game has been 11,000. A market survey indicates that for each dollar the ticket price is lowered, average attendance will increase by 1000. How should the owners of the team set the ticket price to maximize their revenue from ticket sales?

46. Use Newton's method to find all roots of the equation $\sin x = x^2 - 3x + 1$ correct to six decimal places.

47. Use Newton's method to find the absolute maximum value of the function $f(t) = \cos t + t - t^2$ correct to eight decimal places.

48. Use the guidelines in Section 4.4 to sketch the curve $y = x \sin x$, $0 \le x \le 2\pi$. Use Newton's method when necessary.

49–50 ■ Find the most general antiderivative of the function.

49. $f(x) = e^x - (2/\sqrt{x})$

50. $g(t) = (1 + t)/\sqrt{t}$

51–54 ■ Find $f(x)$.

51. $f'(x) = 2/(1 + x^2)$, $\quad f(0) = -1$

52. $f'(u) = \dfrac{u^2 + \sqrt{u}}{u}$, $\quad f(1) = 3$

53. $f''(x) = 1 - 6x + 48x^2$, $\quad f(0) = 1$, $\quad f'(0) = 2$

54. $f''(x) = 2x^3 + 3x^2 - 4x + 5$, $\quad f(0) = 2$, $\quad f(1) = 0$

■ ■ ■ ■ ■ ■ ■ ■ ■ ■ ■ ■ ■ ■

55–56 ■ A particle is moving with the given data. Find the position of the particle.

55. $a(t) = t - 2$, $\quad s(0) = 1$, $\quad v(0) = 3$

56. $a(t) = \cos t + \sin t$, $\quad s(0) = 0$, $\quad v(0) = 5$

■ ■ ■ ■ ■ ■ ■ ■ ■ ■ ■ ■ ■ ■

57. A canister is dropped from a helicopter 500 m above the ground. Its parachute does not open, but the canister has been designed to withstand an impact velocity of 100 m/s. Will it burst?

58. Investigate the family of curves given by

$$f(x) = x^4 + x^3 + cx^2$$

In particular you should determine the transitional value of c at which the number of critical numbers changes and the transitional value at which the number of inflection points changes. Illustrate the various possible shapes with graphs.

59. A rectangular beam will be cut from a cylindrical log of radius 10 inches.
   (a) Show that the beam of maximal cross-sectional area is a square.
   (b) Four rectangular planks will be cut from the four sections of the log that remain after cutting the square beam. Determine the dimensions of the planks that will have maximal cross-sectional area.
   (c) Suppose that the strength of a rectangular beam is proportional to the product of its width and the square of its depth. Find the dimensions of the strongest beam that can be cut from the cylindrical log.

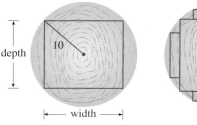
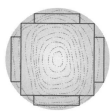

5 INTEGRALS

In Chapter 2 we used the tangent and velocity problems to introduce the derivative, which is the central idea in differential calculus. In much the same way, this chapter starts with the area and distance problems and uses them to formulate the idea of a definite integral, which is the basic concept of integral calculus. We will see in Chapter 7 how to use the integral to solve problems concerning volumes, lengths of curves, work, forces on a dam, and centers of mass, among many others.

There is a connection between integral calculus and differential calculus. The Fundamental Theorem of Calculus relates the integral to the derivative, and we will see in this chapter that it greatly simplifies the solution of many problems.

5.1 AREAS AND DISTANCES

In this section we discover that in trying to find the area under a curve or the distance traveled by a car, we end up with the same special type of limit.

THE AREA PROBLEM

We begin by attempting to solve the *area problem:* Find the area of the region S that lies under the curve $y = f(x)$ from a to b. This means that S, illustrated in Figure 1, is bounded by the graph of a continuous function f [where $f(x) \geq 0$], the vertical lines $x = a$ and $x = b$, and the x-axis.

In trying to solve the area problem we have to ask ourselves: What is the meaning of the word *area*? This question is easy to answer for regions with straight sides. For a rectangle, the area is defined as the product of the length and the width. The area of a triangle is half the base times the height. The area of a polygon is found by dividing it into triangles (as in Figure 2) and adding the areas of the triangles.

FIGURE 1
$S = \{(x, y) \mid a \leq x \leq b, 0 \leq y \leq f(x)\}$

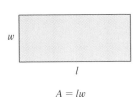
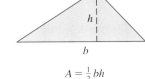
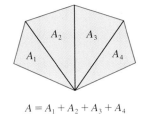

FIGURE 2 $A = lw$ $A = \frac{1}{2}bh$ $A = A_1 + A_2 + A_3 + A_4$

However, it isn't so easy to find the area of a region with curved sides. We all have an intuitive idea of what the area of a region is. But part of the area problem is to make this intuitive idea precise by giving an exact definition of area.

Recall that in defining a tangent we first approximated the slope of the tangent line by slopes of secant lines and then we took the limit of these approximations. We pursue a similar idea for areas. We first approximate the region S by rectangles and then we take the limit of the areas of these rectangles as we increase the number of rectangles. The following example illustrates the procedure.

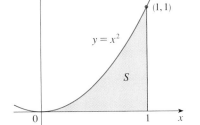

FIGURE 3

▼ EXAMPLE 1 Use rectangles to estimate the area under the parabola $y = x^2$ from 0 to 1 (the parabolic region S illustrated in Figure 3).

SOLUTION We first notice that the area of S must be somewhere between 0 and 1 because S is contained in a square with side length 1, but we can certainly do better than that. Suppose we divide S into four strips S_1, S_2, S_3, and S_4 by drawing the vertical lines $x = \frac{1}{4}$, $x = \frac{1}{2}$, and $x = \frac{3}{4}$ as in Figure 4(a).

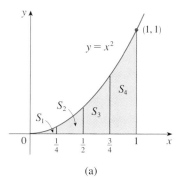
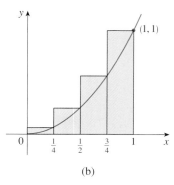

FIGURE 4

(a)   (b)

We can approximate each strip by a rectangle whose base is the same as the strip and whose height is the same as the right edge of the strip [see Figure 4(b)]. In other words, the heights of these rectangles are the values of the function $f(x) = x^2$ at the right endpoints of the subintervals $\left[0, \frac{1}{4}\right]$, $\left[\frac{1}{4}, \frac{1}{2}\right]$, $\left[\frac{1}{2}, \frac{3}{4}\right]$, and $\left[\frac{3}{4}, 1\right]$.

Each rectangle has width $\frac{1}{4}$ and the heights are $\left(\frac{1}{4}\right)^2$, $\left(\frac{1}{2}\right)^2$, $\left(\frac{3}{4}\right)^2$, and 1^2. If we let R_4 be the sum of the areas of these approximating rectangles, we get

$$R_4 = \frac{1}{4} \cdot \left(\frac{1}{4}\right)^2 + \frac{1}{4} \cdot \left(\frac{1}{2}\right)^2 + \frac{1}{4} \cdot \left(\frac{3}{4}\right)^2 + \frac{1}{4} \cdot 1^2 = \frac{15}{32} = 0.46875$$

From Figure 4(b) we see that the area A of S is less than R_4, so

$$A < 0.46875$$

Instead of using the rectangles in Figure 4(b) we could use the smaller rectangles in Figure 5 whose heights are the values of f at the left endpoints of the subintervals. (The leftmost rectangle has collapsed because its height is 0.) The sum of the areas of these approximating rectangles is

$$L_4 = \frac{1}{4} \cdot 0^2 + \frac{1}{4} \cdot \left(\frac{1}{4}\right)^2 + \frac{1}{4} \cdot \left(\frac{1}{2}\right)^2 + \frac{1}{4} \cdot \left(\frac{3}{4}\right)^2 = \frac{7}{32} = 0.21875$$

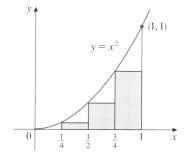

FIGURE 5

We see that the area of S is larger than L_4, so we have lower and upper estimates for A:

$$0.21875 < A < 0.46875$$

We can repeat this procedure with a larger number of strips. Figure 6 shows what happens when we divide the region S into eight strips of equal width.

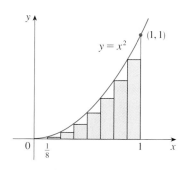
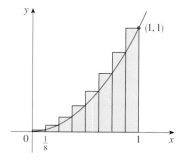

FIGURE 6

Approximating S with eight rectangles

(a) Using left endpoints

(b) Using right endpoints

By computing the sum of the areas of the smaller rectangles (L_8) and the sum of the areas of the larger rectangles (R_8), we obtain better lower and upper estimates for A:

$$0.2734375 < A < 0.3984375$$

So one possible answer to the question is to say that the true area of S lies somewhere between 0.2734375 and 0.3984375.

We could obtain better estimates by increasing the number of strips. The table at the left shows the results of similar calculations (with a computer) using n rectangles whose heights are found with left endpoints (L_n) or right endpoints (R_n). In particular, we see by using 50 strips that the area lies between 0.3234 and 0.3434. With 1000 strips we narrow it down even more: A lies between 0.3328335 and 0.3338335. A good estimate is obtained by averaging these numbers: $A \approx 0.3333335$. ▪

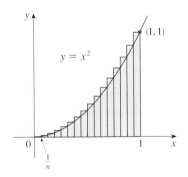

n	L_n	R_n
10	0.2850000	0.3850000
20	0.3087500	0.3587500
30	0.3168519	0.3501852
50	0.3234000	0.3434000
100	0.3283500	0.3383500
1000	0.3328335	0.3338335

From the values in the table in Example 1, it looks as if R_n is approaching $\frac{1}{3}$ as n increases. We confirm this in the next example.

☑ EXAMPLE 2 For the region S in Example 1, show that the sum of the areas of the upper approximating rectangles approaches $\frac{1}{3}$, that is,

$$\lim_{n \to \infty} R_n = \tfrac{1}{3}$$

SOLUTION R_n is the sum of the areas of the n rectangles in Figure 7. Each rectangle has width $1/n$ and the heights are the values of the function $f(x) = x^2$ at the points $1/n, 2/n, 3/n, \ldots, n/n$; that is, the heights are $(1/n)^2, (2/n)^2, (3/n)^2, \ldots, (n/n)^2$. Thus

$$R_n = \frac{1}{n}\left(\frac{1}{n}\right)^2 + \frac{1}{n}\left(\frac{2}{n}\right)^2 + \frac{1}{n}\left(\frac{3}{n}\right)^2 + \cdots + \frac{1}{n}\left(\frac{n}{n}\right)^2$$

$$= \frac{1}{n} \cdot \frac{1}{n^2}(1^2 + 2^2 + 3^2 + \cdots + n^2)$$

$$= \frac{1}{n^3}(1^2 + 2^2 + 3^2 + \cdots + n^2)$$

Here we need the formula for the sum of the squares of the first n positive integers:

1
$$1^2 + 2^2 + 3^2 + \cdots + n^2 = \frac{n(n+1)(2n+1)}{6}$$

Perhaps you have seen this formula before. It is proved in Example 5 in Appendix C.

Putting Formula 1 into our expression for R_n, we get

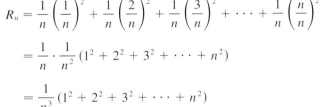
$$R_n = \frac{1}{n^3} \cdot \frac{n(n+1)(2n+1)}{6} = \frac{(n+1)(2n+1)}{6n^2}$$

FIGURE 7

■ Here we are computing the limit of the sequence $\{R_n\}$. Sequences and their limits will be studied in detail in Section 8.1. The idea is very similar to a limit at infinity (Section 1.6) except that in writing $\lim_{n \to \infty}$ we restrict n to be a positive integer. In particular, we know that

$$\lim_{n \to \infty} \frac{1}{n} = 0$$

When we write $\lim_{n \to \infty} R_n = \frac{1}{3}$ we mean that we can make R_n as close to $\frac{1}{3}$ as we like by taking n sufficiently large.

Thus we have

$$\lim_{n \to \infty} R_n = \lim_{n \to \infty} \frac{(n + 1)(2n + 1)}{6n^2}$$

$$= \lim_{n \to \infty} \frac{1}{6} \left(\frac{n + 1}{n} \right) \left(\frac{2n + 1}{n} \right)$$

$$= \lim_{n \to \infty} \frac{1}{6} \left(1 + \frac{1}{n} \right) \left(2 + \frac{1}{n} \right)$$

$$= \frac{1}{6} \cdot 1 \cdot 2 = \frac{1}{3} \qquad ■$$

It can be shown that the lower approximating sums also approach $\frac{1}{3}$, that is,

$$\lim_{n \to \infty} L_n = \frac{1}{3}$$

From Figures 8 and 9 it appears that, as n increases, both L_n and R_n become better and better approximations to the area of S. Therefore, we *define* the area A to be the limit of the sums of the areas of the approximating rectangles, that is,

$$A = \lim_{n \to \infty} R_n = \lim_{n \to \infty} L_n = \frac{1}{3}$$

In Visual 5.1 you can create pictures like those in Figures 8 and 9 for other values of n.

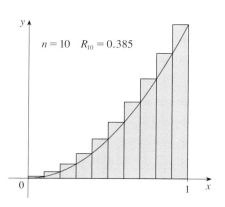
$n = 10 \quad R_{10} = 0.385$

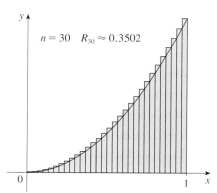
$n = 30 \quad R_{30} \approx 0.3502$

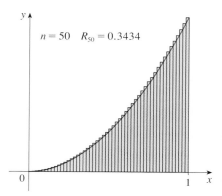
$n = 50 \quad R_{50} = 0.3434$

FIGURE 8

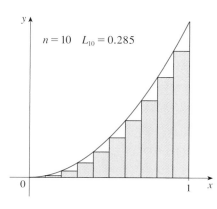
$n = 10 \quad L_{10} = 0.285$

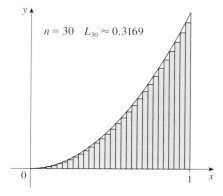
$n = 30 \quad L_{30} \approx 0.3169$

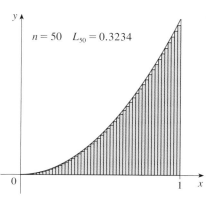
$n = 50 \quad L_{50} = 0.3234$

FIGURE 9 The area is the number that is smaller than all upper sums and larger than all lower sums

Let's apply the idea of Examples 1 and 2 to the more general region S of Figure 1. We start by subdividing S into n strips $S_1, S_2, \ldots, S_n$ of equal width as in Figure 10.

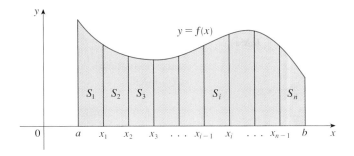

FIGURE 10

The width of the interval $[a, b]$ is $b - a$, so the width of each of the n strips is

$$\Delta x = \frac{b - a}{n}$$

These strips divide the interval $[a, b]$ into n subintervals

$$[x_0, x_1], \quad [x_1, x_2], \quad [x_2, x_3], \quad \ldots, \quad [x_{n-1}, x_n]$$

where $x_0 = a$ and $x_n = b$. The right endpoints of the subintervals are

$$x_1 = a + \Delta x,$$

$$x_2 = a + 2\,\Delta x,$$

$$x_3 = a + 3\,\Delta x,$$

$$\vdots$$

Let's approximate the ith strip S_i by a rectangle with width Δx and height $f(x_i)$, which is the value of f at the right endpoint (see Figure 11). Then the area of the ith rectangle is $f(x_i)\,\Delta x$. What we think of intuitively as the area of S is approximated by the sum of the areas of these rectangles, which is

$$R_n = f(x_1)\,\Delta x + f(x_2)\,\Delta x + \cdots + f(x_n)\,\Delta x$$

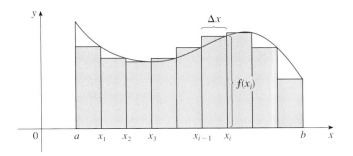

FIGURE 11

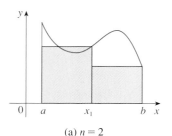

(a) $n = 2$

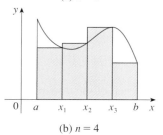

(b) $n = 4$

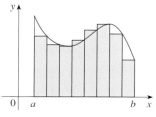

(c) $n = 8$

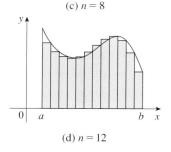

(d) $n = 12$

FIGURE 12

Figure 12 shows this approximation for $n = 2, 4, 8$, and 12. Notice that this approximation appears to become better and better as the number of strips increases, that is, as $n \to \infty$. Therefore, we define the area A of the region S in the following way.

> **2 DEFINITION** The **area** A of the region S that lies under the graph of the continuous function f is the limit of the sum of the areas of approximating rectangles:
>
> $$A = \lim_{n \to \infty} R_n = \lim_{n \to \infty} \left[f(x_1)\, \Delta x + f(x_2)\, \Delta x + \cdots + f(x_n)\, \Delta x \right]$$

It can be proved that the limit in Definition 2 always exists, since we are assuming that f is continuous. It can also be shown that we get the same value if we use left endpoints:

$$\boxed{3} \qquad A = \lim_{n \to \infty} L_n = \lim_{n \to \infty} \left[f(x_0)\, \Delta x + f(x_1)\, \Delta x + \cdots + f(x_{n-1})\, \Delta x \right]$$

In fact, instead of using left endpoints or right endpoints, we could take the height of the ith rectangle to be the value of f at *any* number x_i^* in the ith subinterval $[x_{i-1}, x_i]$. We call the numbers $x_1^*, x_2^*, \ldots, x_n^*$ the **sample points**. Figure 13 shows approximating rectangles when the sample points are not chosen to be endpoints. So a more general expression for the area of S is

$$\boxed{4} \qquad A = \lim_{n \to \infty} \left[f(x_1^*)\, \Delta x + f(x_2^*)\, \Delta x + \cdots + f(x_n^*)\, \Delta x \right]$$

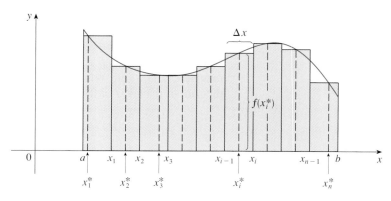

FIGURE 13

This tells us to end with $i = n$.

This tells us to add.

This tells us to start with $i = m$.

$$\sum_{i=m}^{n} f(x_i)\, \Delta x$$

We often use **sigma notation** to write sums with many terms more compactly. For instance,

$$\sum_{i=1}^{n} f(x_i)\, \Delta x = f(x_1)\, \Delta x + f(x_2)\, \Delta x + \cdots + f(x_n)\, \Delta x$$

So the expressions for area in Equations 2, 3, and 4 can be written as follows:

▪ If you need practice with sigma notation, look at the examples and try some
of the exercises in Appendix C.

$$A = \lim_{n \to \infty} \sum_{i=1}^{n} f(x_i) \, \Delta x$$

$$A = \lim_{n \to \infty} \sum_{i=1}^{n} f(x_{i-1}) \, \Delta x$$

$$A = \lim_{n \to \infty} \sum_{i=1}^{n} f(x_i^*) \, \Delta x$$

We can also rewrite Formula 1 in the following way:

$$\sum_{i=1}^{n} i^2 = \frac{n(n+1)(2n+1)}{6}$$

EXAMPLE 3 Let A be the area of the region that lies under the graph of $f(x) = e^{-x}$
between $x = 0$ and $x = 2$.
(a) Using right endpoints, find an expression for A as a limit. Do not evaluate the
limit.
(b) Estimate the area by taking the sample points to be midpoints and using four
subintervals and then ten subintervals.

SOLUTION
(a) Since $a = 0$ and $b = 2$, the width of a subinterval is

$$\Delta x = \frac{2 - 0}{n} = \frac{2}{n}$$

So $x_1 = 2/n$, $x_2 = 4/n$, $x_3 = 6/n$, $x_i = 2i/n$, and $x_n = 2n/n$. The sum of the areas
of the approximating rectangles is

$$R_n = f(x_1) \, \Delta x + f(x_2) \, \Delta x + \cdots + f(x_n) \, \Delta x$$

$$= e^{-x_1} \Delta x + e^{-x_2} \Delta x + \cdots + e^{-x_n} \Delta x$$

$$= e^{-2/n} \left(\frac{2}{n} \right) + e^{-4/n} \left(\frac{2}{n} \right) + \cdots + e^{-2n/n} \left(\frac{2}{n} \right)$$

According to Definition 2, the area is

$$A = \lim_{n \to \infty} R_n = \lim_{n \to \infty} \frac{2}{n} \left(e^{-2/n} + e^{-4/n} + e^{-6/n} + \cdots + e^{-2n/n} \right)$$

Using sigma notation we could write

$$A = \lim_{n \to \infty} \frac{2}{n} \sum_{i=1}^{n} e^{-2i/n}$$

It is difficult to evaluate this limit directly by hand, but with the aid of a computer
algebra system it isn't hard (see Exercise 18). In Section 5.3 we will be able to find
A more easily using a different method.

(b) With $n = 4$ the subintervals of equal width $\Delta x = 0.5$ are $[0, 0.5]$, $[0.5, 1]$,
$[1, 1.5]$, and $[1.5, 2]$. The midpoints of these subintervals are $x_1^* = 0.25$, $x_2^* = 0.75$,
$x_3^* = 1.25$, and $x_4^* = 1.75$, and the sum of the areas of the four approximating

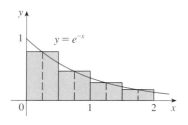

FIGURE 14

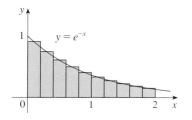

FIGURE 15

rectangles (see Figure 14) is

$$M_4 = \sum_{i=1}^{4} f(x_i^*) \, \Delta x$$

$$= f(0.25) \, \Delta x + f(0.75) \, \Delta x + f(1.25) \, \Delta x + f(1.75) \, \Delta x$$

$$= e^{-0.25}(0.5) + e^{-0.75}(0.5) + e^{-1.25}(0.5) + e^{-1.75}(0.5)$$

$$= \tfrac{1}{2}(e^{-0.25} + e^{-0.75} + e^{-1.25} + e^{-1.75}) \approx 0.8557$$

So an estimate for the area is

$$A \approx 0.8557$$

With $n = 10$ the subintervals are $[0, 0.2]$, $[0.2, 0.4]$, ..., $[1.8, 2]$ and the midpoints are $x_1^* = 0.1$, $x_2^* = 0.3$, $x_3^* = 0.5$, ..., $x_{10}^* = 1.9$. Thus

$$A \approx M_{10} = f(0.1) \, \Delta x + f(0.3) \, \Delta x + f(0.5) \, \Delta x + \cdots + f(1.9) \, \Delta x$$

$$= 0.2(e^{-0.1} + e^{-0.3} + e^{-0.5} + \cdots + e^{-1.9}) \approx 0.8632$$

From Figure 15 it appears that this estimate is better than the estimate with $n = 4$. ▪

THE DISTANCE PROBLEM

Now let's consider the *distance problem:* Find the distance traveled by an object during a certain time period if the velocity of the object is known at all times. (In a sense this is the inverse problem of the velocity problem that we discussed in Section 2.1.) If the velocity remains constant, then the distance problem is easy to solve by means of the formula

$$\text{distance} = \text{velocity} \times \text{time}$$

But if the velocity varies, it's not so easy to find the distance traveled. We investigate the problem in the following example.

▼ EXAMPLE 4 Suppose the odometer on our car is broken and we want to estimate the distance driven over a 30-second time interval. We take speedometer readings every five seconds and record them in the following table:

Time (s)	0	5	10	15	20	25	30
Velocity (mi/h)	17	21	24	29	32	31	28

In order to have the time and the velocity in consistent units, let's convert the velocity readings to feet per second (1 mi/h = 5280/3600 ft/s):

Time (s)	0	5	10	15	20	25	30
Velocity (ft/s)	25	31	35	43	47	46	41

During the first five seconds the velocity doesn't change very much, so we can estimate the distance traveled during that time by assuming that the velocity is constant. If we take the velocity during that time interval to be the initial velocity (25 ft/s), then we obtain the approximate distance traveled during the first five seconds:

$$25 \text{ ft/s} \times 5 \text{ s} = 125 \text{ ft}$$

Similarly, during the second time interval the velocity is approximately constant and we take it to be the velocity when $t = 5$ s. So our estimate for the distance traveled from $t = 5$ s to $t = 10$ s is

$$31 \text{ ft/s} \times 5 \text{ s} = 155 \text{ ft}$$

If we add similar estimates for the other time intervals, we obtain an estimate for the total distance traveled:

$$(25 \times 5) + (31 \times 5) + (35 \times 5) + (43 \times 5) + (47 \times 5) + (46 \times 5) = 1135 \text{ ft}$$

We could just as well have used the velocity at the *end* of each time period instead of the velocity at the beginning as our assumed constant velocity. Then our estimate becomes

$$(31 \times 5) + (35 \times 5) + (43 \times 5) + (47 \times 5) + (46 \times 5) + (41 \times 5) = 1215 \text{ ft}$$

If we had wanted a more accurate estimate, we could have taken velocity readings every two seconds, or even every second.   ▪

Perhaps the calculations in Example 4 remind you of the sums we used earlier to estimate areas. The similarity is explained when we sketch a graph of the velocity function of the car in Figure 16 and draw rectangles whose heights are the initial velocities for each time interval. The area of the first rectangle is $25 \times 5 = 125$, which is also our estimate for the distance traveled in the first five seconds. In fact, the area of each rectangle can be interpreted as a distance because the height represents velocity and the width represents time. The sum of the areas of the rectangles in Figure 16 is $L_6 = 1135$, which is our initial estimate for the total distance traveled.

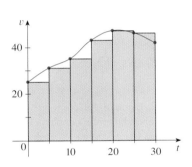

FIGURE 16

In general, suppose an object moves with velocity $v = f(t)$, where $a \le t \le b$ and $f(t) \ge 0$ (so the object always moves in the positive direction). We take velocity readings at times $t_0 (= a)$, t_1, t_2, $\ldots$, $t_n (= b)$ so that the velocity is approximately constant on each subinterval. If these times are equally spaced, then the time between consecutive readings is $\Delta t = (b - a)/n$. During the first time interval the velocity is approximately $f(t_0)$ and so the distance traveled is approximately $f(t_0) \Delta t$. Similarly, the distance traveled during the second time interval is about $f(t_1) \Delta t$ and the total distance traveled during the time interval $[a, b]$ is approximately

$$f(t_0) \Delta t + f(t_1) \Delta t + \cdots + f(t_{n-1}) \Delta t = \sum_{i=1}^{n} f(t_{i-1}) \Delta t$$

If we use the velocity at right endpoints instead of left endpoints, our estimate for the total distance becomes

$$f(t_1) \Delta t + f(t_2) \Delta t + \cdots + f(t_n) \Delta t = \sum_{i=1}^{n} f(t_i) \Delta t$$

The more frequently we measure the velocity, the more accurate our estimates become, so it seems plausible that the *exact* distance d traveled is the *limit* of such expressions:

5
$$d = \lim_{n \to \infty} \sum_{i=1}^{n} f(t_{i-1}) \Delta t = \lim_{n \to \infty} \sum_{i=1}^{n} f(t_i) \Delta t$$

We will see in Section 5.3 that this is indeed true.

Because Equation 5 has the same form as our expressions for area in Equations 2 and 3, it follows that the distance traveled is equal to the area under the graph of the velocity function. In Chapter 7 we will see that other quantities of interest in the natural and social sciences—such as the work done by a variable force—can also be interpreted as the area under a curve. So when we compute areas in this chapter, bear in mind that they can be interpreted in a variety of practical ways.

5.1 EXERCISES

1. (a) By reading values from the given graph of f, use five rectangles to find a lower estimate and an upper estimate for the area under the given graph of f from $x = 0$ to $x = 10$. In each case sketch the rectangles that you use.
(b) Find new estimates using ten rectangles in each case.

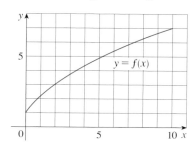

2. (a) Use six rectangles to find estimates of each type for the area under the given graph of f from $x = 0$ to $x = 12$.
  (i) L_6 (sample points are left endpoints)
  (ii) R_6 (sample points are right endpoints)
  (iii) M_6 (sample points are midpoints)
(b) Is L_6 an underestimate or overestimate of the true area?
(c) Is R_6 an underestimate or overestimate of the true area?
(d) Which of the numbers L_6, R_6, or M_6 gives the best estimate? Explain.

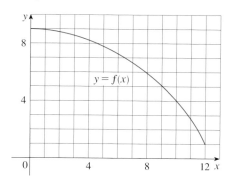

3. (a) Estimate the area under the graph of $f(x) = 1/x$ from $x = 1$ to $x = 5$ using four approximating rectangles and right endpoints. Sketch the graph and the rectangles. Is your estimate an underestimate or an overestimate?
(b) Repeat part (a) using left endpoints.

4. (a) Estimate the area under the graph of $f(x) = 25 - x^2$ from $x = 0$ to $x = 5$ using five approximating rectangles and right endpoints. Sketch the graph and the rectangles. Is your estimate an underestimate or an overestimate?
(b) Repeat part (a) using left endpoints.

5. (a) Estimate the area under the graph of $f(x) = 1 + x^2$ from $x = -1$ to $x = 2$ using three rectangles and right endpoints. Then improve your estimate by using six rectangles. Sketch the curve and the approximating rectangles.
(b) Repeat part (a) using left endpoints.
(c) Repeat part (a) using midpoints.
(d) From your sketches in parts (a)–(c), which appears to be the best estimate?

6. (a) Graph the function $f(x) = e^{-x^2}$, $-2 \leq x \leq 2$.
(b) Estimate the area under the graph of f using four approximating rectangles and taking the sample points to be (i) right endpoints and (ii) midpoints. In each case sketch the curve and the rectangles.
(c) Improve your estimates in part (b) by using 8 rectangles.

7. The speed of a runner increased steadily during the first three seconds of a race. Her speed at half-second intervals is given in the table. Find lower and upper estimates for the distance that she traveled during these three seconds.

t (s)	0	0.5	1.0	1.5	2.0	2.5	3.0
v (ft/s)	0	6.2	10.8	14.9	18.1	19.4	20.2

8. Speedometer readings for a motorcycle at 12-second intervals are given in the table.

t (s)	0	12	24	36	48	60
v (ft/s)	30	28	25	22	24	27

(a) Estimate the distance traveled by the motorcycle during this time period using the velocities at the beginning of the time intervals.

(b) Give another estimate using the velocities at the end of the time periods.

(c) Are your estimates in parts (a) and (b) upper and lower estimates? Explain.

9. Oil leaked from a tank at a rate of $r(t)$ liters per hour. The rate decreased as time passed and values of the rate at two-hour time intervals are shown in the table. Find lower and upper estimates for the total amount of oil that leaked out.

t (h)	0	2	4	6	8	10
$r(t)$ (L/h)	8.7	7.6	6.8	6.2	5.7	5.3

10. When we estimate distances from velocity data, it is sometimes necessary to use times $t_0, t_1, t_2, t_3, \ldots$ that are not equally spaced. We can still estimate distances using the time periods $\Delta t_i = t_i - t_{i-1}$. For example, on May 7, 1992, the space shuttle *Endeavour* was launched on mission STS-49, the purpose of which was to install a new perigee kick motor in an Intelsat communications satellite. The table, provided by NASA, gives the velocity data for the shuttle between liftoff and the jettisoning of the solid rocket boosters. Use these data to estimate the height above the Earth's surface of the space shuttle *Endeavour*, 62 seconds after liftoff.

Event	Time (s)	Velocity (ft/s)
Launch	0	0
Begin roll maneuver	10	185
End roll maneuver	15	319
Throttle to 89%	20	447
Throttle to 67%	32	742
Throttle to 104%	59	1325
Maximum dynamic pressure	62	1445
Solid rocket booster separation	125	4151

11. The velocity graph of a braking car is shown. Use it to estimate the distance traveled by the car while the brakes are applied.

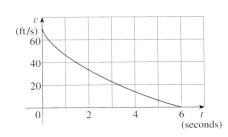

12. The velocity graph of a car accelerating from rest to a speed of 120 km/h over a period of 30 seconds is shown. Estimate the distance traveled during this period.

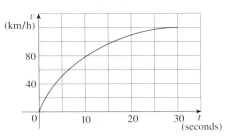

13–14 ▪ Use Definition 2 to find an expression for the area under the graph of f as a limit. Do not evaluate the limit.

13. $f(x) = \sqrt[4]{x}, \quad 1 \le x \le 16$

14. $f(x) = \dfrac{\ln x}{x}, \quad 3 \le x \le 10$

▪   ▪   ▪   ▪   ▪   ▪   ▪   ▪   ▪   ▪   ▪   ▪   ▪

15. Determine a region whose area is equal to

$$\lim_{n \to \infty} \sum_{i=1}^{n} \frac{\pi}{4n} \tan \frac{i\pi}{4n}$$

Do not evaluate the limit.

16. (a) Use Definition 2 to find an expression for the area under the curve $y = x^3$ from 0 to 1 as a limit.

(b) The following formula for the sum of the cubes of the first n integers is proved in Appendix C. Use it to evaluate the limit in part (a).

$$1^3 + 2^3 + 3^3 + \cdots + n^3 = \left[\frac{n(n+1)}{2} \right]^2$$

CAS **17.** (a) Express the area under the curve $y = x^5$ from 0 to 2 as a limit.

(b) Use a computer algebra system to find the sum in your expression from part (a).

(c) Evaluate the limit in part (a).

CAS **18.** Find the exact area of the region under the graph of $y = e^{-x}$ from 0 to 2 by using a computer algebra system to evaluate the sum and then the limit in Example 3(a). Compare your answer with the estimate obtained in Example 3(b).

CAS **19.** Find the exact area under the cosine curve $y = \cos x$ from $x = 0$ to $x = b$, where $0 \le b \le \pi/2$. (Use a computer algebra system both to evaluate the sum and to compute the limit.) In particular, what is the area if $b = \pi/2$?

20. (a) Let A_n be the area of a polygon with n equal sides inscribed in a circle with radius r. By dividing the polygon into n congruent triangles with central angle $2\pi/n$, show that $A_n = \frac{1}{2}nr^2 \sin(2\pi/n)$.

(b) Show that $\lim_{n \to \infty} A_n = \pi r^2$. [*Hint:* Use Equation 1.4.5 on page 42.]

5.2 | THE DEFINITE INTEGRAL

We saw in Section 5.1 that a limit of the form

1
$$\lim_{n \to \infty} \sum_{i=1}^{n} f(x_i^*) \, \Delta x = \lim_{n \to \infty} \left[f(x_1^*) \, \Delta x + f(x_2^*) \, \Delta x + \cdots + f(x_n^*) \, \Delta x \right]$$

arises when we compute an area. We also saw that it arises when we try to find the distance traveled by an object. It turns out that this same type of limit occurs in a wide variety of situations even when f is not necessarily a positive function. Here we consider limits similar to (1) but in which f need not be positive or continuous and the subintervals don't necessarily have the same length.

In general we start with any function f defined on $[a, b]$ and we divide $[a, b]$ into n smaller subintervals by choosing partition points $x_0, x_1, x_2, \ldots, x_n$ so that

$$a = x_0 < x_1 < x_2 < \cdots < x_{n-1} < x_n = b$$

The resulting collection of subintervals

$$[x_0, x_1], \quad [x_1, x_2], \quad [x_2, x_3], \quad \ldots, \quad [x_{n-1}, x_n]$$

is called a **partition** P of $[a, b]$. We use the notation Δx_i for the length of the ith subinterval $[x_{i-1}, x_i]$. Thus

$$\Delta x_i = x_i - x_{i-1}$$

Then we choose **sample points** $x_1^*, x_2^*, \ldots, x_n^*$ in the subintervals with x_i^* in the ith subinterval $[x_{i-1}, x_i]$. These sample points could be left endpoints or right endpoints or any numbers between the endpoints. Figure 1 shows an example of a partition and sample points.

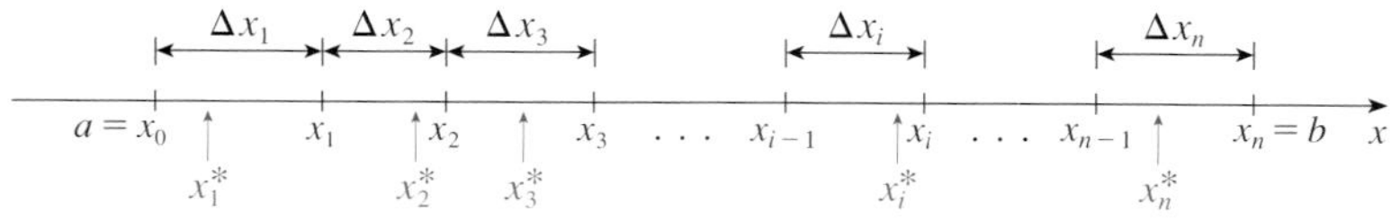

FIGURE 1
A partition of $[a, b]$ with
sample points x_i^*

■ The Riemann sum is named after the German mathematician Bernhard Riemann (1826–1866). See the biographical note on page 263.

A **Riemann sum** associated with a partition P and a function f is constructed by evaluating f at the sample points, multiplying by the lengths of the corresponding subintervals, and adding:

$$\sum_{i=1}^{n} f(x_i^*) \, \Delta x_i = f(x_1^*) \, \Delta x_1 + f(x_2^*) \, \Delta x_2 + \cdots + f(x_n^*) \, \Delta x_n$$

The geometric interpretation of a Riemann sum is shown in Figure 2. Notice that if $f(x_i^*)$ is negative, then $f(x_i^*) \, \Delta x_i$ is negative and so we have to *subtract* the area of the corresponding rectangle.

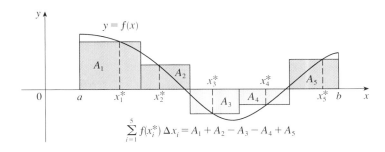

FIGURE 2

A Riemann sum is the sum of the areas of the rectangles above the x-axis and the negatives of the areas of the rectangles below the x-axis.

$$\sum_{i=1}^{5} f(x_i^*)\,\Delta x_i = A_1 + A_2 - A_3 - A_4 + A_5$$

If we imagine all possible partitions of $[a, b]$ and all possible choices of sample points, we can think of taking the limit of all possible Riemann sums as n becomes large by analogy with the definition of area. But because we are now allowing sub-intervals with different lengths, we need to ensure that all of these lengths Δx_i approach 0. We can do that by insisting that the *largest* of these lengths, which we denote by $\max \Delta x_i$, approaches 0. The result is called the *definite integral* of f from a to b.

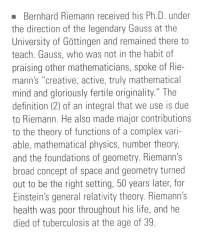

■ Bernhard Riemann received his Ph.D. under the direction of the legendary Gauss at the University of Göttingen and remained there to teach. Gauss, who was not in the habit of praising other mathematicians, spoke of Riemann's "creative, active, truly mathematical mind and gloriously fertile originality." The definition (2) of an integral that we use is due to Riemann. He also made major contributions to the theory of functions of a complex variable, mathematical physics, number theory, and the foundations of geometry. Riemann's broad concept of space and geometry turned out to be the right setting, 50 years later, for Einstein's general relativity theory. Riemann's health was poor throughout his life, and he died of tuberculosis at the age of 39.

> **2 DEFINITION OF A DEFINITE INTEGRAL**   If f is a function defined on $[a, b]$, the **definite integral of f from a to b** is the number
>
> $$\int_a^b f(x)\,dx = \lim_{\max \Delta x_i \to 0} \sum_{i=1}^{n} f(x_i^*)\,\Delta x_i$$
>
> provided that this limit exists. If it does exist, we say that f is **integrable** on $[a, b]$.

The precise meaning of the limit that defines the integral in Definition 2 is as follows: $\int_a^b f(x)\,dx = I$ means that for every $\varepsilon > 0$ there is a corresponding number $\delta > 0$ such that

$$\left| I - \sum_{i=1}^{n} f(x_i^*)\,\Delta x_i \right| < \varepsilon$$

for all partitions P of $[a, b]$ with $\max \Delta x_i < \delta$ and for all possible choices of x_i^* in $[x_{i-1}, x_i]$.

This means that a definite integral can be approximated to within any desired degree of accuracy by a Riemann sum.

NOTE 1   The symbol $\int$ was introduced by Leibniz and is called an **integral sign**. It is an elongated S and was chosen because an integral is a limit of sums. In the notation $\int_a^b f(x)\,dx$, $f(x)$ is called the **integrand** and a and b are called the **limits of integration**; a is the **lower limit** and b is the **upper limit**. The symbol dx has no official meaning by itself; $\int_a^b f(x)\,dx$ is all one symbol. The procedure of calculating an integral is called **integration**.

NOTE 2   The definite integral $\int_a^b f(x)\,dx$ is a number; it does not depend on x. In fact, we could use any letter in place of x without changing the value of the integral:

$$\int_a^b f(x)\,dx = \int_a^b f(t)\,dt = \int_a^b f(r)\,dr$$

We have defined the definite integral for an integrable function, but not all functions are integrable. The following theorem shows that the most commonly occurring functions are in fact integrable. The theorem is proved in more advanced courses.

---

3 **THEOREM** If f is continuous on $[a, b]$, or if f has only a finite number of jump discontinuities, then f is integrable on $[a, b]$; that is, the definite integral $\int_a^b f(x)\,dx$ exists.

If f is integrable on $[a, b]$, then the Riemann sums in Definition 2 must approach $\int_a^b f(x)\,dx$ as max $\Delta x_i \to 0$ no matter how the partitions and sample points are chosen. So in calculating the value of an integral we are free to choose partitions P and sample points x_i^* to simplify the calculation. It's often convenient to take P to be a **regular partition**; that is, all the subintervals have the same length Δx. Then

$$\Delta x = \Delta x_1 = \Delta x_2 = \cdots = \Delta x_n = \frac{b-a}{n}$$

and $\qquad x_0 = a, \quad x_1 = a + \Delta x, \quad x_2 = a + 2\,\Delta x, \quad \ldots, \quad x_i = a + i\,\Delta x$

If we choose x_i^* to be the right endpoint of the ith subinterval, then

$$x_i^* = x_i = a + i\,\Delta x = a + i\frac{b-a}{n}$$

In this case, max $\Delta x_i = \Delta x = (b-a)/n \to 0$ as $n \to \infty$, so Definition 2 gives

$$\int_a^b f(x)\,dx = \lim_{\Delta x \to 0} \sum_{i=1}^n f(x_i)\,\Delta x = \lim_{n \to \infty} \sum_{i=1}^n f(x_i)\,\Delta x$$

---

4 **THEOREM** If f is integrable on $[a, b]$, then

$$\int_a^b f(x)\,dx = \lim_{n \to \infty} \sum_{i=1}^n f(x_i)\,\Delta x$$

where $\qquad \Delta x = \dfrac{b-a}{n} \qquad$ and $\qquad x_i = a + i\,\Delta x$

In computing the value of an integral, Theorem 4 is much simpler to use than Definition 2.

EXAMPLE 1 Express

$$\lim_{n \to \infty} \sum_{i=1}^n (x_i^3 + x_i \sin x_i)\,\Delta x$$

as an integral on the interval $[0, \pi]$.

SOLUTION Comparing the given limit with the limit in Theorem 4, we see that they will be identical if we choose $f(x) = x^3 + x \sin x$. We are given that $a = 0$ and

$b = \pi$. Therefore, by Theorem 4, we have

$$\lim_{n \to \infty} \sum_{i=1}^{n} (x_i^3 + x_i \sin x_i) \Delta x = \int_0^{\pi} (x^3 + x \sin x) \, dx$$

■

Later, when we apply the definite integral to physical situations, it will be important to recognize limits of sums as integrals, as we did in Example 1. When Leibniz chose the notation for an integral, he chose the ingredients as reminders of the limiting process. In general, when we write

$$\lim_{n \to \infty} \sum_{i=1}^{n} f(x_i^*) \, \Delta x = \int_a^b f(x) \, dx$$

we replace $\lim \Sigma$ by $\int$, x_i^* by x, and Δx by dx.

NOTE 3 If f happens to be positive, then the Riemann sum can be interpreted as a sum of areas of approximating rectangles (see Figure 3). By comparing Theorem 4 with the definition of area in Section 5.1, we see that the definite integral $\int_a^b f(x) \, dx$ can be interpreted as the area under the curve $y = f(x)$ from a to b. (See Figure 4.)

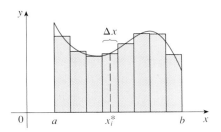

FIGURE 3
If $f(x) \geq 0$, the Riemann sum $\Sigma f(x_i^*) \, \Delta x$
is the sum of areas of rectangles.

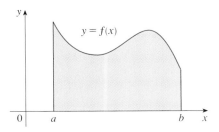

FIGURE 4
If $f(x) \geq 0$, the integral $\int_a^b f(x) \, dx$ is the
area under the curve $y = f(x)$ from a to b.

If f takes on both positive and negative values, as in Figure 5, then the Riemann sum is the sum of the areas of the rectangles that lie above the x-axis and the *negatives* of the areas of the rectangles that lie below the x-axis (the areas of the dark blue rectangles *minus* the areas of the light blue rectangles). When we take the limit of such Riemann sums, we get the situation illustrated in Figure 6. A definite integral can be interpreted as a **net area**, that is, a difference of areas:

$$\int_a^b f(x) \, dx = A_1 - A_2$$

where A_1 is the area of the region above the x-axis and below the graph of f, and A_2 is the area of the region below the x-axis and above the graph of f.

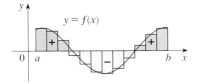

FIGURE 5
$\Sigma f(x_i^*) \, \Delta x$ is an approximation to
the net area

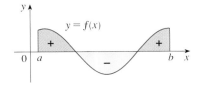

FIGURE 6
$\int_a^b f(x) \, dx$ is the net area

EVALUATING INTEGRALS

When we use the definition or Theorem 4 to evaluate a definite integral, we need to know how to work with sums. The following three equations give formulas for sums of powers of positive integers. Equation 5 may be familiar to you from a course in algebra. Equations 6 and 7 were discussed in Section 5.1 and are proved in Appendix C.

5
$$\sum_{i=1}^{n} i = \frac{n(n + 1)}{2}$$

6
$$\sum_{i=1}^{n} i^2 = \frac{n(n + 1)(2n + 1)}{6}$$

7
$$\sum_{i=1}^{n} i^3 = \left[\frac{n(n + 1)}{2} \right]^2$$

The remaining formulas are simple rules for working with sigma notation:

■ Formulas 8–11 are proved by writing out each side in expanded form. The left side of Equation 9 is

$$ca_1 + ca_2 + \cdots + ca_n$$

The right side is

$$c(a_1 + a_2 + \cdots + a_n)$$

These are equal by the distributive property. The other formulas are discussed in Appendix C.

8
$$\sum_{i=1}^{n} c = nc$$

9
$$\sum_{i=1}^{n} ca_i = c \sum_{i=1}^{n} a_i$$

10
$$\sum_{i=1}^{n} (a_i + b_i) = \sum_{i=1}^{n} a_i + \sum_{i=1}^{n} b_i$$

11
$$\sum_{i=1}^{n} (a_i - b_i) = \sum_{i=1}^{n} a_i - \sum_{i=1}^{n} b_i$$

EXAMPLE 2
(a) Evaluate the Riemann sum for $f(x) = x^3 - 6x$ taking the sample points to be right endpoints and $a = 0$, $b = 3$, and $n = 6$.

(b) Evaluate $\int_{0}^{3} (x^3 - 6x)\, dx$.

SOLUTION
(a) With $n = 6$ the interval width is

$$\Delta x = \frac{b - a}{n} = \frac{3 - 0}{6} = \frac{1}{2}$$

and the right endpoints are $x_1 = 0.5$, $x_2 = 1.0$, $x_3 = 1.5$, $x_4 = 2.0$, $x_5 = 2.5$, and $x_6 = 3.0$. So the Riemann sum is

$$R_6 = \sum_{i=1}^{6} f(x_i)\, \Delta x$$

$$= f(0.5)\, \Delta x + f(1.0)\, \Delta x + f(1.5)\, \Delta x + f(2.0)\, \Delta x + f(2.5)\, \Delta x + f(3.0)\, \Delta x$$

$$= \tfrac{1}{2}(-2.875 - 5 - 5.625 - 4 + 0.625 + 9)$$

$$= -3.9375$$

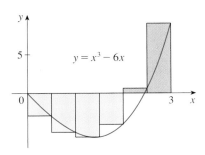

FIGURE 7

Notice that f is not a positive function and so the Riemann sum does not represent a sum of areas of rectangles. But it does represent the sum of the areas of the dark blue rectangles (above the x-axis) minus the sum of the areas of the light blue rectangles (below the x-axis) in Figure 7.

(b) With n subintervals we have

$$\Delta x = \frac{b - a}{n} = \frac{3}{n}$$

Thus $x_0 = 0$, $x_1 = 3/n$, $x_2 = 6/n$, $x_3 = 9/n$, and, in general, $x_i = 3i/n$. Since we are using right endpoints, we can use Theorem 4:

$$\int_0^3 (x^3 - 6x)\, dx = \lim_{n \to \infty} \sum_{i=1}^{n} f(x_i)\, \Delta x = \lim_{n \to \infty} \sum_{i=1}^{n} f\!\left(\frac{3i}{n}\right) \frac{3}{n}$$

■ In the sum, n is a constant (unlike i), so we can move $3/n$ in front of the Σ sign.

$$= \lim_{n \to \infty} \frac{3}{n} \sum_{i=1}^{n} \left[\left(\frac{3i}{n}\right)^3 - 6\left(\frac{3i}{n}\right) \right] \qquad \text{(Equation 9 with } c = 3/n\text{)}$$

$$= \lim_{n \to \infty} \frac{3}{n} \sum_{i=1}^{n} \left[\frac{27}{n^3} i^3 - \frac{18}{n} i \right]$$

$$= \lim_{n \to \infty} \left[\frac{81}{n^4} \sum_{i=1}^{n} i^3 - \frac{54}{n^2} \sum_{i=1}^{n} i \right] \qquad \text{(Equations 11 and 9)}$$

$$= \lim_{n \to \infty} \left\{ \frac{81}{n^4} \left[\frac{n(n + 1)}{2} \right]^2 - \frac{54}{n^2} \frac{n(n + 1)}{2} \right\} \qquad \text{(Equations 7 and 5)}$$

$$= \lim_{n \to \infty} \left[\frac{81}{4} \left(1 + \frac{1}{n}\right)^2 - 27\left(1 + \frac{1}{n}\right) \right]$$

$$= \frac{81}{4} - 27 = -\frac{27}{4} = -6.75$$

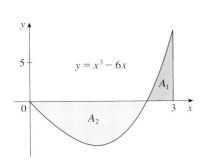

FIGURE 8

$$\int_0^3 (x^3 - 6x)\, dx = A_1 - A_2 = -6.75$$

This integral can't be interpreted as an area because f takes on both positive and negative values. But it can be interpreted as the difference of areas $A_1 - A_2$, where A_1 and A_2 are shown in Figure 8.

Figure 9 illustrates the calculation by showing the positive and negative terms in the right Riemann sum R_n for $n = 40$. The values in the table show the Riemann sums approaching the exact value of the integral, -6.75, as $n \to \infty$.

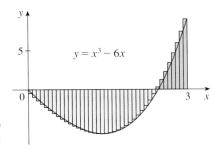

FIGURE 9

$R_{40} \approx -6.3998$

n	R_n
40	-6.3998
100	-6.6130
500	-6.7229
1000	-6.7365
5000	-6.7473

A much simpler method for evaluating the integral in Example 2 will be given in Section 5.3 after we have proved the Evaluation Theorem.

EXAMPLE 3 Evaluate the following integrals by interpreting each in terms of areas.

(a) $\int_0^1 \sqrt{1 - x^2}\, dx$ (b) $\int_0^3 (x - 1)\, dx$

SOLUTION

(a) Since $f(x) = \sqrt{1 - x^2} \geqslant 0$, we can interpret this integral as the area under the curve $y = \sqrt{1 - x^2}$ from 0 to 1. But, since $y^2 = 1 - x^2$, we get $x^2 + y^2 = 1$, which shows that the graph of f is the quarter-circle with radius 1 in Figure 10. Therefore

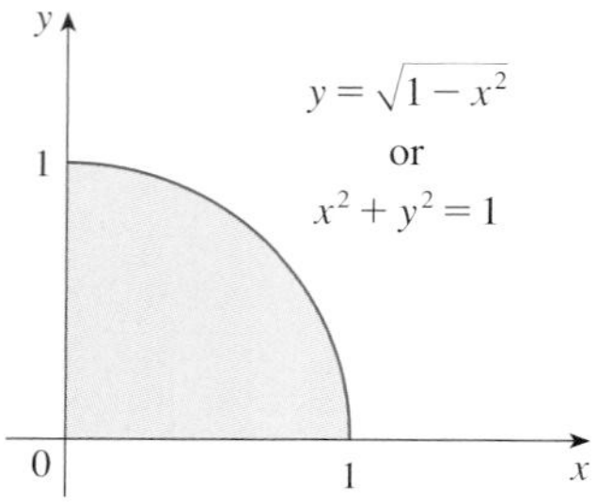

FIGURE 10

$$\int_0^1 \sqrt{1 - x^2}\, dx = \tfrac{1}{4}\pi(1)^2 = \frac{\pi}{4}$$

(In Section 6.2 we will be able to *prove* that the area of a circle of radius r is πr^2.)

(b) The graph of $y = x - 1$ is the line with slope 1 shown in Figure 11. We compute the integral as the difference of the areas of the two triangles:

$$\int_0^3 (x - 1)\, dx = A_1 - A_2 = \tfrac{1}{2}(2 \cdot 2) - \tfrac{1}{2}(1 \cdot 1) = 1.5$$

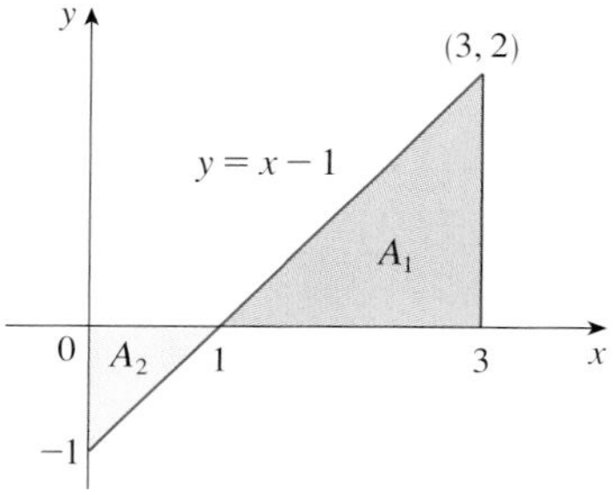

FIGURE 11

■

THE MIDPOINT RULE

We often choose the sample point x_i^* to be the right endpoint of the ith subinterval because it is convenient for computing the limit. But if the purpose is to find an *approximation* to an integral, it is usually better to choose x_i^* to be the midpoint of the interval, which we denote by $\bar{x}_i$. Any Riemann sum is an approximation to an integral, but if we use midpoints and a regular partition we get the following approximation.

TEC Module 5.2/6.5 shows how the Midpoint Rule estimates improve as n increases.

MIDPOINT RULE

$$\int_a^b f(x)\, dx \approx \sum_{i=1}^{n} f(\bar{x}_i)\, \Delta x = \Delta x\, [f(\bar{x}_1) + \cdots + f(\bar{x}_n)]$$

where $\Delta x = \dfrac{b - a}{n}$

and $\bar{x}_i = \tfrac{1}{2}(x_{i-1} + x_i) = \text{midpoint of } [x_{i-1}, x_i]$

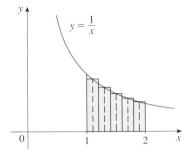

FIGURE 12

✔ EXAMPLE 4 Use the Midpoint Rule with $n = 5$ to approximate $\int_1^2 \dfrac{1}{x}\,dx$.

SOLUTION The endpoints of the five subintervals are 1, 1.2, 1.4, 1.6, 1.8, and 2.0, so the midpoints are 1.1, 1.3, 1.5, 1.7, and 1.9. The width of the subintervals is $\Delta x = (2 - 1)/5 = \frac{1}{5}$, so the Midpoint Rule gives

$$\int_1^2 \frac{1}{x}\,dx \approx \Delta x\,[f(1.1) + f(1.3) + f(1.5) + f(1.7) + f(1.9)]$$

$$= \frac{1}{5}\left(\frac{1}{1.1} + \frac{1}{1.3} + \frac{1}{1.5} + \frac{1}{1.7} + \frac{1}{1.9}\right) \approx 0.691908$$

Since $f(x) = 1/x > 0$ for $1 \leqslant x \leqslant 2$, the integral represents an area, and the approximation given by the Midpoint Rule is the sum of the areas of the rectangles shown in Figure 12. ▪

At the moment we don't know how accurate the approximation in Example 4 is, but in Section 6.5 we will learn a method for estimating the error involved in using the Midpoint Rule. At that time we will discuss other methods for approximating definite integrals.

If we apply the Midpoint Rule to the integral in Example 2, we get the picture in Figure 13. The approximation $M_{40} \approx -6.7563$ is much closer to the true value -6.75 than the right endpoint approximation, $R_{40} \approx -6.3998$, shown in Figure 9.

In Visual 5.2 you can compare left, right, and midpoint approximations to the integral in Example 2 for different values of n.

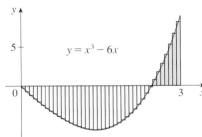

FIGURE 13
$M_{40} \approx -6.7563$

PROPERTIES OF THE DEFINITE INTEGRAL

We now develop some basic properties of integrals that will help us to evaluate integrals in a simple manner. We assume that f and g are integrable functions.

When we defined the definite integral $\int_a^b f(x)\,dx$, we implicitly assumed that $a < b$. But the definition as a limit of Riemann sums makes sense even if $a > b$. Notice that if we reverse a and b in Theorem 4, then Δx changes from $(b - a)/n$ to $(a - b)/n$. Therefore

$$\int_b^a f(x)\,dx = -\int_a^b f(x)\,dx$$

If $a = b$, then $\Delta x = 0$ and so

$$\int_a^a f(x)\,dx = 0$$

PROPERTIES OF THE INTEGRAL Suppose all the following integrals exist.

1. $\displaystyle\int_a^b c \, dx = c(b - a)$, where c is any constant

2. $\displaystyle\int_a^b [f(x) + g(x)] \, dx = \int_a^b f(x) \, dx + \int_a^b g(x) \, dx$

3. $\displaystyle\int_a^b cf(x) \, dx = c \int_a^b f(x) \, dx$, where c is any constant

4. $\displaystyle\int_a^b [f(x) - g(x)] \, dx = \int_a^b f(x) \, dx - \int_a^b g(x) \, dx$

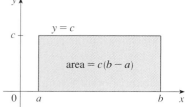

FIGURE 14

$\displaystyle\int_a^b c \, dx = c(b - a)$

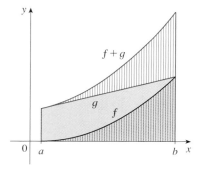

FIGURE 15

$\displaystyle\int_a^b [f(x) + g(x)] \, dx =$
$\displaystyle\int_a^b f(x) \, dx + \int_a^b g(x) \, dx$

■ Property 3 seems intuitively reasonable because we know that multiplying a function by a positive number c stretches or shrinks its graph vertically by a factor of c. So it stretches or shrinks each approximating rectangle by a factor c and therefore it has the effect of multiplying the area by c.

Property 1 says that the integral of a constant function $f(x) = c$ is the constant times the length of the interval. If $c > 0$ and $a < b$, this is to be expected because $c(b - a)$ is the area of the shaded rectangle in Figure 14.

Property 2 says that the integral of a sum is the sum of the integrals. For positive functions it says that the area under $f + g$ is the area under f plus the area under g. Figure 15 helps us understand why this is true: In view of how graphical addition works, the corresponding vertical line segments have equal height.

In general, Property 2 follows from Theorem 4 and the fact that the limit of a sum is the sum of the limits:

$$\int_a^b [f(x) + g(x)] \, dx = \lim_{n \to \infty} \sum_{i=1}^n [f(x_i) + g(x_i)] \, \Delta x$$

$$= \lim_{n \to \infty} \left[\sum_{i=1}^n f(x_i) \, \Delta x + \sum_{i=1}^n g(x_i) \, \Delta x \right]$$

$$= \lim_{n \to \infty} \sum_{i=1}^n f(x_i) \, \Delta x + \lim_{n \to \infty} \sum_{i=1}^n g(x_i) \, \Delta x$$

$$= \int_a^b f(x) \, dx + \int_a^b g(x) \, dx$$

Property 3 can be proved in a similar manner and says that the integral of a constant times a function is the constant times the integral of the function. In other words, a constant (but *only* a constant) can be taken in front of an integral sign. Property 4 is proved by writing $f - g = f + (-g)$ and using Properties 2 and 3 with $c = -1$.

EXAMPLE 5 Use the properties of integrals to evaluate $\displaystyle\int_0^1 (4 + 3x^2) \, dx$.

SOLUTION Using Properties 2 and 3 of integrals, we have

$$\int_0^1 (4 + 3x^2) \, dx = \int_0^1 4 \, dx + \int_0^1 3x^2 \, dx = \int_0^1 4 \, dx + 3 \int_0^1 x^2 \, dx$$

We know from Property 1 that

$$\int_0^1 4 \, dx = 4(1 - 0) = 4$$

and we found in Example 2 in Section 5.1 that $\int_0^1 x^2 \, dx = \frac{1}{3}$. So

$$\int_0^1 (4 + 3x^2) \, dx = \int_0^1 4 \, dx + 3 \int_0^1 x^2 \, dx$$

$$= 4 + 3 \cdot \tfrac{1}{3} = 5 \qquad \blacksquare$$

The next property tells us how to combine integrals of the same function over adjacent intervals:

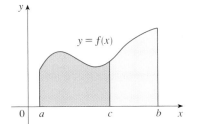

FIGURE 16

5.
$$\int_a^c f(x) \, dx + \int_c^b f(x) \, dx = \int_a^b f(x) \, dx$$

Property 5 is more complicated and is proved in Appendix B, but for the case where $f(x) \geq 0$ and $a < c < b$ it can be seen from the geometric interpretation in Figure 16: The area under $y = f(x)$ from a to c plus the area from c to b is equal to the total area from a to b.

☑ EXAMPLE 6 If it is known that $\int_0^{10} f(x) \, dx = 17$ and $\int_0^8 f(x) \, dx = 12$, find $\int_8^{10} f(x) \, dx$.

SOLUTION By Property 5, we have

$$\int_0^8 f(x) \, dx + \int_8^{10} f(x) \, dx = \int_0^{10} f(x) \, dx$$

so
$$\int_8^{10} f(x) \, dx = \int_0^{10} f(x) \, dx - \int_0^8 f(x) \, dx = 17 - 12 = 5 \qquad \blacksquare$$

Notice that Properties 1–5 are true whether $a < b$, $a = b$, or $a > b$. The following properties, in which we compare sizes of functions and sizes of integrals, are true only if $a \leq b$.

COMPARISON PROPERTIES OF THE INTEGRAL

6. If $f(x) \geq 0$ for $a \leq x \leq b$, then $\int_a^b f(x) \, dx \geq 0$.

7. If $f(x) \geq g(x)$ for $a \leq x \leq b$, then $\int_a^b f(x) \, dx \geq \int_a^b g(x) \, dx$.

8. If $m \leq f(x) \leq M$ for $a \leq x \leq b$, then

$$m(b - a) \leq \int_a^b f(x) \, dx \leq M(b - a)$$

If $f(x) \geq 0$, then $\int_a^b f(x) \, dx$ represents the area under the graph of f, so the geometric interpretation of Property 6 is simply that areas are positive. (It also follows directly from the definition because all the quantities involved are positive.). Property 7 says that a bigger function has a bigger integral. It follows from Properties 6 and 4 because $f - g \geq 0$.

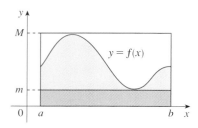

FIGURE 17

Property 8 is illustrated by Figure 17 for the case where $f(x) \geq 0$. If f is continuous we could take m and M to be the absolute minimum and maximum values of f on the interval $[a, b]$. In this case Property 8 says that the area under the graph of f is greater than the area of the rectangle with height m and less than the area of the rectangle with height M.

In general, since $m \leq f(x) \leq M$, Property 7 gives

$$\int_a^b m \, dx \leq \int_a^b f(x) \, dx \leq \int_a^b M \, dx$$

Using Property 1 to evaluate the integrals on the left- and right-hand sides, we obtain

$$m(b - a) \leq \int_a^b f(x) \, dx \leq M(b - a)$$

Property 8 is useful when all we want is a rough estimate of the size of an integral without going to the bother of using the Midpoint Rule.

EXAMPLE 7 Use Property 8 to estimate $\int_0^1 e^{-x^2} \, dx$.

SOLUTION Because $f(x) = e^{-x^2}$ is a decreasing function on $[0, 1]$, its absolute maximum value is $M = f(0) = 1$ and its absolute minimum value is $m = f(1) = e^{-1}$. Thus, by Property 8,

$$e^{-1}(1 - 0) \leq \int_0^1 e^{-x^2} \, dx \leq 1(1 - 0)$$

or

$$e^{-1} \leq \int_0^1 e^{-x^2} \, dx \leq 1$$

Since $e^{-1} \approx 0.3679$, we can write

$$0.367 \leq \int_0^1 e^{-x^2} \, dx \leq 1 \qquad ■$$

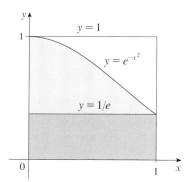

FIGURE 18

The result of Example 7 is illustrated in Figure 18. The integral is greater than the area of the lower rectangle and less than the area of the square.

5.2 | EXERCISES

1. Evaluate the Riemann sum for $f(x) = 2 - x^2$, $0 \leq x \leq 2$, with four equal subintervals, taking the sample points to be right endpoints. Explain, with the aid of a diagram, what the Riemann sum represents.

2. If $f(x) = \ln x - 1$, $1 \leq x \leq 4$, evaluate the Riemann sum for a regular partition with $n = 6$, taking the sample points to be left endpoints. (Give your answer correct to six decimal places.) What does the Riemann sum represent? Illustrate with a diagram.

3. If $f(x) = \sqrt{x} - 2$, $1 \leq x \leq 6$, find the Riemann sum for a regular partition with $n = 5$ correct to six decimal places, taking the sample points to be midpoints. What does the Riemann sum represent? Illustrate with a diagram.

4. (a) Find the Riemann sum for $f(x) = x - 2 \sin 2x$, $0 \leq x \leq 3$, with a regular partition and six terms, taking the sample points to be right endpoints. (Give your answer correct to six decimal places.) Explain what the Riemann sum represents with the aid of a sketch.
(b) Repeat part (a) with midpoints as the sample points.

5. Find the Riemann sum for $f(x) = x^3$, $-1 \leq x \leq 1$, if the partition points are $-1, -0.5, 0, 0.5, 1$ and the sample points are $-1, -0.4, 0.2, 1$.

6. Find the Riemann sum for $f(x) = x + x^2$, $-2 \leq x \leq 0$, if the partition points are $-2, -1.5, -1, -0.7, -0.4, 0$ and the sample points are left endpoints. What is max Δx_i?

7. The graph of a function f is given. Estimate $\int_0^8 f(x)\, dx$ using four subintervals with (a) right endpoints, (b) left endpoints, and (c) midpoints.

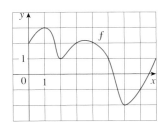

8. The graph of g is shown. Estimate $\int_{-3}^3 g(x)\, dx$ with six subintervals using (a) right endpoints, (b) left endpoints, and (c) midpoints.

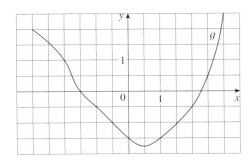

9. A table of values of an increasing function f is shown. Use the table to find lower and upper estimates for $\int_0^{25} f(x)\, dx$.

x	0	5	10	15	20	25
$f(x)$	-42	-37	-25	-6	15	36

10. The table gives the values of a function obtained from an experiment. Use them to estimate $\int_0^6 f(x)\, dx$ using three equal subintervals with (a) right endpoints, (b) left endpoints, and (c) midpoints. If the function is known to be a decreasing function, can you say whether your estimates are less than or greater than the exact value of the integral?

x	0	1	2	3	4	5	6
$f(x)$	9.3	9.0	8.3	6.5	2.3	-7.6	-10.5

11–14 ▪ Use the Midpoint Rule with the given value of n to approximate the integral. Round the answer to four decimal places.

11. $\displaystyle\int_2^{10} \sqrt{x^3 + 1}\, dx$, $\quad n = 4$

12. $\displaystyle\int_0^\pi \sec(x/3)\, dx$, $\quad n = 6$

13. $\displaystyle\int_0^1 \sin(x^2)\, dx$, $\quad n = 5$

14. $\displaystyle\int_1^5 x^2 e^{-x}\, dx$, $\quad n = 4$

15–18 ▪ Express the limit as a definite integral on the given interval.

15. $\displaystyle\lim_{n \to \infty} \sum_{i=1}^n x_i \sin x_i \, \Delta x$, $\quad [0, \pi]$

16. $\displaystyle\lim_{n \to \infty} \sum_{i=1}^n \frac{e^{x_i}}{1 + x_i} \, \Delta x$, $\quad [1, 5]$

17. $\displaystyle\lim_{\max \Delta x_i \to 0} \sum_{i=1}^n \sqrt{2x_i^* + (x_i^*)^2} \, \Delta x_i$, $\quad [1, 8]$

18. $\displaystyle\lim_{\max \Delta x_i \to 0} \sum_{i=1}^n [4 - 3(x_i^*)^2 + 6(x_i^*)^5] \, \Delta x_i$, $\quad [0, 2]$

19–23 ▪ Use the form of the definition of the integral given in Theorem 4 to evaluate the integral.

19. $\displaystyle\int_{-1}^5 (1 + 3x)\, dx$

20. $\displaystyle\int_1^4 (x^2 + 2x - 5)\, dx$

21. $\displaystyle\int_0^2 (2 - x^2)\, dx$

22. $\displaystyle\int_0^5 (1 + 2x^3)\, dx$

23. $\displaystyle\int_1^2 x^3\, dx$

24. (a) Find an approximation to the integral $\int_0^4 (x^2 - 3x)\, dx$ using a Riemann sum with right endpoints and $n = 8$.
(b) Draw a diagram like Figure 2 to illustrate the approximation in part (a).
(c) Use Theorem 4 to evaluate $\int_0^4 (x^2 - 3x)\, dx$.
(d) Interpret the integral in part (c) as a difference of areas and illustrate with a diagram like Figure 6.

25–26 ▪ Express the integral as a limit of Riemann sums. Do not evaluate the limit.

25. $\displaystyle\int_2^6 \frac{x}{1 + x^5}\, dx$

26. $\displaystyle\int_1^{10} (x - 4 \ln x)\, dx$

[CAS] **27–28** ▪ Express the integral as a limit of sums. Then evaluate, using a computer algebra system to find both the sum and the limit.

27. $\displaystyle\int_0^\pi \sin 5x\, dx$

28. $\displaystyle\int_2^{10} x^6\, dx$

29. The graph of f is shown. Evaluate each integral by interpreting it in terms of areas.

(a) $\int_0^2 f(x)\,dx$

(b) $\int_0^5 f(x)\,dx$

(c) $\int_5^7 f(x)\,dx$

(d) $\int_0^9 f(x)\,dx$

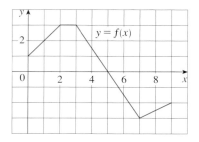

30. The graph of g consists of two straight lines and a semicircle. Use it to evaluate each integral.

(a) $\int_0^2 g(x)\,dx$

(b) $\int_2^6 g(x)\,dx$

(c) $\int_0^7 g(x)\,dx$

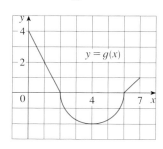

31–36 ■ Evaluate the integral by interpreting it in terms of areas.

31. $\int_0^3 \left(\tfrac{1}{2}x - 1\right) dx$

32. $\int_{-2}^2 \sqrt{4 - x^2}\,dx$

33. $\int_{-3}^0 \left(1 + \sqrt{9 - x^2}\right) dx$

34. $\int_{-1}^3 (3 - 2x)\,dx$

35. $\int_{-1}^2 |x|\,dx$

36. $\int_0^{10} |x - 5|\,dx$

37. Given that $\int_4^9 \sqrt{x}\,dx = \frac{38}{3}$, what is $\int_9^4 \sqrt{t}\,dt$?

38. Evaluate $\int_1^1 x^2 \cos x\,dx$.

39. Write as a single integral in the form $\int_a^b f(x)\,dx$:

$$\int_{-2}^2 f(x)\,dx + \int_2^5 f(x)\,dx - \int_{-2}^{-1} f(x)\,dx$$

40. If $\int_1^5 f(x)\,dx = 12$ and $\int_4^5 f(x)\,dx = 3.6$, find $\int_1^4 f(x)\,dx$.

41. If $\int_0^9 f(x)\,dx = 37$ and $\int_0^9 g(x)\,dx = 16$, find $\int_0^9 [2f(x) + 3g(x)]\,dx$.

42. Find $\int_0^5 f(x)\,dx$ if

$$f(x) = \begin{cases} 3 & \text{for } x < 3 \\ x & \text{for } x \geqslant 3 \end{cases}$$

43. In Example 2 in Section 5.1 we showed that $\int_0^1 x^2\,dx = \frac{1}{3}$. Use this fact and the properties of integrals to evaluate $\int_0^1 (5 - 6x^2)\,dx$.

44. Suppose f has absolute minimum value m and absolute maximum value M. Between what two values must $\int_0^2 f(x)\,dx$ lie? Which property of integrals allows you to make your conclusion?

45. Use the properties of integrals to verify that

$$0 \leqslant \int_1^3 \ln x\,dx \leqslant 2\ln 3$$

without evaluating the integral.

46–50 ■ Use Property 8 to estimate the value of the integral.

46. $\int_0^2 \sqrt{x^3 + 1}\,dx$

47. $\int_1^2 \frac{1}{x}\,dx$

48. $\int_0^2 (x^3 - 3x + 3)\,dx$

49. $\int_{\pi/4}^{\pi/3} \tan x\,dx$

50. $\int_{\pi/4}^{3\pi/4} \sin^2 x\,dx$

51. Express the following limit as a definite integral:

$$\lim_{n \to \infty} \sum_{i=1}^n \frac{i^4}{n^5}$$

5.3 | **EVALUATING DEFINITE INTEGRALS**

In Section 5.2 we computed integrals from the definition as a limit of Riemann sums and we saw that this procedure is sometimes long and difficult. Sir Isaac Newton discovered a much simpler method for evaluating integrals and a few years later Leibniz made the same discovery. They realized that they could calculate $\int_a^b f(x)\,dx$ if they happened to know an antiderivative F of f. Their discovery, called the Evaluation Theorem, is part of the Fundamental Theorem of Calculus, which is discussed in the next section.

> **EVALUATION THEOREM** If f is continuous on the interval $[a, b]$, then
>
> $$\int_a^b f(x)\, dx = F(b) - F(a)$$
>
> where F is any antiderivative of f, that is, $F' = f$.

This theorem states that if we know an antiderivative F of f, then we can evaluate $\int_a^b f(x)\, dx$ simply by subtracting the values of F at the endpoints of the interval $[a, b]$. It is very surprising that $\int_a^b f(x)\, dx$, which was defined by a complicated procedure involving all of the values of $f(x)$ for $a \le x \le b$, can be found by knowing the values of $F(x)$ at only two points, a and b.

For instance, we know from Section 4.7 that an antiderivative of $f(x) = x^2$ is $F(x) = \frac{1}{3}x^3$, so the Evaluation Theorem tells us that

$$\int_0^1 x^2\, dx = F(1) - F(0) = \tfrac{1}{3} \cdot 1^3 - \tfrac{1}{3} \cdot 0^3 = \tfrac{1}{3}$$

Comparing this method with the calculation in Example 2 in Section 5.1, where we found the area under the parabola $y = x^2$ from 0 to 1 by computing a limit of sums, we see that the Evaluation Theorem provides us with a simple and powerful method.

Although the Evaluation Theorem may be surprising at first glance, it becomes plausible if we interpret it in physical terms. If $v(t)$ is the velocity of an object and $s(t)$ is its position at time t, then $v(t) = s'(t)$, so s is an antiderivative of v. In Section 5.1 we considered an object that always moves in the positive direction and made the guess that the area under the velocity curve is equal to the distance traveled. In symbols:

$$\int_a^b v(t)\, dt = s(b) - s(a)$$

That is exactly what the Evaluation Theorem says in this context.

PROOF OF THE EVALUATION THEOREM We divide the interval $[a, b]$ into n subintervals with endpoints $x_0 (= a)$, x_1, x_2, $\ldots$, $x_n (= b)$ and with length $\Delta x = (b - a)/n$. Let F be any antiderivative of f. By subtracting and adding like terms, we can express the total difference in the F values as the sum of the differences over the subintervals:

$$
\begin{aligned}
F(b) - F(a) &= F(x_n) - F(x_0) \\
&= F(x_n) - F(x_{n-1}) + F(x_{n-1}) - F(x_{n-2}) + \cdots + F(x_2) - F(x_1) + F(x_1) - F(x_0) \\
&= \sum_{i=1}^{n} [F(x_i) - F(x_{i-1})]
\end{aligned}
$$

■ See Section 4.2 for The Mean Value Theorem.

Now F is continuous (because it's differentiable) and so we can apply the Mean Value Theorem to F on each subinterval $[x_{i-1}, x_i]$. Thus, there exists a number x_i^* between x_{i-1} and x_i such that

$$F(x_i) - F(x_{i-1}) = F'(x_i^*)(x_i - x_{i-1}) = f(x_i^*)\, \Delta x$$

Therefore
$$F(b) - F(a) = \sum_{i=1}^{n} f(x_i^*)\,\Delta x$$

Now we take the limit of each side of this equation as $n \to \infty$. The left side is a constant and the right side is a Riemann sum for the function f, so

$$F(b) - F(a) = \lim_{n\to\infty} \sum_{i=1}^{n} f(x_i^*)\,\Delta x = \int_a^b f(x)\,dx$$

□

When applying the Evaluation Theorem we use the notation

$$F(x)\Big]_a^b = F(b) - F(a)$$

and so we can write

$$\int_a^b f(x)\,dx = F(x)\Big]_a^b \qquad \text{where} \qquad F' = f$$

Other common notations are $F(x)\big|_a^b$ and $[F(x)]_a^b$.

◤ **EXAMPLE 1** Evaluate $\int_1^3 e^x\,dx$.

SOLUTION An antiderivative of $f(x) = e^x$ is $F(x) = e^x$, so we use the Evaluation Theorem as follows:

$$\int_1^3 e^x\,dx = e^x\Big]_1^3 = e^3 - e$$ ■

■ In applying the Evaluation Theorem we use a particular antiderivative F of f. It is not necessary to use the most general antiderivative ($e^x + C$).

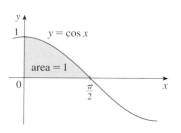

FIGURE 1

EXAMPLE 2 Find the area under the cosine curve from 0 to b, where $0 \le b \le \pi/2$.

SOLUTION Since an antiderivative of $f(x) = \cos x$ is $F(x) = \sin x$, we have

$$A = \int_0^b \cos x\,dx = \sin x\Big]_0^b = \sin b - \sin 0 = \sin b$$

In particular, taking $b = \pi/2$, we have proved that the area under the cosine curve from 0 to $\pi/2$ is $\sin(\pi/2) = 1$. (See Figure 1.) ■

When the French mathematician Gilles de Roberval first found the area under the sine and cosine curves in 1635, this was a very challenging problem that required a great deal of ingenuity. If we didn't have the benefit of the Evaluation Theorem, we would have to compute a difficult limit of sums using obscure trigonometric identities (or a computer algebra system as in Exercise 19 in Section 5.1). It was even more difficult for Roberval because the apparatus of limits had not been invented in 1635. But in the 1660s and 1670s, when the Evaluation Theorem was discovered by Newton and Leibniz, such problems became very easy, as you can see from Example 2.

INDEFINITE INTEGRALS

We need a convenient notation for antiderivatives that makes them easy to work with. Because of the relation given by the Evaluation Theorem between antiderivatives and integrals, the notation $\int f(x)\,dx$ is traditionally used for an antiderivative of f and is called an **indefinite integral**. Thus

$$\int f(x)\,dx = F(x) \qquad \text{means} \qquad F'(x) = f(x)$$

⊘ You should distinguish carefully between definite and indefinite integrals. A definite integral $\int_a^b f(x)\,dx$ is a *number*, whereas an indefinite integral $\int f(x)\,dx$ is a *function* (or family of functions). The connection between them is given by the Evaluation Theorem: If f is continuous on $[a, b]$, then

$$\int_a^b f(x)\,dx = \int f(x)\,dx \Big]_a^b$$

Recall from Section 4.7 that if F is an antiderivative of f on an interval I, then the most general antiderivative of f on I is $F(x) + C$, where C is an arbitrary constant. For instance, the formula

$$\int \frac{1}{x}\,dx = \ln|x| + C$$

is valid (on any interval that doesn't contain 0) because $(d/dx)\ln|x| = 1/x$. So an indefinite integral $\int f(x)\,dx$ can represent either a particular antiderivative of f or an entire *family* of antiderivatives (one for each value of the constant C).

The effectiveness of the Evaluation Theorem depends on having a supply of antiderivatives of functions. We therefore restate the Table of Antidifferentiation Formulas from Section 4.7, together with a few others, in the notation of indefinite integrals. Any formula can be verified by differentiating the function on the right side and obtaining the integrand. For instance,

$$\int \sec^2 x\,dx = \tan x + C \qquad \text{because} \qquad \frac{d}{dx}(\tan x + C) = \sec^2 x$$

---

1 TABLE OF INDEFINITE INTEGRALS

$$\int [f(x) + g(x)]\,dx = \int f(x)\,dx + \int g(x)\,dx \qquad \int cf(x)\,dx = c\int f(x)\,dx$$

$$\int x^n\,dx = \frac{x^{n+1}}{n+1} + C \quad (n \neq -1) \qquad \int \frac{1}{x}\,dx = \ln|x| + C$$

$$\int e^x\,dx = e^x + C \qquad \int a^x\,dx = \frac{a^x}{\ln a} + C$$

■ We adopt the convention that when a formula for a general indefinite integral is given, it is valid only on an interval.

$$\int \sin x\,dx = -\cos x + C \qquad \int \cos x\,dx = \sin x + C$$

$$\int \sec^2 x\,dx = \tan x + C \qquad \int \csc^2 x\,dx = -\cot x + C$$

$$\int \sec x \tan x\,dx = \sec x + C \qquad \int \csc x \cot x\,dx = -\csc x + C$$

$$\int \frac{1}{x^2 + 1}\,dx = \tan^{-1} x + C \qquad \int \frac{1}{\sqrt{1 - x^2}}\,dx = \sin^{-1} x + C$$

EXAMPLE 3 Find the general indefinite integral

$$\int (10x^4 - 2 \sec^2 x)\,dx$$

■ The indefinite integral in Example 3 is graphed in Figure 2 for several values of C. Here the value of C is the y-intercept.

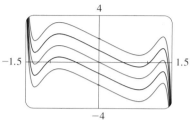

FIGURE 2

SOLUTION Using our convention and Table 1, we have

$$\int (10x^4 - 2 \sec^2 x)\,dx = 10 \int x^4\,dx - 2 \int \sec^2 x\,dx$$

$$= 10\,\frac{x^5}{5} - 2 \tan x + C$$

$$= 2x^5 - 2 \tan x + C$$

You should check this answer by differentiating it. ■

EXAMPLE 4 Evaluate $\displaystyle\int_0^3 (x^3 - 6x)\,dx$.

SOLUTION Using the Evaluation Theorem and Table 1, we have

$$\int_0^3 (x^3 - 6x)\,dx = \frac{x^4}{4} - 6\,\frac{x^2}{2}\,\bigg]_0^3$$

$$= \left(\tfrac{1}{4} \cdot 3^4 - 3 \cdot 3^2\right) - \left(\tfrac{1}{4} \cdot 0^4 - 3 \cdot 0^2\right)$$

$$= \tfrac{81}{4} - 27 - 0 + 0 = -6.75$$

Compare this calculation with Example 2(b) in Section 5.2. ■

Ⅴ EXAMPLE 5 Find $\displaystyle\int_0^2 \left(2x^3 - 6x + \frac{3}{x^2 + 1}\right)dx$ and interpret the result in terms of areas.

■ Figure 3 shows the graph of the integrand in Example 5. We know from Section 5.2 that the value of the integral can be interpreted as the sum of the areas labeled with a plus sign minus the area labeled with a minus sign.

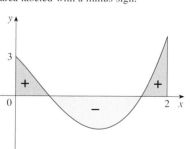

FIGURE 3

SOLUTION The Evaluation Theorem gives

$$\int_0^2 \left(2x^3 - 6x + \frac{3}{x^2 + 1}\right)dx = 2\,\frac{x^4}{4} - 6\,\frac{x^2}{2} + 3 \tan^{-1}x\,\bigg]_0^2$$

$$= \tfrac{1}{2}x^4 - 3x^2 + 3 \tan^{-1}x\,\bigg]_0^2$$

$$= \tfrac{1}{2}(2^4) - 3(2^2) + 3 \tan^{-1} 2 - 0$$

$$= -4 + 3 \tan^{-1} 2$$

This is the exact value of the integral. If a decimal approximation is desired, we can use a calculator to approximate $\tan^{-1} 2$. Doing so, we get

$$\int_0^2 \left(2x^3 - 6x + \frac{3}{x^2 + 1}\right)dx \approx -0.67855 \qquad ■$$

EXAMPLE 6   Evaluate $\displaystyle\int_1^9 \frac{2t^2 + t^2\sqrt{t} - 1}{t^2}\,dt$.

SOLUTION   First we need to write the integrand in a simpler form by carrying out the division:

$$\int_1^9 \frac{2t^2 + t^2\sqrt{t} - 1}{t^2}\,dt = \int_1^9 \left(2 + t^{1/2} - t^{-2}\right)dt$$

$$= 2t + \frac{t^{3/2}}{\frac{3}{2}} - \frac{t^{-1}}{-1}\Bigg]_1^9 = 2t + \tfrac{2}{3}t^{3/2} + \frac{1}{t}\Bigg]_1^9$$

$$= \left[2\cdot 9 + \tfrac{2}{3}(9)^{3/2} + \tfrac{1}{9}\right] - \left(2\cdot 1 + \tfrac{2}{3}\cdot 1^{3/2} + \tfrac{1}{1}\right)$$

$$= 18 + 18 + \tfrac{1}{9} - 2 - \tfrac{2}{3} - 1 = 32\tfrac{4}{9} \qquad\blacksquare$$

APPLICATIONS

The Evaluation Theorem says that if f is continuous on $[a, b]$, then

$$\int_a^b f(x)\,dx = F(b) - F(a)$$

where F is any antiderivative of f. This means that $F' = f$, so the equation can be rewritten as

$$\int_a^b F'(x)\,dx = F(b) - F(a)$$

We know that $F'(x)$ represents the rate of change of $y = F(x)$ with respect to x and $F(b) - F(a)$ is the change in y when x changes from a to b. [Note that y could, for instance, increase, then decrease, then increase again. Although y might change in both directions, $F(b) - F(a)$ represents the *net* change in y.] So we can reformulate the Evaluation Theorem in words as follows.

NET CHANGE THEOREM   The integral of a rate of change is the net change:

$$\int_a^b F'(x)\,dx = F(b) - F(a)$$

This principle can be applied to all of the rates of change in the natural and social sciences. Here are a few instances of this idea:

- If $V(t)$ is the volume of water in a reservoir at time t, then its derivative $V'(t)$ is the rate at which water flows into the reservoir at time t. So

$$\int_{t_1}^{t_2} V'(t)\,dt = V(t_2) - V(t_1)$$

  is the change in the amount of water in the reservoir between time t_1 and time t_2.

- If $[C](t)$ is the concentration of the product of a chemical reaction at time t, then the rate of reaction is the derivative $d[C]/dt$. So

$$\int_{t_1}^{t_2} \frac{d[C]}{dt}\,dt = [C](t_2) - [C](t_1)$$

  is the change in the concentration of C from time t_1 to time t_2.

■ If the rate of growth of a population is dn/dt, then

$$\int_{t_1}^{t_2} \frac{dn}{dt}\, dt = n(t_2) - n(t_1)$$

is the net change in population during the time period from t_1 to t_2. (The population increases when births happen and decreases when deaths occur. The net change takes into account both births and deaths.)

■ If an object moves along a straight line with position function $s(t)$, then its velocity is $v(t) = s'(t)$, so

2
$$\int_{t_1}^{t_2} v(t)\, dt = s(t_2) - s(t_1)$$

is the net change of position, or *displacement,* of the particle during the time period from t_1 to t_2. In Section 5.1 we guessed that this was true for the case where the object moves in the positive direction, but now we have proved that it is always true.

■ If we want to calculate the distance traveled during the time interval, we have to consider the intervals when $v(t) \geqslant 0$ (the particle moves to the right) and also the intervals when $v(t) \leqslant 0$ (the particle moves to the left). In both cases the distance is computed by integrating $|v(t)|$, the speed. Therefore

3
$$\int_{t_1}^{t_2} |v(t)|\, dt = \text{total distance traveled}$$

Figure 4 shows how both displacement and distance traveled can be interpreted in terms of areas under a velocity curve.

■ The acceleration of the object is $a(t) = v'(t)$, so

$$\int_{t_1}^{t_2} a(t)\, dt = v(t_2) - v(t_1)$$

is the change in velocity from time t_1 to time t_2.

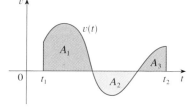

displacement $= \displaystyle\int_{t_1}^{t_2} v(t)\, dt = A_1 - A_2 + A_3$

distance $= \displaystyle\int_{t_1}^{t_2} |v(t)|\, dt = A_1 + A_2 + A_3$

FIGURE 4

▼ EXAMPLE 7 A particle moves along a line so that its velocity at time t is $v(t) = t^2 - t - 6$ (measured in meters per second).
(a) Find the displacement of the particle during the time period $1 \leqslant t \leqslant 4$.
(b) Find the distance traveled during this time period.

SOLUTION
(a) By Equation 2, the displacement is

$$s(4) - s(1) = \int_1^4 v(t)\, dt = \int_1^4 (t^2 - t - 6)\, dt$$

$$= \left[\frac{t^3}{3} - \frac{t^2}{2} - 6t \right]_1^4 = -\frac{9}{2}$$

This means that the particle's position at time $t = 4$ is 4.5 m to the left of its position at the start of the time period.

(b) Note that $v(t) = t^2 - t - 6 = (t - 3)(t + 2)$ and so $v(t) \leqslant 0$ on the interval $[1, 3]$ and $v(t) \geqslant 0$ on $[3, 4]$. Thus, from Equation 3, the distance traveled is

■ To integrate the absolute value of $v(t)$, we use Property 5 of integrals from Section 5.2 to split the integral into two parts, one where $v(t) \leqslant 0$ and one where $v(t) \geqslant 0$.

$$\int_1^4 |v(t)| \, dt = \int_1^3 [-v(t)] \, dt + \int_3^4 v(t) \, dt$$

$$= \int_1^3 (-t^2 + t + 6) \, dt + \int_3^4 (t^2 - t - 6) \, dt$$

$$= \left[-\frac{t^3}{3} + \frac{t^2}{2} + 6t \right]_1^3 + \left[\frac{t^3}{3} - \frac{t^2}{2} - 6t \right]_3^4$$

$$= \frac{61}{6} \approx 10.17 \text{ m}$$

▼ **EXAMPLE 8** Figure 5 shows the power consumption in the city of San Francisco for a day in September (P is measured in megawatts; t is measured in hours starting at midnight). Estimate the energy used on that day.

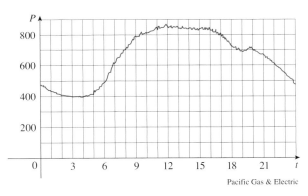

FIGURE 5

Pacific Gas & Electric

SOLUTION Power is the rate of change of energy: $P(t) = E'(t)$. So, by the Net Change Theorem,

$$\int_0^{24} P(t) \, dt = \int_0^{24} E'(t) \, dt = E(24) - E(0)$$

is the total amount of energy used on that day. We approximate the value of the integral using the Midpoint Rule with 12 subintervals and $\Delta t = 2$:

$$\int_0^{24} P(t) \, dt \approx [P(1) + P(3) + P(5) + \cdots + P(21) + P(23)] \Delta t$$

$$\approx (440 + 400 + 420 + 620 + 790 + 840 + 850$$

$$+ 840 + 810 + 690 + 670 + 550)(2)$$

$$= 15{,}840$$

The energy used was approximately 15,840 megawatt-hours. ■

■ A note on units

How did we know what units to use for energy in Example 8? The integral $\int_0^{24} P(t) \, dt$ is defined as the limit of sums of terms of the form $P(t_i^*) \, \Delta t$. Now $P(t_i^*)$ is measured in megawatts and Δt is measured in hours, so their product is measured in megawatt-hours. The same is true of the limit. In general, the unit of measurement for $\int_a^b f(x) \, dx$ is the product of the unit for $f(x)$ and the unit for x.

5.3 EXERCISES

1–28 ■ Evaluate the integral.

1. $\int_{-1}^{3} x^5 \, dx$

2. $\int_{1}^{3} (1 + 2x - 4x^3) \, dx$

3. $\int_{0}^{2} (6x^2 - 4x + 5) \, dx$

4. $\int_{-2}^{0} (u^5 - u^3 + u^2) \, du$

5. $\int_{0}^{1} x^{4/5} \, dx$

6. $\int_{1}^{8} \sqrt[3]{x} \, dx$

7. $\int_{-1}^{0} (2x - e^x) \, dx$

8. $\int_{\pi}^{2\pi} \cos \theta \, d\theta$

9. $\int_{-2}^{2} (3u + 1)^2 \, du$

10. $\int_{0}^{4} (2v + 5)(3v - 1) \, dv$

11. $\int_{-2}^{-1} \left(4y^3 + \frac{2}{y^3} \right) dy$

12. $\int_{1}^{2} \frac{y + 5y^7}{y^3} \, dy$

13. $\int_{0}^{1} x(\sqrt[3]{x} + \sqrt[4]{x}) \, dx$

14. $\int_{1}^{9} \frac{3x - 2}{\sqrt{x}} \, dx$

15. $\int_{0}^{\pi/4} \sec^2 t \, dt$

16. $\int_{0}^{5} (2e^x + 4 \cos x) \, dx$

17. $\int_{1}^{9} \frac{1}{2x} \, dx$

18. $\int_{0}^{1} 10^x \, dx$

19. $\int_{1/2}^{\sqrt{3}/2} \frac{6}{\sqrt{1 - t^2}} \, dt$

20. $\int_{0}^{1} \frac{4}{t^2 + 1} \, dt$

21. $\int_{1}^{64} \frac{1 + \sqrt[3]{x}}{\sqrt{x}} \, dx$

22. $\int_{\pi/4}^{\pi/3} \sec \theta \tan \theta \, d\theta$

23. $\int_{-1}^{1} e^{u+1} \, du$

24. $\int_{0}^{1} (1 + x^2)^3 \, dx$

25. $\int_{0}^{\pi/4} \frac{1 + \cos^2 \theta}{\cos^2 \theta} \, d\theta$

26. $\int_{0}^{\pi/3} \frac{\sin \theta + \sin \theta \tan^2 \theta}{\sec^2 \theta} \, d\theta$

27. $\int_{1}^{e} \frac{x^2 + x + 1}{x} \, dx$

28. $\int_{0}^{3\pi/2} |\sin x| \, dx$

■   ■   ■   ■   ■   ■   ■   ■   ■   ■   ■   ■

29–30 ■ What is wrong with the equation?

29. $\int_{-1}^{3} \frac{1}{x^2} \, dx = \frac{x^{-1}}{-1} \Big]_{-1}^{3} = -\frac{4}{3}$

30. $\int_{0}^{\pi} \sec^2 x \, dx = \tan x \big]_{0}^{\pi} = 0$

■   ■   ■   ■   ■   ■   ■   ■   ■   ■   ■   ■

31–32 ■ Use a graph to give a rough estimate of the area of the region that lies beneath the given curve. Then find the exact area.

31. $y = \sin x$, $0 \le x \le \pi$

32. $y = \sec^2 x$, $0 \le x \le \pi/3$

■   ■   ■   ■   ■   ■   ■   ■   ■   ■   ■   ■

33. Use a graph to estimate the x-intercepts of the curve $y = x + x^2 - x^4$. Then use this information to estimate the area of the region that lies under the curve and above the x-axis.

34. Repeat Exercise 33 for the curve $y = 2x + 3x^4 - 2x^6$.

35–36 ■ Evaluate the integral and interpret it as a difference of areas. Illustrate with a sketch.

35. $\int_{-1}^{2} x^3 \, dx$

36. $\int_{\pi/4}^{5\pi/2} \sin x \, dx$

■   ■   ■   ■   ■   ■   ■   ■   ■   ■   ■   ■

37–38 ■ Verify by differentiation that the formula is correct.

37. $\int \frac{x}{\sqrt{x^2 + 1}} \, dx = \sqrt{x^2 + 1} + C$

38. $\int x \cos x \, dx = x \sin x + \cos x + C$

■   ■   ■   ■   ■   ■   ■   ■   ■   ■   ■   ■

39–40 ■ Find the general indefinite integral. Illustrate by graphing several members of the family on the same screen.

39. $\int x \sqrt{x} \, dx$

40. $\int (\cos x - 2 \sin x) \, dx$

■   ■   ■   ■   ■   ■   ■   ■   ■   ■   ■   ■

41–44 ■ Find the general indefinite integral.

41. $\int (1 - t)(2 + t^2) \, dt$

42. $\int x(1 + 2x^4) \, dx$

43. $\int \frac{\sin x}{1 - \sin^2 x} \, dx$

44. $\int \frac{\sin 2x}{\sin x} \, dx$

■   ■   ■   ■   ■   ■   ■   ■   ■   ■   ■   ■

45. The area of the region that lies to the right of the y-axis and to the left of the parabola $x = 2y - y^2$ (the shaded region in the figure) is given by the integral $\int_{0}^{2} (2y - y^2) \, dy$. (Turn your head clockwise and think of the region as lying below the curve $x = 2y - y^2$ from $y = 0$ to $y = 2$.) Find the area of the region.

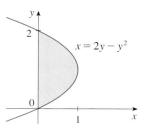

46. The boundaries of the shaded region are the y-axis, the line $y = 1$, and the curve $y = \sqrt[4]{x}$. Find the area of this region by writing x as a function of y and integrating with respect to y (as in Exercise 45).

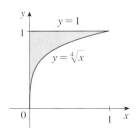

47. If $w'(t)$ is the rate of growth of a child in pounds per year, what does $\int_5^{10} w'(t)\, dt$ represent?

48. The current in a wire is defined as the derivative of the charge: $I(t) = Q'(t)$. What does $\int_a^b I(t)\, dt$ represent?

49. If oil leaks from a tank at a rate of $r(t)$ gallons per minute at time t, what does $\int_0^{120} r(t)\, dt$ represent?

50. A honeybee population starts with 100 bees and increases at a rate of $n'(t)$ bees per week. What does $100 + \int_0^{15} n'(t)\, dt$ represent?

51. In Section 4.5 we defined the marginal revenue function $R'(x)$ as the derivative of the revenue function $R(x)$, where x is the number of units sold. What does $\int_{1000}^{5000} R'(x)\, dx$ represent?

52. If $f(x)$ is the slope of a trail at a distance of x miles from the start of the trail, what does $\int_3^5 f(x)\, dx$ represent?

53. If x is measured in meters and $f(x)$ is measured in newtons, what are the units for $\int_0^{100} f(x)\, dx$?

54. If the units for x are feet and the units for $a(x)$ are pounds per foot, what are the units for da/dx? What units does $\int_2^8 a(x)\, dx$ have?

55–56 ▪ The velocity function (in meters per second) is given for a particle moving along a line. Find (a) the displacement and (b) the distance traveled by the particle during the given time interval.

55. $v(t) = 3t - 5, \quad 0 \leqslant t \leqslant 3$

56. $v(t) = t^2 - 2t - 8, \quad 1 \leqslant t \leqslant 6$

▪ ▪ ▪ ▪ ▪ ▪ ▪ ▪ ▪ ▪ ▪ ▪

57–58 ▪ The acceleration function (in m/s²) and the initial velocity are given for a particle moving along a line. Find (a) the velocity at time t and (b) the distance traveled during the given time interval.

57. $a(t) = t + 4, \quad v(0) = 5, \quad 0 \leqslant t \leqslant 10$

58. $a(t) = 2t + 3, \quad v(0) = -4, \quad 0 \leqslant t \leqslant 3$

▪ ▪ ▪ ▪ ▪ ▪ ▪ ▪ ▪ ▪ ▪ ▪

59. The velocity of a car was read from its speedometer at 10-second intervals and recorded in the table. Use the Midpoint Rule to estimate the distance traveled by the car.

t (s)	v (mi/h)	t (s)	v (mi/h)
0	0	60	56
10	38	70	53
20	52	80	50
30	58	90	47
40	55	100	45
50	51		

60. Suppose that a volcano is erupting and readings of the rate $r(t)$ at which solid materials are spewed into the atmosphere are given in the table. The time t is measured in seconds and the units for $r(t)$ are tonnes (metric tons) per second.

t	0	1	2	3	4	5	6
$r(t)$	2	10	24	36	46	54	60

(a) Give upper and lower estimates for the total quantity $Q(6)$ of erupted materials after 6 seconds.
(b) Use the Midpoint Rule to estimate $Q(6)$.

61. Water flows from the bottom of a storage tank at a rate of $r(t) = 200 - 4t$ liters per minute, where $0 \leqslant t \leqslant 50$. Find the amount of water that flows from the tank during the first 10 minutes.

62. Water flows into and out of a storage tank. A graph of the rate of change $r(t)$ of the volume of water in the tank, in liters per day, is shown. If the amount of water in the tank at time $t = 0$ is 25,000 L, use the Midpoint Rule to estimate the amount of water four days later.

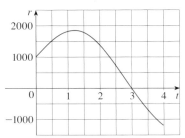

63. Suppose h is a function such that $h(1) = -2$, $h'(1) = 2$, $h''(1) = 3$, $h(2) = 6$, $h'(2) = 5$, $h''(2) = 13$, and h'' is continuous everywhere. Evaluate $\int_1^2 h''(u)\, du$.

64. The area labeled B is three times the area labeled A. Express b in terms of a.

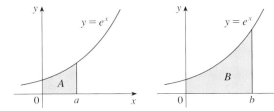

| 5.4 | THE FUNDAMENTAL THEOREM OF CALCULUS |

The Fundamental Theorem of Calculus is appropriately named because it establishes a connection between the two branches of calculus: differential calculus and integral calculus. Differential calculus arose from the tangent problem, whereas integral calculus arose from a seemingly unrelated problem, the area problem. Newton's teacher at Cambridge, Isaac Barrow (1630–1677), discovered that these two problems are actually closely related. In fact, he realized that differentiation and integration are inverse processes. The Fundamental Theorem of Calculus gives the precise inverse relationship between the derivative and the integral. It was Newton and Leibniz who exploited this relationship and used it to develop calculus into a systematic mathematical method.

The first part of the Fundamental Theorem deals with functions defined by an equation of the form

1
$$g(x) = \int_a^x f(t)\, dt$$

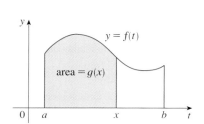

FIGURE 1

where f is a continuous function on $[a, b]$ and x varies between a and b. Observe that g depends only on x, which appears as the variable upper limit in the integral. If x is a fixed number, then the integral $\int_a^x f(t)\, dt$ is a definite number. If we then let x vary, the number $\int_a^x f(t)\, dt$ also varies and defines a function of x denoted by $g(x)$.

If f happens to be a positive function, then $g(x)$ can be interpreted as the area under the graph of f from a to x, where x can vary from a to b. (Think of g as the "area so far" function; see Figure 1.)

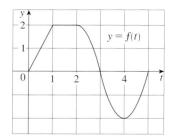

FIGURE 2

▼ **EXAMPLE 1** If f is the function whose graph is shown in Figure 2 and $g(x) = \int_0^x f(t)\, dt$, find the values of $g(0)$, $g(1)$, $g(2)$, $g(3)$, $g(4)$, and $g(5)$. Then sketch a rough graph of g.

SOLUTION First we notice that $g(0) = \int_0^0 f(t)\, dt = 0$. From Figure 3 we see that $g(1)$ is the area of a triangle:

$$g(1) = \int_0^1 f(t)\, dt = \tfrac{1}{2}(1 \cdot 2) = 1$$

To find $g(2)$ we add to $g(1)$ the area of a rectangle:

$$g(2) = \int_0^2 f(t)\, dt = \int_0^1 f(t)\, dt + \int_1^2 f(t)\, dt = 1 + (1 \cdot 2) = 3$$

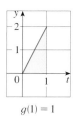

$g(1) = 1$

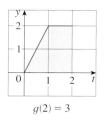

$g(2) = 3$

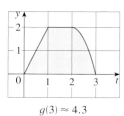

$g(3) \approx 4.3$

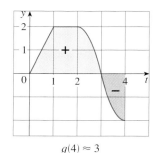

$g(4) \approx 3$

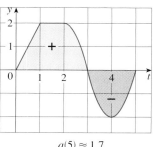

$g(5) \approx 1.7$

FIGURE 3

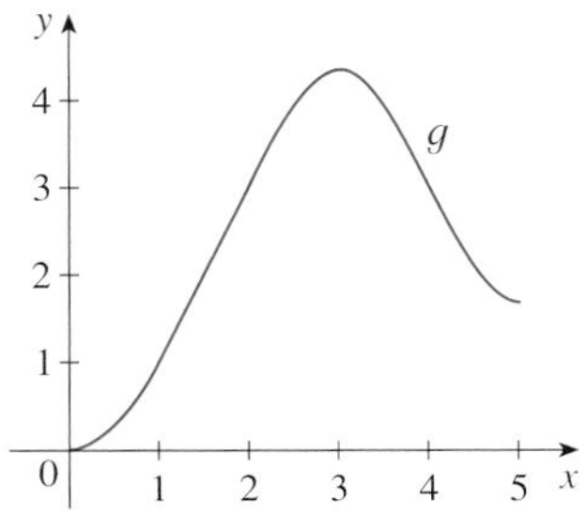

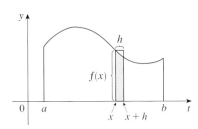

FIGURE 4

$g(x) = \int_a^x f(t)\, dt$

We estimate that the area under f from 2 to 3 is about 1.3, so

$$g(3) = g(2) + \int_2^3 f(t)\, dt \approx 3 + 1.3 = 4.3$$

For $t > 3$, $f(t)$ is negative and so we start subtracting areas:

$$g(4) = g(3) + \int_3^4 f(t)\, dt \approx 4.3 + (-1.3) = 3.0$$

$$g(5) = g(4) + \int_4^5 f(t)\, dt \approx 3 + (-1.3) = 1.7$$

We use these values to sketch the graph of g in Figure 4. Notice that, because $f(t)$ is positive for $t < 3$, we keep adding area for $t < 3$ and so g is increasing up to $x = 3$, where it attains a maximum value. For $x > 3$, g decreases because $f(t)$ is negative. ▪

EXAMPLE 2 If $g(x) = \int_a^x f(t)\, dt$, where $a = 1$ and $f(t) = t^2$, find a formula for $g(x)$ and calculate $g'(x)$.

SOLUTION In this case we can compute $g(x)$ explicitly using the Evaluation Theorem:

$$g(x) = \int_1^x t^2\, dt = \frac{t^3}{3}\bigg]_1^x = \frac{x^3 - 1}{3}$$

Then
$$g'(x) = \frac{d}{dx}\left(\tfrac{1}{3}x^3 - \tfrac{1}{3}\right) = x^2$$ ▪

For the function in Example 2 notice that $g'(x) = x^2$, that is $g' = f$. In other words, if g is defined as the integral of f by Equation 1, then g turns out to be an antiderivative of f, at least in this case. And if we sketch the derivative of the function g shown in Figure 4 by estimating slopes of tangents, we get a graph like that of f in Figure 2. So we suspect that $g' = f$ in Example 1 too.

To see why this might be generally true we consider any continuous function f with $f(x) \geqslant 0$. Then $g(x) = \int_a^x f(t)\, dt$ can be interpreted as the area under the graph of f from a to x, as in Figure 1.

In order to compute $g'(x)$ from the definition of derivative we first observe that, for $h > 0$, $g(x + h) - g(x)$ is obtained by subtracting areas, so it is the area under the graph of f from x to $x + h$ (the shaded area in Figure 5). For small h you can see from the figure that this area is approximately equal to the area of the rectangle with height $f(x)$ and width h:

$$g(x + h) - g(x) \approx hf(x)$$

so
$$\frac{g(x + h) - g(x)}{h} \approx f(x)$$

FIGURE 5

Intuitively, we therefore expect that

$$g'(x) = \lim_{h \to 0} \frac{g(x + h) - g(x)}{h} = f(x)$$

The fact that this is true, even when f is not necessarily positive, is the first part of the Fundamental Theorem of Calculus.

■ We abbreviate the name of this theorem as FTC1. In words, it says that the derivative of a definite integral with respect to its upper limit is the integrand evaluated at the upper limit.

THE FUNDAMENTAL THEOREM OF CALCULUS, PART 1 If f is continuous on $[a, b]$, then the function g defined by

$$g(x) = \int_a^x f(t)\, dt \qquad a \leq x \leq b$$

is an antiderivative of f, that is, $g'(x) = f(x)$ for $a < x < b$.

PROOF If x and $x + h$ are in the open interval (a, b), then

$$g(x + h) - g(x) = \int_a^{x+h} f(t)\, dt - \int_a^x f(t)\, dt$$

Module 5.4 provides visual evidence for FTC1.

$$= \left(\int_a^x f(t)\, dt + \int_x^{x+h} f(t)\, dt \right) - \int_a^x f(t)\, dt \quad \text{(by Property 5)}$$

$$= \int_x^{x+h} f(t)\, dt$$

and so, for $h \neq 0$,

2
$$\frac{g(x + h) - g(x)}{h} = \frac{1}{h} \int_x^{x+h} f(t)\, dt$$

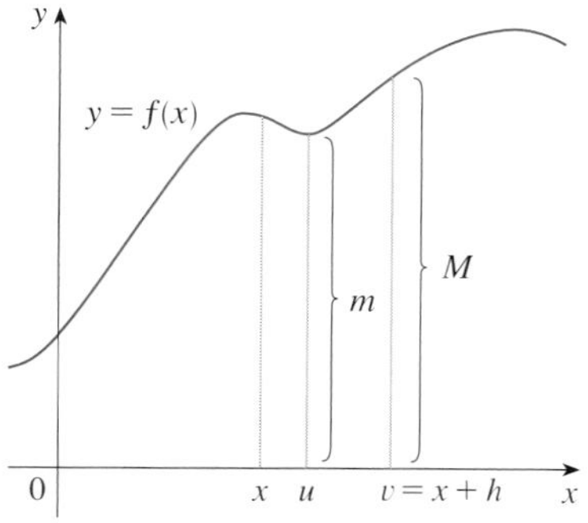

For now let's assume that $h > 0$. Since f is continuous on $[x, x + h]$, the Extreme Value Theorem says that there are numbers u and v in $[x, x + h]$ such that $f(u) = m$ and $f(v) = M$, where m and M are the absolute minimum and maximum values of f on $[x, x + h]$. (See Figure 6.)

By Property 8 of integrals, we have

$$mh \leq \int_x^{x+h} f(t)\, dt \leq Mh$$

FIGURE 6

that is,

$$f(u)h \leq \int_x^{x+h} f(t)\, dt \leq f(v)h$$

Since $h > 0$, we can divide this inequality by h:

$$f(u) \leq \frac{1}{h} \int_x^{x+h} f(t)\, dt \leq f(v)$$

Now we use Equation 2 to replace the middle part of this inequality:

3
$$f(u) \leq \frac{g(x + h) - g(x)}{h} \leq f(v)$$

Inequality 3 can be proved in a similar manner for the case $h < 0$.

Now we let $h \to 0$. Then $u \to x$ and $v \to x$, since u and v lie between x and $x + h$. Thus

$$\lim_{h \to 0} f(u) = \lim_{u \to x} f(u) = f(x) \qquad \text{and} \qquad \lim_{h \to 0} f(v) = \lim_{v \to x} f(v) = f(x)$$

because f is continuous at x. We conclude, from (3) and the Squeeze Theorem, that

$$\boxed{4}\qquad g'(x) = \lim_{h \to 0} \frac{g(x + h) - g(x)}{h} = f(x)$$

If $x = a$ or b, then Equation 4 can be interpreted as a one-sided limit. Then Theorem 2.2.4 (modified for one-sided limits) shows that g is continuous on $[a, b]$.   □

Using Leibniz notation for derivatives, we can write FTC1 as

$$\frac{d}{dx} \int_a^x f(t)\, dt = f(x)$$

when f is continuous. Roughly speaking, this equation says that if we first integrate f and then differentiate the result, we get back to the original function f.

▼ **EXAMPLE 3** Find the derivative of the function $g(x) = \int_0^x \sqrt{1 + t^2}\ dt$.

SOLUTION Since $f(t) = \sqrt{1 + t^2}$ is continuous, Part 1 of the Fundamental Theorem of Calculus gives

$$g'(x) = \sqrt{1 + x^2}$$ ▪

EXAMPLE 4 Although a formula of the form $g(x) = \int_a^x f(t)\, dt$ may seem like a strange way of defining a function, books on physics, chemistry, and statistics are full of such functions. For instance, the **Fresnel function**

$$S(x) = \int_0^x \sin(\pi t^2/2)\, dt$$

is named after the French physicist Augustin Fresnel (1788–1827), who is famous for his works in optics. This function first appeared in Fresnel's theory of the diffraction of light waves, but more recently it has been applied to the design of highways.

Part 1 of the Fundamental Theorem tells us how to differentiate the Fresnel function:

$$S'(x) = \sin(\pi x^2/2)$$

This means that we can apply all the methods of differential calculus to analyze S (see Exercise 29).

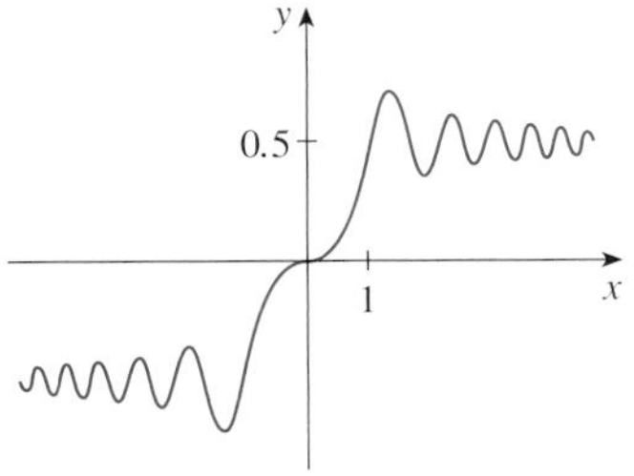

Figure 7 shows the graphs of $f(x) = \sin(\pi x^2/2)$ and the Fresnel function $S(x) = \int_0^x f(t)\, dt$. A computer was used to graph S by computing the value of this integral for many values of x. It does indeed look as if $S(x)$ is the area under the graph of f from 0 to x [until $x \approx 1.4$, when $S(x)$ becomes a difference of areas]. Figure 8 shows a larger part of the graph of S.

If we now start with the graph of S in Figure 7 and think about what its derivative should look like, it seems reasonable that $S'(x) = f(x)$. [For instance, S is increasing when $f(x) > 0$ and decreasing when $f(x) < 0$.] So this gives a visual confirmation of Part 1 of the Fundamental Theorem of Calculus. ▪

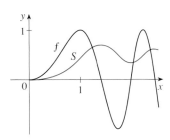

FIGURE 7
$f(x) = \sin(\pi x^2/2)$
$S(x) = \int_0^x \sin(\pi t^2/2)\, dt$

FIGURE 8
The Fresnel function
$S(x) = \int_0^x \sin(\pi t^2/2)\, dt$

EXAMPLE 5 Find $\dfrac{d}{dx}\displaystyle\int_1^{x^4} \sec t \, dt$.

SOLUTION Here we have to be careful to use the Chain Rule in conjunction with Part 1 of the Fundamental Theorem. Let $u = x^4$. Then

$$\frac{d}{dx}\int_1^{x^4} \sec t \, dt = \frac{d}{dx}\int_1^{u} \sec t \, dt$$

$$= \frac{d}{du}\left[\int_1^{u} \sec t \, dt\right]\frac{du}{dx} \qquad \text{(by the Chain Rule)}$$

$$= \sec u \, \frac{du}{dx} \qquad\qquad \text{(by FTC1)}$$

$$= \sec(x^4) \cdot 4x^3 \qquad\qquad\qquad ▪$$

DIFFERENTIATION AND INTEGRATION AS INVERSE PROCESSES

We now bring together the two parts of the Fundamental Theorem. We regard Part 1 as fundamental because it relates integration and differentiation. But the Evaluation Theorem from Section 5.3 also relates integrals and derivatives, so we rename it as Part 2 of the Fundamental Theorem.

THE FUNDAMENTAL THEOREM OF CALCULUS Suppose f is continuous on $[a, b]$.

1. If $g(x) = \int_a^x f(t) \, dt$, then $g'(x) = f(x)$.

2. $\int_a^b f(x) \, dx = F(b) - F(a)$, where F is any antiderivative of f, that is, $F' = f$.

We noted that Part 1 can be rewritten as

$$\frac{d}{dx}\int_a^x f(t) \, dt = f(x)$$

which says that if f is integrated and the result is then differentiated, we arrive back at the original function f. In Section 5.3 we reformulated Part 2 as the Net Change Theorem:

$$\int_a^b F'(x) \, dx = F(b) - F(a)$$

This version says that if we take a function F, first differentiate it, and then integrate the result, we arrive back at the original function F, but in the form $F(b) - F(a)$. Taken together, the two parts of the Fundamental Theorem of Calculus say that differentiation and integration are inverse processes. Each undoes what the other does.

The Fundamental Theorem of Calculus is unquestionably the most important theorem in calculus and, indeed, it ranks as one of the great accomplishments of the human mind. Before it was discovered, from the time of Eudoxus and Archimedes to the time of Galileo and Fermat, problems of finding areas, volumes, and lengths of curves were so difficult that only a genius could meet the challenge. But now, armed with the systematic method that Newton and Leibniz fashioned out of the Fundamental Theorem, we will see in the chapters to come that these challenging problems are accessible to all of us.

AVERAGE VALUE OF A FUNCTION

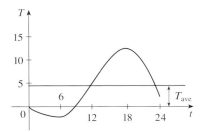

FIGURE 9

It's easy to calculate the average value of finitely many numbers $y_1, y_2, \ldots, y_n$:

$$y_{\text{ave}} = \frac{y_1 + y_2 + \cdots + y_n}{n}$$

But how do we compute the average temperature during a day if infinitely many temperature readings are possible? Figure 9 shows the graph of a temperature function $T(t)$, where t is measured in hours and T in °C, and a guess at the average temperature, T_{ave}.

In general, let's try to compute the average value of a function $y = f(x)$, $a \le x \le b$. We start by dividing the interval $[a, b]$ into n equal subintervals, each with length $\Delta x = (b - a)/n$. Then we choose points $x_1^*, \ldots, x_n^*$ in successive subintervals and calculate the average of the numbers $f(x_1^*), \ldots, f(x_n^*)$:

$$\frac{f(x_1^*) + \cdots + f(x_n^*)}{n}$$

(For example, if f represents a temperature function and $n = 24$, this means that we take temperature readings every hour and then average them.) Since $\Delta x = (b - a)/n$, we can write $n = (b - a)/\Delta x$ and the average value becomes

$$\frac{f(x_1^*) + \cdots + f(x_n^*)}{\dfrac{b - a}{\Delta x}} = \frac{1}{b - a}\left[f(x_1^*)\,\Delta x + \cdots + f(x_n^*)\,\Delta x \right]$$

$$= \frac{1}{b - a} \sum_{i=1}^{n} f(x_i^*)\,\Delta x$$

If we let n increase, we would be computing the average value of a large number of closely spaced values. (For example, we would be averaging temperature readings taken every minute or even every second.) The limiting value is

$$\lim_{n \to \infty} \frac{1}{b - a} \sum_{i=1}^{n} f(x_i^*)\,\Delta x = \frac{1}{b - a} \int_a^b f(x)\,dx$$

by the definition of a definite integral.

Therefore, we define the **average value of f** on the interval $[a, b]$ as

$$f_{\text{ave}} = \frac{1}{b - a} \int_a^b f(x)\,dx$$

▪ For a positive function, we can think of this definition as saying

$$\frac{\text{area}}{\text{width}} = \text{average height}$$

◤ EXAMPLE 6 Find the average value of the function $f(x) = 1 + x^2$ on the interval $[-1, 2]$.

SOLUTION With $a = -1$ and $b = 2$ we have

$$f_{ave} = \frac{1}{b - a} \int_a^b f(x)\,dx = \frac{1}{2 - (-1)} \int_{-1}^2 (1 + x^2)\,dx = \frac{1}{3}\left[x + \frac{x^3}{3}\right]_{-1}^2 = 2 \qquad ■$$

If $T(t)$ is the temperature at time t, we might wonder if there is a specific time when the temperature is the same as the average temperature. For the temperature function graphed in Figure 9, we see that there are two such times—just before noon and just before midnight. In general, is there a number c at which the value of a function f is exactly equal to the average value of the function, that is, $f(c) = f_{ave}$? The following theorem says that this is true for continuous functions.

THE MEAN VALUE THEOREM FOR INTEGRALS If f is continuous on $[a, b]$, then there exists a number c in $[a, b]$ such that

$$f(c) = f_{ave} = \frac{1}{b - a}\int_a^b f(x)\,dx$$

that is,

$$\int_a^b f(x)\,dx = f(c)(b - a)$$

PROOF Let $F(x) = \int_a^x f(t)\,dt$ for $a \leq x \leq b$. By the Mean Value Theorem for derivatives, there is a number c between a and b such that

$$F(b) - F(a) = F'(c)(b - a)$$

But $F'(x) = f(x)$ by FTC1. Therefore

$$\int_a^b f(t)\,dt - 0 = f(c)(b - a) \qquad \square$$

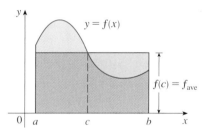

FIGURE 10

The geometric interpretation of the Mean Value Theorem for Integrals is that, for *positive* functions f, there is a number c such that the rectangle with base $[a, b]$ and height $f(c)$ has the same area as the region under the graph of f from a to b. (See Figure 10 and the more picturesque interpretation in the margin note.)

■ You can always chop off the top of a (two-dimensional) mountain at a certain height and use it to fill in the valleys so that the mountaintop becomes completely flat.

◤ EXAMPLE 7 Since $f(x) = 1 + x^2$ is continuous on the interval $[-1, 2]$, the Mean Value Theorem for Integrals says there is a number c in $[-1, 2]$ such that

$$\int_{-1}^2 (1 + x^2)\,dx = f(c)[2 - (-1)]$$

In this particular case we can find c explicitly. From Example 6 we know that $f_{ave} = 2$, so the value of c satisfies

$$f(c) = f_{ave} = 2$$

Therefore

$$1 + c^2 = 2 \qquad \text{so} \qquad c^2 = 1$$

Thus in this case there happen to be two numbers $c = \pm 1$ in the interval $[-1, 2]$ that work in the Mean Value Theorem for Integrals. ■

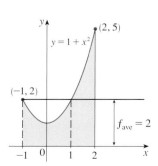

FIGURE 11

Examples 6 and 7 are illustrated by Figure 11.

5.4 EXERCISES

1. Let $g(x) = \int_0^x f(t)\,dt$, where f is the function whose graph is shown.
(a) Evaluate $g(0)$, $g(1)$, $g(2)$, $g(3)$, and $g(6)$.
(b) On what interval is g increasing?
(c) Where does g have a maximum value?
(d) Sketch a rough graph of g.

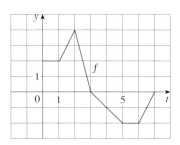

2. Let $g(x) = \int_0^x f(t)\,dt$, where f is the function whose graph is shown.
(a) Evaluate $g(x)$ for $x = 0$, 1, 2, 3, 4, 5, and 6.
(b) Estimate $g(7)$.
(c) Where does g have a maximum value? Where does it have a minimum value?
(d) Sketch a rough graph of g.

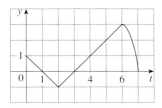

3–4 ▪ Sketch the area represented by $g(x)$. Then find $g'(x)$ in two ways: (a) by using Part 1 of the Fundamental Theorem and (b) by evaluating the integral using Part 2 and then differentiating.

3. $g(x) = \int_0^x (1 + t^2)\,dt$ **4.** $g(x) = \int_0^x (1 + \sqrt{t}\,)\,dt$

▪ ▪ ▪ ▪ ▪ ▪ ▪ ▪ ▪ ▪ ▪ ▪

5–14 ▪ Use Part 1 of the Fundamental Theorem of Calculus to find the derivative of the function.

5. $g(x) = \int_0^x \sqrt{1 + 2t}\,dt$ **6.** $g(x) = \int_1^x \ln t\,dt$

7. $g(y) = \int_2^y t^2 \sin t\,dt$

8. $F(x) = \int_x^{10} \tan \theta\,d\theta$

$$\left[\text{Hint: } \int_x^{10} \tan \theta\,d\theta = -\int_{10}^x \tan \theta\,d\theta \right]$$

9. $h(x) = \int_2^{1/x} \arctan t\,dt$ **10.** $h(x) = \int_0^{x^2} \sqrt{1 + r^3}\,dr$

11. $y = \int_3^{\sqrt{x}} \dfrac{\cos t}{t}\,dt$ **12.** $y = \int_{e^x}^0 \sin^3 t\,dt$

13. $g(x) = \int_{2x}^{3x} \dfrac{u^2 - 1}{u^2 + 1}\,du$

$$\left[\text{Hint: } \int_{2x}^{3x} f(u)\,du = \int_{2x}^0 f(u)\,du + \int_0^{3x} f(u)\,du \right]$$

14. $y = \int_{\sin x}^{\cos x} (1 + v^2)^{10}\,dv$

▪ ▪ ▪ ▪ ▪ ▪ ▪ ▪ ▪ ▪ ▪ ▪ ▪ ▪ ▪ ▪

15–18 ▪ Find the average value of the function on the given interval.

15. $f(x) = x^2$, $[-1, 1]$ **16.** $f(x) = 1/x$, $[1, 4]$

17. $g(x) = \cos x$, $[0, \pi/2]$

18. $f(\theta) = \sec \theta \tan \theta$, $[0, \pi/4]$

▪ ▪ ▪ ▪ ▪ ▪ ▪ ▪ ▪ ▪ ▪ ▪ ▪ ▪ ▪

19–20 ▪
(a) Find the average value of f on the given interval.
(b) Find c such that $f_{\text{ave}} = f(c)$.
(c) Sketch the graph of f and a rectangle whose area is the same as the area under the graph of f.

19. $f(x) = (x - 3)^2$, $[2, 5]$

20. $f(x) = \sqrt{x}$, $[0, 4]$

▪ ▪ ▪ ▪ ▪ ▪ ▪ ▪ ▪ ▪ ▪ ▪ ▪ ▪ ▪

21. The table gives values of a continuous function. Use the Midpoint Rule to estimate the average value of f on $[20, 50]$.

x	20	25	30	35	40	45	50
$f(x)$	42	38	31	29	35	48	60

22. The velocity graph of an accelerating car is shown.
(a) Estimate the average velocity of the car during the first 12 seconds.
(b) At what time was the instantaneous velocity equal to the average velocity?

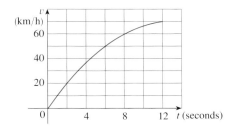

23. If $F(x) = \int_1^x f(t)\,dt$, where $f(t) = \int_1^{t^2} \dfrac{\sqrt{1+u^4}}{u}\,du$,

find $F''(2)$.

24. Find the interval on which the curve

$$y = \int_0^x \frac{1}{1+t+t^2}\,dt$$

is concave upward.

25–26 ■ Let $g(x) = \int_0^x f(t)\,dt$, where f is the function whose graph is shown.
(a) At what values of x do the local maximum and minimum values of g occur?
(b) Where does g attain its absolute maximum value?
(c) On what intervals is g concave downward?
(d) Sketch the graph of g.

25.

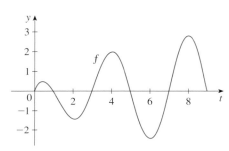

26.

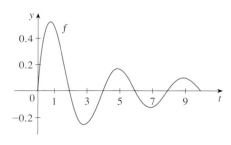

■ ■ ■ ■ ■ ■ ■ ■ ■ ■ ■ ■

27. If $f(1) = 12$, f' is continuous, and $\int_1^4 f'(x)\,dx = 17$, what is the value of $f(4)$?

28. The **error function**

$$\mathrm{erf}(x) = \frac{2}{\sqrt{\pi}} \int_0^x e^{-t^2}\,dt$$

is used in probability, statistics, and engineering.
(a) Show that $\int_a^b e^{-t^2}\,dt = \tfrac{1}{2}\sqrt{\pi}\,[\mathrm{erf}(b) - \mathrm{erf}(a)]$.
(b) Show that the function $y = e^{x^2}\mathrm{erf}(x)$ satisfies the differential equation $y' = 2xy + 2/\sqrt{\pi}$.

29. The Fresnel function S was defined in Example 4 and graphed in Figures 7 and 8.
(a) At what values of x does this function have local maximum values?

(b) On what intervals is the function concave upward?
(CAS) (c) Use a graph to solve the following equation correct to two decimal places:

$$\int_0^x \sin(\pi t^2/2)\,dt = 0.2$$

(CAS) 30. The **sine integral function**

$$\mathrm{Si}(x) = \int_0^x \frac{\sin t}{t}\,dt$$

is important in electrical engineering. [The integrand $f(t) = (\sin t)/t$ is not defined when $t = 0$, but we know that its limit is 1 when $t \to 0$. So we define $f(0) = 1$ and this makes f a continuous function everywhere.]
(a) Draw the graph of Si.
(b) At what values of x does this function have local maximum values?
(c) Find the coordinates of the first inflection point to the right of the origin.
(d) Does this function have horizontal asymptotes?
(e) Solve the following equation correct to one decimal place:

$$\int_0^x \frac{\sin t}{t}\,dt = 1$$

31. Find a function f and a number a such that

$$6 + \int_a^x \frac{f(t)}{t^2}\,dt = 2\sqrt{x}$$

for all $x > 0$.

32. A high-tech company purchases a new computing system whose initial value is V. The system will depreciate at the rate $f = f(t)$ and will accumulate maintenance costs at the rate $g = g(t)$, where t is the time measured in months. The company wants to determine the optimal time to replace the system.
(a) Let

$$C(t) = \frac{1}{t} \int_0^t [f(s) + g(s)]\,ds$$

Show that the critical numbers of C occur at the numbers t where $C(t) = f(t) + g(t)$.
(b) Suppose that

$$f(t) = \begin{cases} \dfrac{V}{15} - \dfrac{V}{450}\,t & \text{if } 0 < t \le 30 \\[2mm] 0 & \text{if } t > 30 \end{cases}$$

and $\qquad g(t) = \dfrac{Vt^2}{12{,}900} \qquad t > 0$

Determine the length of time T for the total depreciation $D(t) = \int_0^t f(s)\,ds$ to equal the initial value V.

(c) Determine the absolute minimum of C on $(0, T]$.

(d) Sketch the graphs of C and $f + g$ in the same coordinate system, and verify the result in part (a) in this case.

33. A manufacturing company owns a major piece of equipment that depreciates at the (continuous) rate $f = f(t)$, where t is the time measured in months since its last overhaul. Because a fixed cost A is incurred each time the machine is overhauled, the company wants to determine the optimal time T (in months) between overhauls.

(a) Explain why $\int_0^t f(s)\,ds$ represents the loss in value of the machine over the period of time t since the last overhaul.

(b) Let $C = C(t)$ be given by

$$C(t) = \frac{1}{t}\left[A + \int_0^t f(s)\,ds\right]$$

What does C represent and why would the company want to minimize C?

(c) Show that C has a minimum value at the numbers $t = T$ where $C(T) = f(T)$.

5.5 THE SUBSTITUTION RULE

Because of the Fundamental Theorem, it's important to be able to find antiderivatives. But our antidifferentiation formulas don't tell us how to evaluate integrals such as

$$\boxed{1} \qquad \int 2x\sqrt{1 + x^2}\,dx$$

To evaluate this integral our strategy is to simplify the integral by changing from the variable x to a new variable u. Suppose that we let u be the quantity under the root sign in (1), $u = 1 + x^2$. Then the differential of u is $du = 2x\,dx$. Notice that if the dx in the notation for an integral were to be interpreted as a differential, then the differential $2x\,dx$ would occur in (1) and, so, formally, without justifying our calculation, we could write

■ Differentials were defined in Section 2.8. If $u = f(x)$, then
$$du = f'(x)\,dx$$

$$\boxed{2} \qquad \int 2x\sqrt{1 + x^2}\,dx = \int \sqrt{1 + x^2}\,2x\,dx = \int \sqrt{u}\,du$$

$$= \tfrac{2}{3}u^{3/2} + C = \tfrac{2}{3}(x^2 + 1)^{3/2} + C$$

But now we can check that we have the correct answer by using the Chain Rule to differentiate the final function of Equation 2:

$$\frac{d}{dx}\left[\tfrac{2}{3}(x^2 + 1)^{3/2} + C\right] = \tfrac{2}{3}\cdot\tfrac{3}{2}(x^2 + 1)^{1/2}\cdot 2x = 2x\sqrt{x^2 + 1}$$

In general, this method works whenever we have an integral that we can write in the form $\int f(g(x))g'(x)\,dx$. Observe that if $F' = f$, then

$$\boxed{3} \qquad \int F'(g(x))g'(x)\,dx = F(g(x)) + C$$

because, by the Chain Rule,

$$\frac{d}{dx}[F(g(x))] = F'(g(x))g'(x)$$

If we make the "change of variable" or "substitution" $u = g(x)$, then from Equation 3 we have

$$\int F'(g(x))g'(x)\,dx = F(g(x)) + C = F(u) + C = \int F'(u)\,du$$

or, writing $F' = f$, we get

$$\int f(g(x))g'(x)\,dx = \int f(u)\,du$$

Thus we have proved the following rule.

---

4 THE SUBSTITUTION RULE If $u = g(x)$ is a differentiable function whose range is an interval I and f is continuous on I, then

$$\int f(g(x))g'(x)\,dx = \int f(u)\,du$$

Notice that the Substitution Rule for integration was proved using the Chain Rule for differentiation. Notice also that if $u = g(x)$, then $du = g'(x)\,dx$, so a way to remember the Substitution Rule is to think of dx and du in (4) as differentials.

Thus the Substitution Rule says: **It is permissible to operate with dx and du after integral signs as if they were differentials.**

EXAMPLE 1 Find $\int x^3 \cos(x^4 + 2)\,dx$.

SOLUTION We make the substitution $u = x^4 + 2$ because its differential is $du = 4x^3\,dx$, which, apart from the constant factor 4, occurs in the integral. Thus, using $x^3\,dx = \frac{1}{4}\,du$ and the Substitution Rule, we have

$$\int x^3 \cos(x^4 + 2)\,dx = \int \cos u \cdot \tfrac{1}{4}\,du = \tfrac{1}{4}\int \cos u\,du$$

$$= \tfrac{1}{4}\sin u + C$$

■ Check the answer by differentiating it.

$$= \tfrac{1}{4}\sin(x^4 + 2) + C$$

Notice that at the final stage we had to return to the original variable x. ■

The idea behind the Substitution Rule is to replace a relatively complicated integral by a simpler integral. This is accomplished by changing from the original variable x to a new variable u that is a function of x. Thus in Example 1 we replaced the integral $\int x^3 \cos(x^4 + 2)\,dx$ by the simpler integral $\frac{1}{4}\int \cos u\,du$.

The main challenge in using the Substitution Rule is to think of an appropriate substitution. You should try to choose u to be some function in the integrand whose differential also occurs (except for a constant factor). This was the case in Example 1. If that is not possible, try choosing u to be some complicated part of the integrand (perhaps the inner function in a composite function). Finding the right substitution is a bit of an art. It's not unusual to guess wrong; if your first guess doesn't work, try another substitution.

EXAMPLE 2 Evaluate $\int \sqrt{2x + 1}\, dx$.

SOLUTION 1 Let $u = 2x + 1$. Then $du = 2\, dx$, so $dx = \frac{1}{2}\, du$. Thus the Substitution Rule gives

$$\int \sqrt{2x + 1}\, dx = \int \sqrt{u} \cdot \tfrac{1}{2}\, du = \tfrac{1}{2} \int u^{1/2}\, du$$

$$= \frac{1}{2} \cdot \frac{u^{3/2}}{3/2} + C = \tfrac{1}{3} u^{3/2} + C$$

$$= \tfrac{1}{3}(2x + 1)^{3/2} + C$$

SOLUTION 2 Another possible substitution is $u = \sqrt{2x + 1}$. Then

$$du = \frac{dx}{\sqrt{2x + 1}} \qquad \text{so} \qquad dx = \sqrt{2x + 1}\, du = u\, du$$

(Or observe that $u^2 = 2x + 1$, so $2u\, du = 2\, dx$.) Therefore

$$\int \sqrt{2x + 1}\, dx = \int u \cdot u\, du = \int u^2\, du$$

$$= \frac{u^3}{3} + C = \tfrac{1}{3}(2x + 1)^{3/2} + C \qquad ▪$$

▼ EXAMPLE 3 Find $\displaystyle\int \frac{x}{\sqrt{1 - 4x^2}}\, dx$.

SOLUTION Let $u = 1 - 4x^2$. Then $du = -8x\, dx$, so $x\, dx = -\tfrac{1}{8}\, du$ and

$$\int \frac{x}{\sqrt{1 - 4x^2}}\, dx = -\tfrac{1}{8} \int \frac{1}{\sqrt{u}}\, du = -\tfrac{1}{8} \int u^{-1/2}\, du$$

$$= -\tfrac{1}{8}\left(2\sqrt{u}\right) + C = -\tfrac{1}{4}\sqrt{1 - 4x^2} + C \qquad ▪$$

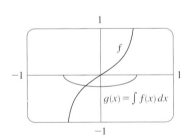

FIGURE 1

$$f(x) = \frac{x}{\sqrt{1 - 4x^2}}$$

$$g(x) = \int f(x)\, dx = -\tfrac{1}{4}\sqrt{1 - 4x^2}$$

The answer to Example 3 could be checked by differentiation, but instead let's check it with a graph. In Figure 1 we have used a computer to graph both the integrand $f(x) = x/\sqrt{1 - 4x^2}$ and its indefinite integral $g(x) = -\tfrac{1}{4}\sqrt{1 - 4x^2}$ (we take the case $C = 0$). Notice that $g(x)$ decreases when $f(x)$ is negative, increases when $f(x)$ is positive, and has its minimum value when $f(x) = 0$. So it seems reasonable, from the graphical evidence, that g is an antiderivative of f.

EXAMPLE 4 Calculate $\int e^{5x}\, dx$.

SOLUTION If we let $u = 5x$, then $du = 5\, dx$, so $dx = \tfrac{1}{5}\, du$. Therefore

$$\int e^{5x}\, dx = \tfrac{1}{5} \int e^{u}\, du = \tfrac{1}{5} e^{u} + C = \tfrac{1}{5} e^{5x} + C \qquad ▪$$

▼ EXAMPLE 5 Calculate $\int \tan x \, dx$.

SOLUTION First we write tangent in terms of sine and cosine:

$$\int \tan x \, dx = \int \frac{\sin x}{\cos x} \, dx$$

This suggests that we should substitute $u = \cos x$, since then $du = -\sin x \, dx$ and so $\sin x \, dx = -du$:

$$\int \tan x \, dx = \int \frac{\sin x}{\cos x} \, dx = -\int \frac{1}{u} \, du$$

$$= -\ln|u| + C = -\ln|\cos x| + C \qquad \blacksquare$$

Since $-\ln|\cos x| = \ln(|\cos x|^{-1}) = \ln(1/|\cos x|) = \ln|\sec x|$, the result of Example 5 can also be written as

5

$$\boxed{\int \tan x \, dx = \ln|\sec x| + C}$$

DEFINITE INTEGRALS

When evaluating a *definite* integral by substitution, two methods are possible. One method is to evaluate the indefinite integral first and then use the Evaluation Theorem. For instance, using the result of Example 2, we have

$$\int_0^4 \sqrt{2x+1} \, dx = \int \sqrt{2x+1} \, dx\Big]_0^4 = \tfrac{1}{3}(2x+1)^{3/2}\Big]_0^4$$

$$= \tfrac{1}{3}(9)^{3/2} - \tfrac{1}{3}(1)^{3/2} = \tfrac{1}{3}(27-1) = \tfrac{26}{3}$$

Another method, which is usually preferable, is to change the limits of integration when the variable is changed.

▪ This rule says that when using a substitution in a definite integral, we must put everything in terms of the new variable u, not only x and dx but also the limits of integration. The new limits of integration are the values of u that correspond to $x = a$ and $x = b$.

6 **THE SUBSTITUTION RULE FOR DEFINITE INTEGRALS** If g' is continuous on $[a, b]$ and f is continuous on the range of $u = g(x)$, then

$$\int_a^b f(g(x))g'(x) \, dx = \int_{g(a)}^{g(b)} f(u) \, du$$

PROOF Let F be an antiderivative of f. Then, by (3), $F(g(x))$ is an antiderivative of $f(g(x))g'(x)$ and so, by the Evaluation Theorem, we have

$$\int_a^b f(g(x))g'(x) \, dx = F(g(x))\Big]_a^b = F(g(b)) - F(g(a))$$

But, applying the Evaluation Theorem a second time, we also have

$$\int_{g(a)}^{g(b)} f(u) \, du = F(u)\Big]_{g(a)}^{g(b)} = F(g(b)) - F(g(a)) \qquad \square$$

■ The integral given in Example 6 is an abbreviation for

$$\int_1^2 \frac{1}{(3 - 5x)^2}\, dx$$

EXAMPLE 6 Evaluate $\displaystyle\int_1^2 \frac{dx}{(3 - 5x)^2}$.

SOLUTION Let $u = 3 - 5x$. Then $du = -5\, dx$, so $dx = -\frac{1}{5}\, du$. To find the new limits of integration we note that

when $x = 1$, $u = 3 - 5(1) = -2$ and when $x = 2$, $u = 3 - 5(2) = -7$

Therefore

$$\int_1^2 \frac{dx}{(3 - 5x)^2} = -\frac{1}{5}\int_{-2}^{-7} \frac{du}{u^2} = -\frac{1}{5}\left[-\frac{1}{u} \right]_{-2}^{-7}$$

$$= \frac{1}{5u}\bigg]_{-2}^{-7} = \frac{1}{5}\left(-\frac{1}{7} + \frac{1}{2} \right) = \frac{1}{14}$$

Observe that when using (6) we do not return to the variable x after integrating. We simply evaluate the expression in u between the appropriate values of u.   ■

■ Since the function $f(x) = (\ln x)/x$ in Example 7 is positive for $x > 1$, the integral represents the area of the shaded region in Figure 2.

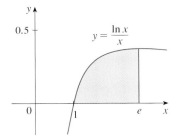

FIGURE 2

▼ EXAMPLE 7 Calculate $\displaystyle\int_1^e \frac{\ln x}{x}\, dx$.

SOLUTION We let $u = \ln x$ because its differential $du = dx/x$ occurs in the integral. When $x = 1$, $u = \ln 1 = 0$; when $x = e$, $u = \ln e = 1$. Thus

$$\int_1^e \frac{\ln x}{x}\, dx = \int_0^1 u\, du = \frac{u^2}{2}\bigg]_0^1 = \frac{1}{2}$$ ■

SYMMETRY

The next theorem uses the Substitution Rule for Definite Integrals (6) to simplify the calculation of integrals of functions that possess symmetry properties.

> **7** **INTEGRALS OF SYMMETRIC FUNCTIONS** Suppose f is continuous on $[-a, a]$.
> (a) If f is even $[f(-x) = f(x)]$, then $\int_{-a}^{a} f(x)\, dx = 2 \int_0^a f(x)\, dx$.
> (b) If f is odd $[f(-x) = -f(x)]$, then $\int_{-a}^{a} f(x)\, dx = 0$.

PROOF We split the integral in two:

$$\boxed{8} \quad \int_{-a}^{a} f(x)\, dx = \int_{-a}^{0} f(x)\, dx + \int_0^a f(x)\, dx = -\int_0^{-a} f(x)\, dx + \int_0^a f(x)\, dx$$

In the first integral on the far right side we make the substitution $u = -x$. Then $du = -dx$ and when $x = -a$, $u = a$. Therefore

$$-\int_0^{-a} f(x)\, dx = -\int_0^a f(-u)\, (-du) = \int_0^a f(-u)\, du$$

and so Equation 8 becomes

$$9 \qquad \int_{-a}^{a} f(x)\,dx = \int_{0}^{a} f(-u)\,du + \int_{0}^{a} f(x)\,dx$$

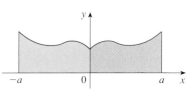

(a) f even, $\int_{-a}^{a} f(x)\,dx = 2\int_{0}^{a} f(x)\,dx$

(a) If f is even, then $f(-u) = f(u)$ so Equation 9 gives

$$\int_{-a}^{a} f(x)\,dx = \int_{0}^{a} f(u)\,du + \int_{0}^{a} f(x)\,dx = 2\int_{0}^{a} f(x)\,dx$$

(b) If f is odd, then $f(-u) = -f(u)$ and so Equation 9 gives

$$\int_{-a}^{a} f(x)\,dx = -\int_{0}^{a} f(u)\,du + \int_{0}^{a} f(x)\,dx = 0$$

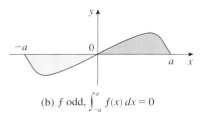

(b) f odd, $\int_{-a}^{a} f(x)\,dx = 0$

FIGURE 3

Theorem 7 is illustrated by Figure 3. For the case where f is positive and even, part (a) says that the area under $y = f(x)$ from $-a$ to a is twice the area from 0 to a because of symmetry. Recall that an integral $\int_{a}^{b} f(x)\,dx$ can be expressed as the area above the x-axis and below $y = f(x)$ minus the area below the axis and above the curve. Thus part (b) says the integral is 0 because the areas cancel.

▼ EXAMPLE 8 Since $f(x) = x^6 + 1$ satisfies $f(-x) = f(x)$, it is even and so

$$\int_{-2}^{2} (x^6 + 1)\,dx = 2\int_{0}^{2} (x^6 + 1)\,dx$$

$$= 2\left[\tfrac{1}{7}x^7 + x\right]_{0}^{2} = 2\left(\tfrac{128}{7} + 2\right) = \tfrac{284}{7} \qquad ■$$

EXAMPLE 9 Since $f(x) = (\tan x)/(1 + x^2 + x^4)$ satisfies $f(-x) = -f(x)$, it is odd and so

$$\int_{-1}^{1} \frac{\tan x}{1 + x^2 + x^4}\,dx = 0 \qquad ■$$

5.5 EXERCISES

1–6 ■ Evaluate the integral by making the given substitution.

1. $\displaystyle\int \cos 3x\,dx, \quad u = 3x$

2. $\displaystyle\int x(4 + x^2)^{10}\,dx, \quad u = 4 + x^2$

3. $\displaystyle\int x^2\sqrt{x^3 + 1}\,dx, \quad u = x^3 + 1$

4. $\displaystyle\int \frac{\sin\sqrt{x}}{\sqrt{x}}\,dx, \quad u = \sqrt{x}$

5. $\displaystyle\int \frac{4}{(1 + 2x)^3}\,dx, \quad u = 1 + 2x$

6. $\displaystyle\int e^{\sin\theta}\cos\theta\,d\theta, \quad u = \sin\theta$

■ ■ ■ ■ ■ ■ ■ ■ ■ ■ ■ ■

7–34 ■ Evaluate the indefinite integral.

7. $\displaystyle\int 2x(x^2 + 3)^4\,dx$

8. $\displaystyle\int x^2(x^3 + 5)^9\,dx$

9. $\displaystyle\int (3x - 2)^{20}\,dx$

10. $\displaystyle\int xe^{x^2}\,dx$

11. $\displaystyle\int \frac{(\ln x)^2}{x}\,dx$

12. $\displaystyle\int (2 - x)^6\,dx$

13. $\displaystyle\int \frac{dx}{5 - 3x}$

14. $\displaystyle\int \frac{x}{(x^2 + 1)^2}\, dx$

15. $\displaystyle\int \frac{a + bx^2}{\sqrt{3ax + bx^3}}\, dx$

16. $\displaystyle\int \frac{1}{(5t + 4)^{2.7}}\, dt$

17. $\displaystyle\int \sin \pi t\, dt$

18. $\displaystyle\int y^3 \sqrt{2y^4 - 1}\, dy$

19. $\displaystyle\int e^x \sqrt{1 + e^x}\, dx$

20. $\displaystyle\int \sec 2\theta \tan 2\theta\, d\theta$

21. $\displaystyle\int \cos \theta \, \sin^6\theta\, d\theta$

22. $\displaystyle\int \frac{x}{x^2 + 1}\, dx$

23. $\displaystyle\int \sqrt{\cot x}\, \csc^2 x\, dx$

24. $\displaystyle\int \frac{\tan^{-1} x}{1 + x^2}\, dx$

25. $\displaystyle\int \frac{dx}{\sqrt{1 - x^2}\, \sin^{-1} x}$

26. $\displaystyle\int \frac{\cos(\pi/x)}{x^2}\, dx$

27. $\displaystyle\int \sec^3 x \tan x\, dx$

28. $\displaystyle\int \sin t \, \sec^2(\cos t)\, dt$

29. $\displaystyle\int \frac{e^x + 1}{e^x}\, dx$

30. $\displaystyle\int \frac{e^x}{e^x + 1}\, dx$

31. $\displaystyle\int \frac{\sin 2x}{1 + \cos^2 x}\, dx$

32. $\displaystyle\int \frac{\sin x}{1 + \cos^2 x}\, dx$

33. $\displaystyle\int \frac{1 + x}{1 + x^2}\, dx$

34. $\displaystyle\int \frac{x}{1 + x^4}\, dx$

▪ ▪ ▪ ▪ ▪ ▪ ▪ ▪ ▪ ▪ ▪ ▪

35–50 ▪ Evaluate the definite integral.

35. $\displaystyle\int_0^2 (x - 1)^{25}\, dx$

36. $\displaystyle\int_0^7 \sqrt{4 + 3x}\, dx$

37. $\displaystyle\int_0^1 x^2(1 + 2x^3)^5\, dx$

38. $\displaystyle\int_0^{\sqrt{\pi}} x \cos(x^2)\, dx$

39. $\displaystyle\int_0^{\pi} \sec^2(t/4)\, dt$

40. $\displaystyle\int_{1/6}^{1/2} \csc \pi t \, \cot \pi t\, dt$

41. $\displaystyle\int_1^4 \frac{e^{\sqrt{x}}}{\sqrt{x}}\, dx$

42. $\displaystyle\int_0^{\pi/2} \cos x \sin(\sin x)\, dx$

43. $\displaystyle\int_1^2 x\sqrt{x - 1}\, dx$

44. $\displaystyle\int_{-\pi/2}^{\pi/2} \frac{x^2 \sin x}{1 + x^6}\, dx$

45. $\displaystyle\int_0^1 \frac{e^z + 1}{e^z + z}\, dz$

46. $\displaystyle\int_0^4 \frac{x}{\sqrt{1 + 2x}}\, dx$

47. $\displaystyle\int_{-\pi/6}^{\pi/6} \tan^3\theta\, d\theta$

48. $\displaystyle\int_0^a x\sqrt{a^2 - x^2}\, dx$

49. $\displaystyle\int_e^{e^4} \frac{dx}{x\sqrt{\ln x}}$

50. $\displaystyle\int_0^{1/2} \frac{\sin^{-1} x}{\sqrt{1 - x^2}}\, dx$

▪ ▪ ▪ ▪ ▪ ▪ ▪ ▪ ▪ ▪ ▪ ▪

51–54 ▪ Find the average value of the function on the given interval.

51. $f(t) = te^{-t^2}$, $[0, 5]$

52. $g(x) = x^2\sqrt{1 + x^3}$, $[0, 2]$

53. $h(x) = \cos^4 x \sin x$, $[0, \pi]$

54. $h(r) = 3/(1 + r)^2$, $[1, 6]$

▪ ▪ ▪ ▪ ▪ ▪ ▪ ▪ ▪ ▪ ▪ ▪

55. Evaluate $\int_{-2}^{2} (x + 3)\sqrt{4 - x^2}\, dx$ by writing it as a sum of two integrals and interpreting one of those integrals in terms of an area.

56. Evaluate $\int_0^1 x\sqrt{1 - x^4}\, dx$ by making a substitution and interpreting the resulting integral in terms of an area.

57. Which of the following areas are equal? Why?

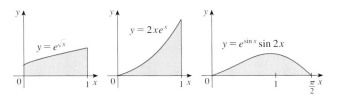

58. A bacteria population starts with 400 bacteria and grows at a rate of $r(t) = (450.268)e^{1.12567t}$ bacteria per hour. How many bacteria will there be after three hours?

59. Breathing is cyclic and a full respiratory cycle from the beginning of inhalation to the end of exhalation takes about 5 s. The maximum rate of air flow into the lungs is about 0.5 L/s. This explains, in part, why the function $f(t) = \frac{1}{2} \sin(2\pi t/5)$ has often been used to model the rate of air flow into the lungs. Use this model to find the volume of inhaled air in the lungs at time t.

60. Alabama Instruments Company has set up a production line to manufacture a new calculator. The rate of production of these calculators after t weeks is

$$\frac{dx}{dt} = 5000\left(1 - \frac{100}{(t + 10)^2}\right) \text{ calculators/week}$$

(Notice that production approaches 5000 per week as time goes on, but the initial production is lower because of the workers' unfamiliarity with the new techniques.) Find the number of calculators produced from the beginning of the third week to the end of the fourth week.

61. If f is continuous and $\int_0^4 f(x)\, dx = 10$, find $\int_0^2 f(2x)\, dx$.

62. If f is continuous and $\int_0^9 f(x)\, dx = 4$, find $\int_0^3 xf(x^2)\, dx$.

63. If f is continuous on $\mathbb{R}$, prove that

$$\int_a^b f(-x)\, dx = \int_{-b}^{-a} f(x)\, dx$$

For the case where $f(x) \geqslant 0$ and $0 < a < b$, draw a diagram to interpret this equation geometrically as an equality of areas.

64. If f is continuous on $\mathbb{R}$, prove that

$$\int_a^b f(x + c)\, dx = \int_{a+c}^{b+c} f(x)\, dx$$

For the case where $f(x) \geqslant 0$, draw a diagram to interpret this equation geometrically as an equality of areas.

65. If a and b are positive numbers, show that

$$\int_0^1 x^a(1 - x)^b\, dx = \int_0^1 x^b(1 - x)^a\, dx$$

---

5 | REVIEW

1. (a) Write an expression for a Riemann sum of a function f. Explain the meaning of the notation that you use.
(b) If $f(x) \geqslant 0$, what is the geometric interpretation of a Riemann sum? Illustrate with a diagram.
(c) If $f(x)$ takes on both positive and negative values, what is the geometric interpretation of a Riemann sum? Illustrate with a diagram.

2. (a) Write the definition of the definite integral of f from a to b. How does the definition simplify if you know that f is continuous and you use equal subintervals?
(b) What is the geometric interpretation of $\int_a^b f(x)\, dx$ if $f(x) \geqslant 0$?
(c) What is the geometric interpretation of $\int_a^b f(x)\, dx$ if $f(x)$ takes on both positive and negative values? Illustrate with a diagram.

3. State the Midpoint Rule.

4. (a) State the Evaluation Theorem.
(b) State the Net Change Theorem.
(c) If $r(t)$ is the rate at which water flows into a reservoir, what does $\int_{t_1}^{t_2} r(t)\, dt$ represent?

5. (a) Explain the meaning of the indefinite integral $\int f(x)\, dx$.
(b) What is the connection between the definite integral $\int_a^b f(x)\, dx$ and the indefinite integral $\int f(x)\, dx$?

6. State both parts of the Fundamental Theorem of Calculus.

7. Suppose a particle moves back and forth along a straight line with velocity $v(t)$, measured in feet per second, and acceleration $a(t)$.
(a) What is the meaning of $\int_{60}^{120} v(t)\, dt$?
(b) What is the meaning of $\int_{60}^{120} |v(t)|\, dt$?
(c) What is the meaning of $\int_{60}^{120} a(t)\, dt$?

8. (a) What is the average value of a function f on an interval $[a, b]$?
(b) What does the Mean Value Theorem for Integrals say? What is its geometric interpretation?

9. Explain exactly what is meant by the statement that "differentiation and integration are inverse processes."

10. State the Substitution Rule. In practice, how do you use it?

Determine whether the statement is true or false. If it is true, explain why. If it is false, explain why or give an example that disproves the statement.

1. If f and g are continuous on $[a, b]$, then

$$\int_a^b [f(x) + g(x)]\, dx = \int_a^b f(x)\, dx + \int_a^b g(x)\, dx$$

2. If f and g are continuous on $[a, b]$, then

$$\int_a^b [f(x)g(x)]\, dx = \left(\int_a^b f(x)\, dx\right)\left(\int_a^b g(x)\, dx\right)$$

3. If f is continuous on $[a, b]$, then

$$\int_a^b 5f(x)\, dx = 5 \int_a^b f(x)\, dx$$

4. If f is continuous on $[a, b]$, then

$$\int_a^b xf(x)\,dx = x \int_a^b f(x)\,dx$$

5. If f is continuous on $[a, b]$ and $f(x) \geqslant 0$, then

$$\int_a^b \sqrt{f(x)}\,dx = \sqrt{\int_a^b f(x)\,dx}$$

6. If f' is continuous on $[1, 3]$, then $\int_1^3 f'(v)\,dv = f(3) - f(1)$.

7. If f and g are continuous and $f(x) \geqslant g(x)$ for $a \leqslant x \leqslant b$, then

$$\int_a^b f(x)\,dx \geqslant \int_a^b g(x)\,dx$$

8. If f and g are differentiable and $f(x) \geqslant g(x)$ for $a < x < b$, then $f'(x) \geqslant g'(x)$ for $a < x < b$.

9. $\int_{-1}^1 \left(x^5 - 6x^9 + \dfrac{\sin x}{(1 + x^4)^2} \right) dx = 0$

10. $\int_{-5}^5 (ax^2 + bx + c)\,dx = 2 \int_0^5 (ax^2 + c)\,dx$

11. $\int_{-2}^1 \dfrac{1}{x^4}\,dx = -\dfrac{3}{8}$

12. $\int_0^2 (x - x^3)\,dx$ represents the area under the curve $y = x - x^3$ from 0 to 2.

13. All continuous functions have antiderivatives.

EXERCISES

---

1. Use the given graph of f to find the Riemann sum with six subintervals. Take the sample points to be (a) left endpoints and (b) midpoints. In each case draw a diagram and explain what the Riemann sum represents.

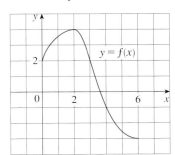

2. (a) Evaluate the Riemann sum for

$$f(x) = x^2 - x \qquad 0 \leqslant x \leqslant 2$$

with four subintervals, taking the sample points to be right endpoints. Explain, with the aid of a diagram, what the Riemann sum represents.

(b) Use the definition of a definite integral (with right end-points) to calculate the value of the integral

$$\int_0^2 (x^2 - x)\,dx$$

(c) Use the Fundamental Theorem to check your answer to part (b).

(d) Draw a diagram to explain the geometric meaning of the integral in part (b).

3. Evaluate

$$\int_0^1 \left(x + \sqrt{1 - x^2} \right) dx$$

by interpreting it in terms of areas.

4. Express

$$\lim_{n \to \infty} \sum_{i=1}^n \sin x_i\,\Delta x$$

as a definite integral on the interval $[0, \pi]$ and then evaluate the integral.

5. The following figure shows the graphs of f, f', and $\int_0^x f(t)\,dt$. Identify each graph, and explain your choices.

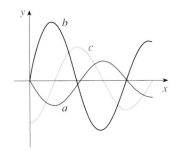

6. Evaluate:

(a) $\int_0^1 \dfrac{d}{dx} \left(e^{\arctan x} \right) dx$

(b) $\dfrac{d}{dx} \int_0^1 e^{\arctan x}\,dx$

(c) $\dfrac{d}{dx} \int_0^x e^{\arctan t}\,dt$

7–32 ■ Evaluate the integral, if it exists.

7. $\int_1^2 (8x^3 + 3x^2)\, dx$

8. $\int_0^T (x^4 - 8x + 7)\, dx$

9. $\int_0^1 (1 - x^9)\, dx$

10. $\int_0^1 (1 - x)^9\, dx$

11. $\int_1^9 \dfrac{\sqrt{u} - 2u^2}{u}\, du$

12. $\int_0^1 (\sqrt[4]{u} + 1)^2\, du$

13. $\int_0^1 y(y^2 + 1)^5\, dy$

14. $\int_0^2 y^2\sqrt{1 + y^3}\, dy$

15. $\int_0^1 v^2 \cos(v^3)\, dv$

16. $\int_0^1 \sin(3\pi t)\, dt$

17. $\int_0^1 e^{\pi t}\, dt$

18. $\int_{-1}^1 \dfrac{\sin x}{1 + x^2}\, dx$

19. $\int_2^4 \dfrac{1 + x - x^2}{x^2}\, dx$

20. $\int_1^2 \dfrac{1}{2 - 3x}\, dx$

21. $\int \dfrac{x + 2}{\sqrt{x^2 + 4x}}\, dx$

22. $\int \csc^2 3t\, dt$

23. $\int \sin \pi t \cos \pi t\, dt$

24. $\int \sin x \cos(\cos x)\, dx$

25. $\int \dfrac{e^{\sqrt{x}}}{\sqrt{x}}\, dx$

26. $\int \dfrac{\cos(\ln x)}{x}\, dx$

27. $\int \tan x \ln(\cos x)\, dx$

28. $\int \dfrac{x}{\sqrt{1 - x^4}}\, dx$

29. $\int \dfrac{x^3}{1 + x^4}\, dx$

30. $\int \sinh(1 + 4x)\, dx$

31. $\int \dfrac{\sec \theta \tan \theta}{1 + \sec \theta}\, d\theta$

32. $\int_0^{\pi/4} (1 + \tan t)^3 \sec^2 t\, dt$

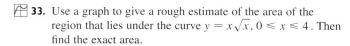

33. Use a graph to give a rough estimate of the area of the region that lies under the curve $y = x\sqrt{x}$, $0 \le x \le 4$. Then find the exact area.

34. Graph the function $f(x) = \cos^2 x \sin^3 x$ and use the graph to guess the value of the integral $\int_0^{2\pi} f(x)\, dx$. Then evaluate the integral to confirm your guess.

35–38 ■ Find the derivative of the function.

35. $F(x) = \int_1^x \sqrt{1 + t^4}\, dt$

36. $g(x) = \int_1^{\cos x} \sqrt[3]{1 - t^2}\, dt$

37. $y = \int_{\sqrt{x}}^x \dfrac{e^t}{t}\, dt$

38. $y = \int_{2x}^{3x+1} \sin(t^4)\, dt$

39. Use Property 8 of integrals to estimate the value of

$$\int_1^3 \sqrt{x^2 + 3}\, dx$$

40. Use the properties of integrals to verify that

$$0 \le \int_0^1 x^4 \cos x\, dx \le 0.2$$

41. Use the Midpoint Rule with $n = 5$ to approximate $\int_0^1 \sqrt{1 + x^3}\, dx$.

42. A particle moves along a line with velocity function $v(t) = t^2 - t$, where v is measured in meters per second. Find (a) the displacement and (b) the distance traveled by the particle during the time interval $[0, 5]$.

43. Let $r(t)$ be the rate at which the world's oil is consumed, where t is measured in years starting at $t = 0$ on January 1, 2000, and $r(t)$ is measured in barrels per year. What does $\int_0^3 r(t)\, dt$ represent?

44. A radar gun was used to record the speed of a runner at the times given in the table. Use the Midpoint Rule to estimate the distance the runner covered during those 5 seconds.

t (s)	v (m/s)	t (s)	v (m/s)
0	0	3.0	10.51
0.5	4.67	3.5	10.67
1.0	7.34	4.0	10.76
1.5	8.86	4.5	10.81
2.0	9.73	5.0	10.81
2.5	10.22		

45. A population of honeybees increased at a rate of $r(t)$ bees per week, where the graph of r is as shown. Use the Midpoint Rule with six subintervals to estimate the increase in the bee population during the first 24 weeks.

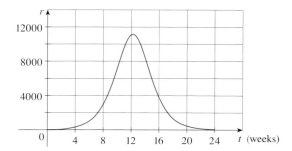

46. Find the average value of the function $f(x) = x^2\sqrt{1 + x^3}$ on the interval $[0, 2]$.

47. If f is a continuous function, what is the limit as $h \to 0$ of the average value of f on the interval $[x, x + h]$?

48. Let

$$f(x) = \begin{cases} -x - 1 & \text{if } -3 \leqslant x \leqslant 0 \\ -\sqrt{1 - x^2} & \text{if } 0 \leqslant x \leqslant 1 \end{cases}$$

Evaluate $\int_{-3}^{1} f(x)\,dx$ by interpreting the integral as a difference of areas.

49. Estimate the value of the number c such that the area under the curve $y = \sinh cx$ between $x = 0$ and $x = 1$ is equal to 1.

50. Suppose that the temperature in a long, thin rod placed along the x-axis is initially $C/(2a)$ if $|x| \leqslant a$ and 0 if $|x| > a$. It can be shown that if the heat diffusivity of the rod is k, then the temperature of the rod at the point x at time t is

$$T(x, t) = \frac{C}{a\sqrt{4\pi kt}} \int_0^a e^{-(x-u)^2/(4kt)}\,du$$

To find the temperature distribution that results from an initial hot spot concentrated at the origin, we need to compute

$$\lim_{a \to 0} T(x, t)$$

Use l'Hospital's Rule to find this limit.

51. If f is a continuous function such that

$$\int_0^x f(t)\,dt = xe^{2x} + \int_0^x e^{-t}f(t)\,dt$$

for all x, find an explicit formula for $f(x)$.

52. Find a function f and a value of the constant a such that

$$2\int_a^x f(t)\,dt = 2\sin x - 1$$

53. If f' is continuous on $[a, b]$, show that

$$2\int_a^b f(x)f'(x)\,dx = [f(b)]^2 - [f(a)]^2$$

54. Evaluate

$$\lim_{n \to \infty} \frac{1}{n}\left[\left(\frac{1}{n}\right)^9 + \left(\frac{2}{n}\right)^9 + \left(\frac{3}{n}\right)^9 + \cdots + \left(\frac{n}{n}\right)^9\right]$$

6 TECHNIQUES OF INTEGRATION

Because of the Fundamental Theorem of Calculus, we can integrate a function if we know an antiderivative, that is, an indefinite integral. We summarize here the most important integrals that we have learned so far.

$$\int x^n \, dx = \frac{x^{n+1}}{n+1} + C \quad (n \neq -1) \qquad\qquad \int \frac{1}{x} \, dx = \ln|x| + C$$

$$\int e^x \, dx = e^x + C \qquad\qquad\qquad\qquad \int a^x \, dx = \frac{a^x}{\ln a} + C$$

$$\int \sin x \, dx = -\cos x + C \qquad\qquad\qquad \int \cos x \, dx = \sin x + C$$

$$\int \sec^2 x \, dx = \tan x + C \qquad\qquad\qquad \int \csc^2 x \, dx = -\cot x + C$$

$$\int \sec x \tan x \, dx = \sec x + C \qquad\qquad \int \csc x \cot x \, dx = -\csc x + C$$

$$\int \sinh x \, dx = \cosh x + C \qquad\qquad\quad \int \cosh x \, dx = \sinh x + C$$

$$\int \tan x \, dx = \ln|\sec x| + C \qquad\qquad \int \cot x \, dx = \ln|\sin x| + C$$

$$\int \frac{1}{x^2 + a^2} \, dx = \frac{1}{a} \tan^{-1}\left(\frac{x}{a}\right) + C \qquad \int \frac{1}{\sqrt{a^2 - x^2}} \, dx = \sin^{-1}\left(\frac{x}{a}\right) + C$$

In this chapter we develop techniques for using these basic integration formulas to obtain indefinite integrals of more complicated functions. We learned the most important method of integration, the Substitution Rule, in Section 5.5. The other general technique, integration by parts, is presented in Section 6.1. Then we learn methods that are special to particular classes of functions such as trigonometric functions and rational functions.

6.1 | INTEGRATION BY PARTS

Every differentiation rule has a corresponding integration rule. For instance, the Substitution Rule for integration corresponds to the Chain Rule for differentiation. The rule that corresponds to the Product Rule for differentiation is called the rule for *integration by parts*.

The Product Rule states that if f and g are differentiable functions, then

$$\frac{d}{dx}[f(x)g(x)] = f(x)g'(x) + g(x)f'(x)$$

In the notation for indefinite integrals this equation becomes

$$\int [f(x)g'(x) + g(x)f'(x)] \, dx = f(x)g(x)$$

or

$$\int f(x)g'(x) \, dx + \int g(x)f'(x) \, dx = f(x)g(x)$$

We can rearrange this equation as

1

$$\int f(x)g'(x)\,dx = f(x)g(x) - \int g(x)f'(x)\,dx$$

Formula 1 is called the **formula for integration by parts**. It is perhaps easier to remember in the following notation. Let $u = f(x)$ and $v = g(x)$. Then the differentials are $du = f'(x)\,dx$ and $dv = g'(x)\,dx$, so, by the Substitution Rule, the formula for integration by parts becomes

2

$$\int u\,dv = uv - \int v\,du$$

EXAMPLE 1 Find $\int x \sin x\,dx$.

SOLUTION USING FORMULA 1 Suppose we choose $f(x) = x$ and $g'(x) = \sin x$. Then $f'(x) = 1$ and $g(x) = -\cos x$. (For g we can choose *any* antiderivative of g'.) Thus, using Formula 1, we have

$$\int x \sin x\,dx = f(x)g(x) - \int g(x)f'(x)\,dx$$

$$= x(-\cos x) - \int (-\cos x)\,dx$$

$$= -x \cos x + \int \cos x\,dx$$

$$= -x \cos x + \sin x + C$$

It's wise to check the answer by differentiating it. If we do so, we get $x \sin x$, as expected.

SOLUTION USING FORMULA 2 Let

$$u = x \qquad dv = \sin x\,dx$$

Then

$$du = dx \qquad v = -\cos x$$

■ It is helpful to use the pattern:
$$u = \square \qquad dv = \square$$
$$du = \square \qquad v = \square$$

and so

$$\int x \sin x\,dx = \int \overbrace{x}^{u}\,\overbrace{\sin x\,dx}^{dv} = \overbrace{x}^{u}\,\overbrace{(-\cos x)}^{v} - \int \overbrace{(-\cos x)}^{v}\,\overbrace{dx}^{du}$$

$$= -x \cos x + \int \cos x\,dx$$

$$= -x \cos x + \sin x + C$$

■

NOTE Our aim in using integration by parts is to obtain a simpler integral than the one we started with. Thus in Example 1 we started with $\int x \sin x\,dx$ and expressed it in terms of the simpler integral $\int \cos x\,dx$. If we had chosen $u = \sin x$ and $dv = x\,dx$, then $du = \cos x\, dx$ and $v = x^2/2$, so integration by parts gives

$$\int x \sin x\, dx = (\sin x)\frac{x^2}{2} - \frac{1}{2}\int x^2 \cos x\, dx$$

Although this is true, $\int x^2 \cos x\, dx$ is a more difficult integral than the one we started with. In general, when deciding on a choice for u and dv, we usually try to choose $u = f(x)$ to be a function that becomes simpler when differentiated (or at least not more complicated) as long as $dv = g'(x)\, dx$ can be readily integrated to give v.

V EXAMPLE 2 Evaluate $\int \ln x\, dx$.

SOLUTION Here we don't have much choice for u and dv. Let

$$u = \ln x \qquad dv = dx$$

Then

$$du = \frac{1}{x}\, dx \qquad v = x$$

Integrating by parts, we get

$$\int \ln x\, dx = x \ln x - \int x\, \frac{dx}{x}$$

- It's customary to write $\int 1\, dx$ as $\int dx$.

$$= x \ln x - \int dx$$

- Check the answer by differentiating it.

$$= x \ln x - x + C$$

Integration by parts is effective in this example because the derivative of the function $f(x) = \ln x$ is simpler than f. ▪

V EXAMPLE 3 Find $\int t^2 e^t\, dt$.

SOLUTION Notice that t^2 becomes simpler when differentiated (whereas e^t is unchanged when differentiated or integrated), so we choose

$$u = t^2 \qquad dv = e^t\, dt$$

Then

$$du = 2t\, dt \qquad v = e^t$$

Integration by parts gives

3
$$\int t^2 e^t\, dt = t^2 e^t - 2\int t e^t\, dt$$

The integral that we obtained, $\int t e^t\, dt$, is simpler than the original integral but is still not obvious. Therefore, we use integration by parts a second time, this time with $u = t$ and $dv = e^t\, dt$. Then $du = dt$, $v = e^t$, and

$$\int t e^t\, dt = t e^t - \int e^t\, dt$$

$$= t e^t - e^t + C$$

Putting this in Equation 3, we get

$$\int t^2 e^t \, dt = t^2 e^t - 2 \int t e^t \, dt$$

$$= t^2 e^t - 2(te^t - e^t + C)$$

$$= t^2 e^t - 2te^t + 2e^t + C_1 \qquad \text{where } C_1 = -2C \qquad ■$$

▼ EXAMPLE 4 Evaluate $\int e^x \sin x \, dx$.

▪ **www.stewartcalculus.com**
An easier method, using complex numbers, is given under *Additional Topics*. Click on *Complex Numbers* and see Exercise 50.

SOLUTION Neither e^x nor $\sin x$ becomes simpler when differentiated, but we try choosing $u = e^x$ and $dv = \sin x \, dx$ anyway. Then $du = e^x \, dx$ and $v = -\cos x$, so integration by parts gives

$$\boxed{4} \qquad \int e^x \sin x \, dx = -e^x \cos x + \int e^x \cos x \, dx$$

The integral that we have obtained, $\int e^x \cos x \, dx$, is no simpler than the original one, but at least it's no more difficult. Having had success in the preceding example integrating by parts twice, we persevere and integrate by parts again. This time we use $u = e^x$ and $dv = \cos x \, dx$. Then $du = e^x \, dx$, $v = \sin x$, and

$$\boxed{5} \qquad \int e^x \cos x \, dx = e^x \sin x - \int e^x \sin x \, dx$$

At first glance, it appears as if we have accomplished nothing because we have arrived at $\int e^x \sin x \, dx$, which is where we started. However, if we put the expression for $\int e^x \cos x \, dx$ from Equation 5 into Equation 4 we get

$$\int e^x \sin x \, dx = -e^x \cos x + e^x \sin x - \int e^x \sin x \, dx$$

This can be regarded as an equation to be solved for the unknown integral. Adding $\int e^x \sin x \, dx$ to both sides, we obtain

$$2 \int e^x \sin x \, dx = -e^x \cos x + e^x \sin x$$

Dividing by 2 and adding the constant of integration, we get

$$\int e^x \sin x \, dx = \tfrac{1}{2} e^x (\sin x - \cos x) + C \qquad ■$$

▪ Figure 1 illustrates Example 4 by showing the graphs of $f(x) = e^x \sin x$ and $F(x) = \frac{1}{2} e^x (\sin x - \cos x)$. As a visual check on our work, notice that $f(x) = 0$ when F has a maximum or minimum.

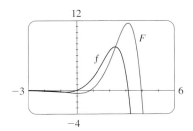

FIGURE 1

If we combine the formula for integration by parts with the Evaluation Theorem, we can evaluate definite integrals by parts. Evaluating both sides of Formula 1 between a and b, assuming f' and g' are continuous, and using the Evaluation Theorem, we obtain

$$\boxed{6} \qquad \int_a^b f(x) g'(x) \, dx = f(x) g(x) \Big]_a^b - \int_a^b g(x) f'(x) \, dx$$

EXAMPLE 5 Calculate $\int_0^1 \tan^{-1}x\,dx$.

SOLUTION Let

$$u = \tan^{-1}x \qquad\qquad dv = dx$$

Then

$$du = \frac{dx}{1+x^2} \qquad\qquad v = x$$

So Formula 6 gives

$$\int_0^1 \tan^{-1}x\,dx = x\tan^{-1}x\Big]_0^1 - \int_0^1 \frac{x}{1+x^2}\,dx$$

$$= 1\cdot\tan^{-1}1 - 0\cdot\tan^{-1}0 - \int_0^1 \frac{x}{1+x^2}\,dx$$

$$= \frac{\pi}{4} - \int_0^1 \frac{x}{1+x^2}\,dx$$

■ Since $\tan^{-1}x \geq 0$ for $x \geq 0$, the integral in Example 5 can be interpreted as the area of the region shown in Figure 2.

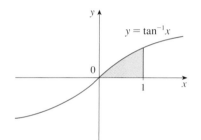

$y = \tan^{-1}x$

FIGURE 2

To evaluate this integral we use the substitution $t = 1 + x^2$ (since u has another meaning in this example). Then $dt = 2x\,dx$, so $x\,dx = \frac{1}{2}\,dt$. When $x = 0$, $t = 1$; when $x = 1$, $t = 2$; so

$$\int_0^1 \frac{x}{1+x^2}\,dx = \frac{1}{2}\int_1^2 \frac{dt}{t} = \frac{1}{2}\ln|t|\Big]_1^2$$

$$= \frac{1}{2}(\ln 2 - \ln 1) = \frac{1}{2}\ln 2$$

Therefore

$$\int_0^1 \tan^{-1}x\,dx = \frac{\pi}{4} - \int_0^1 \frac{x}{1+x^2}\,dx = \frac{\pi}{4} - \frac{\ln 2}{2} \qquad ■$$

EXAMPLE 6 Prove the reduction formula

■ Equation 7 is called a *reduction formula* because the exponent n has been *reduced* to $n - 1$ and $n - 2$.

7 $$\int \sin^n x\,dx = -\frac{1}{n}\cos x\,\sin^{n-1}x + \frac{n-1}{n}\int \sin^{n-2}x\,dx$$

where $n \geq 2$ is an integer.

SOLUTION Let

$$u = \sin^{n-1}x \qquad\qquad dv = \sin x\,dx$$

Then

$$du = (n-1)\sin^{n-2}x\,\cos x\,dx \qquad\qquad v = -\cos x$$

so integration by parts gives

$$\int \sin^n x\,dx = -\cos x\,\sin^{n-1}x + (n-1)\int \sin^{n-2}x\,\cos^2 x\,dx$$

Since $\cos^2 x = 1 - \sin^2 x$, we have

$$\int \sin^n x\,dx = -\cos x\,\sin^{n-1}x + (n-1)\int \sin^{n-2}x\,dx - (n-1)\int \sin^n x\,dx$$

As in Example 4, we solve this equation for the desired integral by taking the last term on the right side to the left side. Thus we have

$$n \int \sin^n x \, dx = -\cos x \sin^{n-1} x + (n-1) \int \sin^{n-2} x \, dx$$

or

$$\int \sin^n x \, dx = -\frac{1}{n} \cos x \sin^{n-1} x + \frac{n-1}{n} \int \sin^{n-2} x \, dx \qquad ▪$$

The reduction formula (7) is useful because by using it repeatedly we could eventually express $\int \sin^n x \, dx$ in terms of $\int \sin x \, dx$ (if n is odd) or $\int (\sin x)^0 \, dx = \int dx$ (if n is even).

6.1   EXERCISES

1–2 ▪ Evaluate the integral using integration by parts with the indicated choices of u and dv.

1. $\int x \ln x \, dx; \quad u = \ln x, \; dv = x \, dx$

2. $\int \theta \sec^2 \theta \, d\theta; \quad u = \theta, \; dv = \sec^2 \theta \, d\theta$

▪ ▪ ▪ ▪ ▪ ▪ ▪ ▪ ▪ ▪ ▪ ▪ ▪

3–24 ▪ Evaluate the integral.

3. $\int x \cos 5x \, dx$

4. $\int x e^{-x} \, dx$

5. $\int r e^{r/2} \, dr$

6. $\int t \sin 2t \, dt$

7. $\int x^2 \sin \pi x \, dx$

8. $\int x^2 \cos mx \, dx$

9. $\int \ln(2x + 1) \, dx$

10. $\int p^5 \ln p \, dp$

11. $\int \arctan 4t \, dt$

12. $\int t^3 e^t \, dt$

13. $\int e^{2\theta} \sin 3\theta \, d\theta$

14. $\int e^{-\theta} \cos 2\theta \, d\theta$

15. $\int_0^\pi t \sin 3t \, dt$

16. $\int_0^1 (x^2 + 1) e^{-x} \, dx$

17. $\int_1^2 \frac{\ln x}{x^2} \, dx$

18. $\int_1^4 \sqrt{t} \ln t \, dt$

19. $\int_0^1 \frac{y}{e^{2y}} \, dy$

20. $\int_1^{\sqrt{3}} \arctan(1/x) \, dx$

21. $\int_0^{1/2} \sin^{-1} x \, dx$

22. $\int_0^1 \frac{r^3}{\sqrt{4 + r^2}} \, dr$

23. $\int_1^2 (\ln x)^2 \, dx$

24. $\int_0^t e^s \sin(t - s) \, ds$

▪ ▪ ▪ ▪ ▪ ▪ ▪ ▪ ▪ ▪ ▪ ▪ ▪

25–28 ▪ First make a substitution and then use integration by parts to evaluate the integral.

25. $\int \sin \sqrt{x} \, dx$

26. $\int x^5 \cos(x^3) \, dx$

27. $\int_{\sqrt{\pi/2}}^{\sqrt{\pi}} \theta^3 \cos(\theta^2) \, d\theta$

28. $\int_1^4 e^{\sqrt{x}} \, dx$

▪ ▪ ▪ ▪ ▪ ▪ ▪ ▪ ▪ ▪ ▪ ▪ ▪

29. (a) Use the reduction formula in Example 6 to show that

$$\int \sin^2 x \, dx = \frac{x}{2} - \frac{\sin 2x}{4} + C$$

(b) Use part (a) and the reduction formula to evaluate $\int \sin^4 x \, dx$.

30. (a) Prove the reduction formula

$$\int \cos^n x \, dx = \frac{1}{n} \cos^{n-1} x \sin x + \frac{n-1}{n} \int \cos^{n-2} x \, dx$$

(b) Use part (a) to evaluate $\int \cos^2 x \, dx$.
(c) Use parts (a) and (b) to evaluate $\int \cos^4 x \, dx$.

31. (a) Use the reduction formula in Example 6 to show that

$$\int_0^{\pi/2} \sin^n x \, dx = \frac{n-1}{n} \int_0^{\pi/2} \sin^{n-2} x \, dx$$

where $n \geq 2$ is an integer.
(b) Use part (a) to evaluate $\int_0^{\pi/2} \sin^3 x \, dx$ and $\int_0^{\pi/2} \sin^5 x \, dx$.
(c) Use part (a) to show that, for odd powers of sine,

$$\int_0^{\pi/2} \sin^{2n+1} x \, dx = \frac{2 \cdot 4 \cdot 6 \cdot \cdots \cdot 2n}{3 \cdot 5 \cdot 7 \cdot \cdots \cdot (2n + 1)}$$

32. Prove that, for even powers of sine,

$$\int_0^{\pi/2} \sin^{2n}x \, dx = \frac{1 \cdot 3 \cdot 5 \cdot \cdots \cdot (2n-1)}{2 \cdot 4 \cdot 6 \cdot \cdots \cdot 2n} \frac{\pi}{2}$$

33–36 ■ Use integration by parts to prove the reduction formula.

33. $\int (\ln x)^n \, dx = x(\ln x)^n - n \int (\ln x)^{n-1} \, dx$

34. $\int x^n e^x \, dx = x^n e^x - n \int x^{n-1} e^x \, dx$

35. $\int (x^2 + a^2)^n \, dx$

$$= \frac{x(x^2 + a^2)^n}{2n+1} + \frac{2na^2}{2n+1} \int (x^2 + a^2)^{n-1} \, dx \quad \left(n \neq -\tfrac{1}{2}\right)$$

36. $\int \sec^n x \, dx = \dfrac{\tan x \sec^{n-2} x}{n-1} + \dfrac{n-2}{n-1} \int \sec^{n-2} x \, dx$
$(n \neq 1)$

■   ■   ■   ■   ■   ■   ■   ■   ■   ■   ■   ■   ■

37. Use Exercise 33 to find $\int (\ln x)^3 \, dx$.

38. Use Exercise 34 to find $\int x^4 e^x \, dx$.

39. Find the average value of $f(x) = x^2 \ln x$ on the interval $[1, 3]$.

40. A rocket accelerates by burning its onboard fuel, so its mass decreases with time. Suppose the initial mass of the rocket at liftoff (including its fuel) is m, the fuel is consumed at rate r, and the exhaust gases are ejected with

constant velocity v_e (relative to the rocket). A model for the velocity of the rocket at time t is given by the equation

$$v(t) = -gt - v_e \ln \frac{m - rt}{m}$$

where g is the acceleration due to gravity and t is not too large. If $g = 9.8 \text{ m/s}^2$, $m = 30{,}000 \text{ kg}$, $r = 160 \text{ kg/s}$, and $v_e = 3000 \text{ m/s}$, find the height of the rocket one minute after liftoff.

41. A particle that moves along a straight line has velocity $v(t) = t^2 e^{-t}$ meters per second after t seconds. How far will it travel during the first t seconds?

42. If $f(0) = g(0) = 0$ and f'' and g'' are continuous, show that

$$\int_0^a f(x)g''(x) \, dx = f(a)g'(a) - f'(a)g(a) + \int_0^a f''(x)g(x) \, dx$$

43. Suppose that $f(1) = 2$, $f(4) = 7$, $f'(1) = 5$, $f'(4) = 3$, and f'' is continuous. Find the value of $\int_1^4 xf''(x) \, dx$.

44. (a) Use integration by parts to show that

$$\int f(x) \, dx = xf(x) - \int xf'(x) \, dx$$

(b) If f and g are inverse functions and f' is continuous, prove that

$$\int_a^b f(x) \, dx = bf(b) - af(a) - \int_{f(a)}^{f(b)} g(y) \, dy$$

[*Hint:* Use part (a) and make the substitution $y = f(x)$.]

(c) In the case where f and g are positive functions and $b > a > 0$, draw a diagram to give a geometric interpretation of part (b).

(d) Use part (b) to evaluate $\int_1^e \ln x \, dx$.

| **6.2** | **TRIGONOMETRIC INTEGRALS AND SUBSTITUTIONS** |

In this section we look at integrals involving trigonometric functions and integrals that can be transformed into trigonometric integrals by substitution.

TRIGONOMETRIC INTEGRALS

Here we use trigonometric identities to integrate certain combinations of trigonometric functions. We start with powers of sine and cosine.

EXAMPLE I Evaluate $\int \cos^3 x \, dx$.

SOLUTION Simply substituting $u = \cos x$ isn't helpful, since then $du = -\sin x \, dx$. In order to integrate powers of cosine, we would need an extra $\sin x$ factor. Similarly, a power of sine would require an extra $\cos x$ factor. Thus here we can separate one cosine factor and convert the remaining $\cos^2 x$ factor to an expression involving sine using the identity $\sin^2 x + \cos^2 x = 1$:

$$\cos^3 x = \cos^2 x \cdot \cos x = (1 - \sin^2 x)\cos x$$

We can then evaluate the integral by substituting $u = \sin x$, so $du = \cos x\, dx$ and

$$\int \cos^3 x\, dx = \int \cos^2 x \cdot \cos x\, dx = \int (1 - \sin^2 x)\cos x\, dx$$

$$= \int (1 - u^2)\, du = u - \tfrac{1}{3}u^3 + C = \sin x - \tfrac{1}{3}\sin^3 x + C \qquad ■$$

In general, we try to write an integrand involving powers of sine and cosine in a form where we have only one sine factor (and the remainder of the expression in terms of cosine) or only one cosine factor (and the remainder of the expression in terms of sine). The identity $\sin^2 x + \cos^2 x = 1$ enables us to convert back and forth between even powers of sine and cosine.

V EXAMPLE 2 Find $\int \sin^5 x \cos^2 x\, dx$

SOLUTION We could convert $\cos^2 x$ to $1 - \sin^2 x$, but we would be left with an expression in terms of $\sin x$ with no extra $\cos x$ factor. Instead, we separate a single sine factor and rewrite the remaining $\sin^4 x$ factor in terms of $\cos x$:

$$\sin^5 x \cos^2 x = (\sin^2 x)^2 \cos^2 x \sin x = (1 - \cos^2 x)^2 \cos^2 x \sin x$$

Substituting $u = \cos x$, we have $du = -\sin x\, dx$ and so

$$\int \sin^5 x \cos^2 x\, dx = \int (\sin^2 x)^2 \cos^2 x \sin x\, dx = \int (1 - \cos^2 x)^2 \cos^2 x \sin x\, dx$$

$$= \int (1 - u^2)^2 u^2 (-du) = -\int (u^2 - 2u^4 + u^6)\, du$$

$$= -\left(\frac{u^3}{3} - 2\frac{u^5}{5} + \frac{u^7}{7}\right) + C$$

$$= -\tfrac{1}{3}\cos^3 x + \tfrac{2}{5}\cos^5 x - \tfrac{1}{7}\cos^7 x + C \qquad ■$$

In the preceding examples, an odd power of sine or cosine enabled us to separate a single factor and convert the remaining even power. If the integrand contains even powers of both sine and cosine, this strategy fails. In this case, we can take advantage of the following half-angle identities (see Equations 17b and 17a in Appendix A):

$$\sin^2 x = \tfrac{1}{2}(1 - \cos 2x) \qquad \text{and} \qquad \cos^2 x = \tfrac{1}{2}(1 + \cos 2x)$$

■ Figure 1 shows the graphs of the integrand $\sin^5 x \cos^2 x$ in Example 2 and its indefinite integral (with $C = 0$). Which is which?

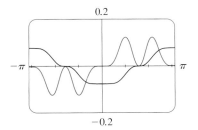

FIGURE 1

■ Example 3 shows that the area of the region shown in Figure 2 is $\pi/2$.

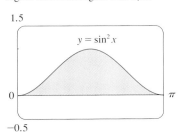

FIGURE 2

V EXAMPLE 3 Evaluate $\int_0^\pi \sin^2 x\, dx$.

SOLUTION If we write $\sin^2 x = 1 - \cos^2 x$, the integral is no simpler to evaluate. Using the half-angle formula for $\sin^2 x$, however, we have

$$\int_0^\pi \sin^2 x\, dx = \tfrac{1}{2}\int_0^\pi (1 - \cos 2x)\, dx = \left[\tfrac{1}{2}\left(x - \tfrac{1}{2}\sin 2x\right)\right]_0^\pi$$

$$= \tfrac{1}{2}\left(\pi - \tfrac{1}{2}\sin 2\pi\right) - \tfrac{1}{2}\left(0 - \tfrac{1}{2}\sin 0\right) = \tfrac{1}{2}\pi$$

Notice that we mentally made the substitution $u = 2x$ when integrating $\cos 2x$. Another method for evaluating this integral was given in Exercise 29 in Section 6.1.

■

EXAMPLE 4 Find $\int \sin^4 x \, dx$.

SOLUTION We could evaluate this integral using the reduction formula for $\int \sin^n x \, dx$ (Equation 6.1.7) together with Example 3 (as in Exercise 29 in Section 6.1), but a better method is to write $\sin^4 x = (\sin^2 x)^2$ and use a half-angle formula:

$$\int \sin^4 x \, dx = \int (\sin^2 x)^2 \, dx$$

$$= \int \left(\frac{1 - \cos 2x}{2} \right)^2 dx$$

$$= \frac{1}{4} \int (1 - 2\cos 2x + \cos^2 2x) \, dx$$

Since $\cos^2 2x$ occurs, we must use another half-angle formula

$$\cos^2 2x = \tfrac{1}{2}(1 + \cos 4x)$$

■ **How to Integrate Powers of $\sin x$ and $\cos x$**

From Examples 1–4 we see that the following strategy works:

(i) If the power of $\cos x$ is odd, save one cosine factor and use $\cos^2 x = 1 - \sin^2 x$ to express the remaining factors in terms of $\sin x$. Then substitute $u = \sin x$.

(ii) If the power of $\sin x$ is odd, save one sine factor and use $\sin^2 x = 1 - \cos^2 x$ to express the remaining factors in terms of $\cos x$. Then substitute $u = \cos x$.

(iii) If the powers of both sine and cosine are even, use the half-angle identities:

$$\sin^2 x = \tfrac{1}{2}(1 - \cos 2x)$$
$$\cos^2 x = \tfrac{1}{2}(1 + \cos 2x)$$

It is sometimes helpful to use the identity

$$\sin x \cos x = \tfrac{1}{2} \sin 2x$$

This gives

$$\int \sin^4 x \, dx = \frac{1}{4} \int \left[1 - 2\cos 2x + \tfrac{1}{2}(1 + \cos 4x) \right] dx$$

$$= \frac{1}{4} \int \left(\tfrac{3}{2} - 2\cos 2x + \tfrac{1}{2}\cos 4x \right) dx$$

$$= \frac{1}{4} \left(\tfrac{3}{2}x - \sin 2x + \tfrac{1}{8}\sin 4x \right) + C$$ ■

We can use a similar strategy to evaluate integrals of the form $\int \tan^m x \, \sec^n x \, dx$. Since $(d/dx) \tan x = \sec^2 x$, we can separate a $\sec^2 x$ factor and convert the remaining (even) power of secant to an expression involving tangent using the identity $\sec^2 x = 1 + \tan^2 x$. Or, since $(d/dx) \sec x = \sec x \tan x$, we can separate a $\sec x \tan x$ factor and convert the remaining (even) power of tangent to secant.

▼ EXAMPLE 5 Evaluate $\int \tan^6 x \, \sec^4 x \, dx$.

SOLUTION If we separate one $\sec^2 x$ factor, we can express the remaining $\sec^2 x$ factor in terms of tangent using the identity $\sec^2 x = 1 + \tan^2 x$. We can then evaluate the integral by substituting $u = \tan x$ with $du = \sec^2 x \, dx$:

$$\int \tan^6 x \, \sec^4 x \, dx = \int \tan^6 x \, \sec^2 x \, \sec^2 x \, dx$$

$$= \int \tan^6 x \, (1 + \tan^2 x) \, \sec^2 x \, dx$$

$$= \int u^6 (1 + u^2) \, du = \int (u^6 + u^8) \, du$$

$$= \frac{u^7}{7} + \frac{u^9}{9} + C$$

$$= \tfrac{1}{7} \tan^7 x + \tfrac{1}{9} \tan^9 x + C$$ ■

EXAMPLE 6 Find $\int \tan^5\theta \, \sec^7\theta \, d\theta$.

SOLUTION If we separate a $\sec^2\theta$ factor, as in the preceding example, we are left with a $\sec^5\theta$ factor, which isn't easily converted to tangent. However, if we separate a $\sec\theta \, \tan\theta$ factor, we can convert the remaining power of tangent to an expression involving only secant using the identity $\tan^2\theta = \sec^2\theta - 1$. We can then evaluate the integral by substituting $u = \sec\theta$, so $du = \sec\theta \, \tan\theta \, d\theta$:

$$\int \tan^5\theta \, \sec^7\theta \, d\theta = \int \tan^4\theta \, \sec^6\theta \, \sec\theta \, \tan\theta \, d\theta$$

$$= \int (\sec^2\theta - 1)^2 \sec^6\theta \, \sec\theta \, \tan\theta \, d\theta$$

$$= \int (u^2 - 1)^2 u^6 \, du = \int (u^{10} - 2u^8 + u^6) \, du$$

$$= \frac{u^{11}}{11} - 2\frac{u^9}{9} + \frac{u^7}{7} + C$$

$$= \tfrac{1}{11} \sec^{11}\theta - \tfrac{2}{9} \sec^9\theta + \tfrac{1}{7} \sec^7\theta + C \qquad ▪$$

▪ **How to Integrate Powers of $\tan x$ and $\sec x$**

From Examples 5 and 6 we have a strategy for two cases:

(i) If the power of $\sec x$ is even, save a factor of $\sec^2 x$ and use $\sec^2 x = 1 + \tan^2 x$ to express the remaining factors in terms of $\tan x$. Then substitute $u = \tan x$.

(ii) If the power of $\tan x$ is odd, save a factor of $\sec x \, \tan x$ and use $\tan^2 x = \sec^2 x - 1$ to express the remaining factors in terms of $\sec x$. Then substitute $u = \sec x$.

For other cases, the guidelines are not as clear-cut. We may need to use identities, integration by parts, and occasionally a little ingenuity. We will sometimes need to be able to integrate $\tan x$ by using the formula established in (5.5.5):

$$\int \tan x \, dx = \ln |\sec x| + C$$

We will also need the indefinite integral of secant:

1

$$\int \sec x \, dx = \ln |\sec x + \tan x| + C$$

We could verify Formula 1 by differentiating the right side, or as follows. First we multiply numerator and denominator by $\sec x + \tan x$:

$$\int \sec x \, dx = \int \sec x \, \frac{\sec x + \tan x}{\sec x + \tan x} \, dx$$

$$= \int \frac{\sec^2 x + \sec x \, \tan x}{\sec x + \tan x} \, dx$$

If we substitute $u = \sec x + \tan x$, then $du = (\sec x \, \tan x + \sec^2 x) \, dx$, so the integral becomes $\int (1/u) \, du = \ln |u| + C$. Thus we have

$$\int \sec x \, dx = \ln |\sec x + \tan x| + C$$

EXAMPLE 7 Find $\int \tan^3 x \, dx$.

SOLUTION Here only $\tan x$ occurs, so we use $\tan^2 x = \sec^2 x - 1$ to rewrite a $\tan^2 x$ factor in terms of $\sec^2 x$:

$$\int \tan^3 x \, dx = \int \tan x \tan^2 x \, dx = \int \tan x \, (\sec^2 x - 1) \, dx$$

$$= \int \tan x \sec^2 x \, dx - \int \tan x \, dx$$

$$= \frac{\tan^2 x}{2} - \ln|\sec x| + C$$

In the first integral we mentally substituted $u = \tan x$ so that $du = \sec^2 x \, dx$. ■

If an even power of tangent appears with an odd power of secant, it is helpful to express the integrand completely in terms of $\sec x$. Powers of $\sec x$ may require integration by parts, as shown in the following example.

EXAMPLE 8 Find $\int \sec^3 x \, dx$.

SOLUTION Here we integrate by parts with

$$u = \sec x \qquad\qquad dv = \sec^2 x \, dx$$
$$du = \sec x \tan x \, dx \qquad\qquad v = \tan x$$

Then

$$\int \sec^3 x \, dx = \sec x \tan x - \int \sec x \tan^2 x \, dx$$

$$= \sec x \tan x - \int \sec x \, (\sec^2 x - 1) \, dx$$

$$= \sec x \tan x - \int \sec^3 x \, dx + \int \sec x \, dx$$

Using Formula 1 and solving for the required integral, we get

$$\int \sec^3 x \, dx = \tfrac{1}{2}\bigl(\sec x \tan x + \ln|\sec x + \tan x|\bigr) + C$$ ■

Integrals such as the one in Example 8 may seem very special but they occur frequently in applications of integration, as we will see in Chapter 7. Integrals of the form $\int \cot^m x \csc^n x \, dx$ can be found by similar methods because of the identity $1 + \cot^2 x = \csc^2 x$.

TRIGONOMETRIC SUBSTITUTIONS

In finding the area of a circle or an ellipse, an integral of the form $\int \sqrt{a^2 - x^2} \, dx$ arises, where $a > 0$. If it were $\int x\sqrt{a^2 - x^2} \, dx$, the substitution $u = a^2 - x^2$ would be effective but, as it stands, $\int \sqrt{a^2 - x^2} \, dx$ is more difficult. If we change the variable from x to θ by the substitution $x = a \sin \theta$, then the identity $1 - \sin^2\theta = \cos^2\theta$ allows us to get rid of the root sign because

$$\sqrt{a^2 - x^2} = \sqrt{a^2 - a^2 \sin^2\theta} = \sqrt{a^2(1 - \sin^2\theta)} = \sqrt{a^2 \cos^2\theta} = a|\cos\theta|$$

Notice the difference between the substitution $u = a^2 - x^2$ (in which the new variable is a function of the old one) and the substitution $x = a \sin \theta$ (the old variable is a function of the new one).

In general we can make a substitution of the form $x = g(t)$ by using the Substitution Rule in reverse. To make our calculations simpler, we assume that g has an inverse function; that is, g is one-to-one. In this case, if we replace u by x and x by t in the Substitution Rule (Equation 5.5.4), we obtain

$$\int f(x)\, dx = \int f(g(t))g'(t)\, dt$$

This kind of substitution is called *inverse substitution.*

We can make the inverse substitution $x = a \sin \theta$ provided that it defines a one-to-one function. We accomplish this by restricting θ to lie in the interval $[-\pi/2, \pi/2]$.

In the following table we list trigonometric substitutions that are effective for the given radical expressions because of the specified trigonometric identities. In each case the restriction on θ is imposed to ensure that the function that defines the substitution is one-to-one. (These are the same intervals used in Section 3.5 in defining the inverse functions.)

TABLE OF TRIGONOMETRIC SUBSTITUTIONS

Expression	Substitution	Identity
$\sqrt{a^2 - x^2}$	$x = a \sin \theta, \quad -\dfrac{\pi}{2} \le \theta \le \dfrac{\pi}{2}$	$1 - \sin^2\theta = \cos^2\theta$
$\sqrt{a^2 + x^2}$	$x = a \tan \theta, \quad -\dfrac{\pi}{2} < \theta < \dfrac{\pi}{2}$	$1 + \tan^2\theta = \sec^2\theta$
$\sqrt{x^2 - a^2}$	$x = a \sec \theta, \quad 0 \le \theta < \dfrac{\pi}{2} \ \text{or}\ \pi \le \theta < \dfrac{3\pi}{2}$	$\sec^2\theta - 1 = \tan^2\theta$

☑ EXAMPLE 9 Evaluate $\displaystyle\int \frac{\sqrt{9 - x^2}}{x^2}\, dx$.

SOLUTION Let $x = 3 \sin \theta$, where $-\pi/2 \le \theta \le \pi/2$. Then $dx = 3 \cos \theta\, d\theta$ and

$$\sqrt{9 - x^2} = \sqrt{9 - 9 \sin^2\theta} = \sqrt{9 \cos^2\theta} = 3\,|\cos \theta| = 3 \cos \theta$$

(Note that $\cos \theta \ge 0$ because $-\pi/2 \le \theta \le \pi/2$.) Thus, using inverse substitution, we get

$$\int \frac{\sqrt{9 - x^2}}{x^2}\, dx = \int \frac{3 \cos \theta}{9 \sin^2\theta}\, 3 \cos \theta\, d\theta = \int \frac{\cos^2\theta}{\sin^2\theta}\, d\theta$$

$$= \int \cot^2\theta\, d\theta = \int (\csc^2\theta - 1)\, d\theta = -\cot \theta - \theta + C$$

Since this is an indefinite integral, we must return to the original variable x. This can be done either by using trigonometric identities to express $\cot \theta$ in terms of $\sin \theta = x/3$ or by drawing a diagram, as in Figure 3, where θ is interpreted as an angle of a right triangle. Since $\sin \theta = x/3$, we label the opposite side and the hypotenuse as having lengths x and 3. Then the Pythagorean Theorem gives the length of

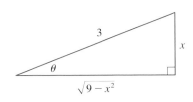

FIGURE 3

$\sin \theta = \dfrac{x}{3}$

the adjacent side as $\sqrt{9 - x^2}$, so we can simply read the value of $\cot \theta$ from the figure:

$$\cot \theta = \frac{\sqrt{9 - x^2}}{x}$$

(Although $\theta > 0$ in the diagram, this expression for $\cot \theta$ is valid even when $\theta < 0$.) Since $\sin \theta = x/3$, we have $\theta = \sin^{-1}(x/3)$ and so

$$\int \frac{\sqrt{9 - x^2}}{x^2} \, dx = -\frac{\sqrt{9 - x^2}}{x} - \sin^{-1}\left(\frac{x}{3}\right) + C \qquad ■$$

▼ EXAMPLE 10 Find the area enclosed by the ellipse

$$\frac{x^2}{a^2} + \frac{y^2}{b^2} = 1$$

SOLUTION Solving the equation of the ellipse for y, we get

$$\frac{y^2}{b^2} = 1 - \frac{x^2}{a^2} = \frac{a^2 - x^2}{a^2} \qquad \text{or} \qquad y = \pm \frac{b}{a}\sqrt{a^2 - x^2}$$

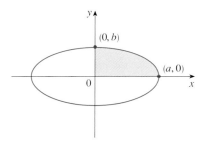

FIGURE 4
$$\frac{x^2}{a^2} + \frac{y^2}{b^2} = 1$$

Because the ellipse is symmetric with respect to both axes, the total area A is four times the area in the first quadrant (see Figure 4). The part of the ellipse in the first quadrant is given by the function

$$y = \frac{b}{a}\sqrt{a^2 - x^2} \qquad 0 \leqslant x \leqslant a$$

and so

$$\tfrac{1}{4}A = \int_0^a \frac{b}{a}\sqrt{a^2 - x^2} \, dx$$

To evaluate this integral we substitute $x = a \sin \theta$. Then $dx = a \cos \theta \, d\theta$. To change the limits of integration we note that when $x = 0$, $\sin \theta = 0$, so $\theta = 0$; when $x = a$, $\sin \theta = 1$, so $\theta = \pi/2$. Also

$$\sqrt{a^2 - x^2} = \sqrt{a^2 - a^2 \sin^2\theta} = \sqrt{a^2 \cos^2\theta} = a\,|\cos \theta| = a \cos \theta$$

since $0 \leqslant \theta \leqslant \pi/2$. Therefore

$$A = 4\frac{b}{a}\int_0^a \sqrt{a^2 - x^2} \, dx = 4\frac{b}{a}\int_0^{\pi/2} a \cos \theta \cdot a \cos \theta \, d\theta$$

$$= 4ab\int_0^{\pi/2} \cos^2\theta \, d\theta = 4ab\int_0^{\pi/2} \tfrac{1}{2}(1 + \cos 2\theta) \, d\theta$$

$$= 2ab\left[\theta + \tfrac{1}{2}\sin 2\theta\right]_0^{\pi/2} = 2ab\left(\frac{\pi}{2} + 0 - 0\right) = \pi ab$$

We have shown that the area of an ellipse with semiaxes a and b is πab. In particular, taking $a = b = r$, we have proved the famous formula that the area of a circle with radius r is πr^2. ■

NOTE Since the integral in Example 10 was a definite integral, we changed the limits of integration and did not have to convert back to the original variable x.

▼ EXAMPLE 11 Find $\int \dfrac{1}{x^2\sqrt{x^2+4}}\,dx$.

SOLUTION Let $x = 2\tan\theta$, $-\pi/2 < \theta < \pi/2$. Then $dx = 2\sec^2\theta\,d\theta$ and

$$\sqrt{x^2+4} = \sqrt{4(\tan^2\theta+1)} = \sqrt{4\sec^2\theta} = 2\,|\sec\theta| = 2\sec\theta$$

Thus we have

$$\int \frac{dx}{x^2\sqrt{x^2+4}} = \int \frac{2\sec^2\theta\,d\theta}{4\tan^2\theta \cdot 2\sec\theta} = \frac{1}{4}\int \frac{\sec\theta}{\tan^2\theta}\,d\theta$$

To evaluate this trigonometric integral we put everything in terms of $\sin\theta$ and $\cos\theta$:

$$\frac{\sec\theta}{\tan^2\theta} = \frac{1}{\cos\theta} \cdot \frac{\cos^2\theta}{\sin^2\theta} = \frac{\cos\theta}{\sin^2\theta}$$

Therefore, making the substitution $u = \sin\theta$, we have

$$\int \frac{dx}{x^2\sqrt{x^2+4}} = \frac{1}{4}\int \frac{\cos\theta}{\sin^2\theta}\,d\theta = \frac{1}{4}\int \frac{du}{u^2}$$

$$= \frac{1}{4}\left(-\frac{1}{u}\right) + C = -\frac{1}{4\sin\theta} + C$$

$$= -\frac{\csc\theta}{4} + C$$

We use Figure 5 to determine that $\csc\theta = \sqrt{x^2+4}/x$ and so

$$\int \frac{dx}{x^2\sqrt{x^2+4}} = -\frac{\sqrt{x^2+4}}{4x} + C \qquad ▪$$

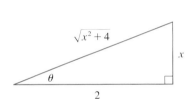

FIGURE 5

$\tan\theta = \dfrac{x}{2}$

EXAMPLE 12 Find $\int \dfrac{x}{\sqrt{x^2+4}}\,dx$.

SOLUTION It would be possible to use the trigonometric substitution $x = 2\tan\theta$ here (as in Example 11). But the direct substitution $u = x^2 + 4$ is simpler, because then $du = 2x\,dx$ and

$$\int \frac{x}{\sqrt{x^2+4}}\,dx = \frac{1}{2}\int \frac{du}{\sqrt{u}} = \sqrt{u} + C = \sqrt{x^2+4} + C \qquad ▪$$

▪ Example 12 illustrates the fact that even when trigonometric substitutions are possible, they may not give the easiest solution. You should look for a simpler method first.

EXAMPLE 13 Evaluate $\int \dfrac{dx}{\sqrt{x^2-a^2}}$, where $a > 0$.

SOLUTION We let $x = a\sec\theta$, where $0 < \theta < \pi/2$ or $\pi < \theta < 3\pi/2$. Then $dx = a\sec\theta\tan\theta\,d\theta$ and

$$\sqrt{x^2-a^2} = \sqrt{a^2(\sec^2\theta-1)} = \sqrt{a^2\tan^2\theta} = a\,|\tan\theta| = a\tan\theta$$

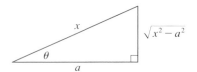

FIGURE 6

$\sec\theta = \dfrac{x}{a}$

Therefore

$$\int \frac{dx}{\sqrt{x^2 - a^2}} = \int \frac{a \sec\theta \tan\theta}{a \tan\theta} \, d\theta$$

$$= \int \sec\theta \, d\theta = \ln|\sec\theta + \tan\theta| + C$$

The triangle in Figure 6 gives $\tan\theta = \sqrt{x^2 - a^2}/a$, so we have

$$\int \frac{dx}{\sqrt{x^2 - a^2}} = \ln\left|\frac{x}{a} + \frac{\sqrt{x^2 - a^2}}{a}\right| + C$$

$$= \ln\left|x + \sqrt{x^2 - a^2}\right| - \ln a + C$$

Writing $C_1 = C - \ln a$, we have

$$\int \frac{dx}{\sqrt{x^2 - a^2}} = \ln\left|x + \sqrt{x^2 - a^2}\right| + C_1 \qquad ■$$

EXAMPLE 14 Find $\displaystyle\int_0^{3\sqrt{3}/2} \frac{x^3}{(4x^2 + 9)^{3/2}} \, dx$.

SOLUTION First we note that $(4x^2 + 9)^{3/2} = (\sqrt{4x^2 + 9})^3$ so trigonometric substitution is appropriate. Although $\sqrt{4x^2 + 9}$ is not quite one of the expressions in the table of trigonometric substitutions, it becomes one of them if we make the preliminary substitution $u = 2x$. When we combine this with the tangent substitution, we have $x = \frac{3}{2}\tan\theta$, which gives $dx = \frac{3}{2}\sec^2\theta \, d\theta$ and

$$\sqrt{4x^2 + 9} = \sqrt{9\tan^2\theta + 9} = 3\sec\theta$$

When $x = 0$, $\tan\theta = 0$, so $\theta = 0$; when $x = 3\sqrt{3}/2$, $\tan\theta = \sqrt{3}$, so $\theta = \pi/3$.

$$\int_0^{3\sqrt{3}/2} \frac{x^3}{(4x^2 + 9)^{3/2}} \, dx = \int_0^{\pi/3} \frac{\frac{27}{8}\tan^3\theta}{27\sec^3\theta} \, \frac{3}{2}\sec^2\theta \, d\theta$$

$$= \frac{3}{16} \int_0^{\pi/3} \frac{\tan^3\theta}{\sec\theta} \, d\theta = \frac{3}{16} \int_0^{\pi/3} \frac{\sin^3\theta}{\cos^2\theta} \, d\theta$$

$$= \frac{3}{16} \int_0^{\pi/3} \frac{1 - \cos^2\theta}{\cos^2\theta} \sin\theta \, d\theta$$

Now we substitute $u = \cos\theta$ so that $du = -\sin\theta \, d\theta$. When $\theta = 0$, $u = 1$; when $\theta = \pi/3$, $u = \frac{1}{2}$. Therefore

$$\int_0^{3\sqrt{3}/2} \frac{x^3}{(4x^2 + 9)^{3/2}} \, dx = -\frac{3}{16} \int_1^{1/2} \frac{1 - u^2}{u^2} \, du = \frac{3}{16} \int_1^{1/2} (1 - u^{-2}) \, du$$

$$= \frac{3}{16}\left[u + \frac{1}{u}\right]_1^{1/2} = \frac{3}{16}\left[\left(\frac{1}{2} + 2\right) - (1 + 1)\right] = \frac{3}{32} \qquad ■$$

| 6.2 | **EXERCISES** |

1–34 ▪ Evaluate the integral.

1. $\displaystyle\int \sin^3x \, \cos^2x \, dx$

2. $\displaystyle\int \sin^6x \, \cos^3x \, dx$

3. $\displaystyle\int_{\pi/2}^{3\pi/4} \sin^5x \, \cos^3x \, dx$

4. $\displaystyle\int_0^{\pi/2} \cos^5x \, dx$

5. $\displaystyle\int_0^{\pi/2} \cos^2\theta \, d\theta$

6. $\displaystyle\int \sin^3(mx) \, dx$

7. $\displaystyle\int_0^{\pi} \sin^4(3t) \, dt$

8. $\displaystyle\int_0^{\pi/2} \sin^2(2\theta) \, d\theta$

9. $\displaystyle\int (1 + \cos\theta)^2 \, d\theta$

10. $\displaystyle\int_0^{\pi} \cos^6\theta \, d\theta$

11. $\displaystyle\int_0^{\pi/4} \sin^4x \, \cos^2x \, dx$

12. $\displaystyle\int x \cos^2x \, dx$

13. $\displaystyle\int \cos^2x \, \tan^3x \, dx$

14. $\displaystyle\int_0^{\pi/2} \sin^2x \, \cos^2x \, dx$

15. $\displaystyle\int \frac{1 - \sin x}{\cos x} \, dx$

16. $\displaystyle\int \cos^2x \, \sin 2x \, dx$

17. $\displaystyle\int \sec^2x \, \tan x \, dx$

18. $\displaystyle\int_0^{\pi/2} \sec^4(t/2) \, dt$

19. $\displaystyle\int \tan^2x \, dx$

20. $\displaystyle\int \tan^4x \, dx$

21. $\displaystyle\int \sec^6t \, dt$

22. $\displaystyle\int_0^{\pi/4} \sec^4\theta \, \tan^4\theta \, d\theta$

23. $\displaystyle\int_0^{\pi/3} \tan^5x \, \sec^4x \, dx$

24. $\displaystyle\int \tan^3(2x) \, \sec^5(2x) \, dx$

25. $\displaystyle\int \tan^3x \, \sec x \, dx$

26. $\displaystyle\int_0^{\pi/3} \tan^5x \, \sec^6x \, dx$

27. $\displaystyle\int \tan^5x \, dx$

28. $\displaystyle\int \tan^6(ay) \, dy$

29. $\displaystyle\int_{\pi/6}^{\pi/2} \cot^2x \, dx$

30. $\displaystyle\int_{\pi/4}^{\pi/2} \cot^3x \, dx$

31. $\displaystyle\int \cot^3\alpha \, \csc^3\alpha \, d\alpha$

32. $\displaystyle\int \csc^4x \, \cot^6x \, dx$

33. $\displaystyle\int \csc x \, dx$

34. $\displaystyle\int \frac{1 - \tan^2x}{\sec^2x} \, dx$

35. (a) Use the formulas for $\cos(A + B)$ and $\cos(A - B)$ to show that
$$\sin A \, \sin B = \tfrac{1}{2}[\cos(A - B) - \cos(A + B)]$$
(b) Use part (a) to evaluate $\int \sin 5x \, \sin 2x \, dx$.

36. (a) Use the formulas for $\sin(A + B)$ and $\sin(A - B)$ to show that
$$\sin A \, \cos B = \tfrac{1}{2}[\sin(A - B) + \sin(A + B)]$$
(b) Use part (a) to evaluate $\int \sin 3x \, \cos x \, dx$.

37–39 ▪ Evaluate the integral using the indicated trigonometric substitution. Sketch and label the associated right triangle.

37. $\displaystyle\int \frac{1}{x^2\sqrt{x^2 - 9}} \, dx; \quad x = 3 \sec\theta$

38. $\displaystyle\int x^3 \sqrt{9 - x^2} \, dx; \quad x = 3 \sin\theta$

39. $\displaystyle\int \frac{x^3}{\sqrt{x^2 + 9}} \, dx; \quad x = 3 \tan\theta$

40–58 ▪ Evaluate the integral.

40. $\displaystyle\int_0^{2\sqrt{3}} \frac{x^3}{\sqrt{16 - x^2}} \, dx$

41. $\displaystyle\int_{\sqrt{2}}^2 \frac{1}{t^3\sqrt{t^2 - 1}} \, dt$

42. $\displaystyle\int_0^2 x^3\sqrt{x^2 + 4} \, dx$

43. $\displaystyle\int \frac{1}{x^2\sqrt{25 - x^2}} \, dx$

44. $\displaystyle\int \frac{\sqrt{x^2 - a^2}}{x^4} \, dx$

45. $\displaystyle\int \frac{dx}{\sqrt{x^2 + 16}}$

46. $\displaystyle\int \frac{t^5}{\sqrt{t^2 + 2}} \, dt$

47. $\displaystyle\int \sqrt{1 - 4x^2} \, dx$

48. $\displaystyle\int_0^1 x\sqrt{x^2 + 4} \, dx$

49. $\displaystyle\int \frac{\sqrt{x^2 - 9}}{x^3} \, dx$

50. $\displaystyle\int \frac{du}{u\sqrt{5 - u^2}}$

51. $\displaystyle\int \frac{x^2}{(a^2 - x^2)^{3/2}} \, dx$

52. $\displaystyle\int \frac{dx}{x^2\sqrt{16x^2 - 9}}$

53. $\displaystyle\int \frac{x}{\sqrt{x^2 - 7}} \, dx$

54. $\displaystyle\int_0^1 \sqrt{x^2 + 1} \, dx$

55. $\displaystyle\int \frac{\sqrt{1 + x^2}}{x} \, dx$

56. $\displaystyle\int \frac{t}{\sqrt{25 - t^2}} \, dt$

57. $\displaystyle\int x\sqrt{1 - x^4} \, dx$

58. $\displaystyle\int_0^{\pi/2} \frac{\cos t}{\sqrt{1 + \sin^2t}} \, dt$

59. Evaluate the integral
$$\int \frac{1}{\sqrt{9x^2 + 6x - 8}} \, dx$$
by first completing the square and using the substitution $u = 3x + 1$.

60–62 • Evaluate the integral by first completing the square.

60. $\displaystyle\int \frac{dt}{\sqrt{t^2 - 6t + 13}}$

61. $\displaystyle\int \frac{dx}{(x^2 + 2x + 2)^2}$

62. $\displaystyle\int \frac{x^2}{\sqrt{4x - x^2}}\, dx$

■   ■   ■   ■   ■   ■   ■   ■   ■   ■   ■   ■   ■

63. A particle moves on a straight line with velocity function $v(t) = \sin \omega t \cos^2 \omega t$. Find its position function $s = f(t)$ if $f(0) = 0$.

64. Household electricity is supplied in the form of alternating current that varies from 155 V to -155 V with a frequency of 60 cycles per second (Hz). The voltage is thus given by the equation

$$E(t) = 155 \sin(120\pi t)$$

where t is the time in seconds. Voltmeters read the RMS (root-mean-square) voltage, which is the square root of the average value of $[E(t)]^2$ over one cycle.
(a) Calculate the RMS voltage of household current.
(b) Many electric stoves require an RMS voltage of 220 V. Find the corresponding amplitude A needed for the voltage $E(t) = A \sin(120\pi t)$.

65. Find the average value of $f(x) = \sqrt{x^2 - 1}/x$, $1 \le x \le 7$.

66. Find the area of the region bounded by the hyperbola $9x^2 - 4y^2 = 36$ and the line $x = 3$.

67. Prove the formula $A = \frac{1}{2}r^2\theta$ for the area of a sector of a circle with radius r and central angle θ. [*Hint:* Assume $0 < \theta < \pi/2$ and place the center of the circle at the origin so it has the equation $x^2 + y^2 = r^2$. Then A is the sum of the area of the triangle POQ and the area of the region PQR in the figure.]

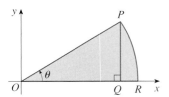

68. A charged rod of length L produces an electric field at point $P(a, b)$ given by

$$E(P) = \int_{-a}^{L-a} \frac{\lambda b}{4\pi\varepsilon_0 (x^2 + b^2)^{3/2}}\, dx$$

where λ is the charge density per unit length on the rod and ε_0 is the free space permittivity (see the figure). Evaluate the integral to determine an expression for the electric field $E(P)$.

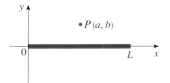

6.3 PARTIAL FRACTIONS

In this section we show how to integrate any rational function (a ratio of polynomials) by expressing it as a sum of simpler fractions, called *partial fractions*, that we already know how to integrate. To illustrate the method, observe that by taking the fractions $2/(x - 1)$ and $1/(x + 2)$ to a common denominator we obtain

$$\frac{2}{x - 1} - \frac{1}{x + 2} = \frac{2(x + 2) - (x - 1)}{(x - 1)(x + 2)} = \frac{x + 5}{x^2 + x - 2}$$

If we now reverse the procedure, we see how to integrate the function on the right side of this equation:

$$\int \frac{x + 5}{x^2 + x - 2}\, dx = \int \left(\frac{2}{x - 1} - \frac{1}{x + 2} \right) dx$$

$$= 2 \ln |x - 1| - \ln |x + 2| + C$$

To see how the method of partial fractions works in general, let's consider a rational function

$$f(x) = \frac{P(x)}{Q(x)}$$

where P and Q are polynomials. It's possible to express f as a sum of simpler fractions provided that the degree of P is less than the degree of Q. Such a rational function is called *proper*. Recall that if

$$P(x) = a_n x^n + a_{n-1} x^{n-1} + \cdots + a_1 x + a_0$$

where $a_n \neq 0$, then the degree of P is n and we write $\deg(P) = n$.

If f is improper, that is, $\deg(P) \geqslant \deg(Q)$, then we must take the preliminary step of dividing Q into P (by long division) until a remainder $R(x)$ is obtained such that $\deg(R) < \deg(Q)$. The division statement is

1 $$f(x) = \frac{P(x)}{Q(x)} = S(x) + \frac{R(x)}{Q(x)}$$

where S and R are also polynomials.

As the following example illustrates, sometimes this preliminary step is all that is required.

☑ EXAMPLE 1 Find $\displaystyle\int \frac{x^3 + x}{x - 1}\, dx$.

SOLUTION Since the degree of the numerator is greater than the degree of the denominator, we first perform the long division. This enables us to write

$$\int \frac{x^3 + x}{x - 1}\, dx = \int \left(x^2 + x + 2 + \frac{2}{x - 1} \right) dx$$

$$= \frac{x^3}{3} + \frac{x^2}{2} + 2x + 2 \ln|x - 1| + C \qquad ▪$$

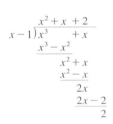

The next step is to factor the denominator $Q(x)$ as far as possible. It can be shown that any polynomial Q can be factored as a product of linear factors (of the form $ax + b$) and irreducible quadratic factors (of the form $ax^2 + bx + c$, where $b^2 - 4ac < 0$). For instance, if $Q(x) = x^4 - 16$, we could factor it as

$$Q(x) = (x^2 - 4)(x^2 + 4) = (x - 2)(x + 2)(x^2 + 4)$$

The third step is to express the proper rational function $R(x)/Q(x)$ (from Equation 1) as a sum of **partial fractions** of the form

$$\frac{A}{(ax + b)^i} \qquad \text{or} \qquad \frac{Ax + B}{(ax^2 + bx + c)^j}$$

A theorem in algebra guarantees that it is always possible to do this. We explain the details for the four cases that occur.

CASE I The denominator $Q(x)$ is a product of distinct linear factors.

This means that we can write

$$Q(x) = (a_1 x + b_1)(a_2 x + b_2) \cdots (a_k x + b_k)$$

where no factor is repeated (and no factor is a constant multiple of another). In this case the partial fraction theorem states that there exist constants $A_1, A_2, \ldots, A_k$ such that

2
$$\frac{R(x)}{Q(x)} = \frac{A_1}{a_1 x + b_1} + \frac{A_2}{a_2 x + b_2} + \cdots + \frac{A_k}{a_k x + b_k}$$

These constants can be determined as in the following example.

▼ EXAMPLE 2 Evaluate $\displaystyle\int \frac{x^2 + 2x - 1}{2x^3 + 3x^2 - 2x} \, dx$.

SOLUTION Since the degree of the numerator is less than the degree of the denominator, we don't need to divide. We factor the denominator as

$$2x^3 + 3x^2 - 2x = x(2x^2 + 3x - 2) = x(2x - 1)(x + 2)$$

Since the denominator has three distinct linear factors, the partial fraction decomposition of the integrand (2) has the form

3
$$\frac{x^2 + 2x - 1}{x(2x - 1)(x + 2)} = \frac{A}{x} + \frac{B}{2x - 1} + \frac{C}{x + 2}$$

■ Another method for finding A, B, and C is given in the note after this example.

To determine the values of A, B, and C, we multiply both sides of this equation by the product of the denominators, $x(2x - 1)(x + 2)$, obtaining

4
$$x^2 + 2x - 1 = A(2x - 1)(x + 2) + Bx(x + 2) + Cx(2x - 1)$$

Expanding the right side of Equation 4 and writing it in the standard form for polynomials, we get

5
$$x^2 + 2x - 1 = (2A + B + 2C)x^2 + (3A + 2B - C)x - 2A$$

■ Figure 1 shows the graphs of the integrand in Example 2 and its indefinite integral (with $K = 0$). Which is which?

The polynomials in Equation 5 are identical, so their coefficients must be equal. The coefficient of x^2 on the right side, $2A + B + 2C$, must equal the coefficient of x^2 on the left side—namely, 1. Likewise, the coefficients of x are equal and the constant terms are equal. This gives the following system of equations for A, B, and C:

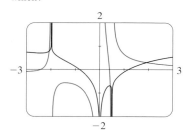

$$2A + B + 2C = 1$$
$$3A + 2B - C = 2$$
$$-2A \qquad\qquad = -1$$

FIGURE I

Solving, we get $A = \frac{1}{2}$, $B = \frac{1}{5}$, and $C = -\frac{1}{10}$, and so

■ We could check our work by taking the terms to a common denominator and adding them.

$$\int \frac{x^2 + 2x - 1}{2x^3 + 3x^2 - 2x} \, dx = \int \left(\frac{1}{2} \frac{1}{x} + \frac{1}{5} \frac{1}{2x - 1} - \frac{1}{10} \frac{1}{x + 2} \right) dx$$

$$= \tfrac{1}{2} \ln |x| + \tfrac{1}{10} \ln |2x - 1| - \tfrac{1}{10} \ln |x + 2| + K$$

In integrating the middle term we have made the mental substitution $u = 2x - 1$, which gives $du = 2 \, dx$ and $dx = du/2$. ■

NOTE We can use an alternative method to find the coefficients A, B, and C in Example 2. Equation 4 is an identity; it is true for every value of x. Let's choose values of x that simplify the equation. If we put $x = 0$ in Equation 4, then the second and third terms on the right side vanish and the equation then becomes $-2A = -1$, or $A = \frac{1}{2}$. Likewise, $x = \frac{1}{2}$ gives $5B/4 = \frac{1}{4}$ and $x = -2$ gives $10C = -1$, so $B = \frac{1}{5}$ and $C = -\frac{1}{10}$. (You may object that Equation 3 is not valid for $x = 0, \frac{1}{2},$ or -2, so why should Equation 4 be valid for those values? In fact, Equation 4 is true for all values of x, even $x = 0, \frac{1}{2},$ and -2. See Exercise 45 for the reason.)

CASE II $Q(x)$ **is a product of linear factors, some of which are repeated.**

Suppose the first linear factor $(a_1 x + b_1)$ is repeated r times; that is, $(a_1 x + b_1)^r$ occurs in the factorization of $Q(x)$. Then instead of the single term $A_1/(a_1 x + b_1)$ in Equation 2, we would use

6
$$\frac{A_1}{a_1 x + b_1} + \frac{A_2}{(a_1 x + b_1)^2} + \cdots + \frac{A_r}{(a_1 x + b_1)^r}$$

By way of illustration, we could write

$$\frac{x^3 - x + 1}{x^2(x - 1)^3} = \frac{A}{x} + \frac{B}{x^2} + \frac{C}{x - 1} + \frac{D}{(x - 1)^2} + \frac{E}{(x - 1)^3}$$

but we prefer to work out in detail a simpler example.

EXAMPLE 3 Find $\displaystyle\int \frac{x^4 - 2x^2 + 4x + 1}{x^3 - x^2 - x + 1}\, dx$.

SOLUTION The first step is to divide. The result of long division is

$$\frac{x^4 - 2x^2 + 4x + 1}{x^3 - x^2 - x + 1} = x + 1 + \frac{4x}{x^3 - x^2 - x + 1}$$

The second step is to factor the denominator $Q(x) = x^3 - x^2 - x + 1$. Since $Q(1) = 0$, we know that $x - 1$ is a factor and we obtain

$$x^3 - x^2 - x + 1 = (x - 1)(x^2 - 1) = (x - 1)(x - 1)(x + 1)$$
$$= (x - 1)^2(x + 1)$$

Since the linear factor $x - 1$ occurs twice, the partial fraction decomposition is

$$\frac{4x}{(x - 1)^2(x + 1)} = \frac{A}{x - 1} + \frac{B}{(x - 1)^2} + \frac{C}{x + 1}$$

Multiplying by the least common denominator, $(x - 1)^2(x + 1)$, we get

7
$$4x = A(x - 1)(x + 1) + B(x + 1) + C(x - 1)^2$$
$$= (A + C)x^2 + (B - 2C)x + (-A + B + C)$$

▪ Another method for finding the coefficients:
Put $x = 1$ in (7): $B = 2$.
Put $x = -1$: $C = -1$.
Put $x = 0$: $A = B + C = 1$.

Now we equate coefficients:

$$A \qquad + \quad C = 0$$
$$B - 2C = 4$$
$$-A + B + \quad C = 0$$

Solving, we obtain $A = 1$, $B = 2$, and $C = -1$, so

$$\int \frac{x^4 - 2x^2 + 4x + 1}{x^3 - x^2 - x + 1} dx = \int \left[x + 1 + \frac{1}{x - 1} + \frac{2}{(x - 1)^2} - \frac{1}{x + 1} \right] dx$$

$$= \frac{x^2}{2} + x + \ln|x - 1| - \frac{2}{x - 1} - \ln|x + 1| + K$$

$$= \frac{x^2}{2} + x - \frac{2}{x - 1} + \ln\left|\frac{x - 1}{x + 1}\right| + K \qquad ■$$

■ Here we use $\ln \dfrac{a}{b} = \ln a - \ln b$.

CASE III $Q(x)$ **contains irreducible quadratic factors, none of which is repeated.**

If $Q(x)$ has the factor $ax^2 + bx + c$, where $b^2 - 4ac < 0$, then, in addition to the partial fractions in Equations 2 and 6, the expression for $R(x)/Q(x)$ will have a term of the form

8
$$\frac{Ax + B}{ax^2 + bx + c}$$

where A and B are constants to be determined. For instance, the function given by $f(x) = x/[(x - 2)(x^2 + 1)(x^2 + 4)]$ has a partial fraction decomposition of the form

$$\frac{x}{(x - 2)(x^2 + 1)(x^2 + 4)} = \frac{A}{x - 2} + \frac{Bx + C}{x^2 + 1} + \frac{Dx + E}{x^2 + 4}$$

The term in (8) can be integrated by completing the square and using the formula

9
$$\int \frac{dx}{x^2 + a^2} = \frac{1}{a} \tan^{-1}\left(\frac{x}{a}\right) + C$$

✓ EXAMPLE 4 Evaluate $\displaystyle\int \frac{2x^2 - x + 4}{x^3 + 4x} dx$.

SOLUTION Since $x^3 + 4x = x(x^2 + 4)$ can't be factored further, we write

$$\frac{2x^2 - x + 4}{x(x^2 + 4)} = \frac{A}{x} + \frac{Bx + C}{x^2 + 4}$$

Multiplying by $x(x^2 + 4)$, we have

$$2x^2 - x + 4 = A(x^2 + 4) + (Bx + C)x$$
$$= (A + B)x^2 + Cx + 4A$$

Equating coefficients, we obtain

$$A + B = 2 \qquad C = -1 \qquad 4A = 4$$

Thus $A = 1$, $B = 1$, and $C = -1$ and so

$$\int \frac{2x^2 - x + 4}{x^3 + 4x} dx = \int \left(\frac{1}{x} + \frac{x - 1}{x^2 + 4} \right) dx$$

In order to integrate the second term we split it into two parts:

$$\int \frac{x-1}{x^2+4}\,dx = \int \frac{x}{x^2+4}\,dx - \int \frac{1}{x^2+4}\,dx$$

We make the substitution $u = x^2 + 4$ in the first of these integrals so that $du = 2x\,dx$. We evaluate the second integral by means of Formula 9 with $a = 2$:

$$\int \frac{2x^2-x+4}{x(x^2+4)}\,dx = \int \frac{1}{x}\,dx + \int \frac{x}{x^2+4}\,dx - \int \frac{1}{x^2+4}\,dx$$

$$= \ln|x| + \tfrac{1}{2}\ln(x^2+4) - \tfrac{1}{2}\tan^{-1}(x/2) + K \qquad \blacksquare$$

EXAMPLE 5 Evaluate $\displaystyle\int \frac{4x^2-3x+2}{4x^2-4x+3}\,dx$.

SOLUTION Since the degree of the numerator is *not less than* the degree of the denominator, we first divide and obtain

$$\frac{4x^2-3x+2}{4x^2-4x+3} = 1 + \frac{x-1}{4x^2-4x+3}$$

Notice that the quadratic $4x^2 - 4x + 3$ is irreducible because its discriminant is $b^2 - 4ac = -32 < 0$. This means it can't be factored, so we don't need to use the partial fraction technique.

To integrate the given function we complete the square in the denominator:

$$4x^2 - 4x + 3 = (2x-1)^2 + 2$$

This suggests that we make the substitution $u = 2x - 1$. Then, $du = 2\,dx$ and $x = (u+1)/2$, so

$$\int \frac{4x^2-3x+2}{4x^2-4x+3}\,dx = \int \left(1 + \frac{x-1}{4x^2-4x+3}\right) dx$$

$$= x + \tfrac{1}{2}\int \frac{\tfrac{1}{2}(u+1)-1}{u^2+2}\,du = x + \tfrac{1}{4}\int \frac{u-1}{u^2+2}\,du$$

$$= x + \tfrac{1}{4}\int \frac{u}{u^2+2}\,du - \tfrac{1}{4}\int \frac{1}{u^2+2}\,du$$

$$= x + \tfrac{1}{8}\ln(u^2+2) - \frac{1}{4}\cdot\frac{1}{\sqrt{2}}\tan^{-1}\left(\frac{u}{\sqrt{2}}\right) + C$$

$$= x + \tfrac{1}{8}\ln(4x^2-4x+3) - \frac{1}{4\sqrt{2}}\tan^{-1}\left(\frac{2x-1}{\sqrt{2}}\right) + C \qquad \blacksquare$$

NOTE Example 5 illustrates the general procedure for integrating a partial fraction of the form

$$\frac{Ax+B}{ax^2+bx+c} \qquad \text{where } b^2 - 4ac < 0$$

We complete the square in the denominator and then make a substitution that brings the integral into the form

$$\int \frac{Cu + D}{u^2 + a^2}\, du = C \int \frac{u}{u^2 + a^2}\, du + D \int \frac{1}{u^2 + a^2}\, du$$

Then the first integral is a logarithm and the second is expressed in terms of $\tan^{-1}$.

CASE IV $Q(x)$ **contains a repeated irreducible quadratic factor.**

If $Q(x)$ has the factor $(ax^2 + bx + c)^r$, where $b^2 - 4ac < 0$, then instead of the single partial fraction (8), the sum

10
$$\frac{A_1 x + B_1}{ax^2 + bx + c} + \frac{A_2 x + B_2}{(ax^2 + bx + c)^2} + \cdots + \frac{A_r x + B_r}{(ax^2 + bx + c)^r}$$

occurs in the partial fraction decomposition of $R(x)/Q(x)$. Each of the terms in (10) can be integrated by first completing the square.

▪ It would be extremely tedious to work out by hand the numerical values of the coefficients in Example 6. Most computer algebra systems, however, can find the numerical values very quickly. For instance, the Maple command

$\qquad$ convert(f, parfrac, x)

or the Mathematica command

$\qquad$ Apart[f]

gives the following values:

$A = -1, \quad B = \frac{1}{8}, \quad C = D = -1,$

$E = \frac{15}{8}, \quad F = -\frac{1}{8}, \quad G = H = \frac{3}{4},$

$\qquad I = -\frac{1}{2}, \quad J = \frac{1}{2}$

EXAMPLE 6 Write out the form of the partial fraction decomposition of the function

$$\frac{x^3 + x^2 + 1}{x(x - 1)(x^2 + x + 1)(x^2 + 1)^3}$$

SOLUTION

$$\frac{x^3 + x^2 + 1}{x(x - 1)(x^2 + x + 1)(x^2 + 1)^3}$$

$$= \frac{A}{x} + \frac{B}{x - 1} + \frac{Cx + D}{x^2 + x + 1} + \frac{Ex + F}{x^2 + 1} + \frac{Gx + H}{(x^2 + 1)^2} + \frac{Ix + J}{(x^2 + 1)^3} \qquad ▪$$

EXAMPLE 7 Evaluate $\displaystyle \int \frac{1 - x + 2x^2 - x^3}{x(x^2 + 1)^2}\, dx.$

SOLUTION The form of the partial fraction decomposition is

$$\frac{1 - x + 2x^2 - x^3}{x(x^2 + 1)^2} = \frac{A}{x} + \frac{Bx + C}{x^2 + 1} + \frac{Dx + E}{(x^2 + 1)^2}$$

Multiplying by $x(x^2 + 1)^2$, we have

$$-x^3 + 2x^2 - x + 1 = A(x^2 + 1)^2 + (Bx + C)x(x^2 + 1) + (Dx + E)x$$

$$= A(x^4 + 2x^2 + 1) + B(x^4 + x^2) + C(x^3 + x) + Dx^2 + Ex$$

$$= (A + B)x^4 + Cx^3 + (2A + B + D)x^2 + (C + E)x + A$$

If we equate coefficients, we get the system

$$A + B = 0 \qquad C = -1 \qquad 2A + B + D = 2 \qquad C + E = -1 \qquad A = 1$$

which has the solution $A = 1$, $B = -1$, $C = -1$, $D = 1$, and $E = 0$. Thus

$$\int \frac{1 - x + 2x^2 - x^3}{x(x^2 + 1)^2} dx = \int \left(\frac{1}{x} - \frac{x + 1}{x^2 + 1} + \frac{x}{(x^2 + 1)^2} \right) dx$$

$$= \int \frac{dx}{x} - \int \frac{x}{x^2 + 1} dx - \int \frac{dx}{x^2 + 1} + \int \frac{x \, dx}{(x^2 + 1)^2}$$

▪ In the second and fourth terms we
made the mental substitution $u = x^2 + 1$.

$$= \ln |x| - \tfrac{1}{2} \ln(x^2 + 1) - \tan^{-1}x - \frac{1}{2(x^2 + 1)} + K$$ ∎

6.3 EXERCISES

1–6 ▪ Write out the form of the partial fraction decomposition
of the function (as in Example 6). Do not determine the numerical values of the coefficients.

1. (a) $\dfrac{2x}{(x + 3)(3x + 1)}$

(b) $\dfrac{1}{x^3 + 2x^2 + x}$

2. (a) $\dfrac{x - 1}{x^3 + x^2}$

(b) $\dfrac{x - 1}{x^3 + x}$

3. (a) $\dfrac{2}{x^2 + 3x - 4}$

(b) $\dfrac{x^2}{(x - 1)(x^2 + x + 1)}$

4. (a) $\dfrac{x^3}{x^2 + 4x + 3}$

(b) $\dfrac{2x + 1}{(x + 1)^3(x^2 + 4)^2}$

5. (a) $\dfrac{x^4}{x^4 - 1}$

(b) $\dfrac{t^4 + t^2 + 1}{(t^2 + 1)(t^2 + 4)^2}$

6. (a) $\dfrac{x^4}{(x^3 + x)(x^2 - x + 3)}$

(b) $\dfrac{1}{x^6 - x^3}$

7–34 ▪ Evaluate the integral.

7. $\displaystyle\int \frac{x}{x - 6} dx$

8. $\displaystyle\int \frac{r^2}{r + 4} dr$

9. $\displaystyle\int \frac{x - 9}{(x + 5)(x - 2)} dx$

10. $\displaystyle\int \frac{1}{(t + 4)(t - 1)} dt$

11. $\displaystyle\int_2^3 \frac{1}{x^2 - 1} dx$

12. $\displaystyle\int_0^1 \frac{x - 1}{x^2 + 3x + 2} dx$

13. $\displaystyle\int \frac{ax}{x^2 - bx} dx$

14. $\displaystyle\int \frac{1}{(x + a)(x + b)} dx$

15. $\displaystyle\int_0^1 \frac{2x + 3}{(x + 1)^2} dx$

16. $\displaystyle\int_0^1 \frac{x^3 - 4x - 10}{x^2 - x - 6} dx$

17. $\displaystyle\int_1^2 \frac{4y^2 - 7y - 12}{y(y + 2)(y - 3)} dy$

18. $\displaystyle\int \frac{x^2 + 2x - 1}{x^3 - x} dx$

19. $\displaystyle\int \frac{1}{(x + 5)^2(x - 1)} dx$

20. $\displaystyle\int \frac{x^2}{(x - 3)(x + 2)^2} dx$

21. $\displaystyle\int \frac{5x^2 + 3x - 2}{x^3 + 2x^2} dx$

22. $\displaystyle\int \frac{x^2 - x + 6}{x^3 + 3x} dx$

23. $\displaystyle\int \frac{10}{(x - 1)(x^2 + 9)} dx$

24. $\displaystyle\int \frac{x^2 - 2x - 1}{(x - 1)^2(x^2 + 1)} dx$

25. $\displaystyle\int \frac{x^3 + x^2 + 2x + 1}{(x^2 + 1)(x^2 + 2)} dx$

26. $\displaystyle\int \frac{x^3 - 2x^2 + x + 1}{x^4 + 5x^2 + 4} dx$

27. $\displaystyle\int \frac{x + 4}{x^2 + 2x + 5} dx$

28. $\displaystyle\int_0^1 \frac{x}{x^2 + 4x + 13} dx$

29. $\displaystyle\int \frac{1}{x^3 - 1} dx$

30. $\displaystyle\int \frac{x^3}{x^3 + 1} dx$

31. $\displaystyle\int \frac{dx}{x^4 - x^2}$

32. $\displaystyle\int_0^1 \frac{2x^3 + 5x}{x^4 + 5x^2 + 4} dx$

33. $\displaystyle\int \frac{x - 3}{(x^2 + 2x + 4)^2} dx$

34. $\displaystyle\int \frac{x^4 + 1}{x(x^2 + 1)^2} dx$

35–40 ▪ Make a substitution to express the integrand as a
rational function and then evaluate the integral.

35. $\displaystyle\int_9^{16} \frac{\sqrt{x}}{x - 4} dx$ $\left(\text{Let } u = \sqrt{x}.\right)$

36. $\displaystyle\int_0^1 \frac{1}{1 + \sqrt[3]{x}} dx$ $\left(\text{Let } u = \sqrt[3]{x}.\right)$

37. $\displaystyle\int \frac{x^3}{\sqrt[3]{x^2 + 1}} dx$

38. $\displaystyle\int_{1/3}^3 \frac{\sqrt{x}}{x^2 + x} dx$

39. $\displaystyle\int \frac{e^{2x}}{e^{2x} + 3e^x + 2} dx$

40. $\displaystyle\int \frac{\cos x}{\sin^2 x + \sin x} dx$

41–42 ■ Use integration by parts, together with the techniques of this section, to evaluate the integral.

41. $\displaystyle\int \ln(x^2 - x + 2)\, dx$

42. $\displaystyle\int x \tan^{-1}x\, dx$

■ ■ ■ ■ ■ ■ ■ ■ ■ ■ ■ ■ ■ ■ ■

43. One method of slowing the growth of an insect population without using pesticides is to introduce into the population a number of sterile males that mate with fertile females but produce no offspring. If P represents the number of female insects in a population, S the number of sterile males introduced each generation, and r the population's natural growth rate, then the female population is related to time t by

$$t = \int \frac{P + S}{P[(r - 1)P - S]}\, dP$$

Suppose an insect population with 10,000 females grows at a rate of $r = 0.10$ and 900 sterile males are added. Evaluate the integral to give an equation relating the female population to time. (Note that the resulting equation can't be solved explicitly for P.)

44. Factor $x^4 + 1$ as a difference of squares by first adding and subtracting the same quantity. Use this factorization to evaluate $\int 1/(x^4 + 1)\, dx$.

45. Suppose that F, G, and Q are polynomials and

$$\frac{F(x)}{Q(x)} = \frac{G(x)}{Q(x)}$$

for all x except when $Q(x) = 0$. Prove that $F(x) = G(x)$ for all x. [*Hint:* Use continuity.]

46. If f is a quadratic function such that $f(0) = 1$ and

$$\int \frac{f(x)}{x^2(x + 1)^3}\, dx$$

is a rational function, find the value of $f'(0)$.

6.4 | **INTEGRATION WITH TABLES AND COMPUTER ALGEBRA SYSTEMS**

In this section we describe how to evaluate integrals using tables and computer algebra systems.

TABLES OF INTEGRALS

Tables of indefinite integrals are very useful when we are confronted by an integral that is difficult to evaluate by hand and we don't have access to a computer algebra system. A relatively brief table of 120 integrals, categorized by form, is provided on the Reference Pages at the back of the book. More extensive tables are available in *CRC Standard Mathematical Tables and Formulae,* 31st ed, by Daniel Zwillinger (Boca Raton, FL: CRC Press, 2002) (709 entries) or in Gradshteyn and Ryzhik's *Table of Integrals, Series, and Products,* 6e, edited by A. Jefferey and D. Zwillinger (San Diego: Academic Press, 2000), which contains hundreds of pages of integrals. It should be remembered, however, that integrals do not often occur in exactly the form listed in a table. Usually we need to use the Substitution Rule or algebraic manipulation to transform a given integral into one of the forms in the table.

■ The Table of Integrals appears on Reference Pages 6–10 at the back of the book.

▼ EXAMPLE 1 Use the Table of Integrals to find $\displaystyle\int \frac{x^2}{\sqrt{5 - 4x^2}}\, dx$.

SOLUTION If we look at the section of the table entitled *Forms involving* $\sqrt{a^2 - u^2}$, we see that the closest entry is number 34:

$$\int \frac{u^2}{\sqrt{a^2 - u^2}}\, du = -\frac{u}{2}\sqrt{a^2 - u^2} + \frac{a^2}{2}\sin^{-1}\!\left(\frac{u}{a}\right) + C$$

This is not exactly what we have, but we will be able to use it if we first make the substitution $u = 2x$:

$$\int \frac{x^2}{\sqrt{5 - 4x^2}} \, dx = \int \frac{(u/2)^2}{\sqrt{5 - u^2}} \frac{du}{2} = \frac{1}{8} \int \frac{u^2}{\sqrt{5 - u^2}} \, du$$

Then we use Formula 34 with $a^2 = 5$ (so $a = \sqrt{5}$):

$$\int \frac{x^2}{\sqrt{5 - 4x^2}} \, dx = \frac{1}{8} \int \frac{u^2}{\sqrt{5 - u^2}} \, du = \frac{1}{8} \left[-\frac{u}{2} \sqrt{5 - u^2} + \frac{5}{2} \sin^{-1} \frac{u}{\sqrt{5}} \right] + C$$

$$= -\frac{x}{8} \sqrt{5 - 4x^2} + \frac{5}{16} \sin^{-1} \left(\frac{2x}{\sqrt{5}} \right) + C \qquad ■$$

EXAMPLE 2 Use the Table of Integrals to find $\int x^3 \sin x \, dx$.

SOLUTION If we look in the section called *Trigonometric Forms*, we see that none of the entries explicitly includes a u^3 factor. However, we can use the reduction formula in entry 84 with $n = 3$:

$$\int x^3 \sin x \, dx = -x^3 \cos x + 3 \int x^2 \cos x \, dx$$

85. $\int u^n \cos u \, du$

$$= u^n \sin u - n \int u^{n-1} \sin u \, du$$

We now need to evaluate $\int x^2 \cos x \, dx$. We can use the reduction formula in entry 85 with $n = 2$, followed by entry 82:

$$\int x^2 \cos x \, dx = x^2 \sin x - 2 \int x \sin x \, dx$$

$$= x^2 \sin x - 2(\sin x - x \cos x) + K$$

Combining these calculations, we get

$$\int x^3 \sin x \, dx = -x^3 \cos x + 3x^2 \sin x + 6x \cos x - 6 \sin x + C$$

where $C = 3K$. ■

▼ EXAMPLE 3 Use the Table of Integrals to find $\int x \sqrt{x^2 + 2x + 4} \, dx$.

SOLUTION Since the table gives forms involving $\sqrt{a^2 + x^2}$, $\sqrt{a^2 - x^2}$, and $\sqrt{x^2 - a^2}$, but not $\sqrt{ax^2 + bx + c}$, we first complete the square:

$$x^2 + 2x + 4 = (x + 1)^2 + 3$$

If we make the substitution $u = x + 1$ (so $x = u - 1$), the integrand will involve the pattern $\sqrt{a^2 + u^2}$:

$$\int x \sqrt{x^2 + 2x + 4} \, dx = \int (u - 1) \sqrt{u^2 + 3} \, du$$

$$= \int u \sqrt{u^2 + 3} \, du - \int \sqrt{u^2 + 3} \, du$$

The first integral is evaluated using the substitution $t = u^2 + 3$:

$$\int u\sqrt{u^2 + 3}\ du = \tfrac{1}{2}\int \sqrt{t}\ dt = \tfrac{1}{2} \cdot \tfrac{2}{3}t^{3/2} = \tfrac{1}{3}(u^2 + 3)^{3/2}$$

21. $\displaystyle\int \sqrt{a^2 + u^2}\ du = \frac{u}{2}\sqrt{a^2 + u^2}$

$\displaystyle\qquad + \frac{a^2}{2}\ln(u + \sqrt{a^2 + u^2}) + C$

For the second integral we use Formula 21 with $a = \sqrt{3}$:

$$\int \sqrt{u^2 + 3}\ du = \frac{u}{2}\sqrt{u^2 + 3} + \tfrac{3}{2}\ln(u + \sqrt{u^2 + 3})$$

Thus

$$\int x\sqrt{x^2 + 2x + 4}\ dx$$

$$= \tfrac{1}{3}(x^2 + 2x + 4)^{3/2} - \frac{x + 1}{2}\sqrt{x^2 + 2x + 4} - \tfrac{3}{2}\ln(x + 1 + \sqrt{x^2 + 2x + 4}) + C$$

■

COMPUTER ALGEBRA SYSTEMS

We have seen that the use of tables involves matching the form of the given integrand with the forms of the integrands in the tables. Computers are particularly good at matching patterns. And just as we used substitutions in conjunction with tables, a CAS can perform substitutions that transform a given integral into one that occurs in its stored formulas. So it isn't surprising that computer algebra systems excel at integration. That doesn't mean that integration by hand is an obsolete skill. We will see that a hand computation sometimes produces an indefinite integral in a form that is more convenient than a machine answer.

To begin, let's see what happens when we ask a machine to integrate the relatively simple function $y = 1/(3x - 2)$. Using the substitution $u = 3x - 2$, an easy calculation by hand gives

$$\int \frac{1}{3x - 2}\ dx = \tfrac{1}{3}\ln|3x - 2| + C$$

whereas Derive, Mathematica, and Maple all return the answer

$$\tfrac{1}{3}\ln(3x - 2)$$

The first thing to notice is that computer algebra systems omit the constant of integration. In other words, they produce a *particular* antiderivative, not the most general one. Therefore, when making use of a machine integration, we might have to add a constant. Second, the absolute value signs are omitted in the machine answer. That is fine if our problem is concerned only with values of x greater than $\tfrac{2}{3}$. But if we are interested in other values of x, then we need to insert the absolute value symbol.

In the next example we reconsider the integral of Example 3, but this time we ask a machine for the answer.

EXAMPLE 4 Use a computer algebra system to find $\displaystyle\int x\sqrt{x^2 + 2x + 4}\ dx$.

SOLUTION Maple responds with the answer

$$\tfrac{1}{3}(x^2 + 2x + 4)^{3/2} - \tfrac{1}{4}(2x + 2)\sqrt{x^2 + 2x + 4} - \frac{3}{2}\operatorname{arcsinh}\frac{\sqrt{3}}{3}(1 + x)$$

This looks different from the answer we found in Example 3, but it is equivalent because the third term can be rewritten using the identity

■ This is Equation 3.6.3.

$$\operatorname{arcsinh} x = \ln\left(x + \sqrt{x^2 + 1}\right)$$

Thus

$$\operatorname{arcsinh} \frac{\sqrt{3}}{3}(1 + x) = \ln\left[\frac{\sqrt{3}}{3}(1 + x) + \sqrt{\tfrac{1}{3}(1 + x)^2 + 1}\right]$$

$$= \ln \frac{1}{\sqrt{3}}\left[1 + x + \sqrt{(1 + x)^2 + 3}\right]$$

$$= \ln \frac{1}{\sqrt{3}} + \ln\left(x + 1 + \sqrt{x^2 + 2x + 4}\right)$$

The resulting extra term $-\frac{3}{2}\ln\left(1/\sqrt{3}\right)$ can be absorbed into the constant of integration. Mathematica gives the answer

$$\left(\frac{5}{6} + \frac{x}{6} + \frac{x^2}{3}\right)\sqrt{x^2 + 2x + 4} - \frac{3}{2}\operatorname{arcsinh}\left(\frac{1 + x}{\sqrt{3}}\right)$$

Mathematica combined the first two terms of Example 3 (and the Maple result) into a single term by factoring.
   Derive gives the answer

$$\tfrac{1}{6}\sqrt{x^2 + 2x + 4}\,(2x^2 + x + 5) - \tfrac{3}{2}\ln\left(\sqrt{x^2 + 2x + 4} + x + 1\right)$$

The first term is like the first term in the Mathematica answer, and the second term is identical to the last term in Example 3. ■

EXAMPLE 5 Use a CAS to evaluate $\int x(x^2 + 5)^8\,dx$.

SOLUTION Maple and Mathematica give the same answer:

$$\tfrac{1}{18}x^{18} + \tfrac{5}{2}x^{16} + 50x^{14} + \tfrac{1750}{3}x^{12} + 4375x^{10} + 21875x^8 + \tfrac{218750}{3}x^6 + 156250x^4 + \tfrac{390625}{2}x^2$$

It's clear that both systems must have expanded $(x^2 + 5)^8$ by the Binomial Theorem and then integrated each term.
   If we integrate by hand instead, using the substitution $u = x^2 + 5$, we get

■ Derive and the TI-89 and TI-92 also give this answer.

$$\int x(x^2 + 5)^8\,dx = \tfrac{1}{18}(x^2 + 5)^9 + C$$

For most purposes, this is a more convenient form of the answer. ■

EXAMPLE 6 Use a CAS to find $\int \sin^5 x \cos^2 x\,dx$.

SOLUTION In Example 2 in Section 6.2 we found that

■ $$\int \sin^5 x \cos^2 x\,dx = -\tfrac{1}{3}\cos^3 x + \tfrac{2}{5}\cos^5 x - \tfrac{1}{7}\cos^7 x + C$$

Derive and Maple report the answer

$$-\tfrac{1}{7} \sin^4x \, \cos^3x - \tfrac{4}{35} \sin^2x \, \cos^3x - \tfrac{8}{105} \cos^3x$$

whereas Mathematica produces

$$-\tfrac{5}{64} \cos x - \tfrac{1}{192} \cos 3x + \tfrac{3}{320} \cos 5x - \tfrac{1}{448} \cos 7x$$

We suspect that there are trigonometric identities which show these three answers are equivalent. Indeed, if we ask Derive, Maple, and Mathematica to simplify their expressions using trigonometric identities, they ultimately produce the same form of the answer as in Equation 1. ∎

CAN WE INTEGRATE ALL CONTINUOUS FUNCTIONS?

The question arises: Will our basic integration formulas, together with the Substitution Rule, integration by parts, tables of integrals, and computer algebra systems, enable us to find the integral of every continuous function? In particular, can we use it to evaluate $\int e^{x^2} dx$? The answer is No, at least not in terms of the functions that we are familiar with.

Most of the functions that we have been dealing with in this book are what are called **elementary functions**. These are the polynomials, rational functions, power functions (x^a), exponential functions (a^x), logarithmic functions, trigonometric and inverse trigonometric functions, and all functions that can be obtained from these by the five operations of addition, subtraction, multiplication, division, and composition. For instance, the function

$$f(x) = \sqrt{\frac{x^2 - 1}{x^3 + 2x - 1}} + \ln(\cos x) - xe^{\sin 2x}$$

is an elementary function.

If f is an elementary function, then f' is an elementary function but $\int f(x) \, dx$ need not be an elementary function. Consider $f(x) = e^{x^2}$. Since f is continuous, its integral exists, and if we define the function F by

$$F(x) = \int_0^x e^{t^2} \, dt$$

then we know from Part 1 of the Fundamental Theorem of Calculus that

$$F'(x) = e^{x^2}$$

Thus $f(x) = e^{x^2}$ has an antiderivative F, but it can be proved that F is not an elementary function. This means that no matter how hard we try, we will never succeed in evaluating $\int e^{x^2} dx$ in terms of the functions we know. (In Chapter 8, however, we will see how to express $\int e^{x^2} dx$ as an infinite series.) The same can be said of the following integrals:

$$\int \frac{e^x}{x} \, dx \qquad \int \sin(x^2) \, dx \qquad \int \cos(e^x) \, dx$$

$$\int \sqrt{x^3 + 1} \, dx \qquad \int \frac{1}{\ln x} \, dx \qquad \int \frac{\sin x}{x} \, dx$$

In fact, the majority of elementary functions don't have elementary antiderivatives.

6.4 EXERCISES

1–22 ▪ Use the Table of Integrals on Reference Pages 6–10 to evaluate the integral.

1. $\displaystyle\int_0^1 2x \cos^{-1}x \, dx$

2. $\displaystyle\int e^{2\theta} \sin 3\theta \, d\theta$

3. $\displaystyle\int \sec^3(\pi x) \, dx$

4. $\displaystyle\int_2^3 \frac{1}{x^2\sqrt{4x^2 - 7}} \, dx$

5. $\displaystyle\int \frac{dx}{x^2\sqrt{4x^2 + 9}}$

6. $\displaystyle\int \frac{\sqrt{2y^2 - 3}}{y^2} \, dy$

7. $\displaystyle\int_0^\pi x^3 \sin x \, dx$

8. $\displaystyle\int \frac{e^{2x}}{\sqrt{2 + e^x}} \, dx$

9. $\displaystyle\int \frac{\tan^3(1/z)}{z^2} \, dz$

10. $\displaystyle\int \sin^{-1}\sqrt{x} \, dx$

11. $\displaystyle\int y\sqrt{6 + 4y - 4y^2} \, dy$

12. $\displaystyle\int x \sin(x^2) \cos(3x^2) \, dx$

13. $\displaystyle\int \sin^2 x \cos x \ln(\sin x) \, dx$

14. $\displaystyle\int_0^\pi \cos^4(3\theta) \, d\theta$

15. $\displaystyle\int \frac{e^x}{3 - e^{2x}} \, dx$

16. $\displaystyle\int_0^2 x^3\sqrt{4x^2 - x^4} \, dx$

17. $\displaystyle\int \frac{x^4 \, dx}{\sqrt{x^{10} - 2}}$

18. $\displaystyle\int_0^1 x^4 e^{-x} \, dx$

19. $\displaystyle\int \frac{\sqrt{4 + (\ln x)^2}}{x} \, dx$

20. $\displaystyle\int \frac{\sec^2\theta \tan^2\theta}{\sqrt{9 - \tan^2\theta}} \, d\theta$

21. $\displaystyle\int \sqrt{e^{2x} - 1} \, dx$

22. $\displaystyle\int e^t \sin(\alpha t - 3) \, dt$

▪ ▪ ▪ ▪ ▪ ▪ ▪ ▪ ▪ ▪ ▪ ▪ ▪ ▪

23. Verify Formula 53 in the Table of Integrals (a) by differentiation and (b) by using the substitution $t = a + bu$.

24. Verify Formula 31 (a) by differentiation and (b) by substituting $u = a \sin\theta$.

CAS **25–32** ▪ Use a computer algebra system to evaluate the integral. Compare the answer with the result of using tables. If the answers are not the same, show that they are equivalent.

25. $\displaystyle\int x^2\sqrt{5 - x^2} \, dx$

26. $\displaystyle\int x^2(1 + x^3)^4 \, dx$

27. $\displaystyle\int \sin^3 x \cos^2 x \, dx$

28. $\displaystyle\int \tan^2 x \sec^4 x \, dx$

29. $\displaystyle\int x\sqrt{1 + 2x} \, dx$

30. $\displaystyle\int \sin^4 x \, dx$

31. $\displaystyle\int \tan^5 x \, dx$

32. $\displaystyle\int x^5\sqrt{x^2 + 1} \, dx$

▪ ▪ ▪ ▪ ▪ ▪ ▪ ▪ ▪ ▪ ▪ ▪ ▪ ▪ ▪ ▪

CAS **33.** Computer algebra systems sometimes need a helping hand from human beings. Ask your CAS to evaluate

$$\int 2^x \sqrt{4^x - 1} \, dx$$

If it doesn't return an answer, ask it to try

$$\int 2^x \sqrt{2^{2x} - 1} \, dx$$

instead. Why do you think it was successful with this form of the integrand?

CAS **34.** Try to evaluate

$$\int (1 + \ln x) \sqrt{1 + (x \ln x)^2} \, dx$$

with a computer algebra system. If it doesn't return an answer, make a substitution that changes the integral into one that the CAS *can* evaluate.

6.5 APPROXIMATE INTEGRATION

There are two situations in which it is impossible to find the exact value of a definite integral.

The first situation arises from the fact that in order to find $\int_a^b f(x) \, dx$ using the Evaluation Theorem we need to know an antiderivative of f. Sometimes, however, it is difficult, or even impossible, to find an antiderivative (see Section 6.4). For example, it is impossible to evaluate the following integrals exactly:

$$\int_0^1 e^{x^2} \, dx \qquad \int_{-1}^1 \sqrt{1 + x^3} \, dx$$

The second situation arises when the function is determined from a scientific experiment through instrument readings or collected data. There may be no formula for the function (see Example 5).

In both cases we need to find approximate values of definite integrals. We already know one such method. Recall that the definite integral is defined as a limit of Riemann sums, so any Riemann sum could be used as an approximation to the integral: If we divide $[a, b]$ into n subintervals of equal length $\Delta x = (b - a)/n$, then we have

$$\int_a^b f(x)\, dx \approx \sum_{i=1}^n f(x_i^*)\, \Delta x$$

where x_i^* is any point in the ith subinterval $[x_{i-1}, x_i]$. If x_i^* is chosen to be the left endpoint of the interval, then $x_i^* = x_{i-1}$ and we have

1
$$\int_a^b f(x)\, dx \approx L_n = \sum_{i=1}^n f(x_{i-1})\, \Delta x$$

If $f(x) \geq 0$, then the integral represents an area and (1) represents an approximation of this area by the rectangles shown in Figure 1(a). If we choose x_i^* to be the right endpoint, then $x_i^* = x_i$ and we have

2
$$\int_a^b f(x)\, dx \approx R_n = \sum_{i=1}^n f(x_i)\, \Delta x$$

[See Figure 1(b).] The approximations L_n and R_n defined by Equations 1 and 2 are called the **left endpoint approximation** and **right endpoint approximation**, respectively.

In Section 5.2 we also considered the case where x_i^* is chosen to be the midpoint $\bar{x}_i$ of the subinterval $[x_{i-1}, x_i]$. Figure 1(c) shows the midpoint approximation M_n, which appears to be better than either L_n or R_n.

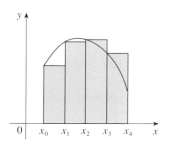

(a) Left endpoint approximation

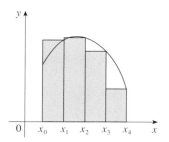

(b) Right endpoint approximation

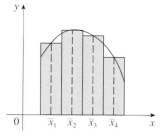

(c) Midpoint approximation

FIGURE 1

MIDPOINT RULE

$$\int_a^b f(x)\, dx \approx M_n = \Delta x \left[f(\bar{x}_1) + f(\bar{x}_2) + \cdots + f(\bar{x}_n) \right]$$

where
$$\Delta x = \frac{b - a}{n}$$

and
$$\bar{x}_i = \tfrac{1}{2}(x_{i-1} + x_i) = \text{midpoint of } [x_{i-1}, x_i]$$

Another approximation, called the Trapezoidal Rule, results from averaging the approximations in Equations 1 and 2:

$$\int_a^b f(x)\, dx \approx \frac{1}{2} \left[\sum_{i=1}^n f(x_{i-1})\, \Delta x + \sum_{i=1}^n f(x_i)\, \Delta x \right] = \frac{\Delta x}{2} \left[\sum_{i=1}^n \left(f(x_{i-1}) + f(x_i) \right) \right]$$

$$= \frac{\Delta x}{2} \left[\left(f(x_0) + f(x_1) \right) + \left(f(x_1) + f(x_2) \right) + \cdots + \left(f(x_{n-1}) + f(x_n) \right) \right]$$

$$= \frac{\Delta x}{2} \left[f(x_0) + 2f(x_1) + 2f(x_2) + \cdots + 2f(x_{n-1}) + f(x_n) \right]$$

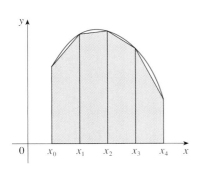

FIGURE 2
Trapezoidal approximation

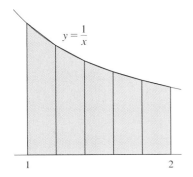

FIGURE 3

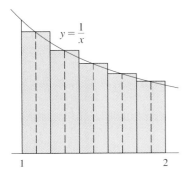

FIGURE 4

TRAPEZOIDAL RULE

$$\int_a^b f(x)\,dx \approx T_n = \frac{\Delta x}{2}\left[f(x_0) + 2f(x_1) + 2f(x_2) + \cdots + 2f(x_{n-1}) + f(x_n)\right]$$

where $\Delta x = (b-a)/n$ and $x_i = a + i\,\Delta x$.

The reason for the name Trapezoidal Rule can be seen from Figure 2, which illustrates the case $f(x) \geqslant 0$. The area of the trapezoid that lies above the ith subinterval is

$$\Delta x\left(\frac{f(x_{i-1}) + f(x_i)}{2}\right) = \frac{\Delta x}{2}\left[f(x_{i-1}) + f(x_i)\right]$$

and if we add the areas of all these trapezoids, we get the right side of the Trapezoidal Rule.

EXAMPLE 1 Use (a) the Trapezoidal Rule and (b) the Midpoint Rule with $n = 5$ to approximate the integral $\int_1^2 (1/x)\,dx$.

SOLUTION
(a) With $n = 5$, $a = 1$, and $b = 2$, we have $\Delta x = (2 - 1)/5 = 0.2$, and so the Trapezoidal Rule gives

$$\int_1^2 \frac{1}{x}\,dx \approx T_5 = \frac{0.2}{2}\left[f(1) + 2f(1.2) + 2f(1.4) + 2f(1.6) + 2f(1.8) + f(2)\right]$$

$$= 0.1\left(\frac{1}{1} + \frac{2}{1.2} + \frac{2}{1.4} + \frac{2}{1.6} + \frac{2}{1.8} + \frac{1}{2}\right)$$

$$\approx 0.695635$$

This approximation is illustrated in Figure 3.

(b) The midpoints of the five subintervals are 1.1, 1.3, 1.5, 1.7, and 1.9, so the Midpoint Rule gives

$$\int_1^2 \frac{1}{x}\,dx \approx \Delta x\left[f(1.1) + f(1.3) + f(1.5) + f(1.7) + f(1.9)\right]$$

$$= \frac{1}{5}\left(\frac{1}{1.1} + \frac{1}{1.3} + \frac{1}{1.5} + \frac{1}{1.7} + \frac{1}{1.9}\right)$$

$$\approx 0.691908$$

This approximation is illustrated in Figure 4. ■

In Example 1 we deliberately chose an integral whose value can be computed explicitly so that we can see how accurate the Trapezoidal and Midpoint Rules are. By the Fundamental Theorem of Calculus,

$$\int_1^2 \frac{1}{x}\,dx = \ln x\,\Big]_1^2 = \ln 2 = 0.693147\ldots$$

$$\int_a^b f(x)\,dx = \text{approximation} + \text{error}$$

The **error** in using an approximation is defined to be the amount that needs to be added to the approximation to make it exact. From the values in Example 1 we see that the errors in the Trapezoidal and Midpoint Rule approximations for $n = 5$ are

$$E_T \approx -0.002488 \qquad \text{and} \qquad E_M \approx 0.001239$$

In general, we have

$$E_T = \int_a^b f(x)\, dx - T_n \qquad \text{and} \qquad E_M = \int_a^b f(x)\, dx - M_n$$

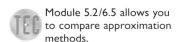

Module 5.2/6.5 allows you to compare approximation methods.

The following tables show the results of calculations similar to those in Example 1, but for $n = 5$, 10, and 20 and for the left and right endpoint approximations as well as the Trapezoidal and Midpoint Rules.

Approximations to $\int_1^2 \frac{1}{x}\, dx$

n	L_n	R_n	T_n	M_n
5	0.745635	0.645635	0.695635	0.691908
10	0.718771	0.668771	0.693771	0.692835
20	0.705803	0.680803	0.693303	0.693069

Corresponding errors

n	E_L	E_R	E_T	E_M
5	−0.052488	0.047512	−0.002488	0.001239
10	−0.025624	0.024376	−0.000624	0.000312
20	−0.012656	0.012344	−0.000156	0.000078

■ It turns out that these observations are true in most cases.

We can make several observations from these tables:

1. In all of the methods we get more accurate approximations when we increase the value of n. (But very large values of n result in so many arithmetic operations that we have to beware of accumulated round-off error.)

2. The errors in the left and right endpoint approximations are opposite in sign and appear to decrease by a factor of about 2 when we double the value of n.

3. The Trapezoidal and Midpoint Rules are much more accurate than the endpoint approximations.

4. The errors in the Trapezoidal and Midpoint Rules are opposite in sign and appear to decrease by a factor of about 4 when we double the value of n.

5. The size of the error in the Midpoint Rule is about half the size of the error in the Trapezoidal Rule.

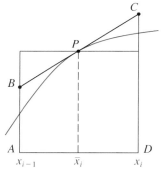

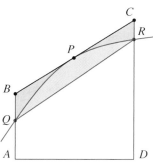

Figure 5 shows why we can usually expect the Midpoint Rule to be more accurate than the Trapezoidal Rule. The area of a typical rectangle in the Midpoint Rule is the same as the trapezoid $ABCD$ whose upper side is tangent to the graph at P. The area of this trapezoid is closer to the area under the graph than is the area of the trapezoid $AQRD$ used in the Trapezoidal Rule. [The midpoint error (shaded gray) is smaller than the trapezoidal error (shaded blue).]

These observations are corroborated in the following error estimates, which are proved in books on numerical analysis. Notice that Observation 4 corresponds to the n^2 in each denominator because $(2n)^2 = 4n^2$. The fact that the estimates depend on the size of the second derivative is not surprising if you look at Figure 5, because $f''(x)$ measures how much the graph is curved. [Recall that $f''(x)$ measures how fast the slope of $y = f(x)$ changes.]

FIGURE 5

> **3** **ERROR BOUNDS** Suppose $|f''(x)| \le K$ for $a \le x \le b$. If E_T and E_M are the errors in the Trapezoidal and Midpoint Rules, then
> $$|E_T| \le \frac{K(b-a)^3}{12n^2} \quad \text{and} \quad |E_M| \le \frac{K(b-a)^3}{24n^2}$$

Let's apply this error estimate to the Trapezoidal Rule approximation in Example 1. If $f(x) = 1/x$, then $f'(x) = -1/x^2$ and $f''(x) = 2/x^3$. Since $1 \le x \le 2$, we have $1/x \le 1$, so

$$|f''(x)| = \left|\frac{2}{x^3}\right| \le \frac{2}{1^3} = 2$$

▪ *K can be any number larger than all the values of $|f''(x)|$, but smaller values of K give better error bounds.*

Therefore, taking $K = 2$, $a = 1$, $b = 2$, and $n = 5$ in the error estimate (3), we see that

$$|E_T| \le \frac{2(2-1)^3}{12(5)^2} = \frac{1}{150} \approx 0.006667$$

Comparing this error estimate of 0.006667 with the actual error of about 0.002488, we see that it can happen that the actual error is substantially less than the upper bound for the error given by (3).

▼ EXAMPLE 2 How large should we take n in order to guarantee that the Trapezoidal and Midpoint Rule approximations for $\int_1^2 (1/x)\,dx$ are accurate to within 0.0001?

SOLUTION We saw in the preceding calculation that $|f''(x)| \le 2$ for $1 \le x \le 2$, so we can take $K = 2$, $a = 1$, and $b = 2$ in (3). Accuracy to within 0.0001 means that the size of the error should be less than 0.0001. Therefore, we choose n so that

$$\frac{2(1)^3}{12n^2} < 0.0001$$

Solving the inequality for n, we get

$$n^2 > \frac{2}{12(0.0001)}$$

or

$$n > \frac{1}{\sqrt{0.0006}} \approx 40.8$$

▪ *It's quite possible that a lower value for n would suffice, but 41 is the smallest value for which the error bound formula can* guarantee *us accuracy to within 0.0001.*

Thus $n = 41$ will ensure the desired accuracy.

For the same accuracy with the Midpoint Rule we choose n so that

$$\frac{2(1)^3}{24n^2} < 0.0001$$

which gives

$$n > \frac{1}{\sqrt{0.0012}} \approx 29$$

■

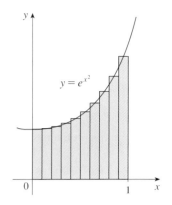

$y = e^{x^2}$

FIGURE 6

■ Error estimates are upper bounds for the error. They give theoretical, worst-case scenarios. The actual error in this case turns out to be about 0.0023.

☑ EXAMPLE 3

(a) Use the Midpoint Rule with $n = 10$ to approximate the integral $\int_0^1 e^{x^2} dx$.

(b) Give an upper bound for the error involved in this approximation.

SOLUTION

(a) Since $a = 0$, $b = 1$, and $n = 10$, the Midpoint Rule gives

$$\int_0^1 e^{x^2} dx \approx \Delta x [f(0.05) + f(0.15) + \cdots + f(0.85) + f(0.95)]$$

$$= 0.1[e^{0.0025} + e^{0.0225} + e^{0.0625} + e^{0.1225} + e^{0.2025} + e^{0.3025}$$

$$+ e^{0.4225} + e^{0.5625} + e^{0.7225} + e^{0.9025}]$$

$$\approx 1.460393$$

Figure 6 illustrates this approximation.

(b) Since $f(x) = e^{x^2}$, we have $f'(x) = 2xe^{x^2}$ and $f''(x) = (2 + 4x^2)e^{x^2}$. Also, since $0 \le x \le 1$, we have $x^2 \le 1$ and so

$$0 \le f''(x) = (2 + 4x^2)e^{x^2} \le 6e$$

Taking $K = 6e$, $a = 0$, $b = 1$, and $n = 10$ in the error estimate (3), we see that an upper bound for the error is

$$\frac{6e(1)^3}{24(10)^2} = \frac{e}{400} \approx 0.007$$ ■

SIMPSON'S RULE

Another rule for approximate integration results from using parabolas instead of straight line segments to approximate a curve. As before, we divide $[a, b]$ into n subintervals of equal length $h = \Delta x = (b - a)/n$, but this time we assume that n is an *even* number. Then on each consecutive pair of intervals we approximate the curve $y = f(x) \ge 0$ by a parabola as shown in Figure 7. If $y_i = f(x_i)$, then $P_i(x_i, y_i)$ is the point on the curve lying above x_i. A typical parabola passes through three consecutive points P_i, P_{i+1}, and P_{i+2}.

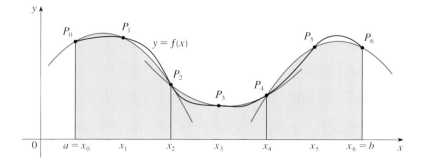

FIGURE 7

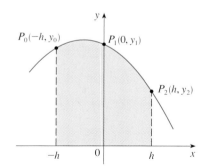

FIGURE 8

To simplify our calculations, we first consider the case where $x_0 = -h$, $x_1 = 0$, and $x_2 = h$. (See Figure 8.) We know that the equation of the parabola through P_0, P_1, and P_2 is of the form $y = Ax^2 + Bx + C$ and so the area under the parabola from $x = -h$

to $x = h$ is

▪ Here we have used Theorem 5.5.7. Notice that $Ax^2 + C$ is even and Bx is odd.

$$\int_{-h}^{h} (Ax^2 + Bx + C)\, dx = 2 \int_{0}^{h} (Ax^2 + C)\, dx$$

$$= 2 \left[A \frac{x^3}{3} + Cx \right]_{0}^{h}$$

$$= 2 \left(A \frac{h^3}{3} + Ch \right) = \frac{h}{3} (2Ah^2 + 6C)$$

But, since the parabola passes through $P_0(-h, y_0)$, $P_1(0, y_1)$, and $P_2(h, y_2)$, we have

$$y_0 = A(-h)^2 + B(-h) + C = Ah^2 - Bh + C$$

$$y_1 = C$$

$$y_2 = Ah^2 + Bh + C$$

and therefore

$$y_0 + 4y_1 + y_2 = 2Ah^2 + 6C$$

Thus we can rewrite the area under the parabola as

$$\frac{h}{3} (y_0 + 4y_1 + y_2)$$

By shifting this parabola horizontally we do not change the area under it. This means that the area under the parabola through P_0, P_1, and P_2 from $x = x_0$ to $x = x_2$ in Figure 7 is still

$$\frac{h}{3} (y_0 + 4y_1 + y_2)$$

Similarly, the area under the parabola through P_2, P_3, and P_4 from $x = x_2$ to $x = x_4$ is

$$\frac{h}{3} (y_2 + 4y_3 + y_4)$$

If we compute the areas under all the parabolas in this manner and add the results, we get

$$\int_{a}^{b} f(x)\, dx \approx \frac{h}{3} (y_0 + 4y_1 + y_2) + \frac{h}{3} (y_2 + 4y_3 + y_4) + \cdots + \frac{h}{3} (y_{n-2} + 4y_{n-1} + y_n)$$

$$= \frac{h}{3} (y_0 + 4y_1 + 2y_2 + 4y_3 + 2y_4 + \cdots + 2y_{n-2} + 4y_{n-1} + y_n)$$

Although we have derived this approximation for the case in which $f(x) \geq 0$, it is a reasonable approximation for any continuous function f and is called Simpson's Rule after the English mathematician Thomas Simpson (1710–1761). Note the pattern of coefficients: 1, 4, 2, 4, 2, 4, 2, ..., 4, 2, 4, 1.

■ Thomas Simpson was a weaver who taught himself mathematics and went on to become one of the best English mathematicians of the 18th century. What we call Simpson's Rule was actually known to Cavalieri and Gregory in the 17th century, but Simpson popularized it in his best-selling calculus textbook, entitled *A New Treatise of Fluxions*.

SIMPSON'S RULE

$$\int_a^b f(x)\,dx \approx S_n = \frac{\Delta x}{3}\left[f(x_0) + 4f(x_1) + 2f(x_2) + 4f(x_3) + \cdots\right.$$

$$\left. + 2f(x_{n-2}) + 4f(x_{n-1}) + f(x_n)\right]$$

where n is even and $\Delta x = (b - a)/n$.

EXAMPLE 4 Use Simpson's Rule with $n = 10$ to approximate $\int_1^2 (1/x)\,dx$.

SOLUTION Putting $f(x) = 1/x$, $n = 10$, and $\Delta x = 0.1$ in Simpson's Rule, we obtain

$$\int_1^2 \frac{1}{x}\,dx \approx S_{10}$$

$$= \frac{\Delta x}{3}\left[f(1) + 4f(1.1) + 2f(1.2) + 4f(1.3) + \cdots + 2f(1.8) + 4f(1.9) + f(2)\right]$$

$$= \frac{0.1}{3}\left(\frac{1}{1} + \frac{4}{1.1} + \frac{2}{1.2} + \frac{4}{1.3} + \frac{2}{1.4} + \frac{4}{1.5} + \frac{2}{1.6} + \frac{4}{1.7} + \frac{2}{1.8} + \frac{4}{1.9} + \frac{1}{2}\right)$$

$$\approx 0.693150 \qquad\blacksquare$$

Notice that, in Example 4, Simpson's Rule gives us a *much* better approximation ($S_{10} \approx 0.693150$) to the true value of the integral ($\ln 2 \approx 0.693147\ldots$) than does the Trapezoidal Rule ($T_{10} \approx 0.693771$) or the Midpoint Rule ($M_{10} \approx 0.692835$). It turns out (see Exercise 40) that the approximations in Simpson's Rule are weighted averages of those in the Trapezoidal and Midpoint Rules:

$$S_{2n} = \tfrac{1}{3}T_n + \tfrac{2}{3}M_n$$

(Recall that E_T and E_M usually have opposite signs and $|E_M|$ is about half the size of $|E_T|$.)

In many applications of calculus we need to evaluate an integral even if no explicit formula is known for y as a function of x. A function may be given graphically or as a table of values of collected data. If there is evidence that the values are not changing rapidly, then the Trapezoidal Rule or Simpson's Rule can still be used to find an approximate value for $\int_a^b y\,dx$, the integral of y with respect to x.

▼ EXAMPLE 5 Figure 9 shows data traffic on the link from the United States to SWITCH, the Swiss education and research network, on February 10, 1998. $D(t)$ is the data throughput, measured in megabits per second (Mb/s). Use Simpson's Rule to estimate the total amount of data transmitted on the link up to noon on that day.

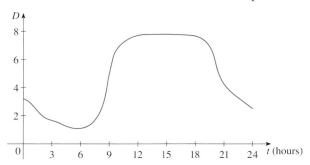

FIGURE 9

SOLUTION Because we want the units to be consistent and $D(t)$ is measured in megabits per second, we convert the units for t from hours to seconds. If we let $A(t)$ be the amount of data (in megabits) transmitted by time t, where t is measured in seconds, then $A'(t) = D(t)$. So, by the Net Change Theorem (see Section 5.3), the total amount of data transmitted by noon (when $t = 12 \times 60^2 = 43{,}200$) is

$$A(43{,}200) = \int_0^{43{,}200} D(t)\, dt$$

We estimate the values of $D(t)$ at hourly intervals from the graph and compile them in the table.

t (hours)	t (seconds)	$D(t)$	t (hours)	t (seconds)	$D(t)$
0	0	3.2	7	25,200	1.3
1	3,600	2.7	8	28,800	2.8
2	7,200	1.9	9	32,400	5.7
3	10,800	1.7	10	36,000	7.1
4	14,400	1.3	11	39,600	7.7
5	18,000	1.0	12	43,200	7.9
6	21,600	1.1			

Then we use Simpson's Rule with $n = 12$ and $\Delta t = 3600$ to estimate the integral:

$$\int_0^{43{,}200} A(t)\, dt \approx \frac{\Delta t}{3}[D(0) + 4D(3600) + 2D(7200) + \cdots + 4D(39{,}600) + D(43{,}200)]$$

$$\approx \frac{3600}{3}[3.2 + 4(2.7) + 2(1.9) + 4(1.7) + 2(1.3) + 4(1.0)$$

$$+ 2(1.1) + 4(1.3) + 2(2.8) + 4(5.7) + 2(7.1) + 4(7.7) + 7.9]$$

$$= 143{,}880$$

Thus the total amount of data transmitted up to noon is about 144,000 megabits, or 144 gigabits. ▪

In Exercise 24 you are asked to demonstrate, in a particular case, that the error in Simpson's Rule decreases by a factor of about 16 when n is doubled. That is consistent with the appearance of n^4 in the denominator of the following error estimate for Simpson's Rule. It is similar to the estimates given in (3) for the Trapezoidal and Midpoint Rules, but it uses the fourth derivative of f.

---

4 ERROR BOUND FOR SIMPSON'S RULE Suppose that $|f^{(4)}(x)| \leqslant K$ for $a \leqslant x \leqslant b$. If E_S is the error involved in using Simpson's Rule, then

$$|E_S| \leqslant \frac{K(b-a)^5}{180 n^4}$$

EXAMPLE 6 How large should we take n in order to guarantee that the Simpson's Rule approximation for $\int_1^2 (1/x)\,dx$ is accurate to within 0.0001?

SOLUTION If $f(x) = 1/x$, then $f^{(4)}(x) = 24/x^5$. Since $x \geq 1$, we have $1/x \leq 1$ and so

$$|f^{(4)}(x)| = \left|\frac{24}{x^5}\right| \leq 24$$

■ Many calculators and computer algebra systems have a built-in algorithm that computes an approximation of a definite integral. Some of these machines use Simpson's Rule; others use more sophisticated techniques such as *adaptive* numerical integration. This means that if a function fluctuates much more on a certain part of the interval than it does elsewhere, then that part gets divided into more subintervals. This strategy reduces the number of calculations required to achieve a prescribed accuracy.

Therefore, we can take $K = 24$ in (4). Thus for an error less than 0.0001 we should choose n so that

$$\frac{24(1)^5}{180n^4} < 0.0001$$

This gives

$$n^4 > \frac{24}{180(0.0001)}$$

or

$$n > \frac{1}{\sqrt[4]{0.00075}} \approx 6.04$$

Therefore, $n = 8$ (n must be even) gives the desired accuracy. (Compare this with Example 2, where we obtained $n = 41$ for the Trapezoidal Rule and $n = 29$ for the Midpoint Rule.) ■

EXAMPLE 7
(a) Use Simpson's Rule with $n = 10$ to approximate the integral $\int_0^1 e^{x^2}\,dx$.
(b) Estimate the error involved in this approximation.

SOLUTION
(a) If $n = 10$, then $\Delta x = 0.1$ and Simpson's Rule gives

■ Figure 10 illustrates the calculation in Example 7. Notice that the parabolic arcs are so close to the graph of $y = e^{x^2}$ that they are practically indistinguishable from it.

$$\int_0^1 e^{x^2}\,dx \approx \frac{\Delta x}{3}\,[f(0) + 4f(0.1) + 2f(0.2) + \cdots + 2f(0.8) + 4f(0.9) + f(1)]$$

$$= \frac{0.1}{3}\,[e^0 + 4e^{0.01} + 2e^{0.04} + 4e^{0.09} + 2e^{0.16} + 4e^{0.25} + 2e^{0.36}$$

$$+ 4e^{0.49} + 2e^{0.64} + 4e^{0.81} + e^1]$$

$$\approx 1.462681$$

(b) The fourth derivative of $f(x) = e^{x^2}$ is

$$f^{(4)}(x) = (12 + 48x^2 + 16x^4)e^{x^2}$$

and so, since $0 \leq x \leq 1$, we have

$$0 \leq f^{(4)}(x) \leq (12 + 48 + 16)e^1 = 76e$$

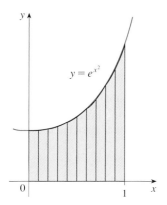

FIGURE 10

Therefore, putting $K = 76e$, $a = 0$, $b = 1$, and $n = 10$ in (4), we see that the error is at most

$$\frac{76e(1)^5}{180(10)^4} \approx 0.000115$$

[Compare this with Example 3(b).] Thus, correct to three decimal places, we have

$$\int_0^1 e^{x^2}\,dx \approx 1.463$$ ■

6.5 EXERCISES

1. Let $I = \int_0^4 f(x)\,dx$, where f is the function whose graph is shown.
(a) Use the graph to find L_2, R_2, and M_2.
(b) Are these underestimates or overestimates of I?
(c) Use the graph to find T_2. How does it compare with I?
(d) For any value of n, list the numbers L_n, R_n, M_n, T_n, and I in increasing order.

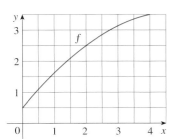

2. The left, right, Trapezoidal, and Midpoint Rule approximations were used to estimate $\int_0^2 f(x)\,dx$, where f is the function whose graph is shown. The estimates were 0.7811, 0.8675, 0.8632, and 0.9540, and the same number of subintervals were used in each case.
(a) Which rule produced which estimate?
(b) Between which two approximations does the true value of $\int_0^2 f(x)\,dx$ lie?

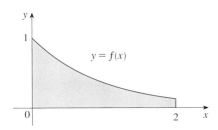

$y = f(x)$

⊞ **3.** Estimate $\int_0^1 \cos(x^2)\,dx$ using (a) the Trapezoidal Rule and (b) the Midpoint Rule, each with $n = 4$. From a graph of the integrand, decide whether your answers are underestimates or overestimates. What can you conclude about the true value of the integral?

⊞ **4.** Draw the graph of $f(x) = \sin(x^2/2)$ in the viewing rectangle $[0, 1]$ by $[0, 0.5]$ and let $I = \int_0^1 f(x)\,dx$.
(a) Use the graph to decide whether L_2, R_2, M_2, and T_2 underestimate or overestimate I.
(b) For any value of n, list the numbers L_n, R_n, M_n, T_n, and I in increasing order.
(c) Compute L_5, R_5, M_5, and T_5. From the graph, which do you think gives the best estimate of I?

5–6 ■ Use (a) the Midpoint Rule and (b) Simpson's Rule to approximate the given integral with the specified value of n. (Round your answers to six decimal places.) Compare your results to the actual value to determine the error in each approximation.

5. $\int_0^\pi x^2 \sin x\,dx$, $\quad n = 8$

6. $\int_0^1 e^{-\sqrt{x}}\,dx$, $\quad n = 6$

■ ■ ■ ■ ■ ■ ■ ■ ■ ■ ■ ■

7–16 ■ Use (a) the Trapezoidal Rule, (b) the Midpoint Rule, and (c) Simpson's Rule to approximate the given integral with the specified value of n. (Round your answers to six decimal places.)

7. $\int_0^2 \sqrt[4]{1 + x^2}\,dx$, $\quad n = 8$

8. $\int_0^{1/2} \sin(x^2)\,dx$, $\quad n = 4$

9. $\int_1^2 \frac{\ln x}{1 + x}\,dx$, $\quad n = 10$

10. $\int_0^3 \frac{dt}{1 + t^2 + t^4}$, $\quad n = 6$

11. $\int_0^4 e^{\sqrt{t}} \sin t\,dt$, $\quad n = 8$

12. $\int_0^4 \sqrt{1 + \sqrt{x}}\,dx$, $\quad n = 8$

13. $\int_1^5 \frac{\cos x}{x}\,dx$, $\quad n = 8$

14. $\int_4^6 \ln(x^3 + 2)\,dx$, $\quad n = 10$

15. $\int_0^3 \frac{1}{1 + y^5}\,dy$, $\quad n = 6$

16. $\int_0^1 \sqrt{z}\,e^{-z}\,dz$, $\quad n = 10$

■ ■ ■ ■ ■ ■ ■ ■ ■ ■ ■ ■

17. (a) Find the approximations T_{10} and M_{10} for the integral $\int_0^2 e^{-x^2}\,dx$.
(b) Estimate the errors in the approximations of part (a).
(c) How large do we have to choose n so that the approximations T_n and M_n to the integral in part (a) are accurate to within 0.00001?

18. (a) Find the approximations T_8 and M_8 for $\int_0^1 \cos(x^2)\,dx$.
(b) Estimate the errors involved in the approximations of part (a).
(c) How large do we have to choose n so that the approximations T_n and M_n to the integral in part (a) are accurate to within 0.00001?

19. (a) Find the approximations T_{10} and S_{10} for $\int_0^1 e^x\,dx$ and the corresponding errors E_T and E_S.
(b) Compare the actual errors in part (a) with the error estimates given by (3) and (4).
(c) How large do we have to choose n so that the approximations T_n, M_n, and S_n to the integral in part (a) are accurate to within 0.00001?

20. How large should n be to guarantee that the Simpson's Rule approximation to $\int_0^1 e^{x^2}\,dx$ is accurate to within 0.00001?

CAS **21.** The trouble with the error estimates is that it is often very difficult to compute four derivatives and obtain a good upper bound K for $|f^{(4)}(x)|$ by hand. But computer algebra systems have no problem computing $f^{(4)}$ and graphing it, so we can easily find a value for K from a machine graph. This exercise deals with approximations to the integral $I = \int_0^{2\pi} f(x)\,dx$, where $f(x) = e^{\cos x}$.
(a) Use a graph to get a good upper bound for $|f''(x)|$.

(b) Use M_{10} to approximate I.

(c) Use part (a) to estimate the error in part (b).

(d) Use the built-in numerical integration capability of your CAS to approximate I.

(e) How does the actual error compare with the error estimate in part (c)?

(f) Use a graph to get a good upper bound for $|f^{(4)}(x)|$.

(g) Use S_{10} to approximate I.

(h) Use part (f) to estimate the error in part (g).

(i) How does the actual error compare with the error estimate in part (h)?

(j) How large should n be to guarantee that the size of the error in using S_n is less than 0.0001?

CAS **22.** Repeat Exercise 21 for the integral $\int_{-1}^{1} \sqrt{4 - x^3} \, dx$.

23. Find the approximations L_n, R_n, T_n, and M_n to the integral $\int_0^1 x^3 \, dx$ for $n = 4$, 8, and 16. Then compute the corresponding errors E_L, E_R, E_T, and E_M. (Round your answers to six decimal places. You may wish to use the sum command on a computer algebra system.) What observations can you make? In particular, what happens to the errors when n is doubled?

24. Find the approximations T_n, M_n, and S_n to the integral $\int_{-1}^{2} xe^x \, dx$ for $n = 6$ and 12. Then compute the corresponding errors E_T, E_M, and E_S. (Round your answers to six decimal places. You may wish to use the sum command on a computer algebra system.) What observations can you make? In particular, what happens to the errors when n is doubled?

25. Estimate the area under the graph in the figure by using (a) the Trapezoidal Rule, (b) the Midpoint Rule, and (c) Simpson's Rule, each with $n = 4$.

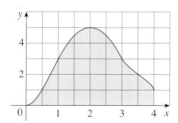

26. A radar gun was used to record the speed of a runner during the first 5 seconds of a race (see the table). Use Simpson's Rule to estimate the distance the runner covered during those 5 seconds.

t (s)	v (m/s)	t (s)	v (m/s)
0	0	3.0	10.51
0.5	4.67	3.5	10.67
1.0	7.34	4.0	10.76
1.5	8.86	4.5	10.81
2.0	9.73	5.0	10.81
2.5	10.22		

27. The graph of the acceleration $a(t)$ of a car measured in ft/s² is shown. Use Simpson's Rule to estimate the increase in the velocity of the car during the 6-second time interval.

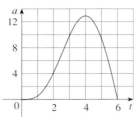

28. Water leaked from a tank at a rate of $r(t)$ liters per hour, where the graph of r is as shown. Use Simpson's Rule to estimate the total amount of water that leaked out during the first six hours.

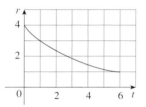

29. The table (supplied by San Diego Gas and Electric) gives the power consumption in megawatts in San Diego County from midnight to 6:00 AM on a day in December. Use Simpson's Rule to estimate the energy used during that time period. (Use the fact that power is the derivative of energy.)

t	P	t	P
0:00	1814	3:30	1611
0:30	1735	4:00	1621
1:00	1686	4:30	1666
1:30	1646	5:00	1745
2:00	1637	5:30	1886
2:30	1609	6:00	2052
3:00	1604		

30. Shown is the graph of traffic on an Internet service provider's T1 data line from midnight to 8:00 AM. D is the data throughput, measured in megabits per second. Use Simpson's Rule to estimate the total amount of data transmitted during that time period.

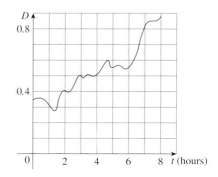

31. (a) Use the Midpoint Rule and the given data to estimate the value of the integral $\int_0^{3.2} f(x)\,dx$.

x	$f(x)$	x	$f(x)$
0.0	6.8	2.0	7.6
0.4	6.5	2.4	8.4
0.8	6.3	2.8	8.8
1.2	6.4	3.2	9.0
1.6	6.9		

(b) If it is known that $-4 \leqslant f''(x) \leqslant 1$ for all x, estimate the error involved in the approximation in part (a).

CAS 32. The figure shows a pendulum with length L that makes a maximum angle θ_0 with the vertical. Using Newton's Second Law it can be shown that the period T (the time for one complete swing) is given by

$$T = 4\sqrt{\frac{L}{g}} \int_0^{\pi/2} \frac{dx}{\sqrt{1 - k^2 \sin^2 x}}$$

where $k = \sin\left(\frac{1}{2}\theta_0\right)$ and g is the acceleration due to gravity. If $L = 1$ m and $\theta_0 = 42°$, use Simpson's Rule with $n = 10$ to find the period.

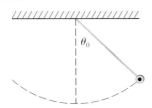

33. The intensity of light with wavelength λ traveling through a diffraction grating with N slits at an angle θ is given by $I(\theta) = N^2 \sin^2 k / k^2$, where $k = (\pi N d \sin\theta)/\lambda$ and d is the distance between adjacent slits. A helium-neon laser with wavelength $\lambda = 632.8 \times 10^{-9}$ m is emitting a narrow band of light, given by $-10^{-6} < \theta < 10^{-6}$, through a grating with 10,000 slits spaced 10^{-4} m apart. Use the Midpoint Rule with $n = 10$ to estimate the total light intensity $\int_{-10^{-6}}^{10^{-6}} I(\theta)\,d\theta$ emerging from the grating.

34. Sketch the graph of a continuous function on $[0, 2]$ for which the right endpoint approximation with $n = 2$ is more accurate than Simpson's Rule.

35. Sketch the graph of a continuous function on $[0, 2]$ for which the Trapezoidal Rule with $n = 2$ is more accurate than the Midpoint Rule.

36. Use the Trapezoidal Rule with $n = 10$ to approximate $\int_0^{20} \cos(\pi x)\,dx$. Compare your result to the actual value. Can you explain the discrepancy?

37. If f is a positive function and $f''(x) < 0$ for $a \leqslant x \leqslant b$, show that

$$T_n < \int_a^b f(x)\,dx < M_n$$

38. Show that if f is a polynomial of degree 3 or lower, then Simpson's Rule gives the exact value of $\int_a^b f(x)\,dx$.

39. Show that $\frac{1}{2}(T_n + M_n) = T_{2n}$.

40. Show that $\frac{1}{3}T_n + \frac{2}{3}M_n = S_{2n}$.

6.6 IMPROPER INTEGRALS

In defining a definite integral $\int_a^b f(x)\,dx$ we dealt with a function f defined on a finite interval $[a, b]$. In this section we extend the concept of a definite integral to the case where the interval is infinite and also to the case where f has an infinite discontinuity in $[a, b]$. In either case the integral is called an *improper* integral.

TYPE 1: INFINITE INTERVALS

Consider the infinite region S that lies under the curve $y = 1/x^2$, above the x-axis, and to the right of the line $x = 1$. You might think that, since S is infinite in extent, its area must be infinite, but let's take a closer look. The area of the part of S that lies to the left of the line $x = t$ (shaded in Figure 1) is

$$A(t) = \int_1^t \frac{1}{x^2}\,dx = -\frac{1}{x}\bigg]_1^t = 1 - \frac{1}{t}$$

Notice that $A(t) < 1$ no matter how large t is chosen.

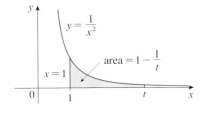

FIGURE 1

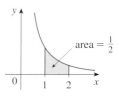

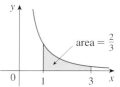

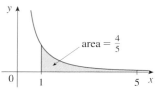

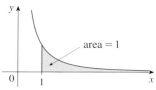

FIGURE 2

We also observe that

$$\lim_{t \to \infty} A(t) = \lim_{t \to \infty} \left(1 - \frac{1}{t} \right) = 1$$

The area of the shaded region approaches 1 as $t \to \infty$ (see Figure 2), so we say that the area of the infinite region S is equal to 1 and we write

$$\int_1^\infty \frac{1}{x^2} \, dx = \lim_{t \to \infty} \int_1^t \frac{1}{x^2} \, dx = 1$$

Using this example as a guide, we define the integral of f (not necessarily a positive function) over an infinite interval as the limit of integrals over finite intervals.

---

1 **DEFINITION OF AN IMPROPER INTEGRAL OF TYPE I**

(a) If $\int_a^t f(x) \, dx$ exists for every number $t \geq a$, then

$$\int_a^\infty f(x) \, dx = \lim_{t \to \infty} \int_a^t f(x) \, dx$$

provided this limit exists (as a finite number).

(b) If $\int_t^b f(x) \, dx$ exists for every number $t \leq b$, then

$$\int_{-\infty}^b f(x) \, dx = \lim_{t \to -\infty} \int_t^b f(x) \, dx$$

provided this limit exists (as a finite number).

The improper integrals $\int_a^\infty f(x) \, dx$ and $\int_{-\infty}^b f(x) \, dx$ are called **convergent** if the corresponding limit exists and **divergent** if the limit does not exist.

(c) If both $\int_a^\infty f(x) \, dx$ and $\int_{-\infty}^a f(x) \, dx$ are convergent, then we define

$$\int_{-\infty}^\infty f(x) \, dx = \int_{-\infty}^a f(x) \, dx + \int_a^\infty f(x) \, dx$$

In part (c) any real number a can be used (see Exercise 52).

Any of the improper integrals in Definition 1 can be interpreted as an area provided that f is a positive function. For instance, in case (a) if $f(x) \geq 0$ and the integral $\int_a^\infty f(x) \, dx$ is convergent, then we define the area of the region

$$S = \{(x, y) \mid x \geq a, 0 \leq y \leq f(x)\}$$

in Figure 3 to be

$$A(S) = \int_a^\infty f(x) \, dx$$

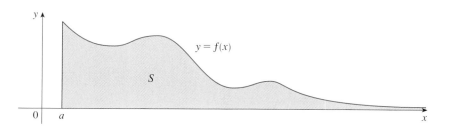

FIGURE 3

This is appropriate because $\int_a^{\infty} f(x)\,dx$ is the limit as $t \to \infty$ of the area under the graph of f from a to t.

▼ **EXAMPLE 1** Determine whether the integral $\int_1^{\infty} (1/x)\,dx$ is convergent or divergent.

SOLUTION According to part (a) of Definition 1, we have

$$\int_1^{\infty} \frac{1}{x}\,dx = \lim_{t \to \infty} \int_1^t \frac{1}{x}\,dx = \lim_{t \to \infty} \ln|x| \Big]_1^t$$

$$= \lim_{t \to \infty} (\ln t - \ln 1) = \lim_{t \to \infty} \ln t = \infty$$

The limit does not exist as a finite number and so the improper integral $\int_1^{\infty} (1/x)\,dx$ is divergent. ∎

Let's compare the result of Example 1 with the example given at the beginning of this section:

$$\int_1^{\infty} \frac{1}{x^2}\,dx \text{ converges} \qquad \int_1^{\infty} \frac{1}{x}\,dx \text{ diverges}$$

Geometrically, this says that although the curves $y = 1/x^2$ and $y = 1/x$ look very similar for $x > 0$, the region under $y = 1/x^2$ to the right of $x = 1$ (the shaded region in Figure 4) has finite area whereas the corresponding region under $y = 1/x$ (in Figure 5) has infinite area. Note that both $1/x^2$ and $1/x$ approach 0 as $x \to \infty$ but $1/x^2$ approaches 0 faster than $1/x$. The values of $1/x$ don't decrease fast enough for its integral to have a finite value.

EXAMPLE 2 Evaluate $\int_{-\infty}^{0} x e^x\,dx$.

SOLUTION Using part (b) of Definition 1, we have

$$\int_{-\infty}^{0} x e^x\,dx = \lim_{t \to -\infty} \int_t^0 x e^x\,dx$$

We integrate by parts with $u = x$, $dv = e^x\,dx$, so that $du = dx$, $v = e^x$:

$$\int_t^0 x e^x\,dx = x e^x \Big]_t^0 - \int_t^0 e^x\,dx = -t e^t - 1 + e^t$$

We know that $e^t \to 0$ as $t \to -\infty$, and by l'Hospital's Rule we have

$$\lim_{t \to -\infty} t e^t = \lim_{t \to -\infty} \frac{t}{e^{-t}} = \lim_{t \to -\infty} \frac{1}{-e^{-t}}$$

$$= \lim_{t \to -\infty} (-e^t) = 0$$

Therefore

$$\int_{-\infty}^{0} x e^x\,dx = \lim_{t \to -\infty} (-t e^t - 1 + e^t)$$

$$= -0 - 1 + 0 = -1 \qquad ∎$$

EXAMPLE 3 Evaluate $\int_{-\infty}^{\infty} \frac{1}{1 + x^2}\,dx$.

SOLUTION It's convenient to choose $a = 0$ in Definition 1(c):

$$\int_{-\infty}^{\infty} \frac{1}{1 + x^2}\,dx = \int_{-\infty}^{0} \frac{1}{1 + x^2}\,dx + \int_0^{\infty} \frac{1}{1 + x^2}\,dx$$

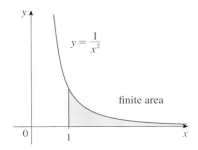

$y = \dfrac{1}{x^2}$

finite area

FIGURE 4

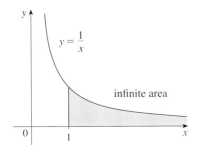

$y = \dfrac{1}{x}$

infinite area

FIGURE 5

In Module 6.6 you can investigate visually and numerically whether several improper integrals are convergent or divergent.

We must now evaluate the integrals on the right side separately:

$$\int_0^\infty \frac{1}{1+x^2}\,dx = \lim_{t\to\infty}\int_0^t \frac{dx}{1+x^2} = \lim_{t\to\infty}\tan^{-1}x\Big]_0^t$$

$$= \lim_{t\to\infty}(\tan^{-1}t - \tan^{-1}0) = \lim_{t\to\infty}\tan^{-1}t = \frac{\pi}{2}$$

$$\int_{-\infty}^0 \frac{1}{1+x^2}\,dx = \lim_{t\to-\infty}\int_t^0 \frac{dx}{1+x^2} = \lim_{t\to-\infty}\tan^{-1}x\Big]_t^0$$

$$= \lim_{t\to-\infty}(\tan^{-1}0 - \tan^{-1}t)$$

$$= 0 - \left(-\frac{\pi}{2}\right) = \frac{\pi}{2}$$

Since both of these integrals are convergent, the given integral is convergent and

$$\int_{-\infty}^\infty \frac{1}{1+x^2}\,dx = \frac{\pi}{2} + \frac{\pi}{2} = \pi$$

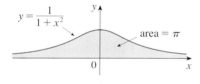

Since $1/(1+x^2) > 0$, the given improper integral can be interpreted as the area of the infinite region that lies under the curve $y = 1/(1+x^2)$ and above the x-axis (see Figure 6). ■

FIGURE 6

EXAMPLE 4 For what values of p is the following integral convergent?

$$\int_1^\infty \frac{1}{x^p}\,dx$$

SOLUTION We know from Example 1 that if $p = 1$, then the integral is divergent, so let's assume that $p \neq 1$. Then

$$\int_1^\infty \frac{1}{x^p}\,dx = \lim_{t\to\infty}\int_1^t x^{-p}\,dx = \lim_{t\to\infty}\frac{x^{-p+1}}{-p+1}\Big]_{x=1}^{x=t}$$

$$= \lim_{t\to\infty}\frac{1}{1-p}\left[\frac{1}{t^{p-1}} - 1\right]$$

If $p > 1$, then $p - 1 > 0$, so as $t \to \infty$, $t^{p-1} \to \infty$ and $1/t^{p-1} \to 0$. Therefore

$$\int_1^\infty \frac{1}{x^p}\,dx = \frac{1}{p-1} \qquad \text{if } p > 1$$

and so the integral converges. But if $p < 1$, then $p - 1 < 0$ and so

$$\frac{1}{t^{p-1}} = t^{1-p} \to \infty \qquad \text{as } t \to \infty$$

and the integral diverges. ■

We summarize the result of Example 4 for future reference:

2 $\displaystyle\int_1^\infty \frac{1}{x^p}\,dx$ is convergent if $p > 1$ and divergent if $p \leq 1$.

TYPE 2: DISCONTINUOUS INTEGRANDS

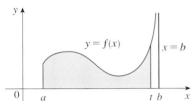

FIGURE 7

Suppose that f is a positive continuous function defined on a finite interval $[a, b]$ but has a vertical asymptote at b. Let S be the unbounded region under the graph of f and above the x-axis between a and b. (For Type 1 integrals, the regions extended indefinitely in a horizontal direction. Here the region is infinite in a vertical direction.) The area of the part of S between a and t (the shaded region in Figure 7) is

$$A(t) = \int_a^t f(x)\,dx$$

If it happens that $A(t)$ approaches a definite number A as $t \to b^-$, then we say that the area of the region S is A and we write

$$\int_a^b f(x)\,dx = \lim_{t \to b^-} \int_a^t f(x)\,dx$$

We use this equation to define an improper integral of Type 2 even when f is not a positive function, no matter what type of discontinuity f has at b.

▪ Parts (b) and (c) of Definition 3 are illustrated in Figures 8 and 9 for the case where $f(x) \geq 0$ and f has vertical asymptotes at a and c, respectively.

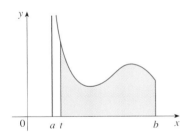

FIGURE 8

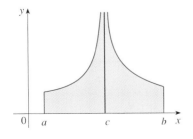

FIGURE 9

3 DEFINITION OF AN IMPROPER INTEGRAL OF TYPE 2

(a) If f is continuous on $[a, b)$ and is discontinuous at b, then

$$\int_a^b f(x)\,dx = \lim_{t \to b^-} \int_a^t f(x)\,dx$$

if this limit exists (as a finite number).

(b) If f is continuous on $(a, b]$ and is discontinuous at a, then

$$\int_a^b f(x)\,dx = \lim_{t \to a^+} \int_t^b f(x)\,dx$$

if this limit exists (as a finite number).

The improper integral $\int_a^b f(x)\,dx$ is called **convergent** if the corresponding limit exists and **divergent** if the limit does not exist.

(c) If f has a discontinuity at c, where $a < c < b$, and both $\int_a^c f(x)\,dx$ and $\int_c^b f(x)\,dx$ are convergent, then we define

$$\int_a^b f(x)\,dx = \int_a^c f(x)\,dx + \int_c^b f(x)\,dx$$

EXAMPLE 5 Find $\displaystyle\int_2^5 \frac{1}{\sqrt{x-2}}\,dx$.

SOLUTION We note first that the given integral is improper because $f(x) = 1/\sqrt{x-2}$ has the vertical asymptote $x = 2$. Since the infinite discontinuity

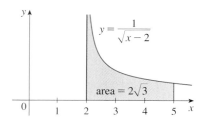

FIGURE 10

occurs at the left endpoint of $[2, 5]$, we use part (b) of Definition 3:

$$\int_2^5 \frac{dx}{\sqrt{x-2}} = \lim_{t \to 2^+} \int_t^5 \frac{dx}{\sqrt{x-2}} = \lim_{t \to 2^+} 2\sqrt{x-2} \,\Big]_t^5$$

$$= \lim_{t \to 2^+} 2(\sqrt{3} - \sqrt{t-2}) = 2\sqrt{3}$$

Thus the given improper integral is convergent and, since the integrand is positive, we can interpret the value of the integral as the area of the shaded region in Figure 10. ■

▼ EXAMPLE 6 Determine whether $\int_0^{\pi/2} \sec x \, dx$ converges or diverges.

SOLUTION Note that the given integral is improper because $\lim_{x \to (\pi/2)^-} \sec x = \infty$. Using part (a) of Definition 3 and Formula 14 from the Table of Integrals, we have

$$\int_0^{\pi/2} \sec x \, dx = \lim_{t \to (\pi/2)^-} \int_0^t \sec x \, dx$$

$$= \lim_{t \to (\pi/2)^-} \ln|\sec x + \tan x| \,\Big]_0^t$$

$$= \lim_{t \to (\pi/2)^-} [\ln(\sec t + \tan t) - \ln 1] = \infty$$

because $\sec t \to \infty$ and $\tan t \to \infty$ as $t \to (\pi/2)^-$. Thus the given improper integral is divergent. ■

EXAMPLE 7 Evaluate $\int_0^3 \frac{dx}{x-1}$ if possible.

SOLUTION Observe that the line $x = 1$ is a vertical asymptote of the integrand. Since it occurs in the middle of the interval $[0, 3]$, we must use part (c) of Definition 3 with $c = 1$:

$$\int_0^3 \frac{dx}{x-1} = \int_0^1 \frac{dx}{x-1} + \int_1^3 \frac{dx}{x-1}$$

where

$$\int_0^1 \frac{dx}{x-1} = \lim_{t \to 1^-} \int_0^t \frac{dx}{x-1} = \lim_{t \to 1^-} \ln|x-1| \,\Big]_0^t$$

$$= \lim_{t \to 1^-} (\ln|t-1| - \ln|-1|)$$

$$= \lim_{t \to 1^-} \ln(1-t) = -\infty$$

because $1 - t \to 0^+$ as $t \to 1^-$. Thus $\int_0^1 dx/(x-1)$ is divergent. This implies that $\int_0^3 dx/(x-1)$ is divergent. [We do not need to evaluate $\int_1^3 dx/(x-1)$.] ■

⊘　**WARNING** If we had not noticed the asymptote $x = 1$ in Example 7 and had instead confused the integral with an ordinary integral, then we might have made the following erroneous calculation:

$$\int_0^3 \frac{dx}{x-1} = \ln|x-1| \,\Big]_0^3 = \ln 2 - \ln 1 = \ln 2$$

This is wrong because the integral is improper and must be calculated in terms of limits.

From now on, whenever you meet the symbol $\int_a^b f(x)\,dx$ you must decide, by looking at the function f on $[a, b]$, whether it is an ordinary definite integral or an improper integral.

A COMPARISON TEST FOR IMPROPER INTEGRALS

Sometimes it is impossible to find the exact value of an improper integral and yet it is important to know whether it is convergent or divergent. In such cases the following theorem is useful. Although we state it for Type 1 integrals, a similar theorem is true for Type 2 integrals.

> **COMPARISON THEOREM** Suppose that f and g are continuous functions with $f(x) \geqslant g(x) \geqslant 0$ for $x \geqslant a$.
>
> (a) If $\int_a^\infty f(x)\,dx$ is convergent, then $\int_a^\infty g(x)\,dx$ is convergent.
>
> (b) If $\int_a^\infty g(x)\,dx$ is divergent, then $\int_a^\infty f(x)\,dx$ is divergent.

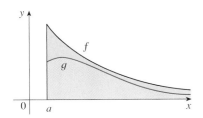

FIGURE 11

We omit the proof of the Comparison Theorem, but Figure 11 makes it seem plausible. If the area under the top curve $y = f(x)$ is finite, then so is the area under the bottom curve $y = g(x)$. And if the area under $y = g(x)$ is infinite, then so is the area under $y = f(x)$. [Note that the reverse is not necessarily true: If $\int_a^\infty g(x)\,dx$ is convergent, $\int_a^\infty f(x)\,dx$ may or may not be convergent, and if $\int_a^\infty f(x)\,dx$ is divergent, $\int_a^\infty g(x)\,dx$ may or may not be divergent.]

▼ EXAMPLE 8 Show that $\displaystyle\int_0^\infty e^{-x^2}\,dx$ is convergent.

SOLUTION We can't evaluate the integral directly because the antiderivative of e^{-x^2} is not an elementary function (as explained in Section 6.4). We write

$$\int_0^\infty e^{-x^2}\,dx = \int_0^1 e^{-x^2}\,dx + \int_1^\infty e^{-x^2}\,dx$$

and observe that the first integral on the right-hand side is just an ordinary definite integral. In the second integral we use the fact that for $x \geqslant 1$ we have $x^2 \geqslant x$, so $-x^2 \leqslant -x$ and therefore $e^{-x^2} \leqslant e^{-x}$. (See Figure 12.) The integral of e^{-x} is easy to evaluate:

$$\int_1^\infty e^{-x}\,dx = \lim_{t\to\infty} \int_1^t e^{-x}\,dx = \lim_{t\to\infty} (e^{-1} - e^{-t}) = e^{-1}$$

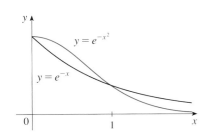

FIGURE 12

Thus, taking $f(x) = e^{-x}$ and $g(x) = e^{-x^2}$ in the Comparison Theorem, we see that $\int_1^\infty e^{-x^2}\,dx$ is convergent. It follows that $\int_0^\infty e^{-x^2}\,dx$ is convergent. ▪

TABLE I

t	$\int_0^t e^{-x^2}\,dx$
1	0.7468241328
2	0.8820813908
3	0.8862073483
4	0.8862269118
5	0.8862269255
6	0.8862269255

In Example 8 we showed that $\int_0^\infty e^{-x^2}\,dx$ is convergent without computing its value. In Exercise 58 we indicate how to show that its value is approximately 0.8862. In probability theory it is important to know the exact value of this improper integral; using the methods of multivariable calculus it can be shown that the exact value is $\sqrt{\pi}/2$. Table 1 illustrates the definition of an improper integral by showing how the (computer-generated) values of $\int_0^t e^{-x^2}\,dx$ approach $\sqrt{\pi}/2$ as t becomes large. In fact, these values converge quite quickly because $e^{-x^2} \to 0$ very rapidly as $x \to \infty$.

EXAMPLE 9 The integral $\int_1^\infty \dfrac{1 + e^{-x}}{x}\, dx$ is divergent by the Comparison Theorem because

$$\frac{1 + e^{-x}}{x} > \frac{1}{x}$$

and $\int_1^\infty (1/x)\, dx$ is divergent by Example 1 [or by (2) with $p = 1$]. ■

Table 2 illustrates the divergence of the integral in Example 9. It appears that the values are not approaching any fixed number.

TABLE 2

t	$\int_1^t [(1 + e^{-x})/x]\, dx$
2	0.8636306042
5	1.8276735512
10	2.5219648704
100	4.8245541204
1000	7.1271392134
10000	9.4297243064

6.6 EXERCISES

1. Explain why each of the following integrals is improper.

(a) $\displaystyle\int_1^\infty x^4 e^{-x^4}\, dx$

(b) $\displaystyle\int_0^{\pi/2} \sec x\, dx$

(c) $\displaystyle\int_0^2 \frac{x}{x^2 - 5x + 6}\, dx$

(d) $\displaystyle\int_{-\infty}^0 \frac{1}{x^2 + 5}\, dx$

2. Which of the following integrals are improper? Why?

(a) $\displaystyle\int_1^2 \frac{1}{2x - 1}\, dx$

(b) $\displaystyle\int_0^1 \frac{1}{2x - 1}\, dx$

(c) $\displaystyle\int_{-\infty}^\infty \frac{\sin x}{1 + x^2}\, dx$

(d) $\displaystyle\int_1^2 \ln(x - 1)\, dx$

3. Find the area under the curve $y = 1/x^3$ from $x = 1$ to $x = t$ and evaluate it for $t = 10$, 100, and 1000. Then find the total area under this curve for $x \geq 1$.

4. (a) Graph the functions $f(x) = 1/x^{1.1}$ and $g(x) = 1/x^{0.9}$ in the viewing rectangles $[0, 10]$ by $[0, 1]$ and $[0, 100]$ by $[0, 1]$.
(b) Find the areas under the graphs of f and g from $x = 1$ to $x = t$ and evaluate for $t = 10$, 100, 10^4, 10^6, 10^{10}, and 10^{20}.
(c) Find the total area under each curve for $x \geq 1$, if it exists.

5–32 ■ Determine whether each integral is convergent or divergent. Evaluate those that are convergent.

5. $\displaystyle\int_1^\infty \frac{1}{(3x + 1)^2}\, dx$

6. $\displaystyle\int_{-\infty}^0 \frac{1}{2x - 5}\, dx$

7. $\displaystyle\int_{-\infty}^{-1} \frac{1}{\sqrt{2 - w}}\, dw$

8. $\displaystyle\int_0^\infty \frac{x}{(x^2 + 2)^2}\, dx$

9. $\displaystyle\int_4^\infty e^{-y/2}\, dy$

10. $\displaystyle\int_{-\infty}^{-1} e^{-2t}\, dt$

11. $\displaystyle\int_{2\pi}^\infty \sin \theta\, d\theta$

12. $\displaystyle\int_{-\infty}^\infty (2 - v^4)\, dv$

13. $\displaystyle\int_{-\infty}^\infty xe^{-x^2}\, dx$

14. $\displaystyle\int_{-\infty}^\infty x^2 e^{-x^3}\, dx$

15. $\displaystyle\int_0^\infty se^{-5s}\, ds$

16. $\displaystyle\int_{-\infty}^\infty \cos \pi t\, dt$

17. $\displaystyle\int_1^\infty \frac{\ln x}{x}\, dx$

18. $\displaystyle\int_{-\infty}^6 re^{r/3}\, dr$

19. $\displaystyle\int_1^\infty \frac{\ln x}{x^2}\, dx$

20. $\displaystyle\int_1^\infty \frac{\ln x}{x^3}\, dx$

21. $\displaystyle\int_{-\infty}^\infty \frac{x^2}{9 + x^6}\, dx$

22. $\displaystyle\int_0^\infty \frac{e^x}{e^{2x} + 3}\, dx$

23. $\displaystyle\int_0^1 \frac{3}{x^5}\, dx$

24. $\displaystyle\int_2^3 \frac{1}{\sqrt{3 - x}}\, dx$

25. $\displaystyle\int_{-2}^{14} \frac{dx}{\sqrt[4]{x + 2}}$

26. $\displaystyle\int_6^8 \frac{4}{(x - 6)^3}\, dx$

27. $\displaystyle\int_0^{33} (x - 1)^{-1/5}\, dx$

28. $\displaystyle\int_0^1 \frac{1}{4y - 1}\, dy$

29. $\displaystyle\int_{-1}^1 \frac{e^x}{e^x - 1}\, dx$

30. $\displaystyle\int_0^1 \frac{dx}{\sqrt{1 - x^2}}$

31. $\displaystyle\int_0^2 z^2 \ln z\, dz$

32. $\displaystyle\int_0^1 \frac{\ln x}{\sqrt{x}}\, dx$

33–38 ■ Sketch the region and find its area (if the area is finite).

33. $S = \{(x, y) \mid x \leq 1,\ 0 \leq y \leq e^x\}$

34. $S = \{(x, y) \mid x \geq -2,\ 0 \leq y \leq e^{-x/2}\}$

35. $S = \{(x, y) \mid 0 \leq y \leq 2/(x^2 + 9)\}$

36. $S = \{(x, y) \mid x \geq 0,\ 0 \leq y \leq x/(x^2 + 9)\}$

37. $S = \{(x, y) \mid 0 \leq x < \pi/2,\ 0 \leq y \leq \sec^2 x\}$

38. $S = \{(x, y) \mid -2 < x \leq 0,\ 0 \leq y \leq 1/\sqrt{x + 2}\}$

39. (a) If $g(x) = (\sin^2 x)/x^2$, use your calculator or computer to make a table of approximate values of $\int_1^t g(x)\,dx$ for $t = 2, 5, 10, 100, 1000$, and $10,000$. Does it appear that $\int_1^\infty g(x)\,dx$ is convergent?

(b) Use the Comparison Theorem with $f(x) = 1/x^2$ to show that $\int_1^\infty g(x)\,dx$ is convergent.

(c) Illustrate part (b) by graphing f and g on the same screen for $1 \leq x \leq 10$. Use your graph to explain intuitively why $\int_1^\infty g(x)\,dx$ is convergent.

40. (a) If $g(x) = 1/(\sqrt{x} - 1)$, use your calculator or computer to make a table of approximate values of $\int_2^t g(x)\,dx$ for $t = 5, 10, 100, 1000$, and $10,000$. Does it appear that $\int_2^\infty g(x)\,dx$ is convergent or divergent?

(b) Use the Comparison Theorem with $f(x) = 1/\sqrt{x}$ to show that $\int_2^\infty g(x)\,dx$ is divergent.

(c) Illustrate part (b) by graphing f and g on the same screen for $2 \leq x \leq 20$. Use your graph to explain intuitively why $\int_2^\infty g(x)\,dx$ is divergent.

41–46 ▪ Use the Comparison Theorem to determine whether the integral is convergent or divergent.

41. $\displaystyle\int_1^\infty \frac{\cos^2 x}{1 + x^2}\,dx$

42. $\displaystyle\int_1^\infty \frac{2 + e^{-x}}{x}\,dx$

43. $\displaystyle\int_1^\infty \frac{dx}{x + e^{2x}}$

44. $\displaystyle\int_1^\infty \frac{x}{\sqrt{1 + x^6}}\,dx$

45. $\displaystyle\int_0^{\pi/2} \frac{dx}{x \sin x}$

46. $\displaystyle\int_0^1 \frac{e^{-x}}{\sqrt{x}}\,dx$

▪ ▪ ▪ ▪ ▪ ▪ ▪ ▪ ▪ ▪ ▪ ▪

47. The integral

$$\int_0^\infty \frac{1}{\sqrt{x}\,(1 + x)}\,dx$$

is improper for two reasons: The interval $[0, \infty)$ is infinite and the integrand has an infinite discontinuity at 0. Evaluate it by expressing it as a sum of improper integrals of Type 2 and Type 1 as follows:

$$\int_0^\infty \frac{1}{\sqrt{x}\,(1 + x)}\,dx = \int_0^1 \frac{1}{\sqrt{x}\,(1 + x)}\,dx + \int_1^\infty \frac{1}{\sqrt{x}\,(1 + x)}\,dx$$

48–49 ▪ Find the values of p for which the integral converges and evaluate the integral for those values of p.

48. $\displaystyle\int_e^\infty \frac{1}{x(\ln x)^p}\,dx$

49. $\displaystyle\int_0^1 \frac{1}{x^p}\,dx$

▪ ▪ ▪ ▪ ▪ ▪ ▪ ▪ ▪ ▪ ▪ ▪

50. (a) Evaluate the integral $\int_0^\infty x^n e^{-x}\,dx$ for $n = 0, 1, 2$, and 3.

(b) Guess the value of $\int_0^\infty x^n e^{-x}\,dx$ when n is an arbitrary positive integer.

(c) Prove your guess using mathematical induction.

51. (a) Show that $\int_{-\infty}^\infty x\,dx$ is divergent.

(b) Show that

$$\lim_{t \to \infty} \int_{-t}^t x\,dx = 0$$

This shows that we can't define

$$\int_{-\infty}^\infty f(x)\,dx = \lim_{t \to \infty} \int_{-t}^t f(x)\,dx$$

52. If $\int_{-\infty}^\infty f(x)\,dx$ is convergent and a and b are real numbers, show that

$$\int_{-\infty}^a f(x)\,dx + \int_a^\infty f(x)\,dx = \int_{-\infty}^b f(x)\,dx + \int_b^\infty f(x)\,dx$$

53. A manufacturer of lightbulbs wants to produce bulbs that last about 700 hours but, of course, some bulbs burn out faster than others. Let $F(t)$ be the fraction of the company's bulbs that burn out before t hours, so $F(t)$ always lies between 0 and 1.

(a) Make a rough sketch of what you think the graph of F might look like.

(b) What is the meaning of the derivative $r(t) = F'(t)$?

(c) What is the value of $\int_0^\infty r(t)\,dt$? Why?

54. The *average speed* of molecules in an ideal gas is

$$\bar{v} = \frac{4}{\sqrt{\pi}}\left(\frac{M}{2RT}\right)^{3/2} \int_0^\infty v^3 e^{-Mv^2/(2RT)}\,dv$$

where M is the molecular weight of the gas, R is the gas constant, T is the gas temperature, and v is the molecular speed. Show that

$$\bar{v} = \sqrt{\frac{8RT}{\pi M}}$$

55. As we saw in Section 3.4, a radioactive substance decays exponentially: The mass at time t is $m(t) = m(0)e^{kt}$, where $m(0)$ is the initial mass and k is a negative constant. The *mean life* M of an atom in the substance is

$$M = -k \int_0^\infty t e^{kt}\,dt$$

For the radioactive carbon isotope, ^{14}C, used in radiocarbon dating, the value of k is -0.000121. Find the mean life of a ^{14}C atom.

56. Astronomers use a technique called *stellar stereography* to determine the density of stars in a star cluster from the observed (two-dimensional) density that can be analyzed from a photograph. Suppose that in a spherical cluster of radius R the density of stars depends only on the distance r from the center of the cluster. If the perceived star density is given by $y(s)$, where s is the observed planar distance from the center of the cluster, and $x(r)$ is the actual density, it can be shown that

$$y(s) = \int_s^R \frac{2r}{\sqrt{r^2 - s^2}} x(r)\, dr$$

If the actual density of stars in a cluster is $x(r) = \frac{1}{2}(R - r)^2$, find the perceived density $y(s)$.

57. Determine how large the number a has to be so that

$$\int_a^\infty \frac{1}{x^2 + 1}\, dx < 0.001$$

58. Estimate the numerical value of $\int_0^\infty e^{-x^2}\, dx$ by writing it as the sum of $\int_0^4 e^{-x^2}\, dx$ and $\int_4^\infty e^{-x^2}\, dx$. Approximate the first integral by using Simpson's Rule with $n = 8$ and show that the second integral is smaller than $\int_4^\infty e^{-4x}\, dx$, which is less than 0.0000001.

59. Show that $\int_0^\infty x^2 e^{-x^2}\, dx = \frac{1}{2} \int_0^\infty e^{-x^2}\, dx$.

60. Show that $\int_0^\infty e^{-x^2}\, dx = \int_0^1 \sqrt{-\ln y}\, dy$ by interpreting the integrals as areas.

61. Find the value of the constant C for which the integral

$$\int_0^\infty \left(\frac{1}{\sqrt{x^2 + 4}} - \frac{C}{x + 2} \right) dx$$

converges. Evaluate the integral for this value of C.

62. Find the value of the constant C for which the integral

$$\int_0^\infty \left(\frac{x}{x^2 + 1} - \frac{C}{3x + 1} \right) dx$$

converges. Evaluate the integral for this value of C.

---

6 ⎮ REVIEW

CONCEPT CHECK

1. State the rule for integration by parts. In practice, how do you use it?

2. How do you evaluate $\int \sin^m x \cos^n x\, dx$ if m is odd? What if n is odd? What if m and n are both even?

3. If the expression $\sqrt{a^2 - x^2}$ occurs in an integral, what substitution might you try? What if $\sqrt{a^2 + x^2}$ occurs? What if $\sqrt{x^2 - a^2}$ occurs?

4. What is the form of the partial fraction expansion of a rational function $P(x)/Q(x)$ if the degree of P is less than the degree of Q and $Q(x)$ has only distinct linear factors? What if a linear factor is repeated? What if $Q(x)$ has an irreducible quadratic factor (not repeated)? What if the quadratic factor is repeated?

5. State the rules for approximating the definite integral $\int_a^b f(x)\, dx$ with the Midpoint Rule, the Trapezoidal Rule, and Simpson's Rule. Which would you expect to give the best estimate? How do you approximate the error for each rule?

6. Define the following improper integrals.

(a) $\int_a^\infty f(x)\, dx$ (b) $\int_{-\infty}^b f(x)\, dx$ (c) $\int_{-\infty}^\infty f(x)\, dx$

7. Define the improper integral $\int_a^b f(x)\, dx$ for each of the following cases.

(a) f has an infinite discontinuity at a.
(b) f has an infinite discontinuity at b.
(c) f has an infinite discontinuity at c, where $a < c < b$.

8. State the Comparison Theorem for improper integrals.

TRUE-FALSE QUIZ

Determine whether the statement is true or false. If it is true, explain why. If it is false, explain why or give an example that disproves the statement.

1. $\dfrac{x(x^2 + 4)}{x^2 - 4}$ can be put in the form $\dfrac{A}{x + 2} + \dfrac{B}{x - 2}$.

2. $\dfrac{x^2 + 4}{x(x^2 - 4)}$ can be put in the form $\dfrac{A}{x} + \dfrac{B}{x + 2} + \dfrac{C}{x - 2}$.

3. $\dfrac{x^2 + 4}{x^2(x - 4)}$ can be put in the form $\dfrac{A}{x^2} + \dfrac{B}{x - 4}$.

4. $\dfrac{x^2 - 4}{x(x^2 + 4)}$ can be put in the form $\dfrac{A}{x} + \dfrac{B}{x^2 + 4}$.

5. $\int_0^4 \dfrac{x}{x^2 - 1}\, dx = \frac{1}{2} \ln 15$

6. $\int_1^\infty \dfrac{1}{x^{\sqrt{2}}}\, dx$ is convergent.

7. If f is continuous, then $\int_{-\infty}^\infty f(x)\, dx = \lim_{t \to \infty} \int_{-t}^t f(x)\, dx$.

8. The Midpoint Rule is always more accurate than the Trapezoidal Rule.

9. (a) Every elementary function has an elementary derivative.
(b) Every elementary function has an elementary anti-derivative.

10. If f is continuous on $[0, \infty)$ and $\int_1^\infty f(x)\,dx$ is convergent, then $\int_0^\infty f(x)\,dx$ is convergent.

11. If f is a continuous, decreasing function on $[1, \infty)$ and $\lim_{x \to \infty} f(x) = 0$, then $\int_1^\infty f(x)\,dx$ is convergent.

12. If $\int_a^\infty f(x)\,dx$ and $\int_a^\infty g(x)\,dx$ are both convergent, then $\int_a^\infty [f(x) + g(x)]\,dx$ is convergent.

13. If $\int_a^\infty f(x)\,dx$ and $\int_a^\infty g(x)\,dx$ are both divergent, then $\int_a^\infty [f(x) + g(x)]\,dx$ is divergent.

14. If $f(x) \le g(x)$ and $\int_0^\infty g(x)\,dx$ diverges, then $\int_0^\infty f(x)\,dx$ also diverges.

EXERCISES

1–40 ▪ Evaluate the integral.

1. $\int_0^5 \dfrac{x}{x + 10}\,dx$

2. $\int_0^5 ye^{-0.6y}\,dy$

3. $\int_0^{\pi/2} \dfrac{\cos\theta}{1 + \sin\theta}\,d\theta$

4. $\int_1^4 \dfrac{dt}{(2t + 1)^3}$

5. $\int \tan^7 x \sec^3 x\,dx$

6. $\int \dfrac{1}{y^2 - 4y - 12}\,dy$

7. $\int \dfrac{\sin(\ln t)}{t}\,dt$

8. $\int \dfrac{dx}{x^2\sqrt{1 + x^2}}$

9. $\int_1^4 x^{3/2} \ln x\,dx$

10. $\int_0^1 \dfrac{\sqrt{\arctan x}}{1 + x^2}\,dx$

11. $\int_1^2 \dfrac{\sqrt{x^2 - 1}}{x}\,dx$

12. $\int_{-1}^1 \dfrac{\sin x}{1 + x^2}\,dx$

13. $\int \dfrac{dx}{x^3 + x}$

14. $\int \dfrac{x^2 + 2}{x + 2}\,dx$

15. $\int \sin^2\theta \cos^5\theta\,d\theta$

16. $\int \dfrac{\sec^6\theta}{\tan^2\theta}\,d\theta$

17. $\int x \sec x \tan x\,dx$

18. $\int \dfrac{x^2 + 8x - 3}{x^3 + 3x^2}\,dx$

19. $\int \dfrac{x + 1}{9x^2 + 6x + 5}\,dx$

20. $\int \dfrac{dt}{\sin^2 t + \cos 2t}$

21. $\int \dfrac{dx}{\sqrt{x^2 - 4x}}$

22. $\int \dfrac{x^3}{(x + 1)^{10}}\,dx$

23. $\int \csc^4 4x\,dx$

24. $\int e^x \cos x\,dx$

25. $\int \dfrac{3x^3 - x^2 + 6x - 4}{(x^2 + 1)(x^2 + 2)}\,dx$

26. $\int \dfrac{dx}{1 + e^x}$

27. $\int_0^{\pi/2} \cos^3 x \sin 2x\,dx$

28. $\int \dfrac{\sqrt[3]{x} + 1}{\sqrt[3]{x} - 1}\,dx$

29. $\int_{-1}^1 x^5 \sec x\,dx$

30. $\int \dfrac{dx}{e^x\sqrt{1 - e^{-2x}}}$

31. $\int_0^{\ln 10} \dfrac{e^x\sqrt{e^x - 1}}{e^x + 8}\,dx$

32. $\int_0^{\pi/4} \dfrac{x \sin x}{\cos^3 x}\,dx$

33. $\int \dfrac{x^2}{(4 - x^2)^{3/2}}\,dx$

34. $\int (\arcsin x)^2\,dx$

35. $\int \dfrac{1}{\sqrt{x} + x^{3/2}}\,dx$

36. $\int \dfrac{1 - \tan\theta}{1 + \tan\theta}\,d\theta$

37. $\int (\cos x + \sin x)^2 \cos 2x\,dx$

38. $\int x(\tan^{-1}x)^2\,dx$

39. $\int_0^{1/2} \dfrac{xe^{2x}}{(1 + 2x)^2}\,dx$

40. $\int_{\pi/4}^{\pi/3} \dfrac{\sqrt{\tan\theta}}{\sin 2\theta}\,d\theta$

41–50 ▪ Evaluate the integral or show that it is divergent.

41. $\int_1^\infty \dfrac{1}{(2x + 1)^3}\,dx$

42. $\int_0^1 \dfrac{t^2 + 1}{t^2 - 1}\,dt$

43. $\int_2^\infty \dfrac{dx}{x \ln x}$

44. $\int_2^6 \dfrac{y}{\sqrt{y - 2}}\,dy$

45. $\int_0^4 \dfrac{\ln x}{\sqrt{x}}\,dx$

46. $\int_0^1 \dfrac{1}{2 - 3x}\,dx$

47. $\int_0^3 \dfrac{dx}{x^2 - x - 2}$

48. $\int_{-1}^1 \dfrac{x + 1}{\sqrt[3]{x^4}}\,dx$

49. $\int_{-\infty}^\infty \dfrac{dx}{4x^2 + 4x + 5}$

50. $\int_1^\infty \dfrac{\tan^{-1}x}{x^2}\,dx$

51–54 ▪ Use the Table of Integrals on the Reference Pages to evaluate the integral.

51. $\int e^x\sqrt{1 - e^{2x}}\,dx$

52. $\int \csc^5 t\,dt$

53. $\int \sqrt{x^2 + x + 1} \, dx$

54. $\int \dfrac{\cot x}{\sqrt{1 + 2\sin x}} \, dx$

55. Is it possible to find a number n such that $\int_0^\infty x^n \, dx$ is convergent?

56. For what values of a is $\int_0^\infty e^{ax} \cos x \, dx$ convergent? Evaluate the integral for those values of a.

57–58 ■ Use (a) the Trapezoidal Rule, (b) the Midpoint Rule, and (c) Simpson's Rule with $n = 10$ to approximate the given integral. Round your answers to six decimal places.

57. $\int_0^1 \sqrt{1 + x^4} \, dx$

58. $\int_0^{\pi/2} \sqrt{\sin x} \, dx$

■ ■ ■ ■ ■ ■ ■ ■ ■ ■ ■ ■ ■ ■

59. Estimate the errors involved in Exercise 57, parts (a) and (b). How large should n be in each case to guarantee an error of less than 0.00001?

60. Use Simpson's Rule with $n = 6$ to estimate the area under the curve $y = e^x/x$ from $x = 1$ to $x = 4$.

61. The speedometer reading (v) on a car was observed at 1-minute intervals and recorded in the chart. Use Simpson's Rule to estimate the distance traveled by the car.

t (min)	v (mi/h)	t (min)	v (mi/h)
0	40	6	56
1	42	7	57
2	45	8	57
3	49	9	55
4	52	10	56
5	54		

62. A population of honeybees increased at a rate of $r(t)$ bees per week, where the graph of r is as shown. Use Simpson's Rule with six subintervals to estimate the increase in the bee population during the first 24 weeks.

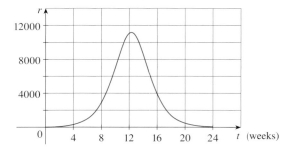

63. (a) If $f(x) = \sin(\sin x)$, use a graph to find an upper bound for $|f^{(4)}(x)|$.
(b) Use Simpson's Rule with $n = 10$ to approximate $\int_0^\pi f(x) \, dx$ and use part (a) to estimate the error.
(c) How large should n be to guarantee that the size of the error in using S_n is less than 0.00001?

64. Use the Comparison Theorem to determine whether the integral

$$\int_1^\infty \frac{x^3}{x^5 + 2} \, dx$$

is convergent or divergent.

65. If f' is continuous on $[0, \infty)$ and $\lim_{x \to \infty} f(x) = 0$, show that

$$\int_0^\infty f'(x) \, dx = -f(0)$$

7 APPLICATIONS OF INTEGRATION

In this chapter we explore some of the applications of the definite integral by using it to compute areas between curves, volumes of solids, lengths of curves, the work done by a varying force, the center of gravity of a plate, and the force on a dam. The common theme in most of these applications is the following general method, which is similar to the one we used to find areas under curves: We break up a quantity Q into a large number of small parts. We next approximate each small part by a quantity of the form $f(x_i^*) \, \Delta x$ and thus approximate Q by a Riemann sum. Then we take the limit and express Q as an integral. Finally we evaluate the integral by using the Evaluation Theorem, or Simpson's Rule, or technology.

In the final section we look at what is perhaps the most important of all the applications of integration: differential equations. When a scientist uses calculus, more often than not it is to solve a differential equation that has arisen in the description of some physical process.

7.1 AREAS BETWEEN CURVES

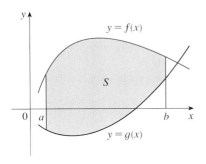

FIGURE 1
$S = \{(x, y) \mid a \leqslant x \leqslant b, g(x) \leqslant y \leqslant f(x)\}$

In Chapter 5 we defined and calculated areas of regions that lie under the graphs of functions. Here we use integrals to find areas of regions that lie between the graphs of two functions.

Consider the region S that lies between two curves $y = f(x)$ and $y = g(x)$ and between the vertical lines $x = a$ and $x = b$, where f and g are continuous functions and $f(x) \geqslant g(x)$ for all x in $[a, b]$. (See Figure 1.)

Just as we did for areas under curves in Section 5.1, we divide S into n strips of equal width and then we approximate the ith strip by a rectangle with base Δx and height $f(x_i^*) - g(x_i^*)$. (See Figure 2. If we like, we could take all of the sample points to be right endpoints, in which case $x_i^* = x_i$.) The Riemann sum

$$\sum_{i=1}^{n} [f(x_i^*) - g(x_i^*)] \, \Delta x$$

is therefore an approximation to what we intuitively think of as the area of S.

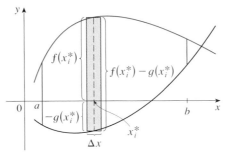

FIGURE 2   (a) Typical rectangle   (b) Approximating rectangles

357

This approximation appears to become better and better as $n \to \infty$. Therefore, we define the **area** A of S as the limiting value of the sum of the areas of these approximating rectangles.

1

$$A = \lim_{n \to \infty} \sum_{i=1}^{n} [f(x_i^*) - g(x_i^*)] \, \Delta x$$

We recognize the limit in (1) as the definite integral of $f - g$. Therefore, we have the following formula for area.

2 The area A of the region bounded by the curves $y = f(x)$, $y = g(x)$, and the lines $x = a$, $x = b$, where f and g are continuous and $f(x) \geqslant g(x)$ for all x in $[a, b]$, is

$$A = \int_a^b [f(x) - g(x)] \, dx$$

Notice that in the special case where $g(x) = 0$, S is the region under the graph of f and our general definition of area (1) reduces to our previous definition (Definition 5.1.2).

In the case where both f and g are positive, you can see from Figure 3 why (2) is true:

$$A = [\text{area under } y = f(x)] - [\text{area under } y = g(x)]$$

$$= \int_a^b f(x) \, dx - \int_a^b g(x) \, dx = \int_a^b [f(x) - g(x)] \, dx$$

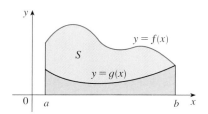

FIGURE 3

$$A = \int_a^b f(x) \, dx - \int_a^b g(x) \, dx$$

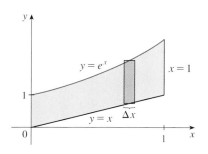

FIGURE 4

EXAMPLE I Find the area of the region bounded above by $y = e^x$, bounded below by $y = x$, and bounded on the sides by $x = 0$ and $x = 1$.

SOLUTION The region is shown in Figure 4. The upper boundary curve is $y = e^x$ and the lower boundary curve is $y = x$. So we use the area formula (2) with $f(x) = e^x$, $g(x) = x$, $a = 0$, and $b = 1$:

$$A = \int_0^1 (e^x - x) \, dx = e^x - \tfrac{1}{2}x^2 \Big]_0^1 = e - \tfrac{1}{2} - 1 = e - 1.5 \qquad \blacksquare$$

In Figure 4 we drew a typical approximating rectangle with width Δx as a reminder of the procedure by which the area is defined in (1). In general, when we set up an integral for an area, it's helpful to sketch the region to identify the top curve y_T, the bottom curve y_B, and a typical approximating rectangle as in Figure 5. Then the area of a typical rectangle is $(y_T - y_B) \, \Delta x$ and the equation

$$A = \lim_{n \to \infty} \sum_{i=1}^{n} (y_T - y_B) \, \Delta x = \int_a^b (y_T - y_B) \, dx$$

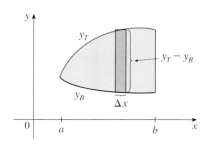

FIGURE 5

summarizes the procedure of adding (in a limiting sense) the areas of all the typical rectangles.

Notice that in Figure 5 the left-hand boundary reduces to a point, whereas in Figure 3 the right-hand boundary reduces to a point. In the next example both of the side boundaries reduce to a point, so the first step is to find a and b.

☑ EXAMPLE 2 Find the area of the region enclosed by the parabolas $y = x^2$ and $y = 2x - x^2$.

SOLUTION We first find the points of intersection of the parabolas by solving their equations simultaneously. This gives $x^2 = 2x - x^2$, or $2x^2 - 2x = 0$. Therefore $2x(x - 1) = 0$, so $x = 0$ or 1. The points of intersection are $(0, 0)$ and $(1, 1)$.

We see from Figure 6 that the top and bottom boundaries are

$$y_T = 2x - x^2 \qquad \text{and} \qquad y_B = x^2$$

The area of a typical rectangle is

$$(y_T - y_B)\, \Delta x = (2x - x^2 - x^2)\, \Delta x = (2x - 2x^2)\, \Delta x$$

and the region lies between $x = 0$ and $x = 1$. So the total area is

$$A = \int_0^1 (2x - 2x^2)\, dx = 2 \int_0^1 (x - x^2)\, dx$$

$$= 2\left[\frac{x^2}{2} - \frac{x^3}{3} \right]_0^1 = 2\left(\frac{1}{2} - \frac{1}{3} \right) = \frac{1}{3} \qquad ■$$

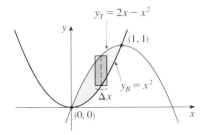

FIGURE 6

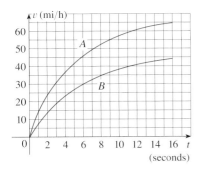

FIGURE 7

EXAMPLE 3 Figure 7 shows velocity curves for two cars, A and B, that start side by side and move along the same road. What does the area between the curves represent? Use Simpson's Rule to estimate it.

SOLUTION We know from Section 5.3 that the area under the velocity curve A represents the distance traveled by car A during the first 16 seconds. Similarly, the area under curve B is the distance traveled by car B during that time period. So the area between these curves, which is the difference of the areas under the curves, is the distance between the cars after 16 seconds. We read the velocities from the graph and convert them to feet per second ($1 \text{ mi/h} = \frac{5280}{3600} \text{ ft/s}$).

t	0	2	4	6	8	10	12	14	16
v_A	0	34	54	67	76	84	89	92	95
v_B	0	21	34	44	51	56	60	63	65
$v_A - v_B$	0	13	20	23	25	28	29	29	30

Using Simpson's Rule with $n = 8$ intervals, so that $\Delta t = 2$, we estimate the distance between the cars after 16 seconds:

$$\int_0^{16} (v_A - v_B)\, dt$$

$$\approx \tfrac{2}{3}[0 + 4(13) + 2(20) + 4(23) + 2(25) + 4(28) + 2(29) + 4(29) + 30]$$

$$\approx 367 \text{ ft} \qquad ■$$

Some regions are best treated by regarding x as a function of y. If a region is bounded by curves with equations $x = f(y)$, $x = g(y)$, $y = c$, and $y = d$, where f and g are continuous and $f(y) \geq g(y)$ for $c \leq y \leq d$ (see Figure 8), then its area is

$$A = \int_c^d [f(y) - g(y)]\, dy$$

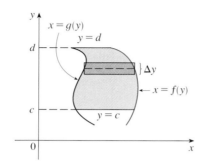

FIGURE 8

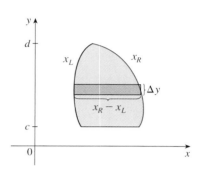

FIGURE 9

If we write x_R for the right boundary and x_L for the left boundary, then, as Figure 9 illustrates, we have

$$A = \int_c^d (x_R - x_L)\, dy$$

Here a typical approximating rectangle has dimensions $x_R - x_L$ and Δy.

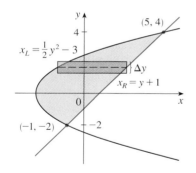

FIGURE 10

✔ EXAMPLE 4 Find the area enclosed by the line $y = x - 1$ and the parabola $y^2 = 2x + 6$.

SOLUTION By solving the two equations we find that the points of intersection are $(-1, -2)$ and $(5, 4)$. We solve the equation of the parabola for x and notice from Figure 10 that the left and right boundary curves are

$$x_L = \tfrac{1}{2}y^2 - 3 \qquad \text{and} \qquad x_R = y + 1$$

We must integrate between the appropriate y-values, $y = -2$ and $y = 4$. Thus

$$A = \int_{-2}^4 (x_R - x_L)\, dy = \int_{-2}^4 \left[(y + 1) - \left(\tfrac{1}{2}y^2 - 3 \right) \right] dy$$

$$= \int_{-2}^4 \left(-\tfrac{1}{2}y^2 + y + 4 \right) dy$$

$$= -\frac{1}{2} \left(\frac{y^3}{3} \right) + \frac{y^2}{2} + 4y \Big]_{-2}^4$$

$$= -\tfrac{1}{6}(64) + 8 + 16 - \left(\tfrac{4}{3} + 2 - 8 \right) = 18 \qquad ∎$$

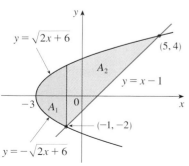

FIGURE 11

We could have found the area in Example 4 by integrating with respect to x instead of y, but the calculation is much more involved. It would have meant splitting the region in two and computing the areas labeled A_1 and A_2 in Figure 11. The method we used in Example 4 is *much* easier.

7.1 EXERCISES

1–4 ■ Find the area of the shaded region.

1.

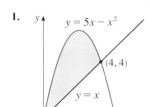

2.

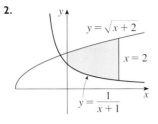

3.

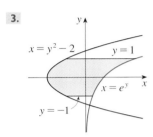

4.

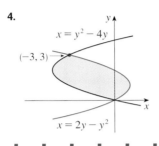

5–16 ■ Sketch the region enclosed by the given curves. Decide whether to integrate with respect to x or y. Draw a typical approximating rectangle and label its height and width. Then find the area of the region.

5. $y = x + 1$, $y = 9 - x^2$, $x = -1$, $x = 2$

6. $y = \sin x$, $y = e^x$, $x = 0$, $x = \pi/2$

7. $y = x$, $y = x^2$

8. $y = 1 + \sqrt{x}$, $y = 1 + \frac{1}{3}x$

9. $y = 12 - x^2$, $y = x^2 - 6$

10. $y = x^2$, $y = 4x - x^2$

11. $x = 2y^2$, $x + y = 1$

12. $4x + y^2 = 12$, $x = y$

13. $x = 2y^2$, $x = 4 + y^2$

14. $y = \sin x$, $y = 2x/\pi$, $x \geqslant 0$

15. $y = 1/x$, $y = x$, $y = \frac{1}{4}x$, $x > 0$

16. $y = |x|$, $y = x^2 - 2$

17–20 ■ Use a graph to find approximate x-coordinates of the points of intersection of the given curves. Then find (approximately) the area of the region bounded by the curves.

17. $y = x \sin(x^2)$, $y = x^4$ **18.** $y = e^x$, $y = 2 - x^2$

19. $y = x^2$, $y = xe^{-x/2}$ **20.** $y = x \cos x$, $y = x^{10}$

21. Sketch the region that lies between the curves $y = \cos x$ and $y = \sin 2x$ and between $x = 0$ and $x = \pi/2$. Notice that the region consists of two separate parts. Find the area of this region.

22. Graph the curves $y = x^2 - x$ and $y = x^3 - 4x^2 + 3x$ on a common screen and observe that the region between them consists of two parts. Find the area of this region.

23. Racing cars driven by Chris and Kelly are side by side at the start of a race. The table shows the velocities of each car (in miles per hour) during the first ten seconds of the race. Use Simpson's Rule to estimate how much farther Kelly travels than Chris does during the first ten seconds.

t	v_C	v_K	t	v_C	v_K
0	0	0	6	69	80
1	20	22	7	75	86
2	32	37	8	81	93
3	46	52	9	86	98
4	54	61	10	90	102
5	62	71			

24. Two cars, A and B, start side by side and accelerate from rest. The figure shows the graphs of their velocity functions.
(a) Which car is ahead after one minute? Explain.
(b) What is the meaning of the area of the shaded region?
(c) Which car is ahead after two minutes? Explain.
(d) Estimate the time at which the cars are again side by side.

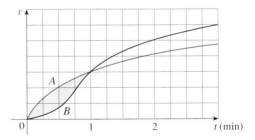

25. The widths (in meters) of a kidney-shaped swimming pool were measured at 2-meter intervals as indicated in the figure. Use Simpson's Rule to estimate the area of the pool.

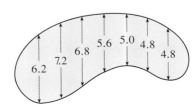

26. A cross-section of an airplane wing is shown. Measurements of the height of the wing, in centimeters, at 20-centimeter intervals are 5.8, 20.3, 26.7, 29.0, 27.6, 27.3, 23.8, 20.5, 15.1, 8.7, and 2.8. Use Simpson's Rule to estimate the area of the wing's cross-section.

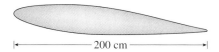

— 200 cm —

27. If the birth rate of a population is $b(t) = 2200e^{0.024t}$ people per year and the death rate is $d(t) = 1460e^{0.018t}$ people per year, find the area between these curves for $0 \leq t \leq 10$. What does this area represent?

28. A water storage tank has the shape of a cylinder with diameter 10 ft. It is mounted so that the circular cross-sections are vertical. If the depth of the water is 7 ft, what percentage of the total capacity is being used?

29. Find the area of the crescent-shaped region (called a *lune*) bounded by arcs of circles with radii r and R (see the figure).

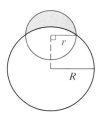

30. Sketch the region in the xy-plane defined by the inequalities $x - 2y^2 \geq 0$, $1 - x - |y| \geq 0$ and find its area.

31. Find the values of c such that the area of the region bounded by the parabolas $y = x^2 - c^2$ and $y = c^2 - x^2$ is 576.

32. Find the area of the region bounded by the parabola $y = x^2$, the tangent line to this parabola at $(1, 1)$, and the x-axis.

33. Find the number b such that the line $y = b$ divides the region bounded by the curves $y = x^2$ and $y = 4$ into two regions with equal area.

34. (a) Find the number a such that the line $x = a$ bisects the area under the curve $y = 1/x^2$, $1 \leq x \leq 4$.
(b) Find the number b such that the line $y = b$ bisects the area in part (a).

35. Find a positive continuous function f such that the area under the graph of f from 0 to t is $A(t) = t^3$ for all $t > 0$.

36. Suppose that $0 < c < \pi/2$. For what value of c is the area of the region enclosed by the curves $y = \cos x$, $y = \cos(x - c)$, and $x = 0$ equal to the area of the region enclosed by the curves $y = \cos(x - c)$, $x = \pi$, and $y = 0$?

37. For what values of m do the line $y = mx$ and the curve $y = x/(x^2 + 1)$ enclose a region? Find the area of the region.

7.2 | VOLUMES

In trying to find the volume of a solid we face the same type of problem as in finding areas. We have an intuitive idea of what volume means, but we must make this idea precise by using calculus to give an exact definition of volume.

We start with a simple type of solid called a **cylinder** (or, more precisely, a *right cylinder*). As illustrated in Figure 1(a), a cylinder is bounded by a plane region B_1, called the **base**, and a congruent region B_2 in a parallel plane. The cylinder consists of all points on line segments that are perpendicular to the base and join B_1 to B_2. If the area of the base is A and the height of the cylinder (the distance from B_1 to B_2) is h, then the volume V of the cylinder is defined as

$$V = Ah$$

In particular, if the base is a circle with radius r, then the cylinder is a circular cylinder with volume $V = \pi r^2 h$ [see Figure 1(b)], and if the base is a rectangle with length l and width w, then the cylinder is a rectangular box (also called a *rectangular parallelepiped*) with volume $V = lwh$ [see Figure 1(c)].

For a solid S that isn't a cylinder we first "cut" S into pieces and approximate each piece by a cylinder. We estimate the volume of S by adding the volumes of the cylin-

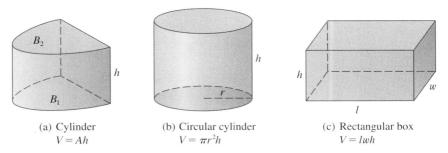

FIGURE 1

(a) Cylinder
$V = Ah$

(b) Circular cylinder
$V = \pi r^2 h$

(c) Rectangular box
$V = lwh$

ders. We arrive at the exact volume of S through a limiting process in which the number of pieces becomes large.

We start by intersecting S with a plane and obtaining a plane region that is called a **cross-section** of S. Let $A(x)$ be the area of the cross-section of S in a plane P_x perpendicular to the x-axis and passing through the point x, where $a \leqslant x \leqslant b$. (See Figure 2. Think of slicing S with a knife through x and computing the area of this slice.) The cross-sectional area $A(x)$ will vary as x increases from a to b.

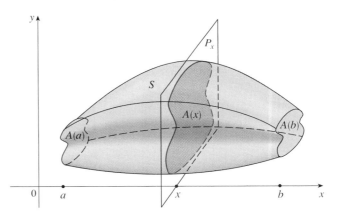

FIGURE 2

We consider a partition of the interval $[a, b]$ into n subintervals with partition points $x_0, x_1, x_2, \ldots, x_n$. We divide S into n "slabs" of width $\Delta x_i = x_i - x_{i-1}$ by using the planes $P_{x_1}, P_{x_2}, \ldots$ to slice the solid. (Think of slicing a loaf of bread.) If we choose sample points x_i^* in $[x_{i-1}, x_i]$, we can approximate the ith slab S_i (the part of S that lies between the planes $P_{x_{i-1}}$ and P_{x_i}) by a cylinder with base area $A(x_i^*)$ and "height" Δx_i. (See Figure 3.)

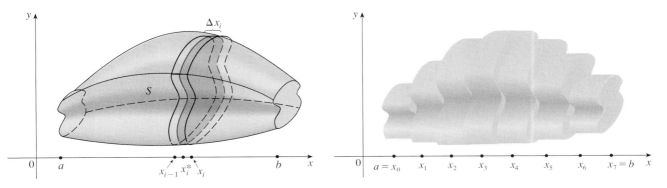

FIGURE 3

The volume of this cylinder is $A(x_i^*)\,\Delta x_i$, so an approximation to our intuitive conception of the volume of the ith slab S_i is

$$V(S_i) \approx A(x_i^*)\,\Delta x_i$$

Adding the volumes of these slabs, we get an approximation to the total volume (that is, what we think of intuitively as the volume):

$$V \approx \sum_{i=1}^{n} A(x_i^*)\,\Delta x_i$$

This approximation appears to become better and better as the slices become thinner and thinner. So we *define* the volume as the limit of these sums as max $\Delta x_i \to 0$. But we recognize the limit of Riemann sums as a definite integral and so we have the following definition.

■ It can be proved that this definition is independent of how S is situated with respect to the x-axis. In other words, no matter how we slice S with parallel planes, we always get the same answer for V.

DEFINITION OF VOLUME Let S be a solid that lies between $x = a$ and $x = b$. If the cross-sectional area of S in the plane P_x, through x and perpendicular to the x-axis, is $A(x)$, where A is an integrable function, then the **volume** of S is

$$V = \lim_{\max \Delta x_i \to 0} \sum_{i=1}^{n} A(x_i^*)\,\Delta x_i = \int_a^b A(x)\,dx$$

When we use the volume formula $V = \int_a^b A(x)\,dx$ it is important to remember that $A(x)$ is the area of a moving cross-section obtained by slicing through x perpendicular to the x-axis.

Notice that, for a cylinder, the cross-sectional area is constant: $A(x) = A$ for all x. So our definition of volume gives $V = \int_a^b A\,dx = A(b - a)$; this agrees with the formula $V = Ah$.

EXAMPLE 1 Show that the volume of a sphere of radius r is $V = \frac{4}{3}\pi r^3$.

SOLUTION If we place the sphere so that its center is at the origin (see Figure 4), then the plane P_x intersects the sphere in a circle whose radius (from the Pythagorean Theorem) is $y = \sqrt{r^2 - x^2}$. So the cross-sectional area is

$$A(x) = \pi y^2 = \pi(r^2 - x^2)$$

Using the definition of volume with $a = -r$ and $b = r$, we have

$$V = \int_{-r}^{r} A(x)\,dx = \int_{-r}^{r} \pi(r^2 - x^2)\,dx$$

$$= 2\pi \int_0^r (r^2 - x^2)\,dx \qquad \text{(The integrand is even.)}$$

$$= 2\pi\left[r^2 x - \frac{x^3}{3}\right]_0^r = 2\pi\left(r^3 - \frac{r^3}{3}\right)$$

$$= \frac{4}{3}\pi r^3 \qquad\qquad ■$$

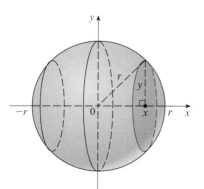

FIGURE 4

Figure 5 illustrates the definition of volume when the solid is a sphere with radius $r = 1$. From the result of Example 1, we know that the volume of the sphere is $\frac{4}{3}\pi \approx 4.18879$. Here the slabs are circular cylinders, or *disks,* and the three parts of

Figure 5 show the geometric interpretations of the Riemann sums

$$\sum_{i=1}^{n} A(\bar{x}_i)\,\Delta x = \sum_{i=1}^{n} \pi(1^2 - \bar{x}_i^2)\,\Delta x$$

when $n = 5$, 10, and 20 if we use regular partitions and choose the sample points x_i^* to be the midpoints $\bar{x}_i$. Notice that as we increase the number of approximating cylinders, the corresponding Riemann sums become closer to the true volume.

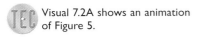
Visual 7.2A shows an animation of Figure 5.

(a) Using 5 disks, $V \approx 4.2726$

(b) Using 10 disks, $V \approx 4.2097$

(c) Using 20 disks, $V \approx 4.1940$

FIGURE 5

Approximating the volume
of a sphere with radius 1

▼ EXAMPLE 2 Find the volume of the solid obtained by rotating about the x-axis the region under the curve $y = \sqrt{x}$ from 0 to 1. Illustrate the definition of volume by sketching a typical approximating cylinder.

SOLUTION The region is shown in Figure 6(a). If we rotate about the x-axis, we get the solid shown in Figure 6(b). When we slice through the point x, we get a disk with radius $\sqrt{x}$. The area of this cross-section is

$$A(x) = \pi\left(\sqrt{x}\right)^2 = \pi x$$

and the volume of the approximating cylinder (a disk with thickness Δx) is

$$A(x)\,\Delta x = \pi x\,\Delta x$$

The solid lies between $x = 0$ and $x = 1$, so its volume is

$$V = \int_0^1 A(x)\,dx = \int_0^1 \pi x\,dx = \pi\,\frac{x^2}{2}\Bigg]_0^1 = \frac{\pi}{2}$$

▪ Did we get a reasonable answer in Example 2? As a check on our work, let's replace the given region by a square with base $[0, 1]$ and height 1. If we rotate this square, we get a cylinder with radius 1, height 1, and volume $\pi \cdot 1^2 \cdot 1 = \pi$. We computed that the given solid has half this volume. That seems about right.

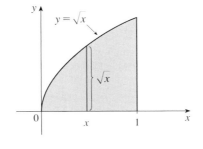

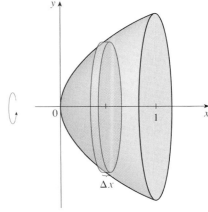

Visual 7.2B shows how the solids of revolution in Examples 2–6 are formed.

FIGURE 6   (a)   (b)

▼ EXAMPLE 3 Find the volume of the solid obtained by rotating the region bounded by $y = x^3$, $y = 8$, and $x = 0$ about the y-axis.

SOLUTION The region is shown in Figure 7(a) and the resulting solid is shown in Figure 7(b). Because the region is rotated about the y-axis, it makes sense to slice the solid perpendicular to the y-axis and therefore to integrate with respect to y. If we slice at height y, we get a circular disk with radius x, where $x = \sqrt[3]{y}$. So the area of a cross-section through y is

$$A(y) = \pi x^2 = \pi(\sqrt[3]{y})^2 = \pi y^{2/3}$$

and the volume of the approximating cylinder pictured in Figure 7(b) is

$$A(y)\,\Delta y = \pi y^{2/3}\,\Delta y$$

Since the solid lies between $y = 0$ and $y = 8$, its volume is

$$V = \int_0^8 A(y)\,dy = \int_0^8 \pi y^{2/3}\,dy = \pi\left[\tfrac{3}{5}y^{5/3}\right]_0^8 = \frac{96\pi}{5}$$

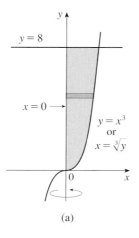

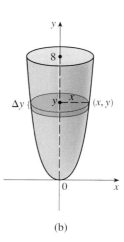

FIGURE 7   (a)   (b)   ■

EXAMPLE 4 The region $\mathcal{R}$ enclosed by the curves $y = x$ and $y = x^2$ is rotated about the x-axis. Find the volume of the resulting solid.

SOLUTION The curves $y = x$ and $y = x^2$ intersect at the points $(0, 0)$ and $(1, 1)$. The region between them, the solid of rotation, and a cross-section perpendicular to the x-axis are shown in Figure 8. A cross-section in the plane P_x has the shape of a *washer* (an annular ring) with inner radius x^2 and outer radius x, so we find the cross-sectional area by subtracting the area of the inner circle from the area of the outer circle:

$$A(x) = \pi x^2 - \pi(x^2)^2 = \pi(x^2 - x^4)$$

Therefore, we have

$$V = \int_0^1 A(x)\,dx = \int_0^1 \pi(x^2 - x^4)\,dx$$

$$= \pi\left[\frac{x^3}{3} - \frac{x^5}{5}\right]_0^1 = \frac{2\pi}{15}$$

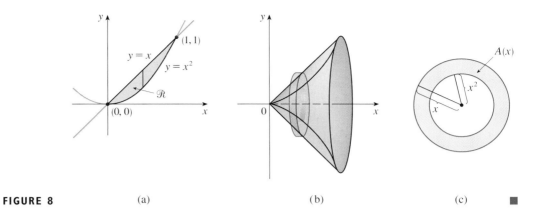

FIGURE 8   (a)   (b)   (c)   ▪

EXAMPLE 5 Find the volume of the solid obtained by rotating the region in
Example 4 about the line $y = 2$.

SOLUTION The solid and a cross-section are shown in Figure 9. Again the cross-
section is a washer, but this time the inner radius is $2 - x$ and the outer radius
is $2 - x^2$. The cross-sectional area is

$$A(x) = \pi(2 - x^2)^2 - \pi(2 - x)^2$$

and so the volume of S is

$$V = \int_0^1 A(x)\, dx = \pi \int_0^1 \left[(2 - x^2)^2 - (2 - x)^2 \right] dx$$

$$= \pi \int_0^1 (x^4 - 5x^2 + 4x)\, dx$$

$$= \pi \left[\frac{x^5}{5} - 5\frac{x^3}{3} + 4\frac{x^2}{2} \right]_0^1 = \frac{8\pi}{15}$$

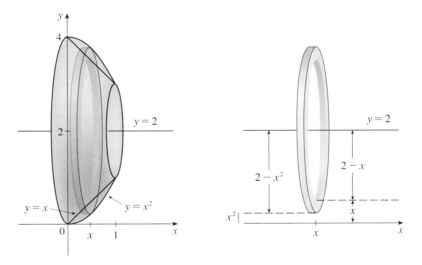

FIGURE 9   ▪

The solids in Examples 1–5 are all called **solids of revolution** because they are
obtained by revolving a region about a line. In general, we calculate the volume of a

solid of revolution by using the basic defining formula

$$V = \int_a^b A(x)\,dx \qquad \text{or} \qquad V = \int_c^d A(y)\,dy$$

and we find the cross-sectional area $A(x)$ or $A(y)$ in one of the following ways:

- If the cross-section is a disk (as in Examples 1–3), we find the radius of the disk (in terms of x or y) and use

$$A = \pi(\text{radius})^2$$

- If the cross-section is a washer (as in Examples 4 and 5), we find the inner radius r_{in} and outer radius r_{out} from a sketch (as in Figures 9 and 10) and compute the area of the washer by subtracting the area of the inner disk from the area of the outer disk:

$$A = \pi(\text{outer radius})^2 - \pi(\text{inner radius})^2$$

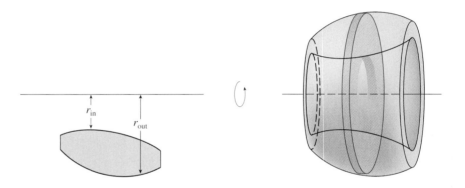

FIGURE 10

The next example gives a further illustration of the procedure.

EXAMPLE 6 Find the volume of the solid obtained by rotating the region in Example 4 about the line $x = -1$.

SOLUTION Figure 11 shows a horizontal cross-section. It is a washer with inner radius $1 + y$ and outer radius $1 + \sqrt{y}$, so the cross-sectional area is

$$A(y) = \pi(\text{outer radius})^2 - \pi(\text{inner radius})^2$$

$$= \pi\left(1 + \sqrt{y}\,\right)^2 - \pi(1 + y)^2$$

The volume is

$$V = \int_0^1 A(y)\,dy = \pi \int_0^1 \left[\left(1 + \sqrt{y}\,\right)^2 - (1 + y)^2\right] dy$$

$$= \pi \int_0^1 \left(2\sqrt{y} - y - y^2\right) dy$$

$$= \pi \left[\frac{4y^{3/2}}{3} - \frac{y^2}{2} - \frac{y^3}{3}\right]_0^1 = \frac{\pi}{2}$$

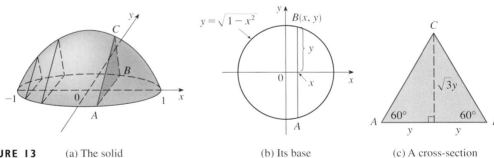

FIGURE 11

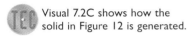

Visual 7.2C shows how the solid in Figure 12 is generated.

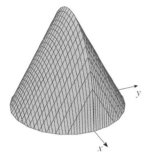

FIGURE 12
Computer-generated picture
of the solid in Example 7

We now find the volumes of two solids that are *not* solids of revolution.

EXAMPLE 7 Figure 12 shows a solid with a circular base of radius 1. Parallel cross-sections perpendicular to the base are equilateral triangles. Find the volume of the solid.

SOLUTION Let's take the circle to be $x^2 + y^2 = 1$. The solid, its base, and a typical cross-section at a distance x from the origin are shown in Figure 13.

FIGURE 13   (a) The solid   (b) Its base   (c) A cross-section

Since B lies on the circle, we have $y = \sqrt{1 - x^2}$ and so the base of the triangle ABC is $|AB| = 2\sqrt{1 - x^2}$. Since the triangle is equilateral, we see from Figure 13(c) that its height is $\sqrt{3}\, y = \sqrt{3}\,\sqrt{1 - x^2}$. The cross-sectional area is therefore

$$A(x) = \tfrac{1}{2} \cdot 2\sqrt{1 - x^2} \cdot \sqrt{3}\,\sqrt{1 - x^2} = \sqrt{3}\,(1 - x^2)$$

and the volume of the solid is

$$V = \int_{-1}^{1} A(x)\, dx = \int_{-1}^{1} \sqrt{3}\,(1 - x^2)\, dx$$

$$= 2\int_{0}^{1} \sqrt{3}\,(1 - x^2)\, dx = 2\sqrt{3}\left[x - \frac{x^3}{3} \right]_{0}^{1} = \frac{4\sqrt{3}}{3}$$

V EXAMPLE 8 Find the volume of a pyramid whose base is a square with side L and whose height is h.

SOLUTION We place the origin O at the vertex of the pyramid and the x-axis along its central axis as in Figure 14. Any plane P_x that passes through x and is perpendicular to the x-axis intersects the pyramid in a square with side of length s, say. We can express s in terms of x by observing from the similar triangles in Figure 15 that

$$\frac{x}{h} = \frac{s/2}{L/2} = \frac{s}{L}$$

and so $s = Lx/h$. [Another method is to observe that the line OP has slope $L/(2h)$ and so its equation is $y = Lx/(2h)$.] Thus the cross-sectional area is

$$A(x) = s^2 = \frac{L^2}{h^2} x^2$$

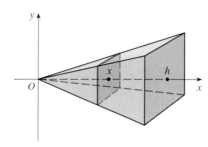

FIGURE 14   **FIGURE 15**

The pyramid lies between $x = 0$ and $x = h$, so its volume is

$$V = \int_0^h A(x)\,dx = \int_0^h \frac{L^2}{h^2} x^2\,dx = \frac{L^2}{h^2}\frac{x^3}{3}\Bigg]_0^h = \frac{L^2 h}{3}$$ ■

NOTE We didn't need to place the vertex of the pyramid at the origin in Example 8. We did so merely to make the equations simple. If, instead, we had placed the center of the base at the origin and the vertex on the positive y-axis, as in Figure 16, you can verify that we would have obtained the integral

$$V = \int_0^h \frac{L^2}{h^2} (h - y)^2\,dy = \frac{L^2 h}{3}$$

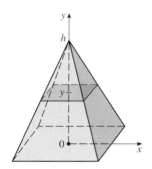

FIGURE 16

7.2	**EXERCISES**

1–12 ■ Find the volume of the solid obtained by rotating the region bounded by the given curves about the specified line. Sketch the region, the solid, and a typical disk or washer.

1. $y = 1/x$, $x = 1$, $x = 2$, $y = 0$;   about the x-axis

2. $y = 1 - x^2$, $y = 0$;   about the x-axis

3. $x = 2\sqrt{y}$, $x = 0$, $y = 9$;   about the y-axis

4. $y = \ln x$, $y = 1$, $y = 2$, $x = 0$;   about the y-axis

5. $y = x^3$, $y = x$, $x \geq 0$; about the *x*-axis

6. $y = \frac{1}{4}x^2$, $y = 5 - x^2$; about the *x*-axis

7. $y^2 = x$, $x = 2y$; about the *y*-axis

8. $y = x^{2/3}$, $x = 1$, $y = 0$; about the *y*-axis

9. $y = x$, $y = \sqrt{x}$; about $y = 1$

10. $y = 1/x$, $y = 0$, $x = 1$, $x = 3$; about $y = -1$

11. $y = x^2$, $x = y^2$; about $x = -1$

12. $y = x$, $y = \sqrt{x}$; about $x = 2$

▪ ▪ ▪ ▪ ▪ ▪ ▪ ▪ ▪ ▪ ▪ ▪ ▪ ▪

13. The region enclosed by the curves $y = x^3$ and $y = \sqrt{x}$ is rotated about the line $x = 1$. Find the volume of the resulting solid.

14. Find the volume of the solid obtained by rotating the region in Exercise 13 about the line $y = 1$.

15–16 ▪ Set up, but do not evaluate, an integral for the volume of the solid obtained by rotating the region bounded by the given curves about the specified line.

15. $y = \tan^3 x$, $y = 1$, $x = 0$; about $y = 1$

16. $y = (x - 2)^4$, $8x - y = 16$; about $x = 10$

▪ ▪ ▪ ▪ ▪ ▪ ▪ ▪ ▪ ▪ ▪ ▪ ▪ ▪

17–18 ▪ Use a graph to find approximate *x*-coordinates of the points of intersection of the given curves. Then find (approximately) the volume of the solid obtained by rotating about the *x*-axis the region bounded by these curves.

17. $y = x^2$, $y = \ln(x + 1)$

18. $y = 3 \sin(x^2)$, $y = e^{x/2} + e^{-2x}$

▪ ▪ ▪ ▪ ▪ ▪ ▪ ▪ ▪ ▪ ▪ ▪ ▪ ▪

19–20 ▪ Use a computer algebra system to find the exact volume of the solid obtained by rotating the region bounded by the given curves about the specified line.

19. $y = \sin^2 x$, $y = 0$, $0 \leq x \leq \pi$; about $y = -1$

20. $y = x$, $y = xe^{1-x/2}$; about $y = 3$

▪ ▪ ▪ ▪ ▪ ▪ ▪ ▪ ▪ ▪ ▪ ▪ ▪ ▪

21–22 ▪ Each integral represents the volume of a solid. Describe the solid.

21. (a) $\pi \int_0^{\pi/2} \cos^2 x \, dx$ (b) $\pi \int_0^1 (y^4 - y^8) \, dy$

22. (a) $\pi \int_2^5 y \, dy$ (b) $\pi \int_0^{\pi/2} [(1 + \cos x)^2 - 1^2] \, dx$

▪ ▪ ▪ ▪ ▪ ▪ ▪ ▪ ▪ ▪ ▪ ▪ ▪ ▪

23. A CAT scan produces equally spaced cross-sectional views of a human organ that provide information about the organ otherwise obtained only by surgery. Suppose that a CAT scan of a human liver shows cross-sections spaced 1.5 cm apart. The liver is 15 cm long and the cross-sectional areas, in square centimeters, are 0, 18, 58, 79, 94, 106, 117, 128, 63, 39, and 0. Use the Midpoint Rule to estimate the volume of the liver.

24. A log 10 m long is cut at 1-meter intervals and its cross-sectional areas *A* (at a distance *x* from the end of the log) are listed in the table. Use the Midpoint Rule with $n = 5$ to estimate the volume of the log.

x (m)	*A* (m²)	*x* (m)	*A* (m²)
0	0.68	6	0.53
1	0.65	7	0.55
2	0.64	8	0.52
3	0.61	9	0.50
4	0.58	10	0.48
5	0.59		

25–37 ▪ Find the volume of the described solid *S*.

25. A right circular cone with height *h* and base radius *r*

26. A frustum of a right circular cone with height *h*, lower base radius *R*, and top radius *r*

27. A cap of a sphere with radius *r* and height *h*

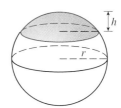

28. A frustum of a pyramid with square base of side *b*, square top of side *a*, and height *h*

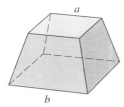

What happens if $a = b$? What happens if $a = 0$?

29. A pyramid with height h and rectangular base with dimensions b and $2b$

30. A pyramid with height h and base an equilateral triangle with side a (a tetrahedron)

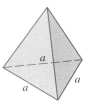

31. A tetrahedron with three mutually perpendicular faces and three mutually perpendicular edges with lengths 3 cm, 4 cm, and 5 cm

32. The base of S is a circular disk with radius r. Parallel cross-sections perpendicular to the base are squares.

33. The base of S is an elliptical region with boundary curve $9x^2 + 4y^2 = 36$. Cross-sections perpendicular to the x-axis are isosceles right triangles with hypotenuse in the base.

34. The base of S is the parabolic region $\{(x, y) \mid x^2 \le y \le 1\}$. Cross-sections perpendicular to the y-axis are equilateral triangles.

35. S has the same base as in Exercise 34, but cross-sections perpendicular to the y-axis are squares.

36. The base of S is the triangular region with vertices $(0, 0)$, $(3, 0)$, and $(0, 2)$. Cross-sections perpendicular to the y-axis are semicircles.

37. S has the same base as in Exercise 36, but cross-sections perpendicular to the y-axis are isosceles triangles with height equal to the base.

■ ■ ■ ■ ■ ■ ■ ■ ■ ■ ■ ■ ■

38. The base of S is a circular disk with radius r. Parallel cross-sections perpendicular to the base are isosceles triangles with height h and unequal side in the base.
   (a) Set up an integral for the volume of S.
   (b) By interpreting the integral as an area, find the volume of S.

39. Some of the pioneers of calculus, such as Kepler and Newton, were inspired by the problem of finding the volumes of wine barrels. (In fact Kepler published a book *Stereometria doliorum* in 1715 devoted to methods for finding the volumes of barrels.) They often approximated the shape of the sides by parabolas.
   (a) A barrel with height h and maximum radius R is constructed by rotating about the x-axis the parabola $y = R - cx^2$, $-h/2 \le x \le h/2$, where c is a positive constant. Show that the radius of each end of the barrel is $r = R - d$, where $d = ch^2/4$.

   (b) Show that the volume enclosed by the barrel is
   $$V = \tfrac{1}{3}\pi h\left(2R^2 + r^2 - \tfrac{2}{5}d^2\right)$$

CAS **40.** (a) A model for the shape of a bird's egg is obtained by rotating about the x-axis the region under the graph of
   $$f(x) = (ax^3 + bx^2 + cx + d)\sqrt{1 - x^2}$$
   Use a CAS to find the volume of such an egg.
   (b) For a Red-throated Loon, $a = -0.06$, $b = 0.04$, $c = 0.1$, and $d = 0.54$. Graph f and find the volume of an egg of this bird.

41. (a) Set up an integral for the volume of a solid *torus* (the donut-shaped solid shown in the figure) with radii r and R.
   (b) By interpreting the integral as an area, find the volume of the torus.

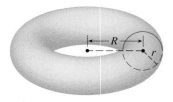

42. A wedge is cut out of a circular cylinder of radius 4 by two planes. One plane is perpendicular to the axis of the cylinder. The other intersects the first at an angle of 30° along a diameter of the cylinder. Find the volume of the wedge.

43. (a) Cavalieri's Principle states that if a family of parallel planes gives equal cross-sectional areas for two solids S_1 and S_2, then the volumes of S_1 and S_2 are equal. Prove this principle.
   (b) Use Cavalieri's Principle to find the volume of the oblique cylinder shown in the figure.

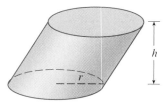

44. Find the volume common to two circular cylinders, each with radius r, if the axes of the cylinders intersect at right angles.

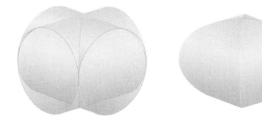

45. Find the volume common to two spheres, each with radius r, if the center of each sphere lies on the surface of the other sphere.

46. A bowl is shaped like a hemisphere with diameter 30 cm. A ball with diameter 10 cm is placed in the bowl and water is poured into the bowl to a depth of h centimeters. Find the volume of water in the bowl.

47. A hole of radius r is bored through a cylinder of radius $R > r$ at right angles to the axis of the cylinder. Set up, but do not evaluate, an integral for the volume cut out.

48. A hole of radius r is bored through the center of a sphere of radius $R > r$. Find the volume of the remaining portion of the sphere.

7.3 VOLUMES BY CYLINDRICAL SHELLS

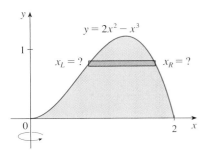

FIGURE 1

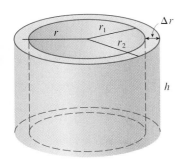

FIGURE 2

Some volume problems are very difficult to handle by the methods of the preceding section. For instance, let's consider the problem of finding the volume of the solid obtained by rotating about the y-axis the region bounded by $y = 2x^2 - x^3$ and $y = 0$. (See Figure 1.) If we slice perpendicular to the y-axis, we get a washer. But to compute the inner radius and the outer radius of the washer, we would have to solve the cubic equation $y = 2x^2 - x^3$ for x in terms of y; that's not easy.

Fortunately, there is a method, called the **method of cylindrical shells**, that is easier to use in such a case. Figure 2 shows a cylindrical shell with inner radius r_1, outer radius r_2, and height h. Its volume V is calculated by subtracting the volume V_1 of the inner cylinder from the volume V_2 of the outer cylinder:

$$V = V_2 - V_1$$
$$= \pi r_2^2 h - \pi r_1^2 h = \pi(r_2^2 - r_1^2)h$$
$$= \pi(r_2 + r_1)(r_2 - r_1)h$$
$$= 2\pi \frac{r_2 + r_1}{2} h(r_2 - r_1)$$

If we let $\Delta r = r_2 - r_1$ (the thickness of the shell) and $r = \frac{1}{2}(r_2 + r_1)$ (the average radius of the shell), then this formula for the volume of a cylindrical shell becomes

1
$$\boxed{V = 2\pi r h\, \Delta r}$$

and it can be remembered as

$$V = [\text{circumference}][\text{height}][\text{thickness}]$$

Now let S be the solid obtained by rotating about the y-axis the region bounded by $y = f(x)$ [where f is continuous and $f(x) \geqslant 0$], $y = 0$, $x = a$, and $x = b$, where $b > a \geqslant 0$. (See Figure 3.)

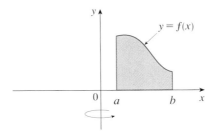

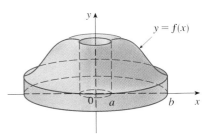

FIGURE 3

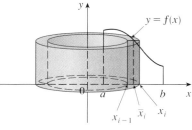

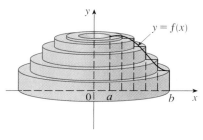

FIGURE 4

We divide the interval $[a, b]$ into n subintervals $[x_{i-1}, x_i]$ of equal width Δx and let $\bar{x}_i$ be the midpoint of the ith subinterval. If the rectangle with base $[x_{i-1}, x_i]$ and height $f(\bar{x}_i)$ is rotated about the y-axis, then the result is a cylindrical shell with average radius $\bar{x}_i$, height $f(\bar{x}_i)$, and thickness Δx (see Figure 4), so by Formula 1 its volume is

$$V_i = (2\pi\bar{x}_i)[f(\bar{x}_i)]\,\Delta x$$

Therefore, an approximation to the volume V of S is given by the sum of the volumes of these shells:

$$V \approx \sum_{i=1}^{n} V_i = \sum_{i=1}^{n} 2\pi\bar{x}_i f(\bar{x}_i)\,\Delta x$$

This approximation appears to become better as $n \to \infty$. But, from the definition of an integral, we know that

$$\lim_{n \to \infty} \sum_{i=1}^{n} 2\pi\bar{x}_i f(\bar{x}_i)\,\Delta x = \int_a^b 2\pi x f(x)\,dx$$

Thus the following appears plausible; a proof is outlined in Exercise 43.

2 The volume of the solid in Figure 3, obtained by rotating about the y-axis the region under the curve $y = f(x)$ from a to b, is

$$V = \int_a^b 2\pi x f(x)\,dx \qquad \text{where } 0 \leqslant a < b$$

The best way to remember Formula 2 is to think of a typical shell, cut and flattened as in Figure 5, with radius x, circumference $2\pi x$, height $f(x)$, and thickness Δx or dx:

$$\int_a^b \underbrace{(2\pi x)}_{\text{circumference}} \underbrace{[f(x)]}_{\text{height}}\,dx$$

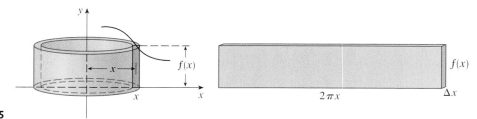

FIGURE 5

This type of reasoning will be helpful in other situations, such as when we rotate about lines other than the y-axis.

EXAMPLE I Find the volume of the solid obtained by rotating about the y-axis the region bounded by $y = 2x^2 - x^3$ and $y = 0$.

SOLUTION From the sketch in Figure 6 we see that a typical shell has radius x, circumference $2\pi x$, and height $f(x) = 2x^2 - x^3$. So, by the shell method, the

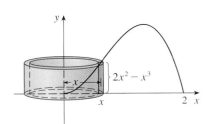

FIGURE 6

Visual 7.3 shows how the solid and shells in Example 1 are formed.

■ Figure 7 shows a computer-generated picture of the solid whose volume we computed in Example 1.

volume is

$$V = \int_0^2 (2\pi x)(2x^2 - x^3)\, dx = 2\pi \int_0^2 (2x^3 - x^4)\, dx$$

$$= 2\pi \left[\tfrac{1}{2}x^4 - \tfrac{1}{5}x^5\right]_0^2 = 2\pi\left(8 - \tfrac{32}{5}\right) = \tfrac{16}{5}\pi$$

It can be verified that the shell method gives the same answer as slicing.   ■

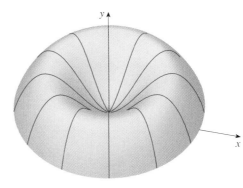

FIGURE 7

NOTE Comparing the solution of Example 1 with the remarks at the beginning of this section, we see that the method of cylindrical shells is much easier than the washer method for this problem. We did not have to find the coordinates of the local maximum and we did not have to solve the equation of the curve for x in terms of y. However, in other examples the methods of the preceding section may be easier.

◤ EXAMPLE 2 Find the volume of the solid obtained by rotating about the y-axis the region between $y = x$ and $y = x^2$.

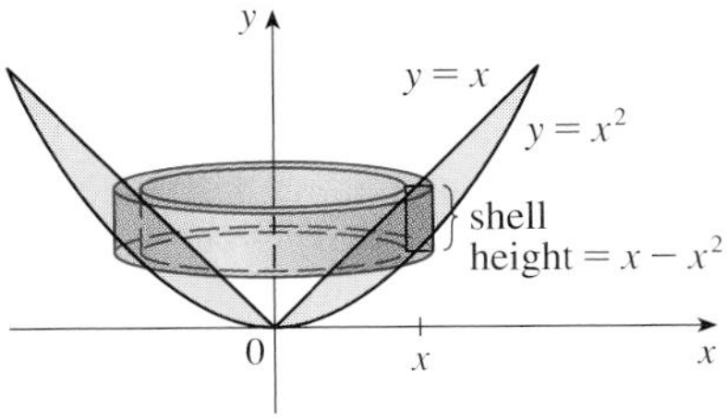

SOLUTION The region and a typical shell are shown in Figure 8. We see that the shell has radius x, circumference $2\pi x$, and height $x - x^2$. So the volume is

$$V = \int_0^1 (2\pi x)(x - x^2)\, dx = 2\pi \int_0^1 (x^2 - x^3)\, dx$$

$$= 2\pi \left[\frac{x^3}{3} - \frac{x^4}{4}\right]_0^1 = \frac{\pi}{6}$$ ■

FIGURE 8

As the following example shows, the shell method works just as well if we rotate about the x-axis. We simply have to draw a diagram to identify the radius and height of a shell.

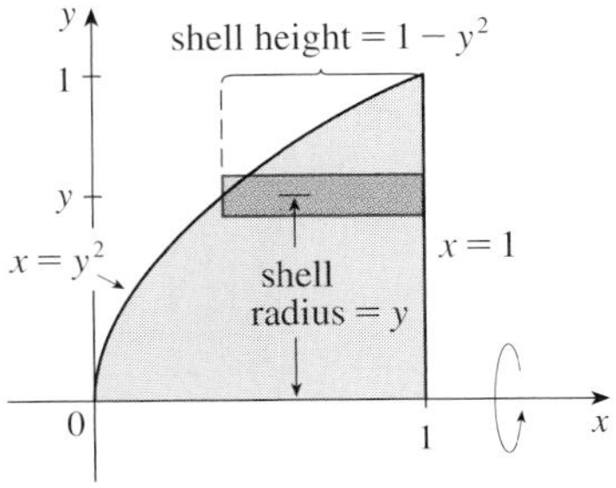

◤ EXAMPLE 3 Use cylindrical shells to find the volume of the solid obtained by rotating about the x-axis the region under the curve $y = \sqrt{x}$ from 0 to 1.

SOLUTION This problem was solved using disks in Example 2 in Section 7.2. To use shells we relabel the curve $y = \sqrt{x}$ (in the figure in that example) as $x = y^2$ in Figure 9. For rotation about the x-axis we see that a typical shell has radius y, circumference $2\pi y$, and height $1 - y^2$. So the volume is

$$V = \int_0^1 (2\pi y)(1 - y^2)\, dy = 2\pi \int_0^1 (y - y^3)\, dy = 2\pi \left[\frac{y^2}{2} - \frac{y^4}{4}\right]_0^1 = \frac{\pi}{2}$$

FIGURE 9

In this problem the disk method was simpler.   ■

☑ EXAMPLE 4 Find the volume of the solid obtained by rotating the region bounded by $y = x - x^2$ and $y = 0$ about the line $x = 2$.

SOLUTION Figure 10 shows the region and a cylindrical shell formed by rotation about the line $x = 2$. It has radius $2 - x$, circumference $2\pi(2 - x)$, and height $x - x^2$.

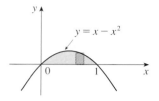

FIGURE 10

The volume of the given solid is

$$V = \int_0^1 2\pi(2 - x)(x - x^2)\,dx = 2\pi \int_0^1 (x^3 - 3x^2 + 2x)\,dx$$

$$= 2\pi\left[\frac{x^4}{4} - x^3 + x^2\right]_0^1 = \frac{\pi}{2}$$ ∎

| **7.3** | **EXERCISES** |

1. Let S be the solid obtained by rotating the region shown in the figure about the y-axis. Explain why it is awkward to use slicing to find the volume V of S. Sketch a typical approximating shell. What are its circumference and height? Use shells to find V.

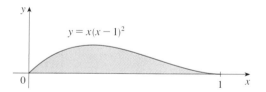

2. Let S be the solid obtained by rotating the region shown in the figure about the y-axis. Sketch a typical cylindrical shell and find its circumference and height. Use shells to find the volume of S. Do you think this method is preferable to slicing? Explain.

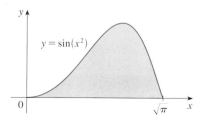

3–7 ■ Use the method of cylindrical shells to find the volume generated by rotating the region bounded by the given curves about the y-axis. Sketch the region and a typical shell.

3. $y = 1/x$, $y = 0$, $x = 1$, $x = 2$

4. $y = x^2$, $y = 0$, $x = 1$

5. $y = e^{-x^2}$, $y = 0$, $x = 0$, $x = 1$

6. $y = 3 + 2x - x^2$, $x + y = 3$

7. $y = 4(x - 2)^2$, $y = x^2 - 4x + 7$

■ ■ ■ ■ ■ ■ ■ ■ ■ ■ ■ ■

8. Let V be the volume of the solid obtained by rotating about the y-axis the region bounded by $y = \sqrt{x}$ and $y = x^2$. Find V both by slicing and by cylindrical shells. In both cases draw a diagram to explain your method.

9–14 ■ Use the method of cylindrical shells to find the volume of the solid obtained by rotating the region bounded by the given curves about the x-axis. Sketch the region and a typical shell.

9. $x = 1 + y^2$, $x = 0$, $y = 1$, $y = 2$

10. $x = \sqrt{y}$, $x = 0$, $y = 1$

11. $y = x^3$, $y = 8$, $x = 0$

12. $x = 4y^2 - y^3$, $x = 0$

13. $y = 4x^2$, $2x + y = 6$

14. $x + y = 3$, $x = 4 - (y - 1)^2$

■ ■ ■ ■ ■ ■ ■ ■ ■ ■ ■ ■ ■

15–20 ■ Use the method of cylindrical shells to find the volume generated by rotating the region bounded by the given curves about the specified axis. Sketch the region and a typical shell.

15. $y = x^2$, $y = 0$, $x = 1$, $x = 2$; about $x = 1$

16. $y = x^2$, $y = 0$, $x = -2$, $x = -1$;   about the y-axis

17. $y = x^2$, $y = 0$, $x = 1$, $x = 2$;   about $x = 4$

18. $y = 4x - x^2$, $y = 8x - 2x^2$;   about $x = -2$

19. $y = \sqrt{x - 1}$, $y = 0$, $x = 5$;   about $y = 3$

20. $y = x^2$, $x = y^2$;   about $y = -1$

■ ■ ■ ■ ■ ■ ■ ■ ■ ■ ■ ■

21–26 ■ Set up, but do not evaluate, an integral for the volume of the solid obtained by rotating the region bounded by the given curves about the specified axis.

21. $y = \ln x$, $y = 0$, $x = 2$;   about the y-axis

22. $y = x$, $y = 4x - x^2$;   about $x = 7$

23. $y = x^4$, $y = \sin(\pi x/2)$;   about $x = -1$

24. $y = 1/(1 + x^2)$, $y = 0$, $x = 0$, $x = 2$;   about $x = 2$

25. $x = \sqrt{\sin y}$, $0 \leqslant y \leqslant \pi$, $x = 0$;   about $y = 4$

26. $x^2 - y^2 = 7$, $x = 4$;   about $y = 5$

■ ■ ■ ■ ■ ■ ■ ■ ■ ■ ■ ■ ■

27. Use the Midpoint Rule with $n = 4$ to estimate the volume obtained by rotating about the y-axis the region under the curve $y = \tan x$, $0 \leqslant x \leqslant \pi/4$.

28. (a) If the region shown in the figure is rotated about the y-axis to form a solid, use Simpson's Rule with $n = 8$ to estimate the volume of the solid.
(b) Estimate the volume if the region is rotated about the x-axis.

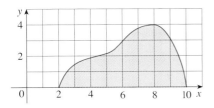

29–32 ■ Each integral represents the volume of a solid. Describe the solid.

29. $\displaystyle\int_0^3 2\pi x^5 \, dx$

30. $\displaystyle 2\pi \int_0^2 \frac{y}{1 + y^2} \, dy$

31. $\displaystyle\int_0^1 2\pi(3 - y)(1 - y^2) \, dy$

32. $\displaystyle\int_0^{\pi/4} 2\pi(\pi - x)(\cos x - \sin x) \, dx$

■ ■ ■ ■ ■ ■ ■ ■ ■ ■ ■ ■

33–38 ■ The region bounded by the given curves is rotated about the specified axis. Find the volume of the resulting solid by any method.

33. $y = x^2 + x - 2$, $y = 0$;   about the x-axis

34. $y = x^2 - 3x + 2$, $y = 0$;   about the y-axis

35. $y = 5$, $y = x + (4/x)$;   about $x = -1$

36. $x = 1 - y^4$, $x = 0$;   about $x = 2$

37. $x^2 + (y - 1)^2 = 1$;   about the y-axis

38. $x^2 + (y - 1)^2 = 1$;   about the x-axis

■ ■ ■ ■ ■ ■ ■ ■ ■ ■ ■ ■

39–41 ■ Use cylindrical shells to find the volume of the solid.

39. A sphere of radius r

40. The solid torus of Exercise 41 in Section 7.2

41. A right circular cone with height h and base radius r

■ ■ ■ ■ ■ ■ ■ ■ ■ ■ ■ ■ ■

42. Suppose you make napkin rings by drilling holes with different diameters through two wooden balls (which also have different diameters). You discover that both napkin rings have the same height h, as shown in the figure.
(a) Guess which ring has more wood in it.
(b) Check your guess: Use cylindrical shells to compute the volume of a napkin ring created by drilling a hole with radius r through the center of a sphere of radius R and express the answer in terms of h.

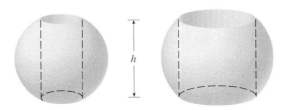

43. Use the following steps to prove Formula 2 for the case where f is one-to-one and therefore has an inverse function f^{-1}: Use the figure to show that

$$V = \pi b^2 d - \pi a^2 c - \int_c^d \pi[f^{-1}(y)]^2 \, dy$$

Make the substitution $y = f(x)$ and then use integration by parts on the resulting integral to prove that

$$V = \int_a^b 2\pi x f(x) \, dx$$

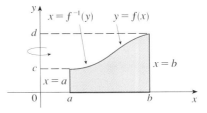

FIGURE 1

7.4 ARC LENGTH

What do we mean by the length of a curve? We might think of fitting a piece of string to the curve in Figure 1 and then measuring the string against a ruler. But that might be difficult to do with much accuracy if we have a complicated curve. We need a precise definition for the length of an arc of a curve, in the same spirit as the definitions we developed for the concepts of area and volume.

If the curve is a polygon, we can easily find its length; we just add the lengths of the line segments that form the polygon. (We can use the distance formula to find the distance between the endpoints of each segment.) We are going to define the length of a general curve by first approximating it by a polygon and then taking a limit as the number of segments of the polygon is increased. This process is familiar for the case of a circle, where the circumference is the limit of lengths of inscribed polygons (see Figure 2).

 Visual 7.4 shows an animation of Figure 2.

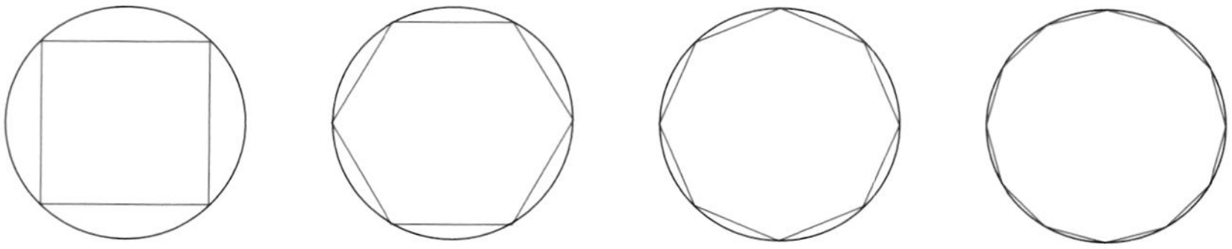

FIGURE 2

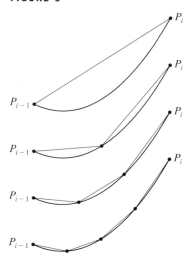

FIGURE 3

Now suppose that a curve C is defined by the equation $y = f(x)$, where f is continuous and $a \leq x \leq b$. We obtain a polygonal approximation to C by dividing the interval $[a, b]$ into n subintervals with endpoints $x_0, x_1, \ldots, x_n$ and equal width Δx. If $y_i = f(x_i)$, then the point $P_i(x_i, y_i)$ lies on C and the polygon with vertices $P_0, P_1, \ldots, P_n$, illustrated in Figure 3, is an approximation to C. The length L of C is approximately the length of this polygon and the approximation gets better as we let n increase. (See Figure 4, where the arc of the curve between P_{i-1} and P_i has been magnified and approximations with successively smaller values of Δx are shown.) Therefore, we define the **length** L of the curve C with equation $y = f(x)$, $a \leq x \leq b$, as the limit of the lengths of these inscribed polygons (if the limit exists):

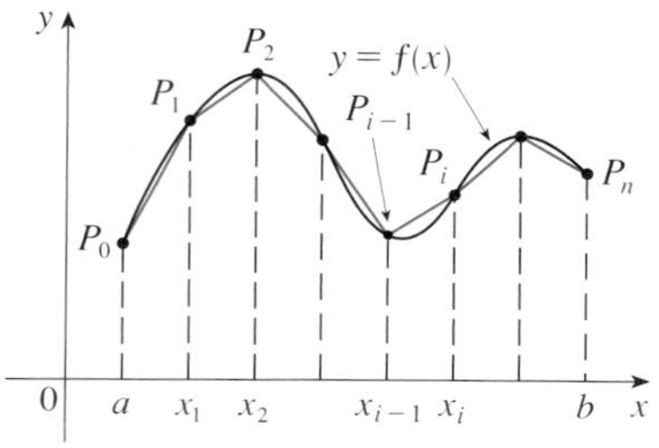

1

$$L = \lim_{n \to \infty} \sum_{i=1}^{n} |P_{i-1}P_i|$$

Notice that the procedure for defining arc length is very similar to the procedure we used for defining area and volume: We divided the curve into a large number of small parts. We then found the approximate lengths of the small parts and added them. Finally, we took the limit as $n \to \infty$.

The definition of arc length given by Equation 1 is not very convenient for computational purposes, but we can derive an integral formula for L in the case where f has a continuous derivative. [Such a function f is called **smooth** because a small change in x produces a small change in $f'(x)$.]

If we let $\Delta y_i = y_i - y_{i-1}$, then

$$|P_{i-1}P_i| = \sqrt{(x_i - x_{i-1})^2 + (y_i - y_{i-1})^2} = \sqrt{(\Delta x)^2 + (\Delta y_i)^2}$$

By applying the Mean Value Theorem to f on the interval $[x_{i-1}, x_i]$, we find that there

FIGURE 4

is a number x_i^* between x_{i-1} and x_i such that

$$f(x_i) - f(x_{i-1}) = f'(x_i^*)(x_i - x_{i-1})$$

that is,

$$\Delta y_i = f'(x_i^*)\,\Delta x$$

Thus we have

$$
\begin{aligned}
|P_{i-1}P_i| &= \sqrt{(\Delta x)^2 + (\Delta y_i)^2} \\
&= \sqrt{(\Delta x)^2 + [f'(x_i^*)\,\Delta x]^2} \\
&= \sqrt{1 + [f'(x_i^*)]^2}\,\sqrt{(\Delta x)^2} \\
&= \sqrt{1 + [f'(x_i^*)]^2}\,\Delta x \qquad \text{(since } \Delta x > 0\text{)}
\end{aligned}
$$

Therefore, by Definition 1,

$$L = \lim_{n \to \infty} \sum_{i=1}^{n} |P_{i-1}P_i| = \lim_{n \to \infty} \sum_{i=1}^{n} \sqrt{1 + [f'(x_i^*)]^2}\,\Delta x$$

We recognize this expression as being equal to

$$\int_a^b \sqrt{1 + [f'(x)]^2}\,dx$$

by the definition of a definite integral. This integral exists because the function $g(x) = \sqrt{1 + [f'(x)]^2}$ is continuous. Thus we have proved the following theorem:

2 THE ARC LENGTH FORMULA If f' is continuous on $[a, b]$, then the length of the curve $y = f(x)$, $a \leqslant x \leqslant b$, is

$$L = \int_a^b \sqrt{1 + [f'(x)]^2}\,dx$$

If we use Leibniz notation for derivatives, we can write the arc length formula as follows:

3
$$L = \int_a^b \sqrt{1 + \left(\frac{dy}{dx}\right)^2}\,dx$$

EXAMPLE 1 Find the length of the arc of the semicubical parabola $y^2 = x^3$ between the points $(1, 1)$ and $(4, 8)$. (See Figure 5.)

SOLUTION For the top half of the curve we have

$$y = x^{3/2} \qquad \frac{dy}{dx} = \tfrac{3}{2}x^{1/2}$$

and so the arc length formula gives

$$L = \int_1^4 \sqrt{1 + \left(\frac{dy}{dx}\right)^2}\,dx = \int_1^4 \sqrt{1 + \tfrac{9}{4}x}\,dx$$

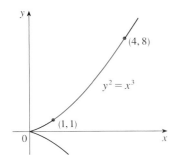

FIGURE 5

■ As a check on our answer to Example 1, notice from Figure 5 that it ought to be slightly larger than the distance from $(1, 1)$ to $(4, 8)$, which is

$$\sqrt{58} \approx 7.615773$$

According to our calculation in Example 1, we have

$$L = \tfrac{1}{27}\left(80\sqrt{10} - 13\sqrt{13}\right) \approx 7.633705$$

Sure enough, this is a bit greater than the length of the line segment.

If we substitute $u = 1 + \tfrac{9}{4}x$, then $du = \tfrac{9}{4}\,dx$. When $x = 1$, $u = \tfrac{13}{4}$; when $x = 4$, $u = 10$. Therefore

$$L = \tfrac{4}{9}\int_{13/4}^{10} \sqrt{u}\,du = \tfrac{4}{9}\cdot\tfrac{2}{3}u^{3/2}\Big]_{13/4}^{10}$$

$$= \tfrac{8}{27}\left[10^{3/2} - \left(\tfrac{13}{4}\right)^{3/2}\right] = \tfrac{1}{27}\left(80\sqrt{10} - 13\sqrt{13}\right) \qquad ■$$

If a curve has the equation $x = g(y)$, $c \le y \le d$, and $g'(y)$ is continuous, then by interchanging the roles of x and y in Formula 2 or Equation 3, we obtain the following formula for its length:

4
$$L = \int_c^d \sqrt{1 + [g'(y)]^2}\,dy = \int_c^d \sqrt{1 + \left(\frac{dx}{dy}\right)^2}\,dy$$

▼ EXAMPLE 2 Find the length of the arc of the parabola $y^2 = x$ from $(0, 0)$ to $(1, 1)$.

SOLUTION Since $x = y^2$, we have $dx/dy = 2y$, and Formula 4 gives

$$L = \int_0^1 \sqrt{1 + \left(\frac{dx}{dy}\right)^2}\,dy = \int_0^1 \sqrt{1 + 4y^2}\,dy$$

We make the trigonometric substitution $y = \tfrac{1}{2}\tan\theta$, which gives $dy = \tfrac{1}{2}\sec^2\theta\,d\theta$ and $\sqrt{1 + 4y^2} = \sqrt{1 + \tan^2\theta} = \sec\theta$. When $y = 0$, $\tan\theta = 0$, so $\theta = 0$; when $y = 1$, $\tan\theta = 2$, so $\theta = \tan^{-1}2 = \alpha$, say. Thus

$$L = \int_0^\alpha \sec\theta \cdot \tfrac{1}{2}\sec^2\theta\,d\theta = \tfrac{1}{2}\int_0^\alpha \sec^3\theta\,d\theta$$

$$= \tfrac{1}{2}\cdot\tfrac{1}{2}\left[\sec\theta\tan\theta + \ln|\sec\theta + \tan\theta|\right]_0^\alpha \qquad \text{(from Example 8 in Section 6.2)}$$

$$= \tfrac{1}{4}\left(\sec\alpha\tan\alpha + \ln|\sec\alpha + \tan\alpha|\right)$$

(We could have used Formula 21 in the Table of Integrals.) Since $\tan\alpha = 2$, we have $\sec^2\alpha = 1 + \tan^2\alpha = 5$, so $\sec\alpha = \sqrt{5}$ and

$$L = \frac{\sqrt{5}}{2} + \frac{\ln(\sqrt{5} + 2)}{4} \qquad ■$$

■ Figure 6 shows the arc of the parabola whose length is computed in Example 2, together with polygonal approximations having $n = 1$ and $n = 2$ line segments, respectively. For $n = 1$ the approximate length is $L_1 = \sqrt{2}$, the diagonal of a square. The table shows the approximations L_n that we get by dividing $[0, 1]$ into n equal subintervals. Notice that each time we double the number of sides of the polygon, we get closer to the exact length, which is

$$L = \frac{\sqrt{5}}{2} + \frac{\ln(\sqrt{5} + 2)}{4} \approx 1.478943$$

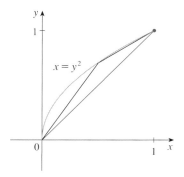

FIGURE 6

n	L_n
1	1.414
2	1.445
4	1.464
8	1.472
16	1.476
32	1.478
64	1.479

Because of the presence of the square root sign in Formulas 2 and 4, the calculation of an arc length often leads to an integral that is very difficult or even impossible to evaluate explicitly. Thus we sometimes have to be content with finding an approximation to the length of a curve as in the following example.

▼ EXAMPLE 3
(a) Set up an integral for the length of the arc of the hyperbola $xy = 1$ from the point $(1, 1)$ to the point $\left(2, \frac{1}{2}\right)$.
(b) Use Simpson's Rule with $n = 10$ to estimate the arc length.

SOLUTION
(a) We have

$$y = \frac{1}{x} \qquad \frac{dy}{dx} = -\frac{1}{x^2}$$

and so the arc length is

$$L = \int_1^2 \sqrt{1 + \left(\frac{dy}{dx}\right)^2}\ dx = \int_1^2 \sqrt{1 + \frac{1}{x^4}}\ dx = \int_1^2 \frac{\sqrt{x^4 + 1}}{x^2}\ dx$$

(b) Using Simpson's Rule (see Section 6.5) with $a = 1$, $b = 2$, $n = 10$, $\Delta x = 0.1$, and $f(x) = \sqrt{1 + 1/x^4}$, we have

$$L = \int_1^2 \sqrt{1 + \frac{1}{x^4}}\ dx$$

▪ Checking the value of the definite integral with a more accurate approximation produced by a computer algebra system, we see that the approximation using Simpson's Rule is accurate to four decimal places.

$$\approx \frac{\Delta x}{3}\left[f(1) + 4f(1.1) + 2f(1.2) + 4f(1.3) + \cdots + 2f(1.8) + 4f(1.9) + f(2)\right]$$

$$\approx 1.1321 \qquad \qquad \blacksquare$$

THE ARC LENGTH FUNCTION

We will find it useful to have a function that measures the arc length of a curve from a particular starting point to any other point on the curve. Thus if a smooth curve C has the equation $y = f(x)$, $a \leq x \leq b$, let $s(x)$ be the distance along C from the initial point $P_0(a, f(a))$ to the point $Q(x, f(x))$. Then s is a function, called the **arc length function**, and, by Formula 2,

5
$$s(x) = \int_a^x \sqrt{1 + [f'(t)]^2}\ dt$$

(We have replaced the variable of integration by t so that x does not have two meanings.) We can use Part 1 of the Fundamental Theorem of Calculus to differentiate Equation 5 (since the integrand is continuous):

6
$$\frac{ds}{dx} = \sqrt{1 + [f'(x)]^2} = \sqrt{1 + \left(\frac{dy}{dx}\right)^2}$$

Equation 6 shows that the rate of change of s with respect to x is always at least 1 and is equal to 1 when $f'(x)$, the slope of the curve, is 0. The differential of arc length is

$$\boxed{7} \qquad ds = \sqrt{1 + \left(\frac{dy}{dx}\right)^2}\, dx$$

and this equation is sometimes written in the symmetric form

$$\boxed{8} \qquad (ds)^2 = (dx)^2 + (dy)^2$$

FIGURE 7

The geometric interpretation of Equation 8 is shown in Figure 7. It can be used as a mnemonic device for remembering both of the Formulas 3 and 4. If we write $L = \int ds$, then from Equation 8 either we can solve to get (7), which gives (3), or we can solve to get

$$ds = \sqrt{1 + \left(\frac{dx}{dy}\right)^2}\, dy$$

which gives (4).

▼ **EXAMPLE 4** Find the arc length function for the curve $y = x^2 - \frac{1}{8}\ln x$ taking $P_0(1, 1)$ as the starting point.

SOLUTION If $f(x) = x^2 - \frac{1}{8}\ln x$, then

$$f'(x) = 2x - \frac{1}{8x}$$

$$1 + [f'(x)]^2 = 1 + \left(2x - \frac{1}{8x}\right)^2 = 1 + 4x^2 - \frac{1}{2} + \frac{1}{64x^2}$$

$$= 4x^2 + \frac{1}{2} + \frac{1}{64x^2} = \left(2x + \frac{1}{8x}\right)^2$$

$$\sqrt{1 + [f'(x)]^2} = 2x + \frac{1}{8x}$$

Thus the arc length function is given by

$$s(x) = \int_1^x \sqrt{1 + [f'(t)]^2}\, dt$$

$$= \int_1^x \left(2t - \frac{1}{8t}\right) dt = t^2 + \tfrac{1}{8}\ln t \Big]_1^x$$

$$= x^2 + \tfrac{1}{8}\ln x - 1$$

For instance, the arc length along the curve from $(1, 1)$ to $(3, f(3))$ is

$$s(3) = 3^2 + \tfrac{1}{8}\ln 3 - 1 = 8 + \frac{\ln 3}{8} \approx 8.1373 \qquad ■$$

■ Figure 8 shows the interpretation of the arc length function in Example 4. Figure 9 shows the graph of this arc length function. Why is $s(x)$ negative when x is less than 1?

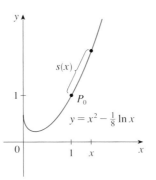

FIGURE 8

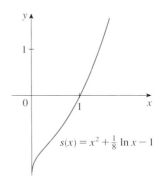

FIGURE 9

7.4 | EXERCISES

1. Use the arc length formula (3) to find the length of the curve $y = 2 - 3x$, $-2 \le x \le 1$. Check your answer by noting that the curve is a line segment and calculating its length by the distance formula.

2. Use the arc length formula to find the length of the curve $y = \sqrt{4 - x^2}$, $0 \le x \le 2$. Check your answer by noting that the curve is a quarter-circle.

3–14 ■ Find the length of the curve.

3. $y = 1 + 6x^{3/2}$, $0 \le x \le 1$

4. $y^2 = 4(x + 4)^3$, $0 \le x \le 2$, $y > 0$

5. $y = \dfrac{x^5}{6} + \dfrac{1}{10x^3}$, $1 \le x \le 2$

6. $y = \dfrac{x^2}{2} - \dfrac{\ln x}{4}$, $2 \le x \le 4$

7. $x = \frac{1}{3}\sqrt{y}\,(y - 3)$, $1 \le y \le 9$

8. $y = \ln(\cos x)$, $0 \le x \le \pi/3$

9. $y = \ln(\sec x)$, $0 \le x \le \pi/4$

10. $y = \ln x$, $1 \le x \le \sqrt{3}$

11. $y = \cosh x$, $0 \le x \le 1$

12. $y^2 = 4x$, $0 \le y \le 2$

13. $y = e^x$, $0 \le x \le 1$

14. $y = \ln\left(\dfrac{e^x + 1}{e^x - 1}\right)$, $a \le x \le b$, $a > 0$

15–18 ■ Set up, but do not evaluate, an integral for the length of the curve.

15. $y = \cos x$, $0 \le x \le 2\pi$

16. $y = 2^x$, $0 \le x \le 3$

17. $x = y + y^3$, $1 \le y \le 4$

18. $\dfrac{x^2}{a^2} + \dfrac{y^2}{b^2} = 1$

19–22 ■ Use Simpson's Rule with $n = 10$ to estimate the arc length of the curve. Compare your answer with the value of the integral produced by your calculator.

19. $y = xe^{-x}$, $0 \le x \le 5$

20. $x = y + \sqrt{y}$, $1 \le y \le 2$

21. $y = \sec x$, $0 \le x \le \pi/3$

22. $y = x \ln x$, $1 \le x \le 3$

CAS 23. Use either a computer algebra system or a table of integrals to find the *exact* length of the arc of the curve $x = \ln(1 - y^2)$ that lies between the points $(0, 0)$ and $\left(\ln\frac{3}{4}, \frac{1}{2}\right)$.

CAS 24. Use either a computer algebra system or a table of integrals to find the *exact* length of the arc of the curve $y = x^{4/3}$ that lies between the points $(0, 0)$ and $(1, 1)$. If your CAS has trouble evaluating the integral, make a substitution that changes the integral into one that the CAS can evaluate.

25. Sketch the curve with equation $x^{2/3} + y^{2/3} = 1$ and use symmetry to find its length.

26. (a) Sketch the curve $y^3 = x^2$.
(b) Use Formulas 3 and 4 to set up two integrals for the arc length from $(0, 0)$ to $(1, 1)$. Observe that one of these is an improper integral and evaluate both of them.
(c) Find the length of the arc of this curve from $(-1, 1)$ to $(8, 4)$.

27. Find the arc length function for the curve $y = 2x^{3/2}$ with starting point $P_0(1, 2)$.

28. (a) Graph the curve $y = \frac{1}{3}x^3 + 1/(4x)$, $x > 0$.
(b) Find the arc length function for this curve with starting point $P_0\left(1, \frac{7}{12}\right)$.
(c) Graph the arc length function.

29. A hawk flying at 15 m/s at an altitude of 180 m accidentally drops its prey. The parabolic trajectory of the falling prey is described by the equation

$$y = 180 - \frac{x^2}{45}$$

until it hits the ground, where y is its height above the ground and x is the horizontal distance traveled in meters. Calculate the distance traveled by the prey from the time it is dropped until the time it hits the ground. Express your answer correct to the nearest tenth of a meter.

30. A steady wind blows a kite due west. The kite's height above ground from horizontal position $x = 0$ to $x = 80$ ft is given by $y = 150 - \frac{1}{40}(x - 50)^2$. Find the distance traveled by the kite.

31. A manufacturer of corrugated metal roofing wants to produce panels that are 28 in. wide and 2 in. thick by processing flat sheets of metal as shown in the figure. The profile of the roofing takes the shape of a sine wave. Verify that the sine curve has equation $y = \sin(\pi x/7)$ and find the width w of a flat metal sheet that is needed to make a 28-inch panel. (Use your calculator to evaluate the integral correct to four significant digits.)

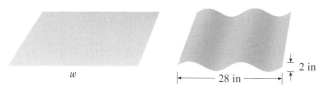

32. The curves with equations $x^n + y^n = 1$, $n = 4, 6, 8, \ldots,$ are called **fat circles**. Graph the curves with $n = 2, 4, 6, 8,$ and 10 to see why. Set up an integral for the length L_{2k} of the fat circle with $n = 2k$. Without attempting to evaluate this integral, state the value of $\lim_{k \to \infty} L_{2k}$.

7.5 | APPLICATIONS TO PHYSICS AND ENGINEERING

■ As a consequence of a calculation of work, you will be able to compute the velocity needed for a rocket to escape the Earth's gravitational field. (See Exercise 22.)

Among the many applications of integral calculus to physics and engineering, we consider three: work, force due to water pressure, and centers of mass. As with our previous applications to geometry (areas, volumes, and lengths), our strategy is to break up the physical quantity into a large number of small parts, approximate each small part, add the results, take the limit, and evaluate the resulting integral.

WORK

The term *work* is used in everyday language to mean the total amount of effort required to perform a task. In physics it has a technical meaning that depends on the idea of a *force*. Intuitively, you can think of a force as describing a push or pull on an object—for example, a horizontal push of a book across a table or the downward pull of the Earth's gravity on a ball. In general, if an object moves along a straight line with position function $s(t)$, then the **force** F on the object (in the same direction) is defined by Newton's Second Law of Motion as the product of its mass m and its acceleration:

1
$$F = m\frac{d^2s}{dt^2}$$

In the SI metric system, the mass is measured in kilograms (kg), the displacement in meters (m), the time in seconds (s), and the force in newtons (N = kg·m/s^2). Thus a force of 1 N acting on a mass of 1 kg produces an acceleration of 1 m/s^2. In the US Customary system the fundamental unit is chosen to be the unit of force, which is the pound.

In the case of constant acceleration, the force F is also constant and the work done is defined to be the product of the force F and the distance d that the object moves:

2
$$W = Fd \qquad \text{work} = \text{force} \times \text{distance}$$

If F is measured in newtons and d in meters, then the unit for W is a newton-meter, which is called a joule (J). If F is measured in pounds and d in feet, then the unit for W is a foot-pound (ft-lb), which is about 1.36 J.

For instance, suppose you lift a 1.2-kg book off the floor to put it on a desk that is 0.7 m high. The force you exert is equal and opposite to that exerted by gravity, so Equation 1 gives

$$F = mg = (1.2)(9.8) = 11.76 \text{ N}$$

and then Equation 2 gives the work done as

$$W = Fd = (11.76)(0.7) \approx 8.2 \text{ J}$$

But if a 20-lb weight is lifted 6 ft off the ground, then the force is given as $F = 20$ lb, so the work done is

$$W = Fd = 20 \cdot 6 = 120 \text{ ft-lb}$$

Here we didn't multiply by g because we were given the *weight* (a force) and not the mass.

Equation 2 defines work as long as the force is constant, but what happens if the force is variable? Let's suppose that the object moves along the x-axis in the positive direction, from $x = a$ to $x = b$, and at each point x between a and b a force $f(x)$ acts on the object, where f is a continuous function. We divide the interval $[a, b]$ into n subintervals with endpoints $x_0, x_1, \ldots, x_n$ and equal width Δx. We choose a sample point x_i^* in the ith subinterval $[x_{i-1}, x_i]$. Then the force at that point is $f(x_i^*)$. If n is large, then Δx is small, and since f is continuous, the values of f don't change very much over the interval $[x_{i-1}, x_i]$. In other words, f is almost constant on the interval and so the work W_i that is done in moving the particle from x_{i-1} to x_i is approximately given by Equation 2:

$$W_i \approx f(x_i^*) \, \Delta x$$

Thus we can approximate the total work by

3
$$W \approx \sum_{i=1}^{n} f(x_i^*) \, \Delta x$$

It seems that this approximation becomes better as we make n larger. Therefore, we define the **work done in moving the object from a to b** as the limit of this quantity as $n \to \infty$. Since the right side of (3) is a Riemann sum, we recognize its limit as being a definite integral and so

4
$$W = \lim_{n \to \infty} \sum_{i=1}^{n} f(x_i^*) \, \Delta x = \int_a^b f(x) \, dx$$

EXAMPLE 1 When a particle is located a distance x feet from the origin, a force of $x^2 + 2x$ pounds acts on it. How much work is done in moving it from $x = 1$ to $x = 3$?

SOLUTION
$$W = \int_1^3 (x^2 + 2x) \, dx = \frac{x^3}{3} + x^2 \bigg]_1^3 = \frac{50}{3}$$

The work done is $16\frac{2}{3}$ ft-lb. ■

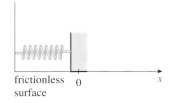

frictionless   0 x
surface

(a) Natural position of spring

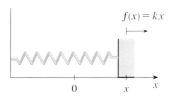

$f(x) = kx$

0   x x

(b) Stretched position of spring

FIGURE 1
Hooke's Law

In the next example we use a law from physics: **Hooke's Law** states that the force required to maintain a spring stretched x units beyond its natural length is proportional to x:

$$f(x) = kx$$

where k is a positive constant (called the **spring constant**). Hooke's Law holds provided that x is not too large (see Figure 1).

▼ **EXAMPLE 2** A force of 40 N is required to hold a spring that has been stretched from its natural length of 10 cm to a length of 15 cm. How much work is done in stretching the spring from 15 cm to 18 cm?

SOLUTION According to Hooke's Law, the force required to hold the spring stretched x meters beyond its natural length is $f(x) = kx$. When the spring is stretched from 10 cm to 15 cm, the amount stretched is 5 cm = 0.05 m. This means that $f(0.05) = 40$, so

$$0.05k = 40 \qquad k = \tfrac{40}{0.05} = 800$$

Thus $f(x) = 800x$ and the work done in stretching the spring from 15 cm to 18 cm is

$$W = \int_{0.05}^{0.08} 800x\, dx = 800\, \frac{x^2}{2}\Big]_{0.05}^{0.08}$$

$$= 400[(0.08)^2 - (0.05)^2] = 1.56 \text{ J} \qquad \blacksquare$$

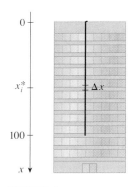

0

x_i^* Δx

100

x

FIGURE 2

▪ If we had placed the origin at the bottom of the cable and the x-axis upward, we would have gotten

$$W = \int_0^{100} 2(100 - x)\, dx$$

which gives the same answer.

▼ **EXAMPLE 3** A 200-lb cable is 100 ft long and hangs vertically from the top of a tall building. How much work is required to lift the cable to the top of the building?

SOLUTION Here we don't have a formula for the force function, but we can use an argument similar to the one that led to Definition 4.

Let's place the origin at the top of the building and the x-axis pointing downward as in Figure 2. We divide the cable into small parts with length Δx. If x_i^* is a point in the ith such interval, then all points in the interval are lifted by approximately the same amount, namely x_i^*. The cable weighs 2 pounds per foot, so the weight of the ith part is $2\Delta x$. Thus the work done on the ith part, in foot-pounds, is

$$\underbrace{(2\,\Delta x)}_{\text{force}} \cdot \underbrace{x_i^*}_{\text{distance}} = 2x_i^*\, \Delta x$$

We get the total work done by adding all these approximations and letting the number of parts become large (so $\Delta x \rightarrow 0$):

$$W = \lim_{n \to \infty} \sum_{i=1}^n 2x_i^*\, \Delta x = \int_0^{100} 2x\, dx = x^2\Big]_0^{100} = 10{,}000 \text{ ft-lb} \qquad \blacksquare$$

EXAMPLE 4 A tank has the shape of an inverted circular cone with height 10 m and base radius 4 m. It is filled with water to a height of 8 m. Find the work required to empty the tank by pumping all of the water to the top of the tank. (The density of water is 1000 kg/m³.)

SOLUTION Let's measure depths from the top of the tank by introducing a vertical coordinate line as in Figure 3. The water extends from a depth of 2 m to a depth of 10 m and so we divide the interval $[2, 10]$ into n subintervals with endpoints $x_0, x_1, \ldots, x_n$ and choose x_i^* in the ith subinterval. This divides the water into n

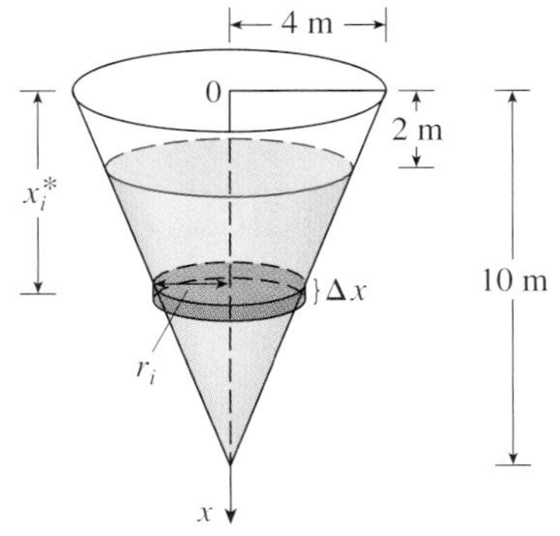

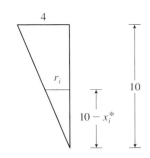

FIGURE 3

FIGURE 4

layers. The ith layer is approximated by a circular cylinder with radius r_i and height Δx. We can compute r_i from similar triangles, using Figure 4, as follows:

$$\frac{r_i}{10 - x_i^*} = \frac{4}{10} \qquad r_i = \tfrac{2}{5}(10 - x_i^*)$$

Thus an approximation to the volume of the ith layer of water is

$$V_i \approx \pi r_i^2 \, \Delta x = \frac{4\pi}{25}(10 - x_i^*)^2 \, \Delta x$$

and so its mass is

$$m_i = \text{density} \times \text{volume}$$

$$\approx 1000 \cdot \frac{4\pi}{25}(10 - x_i^*)^2 \, \Delta x = 160\pi(10 - x_i^*)^2 \, \Delta x$$

The force required to raise this layer must overcome the force of gravity and so

$$F_i = m_i g \approx (9.8)160\pi(10 - x_i^*)^2 \, \Delta x \approx 1568\pi(10 - x_i^*)^2 \, \Delta x$$

Each particle in the layer must travel a distance of approximately x_i^*. The work W_i done to raise this layer to the top is approximately the product of the force F_i and the distance x_i^*:

$$W_i \approx F_i x_i^* \approx 1568\pi x_i^*(10 - x_i^*)^2 \, \Delta x$$

To find the total work done in emptying the entire tank, we add the contributions of each of the n layers and then take the limit as $n \to \infty$:

$$W = \lim_{n \to \infty} \sum_{i=1}^{n} 1568\pi x_i^*(10 - x_i^*)^2 \, \Delta x = \int_2^{10} 1568\pi x(10 - x)^2 \, dx$$

$$= 1568\pi \int_2^{10} (100x - 20x^2 + x^3) \, dx = 1568\pi \left[50x^2 - \frac{20x^3}{3} + \frac{x^4}{4} \right]_2^{10}$$

$$= 1568\pi \left(\tfrac{2048}{3} \right) \approx 3.4 \times 10^6 \text{ J} \qquad \blacksquare$$

HYDROSTATIC PRESSURE AND FORCE

Deep-sea divers realize that water pressure increases as they dive deeper. This is because the weight of the water above them increases.

In general, suppose that a thin horizontal plate with area A square meters is submerged in a fluid of density ρ kilograms per cubic meter at a depth d meters below the surface of the fluid as in Figure 5. The fluid directly above the plate has volume $V = Ad$, so its mass is $m = \rho V = \rho Ad$. The force exerted by the fluid on the plate is therefore

$$F = mg = \rho gAd$$

where g is the acceleration due to gravity. The pressure P on the plate is defined to be the force per unit area:

$$P = \frac{F}{A} = \rho gd$$

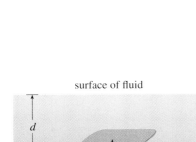

surface of fluid

FIGURE 5

■ When using US Customary units, we write $P = \rho g d = \delta d$, where $\delta = \rho g$ is the *weight density* (as opposed to ρ, which is the *mass density*). For instance, the weight density of water is $\delta = 62.5$ lb/ft³.

The SI unit for measuring pressure is newtons per square meter, which is called a pascal (abbreviation: 1 N/m² = 1 Pa). Since this is a small unit, the kilopascal (kPa) is often used. For instance, because the density of water is $\rho = 1000$ kg/m³, the pressure at the bottom of a swimming pool 2 m deep is

$$P = \rho g d = 1000 \text{ kg/m}^3 \times 9.8 \text{ m/s}^2 \times 2 \text{ m}$$

$$= 19{,}600 \text{ Pa} = 19.6 \text{ kPa}$$

An important principle of fluid pressure is the experimentally verified fact that *at any point in a liquid the pressure is the same in all directions.* (A diver feels the same pressure on nose and both ears.) Thus the pressure in *any* direction at a depth d in a fluid with mass density ρ is given by

5 $$P = \rho g d = \delta d$$

This helps us determine the hydrostatic force against a *vertical* plate or wall or dam in a fluid. This is not a straightforward problem because the pressure is not constant but increases as the depth increases.

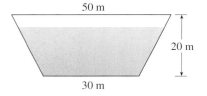

FIGURE 6

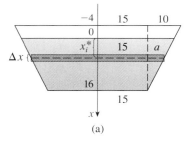

(a)

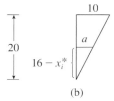

(b)

FIGURE 7

▼ EXAMPLE 5 A dam has the shape of the trapezoid shown in Figure 6. The height is 20 m and the width is 50 m at the top and 30 m at the bottom. Find the force on the dam due to hydrostatic pressure if the water level is 4 m from the top of the dam.

SOLUTION We choose a vertical x-axis with origin at the surface of the water as in Figure 7(a). The depth of the water is 16 m, so we divide the interval $[0, 16]$ into subintervals with endpoints x_i and we choose $x_i^* \in [x_{i-1}, x_i]$. The ith horizontal strip of the dam is approximated by a rectangle with height Δx and width w_i, where, from similar triangles in Figure 7(b),

$$\frac{a}{16 - x_i^*} = \frac{10}{20} \quad \text{or} \quad a = \frac{16 - x_i^*}{2} = 8 - \frac{x_i^*}{2}$$

and so $$w_i = 2(15 + a) = 2\left(15 + 8 - \tfrac{1}{2}x_i^*\right) = 46 - x_i^*$$

If A_i is the area of the ith strip, then

$$A_i \approx w_i \, \Delta x = (46 - x_i^*) \, \Delta x$$

If Δx is small, then the pressure P_i on the ith strip is almost constant and we can use Equation 5 to write

$$P_i \approx 1000 g x_i^*$$

The hydrostatic force F_i acting on the ith strip is the product of the pressure and the area:

$$F_i = P_i A_i \approx 1000 g x_i^* (46 - x_i^*) \, \Delta x$$

Adding these forces and taking the limit as $n \to \infty$, we obtain the total hydrostatic force on the dam:

$$F = \lim_{n \to \infty} \sum_{i=1}^{n} 1000 g x_i^*(46 - x_i^*) \, \Delta x = \int_0^{16} 1000 g x(46 - x) \, dx$$

$$= 1000(9.8) \int_0^{16} (46x - x^2) \, dx = 9800 \left[23x^2 - \frac{x^3}{3} \right]_0^{16}$$

$$\approx 4.43 \times 10^7 \, \text{N}$$ ▪

EXAMPLE 6 Find the hydrostatic force on one end of a cylindrical drum with radius 3 ft if the drum is submerged in water 10 ft deep.

SOLUTION In this example it is convenient to choose the axes as in Figure 8 so that the origin is placed at the center of the drum. Then the circle has a simple equation, $x^2 + y^2 = 9$. As in Example 5 we divide the circular region into horizontal strips of equal width. From the equation of the circle, we see that the length of the ith strip is $2\sqrt{9 - (y_i^*)^2}$ and so its area is

$$A_i = 2\sqrt{9 - (y_i^*)^2} \, \Delta y$$

The pressure on this strip is approximately

$$\delta d_i = 62.5(7 - y_i^*)$$

and so the force on the strip is approximately

$$\delta d_i A_i = 62.5(7 - y_i^*) 2\sqrt{9 - (y_i^*)^2} \, \Delta y$$

The total force is obtained by adding the forces on all the strips and taking the limit:

$$F = \lim_{n \to \infty} \sum_{i=1}^{n} 62.5(7 - y_i^*) 2\sqrt{9 - (y_i^*)^2} \, \Delta y$$

$$= 125 \int_{-3}^{3} (7 - y) \sqrt{9 - y^2} \, dy$$

$$= 125 \cdot 7 \int_{-3}^{3} \sqrt{9 - y^2} \, dy - 125 \int_{-3}^{3} y \sqrt{9 - y^2} \, dy$$

The second integral is 0 because the integrand is an odd function (see Theorem 5.5.7). The first integral can be evaluated using the trigonometric substitution $y = 3 \sin \theta$, but it's simpler to observe that it is the area of a semicircular disk with radius 3. Thus

$$F = 875 \int_{-3}^{3} \sqrt{9 - y^2} \, dy = 875 \cdot \tfrac{1}{2} \pi (3)^2$$

$$= \frac{7875\pi}{2} \approx 12{,}370 \, \text{lb}$$ ▪

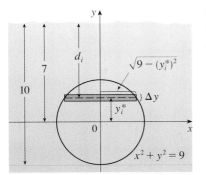

FIGURE 8

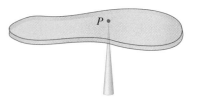

FIGURE 9

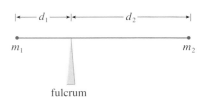

FIGURE 10

MOMENTS AND CENTERS OF MASS

Our main objective here is to find the point P on which a thin plate of any given shape balances horizontally as in Figure 9. This point is called the **center of mass** (or center of gravity) of the plate.

We first consider the simpler situation illustrated in Figure 10, where two masses m_1 and m_2 are attached to a rod of negligible mass on opposite sides of a fulcrum and at distances d_1 and d_2 from the fulcrum. The rod will balance if

6
$$m_1 d_1 = m_2 d_2$$

This is an experimental fact discovered by Archimedes and called the Law of the Lever. (Think of a lighter person balancing a heavier one on a seesaw by sitting farther away from the center.)

Now suppose that the rod lies along the x-axis with m_1 at x_1 and m_2 at x_2 and the center of mass at $\bar{x}$. If we compare Figures 10 and 11, we see that $d_1 = \bar{x} - x_1$ and $d_2 = x_2 - \bar{x}$ and so Equation 6 gives

$$m_1(\bar{x} - x_1) = m_2(x_2 - \bar{x})$$

$$m_1\bar{x} + m_2\bar{x} = m_1 x_1 + m_2 x_2$$

7
$$\bar{x} = \frac{m_1 x_1 + m_2 x_2}{m_1 + m_2}$$

The numbers $m_1 x_1$ and $m_2 x_2$ are called the **moments** of the masses m_1 and m_2 (with respect to the origin), and Equation 7 says that the center of mass $\bar{x}$ is obtained by adding the moments of the masses and dividing by the total mass $m = m_1 + m_2$.

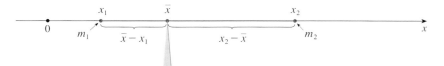

FIGURE 11

In general, if we have a system of n particles with masses $m_1, m_2, \ldots, m_n$ located at the points $x_1, x_2, \ldots, x_n$ on the x-axis, it can be shown similarly that the center of mass of the system is located at

8
$$\bar{x} = \frac{\sum\limits_{i=1}^{n} m_i x_i}{\sum\limits_{i=1}^{n} m_i} = \frac{\sum\limits_{i=1}^{n} m_i x_i}{m}$$

where $m = \sum m_i$ is the total mass of the system, and the sum of the individual moments

$$M = \sum_{i=1}^{n} m_i x_i$$

is called the **moment of the system about the origin**. Then Equation 8 could be rewritten as $m\bar{x} = M$, which says that if the total mass were considered as being concentrated at the center of mass $\bar{x}$, then its moment would be the same as the moment of the system.

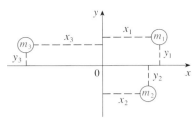

FIGURE 12

Now we consider a system of n particles with masses $m_1, m_2, \ldots, m_n$ located at the points $(x_1, y_1), (x_2, y_2), \ldots, (x_n, y_n)$ in the xy-plane as shown in Figure 12. By analogy with the one-dimensional case, we define the **moment of the system about the y-axis** to be

9
$$M_y = \sum_{i=1}^{n} m_i x_i$$

and the **moment of the system about the x-axis** as

10
$$M_x = \sum_{i=1}^{n} m_i y_i$$

Then M_y measures the tendency of the system to rotate about the y-axis and M_x measures the tendency to rotate about the x-axis.

As in the one-dimensional case, the coordinates $(\bar{x}, \bar{y})$ of the center of mass are given in terms of the moments by the formulas

11
$$\bar{x} = \frac{M_y}{m} \qquad \bar{y} = \frac{M_x}{m}$$

where $m = \Sigma\, m_i$ is the total mass. Since $m\bar{x} = M_y$ and $m\bar{y} = M_x$, the center of mass $(\bar{x}, \bar{y})$ is the point where a single particle of mass m would have the same moments as the system.

◤ EXAMPLE 7 Find the moments and center of mass of the system of objects that have masses 3, 4, and 8 at the points $(-1, 1)$, $(2, -1)$, and $(3, 2)$.

SOLUTION We use Equations 9 and 10 to compute the moments:

$$M_y = 3(-1) + 4(2) + 8(3) = 29$$

$$M_x = 3(1) + 4(-1) + 8(2) = 15$$

Since $m = 3 + 4 + 8 = 15$, we use Equations 11 to obtain

$$\bar{x} = \frac{M_y}{m} = \frac{29}{15} \qquad \bar{y} = \frac{M_x}{m} = \frac{15}{15} = 1$$

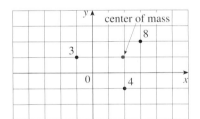

FIGURE 13

Thus the center of mass is $\left(1\tfrac{14}{15}, 1\right)$. (See Figure 13.) ■

Next we consider a flat plate (called a *lamina*) with uniform density ρ that occupies a region $\mathcal{R}$ of the plane. We wish to locate the center of mass of the plate, which is called the **centroid** of $\mathcal{R}$. In doing so we use the following physical principles: The **symmetry principle** says that if $\mathcal{R}$ is symmetric about a line l, then the centroid of $\mathcal{R}$ lies on l. (If $\mathcal{R}$ is reflected about l, then $\mathcal{R}$ remains the same so its centroid remains fixed. But the only fixed points lie on l.) Thus the centroid of a rectangle is its center. Moments should be defined so that if the entire mass of a region is concentrated at the center of mass, then its moments remain unchanged. Also, the moment of the union of two nonoverlapping regions should be the sum of the moments of the individual regions.

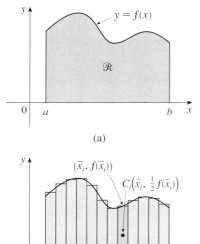

(a)

(b)

FIGURE 14

Suppose that the region $\mathcal{R}$ is of the type shown in Figure 14(a); that is, $\mathcal{R}$ lies between the lines $x = a$ and $x = b$, above the x-axis, and beneath the graph of f, where f is a continuous function. We divide the interval $[a, b]$ into n subintervals with endpoints $x_0, x_1, \ldots, x_n$ and equal width Δx. We choose the sample point x_i^* to be the midpoint $\bar{x}_i$ of the ith subinterval, that is, $\bar{x}_i = (x_{i-1} + x_i)/2$. This determines the polygonal approximation to $\mathcal{R}$ shown in Figure 14(b). The centroid of the ith approximating rectangle R_i is its center $C_i(\bar{x}_i, \frac{1}{2}f(\bar{x}_i))$. Its area is $f(\bar{x}_i)\,\Delta x$, so its mass is

$$\rho f(\bar{x}_i)\,\Delta x$$

The moment of R_i about the y-axis is the product of its mass and the distance from C_i to the y-axis, which is $\bar{x}_i$. Thus

$$M_y(R_i) = [\rho f(\bar{x}_i)\,\Delta x]\,\bar{x}_i = \rho \bar{x}_i f(\bar{x}_i)\,\Delta x$$

Adding these moments, we obtain the moment of the polygonal approximation to $\mathcal{R}$, and then by taking the limit as $n \to \infty$ we obtain the moment of $\mathcal{R}$ itself about the y-axis:

$$M_y = \lim_{n \to \infty} \sum_{i=1}^{n} \rho \bar{x}_i f(\bar{x}_i)\,\Delta x = \rho \int_a^b x f(x)\,dx$$

In a similar fashion we compute the moment of R_i about the x-axis as the product of its mass and the distance from C_i to the x-axis:

$$M_x(R_i) = [\rho f(\bar{x}_i)\,\Delta x]\tfrac{1}{2}f(\bar{x}_i) = \rho \cdot \tfrac{1}{2}[f(\bar{x}_i)]^2\,\Delta x$$

Again we add these moments and take the limit to obtain the moment of $\mathcal{R}$ about the x-axis:

$$M_x = \lim_{n \to \infty} \sum_{i=1}^{n} \rho \cdot \tfrac{1}{2}[f(\bar{x}_i)]^2\,\Delta x = \rho \int_a^b \tfrac{1}{2}[f(x)]^2\,dx$$

Just as for systems of particles, the center of mass of the plate is defined so that $m\bar{x} = M_y$ and $m\bar{y} = M_x$. But the mass of the plate is the product of its density and its area:

$$m = \rho A = \rho \int_a^b f(x)\,dx$$

and so

$$\bar{x} = \frac{M_y}{m} = \frac{\rho \displaystyle\int_a^b x f(x)\,dx}{\rho \displaystyle\int_a^b f(x)\,dx} = \frac{\displaystyle\int_a^b x f(x)\,dx}{\displaystyle\int_a^b f(x)\,dx}$$

$$\bar{y} = \frac{M_x}{m} = \frac{\rho \displaystyle\int_a^b \tfrac{1}{2}[f(x)]^2\,dx}{\rho \displaystyle\int_a^b f(x)\,dx} = \frac{\displaystyle\int_a^b \tfrac{1}{2}[f(x)]^2\,dx}{\displaystyle\int_a^b f(x)\,dx}$$

Notice the cancellation of the ρ's. The location of the center of mass is independent of the density.

In summary, the center of mass of the plate (or the centroid of $\mathcal{R}$) is located at the point $(\bar{x}, \bar{y})$, where

12
$$\bar{x} = \frac{1}{A}\int_a^b xf(x)\,dx \qquad \bar{y} = \frac{1}{A}\int_a^b \tfrac{1}{2}[f(x)]^2\,dx$$

EXAMPLE 8 Find the center of mass of a semicircular plate of radius r.

SOLUTION In order to use (12) we place the semicircle as in Figure 15 so that $f(x) = \sqrt{r^2 - x^2}$ and $a = -r$, $b = r$. Here there is no need to use the formula to calculate $\bar{x}$ because, by the symmetry principle, the center of mass must lie on the y-axis, so $\bar{x} = 0$. The area of the semicircle is $A = \frac{1}{2}\pi r^2$, so

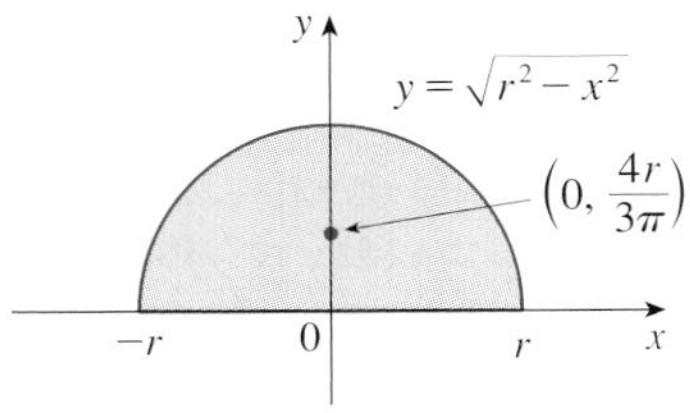

FIGURE 15

$$\begin{aligned}\bar{y} &= \frac{1}{A}\int_{-r}^{r} \tfrac{1}{2}[f(x)]^2\,dx = \frac{1}{\frac{1}{2}\pi r^2}\cdot\frac{1}{2}\int_{-r}^{r}\left(\sqrt{r^2 - x^2}\right)^2 dx \\ &= \frac{2}{\pi r^2}\int_0^r (r^2 - x^2)\,dx = \frac{2}{\pi r^2}\left[r^2x - \frac{x^3}{3}\right]_0^r \\ &= \frac{2}{\pi r^2}\,\frac{2r^3}{3} = \frac{4r}{3\pi}\end{aligned}$$

The center of mass is located at the point $(0, 4r/(3\pi))$. ■

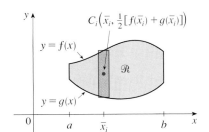

If the region $\mathcal{R}$ lies between two curves $y = f(x)$ and $y = g(x)$, where $f(x) \geqslant g(x)$, as illustrated in Figure 16, then the same sort of argument that led to Formulas 12 can be used to show that the centroid of $\mathcal{R}$ is $(\bar{x}, \bar{y})$, where

FIGURE 16

13
$$\bar{x} = \frac{1}{A}\int_a^b x[f(x) - g(x)]\,dx \qquad \bar{y} = \frac{1}{A}\int_a^b \tfrac{1}{2}\{[f(x)]^2 - [g(x)]^2\}\,dx$$

(See Exercise 51.)

EXAMPLE 9 Find the centroid of the region bounded by the line $y = x$ and the parabola $y = x^2$.

SOLUTION The region is sketched in Figure 17. We take $f(x) = x$, $g(x) = x^2$, $a = 0$, and $b = 1$ in Formulas 13. First we note that the area of the region is

FIGURE 17

$$A = \int_0^1 (x - x^2)\,dx = \frac{x^2}{2} - \frac{x^3}{3}\bigg]_0^1 = \frac{1}{6}$$

Therefore

$$\begin{aligned}\bar{x} &= \frac{1}{A}\int_0^1 x[f(x) - g(x)]\,dx = \frac{1}{\frac{1}{6}}\int_0^1 x(x - x^2)\,dx \\ &= 6\int_0^1 (x^2 - x^3)\,dx = 6\left[\frac{x^3}{3} - \frac{x^4}{4}\right]_0^1 = \frac{1}{2}\end{aligned}$$

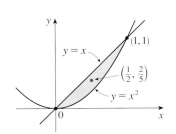

$$\bar{y} = \frac{1}{A} \int_0^1 \frac{1}{2}\{[f(x)]^2 - [g(x)]^2\}\, dx = \frac{1}{\frac{1}{6}} \int_0^1 \frac{1}{2}(x^2 - x^4)\, dx$$

$$= 3\left[\frac{x^3}{3} - \frac{x^5}{5}\right]_0^1 = \frac{2}{5}$$

The centroid is $\left(\frac{1}{2}, \frac{2}{5}\right)$. ∎

We end this section by showing a surprising connection between centroids and volumes of revolution.

▪ This theorem is named after the Greek mathematician Pappus of Alexandria, who lived in the fourth century A.D.

> **THEOREM OF PAPPUS** Let $\mathcal{R}$ be a plane region that lies entirely on one side of a line l in the plane. If $\mathcal{R}$ is rotated about l, then the volume of the resulting solid is the product of the area A of $\mathcal{R}$ and the distance d traveled by the centroid of $\mathcal{R}$.

PROOF We give the proof for the special case in which the region lies between $y = f(x)$ and $y = g(x)$ as in Figure 16 and the line l is the y-axis. Using the method of cylindrical shells (see Section 7.3), we have

$$V = \int_a^b 2\pi x[f(x) - g(x)]\, dx = 2\pi \int_a^b x[f(x) - g(x)]\, dx$$

$$= 2\pi(\bar{x}A) \qquad \text{(by Formulas 13)}$$

$$= (2\pi\bar{x})A = Ad$$

where $d = 2\pi\bar{x}$ is the distance traveled by the centroid during one rotation about the y-axis. ☐

◤ EXAMPLE 10 A torus is formed by rotating a circle of radius r about a line in the plane of the circle that is a distance R $(> r)$ from the center of the circle. Find the volume of the torus.

SOLUTION The circle has area $A = \pi r^2$. By the symmetry principle, its centroid is its center and so the distance traveled by the centroid during a rotation is $d = 2\pi R$. Therefore, by the Theorem of Pappus, the volume of the torus is

$$V = Ad = (\pi r^2)(2\pi R) = 2\pi^2 r^2 R$$ ∎

The method of Example 10 should be compared with the method of Exercise 41 in Section 7.2.

7.5 | **EXERCISES**

---

1. A particle is moved along the x-axis by a force that measures $10/(1 + x)^2$ pounds at a point x feet from the origin. Find the work done in moving the particle from the origin to a distance of 9 ft.

2. When a particle is located a distance x meters from the origin, a force of $\cos(\pi x/3)$ newtons acts on it. How much

work is done in moving the particle from $x = 1$ to $x = 2$? Interpret your answer by considering the work done from $x = 1$ to $x = 1.5$ and from $x = 1.5$ to $x = 2$.

3. Shown is the graph of a force function (in newtons) that increases to its maximum value and then remains constant.

How much work is done by the force in moving an object a distance of 8 m?

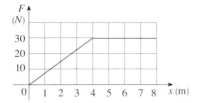

4. The table shows values of a force function $f(x)$ where x is measured in meters and $f(x)$ in newtons. Use Simpson's Rule to estimate the work done by the force in moving an object a distance of 18 m.

x	0	3	6	9	12	15	18
$f(x)$	9.8	9.1	8.5	8.0	7.7	7.5	7.4

5. A force of 10 lb is required to hold a spring stretched 4 in. beyond its natural length. How much work is done in stretching it from its natural length to 6 in. beyond its natural length?

6. A spring has a natural length of 20 cm. If a 25-N force is required to keep it stretched to a length of 30 cm, how much work is required to stretch it from 20 cm to 25 cm?

7. Suppose that 2 J of work is needed to stretch a spring from its natural length of 30 cm to a length of 42 cm.
  (a) How much work is needed to stretch it from 35 cm to 40 cm?
  (b) How far beyond its natural length will a force of 30 N keep the spring stretched?

8. If 6 J of work is needed to stretch a spring from 10 cm to 12 cm and another 10 J is needed to stretch it from 12 cm to 14 cm, what is the natural length of the spring?

9–16 ■ Show how to approximate the required work by a Riemann sum. Then express the work as an integral and evaluate it.

9. A heavy rope, 50 ft long, weighs 0.5 lb/ft and hangs over the edge of a building 120 ft high.
  (a) How much work is done in pulling the rope to the top of the building?
  (b) How much work is done in pulling half the rope to the top of the building?

10. A chain lying on the ground is 10 m long and its mass is 80 kg. How much work is required to raise one end of the chain to a height of 6 m?

11. A cable that weighs 2 lb/ft is used to lift 800 lb of coal up a mine shaft 500 ft deep. Find the work done.

12. A bucket that weighs 4 lb and a rope of negligible weight are used to draw water from a well that is 80 ft deep. The bucket is filled with 40 lb of water and is pulled up at a rate of 2 ft/s, but water leaks out of a hole in the bucket at a rate of 0.2 lb/s. Find the work done in pulling the bucket to the top of the well.

13. A leaky 10-kg bucket is lifted from the ground to a height of 12 m at a constant speed with a rope that weighs 0.8 kg/m. Initially the bucket contains 36 kg of water, but the water leaks at a constant rate and finishes draining just as the bucket reaches the 12 m level. How much work is done?

14. A 10-ft chain weighs 25 lb and hangs from a ceiling. Find the work done in lifting the lower end of the chain to the ceiling so that it's level with the upper end.

15. An aquarium 2 m long, 1 m wide, and 1 m deep is full of water. Find the work needed to pump half of the water out of the aquarium. (Use the fact that the density of water is 1000 kg/m^3.)

16. A circular swimming pool has a diameter of 24 ft, the sides are 5 ft high, and the depth of the water is 4 ft. How much work is required to pump all of the water out over the side? (Use the fact that water weighs 62.5 lb/ft^3.)

■ ■ ■ ■ ■ ■ ■ ■ ■ ■ ■ ■ ■

17. The tank shown is full of water.
  (a) Find the work required to pump the water out of the spout.

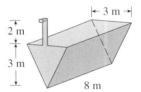

  (b) Suppose that the pump breaks down after 4.7×10^5 J of work has been done. What is the depth of the water remaining in the tank?

18. The hemispherical tank shown is full of water. Given that water weighs 62.5 lb/ft^3, find the work required to pump the water out of the tank.

19. When gas expands in a cylinder with radius r, the pressure at any given time is a function of the volume: $P = P(V)$. The force exerted by the gas on the piston (see the figure) is the product of the pressure and the area: $F = \pi r^2 P$. Show that the work done by the gas when the volume expands from volume V_1 to volume V_2 is

$$W = \int_{V_1}^{V_2} P \, dV$$

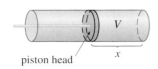

piston head

20. In a steam engine the pressure P and volume V of steam satisfy the equation $PV^{1.4} = k$, where k is a constant. (This is true for adiabatic expansion, that is, expansion in which there is no heat transfer between the cylinder and its surroundings.) Use Exercise 19 to calculate the work done by the engine during a cycle when the steam starts at a pressure of 160 lb/in² and a volume of 100 in³ and expands to a volume of 800 in³.

21. (a) Newton's Law of Gravitation states that two bodies with masses m_1 and m_2 attract each other with a force

$$F = G \frac{m_1 m_2}{r^2}$$

where r is the distance between the bodies and G is the gravitational constant. If one of the bodies is fixed, find the work needed to move the other from $r = a$ to $r = b$.
(b) Compute the work required to launch a 1000-kg satellite vertically to an orbit 1000 km high. You may assume that the Earth's mass is 5.98×10^{24} kg and is concentrated at its center. Take the radius of the Earth to be 6.37×10^6 m and $G = 6.67 \times 10^{-11}$ N·m²/kg².

22. (a) Use an improper integral and information from Exercise 21 to find the work needed to propel a 1000-kg satellite out of the Earth's gravitational field.
(b) Find the *escape velocity* v_0 that is needed to propel a rocket of mass m out of the gravitational field of a planet with mass M and radius R. (Use the fact that the initial kinetic energy of $\frac{1}{2} mv_0^2$ supplies the needed work.)

23–26 ■ A vertical plate is submerged in water and has the indicated shape. Explain how to approximate the hydrostatic force against one side of the plate by a Riemann sum. Then express the force as an integral and evaluate it.

23.

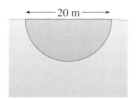

24.

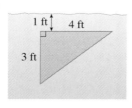

25.

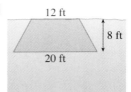

26.

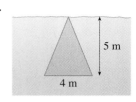

27. A trough is filled with a liquid of density 840 kg/m³. The ends of the trough are equilateral triangles with sides 8 m long and vertex at the bottom. Find the hydrostatic force on one end of the trough.

28. A large tank is designed with ends in the shape of the region between the curves $y = \frac{1}{2}x^2$ and $y = 12$, measured in feet. Find the hydrostatic force on one end of the tank if it is filled to a depth of 8 ft with gasoline. (Assume the gasoline's density is 42.0 lb/ft³.)

29. A swimming pool is 20 ft wide and 40 ft long and its bottom is an inclined plane, the shallow end having a depth of 3 ft and the deep end, 9 ft. If the pool is full of water, find the hydrostatic force on (a) the shallow end, (b) the deep end, (c) one of the sides, and (d) the bottom of the pool.

30. A vertical dam has a semicircular gate as shown in the figure. Find the hydrostatic force against the gate.

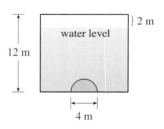

31. A vertical, irregularly shaped plate is submerged in water. The table shows measurements of its width, taken at the indicated depths. Use Simpson's Rule to estimate the force of the water against the plate.

Depth (m)	2.0	2.5	3.0	3.5	4.0	4.5	5.0
Plate width (m)	0	0.8	1.7	2.4	2.9	3.3	3.6

32. Point-masses m_i are located on the x-axis as shown. Find the moment M of the system about the origin and the center of mass $\bar{x}$.

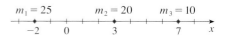

33–34 ■ The masses m_i are located at the points P_i. Find the moments M_x and M_y and the center of mass of the system.

33. $m_1 = 6$, $m_2 = 5$, $m_3 = 10$;
$P_1(1, 5)$, $P_2(3, -2)$, $P_3(-2, -1)$

34. $m_1 = 6$, $m_2 = 5$, $m_3 = 1$, $m_4 = 4$;
$P_1(1, -2)$, $P_2(3, 4)$, $P_3(-3, -7)$, $P_4(6, -1)$

35–38 ■ Sketch the region bounded by the curves, and visually estimate the location of the centroid. Then find the exact coordinates of the centroid.

35. $y = 4 - x^2$, $y = 0$

36. $3x + 2y = 6$, $y = 0$, $x = 0$

37. $y = e^x$, $y = 0$, $x = 0$, $x = 1$

38. $y = 1/x$, $y = 0$, $x = 1$, $x = 2$

39–42 ■ Find the centroid of the region bounded by the given curves.

39. $y = \sqrt{x}$, $y = x$

40. $y = x + 2$, $y = x^2$

41. $y = \sin x$, $y = \cos x$, $x = 0$, $x = \pi/4$

42. $y = x$, $y = 0$, $y = 1/x$, $x = 2$

43–44 ■ Calculate the moments M_x and M_y and the center of mass of a lamina with the given density and shape.

43. $\rho = 1$

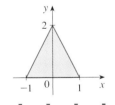

44. $\rho = 2$

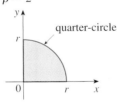

quarter-circle

45. Prove that the centroid of any triangle is located at the point of intersection of the medians. [*Hints:* Place the axes so that the vertices are $(a, 0)$, $(0, b)$, and $(c, 0)$. Recall that a median is a line segment from a vertex to the midpoint of the opposite side. Recall also that the medians intersect at a point two-thirds of the way from each vertex (along the median) to the opposite side.]

46–47 ■ Find the centroid of the region shown, not by integration, but by locating the centroids of the rectangles and triangles (from Exercise 45) and using additivity of moments.

46.

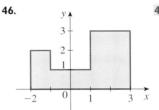

47.

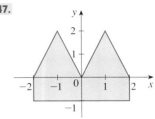

48–50 ■ Use the Theorem of Pappus to find the volume of the given solid.

48. A sphere of radius r (Use Example 8.)

49. A cone with height h and base radius r

50. The solid obtained by rotating the triangle with vertices $(2, 3)$, $(2, 5)$, and $(5, 4)$ about the x-axis

51. Prove Formulas 13.

52. Let $\mathcal{R}$ be the region that lies between the curves $y = x^m$ and $y = x^n$, $0 \le x \le 1$, where m and n are integers with $0 \le n < m$.
(a) Sketch the region $\mathcal{R}$.
(b) Find the coordinates of the centroid of $\mathcal{R}$.
(c) Try to find values of m and n such that the centroid lies *outside* $\mathcal{R}$.

7.6 | **DIFFERENTIAL EQUATIONS**

A **differential equation** is an equation that contains an unknown function and one or more of its derivatives. Here are some examples:

$$y' = xy$$

2

$$y'' + 2y' + y = 0$$

3

$$\frac{d^3y}{dx^3} + x\frac{d^2y}{dx^2} + \frac{dy}{dx} - 2y = e^{-x}$$

In each of these differential equations y is an unknown function x. The importance of differential equations lies in the fact that when a scientist or engineer formulates a physical law in mathematical terms, it frequently turns out to be a differential equation.

The **order** of a differential equation is the order of the highest derivative that occurs in the equation. Thus Equations 1, 2, and 3 are of order 1, 2, and 3, respectively.

A function f is called a **solution** of a differential equation if the equation is satisfied when $y = f(x)$ and its derivatives are substituted into the equation. Thus f is a solution of Equation 1 if

$$f'(x) = xf(x)$$

for all values of x in some interval.

When we are asked to *solve* a differential equation we are expected to find all possible solutions of the equation. We have already solved some particularly simple differential equations, namely, those of the form $y' = f(x)$. For instance, we know that the general solution of the differential equation $y' = x^3$ is given by $y = \frac{1}{4}x^4 + C$, where C is an arbitrary constant.

But, in general, solving a differential equation is not an easy matter. There is no systematic technique that enables us to solve all differential equations. In this section we learn how to solve a certain type of differential equation called a *separable equation*. At the end of the section, however, we will see how to sketch a rough graph of a solution of a first-order differential equation, even when it is impossible to find a formula for the solution.

SEPARABLE EQUATIONS

A **separable equation** is a first-order differential equation that can be written in the form

$$\frac{dy}{dx} = g(x)f(y)$$

The name *separable* comes from the fact that the expression on the right side can be "separated" into a function of x and a function of y. Equivalently, if $f(y) \neq 0$, we could write

4
$$\frac{dy}{dx} = \frac{g(x)}{h(y)}$$

■ The technique for solving separable differential equations was first used by James Bernoulli (in 1690) in solving a problem about pendulums and by Leibniz (in a letter to Huygens in 1691). John Bernoulli explained the general method in a paper published in 1694.

where $h(y) = 1/f(y)$. To solve this equation we rewrite it in the differential form

$$h(y)\,dy = g(x)\,dx$$

so that all y's are on one side of the equation and all x's are on the other side. Then we integrate both sides of the equation:

5
$$\int h(y)\,dy = \int g(x)\,dx$$

Equation 5 defines y implicitly as a function of x. In some cases we may be able to solve for y in terms of x.

We use the Chain Rule to justify this procedure: If h and g satisfy (5), then

$$\frac{d}{dx}\left(\int h(y)\,dy\right) = \frac{d}{dx}\left(\int g(x)\,dx\right)$$

so

$$\frac{d}{dy}\left(\int h(y)\,dy\right)\frac{dy}{dx} = g(x)$$

and

$$h(y)\frac{dy}{dx} = g(x)$$

Thus Equation 4 is satisfied.

When applying differential equations, we are usually not as interested in finding a family of solutions (the *general solution*) as we are in finding a solution that satisfies some additional requirement. In many physical problems we need to find the particular solution that satisfies a condition of the form $y(x_0) = y_0$. This is called an **initial condition**, and the problem of finding a solution of the differential equation that satisfies the initial condition is called an **initial-value problem**.

EXAMPLE I

(a) Solve the differential equation $\dfrac{dy}{dx} = \dfrac{x^2}{y^2}$.

(b) Find the solution of this equation that satisfies the initial condition $y(0) = 2$.

SOLUTION

(a) We write the equation in terms of differentials and integrate both sides:

$$y^2\,dy = x^2\,dx$$

$$\int y^2\,dy = \int x^2\,dx$$

$$\tfrac{1}{3}y^3 = \tfrac{1}{3}x^3 + C$$

▪ Figure 1 shows graphs of several members of the family of solutions of the differential equation in Example 1. The solution of the initial-value problem in part (b) is shown in blue.

where C is an arbitrary constant. (We could have used a constant C_1 on the left side and another constant C_2 on the right side. But then we could combine these constants by writing $C = C_2 - C_1$.)

Solving for y, we get

$$y = \sqrt[3]{x^3 + 3C}$$

We could leave the solution like this or we could write it in the form

$$y = \sqrt[3]{x^3 + K}$$

where $K = 3C$. (Since C is an arbitrary constant, so is K.)

(b) If we put $x = 0$ in the general solution in part (a), we get $y(0) = \sqrt[3]{K}$. To satisfy the initial condition $y(0) = 2$, we must have $\sqrt[3]{K} = 2$ and so $K = 8$.

Thus the solution of the initial-value problem is

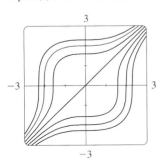

FIGURE I

$$y = \sqrt[3]{x^3 + 8}$$

■

■ Some computer algebra systems can plot curves defined by implicit equations. Figure 2 shows the graphs of several members of the family of solutions of the differential equation in Example 2. As we look at the curves from left to right, the values of C are 3, 2, 1, 0, -1, -2, and -3.

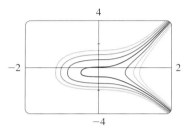

FIGURE 2

V EXAMPLE 2 Solve the differential equation $\dfrac{dy}{dx} = \dfrac{6x^2}{2y + \cos y}$.

SOLUTION Writing the equation in differential form and integrating both sides, we have

$$(2y + \cos y)\,dy = 6x^2\,dx$$

$$\int (2y + \cos y)\,dy = \int 6x^2\,dx$$

6
$$y^2 + \sin y = 2x^3 + C$$

where C is a constant. Equation 6 gives the general solution implicitly. In this case it's impossible to solve the equation to express y explicitly as a function of x. ■

EXAMPLE 3 Solve the equation $y' = x^2 y$.

SOLUTION First we rewrite the equation using Leibniz notation:

$$\frac{dy}{dx} = x^2 y$$

■ If a solution y is a function that satisfies $y(x) \neq 0$ for some x, it follows from a uniqueness theorem for solutions of differential equations that $y(x) \neq 0$ for all x.

If $y \neq 0$, we can rewrite it in differential notation and integrate:

$$\frac{dy}{y} = x^2\,dx \qquad y \neq 0$$

$$\int \frac{dy}{y} = \int x^2\,dx$$

$$\ln |y| = \frac{x^3}{3} + C$$

This equation defines y implicitly as a function of x. But in this case we can solve explicitly for y as follows:

$$|y| = e^{\ln |y|} = e^{(x^3/3)+C} = e^C e^{x^3/3}$$

so
$$y = \pm e^C e^{x^3/3}$$

■ Several solutions of the differential equation in Example 3 are graphed in Figure 3. The values of A are the same as the y-intercepts.

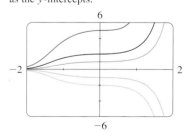

FIGURE 3

We can easily verify that the function $y = 0$ is also a solution of the given differential equation. So we can write the general solution in the form

$$y = Ae^{x^3/3}$$

where A is an arbitrary constant ($A = e^C$, or $A = -e^C$, or $A = 0$). ■

EXAMPLE 4 Solve the equation $\dfrac{dy}{dt} = ky$.

SOLUTION This differential equation was studied in Section 3.4, where it was called the law of natural growth (or decay). Since it is a separable equation, we can solve it by the methods of this section as follows:

$$\int \frac{dy}{y} = \int k \, dt \qquad y \neq 0$$

$$\ln |y| = kt + C$$

$$|y| = e^{kt+C} = e^C e^{kt}$$

$$y = Ae^{kt}$$

where $A \; (= \pm e^C \text{ or } 0)$ is an arbitrary constant. ■

LOGISTIC GROWTH

The differential equation of Example 4 is appropriate for modeling population growth ($y' = ky$ says that the rate of growth is proportional to the size of the population) under conditions of unlimited environment and food supply. However, in a restricted environment and with limited food supply, the population cannot exceed a maximal size M (called the **carrying capacity**) at which it consumes its entire food supply. If we make the assumption that the rate of growth of population is jointly proportional to the size of the population (y) and the amount by which y falls short of the maximal size ($M - y$), then we have the equation

7

$$\frac{dy}{dt} = ky(M - y)$$

where k is a constant. Equation 7 is called the **logistic differential equation** and was used by the Dutch mathematical biologist Pierre-François Verhulst in the 1840s to model world population growth.

The logistic equation is separable, so we write it in the form

$$\int \frac{dy}{y(M - y)} = \int k \, dt$$

Using partial fractions, we have

$$\frac{1}{y(M - y)} = \frac{1}{M} \left[\frac{1}{y} + \frac{1}{M - y} \right]$$

and so

$$\frac{1}{M} \left[\int \frac{dy}{y} + \int \frac{dy}{M - y} \right] = \int k \, dt = kt + C$$

$$\frac{1}{M} \left(\ln |y| - \ln |M - y| \right) = kt + C$$

But $|y| = y$ and $|M - y| = M - y$, since $0 < y < M$, so we have

$$\ln \frac{y}{M - y} = M(kt + C)$$

$$\frac{y}{M - y} = Ae^{kMt} \qquad (A = e^{MC})$$

If the population at time $t = 0$ is $y(0) = y_0$, then $A = y_0/(M - y_0)$, so

$$\frac{y}{M - y} = \frac{y_0}{M - y_0}e^{kMt}$$

If we solve this equation for y, we get

8
$$y = \frac{y_0 M e^{kMt}}{M - y_0 + y_0 e^{kMt}} = \frac{y_0 M}{y_0 + (M - y_0)e^{-kMt}}$$

Using the latter expression for y, we see that

$$\lim_{t \to \infty} y(t) = M$$

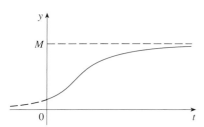

FIGURE 4
Logistic growth function

which is to be expected.

The graph of the logistic growth function is shown in Figure 4. At first the graph is concave upward and the growth curve appears to be almost exponential, but then it is concave downward and approaches the limiting population M.

MIXING PROBLEMS

A typical mixing problem involves a tank of fixed capacity filled with a thoroughly mixed solution of some substance, such as salt. A solution of a given concentration enters the tank at a fixed rate and the mixture, thoroughly stirred, leaves at a fixed rate, which may differ from the entering rate. If $y(t)$ denotes the amount of substance in the tank at time t, then $y'(t)$ is the rate at which the substance is being added minus the rate at which it is being removed. The mathematical description of this situation often leads to a first-order separable differential equation. We can use the same type of reasoning to model a variety of phenomena: chemical reactions, discharge of pollutants into a lake, injection of a drug into the bloodstream.

EXAMPLE 5 A tank contains 20 kg of salt dissolved in 5000 L of water. Brine that contains 0.03 kg of salt per liter of water enters the tank at a rate of 25 L/min. The solution is kept thoroughly mixed and drains from the tank at the same rate. How much salt remains in the tank after half an hour?

SOLUTION Let $y(t)$ be the amount of salt (in kilograms) after t minutes. We are given that $y(0) = 20$ and we want to find $y(30)$. We do this by finding a differential equation satisfied by $y(t)$. Note that dy/dt is the rate of change of the amount of salt, so

9
$$\frac{dy}{dt} = (\text{rate in}) - (\text{rate out})$$

where (rate in) is the rate at which salt enters the tank and (rate out) is the rate at which salt leaves the tank. We have

$$\text{rate in} = \left(0.03 \, \frac{\text{kg}}{\text{L}}\right)\left(25 \, \frac{\text{L}}{\text{min}}\right) = 0.75 \, \frac{\text{kg}}{\text{min}}$$

The tank always contains 5000 L of liquid, so the concentration at time t is $y(t)/5000$ (measured in kilograms per liter). Since the brine flows out at a rate of 25 L/min, we have

$$\text{rate out} = \left(\frac{y(t)}{5000}\frac{\text{kg}}{\text{L}}\right)\left(25\frac{\text{L}}{\text{min}}\right) = \frac{y(t)}{200}\frac{\text{kg}}{\text{min}}$$

Thus from Equation 9 we get

$$\frac{dy}{dt} = 0.75 - \frac{y(t)}{200} = \frac{150 - y(t)}{200}$$

Solving this separable differential equation, we obtain

$$\int \frac{dy}{150 - y} = \int \frac{dt}{200}$$

$$-\ln|150 - y| = \frac{t}{200} + C$$

Since $y(0) = 20$, we have $-\ln 130 = C$, so

$$-\ln|150 - y| = \frac{t}{200} - \ln 130$$

Therefore $\qquad |150 - y| = 130e^{-t/200}$

Since $y(t)$ is continuous and $y(0) = 20$ and the right side is never 0, we deduce that $150 - y(t)$ is always positive. Thus $|150 - y| = 150 - y$ and so

$$y(t) = 150 - 130e^{-t/200}$$

The amount of salt after 30 min is

$$y(30) = 150 - 130e^{-30/200} \approx 38.1 \text{ kg} \qquad ■$$

■ Figure 5 shows the graph of the function $y(t)$ of Example 5. Notice that, as time goes by, the amount of salt approaches 150 kg.

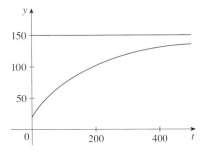

FIGURE 5

DIRECTION FIELDS

Suppose we are given a first-order differential equation of the form

$$y' = F(x, y)$$

where $F(x, y)$ is some expression in x and y. [Recall that a separable equation is the special case in which $F(x, y)$ can be factored as a function of x times a function of y.] Even if it is impossible to find a formula for the solution, we can still visualize the solution curves by means of a direction field. If a solution curve passes through a point (x, y), then its slope at that point is y', which is equal to $F(x, y)$. If we draw short line segments with slope $F(x, y)$ at several points (x, y), the result is called a **direction field** (or **slope field**). These line segments indicate the direction in which a solution curve is heading, so the direction field helps us visualize the general shape of these curves.

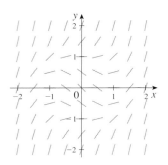

FIGURE 6

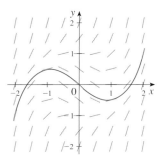

FIGURE 7

Module 7.6 shows direction fields and solution curves for a variety of differential equations.

V EXAMPLE 6

(a) Sketch the direction field for the differential equation $y' = x^2 + y^2 - 1$.
(b) Use part (a) to sketch the solution curve that passes through the origin.

SOLUTION

(a) We start by computing the slope at several points in the following chart:

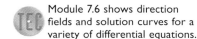

x	-2	-1	0	1	2	-2	-1	0	1	2	$\ldots$
y	0	0	0	0	0	1	1	1	1	1	$\ldots$
$y' = x^2 + y^2 - 1$	3	0	-1	0	3	4	1	0	1	4	$\ldots$

Now we draw short line segments with these slopes at these points. The result is the direction field shown in Figure 6.

(b) We start at the origin and move to the right in the direction of the line segment (which has slope -1). We continue to draw the solution curve so that it moves parallel to the nearby line segments. The resulting solution curve is shown in Figure 7. Returning to the origin, we draw the solution curve to the left as well. ■

The more line segments we draw in a direction field, the clearer the picture becomes. Of course, it's tedious to compute slopes and draw line segments for a huge number of points by hand, but computers are well suited for this task. Figure 8 shows a more detailed, computer-drawn direction field for the differential equation in Example 6. It enables us to draw, with reasonable accuracy, the solution curves shown in Figure 9 with y-intercepts -2, -1, 0, 1, and 2.

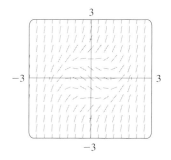

FIGURE 8

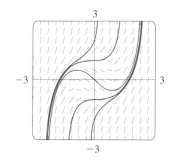

FIGURE 9

| **7.6** | **EXERCISES** |

1–8 ■ Solve the differential equation.

1. $\dfrac{dy}{dx} = \dfrac{y}{x}$

2. $\dfrac{dy}{dx} = \dfrac{\sqrt{x}}{e^y}$

3. $(x^2 + 1)y' = xy$

4. $y' = y^2 \sin x$

5. $(1 + \tan y)y' = x^2 + 1$

6. $\dfrac{dy}{d\theta} = \dfrac{e^y \sin^2\theta}{y \sec\theta}$

7. $\dfrac{du}{dt} = 2 + 2u + t + tu$

8. $\dfrac{dz}{dt} + e^{t+z} = 0$

9–14 ■ Find the solution of the differential equation that satisfies the given initial condition.

9. $\dfrac{du}{dt} = \dfrac{2t + \sec^2 t}{2u}$, $\quad u(0) = -5$

10. $\dfrac{dy}{dx} = \dfrac{y \cos x}{1 + y^2}$, $\quad y(0) = 1$

11. $x \cos x = (2y + e^{3y})y'$, $\quad y(0) = 0$

12. $\dfrac{dP}{dt} = \sqrt{Pt}$, $\quad P(1) = 2$

13. $y' \tan x = a + y$, $y(\pi/3) = a$, $0 < x < \pi/2$

14. $\dfrac{dL}{dt} = kL^2 \ln t$, $L(1) = -1$

▪ ▪ ▪ ▪ ▪ ▪ ▪ ▪ ▪ ▪ ▪

15. Find an equation of the curve that satisfies $dy/dx = 4x^3 y$ and whose y-intercept is 7.

16. Find an equation of the curve that passes through the point $(1, 1)$ and whose slope at (x, y) is y^2/x^3.

17. (a) Solve the differential equation $y' = 2x\sqrt{1 - y^2}$.
   (b) Solve the initial-value problem $y' = 2x\sqrt{1 - y^2}$, $y(0) = 0$, and graph the solution.
   (c) Does the initial-value problem $y' = 2x\sqrt{1 - y^2}$, $y(0) = 2$, have a solution? Explain.

18. Solve the equation $e^{-y}y' + \cos x = 0$ and graph several members of the family of solutions. How does the solution curve change as the constant C varies?

19. Solve the initial-value problem $y' = (\sin x)/\sin y$, $y(0) = \pi/2$, and graph the solution (if your CAS does implicit plots).

20. Solve the equation $y' = x\sqrt{x^2 + 1}/(ye^y)$ and graph several members of the family of solutions (if your CAS does implicit plots). How does the solution curve change as the constant C varies?

21–24 ▪ Match the differential equation with its direction field (labeled I–IV). Give reasons for your answer.

21. $y' = 2 - y$ **23.** $y' = x(2 - y)$

22. $y' = x + y - 1$ **24.** $y' = \sin x \sin y$

I
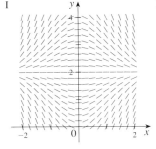

II
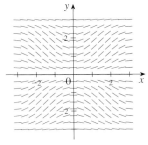

III, IV
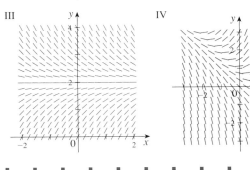

▪ ▪ ▪ ▪ ▪ ▪ ▪ ▪ ▪ ▪ ▪

25–26 ▪ Refer to the direction fields in Exercises 21–24.

25. Use field II to sketch the graphs of the solutions that satisfy the given initial conditions.
   (a) $y(0) = 1$ (b) $y(0) = 2$ (c) $y(0) = -1$

26. Use field IV to sketch the graphs of the solutions that satisfy the given initial conditions.
   (a) $y(0) = -1$ (b) $y(0) = 0$ (c) $y(0) = 1$

27–28 ▪ Sketch a direction field for the differential equation. Then use it to sketch three solution curves.

27. $y' = 1 + y$ **28.** $y' = x^2 - y^2$

▪ ▪ ▪ ▪ ▪ ▪ ▪ ▪ ▪ ▪ ▪

29–32 ▪ Sketch the direction field of the differential equation. Then use it to sketch a solution curve that passes through the given point.

29. $y' = y - 2x$, $(1, 0)$ **30.** $y' = 1 - xy$, $(0, 0)$

31. $y' = y + xy$, $(0, 1)$ **32.** $y' = x - xy$, $(1, 0)$

▪ ▪ ▪ ▪ ▪ ▪ ▪ ▪ ▪ ▪ ▪

33. Psychologists interested in learning theory study **learning curves**. A learning curve is the graph of a function $P(t)$, the performance of someone learning a skill as a function of the training time t. The derivative dP/dt represents the rate at which performance improves.
   (a) If M is the maximum level of performance of which the learner is capable, explain why the differential equation

$$\frac{dP}{dt} = k(M - P) \qquad k \text{ a positive constant}$$

   is a reasonable model for learning.
   (b) Solve the differential equation in part (a) to find an expression for $P(t)$. What is the limit of this expression?

34. A sphere with radius 1 m has temperature 15°C. It lies inside a concentric sphere with radius 2 m and temperature 25°C. The temperature $T(r)$ at a distance r from the common center of the spheres satisfies the differential equation

$$\frac{d^2 T}{dr^2} + \frac{2}{r}\frac{dT}{dr} = 0$$

   If we let $S = dT/dr$, then S satisfies a first-order differential equation. Solve it to find an expression for the temperature $T(r)$ between the spheres.

35. A glucose solution is administered intravenously into the bloodstream at a constant rate r. As the glucose is added, it is converted into other substances and removed from the bloodstream at a rate that is proportional to the concentration at that time. Thus a model for the concentration

$C = C(t)$ of the glucose solution in the bloodstream is

$$\frac{dC}{dt} = r - kC$$

where k is a positive constant.
(a) Suppose that the concentration at time $t = 0$ is C_0. Determine the concentration at any time t by solving the differential equation.
(b) Assuming that $C_0 < r/k$, find $\lim_{t \to \infty} C(t)$ and interpret your answer.

36. A certain small country has \$10 billion in paper currency in circulation, and each day \$50 million comes into the country's banks. The government decides to introduce new currency by having the banks replace old bills with new ones whenever old currency comes into the banks. Let $x = x(t)$ denote the amount of new currency in circulation at time t, with $x(0) = 0$.
(a) Formulate a mathematical model in the form of an initial-value problem that represents the "flow" of the new currency into circulation.
(b) Solve the initial-value problem found in part (a).
(c) How long will it take for the new bills to account for 90% of the currency in circulation?

37. Write the solution of the logistic initial-value problem

$$\frac{dP}{dt} = 0.00008P(1000 - P) \qquad P(0) = 100$$

and use it to find the population sizes $P(40)$ and $P(80)$. At what time does the population reach 900?

38. The Pacific halibut fishery has been modeled by the differential equation

$$\frac{dy}{dt} = ky(M - y)$$

where $y(t)$ is the biomass (the total mass of the members of the population) in kilograms at time t (measured in years), the carrying capacity is estimated to be $M = 8 \times 10^7$ kg, and $k = 8.875 \times 10^{-9}$ per year.
(a) If $y(0) = 2 \times 10^7$ kg, find the biomass a year later.
(b) How long will it take the biomass to reach 4×10^7 kg?

39. One model for the spread of a rumor is that the rate of spread is proportional to the product of the fraction y of the population who have heard the rumor and the fraction who have not heard the rumor.
(a) Write a differential equation that is satisfied by y.
(b) Solve the differential equation.
(c) A small town has 1000 inhabitants. At 8 AM, 80 people have heard a rumor. By noon half the town has heard it. At what time will 90% of the population have heard the rumor?

40. Biologists stocked a lake with 400 fish of one species and estimated the species' carrying capacity in the lake to be 10,000. The number of fish tripled in the first year.
(a) Assuming that the size of the fish population satisfies the logistic equation, find an expression for the size of the population after t years.
(b) How long will it take for the population to increase to 5000?

41. (a) Show that if y satisfies the logistic equation (7), then

$$\frac{d^2y}{dt^2} = k^2y(M - y)(M - 2y)$$

(b) Deduce that a population grows fastest when it reaches half its carrying capacity.

42. For a fixed value of M (say $M = 10$), the family of logistic functions given by Equation 8 depends on the initial value y_0 and the proportionality constant k. Graph several members of this family. How does the graph change when y_0 varies? How does it change when k varies?

43. A tank contains 1000 L of brine with 15 kg of dissolved salt. Pure water enters the tank at a rate of 10 L/min. The solution is kept thoroughly mixed and drains from the tank at the same rate. How much salt is in the tank (a) after t minutes and (b) after 20 minutes?

44. The air in a room with volume 180 m^3 contains 0.15% carbon dioxide initially. Fresher air with only 0.05% carbon dioxide flows into the room at a rate of 2 m^3/min and the mixed air flows out at the same rate. Find the percentage of carbon dioxide in the room as a function of time. What happens in the long run?

45. A vat with 500 gallons of beer contains 4% alcohol (by volume). Beer with 6% alcohol is pumped into the vat at a rate of 5 gal/min and the mixture is pumped out at the same rate. What is the percentage of alcohol after an hour?

46. A tank contains 1000 L of pure water. Brine that contains 0.05 kg of salt per liter of water enters the tank at a rate of 5 L/min. Brine that contains 0.04 kg of salt per liter of water enters the tank at a rate of 10 L/min. The solution is kept thoroughly mixed and drains from the tank at a rate of 15 L/min. How much salt is in the tank (a) after t minutes and (b) after one hour?

47. When a raindrop falls, it increases in size and so its mass at time t is a function of t, $m(t)$. The rate of growth of the mass is $km(t)$ for some positive constant k. When we apply Newton's Law of Motion to the raindrop, we get $(mv)' = gm$, where v is the velocity of the raindrop (directed downward) and g is the acceleration due to gravity. The *terminal velocity* of the raindrop is $\lim_{t \to \infty} v(t)$. Find an expression for the terminal velocity in terms of g and k.

48. An object of mass m is moving horizontally through a medium which resists the motion with a force that is a function of the velocity; that is,

$$m\frac{d^2s}{dt^2} = m\frac{dv}{dt} = f(v)$$

where $v = v(t)$ and $s = s(t)$ represent the velocity and position of the object at time t, respectively. For example, think of a boat moving through the water.

(a) Suppose that the resisting force is proportional to the velocity, that is, $f(v) = -kv$, k a positive constant. (This model is appropriate for small values of v.) Let $v(0) = v_0$ and $s(0) = s_0$ be the initial values of v and s. Determine v and s at any time t. What is the total distance that the object travels from time $t = 0$?

(b) For larger values of v a better model is obtained by supposing that the resisting force is proportional to the square of the velocity, that is, $f(v) = -kv^2$, $k > 0$. (This model was first proposed by Newton.) Let v_0 and s_0 be the initial values of v and s. Determine v and s at any time t. What is the total distance that the object travels in this case?

49. Let $A(t)$ be the area of a tissue culture at time t and let M be the final area of the tissue when growth is complete. Most cell divisions occur on the periphery of the tissue and the number of cells on the periphery is proportional to $\sqrt{A(t)}$. So a reasonable model for the growth of tissue is obtained by assuming that the rate of growth of the area is jointly proportional to $\sqrt{A(t)}$ and $M - A(t)$.

(a) Formulate a differential equation and use it to show that the tissue grows fastest when $A(t) = \frac{1}{3}M$.

(b) Solve the differential equation to find an expression for $A(t)$. Use a computer algebra system to perform the integration.

50. According to Newton's Law of Universal Gravitation, the gravitational force on an object of mass m that has been projected vertically upward from the Earth's surface is

$$F = \frac{mgR^2}{(x + R)^2}$$

where $x = x(t)$ is the object's distance above the surface at time t, R is the Earth's radius, and g is the acceleration due to gravity. Also, by Newton's Second Law, $F = ma = m(dv/dt)$ and so

$$m\frac{dv}{dt} = -\frac{mgR^2}{(x + R)^2}$$

(a) Suppose a rocket is fired vertically upward with an initial velocity v_0. Let h be the maximum height above the surface reached by the object. Show that

$$v_0 = \sqrt{\frac{2gRh}{R + h}}$$

[*Hint:* By the Chain Rule, $m(dv/dt) = mv(dv/dx)$.]

(b) Calculate $v_e = \lim_{h \to \infty} v_0$. This limit is called the *escape velocity* for the Earth.

(c) Use $R = 3960$ mi and $g = 32$ ft/s^2 to calculate v_e in feet per second and in miles per second.

---

7 REVIEW

CONCEPT CHECK

1. (a) Draw two typical curves $y = f(x)$ and $y = g(x)$, where $f(x) \geq g(x)$ for $a \leq x \leq b$. Show how to approximate the area between these curves by a Riemann sum and sketch the corresponding approximating rectangles. Then write an expression for the exact area.

(b) Explain how the situation changes if the curves have equations $x = f(y)$ and $x = g(y)$, where $f(y) \geq g(y)$ for $c \leq y \leq d$.

2. Suppose that Sue runs faster than Kathy throughout a 1500-meter race. What is the physical meaning of the area between their velocity curves for the first minute of the race?

3. (a) Suppose S is a solid with known cross-sectional areas. Explain how to approximate the volume of S by a Riemann sum. Then write an expression for the exact volume.

(b) If S is a solid of revolution, how do you find the cross-sectional areas?

4. (a) What is the volume of a cylindrical shell?

(b) Explain how to use cylindrical shells to find the volume of a solid of revolution.

(c) Why might you want to use the shell method instead of slicing?

5. (a) How is the length of a curve defined?

(b) Write an expression for the length of a smooth curve given by $y = f(x)$, $a \leq x \leq b$.

(c) What if x is given as a function of y?

6. Suppose that you push a book across a 6-meter-long table by exerting a force $f(x)$ at each point from $x = 0$ to $x = 6$. What does $\int_0^6 f(x)\,dx$ represent? If $f(x)$ is measured in newtons, what are the units for the integral?

7. Describe how we can find the hydrostatic force against a vertical wall submersed in a fluid.

8. (a) What is the physical significance of the center of mass of a thin plate?
(b) If the plate lies between $y = f(x)$ and $y = 0$, where $a \leq x \leq b$, write expressions for the coordinates of the center of mass.

9. What does the Theorem of Pappus say?

10. (a) What is a differential equation?
(b) What is the order of a differential equation?
(c) What is an initial condition?

11. What is a direction field for the differential equation $y' = F(x, y)$?

12. What is a separable differential equation? How do you solve it?

EXERCISES

1–4 ■ Find the area of the region bounded by the given curves.

1. $y = x^2 - x - 6$, $y = 0$

2. $y = 20 - x^2$, $y = x^2 - 12$

3. $y = e^x - 1$, $y = x^2 - x$, $x = 1$

4. $x + y = 0$, $x = y^2 + 3y$

■ ■ ■ ■ ■ ■ ■ ■ ■ ■ ■ ■ ■ ■

5–9 ■ Find the volume of the solid obtained by rotating the region bounded by the given curves about the specified axis.

5. $y = 2x$, $y = x^2$; about the x-axis

6. $x = 1 + y^2$, $y = x - 3$; about the y-axis

7. $x = 0$, $x = 9 - y^2$; about $x = -1$

8. $y = x^2 + 1$, $y = 9 - x^2$; about $y = -1$

9. $x^2 - y^2 = a^2$, $x = a + h$ (where $a > 0, h > 0$); about the y-axis

■ ■ ■ ■ ■ ■ ■ ■ ■ ■ ■ ■ ■ ■

10–12 ■ Set up, but do not evaluate, an integral for the volume of the solid obtained by rotating the region bounded by the given curves about the specified axis.

10. $y = \cos x$, $y = 0$, $x = 3\pi/2$, $x = 5\pi/2$; about the y-axis

11. $y = x^3$, $y = x^2$; about $y = 1$

12. $y = x^3$, $y = 8$, $x = 0$; about $x = 2$

■ ■ ■ ■ ■ ■ ■ ■ ■ ■ ■ ■ ■ ■

13. Find the volumes of the solids obtained by rotating the region bounded by the curves $y = x$ and $y = x^2$ about the following lines.
(a) The x-axis   (b) The y-axis   (c) $y = 2$

14. Let $\mathcal{R}$ be the region in the first quadrant bounded by the curves $y = x^3$ and $y = 2x - x^2$. Calculate the following quantities.
(a) The area of $\mathcal{R}$
(b) The volume obtained by rotating $\mathcal{R}$ about the x-axis
(c) The volume obtained by rotating $\mathcal{R}$ about the y-axis

15. Let $\mathcal{R}$ be the region bounded by the curves $y = \tan(x^2)$, $x = 1$, and $y = 0$. Use the Midpoint Rule with $n = 4$ to estimate the following quantities.
(a) The area of $\mathcal{R}$
(b) The volume obtained by rotating $\mathcal{R}$ about the x-axis

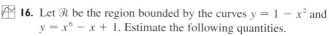 **16.** Let $\mathcal{R}$ be the region bounded by the curves $y = 1 - x^2$ and $y = x^6 - x + 1$. Estimate the following quantities.
(a) The x-coordinates of the points of intersection of the curves
(b) The area of $\mathcal{R}$
(c) The volume generated when $\mathcal{R}$ is rotated about the x-axis
(d) The volume generated when $\mathcal{R}$ is rotated about the y-axis

17–20 ■ Each integral represents the volume of a solid. Describe the solid.

17. $\displaystyle\int_0^{\pi/2} 2\pi x \cos x \, dx$ **18.** $\displaystyle\int_0^{\pi/2} 2\pi \cos^2 x \, dx$

19. $\displaystyle\int_0^2 2\pi y(4 - y^2) \, dy$

20. $\displaystyle\int_0^1 \pi[(2 - x^2)^2 - (2 - \sqrt{x})^2] \, dx$

■ ■ ■ ■ ■ ■ ■ ■ ■ ■ ■ ■ ■ ■

21. The base of a solid is a circular disk with radius 3. Find the volume of the solid if parallel cross-sections perpendicular to the base are isosceles right triangles with hypotenuse lying along the base.

22. The base of a solid is the region bounded by the parabolas $y = x^2$ and $y = 2 - x^2$. Find the volume of the solid if the cross-sections perpendicular to the x-axis are squares with one side lying along the base.

23. The height of a monument is 20 m. A horizontal cross-section at a distance x meters from the top is an equilateral triangle with side $\frac{1}{4}x$ meters. Find the volume of the monument.

24. (a) The base of a solid is a square with vertices located at $(1, 0)$, $(0, 1)$, $(-1, 0)$, and $(0, -1)$. Each cross-section perpendicular to the x-axis is a semicircle. Find the volume of the solid.

(b) Show that by cutting the solid of part (a), we can rearrange it to form a cone. Thus compute its volume more simply.

25–26 ■ Find the length of the curve.

25. $y = \frac{1}{6}(x^2 + 4)^{3/2}, \quad 0 \le x \le 3$

26. $y = 2\ln(\sin\frac{1}{2}x), \quad \pi/3 \le x \le \pi$

■ ■ ■ ■ ■ ■ ■ ■ ■ ■ ■ ■

27. Use Simpson's Rule with $n = 6$ to estimate the length of the curve $y = e^{-x^2}, 0 \le x \le 3$.

28. Find the length of the curve

$$y = \int_1^x \sqrt{\sqrt{t} - 1}\, dt \qquad 1 \le x \le 16$$

29. A force of 30 N is required to maintain a spring stretched from its natural length of 12 cm to a length of 15 cm. How much work is done in stretching the spring from 12 cm to 20 cm?

30. A 1600-lb elevator is suspended by a 200-ft cable that weighs 10 lb/ft. How much work is required to raise the elevator from the basement to the third floor, a distance of 30 ft?

31. A tank full of water has the shape of a paraboloid of revolution as shown in the figure; that is, its shape is obtained by rotating a parabola about a vertical axis.

(a) If its height is 4 ft and the radius at the top is 4 ft, find the work required to pump the water out of the tank.

(b) After 4000 ft-lb of work has been done, what is the depth of the water remaining in the tank?

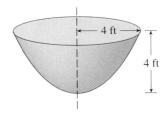

32. A trough is filled with water and its vertical ends have the shape of the parabolic region in the figure. Find the hydrostatic force on one end of the trough.

33. A gate in an irrigation canal is constructed in the form of a trapezoid 3 ft wide at the bottom, 5 ft wide at the top, and 2 ft high. It is placed vertically in the canal so that the water

just covers the gate. Find the hydrostatic force on one side of the gate.

34. Find the centroid of the region shown.

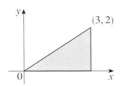

35–36 ■ Find the centroid of the region bounded by the given curves.

35. $y = 4 - x^2, \quad y = x + 2$

36. $y = \sin x, \quad y = 0, \quad x = \pi/4, \quad x = 3\pi/4$

■ ■ ■ ■ ■ ■ ■ ■ ■ ■ ■ ■

37. Find the volume obtained when the circle of radius 1 with center $(1, 0)$ is rotated about the y-axis.

38. Use the Theorem of Pappus and the fact that the volume of a sphere of radius r is $\frac{4}{3}\pi r^3$ to find the centroid of the semicircular region bounded by the curve $y = \sqrt{r^2 - x^2}$ and the x-axis.

39–40 ■ Solve the differential equation.

39. $(3y^2 + 2y)y' = x\cos x$ **40.** $\dfrac{dx}{dt} = 1 - t + x - tx$

■ ■ ■ ■ ■ ■ ■ ■ ■ ■ ■ ■

41–42 ■ Solve the initial-value problem.

41. $\dfrac{dr}{dt} + 2tr = r, \quad r(0) = 5$

42. $(1 + \cos x)y' = (1 + e^{-y})\sin x, \quad y(0) = 0$

■ ■ ■ ■ ■ ■ ■ ■ ■ ■ ■ ■

43. (a) Sketch a direction field for the differential equation $y' = x/y$. Then use it to sketch the four solutions that satisfy the initial conditions $y(0) = 1$, $y(0) = -1$, $y(2) = 1$, and $y(-2) = 1$.

(b) Check your work in part (a) by solving the differential equation explicitly. What type of curve is each solution curve?

44. Let $\mathcal{R}_1$ be the region bounded by $y = x^2$, $y = 0$, and $x = b$, where $b > 0$. Let $\mathcal{R}_2$ be the region bounded by $y = x^2$, $x = 0$, and $y = b^2$.

(a) Is there a value of b such that $\mathcal{R}_1$ and $\mathcal{R}_2$ have the same area?

(b) Is there a value of b such that $\mathcal{R}_1$ sweeps out the same volume when rotated about the x-axis and the y-axis?

(c) Is there a value of b such that $\mathcal{R}_1$ and $\mathcal{R}_2$ sweep out the same volume when rotated about the x-axis?

(d) Is there a value of b such that $\mathcal{R}_1$ and $\mathcal{R}_2$ sweep out the same volume when rotated about the y-axis?

8 SERIES

Infinite series are sums of infinitely many terms. (One of our aims in this chapter is to define exactly what is meant by an infinite sum.) Their importance in calculus stems from Newton's idea of representing functions as sums of infinite series. For instance, in finding areas he often integrated a function by first expressing it as a series and then integrating each term of the series. We will pursue his idea in Section 8.7 in order to integrate such functions as e^{-x^2}. (Recall that we have previously been unable to do this.) Many of the functions that arise in mathematical physics and chemistry, such as Bessel functions, are defined as sums of series, so it is important to be familiar with the basic concepts of convergence of infinite sequences and series.

Physicists also use series in another way, as we will see in Section 8.8. In studying fields as diverse as optics, special relativity, and electromagnetism, they analyze phenomena by replacing a function with the first few terms in the series that represents it.

8.1 SEQUENCES

A **sequence** can be thought of as a list of numbers written in a definite order:

$$a_1, \ a_2, \ a_3, \ a_4, \ \ldots, \ a_n, \ldots$$

The number a_1 is called the *first term*, a_2 is the *second term*, and in general a_n is the *nth term*. We will deal exclusively with infinite sequences and so each term a_n will have a successor a_{n+1}.

Notice that for every positive integer n there is a corresponding number a_n and so a sequence can be defined as a function whose domain is the set of positive integers. But we usually write a_n instead of the function notation $f(n)$ for the value of the function at the number n.

NOTATION The sequence $\{a_1, a_2, a_3, \ldots\}$ is also denoted by

$$\{a_n\} \qquad \text{or} \qquad \{a_n\}_{n=1}^{\infty}$$

EXAMPLE 1 Some sequences can be defined by giving a formula for the nth term. In the following examples we give three descriptions of the sequence: one by using the preceding notation, another by using the defining formula, and a third by writing out the terms of the sequence. Notice that n doesn't have to start at 1.

(a) $\left\{ \dfrac{n}{n+1} \right\}_{n=1}^{\infty}$ $\qquad a_n = \dfrac{n}{n+1}$ $\qquad \left\{ \dfrac{1}{2}, \dfrac{2}{3}, \dfrac{3}{4}, \dfrac{4}{5}, \ldots, \dfrac{n}{n+1}, \ldots \right\}$

(b) $\left\{ \dfrac{(-1)^n(n+1)}{3^n} \right\}$ $\qquad a_n = \dfrac{(-1)^n(n+1)}{3^n}$ $\qquad \left\{ -\dfrac{2}{3}, \dfrac{3}{9}, -\dfrac{4}{27}, \dfrac{5}{81}, \ldots, \dfrac{(-1)^n(n+1)}{3^n}, \ldots \right\}$

(c) $\left\{ \sqrt{n-3} \right\}_{n=3}^{\infty}$ $\qquad a_n = \sqrt{n-3}, \ n \geqslant 3$ $\qquad \{0, 1, \sqrt{2}, \sqrt{3}, \ldots, \sqrt{n-3}, \ldots\}$

(d) $\left\{ \cos \dfrac{n\pi}{6} \right\}_{n=0}^{\infty}$ $\qquad a_n = \cos \dfrac{n\pi}{6}, \ n \geqslant 0$ $\qquad \left\{ 1, \dfrac{\sqrt{3}}{2}, \dfrac{1}{2}, 0, \ldots, \cos \dfrac{n\pi}{6}, \ldots \right\}$ ∎

▼ EXAMPLE 2 Find a formula for the general term a_n of the sequence

$$\left\{ \frac{3}{5}, -\frac{4}{25}, \frac{5}{125}, -\frac{6}{625}, \frac{7}{3125}, \ldots \right\}$$

assuming that the pattern of the first few terms continues.

SOLUTION We are given that

$$a_1 = \frac{3}{5} \qquad a_2 = -\frac{4}{25} \qquad a_3 = \frac{5}{125} \qquad a_4 = -\frac{6}{625} \qquad a_5 = \frac{7}{3125}$$

Notice that the numerators of these fractions start with 3 and increase by 1 whenever we go to the next term. The second term has numerator 4, the third term has numerator 5; in general, the nth term will have numerator $n + 2$. The denominators are the powers of 5, so a_n has denominator 5^n. The signs of the terms are alternately positive and negative, so we need to multiply by a power of -1. In Example 1(b) the factor $(-1)^n$ meant we started with a negative term. Here we want to start with a positive term and so we use $(-1)^{n-1}$ or $(-1)^{n+1}$. Therefore,

$$a_n = (-1)^{n-1} \frac{n+2}{5^n} \qquad\qquad ■$$

EXAMPLE 3 Here are some sequences that don't have a simple defining equation.

(a) The sequence $\{p_n\}$, where p_n is the population of the world as of January 1 in the year n.

(b) If we let a_n be the digit in the nth decimal place of the number e, then $\{a_n\}$ is a well-defined sequence whose first few terms are

$$\{7, 1, 8, 2, 8, 1, 8, 2, 8, 4, 5, \ldots\}$$

(c) The **Fibonacci sequence** $\{f_n\}$ is defined recursively by the conditions

$$f_1 = 1 \qquad f_2 = 1 \qquad f_n = f_{n-1} + f_{n-2} \qquad n \geq 3$$

Each term is the sum of the two preceding terms. The first few terms are

$$\{1, 1, 2, 3, 5, 8, 13, 21, \ldots\}$$

This sequence arose when the 13th-century Italian mathematician known as Fibonacci solved a problem concerning the breeding of rabbits (see Exercise 41).   ■

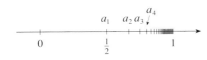

FIGURE 1

A sequence such as the one in Example 1(a), $a_n = n/(n + 1)$, can be pictured either by plotting its terms on a number line as in Figure 1 or by plotting its graph as in Figure 2. Note that, since a sequence is a function whose domain is the set of positive integers, its graph consists of isolated points with coordinates

$$(1, a_1) \qquad (2, a_2) \qquad (3, a_3) \qquad \ldots \qquad (n, a_n) \qquad \ldots$$

From Figure 1 or 2 it appears that the terms of the sequence $a_n = n/(n + 1)$ are approaching 1 as n becomes large. In fact, the difference

$$1 - \frac{n}{n+1} = \frac{1}{n+1}$$

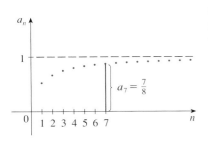

FIGURE 2

can be made as small as we like by taking n sufficiently large. We indicate this by writing

$$\lim_{n \to \infty} \frac{n}{n + 1} = 1$$

In general, the notation

$$\lim_{n \to \infty} a_n = L$$

means that the terms of the sequence $\{a_n\}$ approach L as n becomes large. Notice that the following definition of the limit of a sequence is very similar to the definition of a limit of a function at infinity given in Section 1.6.

---

1 DEFINITION A sequence $\{a_n\}$ has the **limit** L and we write

$$\lim_{n \to \infty} a_n = L \qquad \text{or} \qquad a_n \to L \text{ as } n \to \infty$$

if we can make the terms a_n as close to L as we like by taking n sufficiently large. If $\lim_{n \to \infty} a_n$ exists, we say the sequence **converges** (or is **convergent**). Otherwise, we say the sequence **diverges** (or is **divergent**).

Figure 3 illustrates Definition 1 by showing the graphs of two sequences that have the limit L.

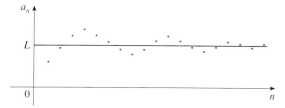

FIGURE 3
Graphs of two sequences with $\lim_{n \to \infty} a_n = L$

A more precise version of Definition 1 is as follows.

---

2 DEFINITION A sequence $\{a_n\}$ has the **limit** L and we write

$$\lim_{n \to \infty} a_n = L \qquad \text{or} \qquad a_n \to L \text{ as } n \to \infty$$

■ Compare this definition with Definition 1.6.7.

if for every $\varepsilon > 0$ there is a corresponding integer N such that

$$\text{if} \quad n > N \quad \text{then} \quad |a_n - L| < \varepsilon$$

Definition 2 is illustrated by Figure 4, in which the terms $a_1, a_2, a_3, \ldots$ are plotted on a number line. No matter how small an interval $(L - \varepsilon, L + \varepsilon)$ is chosen, there exists an N such that all terms of the sequence from a_{N+1} onward must lie in that interval.

FIGURE 4

Another illustration of Definition 2 is given in Figure 5. The points on the graph of $\{a_n\}$ must lie between the horizontal lines $y = L + \varepsilon$ and $y = L - \varepsilon$ if $n > N$. This picture must be valid no matter how small ε is chosen, but usually a smaller ε requires a larger N.

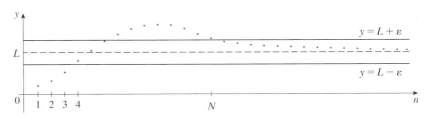

FIGURE 5

If you compare Definition 2 with Definition 1.6.7, you will see that the only difference between $\lim_{n \to \infty} a_n = L$ and $\lim_{x \to \infty} f(x) = L$ is that n is required to be an integer. Thus we have the following theorem, which is illustrated by Figure 6.

3 THEOREM If $\lim_{x \to \infty} f(x) = L$ and $f(n) = a_n$ when n is an integer, then $\lim_{n \to \infty} a_n = L$.

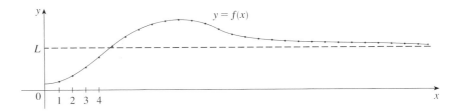

FIGURE 6

In particular, since we know that $\lim_{x \to \infty} (1/x^r) = 0$ when $r > 0$, we have

$$\boxed{4} \qquad \lim_{n \to \infty} \frac{1}{n^r} = 0 \qquad \text{if } r > 0$$

If a_n becomes large as n becomes large, we use the notation $\lim_{n \to \infty} a_n = \infty$. The following precise definition is similar to Definition 1.6.8.

5 DEFINITION $\lim_{n \to \infty} a_n = \infty$ means that for every positive number M there is an integer N such that

$$\text{if} \quad n > N \quad \text{then} \quad a_n > M$$

If $\lim_{n \to \infty} a_n = \infty$, then the sequence $\{a_n\}$ is divergent but in a special way. We say that $\{a_n\}$ diverges to ∞.

The Limit Laws given in Section 1.4 also hold for the limits of sequences and their proofs are similar.

Limit Laws for Sequences

If $\{a_n\}$ and $\{b_n\}$ are convergent sequences and c is a constant, then

$$\lim_{n \to \infty} (a_n + b_n) = \lim_{n \to \infty} a_n + \lim_{n \to \infty} b_n$$

$$\lim_{n \to \infty} (a_n - b_n) = \lim_{n \to \infty} a_n - \lim_{n \to \infty} b_n$$

$$\lim_{n \to \infty} ca_n = c \lim_{n \to \infty} a_n \qquad\qquad \lim_{n \to \infty} c = c$$

$$\lim_{n \to \infty} (a_n b_n) = \lim_{n \to \infty} a_n \cdot \lim_{n \to \infty} b_n$$

$$\lim_{n \to \infty} \frac{a_n}{b_n} = \frac{\lim\limits_{n \to \infty} a_n}{\lim\limits_{n \to \infty} b_n} \quad \text{if } \lim_{n \to \infty} b_n \neq 0$$

$$\lim_{n \to \infty} a_n^p = \left[\lim_{n \to \infty} a_n \right]^p \quad \text{if } p > 0 \text{ and } a_n > 0$$

The Squeeze Theorem can also be adapted for sequences as follows (see Figure 7).

Squeeze Theorem for Sequences

If $a_n \leq b_n \leq c_n$ for $n \geq n_0$ and $\lim\limits_{n \to \infty} a_n = \lim\limits_{n \to \infty} c_n = L$, then $\lim\limits_{n \to \infty} b_n = L$.

Another useful fact about limits of sequences is given by the following theorem, whose proof is left as Exercise 45.

6 THEOREM   If $\lim\limits_{n \to \infty} |a_n| = 0$, then $\lim\limits_{n \to \infty} a_n = 0$.

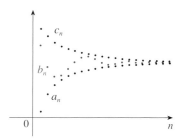

FIGURE 7

The sequence $\{b_n\}$ is squeezed between the sequences $\{a_n\}$ and $\{c_n\}$.

EXAMPLE 4 Find $\lim\limits_{n \to \infty} \dfrac{n}{n + 1}$.

SOLUTION The method is similar to the one we used in Section 1.6: Divide numerator and denominator by the highest power of n that occurs in the denominator and then use the Limit Laws.

$$\lim_{n \to \infty} \frac{n}{n + 1} = \lim_{n \to \infty} \frac{1}{1 + \dfrac{1}{n}} = \frac{\lim\limits_{n \to \infty} 1}{\lim\limits_{n \to \infty} 1 + \lim\limits_{n \to \infty} \dfrac{1}{n}}$$

$$= \frac{1}{1 + 0} = 1$$

■ This shows that the guess we made earlier from Figures 1 and 2 was correct.

Here we used Equation 4 with $r = 1$.

EXAMPLE 5 Calculate $\lim\limits_{n \to \infty} \dfrac{\ln n}{n}$.

SOLUTION Notice that both numerator and denominator approach infinity as $n \to \infty$. We can't apply l'Hospital's Rule directly because it applies not to sequences but to functions of a real variable. However, we can apply l'Hospital's Rule to the related function $f(x) = (\ln x)/x$ and obtain

$$\lim_{x \to \infty} \frac{\ln x}{x} = \lim_{x \to \infty} \frac{1/x}{1} = 0$$

Therefore, by Theorem 3 we have

$$\lim_{n \to \infty} \frac{\ln n}{n} = 0 \qquad \blacksquare$$

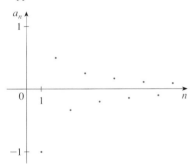

FIGURE 8

EXAMPLE 6 Determine whether the sequence $a_n = (-1)^n$ is convergent or divergent.

SOLUTION If we write out the terms of the sequence, we obtain

$$\{-1, 1, -1, 1, -1, 1, -1, \ldots\}$$

The graph of this sequence is shown in Figure 8. Since the terms oscillate between 1 and -1 infinitely often, a_n does not approach any number. Thus, $\lim_{n \to \infty} (-1)^n$ does not exist; that is, the sequence $\{(-1)^n\}$ is divergent. ■

■ The graph of the sequence in Example 7 is shown in Figure 9 and supports the answer.

EXAMPLE 7 Evaluate $\lim_{n \to \infty} \dfrac{(-1)^n}{n}$ if it exists.

SOLUTION

$$\lim_{n \to \infty} \left| \frac{(-1)^n}{n} \right| = \lim_{n \to \infty} \frac{1}{n} = 0$$

Therefore, by Theorem 6,

$$\lim_{n \to \infty} \frac{(-1)^n}{n} = 0 \qquad \blacksquare$$

FIGURE 9

V EXAMPLE 8 Discuss the convergence of the sequence $a_n = n!/n^n$, where $n! = 1 \cdot 2 \cdot 3 \cdot \cdots \cdot n$.

SOLUTION Both numerator and denominator approach infinity as $n \to \infty$ but here we have no corresponding function for use with l'Hospital's Rule ($x!$ is not defined when x is not an integer). Let's write out a few terms to get a feeling for what happens to a_n as n gets large:

$$a_1 = 1 \qquad a_2 = \frac{1 \cdot 2}{2 \cdot 2} \qquad a_3 = \frac{1 \cdot 2 \cdot 3}{3 \cdot 3 \cdot 3}$$

7

$$a_n = \frac{1 \cdot 2 \cdot 3 \cdot \cdots \cdot n}{n \cdot n \cdot n \cdot \cdots \cdot n}$$

It appears from these expressions and the graph in Figure 10 that the terms are decreasing and perhaps approach 0. To confirm this, observe from Equation 7 that

▪ **CREATING GRAPHS OF SEQUENCES**
Some computer algebra systems have special commands that enable us to create sequences and graph them directly. With most graphing calculators, however, sequences can be graphed by using parametric equations. For instance, the sequence in Example 8 can be graphed by entering the parametric equations

$$x = t \qquad y = t!/t^t$$

and graphing in dot mode starting with $t = 1$, setting the t-step equal to 1. The result is shown in Figure 10.

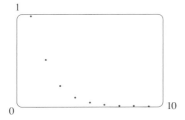

FIGURE 10

Notice that the expression in parentheses is at most 1 because the numerator is less than (or equal to) the denominator. So

$$0 < a_n \leq \frac{1}{n}$$

We know that $1/n \to 0$ as $n \to \infty$. Therefore, $a_n \to 0$ as $n \to \infty$ by the Squeeze Theorem. ∎

☑ **EXAMPLE 9** For what values of r is the sequence $\{r^n\}$ convergent?

SOLUTION We know from Section 1.6 and the graphs of the exponential functions in Section 3.1 that $\lim_{x \to \infty} a^x = \infty$ for $a > 1$ and $\lim_{x \to \infty} a^x = 0$ for $0 < a < 1$. Therefore, putting $a = r$ and using Theorem 3, we have

$$\lim_{n \to \infty} r^n = \begin{cases} \infty & \text{if } r > 1 \\ 0 & \text{if } 0 < r < 1 \end{cases}$$

For the cases $r = 1$ and $r = 0$ we have

$$\lim_{n \to \infty} 1^n = \lim_{n \to \infty} 1 = 1 \qquad \text{and} \qquad \lim_{n \to \infty} 0^n = \lim_{n \to \infty} 0 = 0$$

If $-1 < r < 0$, then $0 < |r| < 1$, so

$$\lim_{n \to \infty} |r^n| = \lim_{n \to \infty} |r|^n = 0$$

and therefore $\lim_{n \to \infty} r^n = 0$ by Theorem 6. If $r \leq -1$, then $\{r^n\}$ diverges as in Example 6. Figure 11 shows the graphs for various values of r. (The case $r = -1$ is shown in Figure 8.)

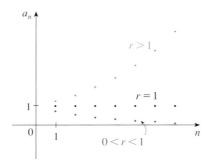
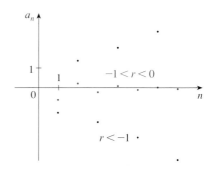

FIGURE 11
The sequence $a_n = r^n$

∎

The results of Example 9 are summarized for future use as follows.

> **8** The sequence $\{r^n\}$ is convergent if $-1 < r \leq 1$ and divergent for all other values of r.
>
> $$\lim_{n \to \infty} r^n = \begin{cases} 0 & \text{if } -1 < r < 1 \\ 1 & \text{if } r = 1 \end{cases}$$

> **9 DEFINITION** A sequence $\{a_n\}$ is called **increasing** if $a_n < a_{n+1}$ for all $n \geq 1$, that is, $a_1 < a_2 < a_3 < \cdots$. It is called **decreasing** if $a_n > a_{n+1}$ for all $n \geq 1$. A sequence is **monotonic** if it is either increasing or decreasing.

EXAMPLE 10 The sequence $\left\{ \dfrac{3}{n+5} \right\}$ is decreasing because

▪ The right side is smaller because it has a larger denominator.

$$\frac{3}{n+5} > \frac{3}{(n+1)+5} = \frac{3}{n+6}$$

and so $a_n > a_{n+1}$ for all $n \geq 1$. ▪

EXAMPLE 11 Show that the sequence $a_n = \dfrac{n}{n^2+1}$ is decreasing.

SOLUTION We must show that $a_{n+1} < a_n$, that is,

$$\frac{n+1}{(n+1)^2+1} < \frac{n}{n^2+1}$$

▪ Another way to do Example 11 is to show that the function

$$f(x) = \frac{x}{x^2+1} \qquad x \geq 1$$

is decreasing because $f'(x) < 0$ for $x > 1$.

This inequality is equivalent to the one we get by cross-multiplication:

$$\frac{n+1}{(n+1)^2+1} < \frac{n}{n^2+1} \quad \Longleftrightarrow \quad (n+1)(n^2+1) < n[(n+1)^2+1]$$

$$\Longleftrightarrow \quad n^3 + n^2 + n + 1 < n^3 + 2n^2 + 2n$$

$$\Longleftrightarrow \quad 1 < n^2 + n$$

Since $n \geq 1$, we know that the inequality $n^2 + n > 1$ is true. Therefore, $a_{n+1} < a_n$ and so $\{a_n\}$ is decreasing. ▪

> **10 DEFINITION** A sequence $\{a_n\}$ is **bounded above** if there is a number M such that
> $$a_n \leq M \qquad \text{for all } n \geq 1$$
> It is **bounded below** if there is a number m such that
> $$m \leq a_n \qquad \text{for all } n \geq 1$$
> If it is bounded above and below, then $\{a_n\}$ is a **bounded sequence**.

For instance, the sequence $a_n = n$ is bounded below $(a_n > 0)$ but not above. The sequence $a_n = n/(n+1)$ is bounded because $0 < a_n < 1$ for all n.

We know that not every bounded sequence is convergent [for instance, the sequence $a_n = (-1)^n$ satisfies $-1 \leq a_n \leq 1$ but is divergent from Example 6] and not every monotonic sequence is convergent $(a_n = n \rightarrow \infty)$. But if a sequence is

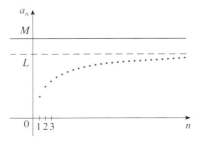

FIGURE 12

both bounded *and* monotonic, then it must be convergent. This fact is proved as Theorem 11, but intuitively you can understand why it is true by looking at Figure 12. If $\{a_n\}$ is increasing and $a_n \leq M$ for all n, then the terms are forced to crowd together and approach some number L.

The proof of Theorem 11 is based on the **Completeness Axiom** for the set $\mathbb{R}$ of real numbers, which says that if S is a nonempty set of real numbers that has an upper bound M ($x \leq M$ for all x in S), then S has a **least upper bound** b. (This means that b is an upper bound for S, but if M is any other upper bound, then $b \leq M$.) The Completeness Axiom is an expression of the fact that there is no gap or hole in the real number line.

> **11 MONOTONIC SEQUENCE THEOREM** Every bounded, monotonic sequence is convergent.

PROOF Suppose $\{a_n\}$ is an increasing sequence. Since $\{a_n\}$ is bounded, the set $S = \{a_n \mid n \geq 1\}$ has an upper bound. By the Completeness Axiom it has a least upper bound L. Given $\varepsilon > 0$, $L - \varepsilon$ is *not* an upper bound for S (since L is the *least* upper bound). Therefore

$$a_N > L - \varepsilon \qquad \text{for some integer } N$$

But the sequence is increasing so $a_n \geq a_N$ for every $n > N$. Thus if $n > N$ we have

$$a_n > L - \varepsilon$$

so

$$0 \leq L - a_n < \varepsilon$$

since $a_n \leq L$. Thus

$$|L - a_n| < \varepsilon \qquad \text{whenever } n > N$$

so $\lim_{n \to \infty} a_n = L$.

A similar proof (using the greatest lower bound) works if $\{a_n\}$ is decreasing. ☐

The proof of Theorem 11 shows that a sequence that is increasing and bounded above is convergent. (Likewise, a decreasing sequence that is bounded below is convergent.) This fact is used many times in dealing with infinite series in Sections 8.2 and 8.3.

Another use of Theorem 11 is indicated in Exercises 38–40.

| **8.1** | **EXERCISES** |

1. (a) What is a sequence?
  (b) What does it mean to say that $\lim_{n \to \infty} a_n = 8$?
  (c) What does it mean to say that $\lim_{n \to \infty} a_n = \infty$?

2. (a) What is a convergent sequence? Give two examples.
  (b) What is a divergent sequence? Give two examples.

3. List the first six terms of the sequence defined by

$$a_n = \frac{n}{2n + 1}$$

Does the sequence appear to have a limit? If so, find it.

4. List the first nine terms of the sequence $\{\cos(n\pi/3)\}$. Does this sequence appear to have a limit? If so, find it. If not, explain why.

5–8 ■ Find a formula for the general term a_n of the sequence, assuming that the pattern of the first few terms continues.

5. $\left\{1, -\frac{2}{3}, \frac{4}{9}, -\frac{8}{27}, \ldots\right\}$

6. $\left\{-\frac{1}{4}, \frac{2}{9}, -\frac{3}{16}, \frac{4}{25}, \ldots\right\}$

7. $\{2, 7, 12, 17, \ldots\}$

8. $\{5, 1, 5, 1, 5, 1, \ldots\}$

■   ■   ■   ■   ■   ■   ■   ■   ■   ■   ■   ■   ■   ■

9–28 ■ Determine whether the sequence converges or diverges. If it converges, find the limit.

9. $a_n = \dfrac{3 + 5n^2}{n + n^2}$

10. $a_n = \dfrac{n + 1}{3n - 1}$

11. $a_n = \dfrac{2^n}{3^{n+1}}$

12. $a_n = \dfrac{\sqrt{n}}{1 + \sqrt{n}}$

13. $a_n = \dfrac{(n + 2)!}{n!}$

14. $a_n = \dfrac{n}{1 + \sqrt{n}}$

15. $a_n = \dfrac{(-1)^{n-1}n}{n^2 + 1}$

16. $a_n = \dfrac{(-1)^n n^3}{n^3 + 2n^2 + 1}$

17. $\left\{\dfrac{e^n + e^{-n}}{e^{2n} - 1}\right\}$

18. $a_n = \cos(2/n)$

19. $\{n^2 e^{-n}\}$

20. $\{\arctan 2n\}$

21. $a_n = \dfrac{\cos^2 n}{2^n}$

22. $\{n \cos n\pi\}$

23. $a_n = \left(1 + \dfrac{2}{n}\right)^n$

24. $a_n = \dfrac{\sin 2n}{1 + \sqrt{n}}$

25. $\{0, 1, 0, 0, 1, 0, 0, 0, 1, \ldots\}$

26. $a_n = \dfrac{(\ln n)^2}{n}$

27. $a_n = \ln(2n^2 + 1) - \ln(n^2 + 1)$

28. $a_n = \dfrac{(-3)^n}{n!}$

■   ■   ■   ■   ■   ■   ■   ■   ■   ■   ■   ■   ■   ■

29. If \$1000 is invested at 6% interest, compounded annually, then after n years the investment is worth $a_n = 1000(1.06)^n$ dollars.
(a) Find the first five terms of the sequence $\{a_n\}$.
(b) Is the sequence convergent or divergent? Explain.

30. Find the first 40 terms of the sequence defined by

$$a_{n+1} = \begin{cases} \frac{1}{2}a_n & \text{if } a_n \text{ is an even number} \\ 3a_n + 1 & \text{if } a_n \text{ is an odd number} \end{cases}$$

and $a_1 = 11$. Do the same if $a_1 = 25$. Make a conjecture about this type of sequence.

31. Suppose you know that $\{a_n\}$ is a decreasing sequence and all its terms lie between the numbers 5 and 8. Explain why the sequence has a limit. What can you say about the value of the limit?

32. (a) If $\{a_n\}$ is convergent, show that

$$\lim_{n \to \infty} a_{n+1} = \lim_{n \to \infty} a_n$$

(b) A sequence $\{a_n\}$ is defined by $a_1 = 1$ and $a_{n+1} = 1/(1 + a_n)$ for $n \geq 1$. Assuming that $\{a_n\}$ is convergent, find its limit.

33–36 ■ Determine whether the sequence is increasing, decreasing, or not monotonic. Is the sequence bounded?

33. $a_n = \dfrac{1}{2n + 3}$

34. $a_n = \dfrac{2n - 3}{3n + 4}$

35. $a_n = \cos(n\pi/2)$

36. $a_n = n + \dfrac{1}{n}$

■   ■   ■   ■   ■   ■   ■   ■   ■   ■   ■   ■   ■   ■

37. Find the limit of the sequence

$$\left\{\sqrt{2}, \sqrt{2\sqrt{2}}, \sqrt{2\sqrt{2\sqrt{2}}}, \ldots\right\}$$

38. A sequence $\{a_n\}$ is given by $a_1 = \sqrt{2}$, $a_{n+1} = \sqrt{2 + a_n}$.
(a) By induction or otherwise, show that $\{a_n\}$ is increasing and bounded above by 3. Apply the Monotonic Sequence Theorem to show that $\lim_{n \to \infty} a_n$ exists.
(b) Find $\lim_{n \to \infty} a_n$.

39. Use induction to show that the sequence defined by $a_1 = 1$, $a_{n+1} = 3 - 1/a_n$ is increasing and $a_n < 3$ for all n. Deduce that $\{a_n\}$ is convergent and find its limit.

40. Show that the sequence defined by

$$a_1 = 2 \qquad a_{n+1} = \dfrac{1}{3 - a_n}$$

satisfies $0 < a_n \leq 2$ and is decreasing. Deduce that the sequence is convergent and find its limit.

41. (a) Fibonacci posed the following problem: Suppose that rabbits live forever and that every month each pair produces a new pair which becomes productive at age 2 months. If we start with one newborn pair, how many pairs of rabbits will we have in the nth month? Show that the answer is f_n, where $\{f_n\}$ is the Fibonacci sequence defined in Example 3(c).
(b) Let $a_n = f_{n+1}/f_n$ and show that $a_{n-1} = 1 + 1/a_{n-2}$. Assuming that $\{a_n\}$ is convergent, find its limit.

42. (a) Let $a_1 = a$, $a_2 = f(a)$, $a_3 = f(a_2) = f(f(a))$, ..., $a_{n+1} = f(a_n)$, where f is a continuous function. If $\lim_{n \to \infty} a_n = L$, show that $f(L) = L$.
(b) Illustrate part (a) by taking $f(x) = \cos x$, $a = 1$, and estimating the value of L to five decimal places.

43. We know that $\lim_{n\to\infty} (0.8)^n = 0$ [from (8) with $r = 0.8$]. Use logarithms to determine how large n has to be so that $(0.8)^n < 0.000001$.

44. Use Definition 2 directly to prove that $\lim_{n\to\infty} r^n = 0$ when $|r| < 1$.

45. Prove Theorem 6.
[*Hint:* Use either Definition 2 or the Squeeze Theorem.]

46. (a) Show that if $\lim_{n\to\infty} a_{2n} = L$ and $\lim_{n\to\infty} a_{2n+1} = L$, then $\{a_n\}$ is convergent and $\lim_{n\to\infty} a_n = L$.
(b) If $a_1 = 1$ and
$$a_{n+1} = 1 + \frac{1}{1 + a_n}$$
find the first eight terms of the sequence $\{a_n\}$. Then use part (a) to show that $\lim_{n\to\infty} a_n = \sqrt{2}$. This gives the **continued fraction expansion**
$$\sqrt{2} = 1 + \cfrac{1}{2 + \cfrac{1}{2 + \cdots}}$$

47. The size of an undisturbed fish population has been modeled by the formula
$$p_{n+1} = \frac{bp_n}{a + p_n}$$
where p_n is the fish population after n years and a and b are positive constants that depend on the species and its environment. Suppose that the population in year 0 is $p_0 > 0$.
(a) Show that if $\{p_n\}$ is convergent, then the only possible values for its limit are 0 and $b - a$.
(b) Show that $p_{n+1} < (b/a)p_n$.
(c) Use part (b) to show that if $a > b$, then $\lim_{n\to\infty} p_n = 0$; in other words, the population dies out.
(d) Now assume that $a < b$. Show that if $p_0 < b - a$, then $\{p_n\}$ is increasing and $0 < p_n < b - a$. Show also that if $p_0 > b - a$, then $\{p_n\}$ is decreasing and $p_n > b - a$. Deduce that if $a < b$, then $\lim_{n\to\infty} p_n = b - a$.

8.2 | SERIES

If we try to add the terms of an infinite sequence $\{a_n\}_{n=1}^{\infty}$ we get an expression of the form

1 $\qquad\qquad a_1 + a_2 + a_3 + \cdots + a_n + \cdots$

which is called an **infinite series** (or just a **series**) and is denoted, for short, by the symbol

$$\sum_{n=1}^{\infty} a_n \qquad \text{or} \qquad \sum a_n$$

But does it make sense to talk about the sum of infinitely many terms?

It would be impossible to find a finite sum for the series

$$1 + 2 + 3 + 4 + 5 + \cdots + n + \cdots$$

because if we start adding the terms we get the cumulative sums 1, 3, 6, 10, 15, 21, . . . and, after the nth term, we get $n(n + 1)/2$, which becomes very large as n increases.

However, if we start to add the terms of the series

$$\frac{1}{2} + \frac{1}{4} + \frac{1}{8} + \frac{1}{16} + \frac{1}{32} + \frac{1}{64} + \cdots + \frac{1}{2^n} + \cdots$$

we get $\frac{1}{2}, \frac{3}{4}, \frac{7}{8}, \frac{15}{16}, \frac{31}{32}, \frac{63}{64}, \ldots, 1 - 1/2^n, \ldots$. The table shows that as we add more and more terms, these *partial sums* become closer and closer to 1. In fact, by adding sufficiently many terms of the series we can make the partial sums as close as we like to 1. So it seems reasonable to say that the sum of this infinite series is 1 and to write

$$\sum_{n=1}^{\infty} \frac{1}{2^n} = \frac{1}{2} + \frac{1}{4} + \frac{1}{8} + \frac{1}{16} + \cdots + \frac{1}{2^n} + \cdots = 1$$

n	Sum of first n terms
1	0.50000000
2	0.75000000
3	0.87500000
4	0.93750000
5	0.96875000
6	0.98437500
7	0.99218750
10	0.99902344
15	0.99996948
20	0.99999905
25	0.99999997

We use a similar idea to determine whether or not a general series (1) has a sum. We consider the **partial sums**

$$s_1 = a_1$$

$$s_2 = a_1 + a_2$$

$$s_3 = a_1 + a_2 + a_3$$

$$s_4 = a_1 + a_2 + a_3 + a_4$$

and, in general,

$$s_n = a_1 + a_2 + a_3 + \cdots + a_n = \sum_{i=1}^{n} a_i$$

These partial sums form a new sequence $\{s_n\}$, which may or may not have a limit. If $\lim_{n \to \infty} s_n = s$ exists (as a finite number), then, as in the preceding example, we call it the sum of the infinite series $\Sigma\, a_n$.

---

2 DEFINITION Given a series $\sum_{n=1}^{\infty} a_n = a_1 + a_2 + a_3 + \cdots$, let s_n denote its nth partial sum:

$$s_n = \sum_{i=1}^{n} a_i = a_1 + a_2 + \cdots + a_n$$

If the sequence $\{s_n\}$ is convergent and $\lim_{n \to \infty} s_n = s$ exists as a real number, then the series $\Sigma\, a_n$ is called **convergent** and we write

$$a_1 + a_2 + \cdots + a_n + \cdots = s \qquad \text{or} \qquad \sum_{n=1}^{\infty} a_n = s$$

The number s is called the **sum** of the series. If the sequence $\{s_n\}$ is divergent, then the series is called **divergent**.

▪ Compare with the improper integral

$$\int_{1}^{\infty} f(x)\, dx = \lim_{t \to \infty} \int_{1}^{t} f(x)\, dx$$

To find this integral we integrate from 1 to t and then let $t \to \infty$. For a series, we sum from 1 to n and then let $n \to \infty$.

Thus the sum of a series is the limit of the sequence of partial sums. So when we write $\sum_{n=1}^{\infty} a_n = s$ we mean that by adding sufficiently many terms of the series we can get as close as we like to the number s. Notice that

$$\sum_{n=1}^{\infty} a_n = \lim_{n \to \infty} \sum_{i=1}^{n} a_i$$

EXAMPLE 1 An important example of an infinite series is the **geometric series**

$$a + ar + ar^2 + ar^3 + \cdots + ar^{n-1} + \cdots = \sum_{n=1}^{\infty} ar^{n-1} \qquad a \neq 0$$

Each term is obtained from the preceding one by multiplying it by the **common ratio** r. (We have already considered the special case where $a = \frac{1}{2}$ and $r = \frac{1}{2}$ on page 420.)

If $r = 1$, then $s_n = a + a + \cdots + a = na \to \pm\infty$. Since $\lim_{n \to \infty} s_n$ doesn't exist, the geometric series diverges in this case.

If $r \neq 1$, we have

$$s_n = a + ar + ar^2 + \cdots + ar^{n-1}$$

and

$$rs_n = \qquad ar + ar^2 + \cdots + ar^{n-1} + ar^{n}$$

■ Figure 1 provides a geometric demonstration of the result in Example 1. If the triangles are constructed as shown and s is the sum of the series, then, by similar triangles,

$$\frac{s}{a} = \frac{a}{a - ar} \qquad \text{so} \qquad s = \frac{a}{1 - r}$$

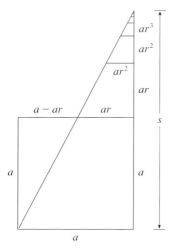

FIGURE I

■ In words: The sum of a convergent geometric series is

$$\frac{\text{first term}}{1 - \text{common ratio}}$$

Subtracting these equations, we get

$$s_n - rs_n = a - ar^n$$

3 $$s_n = \frac{a(1 - r^n)}{1 - r}$$

If $-1 < r < 1$, we know from (8.1.8) that $r^n \to 0$ as $n \to \infty$, so

$$\lim_{n \to \infty} s_n = \lim_{n \to \infty} \frac{a(1 - r^n)}{1 - r} = \frac{a}{1 - r} - \frac{a}{1 - r} \lim_{n \to \infty} r^n = \frac{a}{1 - r}$$

Thus when $|r| < 1$ the geometric series is convergent and its sum is $a/(1 - r)$.

If $r \leq -1$ or $r > 1$, the sequence $\{r^n\}$ is divergent by (8.1.8) and so, by Equation 3, $\lim_{n \to \infty} s_n$ does not exist. Therefore, the geometric series diverges in those cases. ■

We summarize the results of Example 1 as follows.

---

4 The geometric series

$$\sum_{n=1}^{\infty} ar^{n-1} = a + ar + ar^2 + \cdots$$

is convergent if $|r| < 1$ and its sum is

$$\sum_{n=1}^{\infty} ar^{n-1} = \frac{a}{1 - r} \qquad |r| < 1$$

If $|r| \geq 1$, the geometric series is divergent.

V EXAMPLE 2 Find the sum of the geometric series

$$5 - \frac{10}{3} + \frac{20}{9} - \frac{40}{27} + \cdots$$

SOLUTION The first term is $a = 5$ and the common ratio is $r = -\frac{2}{3}$. Since $|r| = \frac{2}{3} < 1$, the series is convergent by (4) and its sum is

$$5 - \frac{10}{3} + \frac{20}{9} - \frac{40}{27} + \cdots = \frac{5}{1 - \left(-\frac{2}{3}\right)} = \frac{5}{\frac{5}{3}} = 3 \qquad ■$$

■ What do we really mean when we say that the sum of the series in Example 2 is 3? Of course, we can't literally add an infinite number of terms, one by one. But, according to Definition 2, the total sum is the limit of the sequence of partial sums. So, by taking the sum of sufficiently many terms, we can get as close as we like to the number 3. The table shows the first ten partial sums s_n and the graph in Figure 2 shows how the sequence of partial sums approaches 3.

n	s_n
1	5.000000
2	1.666667
3	3.888889
4	2.407407
5	3.395062
6	2.736626
7	3.175583
8	2.882945
9	3.078037
10	2.947975

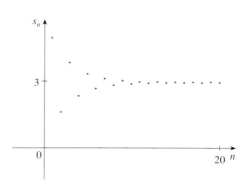

FIGURE 2

EXAMPLE 3 Is the series $\sum_{n=1}^{\infty} 2^{2n}3^{1-n}$ convergent or divergent?

SOLUTION Let's rewrite the nth term of the series in the form ar^{n-1}:

$$\sum_{n=1}^{\infty} 2^{2n}3^{1-n} = \sum_{n=1}^{\infty} (2^2)^n 3^{-(n-1)} = \sum_{n=1}^{\infty} \frac{4^n}{3^{n-1}} = \sum_{n=1}^{\infty} 4\left(\tfrac{4}{3}\right)^{n-1}$$

We recognize this series as a geometric series with $a = 4$ and $r = \frac{4}{3}$. Since $r > 1$, the series diverges by (4). ▪

■ Another way to identify a and r is to write out the first few terms:
$$4 + \tfrac{16}{3} + \tfrac{64}{9} + \cdots$$

V EXAMPLE 4 Write the number $2.3\overline{17} = 2.3171717\ldots$ as a ratio of integers.

SOLUTION

$$2.3171717\ldots = 2.3 + \frac{17}{10^3} + \frac{17}{10^5} + \frac{17}{10^7} + \cdots$$

After the first term we have a geometric series with $a = 17/10^3$ and $r = 1/10^2$. Therefore

$$2.3\overline{17} = 2.3 + \frac{\dfrac{17}{10^3}}{1 - \dfrac{1}{10^2}} = 2.3 + \frac{\dfrac{17}{1000}}{\dfrac{99}{100}}$$

$$= \frac{23}{10} + \frac{17}{990} = \frac{1147}{495}$$ ▪

Module 8.2 explores a series that depends on an angle θ in a triangle and enables you to see how rapidly the series converges when θ varies.

EXAMPLE 5 Find the sum of the series $\sum_{n=0}^{\infty} x^n$, where $|x| < 1$.

SOLUTION Notice that this series starts with $n = 0$ and so the first term is $x^0 = 1$. (With series, we adopt the convention that $x^0 = 1$ even when $x = 0$.) Thus

$$\sum_{n=0}^{\infty} x^n = 1 + x + x^2 + x^3 + x^4 + \cdots$$

This is a geometric series with $a = 1$ and $r = x$. Since $|r| = |x| < 1$, it converges and (4) gives

5
$$\sum_{n=0}^{\infty} x^n = \frac{1}{1 - x}$$ ▪

EXAMPLE 6 Show that the series $\sum_{n=1}^{\infty} \frac{1}{n(n + 1)}$ is convergent, and find its sum.

SOLUTION This is not a geometric series, so we go back to the definition of a convergent series and compute the partial sums.

$$s_n = \sum_{i=1}^{n} \frac{1}{i(i + 1)} = \frac{1}{1 \cdot 2} + \frac{1}{2 \cdot 3} + \frac{1}{3 \cdot 4} + \cdots + \frac{1}{n(n + 1)}$$

We can simplify this expression if we use the partial fraction decomposition

$$\frac{1}{i(i + 1)} = \frac{1}{i} - \frac{1}{i + 1}$$

(see Section 6.3). Thus we have

$$s_n = \sum_{i=1}^{n} \frac{1}{i(i+1)} = \sum_{i=1}^{n} \left(\frac{1}{i} - \frac{1}{i+1} \right)$$

$$= \left(1 - \frac{1}{2} \right) + \left(\frac{1}{2} - \frac{1}{3} \right) + \left(\frac{1}{3} - \frac{1}{4} \right) + \cdots + \left(\frac{1}{n} - \frac{1}{n+1} \right)$$

$$= 1 - \frac{1}{n+1}$$

▪ Notice that the terms cancel in pairs. This is an example of a **telescoping sum:** Because of all the cancellations, the sum collapses (like a pirate's collapsing telescope) into just two terms.

and so
$$\lim_{n \to \infty} s_n = \lim_{n \to \infty} \left(1 - \frac{1}{n+1} \right) = 1 - 0 = 1$$

Therefore, the given series is convergent and

$$\sum_{n=1}^{\infty} \frac{1}{n(n+1)} = 1$$

▪ Figure 3 illustrates Example 6 by showing the graphs of the sequence of terms $a_n = 1/[n(n+1)]$ and the sequence $\{s_n\}$ of partial sums. Notice that $a_n \to 0$ and $s_n \to 1$. See Exercises 36 and 37 for two geometric interpretations of Example 6.

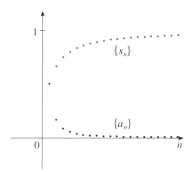

FIGURE 3

☑ **EXAMPLE 7** Show that the **harmonic series**

$$\sum_{n=1}^{\infty} \frac{1}{n} = 1 + \frac{1}{2} + \frac{1}{3} + \frac{1}{4} + \cdots$$

is divergent.

SOLUTION For this particular series it's convenient to consider the partial sums s_2, s_4, s_8, s_{16}, s_{32}, . . . and show that they become large.

$$s_2 = 1 + \tfrac{1}{2}$$

$$s_4 = 1 + \tfrac{1}{2} + \left(\tfrac{1}{3} + \tfrac{1}{4} \right) > 1 + \tfrac{1}{2} + \left(\tfrac{1}{4} + \tfrac{1}{4} \right) = 1 + \tfrac{2}{2}$$

$$s_8 = 1 + \tfrac{1}{2} + \left(\tfrac{1}{3} + \tfrac{1}{4} \right) + \left(\tfrac{1}{5} + \tfrac{1}{6} + \tfrac{1}{7} + \tfrac{1}{8} \right)$$

$$> 1 + \tfrac{1}{2} + \left(\tfrac{1}{4} + \tfrac{1}{4} \right) + \left(\tfrac{1}{8} + \tfrac{1}{8} + \tfrac{1}{8} + \tfrac{1}{8} \right)$$

$$= 1 + \tfrac{1}{2} + \tfrac{1}{2} + \tfrac{1}{2} = 1 + \tfrac{3}{2}$$

$$s_{16} = 1 + \tfrac{1}{2} + \left(\tfrac{1}{3} + \tfrac{1}{4} \right) + \left(\tfrac{1}{5} + \cdots + \tfrac{1}{8} \right) + \left(\tfrac{1}{9} + \cdots + \tfrac{1}{16} \right)$$

$$> 1 + \tfrac{1}{2} + \left(\tfrac{1}{4} + \tfrac{1}{4} \right) + \left(\tfrac{1}{8} + \cdots + \tfrac{1}{8} \right) + \left(\tfrac{1}{16} + \cdots + \tfrac{1}{16} \right)$$

$$= 1 + \tfrac{1}{2} + \tfrac{1}{2} + \tfrac{1}{2} + \tfrac{1}{2} = 1 + \tfrac{4}{2}$$

Similarly, $s_{32} > 1 + \tfrac{5}{2}$, $s_{64} > 1 + \tfrac{6}{2}$, and in general

$$s_{2^n} > 1 + \frac{n}{2}$$

▪ The method used in Example 7 for showing that the harmonic series diverges is due to the French scholar Nicole Oresme (1323–1382).

This shows that $s_{2^n} \to \infty$ as $n \to \infty$ and so $\{s_n\}$ is divergent. Therefore, the harmonic series diverges.

6 THEOREM If the series $\displaystyle\sum_{n=1}^{\infty} a_n$ is convergent, then $\displaystyle\lim_{n \to \infty} a_n = 0$.

PROOF Let $s_n = a_1 + a_2 + \cdots + a_n$. Then $a_n = s_n - s_{n-1}$. Since $\Sigma\, a_n$ is convergent, the sequence $\{s_n\}$ is convergent. Let $\lim_{n \to \infty} s_n = s$. Since $n - 1 \to \infty$ as $n \to \infty$, we also have $\lim_{n \to \infty} s_{n-1} = s$. Therefore

$$\lim_{n \to \infty} a_n = \lim_{n \to \infty} (s_n - s_{n-1}) = \lim_{n \to \infty} s_n - \lim_{n \to \infty} s_{n-1} = s - s = 0 \qquad \square$$

NOTE 1 With any *series* $\Sigma\, a_n$ we associate two *sequences:* the sequence $\{s_n\}$ of its partial sums and the sequence $\{a_n\}$ of its terms. If $\Sigma\, a_n$ is convergent, then the limit of the sequence $\{s_n\}$ is s (the sum of the series) and, as Theorem 6 asserts, the limit of the sequence $\{a_n\}$ is 0.

⊘   **NOTE 2** The converse of Theorem 6 is not true in general. If $\lim_{n \to \infty} a_n = 0$, we cannot conclude that $\Sigma\, a_n$ is convergent. Observe that for the harmonic series $\Sigma\, 1/n$ we have $a_n = 1/n \to 0$ as $n \to \infty$, but we showed in Example 7 that $\Sigma\, 1/n$ is divergent.

---

7 **THE TEST FOR DIVERGENCE** If $\lim\limits_{n \to \infty} a_n$ does not exist or if $\lim\limits_{n \to \infty} a_n \neq 0$, then the series $\sum\limits_{n=1}^{\infty} a_n$ is divergent.

The Test for Divergence follows from Theorem 6 because, if the series is not divergent, then it is convergent, and so $\lim_{n \to \infty} a_n = 0$.

EXAMPLE 8 Show that the series $\sum\limits_{n=1}^{\infty} \dfrac{n^2}{5n^2 + 4}$ diverges.

SOLUTION

$$\lim_{n \to \infty} a_n = \lim_{n \to \infty} \frac{n^2}{5n^2 + 4} = \lim_{n \to \infty} \frac{1}{5 + 4/n^2} = \frac{1}{5} \neq 0$$

So the series diverges by the Test for Divergence. ■

NOTE 3 If we find that $\lim_{n \to \infty} a_n \neq 0$, we know that $\Sigma\, a_n$ is divergent. If we find that $\lim_{n \to \infty} a_n = 0$, we know *nothing* about the convergence or divergence of $\Sigma\, a_n$. Remember the warning in Note 2: If $\lim_{n \to \infty} a_n = 0$, the series $\Sigma\, a_n$ might converge or it might diverge.

---

8 **THEOREM** If $\Sigma\, a_n$ and $\Sigma\, b_n$ are convergent series, then so are the series $\Sigma\, ca_n$ (where c is a constant), $\Sigma\, (a_n + b_n)$, and $\Sigma\, (a_n - b_n)$, and

(i) $\sum\limits_{n=1}^{\infty} ca_n = c \sum\limits_{n=1}^{\infty} a_n$ (ii) $\sum\limits_{n=1}^{\infty} (a_n + b_n) = \sum\limits_{n=1}^{\infty} a_n + \sum\limits_{n=1}^{\infty} b_n$

(iii) $\sum\limits_{n=1}^{\infty} (a_n - b_n) = \sum\limits_{n=1}^{\infty} a_n - \sum\limits_{n=1}^{\infty} b_n$

These properties of convergent series follow from the corresponding Limit Laws for Sequences in Section 8.1. For instance, here is how part (ii) of Theorem 8 is proved:

Let

$$s_n = \sum_{i=1}^{n} a_i \qquad s = \sum_{n=1}^{\infty} a_n \qquad t_n = \sum_{i=1}^{n} b_i \qquad t = \sum_{n=1}^{\infty} b_n$$

The nth partial sum for the series $\Sigma\,(a_n + b_n)$ is

$$u_n = \sum_{i=1}^{n} (a_i + b_i)$$

and, using Equation 5.2.10, we have

$$\lim_{n \to \infty} u_n = \lim_{n \to \infty} \sum_{i=1}^{n} (a_i + b_i) = \lim_{n \to \infty} \left(\sum_{i=1}^{n} a_i + \sum_{i=1}^{n} b_i \right)$$

$$= \lim_{n \to \infty} \sum_{i=1}^{n} a_i + \lim_{n \to \infty} \sum_{i=1}^{n} b_i = \lim_{n \to \infty} s_n + \lim_{n \to \infty} t_n = s + t$$

Therefore, $\Sigma\,(a_n + b_n)$ is convergent and its sum is

$$\sum_{n=1}^{\infty} (a_n + b_n) = s + t = \sum_{n=1}^{\infty} a_n + \sum_{n=1}^{\infty} b_n \qquad \qquad \square$$

EXAMPLE 9 Find the sum of the series $\displaystyle\sum_{n=1}^{\infty} \left(\frac{3}{n(n+1)} + \frac{1}{2^n} \right)$.

SOLUTION The series $\Sigma\,1/2^n$ is a geometric series with $a = \frac{1}{2}$ and $r = \frac{1}{2}$, so

$$\sum_{n=1}^{\infty} \frac{1}{2^n} = \frac{\frac{1}{2}}{1 - \frac{1}{2}} = 1$$

In Example 6 we found that

$$\sum_{n=1}^{\infty} \frac{1}{n(n+1)} = 1$$

So, by Theorem 8, the given series is convergent and

$$\sum_{n=1}^{\infty} \left(\frac{3}{n(n+1)} + \frac{1}{2^n} \right) = 3 \sum_{n=1}^{\infty} \frac{1}{n(n+1)} + \sum_{n=1}^{\infty} \frac{1}{2^n} = 3 \cdot 1 + 1 = 4 \qquad \blacksquare$$

NOTE 4 A finite number of terms doesn't affect the convergence or divergence of a series. For instance, suppose that we were able to show that the series

$$\sum_{n=4}^{\infty} \frac{n}{n^3 + 1}$$

is convergent. Since

$$\sum_{n=1}^{\infty} \frac{n}{n^3 + 1} = \frac{1}{2} + \frac{2}{9} + \frac{3}{28} + \sum_{n=4}^{\infty} \frac{n}{n^3 + 1}$$

it follows that the entire series $\sum_{n=1}^{\infty} n/(n^3 + 1)$ is convergent. Similarly, if it is known that the series $\sum_{n=N+1}^{\infty} a_n$ converges, then the full series

$$\sum_{n=1}^{\infty} a_n = \sum_{n=1}^{N} a_n + \sum_{n=N+1}^{\infty} a_n$$

is also convergent.

8.2 EXERCISES

1. (a) What is the difference between a sequence and a series?
   (b) What is a convergent series? What is a divergent series?

2. Explain what it means to say that $\sum_{n=1}^{\infty} a_n = 5$.

3–8 ■ Determine whether the geometric series is convergent or divergent. If it is convergent, find its sum.

3. $5 - \frac{10}{3} + \frac{20}{9} - \frac{40}{27} + \cdots$

4. $1 + 0.4 + 0.16 + 0.064 + \cdots$

5. $\sum_{n=1}^{\infty} 5\left(\frac{2}{3}\right)^{n-1}$

6. $\sum_{n=1}^{\infty} \frac{(-6)^{n-1}}{5^{n-1}}$

7. $\sum_{n=0}^{\infty} \frac{\pi^n}{3^{n+1}}$

8. $\sum_{n=0}^{\infty} \frac{1}{(\sqrt{2})^n}$

9–18 ■ Determine whether the series is convergent or divergent. If it is convergent, find its sum.

9. $\sum_{n=1}^{\infty} \frac{1}{2n}$

10. $\sum_{n=1}^{\infty} \frac{n+1}{2n-3}$

11. $\sum_{k=2}^{\infty} \frac{k^2}{k^2-1}$

12. $\sum_{k=1}^{\infty} \frac{k(k+2)}{(k+3)^2}$

13. $\sum_{n=1}^{\infty} \frac{1+2^n}{3^n}$

14. $\sum_{n=1}^{\infty} \frac{1+3^n}{2^n}$

15. $\sum_{n=1}^{\infty} \sqrt[n]{2}$

16. $\sum_{n=1}^{\infty} [(0.8)^{n-1} - (0.3)^n]$

17. $\sum_{n=1}^{\infty} \arctan n$

18. $\sum_{k=1}^{\infty} (\cos 1)^k$

19–22 ■ Determine whether the series is convergent or divergent by expressing s_n as a telescoping sum (as in Example 6). If it is convergent, find its sum.

19. $\sum_{n=2}^{\infty} \frac{2}{n^2-1}$

20. $\sum_{n=1}^{\infty} \frac{2}{n^2+4n+3}$

21. $\sum_{n=1}^{\infty} \frac{3}{n(n+3)}$

22. $\sum_{n=1}^{\infty} \ln \frac{n}{n+1}$

23–26 ■ Express the number as a ratio of integers.

23. $0.\overline{2} = 0.2222\ldots$

24. $0.\overline{73} = 0.73737373\ldots$

25. $3.\overline{417} = 3.417417417\ldots$

26. $6.2\overline{54} = 6.2545454\ldots$

27–29 ■ Find the values of x for which the series converges. Find the sum of the series for those values of x.

27. $\sum_{n=1}^{\infty} \frac{x^n}{3^n}$

28. $\sum_{n=0}^{\infty} 2^n(x+1)^n$

29. $\sum_{n=0}^{\infty} \frac{\cos^n x}{2^n}$

30. We have seen that the harmonic series is a divergent series whose terms approach 0. Show that

$$\sum_{n=1}^{\infty} \ln\left(1 + \frac{1}{n}\right)$$

is another series with this property.

31. If the nth partial sum of a series $\sum_{n=1}^{\infty} a_n$ is

$$s_n = \frac{n-1}{n+1}$$

find a_n and $\sum_{n=1}^{\infty} a_n$.

32. If the nth partial sum of a series $\sum_{n=1}^{\infty} a_n$ is $s_n = 3 - n2^{-n}$, find a_n and $\sum_{n=1}^{\infty} a_n$.

33. When money is spent on goods and services, those that receive the money also spend some of it. The people receiving some of the twice-spent money will spend some of that, and so on. Economists call this chain reaction the *multiplier effect*. In a hypothetical isolated community, the local government begins the process by spending D dollars. Suppose that each recipient of spent money spends $100c\%$ and saves $100s\%$ of the money that he or she receives. The values c and s are called the *marginal propensity to consume* and the *marginal propensity to save* and, of course, $c + s = 1$.
    (a) Let S_n be the total spending that has been generated after n transactions. Find an equation for S_n.
    (b) Show that $\lim_{n \to \infty} S_n = kD$, where $k = 1/s$. The number k is called the *multiplier*. What is the multiplier if the marginal propensity to consume is 80%?

    Note: The federal government uses this principle to justify deficit spending. Banks use this principle to justify lending a large percentage of the money that they receive in deposits.

34. A certain ball has the property that each time it falls from a height h onto a hard, level surface, it rebounds to a height rh, where $0 < r < 1$. Suppose that the ball is dropped from an initial height of H meters.
    (a) Assuming that the ball continues to bounce indefinitely, find the total distance that it travels. (Use the fact that the ball falls $\frac{1}{2}gt^2$ meters in t seconds.)
    (b) Calculate the total time that the ball travels.
    (c) Suppose that each time the ball strikes the surface with velocity v it rebounds with velocity $-kv$, where

$0 < k < 1$. How long will it take for the ball to come to rest?

35. What is the value of c if $\displaystyle\sum_{n=2}^{\infty} (1 + c)^{-n} = 2$?

36. Graph the curves $y = x^n$, $0 \leqslant x \leqslant 1$, for $n = 0, 1, 2, 3, 4, \ldots$ on a common screen. By finding the areas between successive curves, give a geometric demonstration of the fact, shown in Example 6, that

$$\sum_{n=1}^{\infty} \frac{1}{n(n+1)} = 1$$

37. The figure shows two circles C and D of radius 1 that touch at P. T is a common tangent line; C_1 is the circle that touches C, D, and T; C_2 is the circle that touches C, D, and C_1; C_3 is the circle that touches C, D, and C_2. This procedure can be continued indefinitely and produces an infinite sequence of circles $\{C_n\}$. Find an expression for the diameter of C_n and thus provide another geometric demonstration of Example 6.

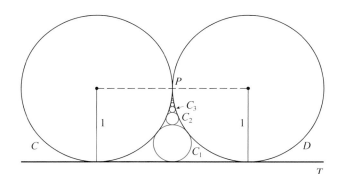

38. A right triangle ABC is given with $\angle A = \theta$ and $|AC| = b$. CD is drawn perpendicular to AB, DE is drawn perpendicular to BC, $EF \perp AB$, and this process is continued indefinitely as shown in the figure. Find the total length of all the perpendiculars

$$|CD| + |DE| + |EF| + |FG| + \cdots$$

in terms of b and θ.

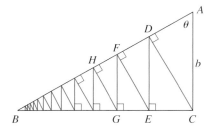

39. What is wrong with the following calculation?

$$0 = 0 + 0 + 0 + \cdots$$
$$= (1 - 1) + (1 - 1) + (1 - 1) + \cdots$$
$$= 1 - 1 + 1 - 1 + 1 - 1 + \cdots$$
$$= 1 + (-1 + 1) + (-1 + 1) + (-1 + 1) + \cdots$$
$$= 1 + 0 + 0 + 0 + \cdots = 1$$

(Guido Ubaldus thought that this proved the existence of God because "something has been created out of nothing.")

40. Suppose that $\sum_{n=1}^{\infty} a_n$ $(a_n \neq 0)$ is known to be a convergent series. Prove that $\sum_{n=1}^{\infty} 1/a_n$ is a divergent series.

41. Prove part (i) of Theorem 8.

42. If $\sum a_n$ is divergent and $c \neq 0$, show that $\sum ca_n$ is divergent.

43. If $\sum a_n$ is convergent and $\sum b_n$ is divergent, show that the series $\sum (a_n + b_n)$ is divergent. [*Hint:* Argue by contradiction.]

44. If $\sum a_n$ and $\sum b_n$ are both divergent, is $\sum (a_n + b_n)$ necessarily divergent?

45. Suppose that a series $\sum a_n$ has positive terms and its partial sums s_n satisfy the inequality $s_n \leqslant 1000$ for all n. Explain why $\sum a_n$ must be convergent.

46. The Fibonacci sequence was defined in Section 8.1 by the equations

$$f_1 = 1, \quad f_2 = 1, \quad f_n = f_{n-1} + f_{n-2} \quad n \geqslant 3$$

Show that each of the following statements is true.

(a) $\dfrac{1}{f_{n-1} f_{n+1}} = \dfrac{1}{f_{n-1} f_n} - \dfrac{1}{f_n f_{n+1}}$

(b) $\displaystyle\sum_{n=2}^{\infty} \frac{1}{f_{n-1} f_{n+1}} = 1$

(c) $\displaystyle\sum_{n=2}^{\infty} \frac{f_n}{f_{n-1} f_{n+1}} = 2$

47. The **Cantor set**, named after the German mathematician Georg Cantor (1845–1918), is constructed as follows. We start with the closed interval $[0, 1]$ and remove the open interval $\left(\frac{1}{3}, \frac{2}{3}\right)$. That leaves the two intervals $\left[0, \frac{1}{3}\right]$ and $\left[\frac{2}{3}, 1\right]$ and we remove the open middle third of each. Four intervals remain and again we remove the open middle third of each of them. We continue this procedure indefinitely, at each step removing the open middle third of every interval that remains from the preceding step. The Cantor set consists of the numbers that remain in [0, 1] after all those intervals have been removed.

(a) Show that the total length of all the intervals that are removed is 1. Despite that, the Cantor set contains infinitely many numbers. Give examples of some numbers in the Cantor set.

(b) The **Sierpinski carpet** is a two-dimensional counterpart of the Cantor set. It is constructed by removing the center one-ninth of a square of side 1, then removing the centers of the eight smaller remaining squares, and so on. (The figure shows the first three steps of the construction.) Show that the sum of the areas of the removed squares is 1. This implies that the Sierpinski carpet has area 0.

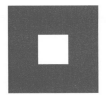  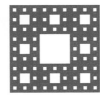

48. (a) A sequence $\{a_n\}$ is defined recursively by the equation $a_n = \frac{1}{2}(a_{n-1} + a_{n-2})$ for $n \geq 3$, where a_1 and a_2 can be any real numbers. Experiment with various values of a_1 and a_2 and use your calculator to guess the limit of the sequence.

(b) Find $\lim_{n \to \infty} a_n$ in terms of a_1 and a_2 by expressing $a_{n+1} - a_n$ in terms of $a_2 - a_1$ and summing a series.

49. Consider the series

$$\sum_{n=1}^{\infty} \frac{n}{(n+1)!}$$

(a) Find the partial sums s_1, s_2, s_3, and s_4. Do you recognize the denominators? Use the pattern to guess a formula for s_n.

(b) Use mathematical induction to prove your guess.

(c) Show that the given infinite series is convergent, and find its sum.

50. In the figure there are infinitely many circles approaching the vertices of an equilateral triangle, each circle touching other circles and sides of the triangle. If the triangle has sides of length 1, find the total area occupied by the circles.

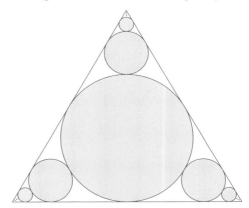

8.3 | THE INTEGRAL AND COMPARISON TESTS

In general, it is difficult to find the exact sum of a series. We were able to accomplish this for geometric series and the series $\sum 1/[n(n+1)]$ because in each of those cases we could find a simple formula for the nth partial sum s_n. But usually it isn't easy to compute $\lim_{n \to \infty} s_n$. Therefore, in this section and the next we develop tests that enable us to determine whether a series is convergent or divergent without explicitly finding its sum.

In this section we deal only with series with positive terms, so the partial sums are increasing. In view of the Monotonic Sequence Theorem, to decide whether a series is convergent or divergent, we need to determine whether the partial sums are bounded or not.

TESTING WITH AN INTEGRAL

Let's investigate the series whose terms are the reciprocals of the squares of the positive integers:

$$\sum_{n=1}^{\infty} \frac{1}{n^2} = \frac{1}{1^2} + \frac{1}{2^2} + \frac{1}{3^2} + \frac{1}{4^2} + \frac{1}{5^2} + \cdots$$

There's no simple formula for the sum s_n of the first n terms, but the computer-generated table of values given in the margin suggests that the partial sums are approaching a number near 1.64 as $n \to \infty$ and so it looks as if the series is convergent.

n	$s_n = \displaystyle\sum_{i=1}^{n} \frac{1}{i^2}$
5	1.4636
10	1.5498
50	1.6251
100	1.6350
500	1.6429
1000	1.6439
5000	1.6447

We can confirm this impression with a geometric argument. Figure 1 shows the curve $y = 1/x^2$ and rectangles that lie below the curve. The base of each rectangle is an interval of length 1; the height is equal to the value of the function $y = 1/x^2$ at the right endpoint of the interval. So the sum of the areas of the rectangles is

$$\frac{1}{1^2} + \frac{1}{2^2} + \frac{1}{3^2} + \frac{1}{4^2} + \frac{1}{5^2} + \cdots = \sum_{n=1}^{\infty} \frac{1}{n^2}$$

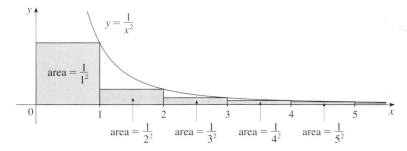

FIGURE 1

If we exclude the first rectangle, the total area of the remaining rectangles is smaller than the area under the curve $y = 1/x^2$ for $x \geq 1$, which is the value of the integral $\int_1^{\infty} (1/x^2)\, dx$. In Section 6.6 we discovered that this improper integral is convergent and has value 1. So the picture shows that all the partial sums are less than

$$\frac{1}{1^2} + \int_1^{\infty} \frac{1}{x^2}\, dx = 2$$

Thus the partial sums are bounded and the series converges. The sum of the series (the limit of the partial sums) is also less than 2:

$$\sum_{n=1}^{\infty} \frac{1}{n^2} = \frac{1}{1^2} + \frac{1}{2^2} + \frac{1}{3^2} + \frac{1}{4^2} + \cdots < 2$$

[The exact sum of this series was found by the Swiss mathematician Leonhard Euler (1707–1783) to be $\pi^2/6$, but the proof of this fact is beyond the scope of this book.] Now let's look at the series

$$\sum_{n=1}^{\infty} \frac{1}{\sqrt{n}} = \frac{1}{\sqrt{1}} + \frac{1}{\sqrt{2}} + \frac{1}{\sqrt{3}} + \frac{1}{\sqrt{4}} + \frac{1}{\sqrt{5}} + \cdots$$

The table of values of s_n suggests that the partial sums aren't approaching a finite number, so we suspect that the given series may be divergent. Again we use a picture for confirmation. Figure 2 shows the curve $y = 1/\sqrt{x}$, but this time we use rectangles whose tops lie *above* the curve.

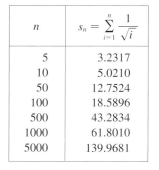

n	$s_n = \sum_{i=1}^{n} \frac{1}{\sqrt{i}}$
5	3.2317
10	5.0210
50	12.7524
100	18.5896
500	43.2834
1000	61.8010
5000	139.9681

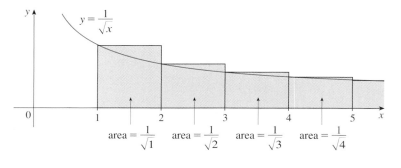

FIGURE 2

The base of each rectangle is an interval of length 1. The height is equal to the value of the function $y = 1/\sqrt{x}$ at the *left* endpoint of the interval. So the sum of the areas of all the rectangles is

$$\frac{1}{\sqrt{1}} + \frac{1}{\sqrt{2}} + \frac{1}{\sqrt{3}} + \frac{1}{\sqrt{4}} + \frac{1}{\sqrt{5}} + \cdots = \sum_{n=1}^{\infty} \frac{1}{\sqrt{n}}$$

This total area is greater than the area under the curve $y = 1/\sqrt{x}$ for $x \geqslant 1$, which is equal to the integral $\int_1^{\infty} (1/\sqrt{x})\, dx$. But we know from Section 6.6 that this improper integral is divergent. In other words, the area under the curve is infinite. So the sum of the series must be infinite, that is, the series is divergent.

The same sort of geometric reasoning that we used for these two series can be used to prove the following test. (The proof is given at the end of this section.)

> **THE INTEGRAL TEST** Suppose f is a continuous, positive, decreasing function on $[1, \infty)$ and let $a_n = f(n)$. Then the series $\sum_{n=1}^{\infty} a_n$ is convergent if and only if the improper integral $\int_1^{\infty} f(x)\, dx$ is convergent. In other words:
>
> (a) If $\displaystyle\int_1^{\infty} f(x)\, dx$ is convergent, then $\displaystyle\sum_{n=1}^{\infty} a_n$ is convergent.
>
> (b) If $\displaystyle\int_1^{\infty} f(x)\, dx$ is divergent, then $\displaystyle\sum_{n=1}^{\infty} a_n$ is divergent.

NOTE When we use the Integral Test it is not necessary to start the series or the integral at $n = 1$. For instance, in testing the series

$$\sum_{n=4}^{\infty} \frac{1}{(n-3)^2} \qquad \text{we use} \qquad \int_4^{\infty} \frac{1}{(x-3)^2}\, dx$$

Also, it is not necessary that f be always decreasing. What is important is that f be *ultimately* decreasing, that is, decreasing for x larger than some number N. Then $\sum_{n=N}^{\infty} a_n$ is convergent, so $\sum_{n=1}^{\infty} a_n$ is convergent by Note 4 of Section 8.2.

▼ EXAMPLE 1 Determine whether the series $\displaystyle\sum_{n=1}^{\infty} \frac{\ln n}{n}$ converges or diverges.

SOLUTION The function $f(x) = (\ln x)/x$ is positive and continuous for $x > 1$ because the logarithm function is positive and continuous there. But it is not obvious whether or not f is decreasing, so we compute its derivative:

$$f'(x) = \frac{x(1/x) - \ln x}{x^2} = \frac{1 - \ln x}{x^2}$$

▪ In order to use the Integral Test we need to be able to evaluate $\int_1^{\infty} f(x)\, dx$ and therefore we have to be able to find an antiderivative of f. Frequently this is difficult or impossible, so we need other tests for convergence too.

Thus $f'(x) < 0$ when $\ln x > 1$, that is, $x > e$. It follows that f is decreasing when $x > e$ and so we can apply the Integral Test:

$$\int_1^{\infty} \frac{\ln x}{x}\, dx = \lim_{t \to \infty} \int_1^t \frac{\ln x}{x}\, dx = \lim_{t \to \infty} \frac{(\ln x)^2}{2} \bigg]_1^t$$

$$= \lim_{t \to \infty} \frac{(\ln t)^2}{2} = \infty$$

Since this improper integral is divergent, the series $\sum (\ln n)/n$ is also divergent by the Integral Test. ▪

V **EXAMPLE 2** For what values of p is the series $\sum_{n=1}^{\infty} \dfrac{1}{n^p}$ convergent?

SOLUTION If $p < 0$, then $\lim_{n \to \infty} (1/n^p) = \infty$. If $p = 0$, then $\lim_{n \to \infty} (1/n^p) = 1$. In either case $\lim_{n \to \infty} (1/n^p) \neq 0$, so the given series diverges by the Test for Divergence [see (8.2.7)].

If $p > 0$, then the function $f(x) = 1/x^p$ is clearly continuous, positive, and decreasing on $[1, \infty)$. We found in Chapter 6 [see (6.6.2)] that

$$\int_1^{\infty} \frac{1}{x^p}\, dx \quad \text{converges if } p > 1 \text{ and diverges if } p \leqslant 1$$

It follows from the Integral Test that the series $\sum 1/n^p$ converges if $p > 1$ and diverges if $0 < p \leqslant 1$. (For $p = 1$, this series is the harmonic series discussed in Example 7 in Section 8.2.) ▪

■ Exercises 29–34 show how to estimate the sum of a series that is convergent by the Integral Test.

The series in Example 2 is called the **p-series**. It is important in the rest of this chapter, so we summarize the results of Example 2 for future reference as follows.

> **1** The p-series $\sum_{n=1}^{\infty} \dfrac{1}{n^p}$ is convergent if $p > 1$ and divergent if $p \leqslant 1$.

For instance, the series

$$\sum_{n=1}^{\infty} \frac{1}{n^3} = \frac{1}{1^3} + \frac{1}{2^3} + \frac{1}{3^3} + \frac{1}{4^3} + \cdots$$

is convergent because it is a p-series with $p = 3 > 1$. But the series

$$\sum_{n=1}^{\infty} \frac{1}{n^{1/3}} = \sum_{n=1}^{\infty} \frac{1}{\sqrt[3]{n}} = 1 + \frac{1}{\sqrt[3]{2}} + \frac{1}{\sqrt[3]{3}} + \frac{1}{\sqrt[3]{4}} + \cdots$$

is divergent because it is a p-series with $p = \frac{1}{3} < 1$.

TESTING BY COMPARING

The series

2
$$\sum_{n=1}^{\infty} \frac{1}{2^n + 1}$$

reminds us of the series $\sum_{n=1}^{\infty} 1/2^n$, which is a geometric series with $a = \frac{1}{2}$ and $r = \frac{1}{2}$ and is therefore convergent. Because the series (2) is so similar to a convergent series, we have the feeling that it too must be convergent. Indeed, it is. The inequality

$$\frac{1}{2^n + 1} < \frac{1}{2^n}$$

shows that our given series (2) has smaller terms than those of the geometric series and therefore all its partial sums are also smaller than 1 (the sum of the geometric series). This means that its partial sums form a bounded increasing sequence, which is convergent. It also follows that the sum of the series is less than the sum of the geometric series:

$$\sum_{n=1}^{\infty} \frac{1}{2^n + 1} < 1$$

Similar reasoning can be used to prove the following test, which applies only to series whose terms are positive. The first part says that if we have a series whose terms are *smaller* than those of a known *convergent* series, then our series is also convergent. The second part says that if we start with a series whose terms are *larger* than those of a known *divergent* series, then it too is divergent.

THE COMPARISON TEST Suppose that $\Sigma \, a_n$ and $\Sigma \, b_n$ are series with positive terms.

(a) If $\Sigma \, b_n$ is convergent and $a_n \leqslant b_n$ for all n, then $\Sigma \, a_n$ is also convergent.

(b) If $\Sigma \, b_n$ is divergent and $a_n \geqslant b_n$ for all n, then $\Sigma \, a_n$ is also divergent.

▪ It is important to keep in mind the distinction between a sequence and a series. A sequence is a list of numbers, whereas a series is a sum. With every series $\Sigma \, a_n$ there are associated two sequences: the sequence $\{a_n\}$ of terms and the sequence $\{s_n\}$ of partial sums.

PROOF

(i) Let

$$s_n = \sum_{i=1}^{n} a_i \qquad t_n = \sum_{i=1}^{n} b_i \qquad t = \sum_{n=1}^{\infty} b_n$$

Since both series have positive terms, the sequences $\{s_n\}$ and $\{t_n\}$ are increasing $(s_{n+1} = s_n + a_{n+1} \geqslant s_n)$. Also $t_n \to t$, so $t_n \leqslant t$ for all n. Since $a_i \leqslant b_i$, we have $s_n \leqslant t_n$. Thus $s_n \leqslant t$ for all n. This means that $\{s_n\}$ is increasing and bounded above and therefore converges by the Monotonic Sequence Theorem. Thus $\Sigma \, a_n$ converges.

(ii) If $\Sigma \, b_n$ is divergent, then $t_n \to \infty$ (since $\{t_n\}$ is increasing). But $a_i \geqslant b_i$ so $s_n \geqslant t_n$. Thus $s_n \to \infty$. Therefore, $\Sigma \, a_n$ diverges. $\quad\square$

Standard Series for Use with the Comparison Test

In using the Comparison Test we must, of course, have some known series $\Sigma \, b_n$ for the purpose of comparison. Most of the time we use one of these series:

▪ A p-series $\left[\Sigma \, 1/n^p \text{ converges if } p > 1 \text{ and diverges if } p \leqslant 1; \text{ see (1)}\right]$

▪ A geometric series $\left[\Sigma \, ar^{n-1} \text{ converges if } |r| < 1 \text{ and diverges if } |r| \geqslant 1; \text{ see (8.2.4)}\right]$

Ⅴ EXAMPLE 3 Determine whether the series $\displaystyle\sum_{n=1}^{\infty} \frac{5}{2n^2 + 4n + 3}$ converges or diverges.

SOLUTION For large n the dominant term in the denominator is $2n^2$, so we compare the given series with the series $\Sigma \, 5/(2n^2)$. Observe that

$$\frac{5}{2n^2 + 4n + 3} < \frac{5}{2n^2}$$

because the left side has a bigger denominator. (In the notation of the Comparison Test, a_n is the left side and b_n is the right side.) We know that

$$\sum_{n=1}^{\infty} \frac{5}{2n^2} = \frac{5}{2} \sum_{n=1}^{\infty} \frac{1}{n^2}$$

is convergent (p-series with $p = 2 > 1$). Therefore

$$\sum_{n=1}^{\infty} \frac{5}{2n^2 + 4n + 3}$$

is convergent by part (a) of the Comparison Test. ▪

Although the condition $a_n \leqslant b_n$ or $a_n \geqslant b_n$ in the Comparison Test is given for all n, we need verify only that it holds for $n \geqslant N$, where N is some fixed integer, because the convergence of a series is not affected by a finite number of terms. This is illustrated in the next example.

▼ EXAMPLE 4 Test the series $\displaystyle\sum_{n=1}^{\infty} \frac{\ln n}{n}$ for convergence or divergence.

SOLUTION We used the Integral Test to test this series in Example 1, but we can also test it by comparing it with the harmonic series. Observe that $\ln n > 1$ for $n \geqslant 3$ and so

$$\frac{\ln n}{n} > \frac{1}{n} \qquad n \geqslant 3$$

We know that $\Sigma \, 1/n$ is divergent (p-series with $p = 1$). Thus the given series is divergent by the Comparison Test. ■

NOTE The terms of the series being tested must be smaller than those of a convergent series or larger than those of a divergent series. If the terms are larger than the terms of a convergent series or smaller than those of a divergent series, then the Comparison Test doesn't apply. Consider, for instance, the series

$$\sum_{n=1}^{\infty} \frac{1}{2^n - 1}$$

The inequality

$$\frac{1}{2^n - 1} > \frac{1}{2^n}$$

is useless as far as the Comparison Test is concerned because $\Sigma \, b_n = \Sigma \left(\frac{1}{2}\right)^n$ is convergent and $a_n > b_n$. Nonetheless, we have the feeling that $\Sigma \, 1/(2^n - 1)$ ought to be convergent because it is very similar to the convergent geometric series $\Sigma \left(\frac{1}{2}\right)^n$. In such cases the following test can be used.

■ Exercises 38 and 39 deal with the cases $c = 0$ and $c = \infty$.

> **THE LIMIT COMPARISON TEST** Suppose that $\Sigma \, a_n$ and $\Sigma \, b_n$ are series with positive terms. If
>
> $$\lim_{n \to \infty} \frac{a_n}{b_n} = c$$
>
> where c is a finite number and $c > 0$, then either both series converge or both diverge.

PROOF Let m and M be positive numbers such that $m < c < M$. Because a_n/b_n is close to c for large n, there is an integer N such that

$$m < \frac{a_n}{b_n} < M \qquad \text{when } n > N$$

and so

$$mb_n < a_n < Mb_n \qquad \text{when } n > N$$

If $\Sigma \, b_n$ converges, so does $\Sigma \, Mb_n$. Thus $\Sigma \, a_n$ converges by part (i) of the Comparison Test. If $\Sigma \, b_n$ diverges, so does $\Sigma \, mb_n$ and part (ii) of the Comparison Test shows that $\Sigma \, a_n$ diverges. ☐

EXAMPLE 5 Test the series $\sum_{n=1}^{\infty} \dfrac{1}{2^n - 1}$ for convergence or divergence.

SOLUTION We use the Limit Comparison Test with

$$a_n = \frac{1}{2^n - 1} \qquad b_n = \frac{1}{2^n}$$

and obtain

$$\lim_{n \to \infty} \frac{a_n}{b_n} = \lim_{n \to \infty} \frac{1/(2^n - 1)}{1/2^n} = \lim_{n \to \infty} \frac{2^n}{2^n - 1} = \lim_{n \to \infty} \frac{1}{1 - 1/2^n} = 1 > 0$$

Since this limit exists and $\sum 1/2^n$ is a convergent geometric series, the given series converges by the Limit Comparison Test. ■

PROOF OF THE INTEGRAL TEST

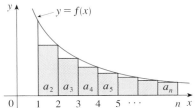

FIGURE 3

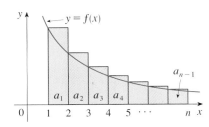

FIGURE 4

We have already seen the basic idea behind the proof of the Integral Test in Figures 1 and 2 for the series $\sum 1/n^2$ and $\sum 1/\sqrt{n}$. For the general series $\sum a_n$ look at Figures 3 and 4. The area of the first shaded rectangle in Figure 3 is the value of f at the right endpoint of $[1, 2]$, that is, $f(2) = a_2$. So, comparing the areas of the shaded rectangles with the area under $y = f(x)$ from 1 to n, we see that

3 $$a_2 + a_3 + \cdots + a_n \leqslant \int_1^n f(x)\, dx$$

(Notice that this inequality depends on the fact that f is decreasing.) Likewise, Figure 4 shows that

4 $$\int_1^n f(x)\, dx \leqslant a_1 + a_2 + \cdots + a_{n-1}$$

(i) If $\int_1^\infty f(x)\, dx$ is convergent, then (3) gives

$$\sum_{i=2}^n a_i \leqslant \int_1^n f(x)\, dx \leqslant \int_1^\infty f(x)\, dx$$

since $f(x) \geqslant 0$. Therefore

$$s_n = a_1 + \sum_{i=2}^n a_i \leqslant a_1 + \int_1^\infty f(x)\, dx = M$$

where M is a constant. Since $s_n \leqslant M$ for all n, the sequence $\{s_n\}$ is bounded above. Also

$$s_{n+1} = s_n + a_{n+1} \geqslant s_n$$

since $a_{n+1} = f(n + 1) \geqslant 0$. Thus $\{s_n\}$ is an increasing bounded sequence and so it is convergent by the Monotonic Sequence Theorem (8.1.11). This means that $\sum a_n$ is convergent.

(ii) If $\int_1^\infty f(x)\, dx$ is divergent, then $\int_1^n f(x)\, dx \to \infty$ as $n \to \infty$ because $f(x) \geqslant 0$. But (4) gives

$$\int_1^n f(x)\, dx \leqslant \sum_{i=1}^{n-1} a_i = s_{n-1}$$

and so $s_{n-1} \to \infty$. This implies that $s_n \to \infty$ and so $\sum a_n$ diverges. □

| 8.3 | EXERCISES |

1. Draw a picture to show that

$$\sum_{n=2}^{\infty} \frac{1}{n^{1.3}} < \int_1^{\infty} \frac{1}{x^{1.3}} \, dx$$

What can you conclude about the series?

2. Suppose f is a continuous positive decreasing function for $x \geq 1$ and $a_n = f(n)$. By drawing a picture, rank the following three quantities in increasing order:

$$\int_1^6 f(x) \, dx \qquad \sum_{i=1}^5 a_i \qquad \sum_{i=2}^6 a_i$$

3. Suppose $\Sigma \, a_n$ and $\Sigma \, b_n$ are series with positive terms and $\Sigma \, b_n$ is known to be convergent.
(a) If $a_n > b_n$ for all n, what can you say about $\Sigma \, a_n$? Why?
(b) If $a_n < b_n$ for all n, what can you say about $\Sigma \, a_n$? Why?

4. Suppose $\Sigma \, a_n$ and $\Sigma \, b_n$ are series with positive terms and $\Sigma \, b_n$ is known to be divergent.
(a) If $a_n > b_n$ for all n, what can you say about $\Sigma \, a_n$? Why?
(b) If $a_n < b_n$ for all n, what can you say about $\Sigma \, a_n$? Why?

5. It is important to distinguish between

$$\sum_{n=1}^{\infty} n^b \qquad \text{and} \qquad \sum_{n=1}^{\infty} b^n$$

What name is given to the first series? To the second? For what values of b does the first series converge? For what values of b does the second series converge?

6–8 ■ Use the Integral Test to determine whether the series is convergent or divergent.

6. $\displaystyle\sum_{n=1}^{\infty} \frac{1}{\sqrt[4]{n}}$ **7.** $\displaystyle\sum_{n=1}^{\infty} \frac{1}{n^4}$ **8.** $\displaystyle\sum_{n=1}^{\infty} \frac{1}{n^2 + 1}$

■ ■ ■ ■ ■ ■ ■ ■ ■ ■ ■ ■ ■

9–10 ■ Use the Comparison Test to determine whether the series is convergent or divergent.

9. $\displaystyle\sum_{n=1}^{\infty} \frac{1}{n^2 + n + 1}$ **10.** $\displaystyle\sum_{n=2}^{\infty} \frac{\sqrt{n}}{n - 1}$

■ ■ ■ ■ ■ ■ ■ ■ ■ ■ ■ ■ ■

11–26 ■ Determine whether the series is convergent or divergent.

11. $1 + \dfrac{1}{8} + \dfrac{1}{27} + \dfrac{1}{64} + \dfrac{1}{125} + \cdots$

12. $\displaystyle\sum_{n=1}^{\infty} \left(\frac{5}{n^4} + \frac{4}{n\sqrt{n}} \right)$

13. $\displaystyle\sum_{n=1}^{\infty} n e^{-n}$ **14.** $\displaystyle\sum_{n=1}^{\infty} \frac{n^2}{n^3 + 1}$

15. $\displaystyle\sum_{n=2}^{\infty} \frac{1}{n \ln n}$ **16.** $\displaystyle\sum_{n=1}^{\infty} \frac{n^2 - 1}{3n^4 + 1}$

17. $\displaystyle\sum_{n=1}^{\infty} \frac{\cos^2 n}{n^2 + 1}$ **18.** $\displaystyle\sum_{n=1}^{\infty} \frac{4 + 3^n}{2^n}$

19. $\displaystyle\sum_{n=1}^{\infty} \frac{n - 1}{n 4^n}$ **20.** $\displaystyle\sum_{n=1}^{\infty} \frac{1}{\sqrt{n^3 + 1}}$

21. $\displaystyle\sum_{n=1}^{\infty} \frac{1}{\sqrt{n^2 + 1}}$ **22.** $\displaystyle\sum_{n=1}^{\infty} \frac{1}{2n + 3}$

23. $\displaystyle\sum_{n=1}^{\infty} \frac{2 + (-1)^n}{n\sqrt{n}}$ **24.** $\displaystyle\sum_{n=0}^{\infty} \frac{1 + \sin n}{10^n}$

25. $\displaystyle\sum_{n=1}^{\infty} \sin\left(\frac{1}{n} \right)$ **26.** $\displaystyle\sum_{n=1}^{\infty} \frac{n + 5}{\sqrt[3]{n^7 + n^2}}$

■ ■ ■ ■ ■ ■ ■ ■ ■ ■ ■ ■ ■

27–28 ■ Find the values of p for which the series is convergent.

27. $\displaystyle\sum_{n=2}^{\infty} \frac{1}{n(\ln n)^p}$ **28.** $\displaystyle\sum_{n=1}^{\infty} \frac{\ln n}{n^p}$

■ ■ ■ ■ ■ ■ ■ ■ ■ ■ ■ ■ ■

29. Let s be the sum of a series $\Sigma \, a_n$ that has been shown to be convergent by the Integral Test and let $f(x)$ be the function in that test. The remainder after n terms is

$$R_n = s - s_n = a_{n+1} + a_{n+2} + a_{n+3} + \cdots$$

Thus R_n is the error made when s_n, the sum of the first n terms, is used as an approximation to the total sum s.
(a) By comparing areas in a diagram like Figures 3 and 4 (but with $x \geq n$), show that

$$\int_{n+1}^{\infty} f(x) \, dx \leq R_n \leq \int_n^{\infty} f(x) \, dx$$

(b) Deduce from part (a) that

$$s_n + \int_{n+1}^{\infty} f(x) \, dx \leq s \leq s_n + \int_n^{\infty} f(x) \, dx$$

30. (a) Find the partial sum s_{10} of the series $\Sigma_{n=1}^{\infty} 1/n^4$. Use Exercise 29(a) to estimate the error in using s_{10} as an approximation to the sum of the series.
(b) Use Exercise 29(b) with $n = 10$ to give an improved estimate of the sum.
(c) Find a value of n so that s_n is within 0.00001 of the sum.

31. (a) Use the sum of the first 10 terms and Exercise 29(a) to estimate the sum of the series $\sum_{n=1}^{\infty} 1/n^2$. How good is this estimate?
(b) Improve this estimate using Exercise 29(b) with $n = 10$.
(c) Find a value of n that will ensure that the error in the approximation $s \approx s_n$ is less than 0.001.

32. Find the sum of the series $\sum_{n=1}^{\infty} 1/n^5$ correct to three decimal places.

33. (a) Use a graph of $y = 1/x$ to show that if s_n is the nth partial sum of the harmonic series, then
$$s_n \leq 1 + \ln n$$
(b) The harmonic series diverges, but very slowly. Use part (a) to show that the sum of the first million terms is less than 15 and the sum of the first billion terms is less than 22.

34. Show that if we want to approximate the sum of the series $\sum_{n=1}^{\infty} n^{-1.001}$ so that the error is less than 5 in the ninth decimal place, then we need to add more than $10^{11,301}$ terms!

35. The meaning of the decimal representation of a number $0.d_1 d_2 d_3 \ldots$ (where the digit d_i is one of the numbers 0, 1, 2, $\ldots$, 9) is that
$$0.d_1 d_2 d_3 d_4 \ldots = \frac{d_1}{10} + \frac{d_2}{10^2} + \frac{d_3}{10^3} + \frac{d_4}{10^4} + \cdots$$
Show that this series always converges.

36. Show that if $a_n > 0$ and $\sum a_n$ is convergent, then $\sum \ln(1 + a_n)$ is convergent.

37. If $\sum a_n$ is a convergent series with positive terms, is it true that $\sum \sin(a_n)$ is also convergent?

38. (a) Suppose that $\sum a_n$ and $\sum b_n$ are series with positive terms and $\sum b_n$ is convergent. Prove that if
$$\lim_{n \to \infty} \frac{a_n}{b_n} = 0$$
then $\sum a_n$ is also convergent.
(b) Use part (a) to show that the series converges.
(i) $\sum_{n=1}^{\infty} \frac{\ln n}{n^3}$ (ii) $\sum_{n=1}^{\infty} \frac{\ln n}{\sqrt{n}\, e^n}$

39. (a) Suppose that $\sum a_n$ and $\sum b_n$ are series with positive terms and $\sum b_n$ is divergent. Prove that if
$$\lim_{n \to \infty} \frac{a_n}{b_n} = \infty$$
then $\sum a_n$ is also divergent.
(b) Use part (a) to show that the series diverges.
(i) $\sum_{n=2}^{\infty} \frac{1}{\ln n}$ (ii) $\sum_{n=1}^{\infty} \frac{\ln n}{n}$

40. Give an example of a pair of series $\sum a_n$ and $\sum b_n$ with positive terms where $\lim_{n \to \infty}(a_n/b_n) = 0$ and $\sum b_n$ diverges, but $\sum a_n$ converges. [Compare with Exercise 38.]

41. Prove that if $a_n \geq 0$ and $\sum a_n$ converges, then $\sum a_n^2$ also converges.

42. Find all positive values of b for which the series $\sum_{n=1}^{\infty} b^{\ln n}$ converges.

8.4   OTHER CONVERGENCE TESTS

The convergence tests that we have looked at so far apply only to series with positive terms. In this section we learn how to deal with series whose terms are not necessarily positive.

ALTERNATING SERIES

An **alternating series** is a series whose terms are alternately positive and negative. Here are two examples:

$$1 - \frac{1}{2} + \frac{1}{3} - \frac{1}{4} + \frac{1}{5} - \frac{1}{6} + \cdots = \sum_{n=1}^{\infty} (-1)^{n-1} \frac{1}{n}$$

$$-\frac{1}{2} + \frac{2}{3} - \frac{3}{4} + \frac{4}{5} - \frac{5}{6} + \frac{6}{7} - \cdots = \sum_{n=1}^{\infty} (-1)^n \frac{n}{n+1}$$

We see from these examples that the nth term of an alternating series is of the form
$$a_n = (-1)^{n-1} b_n \qquad \text{or} \qquad a_n = (-1)^n b_n$$
where b_n is a positive number. $\big($In fact, $b_n = |a_n|.\big)$

The following test says that if the terms of an alternating series decrease to 0 in absolute value, then the series converges.

THE ALTERNATING SERIES TEST If the alternating series

$$\sum_{n=1}^{\infty} (-1)^{n-1} b_n = b_1 - b_2 + b_3 - b_4 + b_5 - b_6 + \cdots \qquad (b_n > 0)$$

satisfies

(i) $\quad b_{n+1} \le b_n \qquad$ for all n

(ii) $\quad \lim_{n \to \infty} b_n = 0$

then the series is convergent.

Before giving the proof let's look at Figure 1, which gives a picture of the idea behind the proof. We first plot $s_1 = b_1$ on a number line. To find s_2 we subtract b_2, so s_2 is to the left of s_1. Then to find s_3 we add b_3, so s_3 is to the right of s_2. But, since $b_3 < b_2$, s_3 is to the left of s_1. Continuing in this manner, we see that the partial sums oscillate back and forth. Since $b_n \to 0$, the successive steps are becoming smaller and smaller. The even partial sums s_2, s_4, s_6, ... are increasing and the odd partial sums s_1, s_3, s_5, ... are decreasing. Thus it seems plausible that both are converging to some number s, which is the sum of the series. Therefore, in the following proof we consider the even and odd partial sums separately.

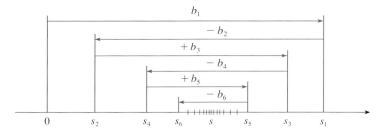

FIGURE 1

PROOF OF THE ALTERNATING SERIES TEST We first consider the even partial sums:

$$s_2 = b_1 - b_2 \ge 0 \qquad \text{since } b_2 \le b_1$$

$$s_4 = s_2 + (b_3 - b_4) \ge s_2 \qquad \text{since } b_4 \le b_3$$

In general $\quad s_{2n} = s_{2n-2} + (b_{2n-1} - b_{2n}) \ge s_{2n-2} \qquad \text{since } b_{2n} \le b_{2n-1}$

Thus $\qquad\qquad\qquad 0 \le s_2 \le s_4 \le s_6 \le \cdots \le s_{2n} \le \cdots$

But we can also write

$$s_{2n} = b_1 - (b_2 - b_3) - (b_4 - b_5) - \cdots - (b_{2n-2} - b_{2n-1}) - b_{2n}$$

Every term in brackets is positive, so $s_{2n} \le b_1$ for all n. Therefore, the sequence $\{s_{2n}\}$ of even partial sums is increasing and bounded above. It is therefore convergent by the Monotonic Sequence Theorem. Let's call its limit s, that is,

$$\lim_{n \to \infty} s_{2n} = s$$

Now we compute the limit of the odd partial sums:

$$\lim_{n \to \infty} s_{2n+1} = \lim_{n \to \infty} (s_{2n} + b_{2n+1})$$

$$= \lim_{n \to \infty} s_{2n} + \lim_{n \to \infty} b_{2n+1}$$

$$= s + 0 \qquad \text{[by condition (ii)]}$$

$$= s$$

Since both the even and odd partial sums converge to s, we have $\lim_{n \to \infty} s_n = s$ (see Exercise 46 in Section 8.1) and so the series is convergent.   □

■ Figure 2 illustrates Example 1 by showing the graphs of the terms $a_n = (-1)^{n-1}/n$ and the partial sums s_n. Notice how the values of s_n zigzag across the limiting value, which appears to be about 0.7. In fact, it can be proved that the exact sum of the series is $\ln 2 \approx 0.693$.

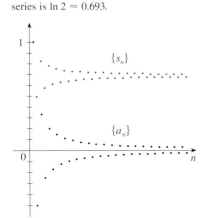

FIGURE 2

◪ EXAMPLE 1   The alternating harmonic series

$$1 - \frac{1}{2} + \frac{1}{3} - \frac{1}{4} + \cdots = \sum_{n=1}^{\infty} \frac{(-1)^{n-1}}{n}$$

satisfies

(i) $b_{n+1} < b_n$ because $\dfrac{1}{n+1} < \dfrac{1}{n}$

(ii) $\displaystyle\lim_{n \to \infty} b_n = \lim_{n \to \infty} \frac{1}{n} = 0$

so the series is convergent by the Alternating Series Test.   ■

◪ EXAMPLE 2   The series $\displaystyle\sum_{n=1}^{\infty} \frac{(-1)^n 3n}{4n - 1}$ is alternating, but

$$\lim_{n \to \infty} b_n = \lim_{n \to \infty} \frac{3n}{4n - 1} = \lim_{n \to \infty} \frac{3}{4 - \dfrac{1}{n}} = \frac{3}{4}$$

so condition (ii) is not satisfied. Instead, we look at the limit of the nth term of the series:

$$\lim_{n \to \infty} a_n = \lim_{n \to \infty} \frac{(-1)^n 3n}{4n - 1}$$

This limit does not exist, so the series diverges by the Test for Divergence.   ■

EXAMPLE 3   Test the series $\displaystyle\sum_{n=1}^{\infty} (-1)^{n+1} \frac{n^2}{n^3 + 1}$ for convergence or divergence.

SOLUTION   The given series is alternating so we try to verify conditions (i) and (ii) of the Alternating Series Test.

Unlike the situation in Example 1, it is not obvious that the sequence given by $b_n = n^2/(n^3 + 1)$ is decreasing. However, if we consider the related function $f(x) = x^2/(x^3 + 1)$, we find that

$$f'(x) = \frac{x(2 - x^3)}{(x^3 + 1)^2}$$

■ Instead of verifying condition (i) of the Alternating Series Test by computing a derivative, we could verify that $b_{n+1} < b_n$ directly by using the technique of Example 11 in Section 8.1.

Since we are considering only positive x, we see that $f'(x) < 0$ if $2 - x^3 < 0$, that is, $x > \sqrt[3]{2}$. Thus f is decreasing on the interval $(\sqrt[3]{2}, \infty)$. This means that $f(n + 1) < f(n)$ and therefore $b_{n+1} < b_n$ when $n \geq 2$. (The inequality $b_2 < b_1$ can be verified directly but all that really matters is that the sequence $\{b_n\}$ is *eventually* decreasing.)

Condition (ii) is readily verified:

$$\lim_{n \to \infty} b_n = \lim_{n \to \infty} \frac{n^2}{n^3 + 1} = \lim_{n \to \infty} \frac{\dfrac{1}{n}}{1 + \dfrac{1}{n^3}} = 0$$

Thus the given series is convergent by the Alternating Series Test. ■

A partial sum s_n of any convergent series can be used as an approximation to the total sum s, but this is not of much use unless we can estimate the accuracy of the approximation. The error involved in using $s \approx s_n$ is the remainder $R_n = s - s_n$. The next theorem says that for series that satisfy the conditions of the Alternating Series Test, the size of the error is smaller than b_{n+1}, which is the absolute value of the first neglected term.

■ You can see geometrically why the Alternating Series Estimation Theorem is true by looking at Figure 1 (on page 438). Notice that $s - s_4 < b_5$, $|s - s_5| < b_6$, and so on. Notice also that s lies between any two consecutive partial sums.

ALTERNATING SERIES ESTIMATION THEOREM   If $s = \Sigma (-1)^{n-1} b_n$ is the sum of an alternating series that satisfies

(i) $0 \leq b_{n+1} \leq b_n$ and   (ii) $\lim_{n \to \infty} b_n = 0$

then

$$|R_n| = |s - s_n| \leq b_{n+1}$$

PROOF   We know from the proof of the Alternating Series Test that s lies between any two consecutive partial sums s_n and s_{n+1}. It follows that

$$|s - s_n| \leq |s_{n+1} - s_n| = b_{n+1} \qquad \square$$

▼ **EXAMPLE 4**   Find the sum of the series $\displaystyle\sum_{n=0}^{\infty} \frac{(-1)^n}{n!}$ correct to three decimal places. (By definition, $0! = 1$.)

SOLUTION   We first observe that the series is convergent by the Alternating Series Test because

(i) $b_{n+1} = \dfrac{1}{(n + 1)!} = \dfrac{1}{n!(n + 1)} < \dfrac{1}{n!} = b_n$

(ii) $0 < \dfrac{1}{n!} < \dfrac{1}{n} \to 0$ so $b_n = \dfrac{1}{n!} \to 0$ as $n \to \infty$

To get a feel for how many terms we need to use in our approximation, let's write out the first few terms of the series:

$$s = \frac{1}{0!} - \frac{1}{1!} + \frac{1}{2!} - \frac{1}{3!} + \frac{1}{4!} - \frac{1}{5!} + \frac{1}{6!} - \frac{1}{7!} + \cdots$$

$$= 1 - 1 + \tfrac{1}{2} - \tfrac{1}{6} + \tfrac{1}{24} - \tfrac{1}{120} + \tfrac{1}{720} - \tfrac{1}{5040} + \cdots$$

Notice that $$b_7 = \tfrac{1}{5040} < \tfrac{1}{5000} = 0.0002$$

and $$s_6 = 1 - 1 + \tfrac{1}{2} - \tfrac{1}{6} + \tfrac{1}{24} - \tfrac{1}{120} + \tfrac{1}{720} \approx 0.368056$$

By the Alternating Series Estimation Theorem we know that

$$|s - s_6| \le b_7 < 0.0002$$

This error of less than 0.0002 does not affect the third decimal place, so we have

$$s \approx 0.368$$

correct to three decimal places. ▪

⊘ **NOTE** The rule that the error (in using s_n to approximate s) is smaller than the first neglected term is, in general, valid only for alternating series that satisfy the conditions of the Alternating Series Estimation Theorem. The rule does not apply to other types of series.

▪ In Section 8.7 we will prove that $e^x = \sum_{n=0}^{\infty} x^n/n!$ for all x, so what we have obtained in Example 4 is actually an approximation to the number e^{-1}.

ABSOLUTE CONVERGENCE

Given any series $\Sigma\, a_n$, we can consider the corresponding series

$$\sum_{n=1}^{\infty} |a_n| = |a_1| + |a_2| + |a_3| + \cdots$$

whose terms are the absolute values of the terms of the original series.

▪ We have convergence tests for series with positive terms and for alternating series. But what if the signs of the terms switch back and forth irregularly? We will see in Example 7 that the idea of absolute convergence sometimes helps in such cases.

> **DEFINITION** A series $\Sigma\, a_n$ is called **absolutely convergent** if the series of absolute values $\Sigma\, |a_n|$ is convergent.

Notice that if $\Sigma\, a_n$ is a series with positive terms, then $|a_n| = a_n$ and so absolute convergence is the same as convergence.

EXAMPLE 5 The series

$$\sum_{n=1}^{\infty} \frac{(-1)^{n-1}}{n^2} = 1 - \frac{1}{2^2} + \frac{1}{3^2} - \frac{1}{4^2} + \cdots$$

is absolutely convergent because

$$\sum_{n=1}^{\infty} \left| \frac{(-1)^{n-1}}{n^2} \right| = \sum_{n=1}^{\infty} \frac{1}{n^2} = 1 + \frac{1}{2^2} + \frac{1}{3^2} + \frac{1}{4^2} + \cdots$$

is a convergent p-series ($p = 2$). ▪

EXAMPLE 6 We know that the alternating harmonic series

$$\sum_{n=1}^{\infty} \frac{(-1)^{n-1}}{n} = 1 - \frac{1}{2} + \frac{1}{3} - \frac{1}{4} + \cdots$$

is convergent (see Example 1), but it is not absolutely convergent because the corresponding series of absolute values is

$$\sum_{n=1}^{\infty} \left| \frac{(-1)^{n-1}}{n} \right| = \sum_{n=1}^{\infty} \frac{1}{n} = 1 + \frac{1}{2} + \frac{1}{3} + \frac{1}{4} + \cdots$$

which is the harmonic series (*p*-series with $p = 1$) and is therefore divergent. ■

> **DEFINITION**   A series $\Sigma\, a_n$ is called **conditionally convergent** if it is convergent but not absolutely convergent.

■ It can be proved that if the terms of an absolutely convergent series are rearranged in a different order, then the sum is unchanged. But if a conditionally convergent series is rearranged, the sum could be different.

Example 6 shows that the alternating harmonic series is conditionally convergent. Thus it is possible for a series to be convergent but not absolutely convergent. However, the next theorem shows that absolute convergence implies convergence.

> **1   THEOREM**   If a series $\Sigma\, a_n$ is absolutely convergent, then it is convergent.

PROOF   Observe that the inequality

$$0 \le a_n + |a_n| \le 2|a_n|$$

is true because $|a_n|$ is either a_n or $-a_n$. If $\Sigma\, a_n$ is absolutely convergent, then $\Sigma\, |a_n|$ is convergent, so $\Sigma\, 2|a_n|$ is convergent. Therefore, by the Comparison Test, $\Sigma\, (a_n + |a_n|)$ is convergent. Then

$$\sum a_n = \sum (a_n + |a_n|) - \sum |a_n|$$

is the difference of two convergent series and is therefore convergent. ☐

■ Figure 3 shows the graphs of the terms a_n and partial sums s_n of the series in Example 7. Notice that the series is not alternating but has positive and negative terms.

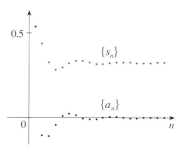

FIGURE 3

☑ EXAMPLE 7   Determine whether the series

$$\sum_{n=1}^{\infty} \frac{\cos n}{n^2} = \frac{\cos 1}{1^2} + \frac{\cos 2}{2^2} + \frac{\cos 3}{3^2} + \cdots$$

is convergent or divergent.

SOLUTION   This series has both positive and negative terms, but it is not alternating. (The first term is positive, the next three are negative, and the following three are positive. The signs change irregularly.) We can apply the Comparison Test to the series of absolute values

$$\sum_{n=1}^{\infty} \left| \frac{\cos n}{n^2} \right| = \sum_{n=1}^{\infty} \frac{|\cos n|}{n^2}$$

Since $|\cos n| \le 1$ for all n, we have

$$\frac{|\cos n|}{n^2} \le \frac{1}{n^2}$$

We know that $\Sigma\, 1/n^2$ is convergent (*p*-series with $p = 2$) and therefore $\Sigma\, |\cos n|/n^2$ is convergent by the Comparison Test. Thus the given series $\Sigma\, (\cos n)/n^2$ is absolutely convergent and therefore convergent by Theorem 1. ■

THE RATIO TEST

The following test is very useful in determining whether a given series is absolutely convergent.

THE RATIO TEST

(i) If $\lim\limits_{n \to \infty} \left| \dfrac{a_{n+1}}{a_n} \right| = L < 1$, then the series $\sum\limits_{n=1}^{\infty} a_n$ is absolutely convergent (and therefore convergent).

(ii) If $\lim\limits_{n \to \infty} \left| \dfrac{a_{n+1}}{a_n} \right| = L > 1$ or $\lim\limits_{n \to \infty} \left| \dfrac{a_{n+1}}{a_n} \right| = \infty$, then the series $\sum\limits_{n=1}^{\infty} a_n$ is divergent.

(iii) If $\lim\limits_{n \to \infty} \left| \dfrac{a_{n+1}}{a_n} \right| = 1$, the Ratio Test is inconclusive; that is, no conclusion can be drawn about the convergence or divergence of $\sum a_n$.

PROOF

(i) The idea is to compare the given series with a convergent geometric series. Since $L < 1$, we can choose a number r such that $L < r < 1$. Since

$$\lim_{n \to \infty} \left| \frac{a_{n+1}}{a_n} \right| = L \qquad \text{and} \qquad L < r$$

the ratio $\left| a_{n+1}/a_n \right|$ will eventually be less than r; that is, there exists an integer N such that

$$\left| \frac{a_{n+1}}{a_n} \right| < r \qquad \text{whenever } n \geqslant N$$

or, equivalently,

2
$$\left| a_{n+1} \right| < \left| a_n \right| r \qquad \text{whenever } n \geqslant N$$

Putting n successively equal to $N, N + 1, N + 2, \ldots$ in (2), we obtain

$$\left| a_{N+1} \right| < \left| a_N \right| r$$

$$\left| a_{N+2} \right| < \left| a_{N+1} \right| r < \left| a_N \right| r^2$$

$$\left| a_{N+3} \right| < \left| a_{N+2} \right| r < \left| a_N \right| r^3$$

and, in general,

3
$$\left| a_{N+k} \right| < \left| a_N \right| r^k \qquad \text{for all } k \geqslant 1$$

Now the series

$$\sum_{k=1}^{\infty} \left| a_N \right| r^k = \left| a_N \right| r + \left| a_N \right| r^2 + \left| a_N \right| r^3 + \cdots$$

is convergent because it is a geometric series with $0 < r < 1$. So the inequality (3), together with the Comparison Test, shows that the series

$$\sum_{n=N+1}^{\infty} |a_n| = \sum_{k=1}^{\infty} |a_{N+k}| = |a_{N+1}| + |a_{N+2}| + |a_{N+3}| + \cdots$$

is also convergent. It follows that the series $\sum_{n=1}^{\infty} |a_n|$ is convergent. (Recall that a finite number of terms doesn't affect convergence.) Therefore, $\sum a_n$ is absolutely convergent.

(ii) If $|a_{n+1}/a_n| \to L > 1$ or $|a_{n+1}/a_n| \to \infty$, then the ratio $|a_{n+1}/a_n|$ will eventually be greater than 1; that is, there exists an integer N such that

$$\left| \frac{a_{n+1}}{a_n} \right| > 1 \qquad \text{whenever } n \geq N$$

This means that $|a_{n+1}| > |a_n|$ whenever $n \geq N$ and so

$$\lim_{n \to \infty} a_n \neq 0$$

Therefore, $\sum a_n$ diverges by the Test for Divergence. ☐

NOTE Part (iii) of the Ratio Test says that if $\lim_{n \to \infty} |a_{n+1}/a_n| = 1$, the test gives no information. For instance, for the convergent series $\sum 1/n^2$ we have

$$\left| \frac{a_{n+1}}{a_n} \right| = \frac{\dfrac{1}{(n+1)^2}}{\dfrac{1}{n^2}} = \frac{n^2}{(n+1)^2} = \frac{1}{\left(1 + \dfrac{1}{n}\right)^2} \to 1 \qquad \text{as } n \to \infty$$

whereas for the divergent series $\sum 1/n$ we have

$$\left| \frac{a_{n+1}}{a_n} \right| = \frac{\dfrac{1}{n+1}}{\dfrac{1}{n}} = \frac{n}{n+1} = \frac{1}{1 + \dfrac{1}{n}} \to 1 \qquad \text{as } n \to \infty$$

Therefore, if $\lim_{n \to \infty} |a_{n+1}/a_n| = 1$, the series $\sum a_n$ might converge or it might diverge. In this case the Ratio Test fails and we must use some other test.

EXAMPLE 8 Test the series $\displaystyle\sum_{n=1}^{\infty} (-1)^n \frac{n^3}{3^n}$ for absolute convergence.

■ Series that involve factorials or other products (including a constant raised to the nth power) are often conveniently tested using the Ratio Test.

SOLUTION We use the Ratio Test with $a_n = (-1)^n n^3/3^n$:

$$\left| \frac{a_{n+1}}{a_n} \right| = \left| \frac{\dfrac{(-1)^{n+1}(n+1)^3}{3^{n+1}}}{\dfrac{(-1)^n n^3}{3^n}} \right| = \frac{(n+1)^3}{3^{n+1}} \cdot \frac{3^n}{n^3}$$

$$= \frac{1}{3}\left(\frac{n+1}{n}\right)^3 = \frac{1}{3}\left(1 + \frac{1}{n}\right)^3 \to \frac{1}{3} < 1$$

Thus, by the Ratio Test, the given series is absolutely convergent and therefore convergent. ■

V EXAMPLE 9 Test the convergence of the series $\sum_{n=1}^{\infty} \dfrac{n^n}{n!}$.

SOLUTION Since the terms $a_n = n^n/n!$ are positive, we don't need the absolute value signs.

$$\frac{a_{n+1}}{a_n} = \frac{(n+1)^{n+1}}{(n+1)!} \cdot \frac{n!}{n^n} = \frac{(n+1)(n+1)^n}{(n+1)n!} \cdot \frac{n!}{n^n}$$

$$= \left(\frac{n+1}{n}\right)^n = \left(1 + \frac{1}{n}\right)^n \to e \qquad \text{as } n \to \infty$$

■ We know that

$$\lim_{x \to 0} (1+x)^{1/x} = e$$

by the definition of e. If we let $n = 1/x$, then $n \to \infty$ as $x \to 0^+$ and so

$$\lim_{n \to \infty} (1 + 1/n)^n = e$$

Since $e > 1$, the given series is divergent by the Ratio Test. ■

The following test is convenient to apply when nth powers occur. Its proof is similar to the proof of the Ratio Test and is left as Exercise 43.

THE ROOT TEST

(i) If $\displaystyle\lim_{n \to \infty} \sqrt[n]{|a_n|} = L < 1$, then the series $\displaystyle\sum_{n=1}^{\infty} a_n$ is absolutely convergent (and therefore convergent).

(ii) If $\displaystyle\lim_{n \to \infty} \sqrt[n]{|a_n|} = L > 1$ or $\displaystyle\lim_{n \to \infty} \sqrt[n]{|a_n|} = \infty$, then the series $\displaystyle\sum_{n=1}^{\infty} a_n$ is divergent.

(iii) If $\displaystyle\lim_{n \to \infty} \sqrt[n]{|a_n|} = 1$, the Root Test is inconclusive.

If $\lim_{n \to \infty} \sqrt[n]{|a_n|} = 1$, then part (iii) of the Root Test says that the test gives no information. The series $\sum a_n$ could converge or diverge. (If $L = 1$ in the Ratio Test, don't try the Root Test because L will again be 1.)

V EXAMPLE 10 Test the convergence of the series $\sum_{n=1}^{\infty} \left(\dfrac{2n+3}{3n+2}\right)^n$.

SOLUTION

$$a_n = \left(\frac{2n+3}{3n+2}\right)^n$$

■ www.stewartcalculus.com
We now have several tests for convergence of series. So, given a series, how do you know which test to use? For advice, click on *Additional Topics* and then on *Strategy for Testing Series*.

$$\sqrt[n]{|a_n|} = \frac{2n+3}{3n+2} = \frac{2 + \dfrac{3}{n}}{3 + \dfrac{2}{n}} \to \frac{2}{3} < 1$$

Thus the given series converges by the Root Test. ■

8.4 | EXERCISES

1. (a) What is an alternating series?
(b) Under what conditions does an alternating series converge?
(c) If these conditions are satisfied, what can you say about the remainder after n terms?

2. What can you say about the series $\Sigma\, a_n$ in each of the following cases?

(a) $\displaystyle\lim_{n\to\infty}\left|\frac{a_{n+1}}{a_n}\right| = 8$ 　　(b) $\displaystyle\lim_{n\to\infty}\left|\frac{a_{n+1}}{a_n}\right| = 0.8$

(c) $\displaystyle\lim_{n\to\infty}\left|\frac{a_{n+1}}{a_n}\right| = 1$

3–8 ■ Test the series for convergence or divergence.

3. $\frac{4}{7} - \frac{4}{8} + \frac{4}{9} - \frac{4}{10} + \frac{4}{11} - \cdots$

4. $-\frac{1}{3} + \frac{2}{4} - \frac{3}{5} + \frac{4}{6} - \frac{5}{7} + \cdots$

5. $\displaystyle\sum_{n=1}^{\infty}\frac{(-1)^{n-1}}{\sqrt{n}}$ 　　**6.** $\displaystyle\sum_{n=1}^{\infty}(-1)^n\frac{\sqrt{n}}{1 + 2\sqrt{n}}$

7. $\displaystyle\sum_{n=1}^{\infty}(-1)^n\frac{3n-1}{2n+1}$ 　　**8.** $\displaystyle\sum_{n=1}^{\infty}(-1)^{n-1}\frac{\ln n}{n}$

9–12 ■ Show that the series is convergent. How many terms of the series do we need to add in order to find the sum to the indicated accuracy?

9. $\displaystyle\sum_{n=1}^{\infty}\frac{(-2)^n}{n!}$ 　$(\,|\,\text{error}\,| < 0.01)$

10. $\displaystyle\sum_{n=1}^{\infty}\frac{(-1)^n}{n5^n}$ 　$(\,|\,\text{error}\,| < 0.0001)$

11. $\displaystyle\sum_{n=1}^{\infty}\frac{(-1)^{n+1}}{n^6}$ 　$(\,|\,\text{error}\,| < 0.00005)$

12. $\displaystyle\sum_{n=1}^{\infty}(-1)^{n-1}ne^{-n}$ 　$(\,|\,\text{error}\,| < 0.01)$

13–16 ■ Approximate the sum of the series correct to four decimal places.

13. $\displaystyle\sum_{n=1}^{\infty}\frac{(-1)^{n+1}}{n^5}$ 　　**14.** $\displaystyle\sum_{n=1}^{\infty}\frac{(-1)^n n}{8^n}$

15. $\displaystyle\sum_{n=1}^{\infty}\frac{(-1)^{n-1}n^2}{10^n}$ 　　**16.** $\displaystyle\sum_{n=1}^{\infty}\frac{(-1)^n}{3^n n!}$

17. Is the 50th partial sum s_{50} of the alternating series $\sum_{n=1}^{\infty}(-1)^{n-1}/n$ an overestimate or an underestimate of the total sum? Explain.

18. For what values of p is the following series convergent?

$$\sum_{n=1}^{\infty}\frac{(-1)^{n-1}}{n^p}$$

19–38 ■ Determine whether the series is absolutely convergent, conditionally convergent, or divergent.

19. $\displaystyle\sum_{n=1}^{\infty}\frac{(-3)^n}{n^3}$ 　　**20.** $\displaystyle\sum_{n=1}^{\infty}\frac{n^2}{2^n}$

21. $\displaystyle\sum_{n=0}^{\infty}\frac{(-10)^n}{n!}$ 　　**22.** $\displaystyle\sum_{n=1}^{\infty}(-1)^n\frac{n}{n^2 + 1}$

23. $\displaystyle\sum_{n=1}^{\infty}\frac{(-1)^{n+1}}{\sqrt[4]{n}}$ 　　**24.** $\displaystyle\sum_{n=1}^{\infty}(-1)^{n-1}\frac{2^n}{n^4}$

25. $\displaystyle\sum_{n=1}^{\infty}\frac{10^n}{(n+1)4^{2n+1}}$ 　　**26.** $\displaystyle\sum_{n=1}^{\infty}\frac{\sin 4n}{4^n}$

27. $\displaystyle\sum_{n=1}^{\infty}\frac{\cos(n\pi/3)}{n!}$ 　　**28.** $\displaystyle\sum_{n=1}^{\infty}\frac{(-1)^{n+1}5^{n-1}}{(n+1)^2 4^{n+2}}$

29. $\displaystyle\sum_{n=1}^{\infty}\frac{(-1)^n \arctan n}{n^2}$ 　　**30.** $\displaystyle\sum_{n=2}^{\infty}\frac{(-1)^n}{(\ln n)^n}$

31. $\displaystyle\sum_{n=1}^{\infty}\frac{n^n}{3^{1+3n}}$ 　　**32.** $\displaystyle\sum_{n=2}^{\infty}\frac{(-1)^n}{n \ln n}$

33. $\displaystyle\sum_{n=1}^{\infty}\left(\frac{n^2+1}{2n^2+1}\right)^n$ 　　**34.** $\displaystyle\sum_{n=1}^{\infty}\frac{(-1)^n}{(\arctan n)^n}$

35. $1 - \dfrac{1\cdot 3}{3!} + \dfrac{1\cdot 3\cdot 5}{5!} - \dfrac{1\cdot 3\cdot 5\cdot 7}{7!} + \cdots$
$\quad + (-1)^{n-1}\dfrac{1\cdot 3\cdot 5\cdot\,\cdots\,\cdot(2n-1)}{(2n-1)!} + \cdots$

36. $\dfrac{2}{5} + \dfrac{2\cdot 6}{5\cdot 8} + \dfrac{2\cdot 6\cdot 10}{5\cdot 8\cdot 11} + \dfrac{2\cdot 6\cdot 10\cdot 14}{5\cdot 8\cdot 11\cdot 14} + \cdots$

37. $\displaystyle\sum_{n=1}^{\infty}\frac{2\cdot 4\cdot 6\cdot\,\cdots\,\cdot(2n)}{n!}$

38. $\displaystyle\sum_{n=1}^{\infty}(-1)^n\frac{2^n n!}{5\cdot 8\cdot 11\cdot\,\cdots\,\cdot(3n+2)}$

39. For which of the following series is the Ratio Test inconclusive (that is, it fails to give a definite answer)?

(a) $\displaystyle\sum_{n=1}^{\infty}\frac{1}{n^3}$ 　　(b) $\displaystyle\sum_{n=1}^{\infty}\frac{n}{2^n}$

(c) $\displaystyle\sum_{n=1}^{\infty}\frac{(-3)^{n-1}}{\sqrt{n}}$ 　　(d) $\displaystyle\sum_{n=1}^{\infty}\frac{\sqrt{n}}{1+n^2}$

40. For which positive integers k is the following series convergent?

$$\sum_{n=1}^{\infty} \frac{(n!)^2}{(kn)!}$$

41. (a) Show that $\sum_{n=0}^{\infty} x^n/n!$ converges for all x.
(b) Deduce that $\lim_{n\to\infty} x^n/n! = 0$ for all x.

42. Around 1910, the Indian mathematician Srinivasa Ramanujan discovered the formula

$$\frac{1}{\pi} = \frac{2\sqrt{2}}{9801} \sum_{n=0}^{\infty} \frac{(4n)!(1103 + 26390n)}{(n!)^4 396^{4n}}$$

William Gosper used this series in 1985 to compute the first 17 million digits of π.
(a) Verify that the series is convergent.
(b) How many correct decimal places of π do you get if you use just the first term of the series? What if you use two terms?

43. Prove the Root Test. [*Hint for part (i):* Take any number r such that $L < r < 1$ and use the fact that there is an integer N such that $\sqrt[n]{|a_n|} < r$ whenever $n \geq N$.]

8.5 POWER SERIES

A **power series** is a series of the form

$$\boxed{1} \qquad \sum_{n=0}^{\infty} c_n x^n = c_0 + c_1 x + c_2 x^2 + c_3 x^3 + \cdots$$

where x is a variable and the c_n's are constants called the **coefficients** of the series. For each fixed x, the series (1) is a series of constants that we can test for convergence or divergence. A power series may converge for some values of x and diverge for other values of x. The sum of the series is a function

$$f(x) = c_0 + c_1 x + c_2 x^2 + \cdots + c_n x^n + \cdots$$

whose domain is the set of all x for which the series converges. Notice that f resembles a polynomial. The only difference is that f has infinitely many terms.

For instance, if we take $c_n = 1$ for all n, the power series becomes the geometric series

$$\sum_{n=0}^{\infty} x^n = 1 + x + x^2 + \cdots + x^n + \cdots$$

which converges when $-1 < x < 1$ and diverges when $|x| \geq 1$ (see Equation 8.2.5).
More generally, a series of the form

$$\boxed{2} \qquad \sum_{n=0}^{\infty} c_n(x - a)^n = c_0 + c_1(x - a) + c_2(x - a)^2 + \cdots$$

is called a **power series in** $(x - a)$ or a **power series centered at** a or a **power series about** a. Notice that in writing out the term corresponding to $n = 0$ in Equations 1 and 2 we have adopted the convention that $(x - a)^0 = 1$ even when $x = a$. Notice also that when $x = a$ all of the terms are 0 for $n \geq 1$ and so the power series (2) always converges when $x = a$.

■ Trigonometric series
A power series is a series in which each term is a power function. A **trigonometric series**

$$\sum_{n=0}^{\infty} (a_n \cos nx + b_n \sin nx)$$

is a series whose terms are trigonometric functions. This type of series is discussed on the website

www.stewartcalculus.com

Click on *Additional Topics* and then on *Fourier Series*.

▼ EXAMPLE 1 For what values of x is the series $\sum_{n=0}^{\infty} n! x^n$ convergent?

SOLUTION We use the Ratio Test. If we let a_n, as usual, denote the nth term of the series, then $a_n = n! x^n$. If $x \neq 0$, we have

■ Notice that
$(n + 1)! = (n + 1)n(n - 1) \cdots \cdots 3 \cdot 2 \cdot 1$
$= (n + 1)n!$

$$\lim_{n\to\infty} \left| \frac{a_{n+1}}{a_n} \right| = \lim_{n\to\infty} \left| \frac{(n + 1)! x^{n+1}}{n! x^n} \right| = \lim_{n\to\infty} (n + 1)|x| = \infty$$

By the Ratio Test, the series diverges when $x \neq 0$. Thus the given series converges only when $x = 0$. ■

V EXAMPLE 2 For what values of x does the series $\sum_{n=1}^{\infty} \dfrac{(x-3)^n}{n}$ converge?

SOLUTION Let $a_n = (x-3)^n/n$. Then

$$
\left| \frac{a_{n+1}}{a_n} \right| = \left| \frac{(x-3)^{n+1}}{n+1} \cdot \frac{n}{(x-3)^n} \right|
$$

$$
= \frac{1}{1 + \dfrac{1}{n}} |x - 3| \to |x - 3| \qquad \text{as } n \to \infty
$$

By the Ratio Test, the given series is absolutely convergent, and therefore convergent, when $|x - 3| < 1$ and divergent when $|x - 3| > 1$. Now

$$
|x - 3| < 1 \quad \Longleftrightarrow \quad -1 < x - 3 < 1 \quad \Longleftrightarrow \quad 2 < x < 4
$$

so the series converges when $2 < x < 4$ and diverges when $x < 2$ or $x > 4$.

The Ratio Test gives no information when $|x - 3| = 1$ so we must consider $x = 2$ and $x = 4$ separately. If we put $x = 4$ in the series, it becomes $\Sigma \, 1/n$, the harmonic series, which is divergent. If $x = 2$, the series is $\Sigma \, (-1)^n/n$, which converges by the Alternating Series Test. Thus the given power series converges for $2 \leqslant x < 4$. ■

We will see that the main use of a power series is that it provides a way to represent some of the most important functions that arise in mathematics, physics, and chemistry. In particular, the sum of the power series in the next example is called a **Bessel function**, after the German astronomer Friedrich Bessel (1784–1846), and the function given in Exercise 23 is another example of a Bessel function. In fact, these functions first arose when Bessel solved Kepler's equation for describing planetary motion. Since that time, these functions have been applied in many different physical situations, including the temperature distribution in a circular plate and the shape of a vibrating drumhead.

EXAMPLE 3 Find the domain of the Bessel function of order 0 defined by

$$
J_0(x) = \sum_{n=0}^{\infty} \frac{(-1)^n x^{2n}}{2^{2n}(n!)^2}
$$

SOLUTION Let $a_n = (-1)^n x^{2n}/[2^{2n}(n!)^2]$. Then

$$
\left| \frac{a_{n+1}}{a_n} \right| = \left| \frac{(-1)^{n+1} x^{2(n+1)}}{2^{2(n+1)}[(n+1)!]^2} \cdot \frac{2^{2n}(n!)^2}{(-1)^n x^{2n}} \right|
$$

$$
= \frac{x^{2n+2}}{2^{2n+2}(n+1)^2(n!)^2} \cdot \frac{2^{2n}(n!)^2}{x^{2n}}
$$

$$
= \frac{x^2}{4(n+1)^2} \to 0 < 1 \qquad \text{for all } x
$$

Thus, by the Ratio Test, the given series converges for all values of x. In other words, the domain of the Bessel function J_0 is $(-\infty, \infty) = \mathbb{R}$. ■

Notice how closely the computer-generated model (which involves Bessel functions and cosine functions) matches the photograph of a vibrating rubber membrane.

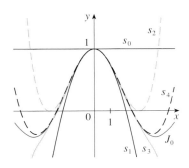

FIGURE 1
Partial sums of the Bessel function J_0

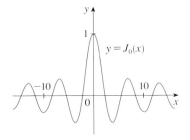

FIGURE 2

Recall that the sum of a series is equal to the limit of the sequence of partial sums. So when we define the Bessel function in Example 3 as the sum of a series we mean that, for every real number x,

$$J_0(x) = \lim_{n \to \infty} s_n(x) \qquad \text{where} \qquad s_n(x) = \sum_{i=0}^{n} \frac{(-1)^i x^{2i}}{2^{2i}(i!)^2}$$

The first few partial sums are

$$s_0(x) = 1 \qquad s_1(x) = 1 - \frac{x^2}{4} \qquad s_2(x) = 1 - \frac{x^2}{4} + \frac{x^4}{64}$$

$$s_3(x) = 1 - \frac{x^2}{4} + \frac{x^4}{64} - \frac{x^6}{2304} \qquad s_4(x) = 1 - \frac{x^2}{4} + \frac{x^4}{64} - \frac{x^6}{2304} + \frac{x^8}{147{,}456}$$

Figure 1 shows the graphs of these partial sums, which are polynomials. They are all approximations to the function J_0, but notice that the approximations become better when more terms are included. Figure 2 shows a more complete graph of the Bessel function.

For the power series that we have looked at so far, the set of values of x for which the series is convergent has always turned out to be an interval [a finite interval for the geometric series and the series in Example 2, the infinite interval $(-\infty, \infty)$ in Example 3, and a collapsed interval $[0, 0] = \{0\}$ in Example 1]. The following theorem, proved in Appendix B, says that this is true in general.

---

3 **THEOREM** For a given power series $\displaystyle\sum_{n=0}^{\infty} c_n(x - a)^n$ there are only three possibilities:

(i) The series converges only when $x = a$.

(ii) The series converges for all x.

(iii) There is a positive number R such that the series converges if $|x - a| < R$ and diverges if $|x - a| > R$.

The number R in case (iii) is called the **radius of convergence** of the power series. By convention, the radius of convergence is $R = 0$ in case (i) and $R = \infty$ in case (ii). The **interval of convergence** of a power series is the interval that consists of all values of x for which the series converges. In case (i) the interval consists of just a single point a. In case (ii) the interval is $(-\infty, \infty)$. In case (iii) note that the inequality $|x - a| < R$ can be rewritten as $a - R < x < a + R$. When x is an *endpoint* of the interval, that is, $x = a \pm R$, anything can happen—the series might converge at one or both endpoints or it might diverge at both endpoints. Thus in case (iii) there are four possibilities for the interval of convergence:

$$(a - R, a + R) \qquad (a - R, a + R] \qquad [a - R, a + R) \qquad [a - R, a + R]$$

The situation is illustrated in Figure 3.

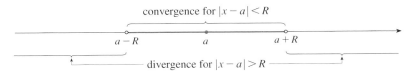

FIGURE 3

We summarize here the radius and interval of convergence for each of the examples already considered in this section.

	Series	Radius of convergence	Interval of convergence
Geometric series	$\sum\limits_{n=0}^{\infty} x^n$	$R = 1$	$(-1, 1)$
Example 1	$\sum\limits_{n=0}^{\infty} n!\, x^n$	$R = 0$	$\{0\}$
Example 2	$\sum\limits_{n=1}^{\infty} \dfrac{(x - 3)^n}{n}$	$R = 1$	$[2, 4)$
Example 3	$\sum\limits_{n=0}^{\infty} \dfrac{(-1)^n x^{2n}}{2^{2n}(n!)^2}$	$R = \infty$	$(-\infty, \infty)$

The Ratio Test (or sometimes the Root Test) should be used to determine the radius of convergence R in most cases. The Ratio and Root Tests always fail when x is an endpoint of the interval of convergence, so the endpoints must be checked with some other test.

EXAMPLE 4 Find the radius of convergence and interval of convergence of the series

$$\sum_{n=0}^{\infty} \frac{(-3)^n x^n}{\sqrt{n + 1}}$$

SOLUTION Let $a_n = (-3)^n x^n / \sqrt{n + 1}$. Then

$$\left| \frac{a_{n+1}}{a_n} \right| = \left| \frac{(-3)^{n+1} x^{n+1}}{\sqrt{n + 2}} \cdot \frac{\sqrt{n + 1}}{(-3)^n x^n} \right| = \left| -3x \sqrt{\frac{n + 1}{n + 2}} \right|$$

$$= 3 \sqrt{\frac{1 + (1/n)}{1 + (2/n)}} \, |x| \ \rightarrow \ 3\,|x| \qquad \text{as } n \rightarrow \infty$$

By the Ratio Test, the given series converges if $3\,|x| < 1$ and diverges if $3\,|x| > 1$. Thus it converges if $|x| < \frac{1}{3}$ and diverges if $|x| > \frac{1}{3}$. This means that the radius of convergence is $R = \frac{1}{3}$.

We know the series converges in the interval $\left(-\frac{1}{3}, \frac{1}{3}\right)$, but we must now test for convergence at the endpoints of this interval. If $x = -\frac{1}{3}$, the series becomes

$$\sum_{n=0}^{\infty} \frac{(-3)^n \left(-\frac{1}{3}\right)^n}{\sqrt{n + 1}} = \sum_{n=0}^{\infty} \frac{1}{\sqrt{n + 1}} = \frac{1}{\sqrt{1}} + \frac{1}{\sqrt{2}} + \frac{1}{\sqrt{3}} + \frac{1}{\sqrt{4}} + \cdots$$

which diverges. (Use the Integral Test or simply observe that it is a p-series with $p = \frac{1}{2} < 1$.) If $x = \frac{1}{3}$, the series is

$$\sum_{n=0}^{\infty} \frac{(-3)^n \left(\frac{1}{3}\right)^n}{\sqrt{n + 1}} = \sum_{n=0}^{\infty} \frac{(-1)^n}{\sqrt{n + 1}}$$

which converges by the Alternating Series Test. Therefore, the given power series converges when $-\frac{1}{3} < x \leqslant \frac{1}{3}$, so the interval of convergence is $\left(-\frac{1}{3}, \frac{1}{3}\right]$. ■

▼ EXAMPLE 5 Find the radius of convergence and interval of convergence of the series

$$\sum_{n=0}^{\infty} \frac{n(x + 2)^n}{3^{n+1}}$$

SOLUTION If $a_n = n(x + 2)^n/3^{n+1}$, then

$$\left| \frac{a_{n+1}}{a_n} \right| = \left| \frac{(n + 1)(x + 2)^{n+1}}{3^{n+2}} \cdot \frac{3^{n+1}}{n(x + 2)^n} \right|$$

$$= \left(1 + \frac{1}{n} \right) \frac{|x + 2|}{3} \rightarrow \frac{|x + 2|}{3} \qquad \text{as } n \rightarrow \infty$$

Using the Ratio Test, we see that the series converges if $|x + 2|/3 < 1$ and it diverges if $|x + 2|/3 > 1$. So it converges if $|x + 2| < 3$ and diverges if $|x + 2| > 3$. Thus the radius of convergence is $R = 3$.

The inequality $|x + 2| < 3$ can be written as $-5 < x < 1$, so we test the series at the endpoints -5 and 1. When $x = -5$, the series is

$$\sum_{n=0}^{\infty} \frac{n(-3)^n}{3^{n+1}} = \tfrac{1}{3} \sum_{n=0}^{\infty} (-1)^n n$$

which diverges by the Test for Divergence $[(-1)^n n$ doesn't converge to $0]$. When $x = 1$, the series is

$$\sum_{n=0}^{\infty} \frac{n(3)^n}{3^{n+1}} = \tfrac{1}{3} \sum_{n=0}^{\infty} n$$

which also diverges by the Test for Divergence. Thus the series converges only when $-5 < x < 1$, so the interval of convergence is $(-5, 1)$. ∎

8.5 | EXERCISES

1. What is a power series?

2. (a) What is the radius of convergence of a power series? How do you find it?
   (b) What is the interval of convergence of a power series? How do you find it?

3–18 ▪ Find the radius of convergence and interval of convergence of the series.

3. $\displaystyle\sum_{n=1}^{\infty} \frac{x^n}{\sqrt{n}}$

4. $\displaystyle\sum_{n=0}^{\infty} \frac{(-1)^n x^n}{n + 1}$

5. $\displaystyle\sum_{n=1}^{\infty} \frac{(-1)^{n-1} x^n}{n^3}$

6. $\displaystyle\sum_{n=1}^{\infty} \sqrt{n}\, x^n$

7. $\displaystyle\sum_{n=0}^{\infty} \frac{x^n}{n!}$

8. $\displaystyle\sum_{n=1}^{\infty} \frac{x^n}{n3^n}$

9. $\displaystyle\sum_{n=1}^{\infty} \frac{(-2)^n x^n}{\sqrt[4]{n}}$

10. $\displaystyle\sum_{n=1}^{\infty} \frac{x^n}{5^n n^5}$

11. $\displaystyle\sum_{n=2}^{\infty} (-1)^n \frac{x^n}{4^n \ln n}$

12. $\displaystyle\sum_{n=0}^{\infty} (-1)^n \frac{x^{2n}}{(2n)!}$

13. $\displaystyle\sum_{n=1}^{\infty} (-1)^n \frac{(x + 2)^n}{n2^n}$

14. $\displaystyle\sum_{n=1}^{\infty} \frac{(-2)^n}{\sqrt{n}} (x + 3)^n$

15. $\displaystyle\sum_{n=1}^{\infty} \frac{n}{b^n} (x - a)^n, \quad b > 0$

16. $\displaystyle\sum_{n=1}^{\infty} \frac{n(x - 4)^n}{n^3 + 1}$

17. $\displaystyle\sum_{n=1}^{\infty} n!(2x - 1)^n$

18. $\displaystyle\sum_{n=1}^{\infty} \frac{n^2 x^n}{2 \cdot 4 \cdot 6 \cdot \,\cdots\, \cdot (2n)}$

▪ ▪ ▪ ▪ ▪ ▪ ▪ ▪ ▪ ▪ ▪ ▪ ▪

19. If $\sum_{n=0}^{\infty} c_n 4^n$ is convergent, does it follow that the following series are convergent?

   (a) $\displaystyle\sum_{n=0}^{\infty} c_n(-2)^n$

   (b) $\displaystyle\sum_{n=0}^{\infty} c_n(-4)^n$

20. Suppose that $\sum_{n=0}^{\infty} c_n x^n$ converges when $x = -4$ and diverges when $x = 6$. What can be said about the convergence or divergence of the following series?

(a) $\sum_{n=0}^{\infty} c_n$

(b) $\sum_{n=0}^{\infty} c_n 8^n$

(c) $\sum_{n=0}^{\infty} c_n(-3)^n$

(d) $\sum_{n=0}^{\infty} (-1)^n c_n 9^n$

21. If k is a positive integer, find the radius of convergence of the series

$$\sum_{n=0}^{\infty} \frac{(n!)^k}{(kn)!} x^n$$

22. Graph the first several partial sums $s_n(x)$ of the series $\sum_{n=0}^{\infty} x^n$, together with the sum function $f(x) = 1/(1 - x)$, on a common screen. On what interval do these partial sums appear to be converging to $f(x)$?

23. The function J_1 defined by

$$J_1(x) = \sum_{n=0}^{\infty} \frac{(-1)^n x^{2n+1}}{n!(n + 1)! 2^{2n+1}}$$

is called the *Bessel function of order 1*.
(a) Find its domain.
(b) Graph the first several partial sums on a common screen.
(c) If your CAS has built-in Bessel functions, graph J_1 on the same screen as the partial sums in part (b) and observe how the partial sums approximate J_1.

24. The function A defined by

$$A(x) = 1 + \frac{x^3}{2 \cdot 3} + \frac{x^6}{2 \cdot 3 \cdot 5 \cdot 6} + \frac{x^9}{2 \cdot 3 \cdot 5 \cdot 6 \cdot 8 \cdot 9} + \cdots$$

is called the *Airy function* after the English mathematician and astronomer Sir George Airy (1801–1892).
(a) Find the domain of the Airy function.
(b) Graph the first several partial sums $s_n(x)$ on a common screen.
(c) If your CAS has built-in Airy functions, graph A on the same screen as the partial sums in part (b) and observe how the partial sums approximate A.

25. A function f is defined by

$$f(x) = 1 + 2x + x^2 + 2x^3 + x^4 + \cdots$$

that is, its coefficients are $c_{2n} = 1$ and $c_{2n+1} = 2$ for all $n \geq 0$. Find the interval of convergence of the series and find an explicit formula for $f(x)$.

26. If $f(x) = \sum_{n=0}^{\infty} c_n x^n$, where $c_{n+4} = c_n$ for all $n \geq 0$, find the interval of convergence of the series and a formula for $f(x)$.

27. Show that if $\lim_{n \to \infty} \sqrt[n]{|c_n|} = c$, where $c \neq 0$, then the radius of convergence of the power series $\sum c_n x^n$ is $R = 1/c$.

28. Suppose that the power series $\sum c_n(x - a)^n$ satisfies $c_n \neq 0$ for all n. Show that if $\lim_{n \to \infty} |c_n/c_{n+1}|$ exists, then it is equal to the radius of convergence of the power series.

29. Suppose the series $\sum c_n x^n$ has radius of convergence 2 and the series $\sum d_n x^n$ has radius of convergence 3. What is the radius of convergence of the series $\sum (c_n + d_n)x^n$?

30. Suppose that the radius of convergence of the power series $\sum c_n x^n$ is R. What is the radius of convergence of the power series $\sum c_n x^{2n}$?

8.6 | REPRESENTING FUNCTIONS AS POWER SERIES

In this section we learn how to represent certain types of functions as sums of power series by manipulating geometric series or by differentiating or integrating such a series. You might wonder why we would ever want to express a known function as a sum of infinitely many terms. This strategy is useful for integrating functions that don't have elementary antiderivatives, for solving differential equations, and for approximating functions by polynomials. (Scientists do this to simplify the expressions they deal with; computer scientists do this to represent functions on calculators and computers.)

We start with an equation that we have seen before:

$$\boxed{1} \qquad \frac{1}{1 - x} = 1 + x + x^2 + x^3 + \cdots = \sum_{n=0}^{\infty} x^n \qquad |x| < 1$$

We first encountered this equation in Example 5 in Section 8.2, where we obtained it by observing that the series is a geometric series with $a = 1$ and $r = x$. But here our

- A geometric illustration of Equation 1 is shown in Figure 1. Because the sum of a series is the limit of the sequence of partial sums, we have

$$\frac{1}{1-x} = \lim_{n \to \infty} s_n(x)$$

where

$$s_n(x) = 1 + x + x^2 + \cdots + x^n$$

is the nth partial sum. Notice that as n increases, $s_n(x)$ becomes a better approximation to $f(x)$ for $-1 < x < 1$.

FIGURE 1

point of view is different. We now regard Equation 1 as expressing the function $f(x) = 1/(1-x)$ as a sum of a power series.

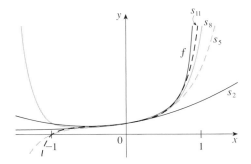

◆ EXAMPLE 1 Express $1/(1 + x^2)$ as the sum of a power series and find the interval of convergence.

SOLUTION Replacing x by $-x^2$ in Equation 1, we have

$$\frac{1}{1 + x^2} = \frac{1}{1 - (-x^2)} = \sum_{n=0}^{\infty} (-x^2)^n$$

$$= \sum_{n=0}^{\infty} (-1)^n x^{2n} = 1 - x^2 + x^4 - x^6 + x^8 - \cdots$$

Because this is a geometric series, it converges when $|-x^2| < 1$, that is, $x^2 < 1$, or $|x| < 1$. Therefore, the interval of convergence is $(-1, 1)$. (Of course, we could have determined the radius of convergence by applying the Ratio Test, but that much work is unnecessary here.) ▪

EXAMPLE 2 Find a power series representation for $1/(x + 2)$.

SOLUTION In order to put this function in the form of the left side of Equation 1 we first factor a 2 from the denominator:

$$\frac{1}{2 + x} = \frac{1}{2\left(1 + \dfrac{x}{2}\right)} = \frac{1}{2\left[1 - \left(-\dfrac{x}{2}\right)\right]}$$

$$= \frac{1}{2} \sum_{n=0}^{\infty} \left(-\frac{x}{2}\right)^n = \sum_{n=0}^{\infty} \frac{(-1)^n}{2^{n+1}} x^n$$

This series converges when $|-x/2| < 1$, that is, $|x| < 2$. So the interval of convergence is $(-2, 2)$. ▪

EXAMPLE 3 Find a power series representation of $x^3/(x + 2)$.

SOLUTION Since this function is just x^3 times the function in Example 2, all we have to do is to multiply that series by x^3:

- It's legitimate to move x^3 across the sigma sign because it doesn't depend on n. [Use Theorem 8.2.8(i) with $c = x^3$.]

$$\frac{x^3}{x + 2} = x^3 \cdot \frac{1}{x + 2} = x^3 \sum_{n=0}^{\infty} \frac{(-1)^n}{2^{n+1}} x^n = \sum_{n=0}^{\infty} \frac{(-1)^n}{2^{n+1}} x^{n+3}$$

$$= \tfrac{1}{2} x^3 - \tfrac{1}{4} x^4 + \tfrac{1}{8} x^5 - \tfrac{1}{16} x^6 + \cdots$$

Another way of writing this series is as follows:

$$\frac{x^3}{x+2} = \sum_{n=3}^{\infty} \frac{(-1)^{n-1}}{2^{n-2}} x^n$$

As in Example 2, the interval of convergence is $(-2, 2)$. ∎

DIFFERENTIATION AND INTEGRATION OF POWER SERIES

The sum of a power series is a function $f(x) = \sum_{n=0}^{\infty} c_n(x-a)^n$ whose domain is the interval of convergence of the series. We would like to be able to differentiate and integrate such functions, and the following theorem (which we won't prove) says that we can do so by differentiating or integrating each individual term in the series, just as we would for a polynomial. This is called **term-by-term differentiation and integration**.

> **2 THEOREM** If the power series $\sum c_n(x-a)^n$ has radius of convergence $R > 0$, then the function f defined by
>
> $$f(x) = c_0 + c_1(x-a) + c_2(x-a)^2 + \cdots = \sum_{n=0}^{\infty} c_n(x-a)^n$$
>
> is differentiable (and therefore continuous) on the interval $(a-R, a+R)$ and
>
> (i) $f'(x) = c_1 + 2c_2(x-a) + 3c_3(x-a)^2 + \cdots = \sum_{n=1}^{\infty} nc_n(x-a)^{n-1}$
>
> (ii) $\displaystyle\int f(x)\,dx = C + c_0(x-a) + c_1\frac{(x-a)^2}{2} + c_2\frac{(x-a)^3}{3} + \cdots$
>
> $$= C + \sum_{n=0}^{\infty} c_n \frac{(x-a)^{n+1}}{n+1}$$
>
> The radii of convergence of the power series in Equations (i) and (ii) are both R.

∎ In part (ii), $\int c_0\,dx = c_0 x + C_1$ is written as $c_0(x-a) + C$, where $C = C_1 + ac_0$, so all the terms of the series have the same form.

NOTE 1 Equations (i) and (ii) in Theorem 2 can be rewritten in the form

(iii) $\displaystyle\frac{d}{dx}\left[\sum_{n=0}^{\infty} c_n(x-a)^n\right] = \sum_{n=0}^{\infty} \frac{d}{dx}\left[c_n(x-a)^n\right]$

(iv) $\displaystyle\int\left[\sum_{n=0}^{\infty} c_n(x-a)^n\right]dx = \sum_{n=0}^{\infty} \int c_n(x-a)^n\,dx$

∎ **www.stewartcalculus.com**
The idea of differentiating a power series term by term is the basis for a powerful method for solving differential equations. Click on *Additional Topics* and then on *Using Series to Solve Differential Equations*.

We know that, for finite sums, the derivative of a sum is the sum of the derivatives and the integral of a sum is the sum of the integrals. Equations (iii) and (iv) assert that the same is true for infinite sums, provided we are dealing with *power series*. (For other types of series of functions the situation is not as simple; see Exercise 36.)

NOTE 2 Although Theorem 2 says that the radius of convergence remains the same when a power series is differentiated or integrated, this does not mean that the *interval* of convergence remains the same. It may happen that the original series converges at an endpoint, whereas the differentiated series diverges there. (See Exercise 37.)

EXAMPLE 4 In Example 3 in Section 8.5 we saw that the Bessel function

$$J_0(x) = \sum_{n=0}^{\infty} \frac{(-1)^n x^{2n}}{2^{2n}(n!)^2}$$

is defined for all x. Thus by Theorem 2, J_0 is differentiable for all x and its derivative is found by term-by-term differentiation as follows:

$$J_0'(x) = \sum_{n=0}^{\infty} \frac{d}{dx} \frac{(-1)^n x^{2n}}{2^{2n}(n!)^2} = \sum_{n=1}^{\infty} \frac{(-1)^n 2n x^{2n-1}}{2^{2n}(n!)^2}$$ ■

▼ EXAMPLE 5 Express $1/(1-x)^2$ as a power series by differentiating Equation 1. What is the radius of convergence?

SOLUTION Differentiating each side of the equation

$$\frac{1}{1-x} = 1 + x + x^2 + x^3 + \cdots = \sum_{n=0}^{\infty} x^n$$

we get

$$\frac{1}{(1-x)^2} = 1 + 2x + 3x^2 + \cdots = \sum_{n=1}^{\infty} n x^{n-1}$$

If we wish, we can replace n by $n+1$ and write the answer as

$$\frac{1}{(1-x)^2} = \sum_{n=0}^{\infty} (n+1)x^n$$

According to Theorem 2, the radius of convergence of the differentiated series is the same as the radius of convergence of the original series, namely, $R = 1$. ■

EXAMPLE 6 Find a power series representation for $\ln(1-x)$ and its radius of convergence.

SOLUTION We notice that, except for a factor of -1, the derivative of this function is $1/(1-x)$. So we integrate both sides of Equation 1:

$$-\ln(1-x) = \int \frac{1}{1-x}\, dx = \int (1 + x + x^2 + \cdots)\, dx$$

$$= x + \frac{x^2}{2} + \frac{x^3}{3} + \cdots + C = \sum_{n=0}^{\infty} \frac{x^{n+1}}{n+1} + C$$

$$= \sum_{n=1}^{\infty} \frac{x^n}{n} + C \qquad |x| < 1$$

To determine the value of C we put $x = 0$ in this equation and obtain $-\ln(1-0) = C$. Thus $C = 0$ and

$$\ln(1-x) = -x - \frac{x^2}{2} - \frac{x^3}{3} - \cdots = -\sum_{n=1}^{\infty} \frac{x^n}{n} \qquad |x| < 1$$

The radius of convergence is the same as for the original series: $R = 1$. ■

Notice what happens if we put $x = \frac{1}{2}$ in the result of Example 6. Since $\ln \frac{1}{2} = -\ln 2$, we see that

$$\ln 2 = \frac{1}{2} + \frac{1}{8} + \frac{1}{24} + \frac{1}{64} + \cdots = \sum_{n=1}^{\infty} \frac{1}{n2^n}$$

V EXAMPLE 7 Find a power series representation for $f(x) = \tan^{-1}x$.

SOLUTION We observe that $f'(x) = 1/(1 + x^2)$ and find the required series by integrating the power series for $1/(1 + x^2)$ found in Example 1.

$$\tan^{-1}x = \int \frac{1}{1 + x^2}\,dx = \int (1 - x^2 + x^4 - x^6 + \cdots)\,dx$$

$$= C + x - \frac{x^3}{3} + \frac{x^5}{5} - \frac{x^7}{7} + \cdots$$

■ The power series for $\tan^{-1}x$ obtained in Example 7 is called *Gregory's series* after the Scottish mathematician James Gregory (1638–1675), who had anticipated some of Newton's discoveries. We have shown that Gregory's series is valid when $-1 < x < 1$, but it turns out (although it isn't easy to prove) that it is also valid when $x = \pm 1$. Notice that when $x = 1$ the series becomes

$$\frac{\pi}{4} = 1 - \frac{1}{3} + \frac{1}{5} - \frac{1}{7} + \cdots$$

This beautiful result is known as the Leibniz formula for π.

To find C we put $x = 0$ and obtain $C = \tan^{-1}0 = 0$. Therefore

$$\tan^{-1}x = x - \frac{x^3}{3} + \frac{x^5}{5} - \frac{x^7}{7} + \cdots = \sum_{n=0}^{\infty} (-1)^n \frac{x^{2n+1}}{2n + 1}$$

Since the radius of convergence of the series for $1/(1 + x^2)$ is 1, the radius of convergence of this series for $\tan^{-1}x$ is also 1.   ■

EXAMPLE 8 Evaluate $\int [1/(1 + x^7)]\,dx$ as a power series.

SOLUTION The first step is to express the integrand, $1/(1 + x^7)$, as the sum of a power series. As in Example 1, we start with Equation 1 and replace x by $-x^7$:

$$\frac{1}{1 + x^7} = \frac{1}{1 - (-x^7)} = \sum_{n=0}^{\infty} (-x^7)^n$$

$$= \sum_{n=0}^{\infty} (-1)^n x^{7n} = 1 - x^7 + x^{14} - \cdots$$

■ This example demonstrates one way in which power series representations are useful. Integrating $1/(1 + x^7)$ by hand is incredibly difficult. Different computer algebra systems return different forms of the answer, but they are all extremely complicated. (If you have a CAS, try it yourself.) The infinite series answer that we obtain in Example 8 is actually much easier to deal with than the finite answer provided by a CAS.

Now we integrate term by term:

$$\int \frac{1}{1 + x^7}\,dx = \int \sum_{n=0}^{\infty} (-1)^n x^{7n}\,dx = C + \sum_{n=0}^{\infty} (-1)^n \frac{x^{7n+1}}{7n + 1}$$

$$= C + x - \frac{x^8}{8} + \frac{x^{15}}{15} - \frac{x^{22}}{22} + \cdots$$

This series converges for $|-x^7| < 1$, that is, for $|x| < 1$.   ■

8.6 EXERCISES

1. If the radius of convergence of the power series $\sum_{n=0}^{\infty} c_n x^n$ is 10, what is the radius of convergence of the series $\sum_{n=1}^{\infty} nc_n x^{n-1}$? Why?

2. Suppose you know that the series $\sum_{n=0}^{\infty} b_n x^n$ converges for $|x| < 2$. What can you say about the following series? Why?

$$\sum_{n=0}^{\infty} \frac{b_n}{n + 1} x^{n+1}$$

3–10 ■ Find a power series representation for the function and determine the interval of convergence.

3. $f(x) = \dfrac{1}{1 + x}$

4. $f(x) = \dfrac{3}{1 - x^4}$

5. $f(x) = \dfrac{1}{1 - x^3}$

6. $f(x) = \dfrac{1}{1 + 9x^2}$

7. $f(x) = \dfrac{1}{x - 5}$

8. $f(x) = \dfrac{x}{4x + 1}$

9. $f(x) = \dfrac{x}{9 + x^2}$

10. $f(x) = \dfrac{x^2}{a^3 - x^3}$

▪ ▪ ▪ ▪ ▪ ▪ ▪ ▪ ▪ ▪ ▪ ▪ ▪ ▪

11–12 ▪ Express the function as the sum of a power series by first using partial fractions. Find the interval of convergence.

11. $f(x) = \dfrac{3}{x^2 + x - 2}$

12. $f(x) = \dfrac{7x - 1}{3x^2 + 2x - 1}$

▪ ▪ ▪ ▪ ▪ ▪ ▪ ▪ ▪ ▪ ▪ ▪ ▪ ▪

13. (a) Use differentiation to find a power series representation for

$$f(x) = \frac{1}{(1 + x)^2}$$

What is the radius of convergence?
(b) Use part (a) to find a power series for

$$f(x) = \frac{1}{(1 + x)^3}$$

(c) Use part (b) to find a power series for

$$f(x) = \frac{x^2}{(1 + x)^3}$$

14. (a) Find a power series representation for $f(x) = \ln(1 + x)$. What is the radius of convergence?
(b) Use part (a) to find a power series for
$f(x) = x \ln(1 + x)$.
(c) Use part (a) to find a power series for $f(x) = \ln(x^2 + 1)$.

15–18 ▪ Find a power series representation for the function and determine the radius of convergence.

15. $f(x) = \ln(5 - x)$

16. $f(x) = \dfrac{x^2}{(1 - 2x)^2}$

17. $f(x) = \dfrac{x^3}{(x - 2)^2}$

18. $f(x) = \arctan(x/3)$

▪ ▪ ▪ ▪ ▪ ▪ ▪ ▪ ▪ ▪ ▪ ▪ ▪ ▪

⊞ **19–22** ▪ Find a power series representation for f, and graph f and several partial sums $s_n(x)$ on the same screen. What happens as n increases?

19. $f(x) = \ln(3 + x)$

20. $f(x) = \dfrac{1}{x^2 + 25}$

21. $f(x) = \ln\left(\dfrac{1 + x}{1 - x}\right)$

22. $f(x) = \tan^{-1}(2x)$

▪ ▪ ▪ ▪ ▪ ▪ ▪ ▪ ▪ ▪ ▪ ▪ ▪ ▪

23–26 ▪ Evaluate the indefinite integral as a power series. What is the radius of convergence?

23. $\displaystyle\int \frac{t}{1 - t^8}\, dt$

24. $\displaystyle\int \frac{\ln(1 - t)}{t}\, dt$

25. $\displaystyle\int \frac{x - \tan^{-1}x}{x^3}\, dx$

26. $\displaystyle\int \tan^{-1}(x^2)\, dx$

▪ ▪ ▪ ▪ ▪ ▪ ▪ ▪ ▪ ▪ ▪ ▪ ▪ ▪

27–30 ▪ Use a power series to approximate the definite integral to six decimal places.

27. $\displaystyle\int_0^{0.2} \frac{1}{1 + x^5}\, dx$

28. $\displaystyle\int_0^{0.4} \ln(1 + x^4)\, dx$

29. $\displaystyle\int_0^{0.1} x \arctan(3x)\, dx$

30. $\displaystyle\int_0^{0.3} \frac{x^2}{1 + x^4}\, dx$

▪ ▪ ▪ ▪ ▪ ▪ ▪ ▪ ▪ ▪ ▪ ▪ ▪ ▪

31. Use the result of Example 6 to compute $\ln 1.1$ correct to five decimal places.

32. Show that the function

$$f(x) = \sum_{n=0}^{\infty} \frac{(-1)^n x^{2n}}{(2n)!}$$

is a solution of the differential equation

$$f''(x) + f(x) = 0$$

33. (a) Show that J_0 (the Bessel function of order 0 given in Example 4) satisfies the differential equation

$$x^2 J_0''(x) + x J_0'(x) + x^2 J_0(x) = 0$$

(b) Evaluate $\int_0^1 J_0(x)\, dx$ correct to three decimal places.

34. The Bessel function of order 1 is defined by

$$J_1(x) = \sum_{n=0}^{\infty} \frac{(-1)^n x^{2n+1}}{n!(n + 1)!2^{2n+1}}$$

(a) Show that J_1 satisfies the differential equation

$$x^2 J_1''(x) + x J_1'(x) + (x^2 - 1)J_1(x) = 0$$

(b) Show that $J_0'(x) = -J_1(x)$.

35. (a) Show that the function

$$f(x) = \sum_{n=0}^{\infty} \frac{x^n}{n!}$$

is a solution of the differential equation

$$f'(x) = f(x)$$

(b) Show that $f(x) = e^x$.

36. Let $f_n(x) = (\sin nx)/n^2$. Show that the series $\Sigma f_n(x)$ converges for all values of x but the series of derivatives $\Sigma f_n'(x)$ diverges when $x = 2n\pi$, n an integer. For what values of x does the series $\Sigma f_n''(x)$ converge?

37. Let

$$f(x) = \sum_{n=1}^{\infty} \frac{x^n}{n^2}$$

Find the intervals of convergence for f, f', and f''.

38. (a) Starting with the geometric series $\sum_{n=0}^{\infty} x^n$, find the sum of the series

$$\sum_{n=1}^{\infty} nx^{n-1} \qquad |x| < 1$$

(b) Find the sum of each of the following series.

　(i) $\displaystyle\sum_{n=1}^{\infty} nx^n$, $|x| < 1$ 　(ii) $\displaystyle\sum_{n=1}^{\infty} \frac{n}{2^n}$

(c) Find the sum of each of the following series.

　(i) $\displaystyle\sum_{n=2}^{\infty} n(n-1)x^n$, $|x| < 1$

　(ii) $\displaystyle\sum_{n=2}^{\infty} \frac{n^2 - n}{2^n}$ 　(iii) $\displaystyle\sum_{n=1}^{\infty} \frac{n^2}{2^n}$

39. Use the power series for $\tan^{-1}x$ to prove the following expression for π as the sum of an infinite series:

$$\pi = 2\sqrt{3} \sum_{n=0}^{\infty} \frac{(-1)^n}{(2n+1)3^n}$$

8.7 TAYLOR AND MACLAURIN SERIES

In the preceding section we were able to find power series representations for a certain restricted class of functions. Here we investigate more general problems: Which functions have power series representations? How can we find such representations?

We start by supposing that f is any function that can be represented by a power series:

1 $\quad f(x) = c_0 + c_1(x-a) + c_2(x-a)^2 + c_3(x-a)^3 + c_4(x-a)^4 + \cdots$
$$|x - a| < R$$

Let's try to determine what the coefficients c_n must be in terms of f. To begin, notice that if we put $x = a$ in Equation 1, then all terms after the first one are 0 and we get

$$f(a) = c_0$$

By Theorem 8.6.2, we can differentiate the series in Equation 1 term by term:

2 $\quad f'(x) = c_1 + 2c_2(x-a) + 3c_3(x-a)^2 + 4c_4(x-a)^3 + \cdots \qquad |x-a| < R$

and substitution of $x = a$ in Equation 2 gives

$$f'(a) = c_1$$

Now we differentiate both sides of Equation 2 and obtain

3 $\quad f''(x) = 2c_2 + 2 \cdot 3c_3(x-a) + 3 \cdot 4c_4(x-a)^2 + \cdots \qquad |x-a| < R$

Again we put $x = a$ in Equation 3. The result is

$$f''(a) = 2c_2$$

Let's apply the procedure one more time. Differentiation of the series in Equation 3 gives

4 $\quad f'''(x) = 2 \cdot 3c_3 + 2 \cdot 3 \cdot 4c_4(x-a) + 3 \cdot 4 \cdot 5c_5(x-a)^2 + \cdots \qquad |x-a| < R$

and substitution of $x = a$ in Equation 4 gives

$$f'''(a) = 2 \cdot 3c_3 = 3!c_3$$

By now you can see the pattern. If we continue to differentiate and substitute $x = a$, we obtain

$$f^{(n)}(a) = 2 \cdot 3 \cdot 4 \cdot \cdots \cdot nc_n = n!c_n$$

Solving this equation for the nth coefficient c_n, we get

$$c_n = \frac{f^{(n)}(a)}{n!}$$

This formula remains valid even for $n = 0$ if we adopt the conventions that $0! = 1$ and $f^{(0)} = f$. Thus we have proved the following theorem.

---

5 THEOREM If f has a power series representation (expansion) at a, that is, if

$$f(x) = \sum_{n=0}^{\infty} c_n(x - a)^n \qquad |x - a| < R$$

then its coefficients are given by the formula

$$c_n = \frac{f^{(n)}(a)}{n!}$$

Substituting this formula for c_n back into the series, we see that *if f has a power series expansion at a, then it must be of the following form.*

---

6 $\displaystyle f(x) = \sum_{n=0}^{\infty} \frac{f^{(n)}(a)}{n!} (x - a)^n$

$$= f(a) + \frac{f'(a)}{1!} (x - a) + \frac{f''(a)}{2!} (x - a)^2 + \frac{f'''(a)}{3!} (x - a)^3 + \cdots$$

■ The Taylor series is named after the English mathematician Brook Taylor (1685–1731) and the Maclaurin series is named in honor of the Scottish mathematician Colin Maclaurin (1698–1746) despite the fact that the Maclaurin series is really just a special case of the Taylor series. But the idea of representing particular functions as sums of power series goes back to Newton, and the general Taylor series was known to the Scottish mathematician James Gregory in 1668 and to the Swiss mathematician John Bernoulli in the 1690s. Taylor was apparently unaware of the work of Gregory and Bernoulli when he published his discoveries on series in 1715 in his book *Methodus incrementorum directa et inversa.* Maclaurin series are named after Colin Maclaurin because he popularized them in his calculus textbook *Treatise of Fluxions* published in 1742.

The series in Equation 6 is called the **Taylor series of the function f at a** (or **about** a or **centered at a**). For the special case $a = 0$ the Taylor series becomes

---

7 $\displaystyle f(x) = \sum_{n=0}^{\infty} \frac{f^{(n)}(0)}{n!} x^n = f(0) + \frac{f'(0)}{1!} x + \frac{f''(0)}{2!} x^2 + \cdots$

This case arises frequently enough that it is given the special name **Maclaurin series**.

NOTE We have shown that *if* f can be represented as a power series about a, then f is equal to the sum of its Taylor series. But there exist functions that are not equal to the sum of their Taylor series. An example of such a function is given in Exercise 70.

☑ EXAMPLE 1 Find the Maclaurin series of the function $f(x) = e^x$ and its radius of convergence.

SOLUTION If $f(x) = e^x$, then $f^{(n)}(x) = e^x$, so $f^{(n)}(0) = e^0 = 1$ for all n. Therefore, the Taylor series for f at 0 (that is, the Maclaurin series) is

$$\sum_{n=0}^{\infty} \frac{f^{(n)}(0)}{n!} x^n = \sum_{n=0}^{\infty} \frac{x^n}{n!} = 1 + \frac{x}{1!} + \frac{x^2}{2!} + \frac{x^3}{3!} + \cdots$$

To find the radius of convergence we let $a_n = x^n/n!$. Then

$$\left| \frac{a_{n+1}}{a_n} \right| = \left| \frac{x^{n+1}}{(n+1)!} \cdot \frac{n!}{x^n} \right| = \frac{|x|}{n+1} \to 0 < 1$$

so, by the Ratio Test, the series converges for all x and the radius of convergence is $R = \infty$. ∎

The conclusion we can draw from Theorem 5 and Example 1 is that *if e^x has a power series expansion at 0, then*

$$e^x = \sum_{n=0}^{\infty} \frac{x^n}{n!}$$

So how can we determine whether e^x *does* have a power series representation?

Let's investigate the more general question: Under what circumstances is a function equal to the sum of its Taylor series? In other words, if f has derivatives of all orders, when is it true that

$$f(x) = \sum_{n=0}^{\infty} \frac{f^{(n)}(a)}{n!} (x-a)^n$$

As with any convergent series, this means that $f(x)$ is the limit of the sequence of partial sums. In the case of the Taylor series, the partial sums are

$$T_n(x) = \sum_{i=0}^{n} \frac{f^{(i)}(a)}{i!} (x-a)^i$$

$$= f(a) + \frac{f'(a)}{1!}(x-a) + \frac{f''(a)}{2!}(x-a)^2 + \cdots + \frac{f^{(n)}(a)}{n!}(x-a)^n$$

Notice that T_n is a polynomial of degree n called the **nth-degree Taylor polynomial of f at a.** For instance, for the exponential function $f(x) = e^x$, the result of Example 1 shows that the Taylor polynomials at 0 (or Maclaurin polynomials) with $n = 1, 2,$ and 3 are

$$T_1(x) = 1 + x \qquad T_2(x) = 1 + x + \frac{x^2}{2!} \qquad T_3(x) = 1 + x + \frac{x^2}{2!} + \frac{x^3}{3!}$$

The graphs of the exponential function and these three Taylor polynomials are drawn in Figure 1.

In general, $f(x)$ is the sum of its Taylor series if

$$f(x) = \lim_{n \to \infty} T_n(x)$$

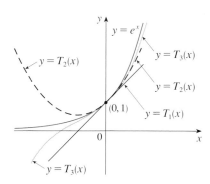

FIGURE 1

▪ As n increases, $T_n(x)$ appears to approach e^x in Figure 1. This suggests that e^x is equal to the sum of its Taylor series.

If we let

$$R_n(x) = f(x) - T_n(x) \qquad \text{so that} \qquad f(x) = T_n(x) + R_n(x)$$

then $R_n(x)$ is called the **remainder** of the Taylor series. If we can somehow show that $\lim_{n \to \infty} R_n(x) = 0$, then it follows that

$$\lim_{n \to \infty} T_n(x) = \lim_{n \to \infty} [f(x) - R_n(x)] = f(x) - \lim_{n \to \infty} R_n(x) = f(x)$$

We have therefore proved the following.

---

8 **THEOREM** If $f(x) = T_n(x) + R_n(x)$, where T_n is the nth-degree Taylor polynomial of f at a and

$$\lim_{n \to \infty} R_n(x) = 0$$

for $|x - a| < R$, then f is equal to the sum of its Taylor series on the interval $|x - a| < R$.

In trying to show that $\lim_{n \to \infty} R_n(x) = 0$ for a specific function f, we usually use the expression in the next theorem.

---

9 **TAYLOR'S FORMULA** If f has $n + 1$ derivatives in an interval I that contains the number a, then for x in I there is a number z strictly between x and a such that the remainder term in the Taylor series can be expressed as

$$R_n(x) = \frac{f^{(n+1)}(z)}{(n + 1)!} (x - a)^{n+1}$$

NOTE 1 For the special case $n = 0$, if we put $x = b$ and $z = c$ in Taylor's Formula, we get $f(b) = f(a) + f'(c)(b - a)$, which is the Mean Value Theorem. In fact, Theorem 9 can be proved by a method similar to the proof of the Mean Value Theorem. The proof is given at the end of this section.

NOTE 2 Notice that the remainder term

10
$$R_n(x) = \frac{f^{(n+1)}(z)}{(n + 1)!} (x - a)^{n+1}$$

is very similar to the terms in the Taylor series except that $f^{(n+1)}$ is evaluated at z instead of at a. All we can say about the number z is that it lies somewhere between x and a. The expression for $R_n(x)$ in Equation 10 is known as **Lagrange's form of the remainder term**.

NOTE 3 In Section 8.8 we will explore the use of Taylor's Formula in approximating functions. Our immediate use of it is in conjunction with Theorem 8.

In applying Theorems 8 and 9 it is often helpful to make use of the following fact.

11
$$\lim_{n \to \infty} \frac{x^n}{n!} = 0 \qquad \text{for every real number } x$$

This is true because we know from Example 1 that the series $\Sigma\, x^n/n!$ converges for all x and so its nth term approaches 0.

EXAMPLE 2 Prove that e^x is equal to the sum of its Taylor series.

SOLUTION If $f(x) = e^x$, then $f^{(n+1)}(x) = e^x$, so the remainder term in Taylor's Formula is

$$R_n(x) = \frac{e^z}{(n+1)!}\, x^{n+1}$$

where z lies between 0 and x. (Note, however, that z depends on n.) If $x > 0$, then $0 < z < x$, so $e^z < e^x$. Therefore

$$0 < R_n(x) = \frac{e^z}{(n+1)!}\, x^{n+1} < e^x \frac{x^{n+1}}{(n+1)!} \to 0$$

by Equation 11, so $R_n(x) \to 0$ as $n \to \infty$ by the Squeeze Theorem. If $x < 0$, then $x < z < 0$, so $e^z < e^0 = 1$ and

$$|R_n(x)| < \frac{|x|^{n+1}}{(n+1)!} \to 0$$

Again $R_n(x) \to 0$. Thus, by Theorem 8, e^x is equal to the sum of its Taylor series, that is,

12

$$e^x = \sum_{n=0}^{\infty} \frac{x^n}{n!} \qquad \text{for all } x$$ ■

In particular, if we put $x = 1$ in Equation 12, we obtain the following expression for the number e as a sum of an infinite series:

■ In 1748 Leonard Euler used Equation 13 to find the value of e correct to 23 digits. In 2003 Shigeru Kondo, again using the series in (13), computed e to more than fifty billion decimal places! The special techniques employed to speed up the computation are explained on the web page

numbers.computation.free.fr

13

$$e = \sum_{n=0}^{\infty} \frac{1}{n!} = 1 + \frac{1}{1!} + \frac{1}{2!} + \frac{1}{3!} + \cdots$$

EXAMPLE 3 Find the Taylor series for $f(x) = e^x$ at $a = 2$.

SOLUTION We have $f^{(n)}(2) = e^2$ and so, putting $a = 2$ in the definition of a Taylor series (6), we get

$$\sum_{n=0}^{\infty} \frac{f^{(n)}(2)}{n!} (x-2)^n = \sum_{n=0}^{\infty} \frac{e^2}{n!} (x-2)^n$$

Again it can be verified, as in Example 1, that the radius of convergence is $R = \infty$. As in Example 2 we can verify that $\lim_{n\to\infty} R_n(x) = 0$, so

14

$$e^x = \sum_{n=0}^{\infty} \frac{e^2}{n!} (x-2)^n \qquad \text{for all } x$$ ■

We have two power series expansions for e^x, the Maclaurin series in Equation 12 and the Taylor series in Equation 14. The first is better if we are interested in values of x near 0 and the second is better if x is near 2.

EXAMPLE 4 Find the Maclaurin series for $\sin x$ and prove that it represents $\sin x$ for all x.

SOLUTION We arrange our computation in two columns as follows:

$$f(x) = \sin x \qquad f(0) = 0$$
$$f'(x) = \cos x \qquad f'(0) = 1$$
$$f''(x) = -\sin x \qquad f''(0) = 0$$
$$f'''(x) = -\cos x \qquad f'''(0) = -1$$
$$f^{(4)}(x) = \sin x \qquad f^{(4)}(0) = 0$$

Since the derivatives repeat in a cycle of four, we can write the Maclaurin series as follows:

$$f(0) + \frac{f'(0)}{1!}x + \frac{f''(0)}{2!}x^2 + \frac{f'''(0)}{3!}x^3 + \cdots$$

$$= x - \frac{x^3}{3!} + \frac{x^5}{5!} - \frac{x^7}{7!} + \cdots = \sum_{n=0}^{\infty}(-1)^n \frac{x^{2n+1}}{(2n+1)!}$$

Using the remainder term (10) with $a = 0$, we have

$$R_n(x) = \frac{f^{(n+1)}(z)}{(n+1)!}x^{n+1}$$

where $f(x) = \sin x$ and z lies between 0 and x. But $f^{(n+1)}(z)$ is $\pm\sin z$ or $\pm\cos z$. In any case, $|f^{(n+1)}(z)| \leq 1$ and so

15
$$0 \leq |R_n(x)| = \frac{|f^{(n+1)}(z)|}{(n+1)!}|x^{n+1}| \leq \frac{|x|^{n+1}}{(n+1)!}$$

By Equation 11 the right side of this inequality approaches 0 as $n \to \infty$, so $|R_n(x)| \to 0$ by the Squeeze Theorem. It follows that $R_n(x) \to 0$ as $n \to \infty$, so $\sin x$ is equal to the sum of its Maclaurin series by Theorem 8. ■

We state the result of Example 4 for future reference.

16
$$\sin x = x - \frac{x^3}{3!} + \frac{x^5}{5!} - \frac{x^7}{7!} + \cdots$$

$$= \sum_{n=0}^{\infty}(-1)^n \frac{x^{2n+1}}{(2n+1)!} \qquad \text{for all } x$$

EXAMPLE 5 Find the Maclaurin series for $\cos x$.

SOLUTION We could proceed directly as in Example 4 but it's easier to differentiate the Maclaurin series for $\sin x$ given by Equation 16:

$$\cos x = \frac{d}{dx}(\sin x) = \frac{d}{dx}\left(x - \frac{x^3}{3!} + \frac{x^5}{5!} - \frac{x^7}{7!} + \cdots\right)$$

$$= 1 - \frac{3x^2}{3!} + \frac{5x^4}{5!} - \frac{7x^6}{7!} + \cdots = 1 - \frac{x^2}{2!} + \frac{x^4}{4!} - \frac{x^6}{6!} + \cdots$$

■ Figure 2 shows the graph of $\sin x$ together with its Taylor (or Maclaurin) polynomials

$$T_1(x) = x$$

$$T_3(x) = x - \frac{x^3}{3!}$$

$$T_5(x) = x - \frac{x^3}{3!} + \frac{x^5}{5!}$$

Notice that, as n increases, $T_n(x)$ becomes a better approximation to $\sin x$.

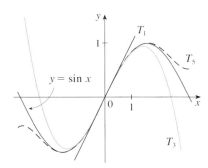

FIGURE 2

■ The Maclaurin series for e^x, $\sin x$, and $\cos x$ that we found in Examples 2, 4, and 5 were discovered, using different methods, by Newton. These equations are remarkable because they say we know everything about each of these functions if we know all its derivatives at the single number 0.

Since the Maclaurin series for $\sin x$ converges for all x, Theorem 8.6.2 tells us that the differentiated series for $\cos x$ also converges for all x. Thus

17

$$\cos x = 1 - \frac{x^2}{2!} + \frac{x^4}{4!} - \frac{x^6}{6!} + \cdots$$

$$= \sum_{n=0}^{\infty} (-1)^n \frac{x^{2n}}{(2n)!} \qquad \text{for all } x \qquad ■$$

EXAMPLE 6 Find the Maclaurin series for the function $f(x) = x \cos x$.

SOLUTION Instead of computing derivatives and substituting in Equation 7, it's easier to multiply the series for $\cos x$ (Equation 17) by x:

$$x \cos x = x \sum_{n=0}^{\infty} (-1)^n \frac{x^{2n}}{(2n)!} = \sum_{n=0}^{\infty} (-1)^n \frac{x^{2n+1}}{(2n)!} \qquad ■$$

The power series that we obtained by indirect methods in Examples 5 and 6 and in Section 8.6 are indeed the Taylor or Maclaurin series of the given functions because Theorem 5 asserts that, no matter how we obtain a power series representation $f(x) = \Sigma c_n(x - a)^n$, it is always true that $c_n = f^{(n)}(a)/n!$. In other words, the coefficients are uniquely determined.

EXAMPLE 7 Find the Maclaurin series for $f(x) = (1 + x)^k$, where k is any real number.

SOLUTION Arranging our work in columns, we have

$$f(x) = (1 + x)^k \qquad\qquad f(0) = 1$$

$$f'(x) = k(1 + x)^{k-1} \qquad\qquad f'(0) = k$$

$$f''(x) = k(k - 1)(1 + x)^{k-2} \qquad\qquad f''(0) = k(k - 1)$$

$$f'''(x) = k(k - 1)(k - 2)(1 + x)^{k-3} \qquad\qquad f'''(0) = k(k - 1)(k - 2)$$

$$\vdots \qquad\qquad\qquad \vdots$$

$$f^{(n)}(x) = k(k - 1) \cdots (k - n + 1)(1 + x)^{k-n} \qquad f^{(n)}(0) = k(k - 1) \cdots (k - n + 1)$$

Therefore, the Maclaurin series of $f(x) = (1 + x)^k$ is

$$\sum_{n=0}^{\infty} \frac{f^{(n)}(0)}{n!} x^n = \sum_{n=0}^{\infty} \frac{k(k - 1) \cdots (k - n + 1)}{n!} x^n$$

This series is called the **binomial series**. If its nth term is a_n, then

$$\left| \frac{a_{n+1}}{a_n} \right| = \left| \frac{k(k - 1) \cdots (k - n + 1)(k - n)x^{n+1}}{(n + 1)!} \cdot \frac{n!}{k(k - 1) \cdots (k - n + 1)x^n} \right|$$

$$= \frac{|k - n|}{n + 1} |x| = \frac{\left| 1 - \dfrac{k}{n} \right|}{1 + \dfrac{1}{n}} |x| \to |x| \qquad \text{as } n \to \infty$$

Thus by the Ratio Test the binomial series converges if $|x| < 1$ and diverges if $|x| > 1$. ∎

The traditional notation for the coefficients in the binomial series is

$$\binom{k}{n} = \frac{k(k-1)(k-2)\cdots(k-n+1)}{n!}$$

and these numbers are called the **binomial coefficients**.

The following theorem states that $(1 + x)^k$ is equal to the sum of its Maclaurin series. It is possible to prove this by showing that the remainder term $R_n(x)$ approaches 0, but that turns out to be quite difficult. The proof outlined in Exercise 69 is much easier.

---

18 THE BINOMIAL SERIES If k is any real number and $|x| < 1$, then

$$(1 + x)^k = \sum_{n=0}^{\infty} \binom{k}{n} x^n = 1 + kx + \frac{k(k-1)}{2!} x^2 + \frac{k(k-1)(k-2)}{3!} x^3 + \cdots$$

Although the binomial series always converges when $|x| < 1$, the question of whether or not it converges at the endpoints, ± 1, depends on the value of k. It turns out that the series converges at 1 if $-1 < k \le 0$ and at both endpoints if $k \ge 0$. Notice that if k is a positive integer and $n > k$, then the expression for $\binom{k}{n}$ contains a factor $(k - k)$, so $\binom{k}{n} = 0$ for $n > k$. This means that the series terminates and reduces to the ordinary Binomial Theorem when k is a positive integer. (See Reference Page 1.)

▼ EXAMPLE 8 Find the Maclaurin series for the function $f(x) = \dfrac{1}{\sqrt{4-x}}$ and its radius of convergence.

SOLUTION We write $f(x)$ in a form where we can use the binomial series:

$$\frac{1}{\sqrt{4-x}} = \frac{1}{\sqrt{4\left(1 - \dfrac{x}{4}\right)}} = \frac{1}{2\sqrt{1 - \dfrac{x}{4}}} = \frac{1}{2}\left(1 - \frac{x}{4}\right)^{-1/2}$$

Using the binomial series with $k = -\frac{1}{2}$ and with x replaced by $-x/4$, we have

$$\frac{1}{\sqrt{4-x}} = \frac{1}{2}\left(1 - \frac{x}{4}\right)^{-1/2} = \frac{1}{2}\sum_{n=0}^{\infty}\binom{-\frac{1}{2}}{n}\left(-\frac{x}{4}\right)^n$$

$$= \frac{1}{2}\left[1 + \left(-\frac{1}{2}\right)\left(-\frac{x}{4}\right) + \frac{\left(-\frac{1}{2}\right)\left(-\frac{3}{2}\right)}{2!}\left(-\frac{x}{4}\right)^2 + \frac{\left(-\frac{1}{2}\right)\left(-\frac{3}{2}\right)\left(-\frac{5}{2}\right)}{3!}\left(-\frac{x}{4}\right)^3\right.$$

$$\left. + \cdots + \frac{\left(-\frac{1}{2}\right)\left(-\frac{3}{2}\right)\left(-\frac{5}{2}\right)\cdots\left(-\frac{1}{2} - n + 1\right)}{n!}\left(-\frac{x}{4}\right)^n + \cdots\right]$$

$$= \frac{1}{2}\left[1 + \frac{1}{8}x + \frac{1\cdot3}{2!8^2}x^2 + \frac{1\cdot3\cdot5}{3!8^3}x^3 + \cdots + \frac{1\cdot3\cdot5\cdot\cdots\cdot(2n-1)}{n!8^n}x^n + \cdots\right]$$

We know from (18) that this series converges when $|-x/4| < 1$, that is, $|x| < 4$, so the radius of convergence is $R = 4$.   ■

We collect in the following table, for future reference, some important Maclaurin series that we have derived in this section and the preceding one.

Important Maclaurin series and their radii of convergence

$\dfrac{1}{1-x} = \displaystyle\sum_{n=0}^{\infty} x^n = 1 + x + x^2 + x^3 + \cdots$	$R = 1$
$e^x = \displaystyle\sum_{n=0}^{\infty} \dfrac{x^n}{n!} = 1 + \dfrac{x}{1!} + \dfrac{x^2}{2!} + \dfrac{x^3}{3!} + \cdots$	$R = \infty$
$\sin x = \displaystyle\sum_{n=0}^{\infty} (-1)^n \dfrac{x^{2n+1}}{(2n+1)!} = x - \dfrac{x^3}{3!} + \dfrac{x^5}{5!} - \dfrac{x^7}{7!} + \cdots$	$R = \infty$
$\cos x = \displaystyle\sum_{n=0}^{\infty} (-1)^n \dfrac{x^{2n}}{(2n)!} = 1 - \dfrac{x^2}{2!} + \dfrac{x^4}{4!} - \dfrac{x^6}{6!} + \cdots$	$R = \infty$
$\tan^{-1}x = \displaystyle\sum_{n=0}^{\infty} (-1)^n \dfrac{x^{2n+1}}{2n+1} = x - \dfrac{x^3}{3} + \dfrac{x^5}{5} - \dfrac{x^7}{7} + \cdots$	$R = 1$
$(1+x)^k = \displaystyle\sum_{n=0}^{\infty} \binom{k}{n} x^n = 1 + kx + \dfrac{k(k-1)}{2!}x^2 + \dfrac{k(k-1)(k-2)}{3!} + \cdots$	$R = 1$

Module 8.7/8.8 enables you to see how successive Taylor polynomials approach the original function.

One reason that Taylor series are important is that they enable us to integrate functions that we couldn't previously handle. In fact, in the introduction to this chapter we mentioned that Newton often integrated functions by first expressing them as power series and then integrating the series term by term. The function $f(x) = e^{-x^2}$ can't be integrated by techniques discussed so far because its antiderivative is not an elementary function (see Section 6.4). In the following example we use Newton's idea to integrate this function.

◩ EXAMPLE 9
(a) Evaluate $\int e^{-x^2}\, dx$ as an infinite series.
(b) Evaluate $\int_0^1 e^{-x^2}\, dx$ correct to within an error of 0.001.

SOLUTION
(a) First we find the Maclaurin series for $f(x) = e^{-x^2}$. Although it's possible to use the direct method, let's find it simply by replacing x with $-x^2$ in the series for e^x given in the table of Maclaurin series. Thus, for all values of x,

$$e^{-x^2} = \sum_{n=0}^{\infty} \frac{(-x^2)^n}{n!} = \sum_{n=0}^{\infty} (-1)^n \frac{x^{2n}}{n!} = 1 - \frac{x^2}{1!} + \frac{x^4}{2!} - \frac{x^6}{3!} + \cdots$$

Now we integrate term by term:

$$\int e^{-x^2}\, dx = \int \left(1 - \frac{x^2}{1!} + \frac{x^4}{2!} - \frac{x^6}{3!} + \cdots + (-1)^n \frac{x^{2n}}{n!} + \cdots \right) dx$$

$$= C + x - \frac{x^3}{3 \cdot 1!} + \frac{x^5}{5 \cdot 2!} - \frac{x^7}{7 \cdot 3!} + \cdots + (-1)^n \frac{x^{2n+1}}{(2n+1)n!} + \cdots$$

This series converges for all x because the original series for e^{-x^2} converges for all x.

(b) The Evaluation Theorem gives

$$\int_0^1 e^{-x^2}\,dx = \left[x - \frac{x^3}{3 \cdot 1!} + \frac{x^5}{5 \cdot 2!} - \frac{x^7}{7 \cdot 3!} + \frac{x^9}{9 \cdot 4!} - \cdots \right]_0^1$$

$$= 1 - \tfrac{1}{3} + \tfrac{1}{10} - \tfrac{1}{42} + \tfrac{1}{216} - \cdots$$

$$\approx 1 - \tfrac{1}{3} + \tfrac{1}{10} - \tfrac{1}{42} + \tfrac{1}{216} \approx 0.7475$$

■ We can take $C = 0$ in the antiderivative in part (a).

The Alternating Series Estimation Theorem shows that the error involved in this approximation is less than

$$\frac{1}{11 \cdot 5!} = \frac{1}{1320} < 0.001$$

■

   Another use of Taylor series is illustrated in the next example. The limit could be found with l'Hospital's Rule, but instead we use a series.

EXAMPLE 10 Evaluate $\displaystyle\lim_{x \to 0} \frac{e^x - 1 - x}{x^2}$.

SOLUTION Using the Maclaurin series for e^x, we have

■ Some computer algebra systems compute limits in this way.

$$\lim_{x \to 0} \frac{e^x - 1 - x}{x^2} = \lim_{x \to 0} \frac{\left(1 + \dfrac{x}{1!} + \dfrac{x^2}{2!} + \dfrac{x^3}{3!} + \cdots \right) - 1 - x}{x^2}$$

$$= \lim_{x \to 0} \frac{\dfrac{x^2}{2!} + \dfrac{x^3}{3!} + \dfrac{x^4}{4!} + \cdots}{x^2}$$

$$= \lim_{x \to 0} \left(\frac{1}{2} + \frac{x}{3!} + \frac{x^2}{4!} + \frac{x^3}{5!} + \cdots \right) = \frac{1}{2}$$

because power series are continuous functions.   ■

MULTIPLICATION AND DIVISION OF POWER SERIES

If power series are added or subtracted, they behave like polynomials (Theorem 8.2.8 shows this). In fact, as the following example illustrates, they can also be multiplied and divided like polynomials. We find only the first few terms because the calculations for the later terms become tedious and the initial terms are the most important ones.

EXAMPLE 11 Find the first three nonzero terms in the Maclaurin series for
(a) $e^x \sin x$ and (b) $\tan x$.

SOLUTION
(a) Using the Maclaurin series for e^x and $\sin x$ in the table on page 466, we have

$$e^x \sin x = \left(1 + \frac{x}{1!} + \frac{x^2}{2!} + \frac{x^3}{3!} + \cdots \right)\left(x - \frac{x^3}{3!} + \cdots \right)$$

We multiply these expressions, collecting like terms just as for polynomials:

$$
\begin{array}{r}
1 + x + \tfrac{1}{2}x^2 + \tfrac{1}{6}x^3 + \cdots \\
\times \qquad\qquad x \qquad\qquad -\tfrac{1}{6}x^3 + \cdots \\
\hline
x + \quad x^2 + \tfrac{1}{2}x^3 + \tfrac{1}{6}x^4 + \cdots \\
+ \qquad\qquad\qquad\qquad -\tfrac{1}{6}x^3 - \tfrac{1}{6}x^4 - \cdots \\
\hline
x + \quad x^2 + \tfrac{1}{3}x^3 + \cdots
\end{array}
$$

Thus $$e^x \sin x = x + x^2 + \tfrac{1}{3}x^3 + \cdots$$

(b) Using the Maclaurin series in the table, we have

$$
\tan x = \frac{\sin x}{\cos x} = \frac{x - \dfrac{x^3}{3!} + \dfrac{x^5}{5!} - \cdots}{1 - \dfrac{x^2}{2!} + \dfrac{x^4}{4!} - \cdots}
$$

We use a procedure like long division:

$$
\begin{array}{r}
x + \tfrac{1}{3}x^3 + \tfrac{2}{15}x^5 + \cdots \\
1 - \tfrac{1}{2}x^2 + \tfrac{1}{24}x^4 - \cdots \overline{\smash{\big)}\, x - \tfrac{1}{6}x^3 + \tfrac{1}{120}x^5 - \cdots} \\
\underline{x - \tfrac{1}{2}x^3 + \tfrac{1}{24}x^5 - \cdots} \\
\tfrac{1}{3}x^3 - \tfrac{1}{30}x^5 + \cdots \\
\underline{\tfrac{1}{3}x^3 - \tfrac{1}{6}x^5 + \cdots} \\
\tfrac{2}{15}x^5 + \cdots
\end{array}
$$

Thus $$\tan x = x + \tfrac{1}{3}x^3 + \tfrac{2}{15}x^5 + \cdots$$ ∎

Although we have not attempted to justify the formal manipulations used in Example 11, they are legitimate. There is a theorem which states that if both $f(x) = \Sigma\, c_n x^n$ and $g(x) = \Sigma\, b_n x^n$ converge for $|x| < R$ and the series are multiplied as if they were polynomials, then the resulting series also converges for $|x| < R$ and represents $f(x)g(x)$. For division we require $b_0 \neq 0$; the resulting series converges for sufficiently small $|x|$.

PROOF OF TAYLOR'S FORMULA

We conclude this section by giving the promised proof of Theorem 9.

Let $R_n(x) = f(x) - T_n(x)$, where T_n is the nth-degree Taylor polynomial of f at a. The idea for the proof is the same as that for the Mean Value Theorem: We apply Rolle's Theorem to a specially constructed function. We think of x as a constant, $x \neq a$, and we define a function g on I by

$$
g(t) = f(x) - f(t) - f'(t)(x - t) - \frac{f''(t)}{2!}(x - t)^2 - \cdots
$$

$$
- \frac{f^{(n)}(t)}{n!}(x - t)^n - R_n(x)\frac{(x - t)^{n+1}}{(x - a)^{n+1}}
$$

Then

$$g(x) = f(x) - f(x) - 0 - \cdots - 0 = 0$$

$$g(a) = f(x) - [T_n(x) + R_n(x)] = f(x) - f(x) = 0$$

Thus, by Rolle's Theorem (applied to g on the interval from a to x), there is a number z between x and a such that $g'(z) = 0$. If we differentiate the expression for g, then most terms cancel. We leave it to you to verify that the expression for $g'(t)$ simplifies to

$$g'(t) = -\frac{f^{(n+1)}(t)}{n!}(x - t)^n + (n + 1)R_n(x)\frac{(x - t)^n}{(x - a)^{n+1}}$$

Thus we have

$$g'(z) = -\frac{f^{(n+1)}(z)}{n!}(x - z)^n + (n + 1)R_n(x)\frac{(x - z)^n}{(x - a)^{n+1}} = 0$$

and so

$$R_n(x) = \frac{f^{(n+1)}(z)}{(n + 1)!}(x - a)^{n+1} \qquad \square$$

8.7   EXERCISES

1. If $f(x) = \sum_{n=0}^{\infty} b_n(x - 5)^n$ for all x, write a formula for b_8.

2. The graph of f is shown.

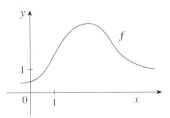

(a) Explain why the series

$$1.6 - 0.8(x - 1) + 0.4(x - 1)^2 - 0.1(x - 1)^3 + \cdots$$

is *not* the Taylor series of f centered at 1.

(b) Explain why the series

$$2.8 + 0.5(x - 2) + 1.5(x - 2)^2 - 0.1(x - 2)^3 + \cdots$$

is *not* the Taylor series of f centered at 2.

3. If $f^{(n)}(0) = (n + 1)!$ for $n = 0, 1, 2, \ldots$, find the Maclaurin series for f and its radius of convergence.

4. Find the Taylor series for f centered at 4 if

$$f^{(n)}(4) = \frac{(-1)^n n!}{3^n(n + 1)}$$

What is the radius of convergence of the Taylor series?

5–10 ■ Find the Maclaurin series for $f(x)$ using the definition of a Maclaurin series. [Assume that f has a power series expansion. Do not show that $R_n(x) \to 0$.] Also find the associated radius of convergence.

5. $f(x) = \cos x$

6. $f(x) = \sin 2x$

7. $f(x) = e^{5x}$

8. $f(x) = xe^x$

9. $f(x) = \sinh x$

10. $f(x) = \cosh x$

■   ■   ■   ■   ■   ■   ■   ■   ■   ■   ■

11–18 ■ Find the Taylor series for $f(x)$ centered at the given value of a. [Assume that f has a power series expansion. Do not show that $R_n(x) \to 0$.]

11. $f(x) = 1 + x + x^2$, $a = 2$

12. $f(x) = x^3$, $a = -1$

13. $f(x) = e^x$, $a = 3$

14. $f(x) = \ln x$, $a = 2$

15. $f(x) = \cos x$, $a = \pi$

16. $f(x) = \sin x$, $a = \pi/2$

17. $f(x) = 1/\sqrt{x}$, $a = 9$

18. $f(x) = x^{-2}$, $a = 1$

■   ■   ■   ■   ■   ■   ■   ■   ■   ■   ■

19. Prove that the series obtained in Exercise 5 represents $\cos x$ for all x.

20. Prove that the series obtained in Exercise 16 represents $\sin x$ for all x.

21. Prove that the series obtained in Exercise 9 represents $\sinh x$ for all x.

22. Prove that the series obtained in Exercise 10 represents $\cosh x$ for all x.

23–26 ■ Use the binomial series to expand the function as a power series. State the radius of convergence.

23. $\sqrt{1 + x}$

24. $\dfrac{1}{(1 + x)^4}$

25. $\dfrac{1}{(2 + x)^3}$

26. $(1 - x)^{2/3}$

■ ■ ■ ■ ■ ■ ■ ■ ■ ■ ■ ■ ■

27–36 ■ Use a Maclaurin series derived in this section to obtain the Maclaurin series for the given function.

27. $f(x) = \cos \pi x$

28. $f(x) = e^{-x/2}$

29. $f(x) = x \tan^{-1}x$

30. $f(x) = \sin(x^4)$

31. $f(x) = x^2 e^{-x}$

32. $f(x) = x \cos 2x$

33. $f(x) = \dfrac{x}{\sqrt{4 + x^2}}$

34. $f(x) = \dfrac{x^2}{\sqrt{2 + x}}$

35. $f(x) = \sin^2 x$ [*Hint:* Use $\sin^2 x = \frac{1}{2}(1 - \cos 2x)$.]

36. $f(x) = \begin{cases} \dfrac{x - \sin x}{x^3} & \text{if } x \neq 0 \\ \frac{1}{6} & \text{if } x = 0 \end{cases}$

■ ■ ■ ■ ■ ■ ■ ■ ■ ■ ■ ■ ■

⊞ **37–38** ■ Find the Maclaurin series of f (by any method) and its radius of convergence. Graph f and its first few Taylor polynomials on the same screen. What do you notice about the relationship between these polynomials and f?

37. $f(x) = \cos(x^2)$

38. $f(x) = e^{-x^2} + \cos x$

■ ■ ■ ■ ■ ■ ■ ■ ■ ■ ■ ■ ■

39. Use the Maclaurin series for e^x to calculate $e^{-0.2}$ correct to five decimal places.

40. Use the Maclaurin series for $\sin x$ to compute $\sin 3°$ correct to five decimal places.

41. (a) Use the binomial series to expand $1/\sqrt{1 - x^2}$.
   (b) Use part (a) to find the Maclaurin series for $\sin^{-1}x$.

42. (a) Expand $1/\sqrt[4]{1 + x}$ as a power series.
   (b) Use part (a) to estimate $1/\sqrt[4]{1.1}$ correct to three decimal places.

43–46 ■ Evaluate the indefinite integral as an infinite series.

43. $\displaystyle\int x \cos(x^3)\, dx$

44. $\displaystyle\int \dfrac{\sin x}{x}\, dx$

45. $\displaystyle\int \sqrt{x^3 + 1}\, dx$

46. $\displaystyle\int \dfrac{e^x - 1}{x}\, dx$

■ ■ ■ ■ ■ ■ ■ ■ ■ ■ ■ ■ ■

47–50 ■ Use series to approximate the definite integral to within the indicated accuracy.

47. $\displaystyle\int_0^1 x \cos(x^3)\, dx$ (three decimal places)

48. $\displaystyle\int_0^{0.2} \left[\tan^{-1}(x^3) + \sin(x^3)\right] dx$ (five decimal places)

49. $\displaystyle\int_0^{0.1} \dfrac{dx}{\sqrt{1 + x^3}}$ ($|\,\text{error}\,| < 10^{-8}$)

50. $\displaystyle\int_0^{0.5} x^2 e^{-x^2}\, dx$ ($|\,\text{error}\,| < 0.001$)

■ ■ ■ ■ ■ ■ ■ ■ ■ ■ ■ ■ ■

51–53 ■ Use series to evaluate the limit.

51. $\displaystyle\lim_{x \to 0} \dfrac{x - \tan^{-1}x}{x^3}$

52. $\displaystyle\lim_{x \to 0} \dfrac{1 - \cos x}{1 + x - e^x}$

53. $\displaystyle\lim_{x \to 0} \dfrac{\sin x - x + \frac{1}{6}x^3}{x^5}$

■ ■ ■ ■ ■ ■ ■ ■ ■ ■ ■ ■ ■

54. Use the series in Example 11(b) to evaluate

$$\lim_{x \to 0} \dfrac{\tan x - x}{x^3}$$

We found this limit in Example 4 in Section 3.7 using l'Hospital's Rule three times. Which method do you prefer?

55–58 ■ Use multiplication or division of power series to find the first three nonzero terms in the Maclaurin series for the function.

55. $y = e^{-x^2} \cos x$

56. $y = \sec x$

57. $y = \dfrac{x}{\sin x}$

58. $y = e^x \ln(1 - x)$

■ ■ ■ ■ ■ ■ ■ ■ ■ ■ ■ ■ ■

59–64 ■ Find the sum of the series.

59. $\displaystyle\sum_{n=0}^{\infty} (-1)^n \dfrac{x^{4n}}{n!}$

60. $\displaystyle\sum_{n=0}^{\infty} \dfrac{(-1)^n \pi^{2n}}{6^{2n}(2n)!}$

61. $\displaystyle\sum_{n=0}^{\infty} \dfrac{(-1)^n \pi^{2n+1}}{4^{2n+1}(2n + 1)!}$

62. $\displaystyle\sum_{n=0}^{\infty} \dfrac{3^n}{5^n n!}$

63. $3 + \dfrac{9}{2!} + \dfrac{27}{3!} + \dfrac{81}{4!} + \cdots$

64. $1 - \ln 2 + \dfrac{(\ln 2)^2}{2!} - \dfrac{(\ln 2)^3}{3!} + \cdots$

■ ■ ■ ■ ■ ■ ■ ■ ■ ■ ■ ■ ■

65. (a) Expand $f(x) = x/(1 - x)^2$ as a power series.
(b) Use part (a) to find the sum of the series
$$\sum_{n=1}^{\infty} \frac{n}{2^n}$$

66. (a) Expand $f(x) = (x + x^2)/(1 - x)^3$ as a power series.
(b) Use part (a) to find the sum of the series
$$\sum_{n=1}^{\infty} \frac{n^2}{2^n}$$

67. (a) Use the binomial series to find the Maclaurin series of $f(x) = \sqrt{1 + x^2}$.
(b) Use part (a) to evaluate $f^{(10)}(0)$.

68. (a) Use the binomial series to find the Maclaurin series of $f(x) = 1/\sqrt{1 + x^3}$.
(b) Use part (a) to evaluate $f^{(9)}(0)$.

69. Use the following steps to prove (18).
(a) Let $g(x) = \sum_{n=0}^{\infty} \binom{k}{n} x^n$. Differentiate this series to show that
$$g'(x) = \frac{kg(x)}{1 + x} \qquad -1 < x < 1$$
(b) Let $h(x) = (1 + x)^{-k} g(x)$ and show that $h'(x) = 0$.
(c) Deduce that $g(x) = (1 + x)^k$.

70. (a) Show that the function defined by
$$f(x) = \begin{cases} e^{-1/x^2} & \text{if } x \neq 0 \\ 0 & \text{if } x = 0 \end{cases}$$
is not equal to its Maclaurin series.

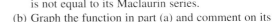

(b) Graph the function in part (a) and comment on its behavior near the origin.

8.8 APPLICATIONS OF TAYLOR POLYNOMIALS

In this section we explore two types of applications of Taylor polynomials. First we look at how they are used to approximate functions—computer scientists like them because polynomials are the simplest of functions. Then we investigate how physicists and engineers use them in such fields as relativity, electric dipoles, the velocity of water waves, and building highways across a desert.

APPROXIMATING FUNCTIONS BY POLYNOMIALS

Suppose that $f(x)$ is equal to the sum of its Taylor series at a:
$$f(x) = \sum_{n=0}^{\infty} \frac{f^{(n)}(a)}{n!} (x - a)^n$$

In Section 8.7 we introduced the notation $T_n(x)$ for the nth partial sum of this series and called it the nth-degree Taylor polynomial of f at a. Thus
$$T_n(x) = \sum_{i=0}^{n} \frac{f^{(i)}(a)}{i!} (x - a)^i$$
$$= f(a) + \frac{f'(a)}{1!} (x - a) + \frac{f''(a)}{2!} (x - a)^2 + \cdots + \frac{f^{(n)}(a)}{n!} (x - a)^n$$

Since f is the sum of its Taylor series, we know that $T_n(x) \to f(x)$ as $n \to \infty$ and so T_n can be used as an approximation to f: $f(x) \approx T_n(x)$.

Notice that the first-degree Taylor polynomial
$$T_1(x) = f(a) + f'(a)(x - a)$$

is the same as the linearization of f at a that we discussed in Section 2.8. Notice also that T_1 and its derivative have the same values at a that f and f' have. In general, it can be shown that the derivatives of T_n at a agree with those of f up to and including derivatives of order n.

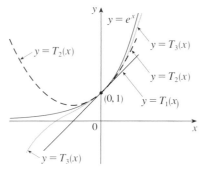

FIGURE I

x	$x = 0.2$	$x = 3.0$
$T_2(x)$	1.220000	8.500000
$T_4(x)$	1.221400	16.375000
$T_6(x)$	1.221403	19.412500
$T_8(x)$	1.221403	20.009152
$T_{10}(x)$	1.221403	20.079665
e^x	1.221403	20.085537

To illustrate these ideas let's take another look at the graphs of $y = e^x$ and its first few Taylor polynomials, as shown in Figure 1. The graph of T_1 is the tangent line to $y = e^x$ at $(0, 1)$; this tangent line is the best linear approximation to e^x near $(0, 1)$. The graph of T_2 is the parabola $y = 1 + x + x^2/2$, and the graph of T_3 is the cubic curve $y = 1 + x + x^2/2 + x^3/6$, which is a closer fit to the exponential curve $y = e^x$ than T_2. The next Taylor polynomial T_4 would be an even better approximation, and so on.

The values in the table give a numerical demonstration of the convergence of the Taylor polynomials $T_n(x)$ to the function $y = e^x$. We see that when $x = 0.2$ the convergence is very rapid, but when $x = 3$ it is somewhat slower. In fact, the farther x is from 0, the more slowly $T_n(x)$ converges to e^x.

When using a Taylor polynomial T_n to approximate a function f, we have to ask the questions: How good an approximation is it? How large should we take n to be in order to achieve a desired accuracy? To answer these questions we need to look at the absolute value of the remainder:

$$|R_n(x)| = |f(x) - T_n(x)|$$

There are three possible methods for estimating the size of the error:

1. If a graphing device is available, we can use it to graph $|R_n(x)|$ and thereby estimate the error.

2. If the series happens to be an alternating series, we can use the Alternating Series Estimation Theorem.

3. In all cases we can use Taylor's Formula (8.7.9), which says that

$$R_n(x) = \frac{f^{(n+1)}(z)}{(n+1)!}(x - a)^{n+1}$$

where z is a number that lies between x and a.

✔ EXAMPLE I
(a) Approximate the function $f(x) = \sqrt[3]{x}$ by a Taylor polynomial of degree 2 at $a = 8$.
(b) How accurate is this approximation when $7 \leqslant x \leqslant 9$?

SOLUTION
(a)

$$f(x) = \sqrt[3]{x} = x^{1/3} \qquad f(8) = 2$$

$$f'(x) = \tfrac{1}{3}x^{-2/3} \qquad f'(8) = \tfrac{1}{12}$$

$$f''(x) = -\tfrac{2}{9}x^{-5/3} \qquad f''(8) = -\tfrac{1}{144}$$

$$f'''(x) = \tfrac{10}{27}x^{-8/3}$$

Thus the second-degree Taylor polynomial is

$$T_2(x) = f(8) + \frac{f'(8)}{1!}(x - 8) + \frac{f''(8)}{2!}(x - 8)^2$$

$$= 2 + \tfrac{1}{12}(x - 8) - \tfrac{1}{288}(x - 8)^2$$

The desired approximation is

$$\sqrt[3]{x} \approx T_2(x) = 2 + \tfrac{1}{12}(x - 8) - \tfrac{1}{288}(x - 8)^2$$

(b) The Taylor series is not alternating when $x < 8$, so we can't use the Alternating Series Estimation Theorem in this example. But using Taylor's Formula we can write

$$R_2(x) = \frac{f'''(z)}{3!}(x - 8)^3 = \tfrac{10}{27} z^{-8/3} \frac{(x - 8)^3}{3!} = \frac{5(x - 8)^3}{81 z^{8/3}}$$

where z lies between 8 and x. In order to estimate the error we note that if $7 \leqslant x \leqslant 9$, then $-1 \leqslant x - 8 \leqslant 1$, so $|x - 8| \leqslant 1$ and therefore $|x - 8|^3 \leqslant 1$. Also, since $z > 7$, we have

$$z^{8/3} > 7^{8/3} > 179$$

and so

$$|R_2(x)| \leqslant \frac{5|x - 8|^3}{81 z^{8/3}} < \frac{5 \cdot 1}{81 \cdot 179} < 0.0004$$

Thus if $7 \leqslant x \leqslant 9$, the approximation in part (a) is accurate to within 0.0004. ▪

Let's use a graphing device to check the calculation in Example 1. Figure 2 shows that the graphs of $y = \sqrt[3]{x}$ and $y = T_2(x)$ are very close to each other when x is near 8. Figure 3 shows the graph of $|R_2(x)|$ computed from the expression

$$|R_2(x)| = |\sqrt[3]{x} - T_2(x)|$$

We see from this graph that

$$|R_2(x)| < 0.0003$$

when $7 \leqslant x \leqslant 9$. Thus the error estimate from graphical methods is slightly better than the error estimate from Taylor's Formula in this case.

▼ EXAMPLE 2

(a) What is the maximum error possible in using the approximation

$$\sin x \approx x - \frac{x^3}{3!} + \frac{x^5}{5!}$$

when $-0.3 \leqslant x \leqslant 0.3$? Use this approximation to find $\sin 12°$ correct to six decimal places.
(b) For what values of x is this approximation accurate to within 0.00005?

SOLUTION

(a) Notice that the Maclaurin series

$$\sin x = x - \frac{x^3}{3!} + \frac{x^5}{5!} - \frac{x^7}{7!} + \cdots$$

is alternating for all nonzero values of x, and the successive terms decrease in size because $|x| < 1$, so we can use the Alternating Series Estimation Theorem. The error in approximating $\sin x$ by the first three terms of its Maclaurin series is at most

$$\left| \frac{x^7}{7!} \right| = \frac{|x|^7}{5040}$$

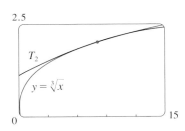

2.5

T_2

$y = \sqrt[3]{x}$

0   15

FIGURE 2

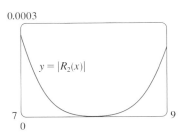

0.0003

$y = |R_2(x)|$

7   9
0

FIGURE 3

If $-0.3 \leq x \leq 0.3$, then $|x| \leq 0.3$, so the error is smaller than

$$\frac{(0.3)^7}{5040} \approx 4.3 \times 10^{-8}$$

To find $\sin 12°$ we first convert to radian measure.

$$\sin 12° = \sin\left(\frac{12\pi}{180}\right) = \sin\left(\frac{\pi}{15}\right)$$

$$\approx \frac{\pi}{15} - \left(\frac{\pi}{15}\right)^3 \frac{1}{3!} + \left(\frac{\pi}{15}\right)^5 \frac{1}{5!}$$

$$\approx 0.20791169$$

Thus, correct to six decimal places, $\sin 12° \approx 0.207912$.

(b) The error will be smaller than 0.00005 if

$$\frac{|x|^7}{5040} < 0.00005$$

Solving this inequality for x, we get

$$|x|^7 < 0.252 \qquad \text{or} \qquad |x| < (0.252)^{1/7} \approx 0.821$$

So the given approximation is accurate to within 0.00005 when $|x| < 0.82$. ■

Module 8.7/8.8 graphically shows the remainders in Taylor polynomial approximations.

What if we had used Taylor's Formula to solve Example 2? The remainder term is

$$R_6(x) = \frac{f^{(7)}(z)}{7!} x^7 = -\cos z \frac{x^7}{7!}$$

(Note that $T_5 = T_6$.) But $|-\cos z| \leq 1$, so $|R_6(x)| \leq |x|^7/7!$ and we get the same estimates as with the Alternating Series Estimation Theorem.

What about graphical methods? Figure 4 shows the graph of

$$|R_6(x)| = \left|\sin x - \left(x - \tfrac{1}{6}x^3 + \tfrac{1}{120}x^5\right)\right|$$

and we see from it that $|R_6(x)| < 4.3 \times 10^{-8}$ when $|x| \leq 0.3$. This is the same estimate that we obtained in Example 2. For part (b) we want $|R_6(x)| < 0.00005$, so we graph both $y = |R_6(x)|$ and $y = 0.00005$ in Figure 5. By placing the cursor on the right intersection point we find that the inequality is satisfied when $|x| < 0.82$. Again this is the same estimate that we obtained in the solution to Example 2.

If we had been asked to approximate $\sin 72°$ instead of $\sin 12°$ in Example 2, it would have been wise to use the Taylor polynomials at $a = \pi/3$ (instead of $a = 0$) because they are better approximations to $\sin x$ for values of x close to $\pi/3$. Notice that 72° is close to 60° (or $\pi/3$ radians) and the derivatives of $\sin x$ are easy to compute at $\pi/3$.

Figure 6 shows the graphs of the Maclaurin polynomial approximations

$$T_1(x) = x \qquad\qquad T_3(x) = x - \frac{x^3}{3!}$$

$$T_5(x) = x - \frac{x^3}{3!} + \frac{x^5}{5!} \qquad T_7(x) = x - \frac{x^3}{3!} + \frac{x^5}{5!} - \frac{x^7}{7!}$$

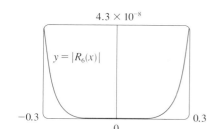

FIGURE 4

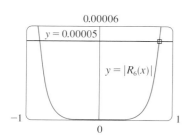

FIGURE 5

to the sine curve. You can see that as n increases, $T_n(x)$ is a good approximation to $\sin x$ on a larger and larger interval.

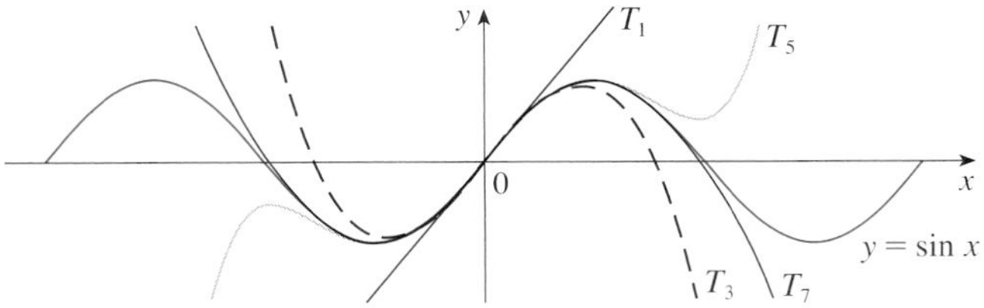

FIGURE 6

One use of the type of calculation done in Examples 1 and 2 occurs in calculators and computers. For instance, when you press the sin or e^x key on your calculator, or when a computer programmer uses a subroutine for a trigonometric or exponential or Bessel function, in many machines a polynomial approximation is calculated. The polynomial is often a Taylor polynomial that has been modified so that the error is spread more evenly throughout an interval.

APPLICATIONS TO PHYSICS

Taylor polynomials are also used frequently in physics. In order to gain insight into an equation, a physicist often simplifies a function by considering only the first two or three terms in its Taylor series. In other words, the physicist uses a Taylor polynomial as an approximation to the function. Taylor's Formula can then be used to gauge the accuracy of the approximation. The following example shows one way in which this idea is used in special relativity.

V EXAMPLE 3 In Einstein's theory of special relativity the mass of an object moving with velocity v is

$$m = \frac{m_0}{\sqrt{1 - v^2/c^2}}$$

where m_0 is the mass of the object when at rest and c is the speed of light. The kinetic energy of the object is the difference between its total energy and its energy at rest:

$$K = mc^2 - m_0c^2$$

(a) Show that when v is very small compared with c, this expression for K agrees with classical Newtonian physics: $K = \frac{1}{2}m_0v^2$.
(b) Use Taylor's Formula to estimate the difference in these expressions for K when $|v| \leqslant 100$ m/s.

SOLUTION
(a) Using the expressions given for K and m, we get

$$K = mc^2 - m_0c^2 = \frac{m_0c^2}{\sqrt{1 - v^2/c^2}} - m_0c^2$$
$$= m_0c^2\left[\left(1 - \frac{v^2}{c^2}\right)^{-1/2} - 1\right]$$

With $x = -v^2/c^2$, the Maclaurin series for $(1 + x)^{-1/2}$ is most easily computed as a binomial series with $k = -\frac{1}{2}$. (Notice that $|x| < 1$ because $v < c$.) Therefore, we

■ The upper curve in Figure 7 is the graph of the expression for the kinetic energy K of an object with velocity v in special relativity. The lower curve shows the function used for K in classical Newtonian physics. When v is much smaller than the speed of light, the curves are practically identical.

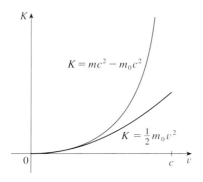

$$K = mc^2 - m_0 c^2$$

$$K = \tfrac{1}{2} m_0 v^2$$

FIGURE 7

have

$$(1 + x)^{-1/2} = 1 - \tfrac{1}{2}x + \frac{\left(-\frac{1}{2}\right)\left(-\frac{3}{2}\right)}{2!} x^2 + \frac{\left(-\frac{1}{2}\right)\left(-\frac{3}{2}\right)\left(-\frac{5}{2}\right)}{3!} x^3 + \cdots$$

$$= 1 - \tfrac{1}{2}x + \tfrac{3}{8}x^2 - \tfrac{5}{16}x^3 + \cdots$$

and

$$K = m_0 c^2 \left[\left(1 + \frac{1}{2}\frac{v^2}{c^2} + \frac{3}{8}\frac{v^4}{c^4} + \frac{5}{16}\frac{v^6}{c^6} + \cdots \right) - 1 \right]$$

$$= m_0 c^2 \left(\frac{1}{2}\frac{v^2}{c^2} + \frac{3}{8}\frac{v^4}{c^4} + \frac{5}{16}\frac{v^6}{c^6} + \cdots \right)$$

If v is much smaller than c, then all terms after the first are very small when compared with the first term. If we omit them, we get

$$K \approx m_0 c^2 \left(\frac{1}{2}\frac{v^2}{c^2} \right) = \tfrac{1}{2} m_0 v^2$$

(b) By Taylor's Formula we can write the remainder term as

$$R_1(x) = \frac{f''(z)}{2!} x^2$$

where $f(x) = m_0 c^2 [(1 + x)^{-1/2} - 1]$ and $x = -v^2/c^2$. Since $f''(x) = \tfrac{3}{4} m_0 c^2 (1 + x)^{-5/2}$, we get

$$R_1(x) = \frac{3 m_0 c^2}{8(1 + z)^{5/2}} \cdot \frac{v^4}{c^4}$$

where z lies between 0 and $-v^2/c^2$. We have $c = 3 \times 10^8$ m/s and $|v| \le 100$ m/s, so

$$R_1(x) \le \frac{\tfrac{3}{8} m_0 (9 \times 10^{16})(100/c)^4}{(1 - 100^2/c^2)^{5/2}} < (4.17 \times 10^{-10}) m_0$$

Thus when $|v| \le 100$ m/s, the magnitude of the error in using the Newtonian expression for kinetic energy is at most $(4.2 \times 10^{-10}) m_0$. ■

8.8 | EXERCISES

1. (a) Find the Taylor polynomials up to degree 6 for $f(x) = \cos x$ centered at $a = 0$. Graph f and these polynomials on a common screen.
(b) Evaluate f and these polynomials at $x = \pi/4$, $\pi/2$, and π.
(c) Comment on how the Taylor polynomials converge to $f(x)$.

2. (a) Find the Taylor polynomials up to degree 3 for $f(x) = 1/x$ centered at $a = 1$. Graph f and these polynomials on a common screen.
(b) Evaluate f and these polynomials at $x = 0.9$ and 1.3.

(c) Comment on how the Taylor polynomials converge to $f(x)$.

3–8 ■ Find the Taylor polynomial $T_n(x)$ for the function f at the number a. Graph f and T_n on the same screen.

3. $f(x) = \sin x$, $a = \pi/6$, $n = 3$

4. $f(x) = e^x$, $a = 2$, $n = 3$

5. $f(x) = \arcsin x$, $a = 0$, $n = 3$

6. $f(x) = \dfrac{\ln x}{x}$, $a = 1$, $n = 3$

7. $f(x) = xe^{-2x}$, $\quad a = 0$, $\quad n = 3$

8. $f(x) = \sqrt{3 + x^2}$, $\quad a = 1$, $\quad n = 2$

■   ■   ■   ■   ■   ■   ■   ■   ■   ■   ■

9–16 ■
(a) Approximate f by a Taylor polynomial with degree n at the number a.
(b) Use Taylor's Formula to estimate the accuracy of the approximation $f(x) \approx T_n(x)$ when x lies in the given interval.
(c) Check your result in part (b) by graphing $|R_n(x)|$.

9. $f(x) = \sqrt{1 + x}$, $\quad a = 0$, $\quad n = 1$, $\quad 0 \leqslant x \leqslant 0.1$

10. $f(x) = 1/x$, $\quad a = 1$, $\quad n = 3$, $\quad 0.8 \leqslant x \leqslant 1.2$

11. $f(x) = \tan x$, $\quad a = 0$, $\quad n = 3$, $\quad 0 \leqslant x \leqslant \pi/6$

12. $f(x) = \cos x$, $\quad a = \pi/3$, $\quad n = 4$, $\quad 0 \leqslant x \leqslant 2\pi/3$

13. $f(x) = e^{x^2}$, $\quad a = 0$, $\quad n = 3$, $\quad 0 \leqslant x \leqslant 0.1$

14. $f(x) = \cosh x$, $\quad a = 0$, $\quad n = 5$, $\quad |x| \leqslant 1$

15. $f(x) = x^{3/4}$, $\quad a = 16$, $\quad n = 3$, $\quad 15 \leqslant x \leqslant 17$

16. $f(x) = \ln x$, $\quad a = 4$, $\quad n = 3$, $\quad 3 \leqslant x \leqslant 5$

■   ■   ■   ■   ■   ■   ■   ■   ■   ■   ■   ■

17. Use the information from Exercise 3 to estimate $\sin 35°$ correct to five decimal places.

18. Use the information from Exercise 12 to estimate $\cos 69°$ correct to five decimal places.

19. Use Taylor's Formula to determine the number of terms of the Maclaurin series for e^x that should be used to estimate $e^{0.1}$ to within 0.00001.

20. Suppose you know that

$$f^{(n)}(4) = \frac{(-1)^n n!}{3^n (n + 1)}$$

and the Taylor series of f centered at 4 converges to $f(x)$ for all x in the interval of convergence. Show that the fifth-degree Taylor polynomial approximates $f(5)$ with error less than 0.0002.

21–22 ■ Use the Alternating Series Estimation Theorem or Taylor's Formula to estimate the range of values of x for which the given approximation is accurate to within the stated error. Check your answer graphically.

21. $\sin x \approx x - \dfrac{x^3}{6}$ $\quad (|\,\text{error}\,| < 0.01)$

22. $\cos x \approx 1 - \dfrac{x^2}{2} + \dfrac{x^4}{24}$ $\quad (|\,\text{error}\,| < 0.005)$

■   ■   ■   ■   ■   ■   ■   ■   ■   ■   ■   ■

23. A car is moving with speed 20 m/s and acceleration 2 m/s² at a given instant. Using a second-degree Taylor polynomial, estimate how far the car moves in the next second. Would it be reasonable to use this polynomial to estimate the distance traveled during the next minute?

24. The resistivity ρ of a conducting wire is the reciprocal of the conductivity and is measured in units of ohm-meters (Ω-m). The resistivity of a given metal depends on the temperature according to the equation

$$\rho(t) = \rho_{20} e^{\alpha(t - 20)}$$

where t is the temperature in °C. There are tables that list the values of α (called the temperature coefficient) and ρ_{20} (the resistivity at 20°C) for various metals. Except at very low temperatures, the resistivity varies almost linearly with temperature and so it is common to approximate the expression for $\rho(t)$ by its first- or second-degree Taylor polynomial at $t = 20$.
(a) Find expressions for these linear and quadratic approximations.
(b) For copper, the tables give $\alpha = 0.0039$/°C and $\rho_{20} = 1.7 \times 10^{-8}$ Ω-m. Graph the resistivity of copper and the linear and quadratic approximations for $-250°C \leqslant t \leqslant 1000°C$.
(c) For what values of t does the linear approximation agree with the exponential expression to within one percent?

25. An electric dipole consists of two electric charges of equal magnitude and opposite sign. If the charges are q and $-q$ and are located at a distance d from each other, then the electric field E at the point P in the figure is

$$E = \frac{q}{D^2} - \frac{q}{(D + d)^2}$$

By expanding this expression for E as a series in powers of d/D, show that E is approximately proportional to $1/D^3$ when P is far away from the dipole.

26. If a water wave with length L moves with velocity v across a body of water with depth d, as in the figure, then

$$v^2 = \frac{gL}{2\pi} \tanh \frac{2\pi d}{L}$$

(a) If the water is deep, show that $v \approx \sqrt{gL/(2\pi)}$.
(b) If the water is shallow, use the Maclaurin series for tanh to show that $v \approx \sqrt{gd}$. (Thus in shallow water the velocity of a wave tends to be independent of the length of the wave.)

(c) Use the Alternating Series Estimation Theorem to show that if $L > 10d$, then the estimate $v^2 \approx gd$ is accurate to within $0.014gL$.

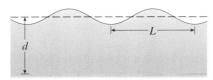

27. If a surveyor measures differences in elevation when making plans for a highway across a desert, corrections must be made for the curvature of the Earth.

(a) If R is the radius of the Earth and L is the length of the highway, show that the correction is

$$C = R \sec(L/R) - R$$

(b) Use a Taylor polynomial to show that

$$C \approx \frac{L^2}{2R} + \frac{5L^4}{24R^3}$$

(c) Compare the corrections given by the formulas in parts (a) and (b) for a highway that is 100 km long. (Take the radius of the Earth to be 6370 km.)

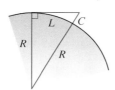

28. The period of a pendulum with length L that makes a maximum angle θ_0 with the vertical is

$$T = 4 \sqrt{\frac{L}{g}} \int_0^{\pi/2} \frac{dx}{\sqrt{1 - k^2 \sin^2 x}}$$

where $k = \sin\left(\frac{1}{2}\theta_0\right)$ and g is the acceleration due to gravity. (In Exercise 32 in Section 6.5 we approximated this integral using Simpson's Rule.)

(a) Expand the integrand as a binomial series and use the result of Exercise 32 in Section 6.1 to show that

$$T = 2\pi \sqrt{\frac{L}{g}} \left[1 + \frac{1^2}{2^2} k^2 + \frac{1^2 3^2}{2^2 4^2} k^4 + \frac{1^2 3^2 5^2}{2^2 4^2 6^2} k^6 + \cdots \right]$$

If θ_0 is not too large, the approximation $T \approx 2\pi\sqrt{L/g}$, obtained by using only the first term in the series, is often used. A better approximation is obtained by using

two terms:

$$T \approx 2\pi \sqrt{\frac{L}{g}} \left(1 + \tfrac{1}{4}k^2\right)$$

(b) Notice that all the terms in the series after the first one have coefficients that are at most $\frac{1}{4}$. Use this fact to compare this series with a geometric series and show that

$$2\pi \sqrt{\frac{L}{g}} \left(1 + \tfrac{1}{4}k^2\right) \leqslant T \leqslant 2\pi \sqrt{\frac{L}{g}} \frac{4 - 3k^2}{4 - 4k^2}$$

(c) Use the inequalities in part (b) to estimate the period of a pendulum with $L = 1$ meter and $\theta_0 = 10°$. How does it compare with the estimate $T \approx 2\pi\sqrt{L/g}$? What if $\theta_0 = 42°$?

29. In Section 4.6 we considered Newton's method for approximating a root r of the equation $f(x) = 0$, and from an initial approximation x_1 we obtained successive approximations $x_2, x_3, \ldots$, where

$$x_{n+1} = x_n - \frac{f(x_n)}{f'(x_n)}$$

Use Taylor's Formula with $n = 1$, $a = x_n$, and $x = r$ to show that if $f''(x)$ exists on an interval I containing r, x_n, and x_{n+1}, and $|f''(x)| \leqslant M$, $|f'(x)| \geqslant K$ for all $x \in I$, then

$$|x_{n+1} - r| \leqslant \frac{M}{2K} |x_n - r|^2$$

[This means that if x_n is accurate to d decimal places, then x_{n+1} is accurate to about $2d$ decimal places. More precisely, if the error at stage n is at most 10^{-m}, then the error at stage $n + 1$ is at most $(M/2K)10^{-2m}$.]

30. Use the following outline to prove that e is an irrational number.

(a) If e were rational, then it would be of the form $e = p/q$, where p and q are positive integers and $q > 2$. Use Taylor's Formula to write

$$\frac{p}{q} = e = 1 + \frac{1}{1!} + \frac{1}{2!} + \cdots + \frac{1}{q!} + \frac{e^z}{(q + 1)!}$$

$$= s_q + \frac{e^z}{(q + 1)!}$$

where $0 < z < 1$.

(b) Show that $q!(e - s_q)$ is an integer.

(c) Show that $q!(e - s_q) < 1$.

(d) Use parts (b) and (c) to deduce that e is irrational.

8 REVIEW

CONCEPT CHECK

1. (a) What is a convergent sequence?
   (b) What is a convergent series?
   (c) What does $\lim_{n \to \infty} a_n = 3$ mean?
   (d) What does $\sum_{n=1}^{\infty} a_n = 3$ mean?

2. (a) What is a bounded sequence?
   (b) What is a monotonic sequence?
   (c) What can you say about a bounded monotonic sequence?

3. (a) What is a geometric series? Under what circumstances is it convergent? What is its sum?
   (b) What is a p-series? Under what circumstances is it convergent?

4. Suppose $\sum a_n = 3$ and s_n is the nth partial sum of the series. What is $\lim_{n \to \infty} a_n$? What is $\lim_{n \to \infty} s_n$?

5. State the following.
   (a) The Test for Divergence
   (b) The Integral Test
   (c) The Comparison Test
   (d) The Limit Comparison Test
   (e) The Alternating Series Test
   (f) The Ratio Test
   (g) The Root Test

6. (a) What is an absolutely convergent series?
   (b) What can you say about such a series?
   (c) What is a conditionally convergent series?

7. If a series is convergent by the Alternating Series Test, how do you estimate its sum?

8. (a) Write the general form of a power series.
   (b) What is the radius of convergence of a power series?
   (c) What is the interval of convergence of a power series?

9. Suppose $f(x)$ is the sum of a power series with radius of convergence R.
   (a) How do you differentiate f? What is the radius of convergence of the series for f'?
   (b) How do you integrate f? What is the radius of convergence of the series for $\int f(x)\,dx$?

10. (a) Write an expression for the nth-degree Taylor polynomial of f centered at a.
    (b) Write an expression for the Taylor series of f centered at a.
    (c) Write an expression for the Maclaurin series of f.
    (d) How do you show that $f(x)$ is equal to the sum of its Taylor series?
    (e) State Taylor's Formula.

11. Write the Maclaurin series and the interval of convergence for each of the following functions.
    (a) $1/(1 - x)$ (b) e^x (c) $\sin x$
    (d) $\cos x$ (e) $\tan^{-1}x$

12. Write the binomial series expansion of $(1 + x)^k$. What is the radius of convergence of this series?

TRUE-FALSE QUIZ

Determine whether the statement is true or false. If it is true, explain why. If it is false, explain why or give an example that disproves the statement.

1. If $\lim_{n \to \infty} a_n = 0$, then $\sum a_n$ is convergent.

2. The series $\sum_{n=1}^{\infty} n^{-\sin 1}$ is convergent.

3. If $\lim_{n \to \infty} a_n = L$, then $\lim_{n \to \infty} a_{2n+1} = L$.

4. If $\sum c_n 6^n$ is convergent, then $\sum c_n(-2)^n$ is convergent.

5. If $\sum c_n 6^n$ is convergent, then $\sum c_n(-6)^n$ is convergent.

6. If $\sum c_n x^n$ diverges when $x = 6$, then it diverges when $x = 10$.

7. The Ratio Test can be used to determine whether $\sum 1/n^3$ converges.

8. The Ratio Test can be used to determine whether $\sum 1/n!$ converges.

9. If $0 \le a_n \le b_n$ and $\sum b_n$ diverges, then $\sum a_n$ diverges.

10. $\sum_{n=0}^{\infty} \dfrac{(-1)^n}{n!} = \dfrac{1}{e}$

11. If $-1 < \alpha < 1$, then $\lim_{n \to \infty} \alpha^n = 0$.

12. If $\sum a_n$ is divergent, then $\sum |a_n|$ is divergent.

13. If $f(x) = 2x - x^2 + \frac{1}{3}x^3 - \cdots$ converges for all x, then $f'''(0) = 2$.

14. If $\{a_n\}$ and $\{b_n\}$ are divergent, then $\{a_n + b_n\}$ is divergent.

15. If $\{a_n\}$ and $\{b_n\}$ are divergent, then $\{a_n b_n\}$ is divergent.

16. If $\{a_n\}$ is decreasing and $a_n > 0$ for all n, then $\{a_n\}$ is convergent.

17. If $a_n > 0$ and $\sum a_n$ converges, then $\sum (-1)^n a_n$ converges.

18. If $a_n > 0$ and $\lim_{n \to \infty} (a_{n+1}/a_n) < 1$, then $\lim_{n \to \infty} a_n = 0$.

EXERCISES

1–8 ■ Determine whether the sequence is convergent or divergent. If it is convergent, find its limit.

1. $a_n = \dfrac{2 + n^3}{1 + 2n^3}$

2. $a_n = \dfrac{9^{n+1}}{10^n}$

3. $a_n = \dfrac{n^3}{1 + n^2}$

4. $a_n = \cos(n\pi/2)$

5. $a_n = \dfrac{n \sin n}{n^2 + 1}$

6. $a_n = \dfrac{\ln n}{\sqrt{n}}$

7. $\{(1 + 3/n)^{4n}\}$

8. $\{(-10)^n/n!\}$

■ ■ ■ ■ ■ ■ ■ ■ ■ ■ ■

9–20 ■ Determine whether the series is convergent or divergent.

9. $\displaystyle\sum_{n=1}^{\infty} \dfrac{n}{n^3 + 1}$

10. $\displaystyle\sum_{n=1}^{\infty} \dfrac{n^2 + 1}{n^3 + 1}$

11. $\displaystyle\sum_{n=1}^{\infty} \dfrac{n^3}{5^n}$

12. $\displaystyle\sum_{n=1}^{\infty} \dfrac{(-1)^n}{\sqrt{n+1}}$

13. $\displaystyle\sum_{n=2}^{\infty} \dfrac{1}{n\sqrt{\ln n}}$

14. $\displaystyle\sum_{n=1}^{\infty} \ln\!\left(\dfrac{n}{3n + 1}\right)$

15. $\displaystyle\sum_{n=1}^{\infty} \dfrac{\cos 3n}{1 + (1.2)^n}$

16. $\displaystyle\sum_{n=1}^{\infty} \dfrac{n^{2n}}{(1 + 2n^2)^n}$

17. $\displaystyle\sum_{n=1}^{\infty} \dfrac{1 \cdot 3 \cdot 5 \cdot \cdots \cdot (2n - 1)}{5^n n!}$

18. $\displaystyle\sum_{n=1}^{\infty} \dfrac{(-5)^{2n}}{n^2 9^n}$

19. $\displaystyle\sum_{n=1}^{\infty} (-1)^{n-1} \dfrac{\sqrt{n}}{n + 1}$

20. $\displaystyle\sum_{n=1}^{\infty} \dfrac{\sqrt{n + 1} - \sqrt{n - 1}}{n}$

■ ■ ■ ■ ■ ■ ■ ■ ■ ■ ■

21–24 ■ Determine whether the series is conditionally convergent, absolutely convergent, or divergent.

21. $\displaystyle\sum_{n=1}^{\infty} (-1)^{n-1} n^{-1/3}$

22. $\displaystyle\sum_{n=1}^{\infty} (-1)^{n-1} n^{-3}$

23. $\displaystyle\sum_{n=1}^{\infty} \dfrac{(-1)^n (n + 1)3^n}{2^{2n+1}}$

24. $\displaystyle\sum_{n=2}^{\infty} \dfrac{(-1)^n \sqrt{n}}{\ln n}$

■ ■ ■ ■ ■ ■ ■ ■ ■ ■ ■

25–29 ■ Find the sum of the series.

25. $\displaystyle\sum_{n=1}^{\infty} \dfrac{2^{2n+1}}{5^n}$

26. $\displaystyle\sum_{n=1}^{\infty} \dfrac{1}{n(n + 3)}$

27. $\displaystyle\sum_{n=1}^{\infty} [\tan^{-1}(n + 1) - \tan^{-1}n]$

28. $\displaystyle\sum_{n=0}^{\infty} \dfrac{(-1)^n \pi^n}{3^{2n}(2n)!}$

29. $1 - e + \dfrac{e^2}{2!} - \dfrac{e^3}{3!} + \dfrac{e^4}{4!} - \cdots$

■ ■ ■ ■ ■ ■ ■ ■ ■ ■ ■ ■

30. Express the repeating decimal $4.17326326326\ldots$ as a fraction.

31. Show that $\cosh x \geqslant 1 + \tfrac{1}{2}x^2$ for all x.

32. For what values of x does the series $\sum_{n=1}^{\infty} (\ln x)^n$ converge?

33. Find the sum of the series $\displaystyle\sum_{n=1}^{\infty} \dfrac{(-1)^{n+1}}{n^5}$ correct to four decimal places.

34. (a) Show that the series $\displaystyle\sum_{n=1}^{\infty} \dfrac{n^n}{(2n)!}$ is convergent.

(b) Deduce that $\displaystyle\lim_{n\to\infty} \dfrac{n^n}{(2n)!} = 0$.

35. Prove that if the series $\sum_{n=1}^{\infty} a_n$ is absolutely convergent, then the series

$$\sum_{n=1}^{\infty} \left(\dfrac{n + 1}{n}\right) a_n$$

is also absolutely convergent.

36–39 ■ Find the radius of convergence and interval of convergence of the series.

36. $\displaystyle\sum_{n=1}^{\infty} (-1)^n \dfrac{x^n}{n^2 5^n}$

37. $\displaystyle\sum_{n=1}^{\infty} \dfrac{(x + 2)^n}{n 4^n}$

38. $\displaystyle\sum_{n=1}^{\infty} \dfrac{2^n(x - 2)^n}{(n + 2)!}$

39. $\displaystyle\sum_{n=0}^{\infty} \dfrac{2^n(x - 3)^n}{\sqrt{n + 3}}$

■ ■ ■ ■ ■ ■ ■ ■ ■ ■ ■ ■

40. Find the radius of convergence of the series

$$\sum_{n=1}^{\infty} \dfrac{(2n)!}{(n!)^2} x^n$$

41. Find the Taylor series of $f(x) = \sin x$ at $a = \pi/6$.

42. Find the Taylor series of $f(x) = \cos x$ at $a = \pi/3$.

43–50 ■ Find the Maclaurin series for f and its radius of convergence. You may use either the direct method (definition of a Maclaurin series) or known series such as geometric series, binomial series, or the Maclaurin series for e^x, $\sin x$, and $\tan^{-1}x$.

43. $f(x) = \dfrac{x^2}{1 + x}$

44. $f(x) = \tan^{-1}(x^2)$

45. $f(x) = \ln(1 - x)$

46. $f(x) = xe^{2x}$

47. $f(x) = \sin(x^4)$

48. $f(x) = 10^x$

49. $f(x) = 1/\sqrt[4]{16 - x}$

50. $f(x) = (1 - 3x)^{-5}$

▪ ▪ ▪ ▪ ▪ ▪ ▪ ▪ ▪ ▪ ▪ ▪

51. Evaluate $\int \dfrac{e^x}{x}\,dx$ as an infinite series.

52. Use series to approximate $\int_0^1 \sqrt{1 + x^4}\,dx$ correct to two decimal places.

53–54 ▪

(a) Approximate f by a Taylor polynomial with degree n at the number a. ▪

(b) Graph f and T_n on a common screen.

(c) Use Taylor's Formula to estimate the accuracy of the approximation $f(x) \approx T_n(x)$ when x lies in the given interval.

(d) Check your result in part (c) by graphing $|R_n(x)|$.

53. $f(x) = \sqrt{x}$, $\quad a = 1$, $\quad n = 3$, $\quad 0.9 \le x \le 1.1$

54. $f(x) = \sec x$, $\quad a = 0$, $\quad n = 2$, $\quad 0 \le x \le \pi/6$

▪ ▪ ▪ ▪ ▪ ▪ ▪ ▪ ▪ ▪ ▪ ▪

55. Use series to evaluate the following limit.

$$\lim_{x \to 0} \frac{\sin x - x}{x^3}$$

56. The force due to gravity on an object with mass m at a height h above the surface of the Earth is

$$F = \frac{mgR^2}{(R + h)^2}$$

where R is the radius of the Earth and g is the acceleration due to gravity.

(a) Express F as a series in powers of h/R.

(b) Observe that if we approximate F by the first term in the series, we get the expression $F \approx mg$ that is usually used when h is much smaller than R. Use the Alternating Series Estimation Theorem to estimate the range of values of h for which the approximation $F \approx mg$ is accurate to within one percent. (Use $R = 6400$ km.)

57. Suppose that $f(x) = \sum_{n=0}^{\infty} c_n x^n$ for all x.

(a) If f is an odd function, show that

$$c_0 = c_2 = c_4 = \cdots = 0$$

(b) If f is an even function, show that

$$c_1 = c_3 = c_5 = \cdots = 0$$

58. If $f(x) = e^{x^2}$, show that $f^{(2n)}(0) = \dfrac{(2n)!}{n!}$.

9 ☐ DIFFERENTIAL EQUATIONS

9.6 Predator-Prey Systems

1. (a) $dx/dt = -0.05x + 0.0001xy$. If $y = 0$, we have $dx/dt = -0.05x$, which indicates that in the absence of y, x declines at

a rate proportional to itself. So x represents the predator population and y represents the prey population. The growth of

the prey population, $0.1y$ (from $dy/dt = 0.1y - 0.005xy$), is restricted only by encounters with predators (the term

$-0.005xy$). The predator population increases only through the term $0.0001xy$; that is, by encounters with the prey and

not through additional food sources.

(b) $dy/dt = -0.015y + 0.00008xy$. If $x = 0$, we have $dy/dt = -0.015y$, which indicates that in the absence of x, y would

decline at a rate proportional to itself. So y represents the predator population and x represents the prey population. The

growth of the prey population, $0.2x$ (from $dx/dt = 0.2x - 0.0002x^2 - 0.006xy = 0.2x(1 - 0.001x) - 0.006xy$), is

restricted by a carrying capacity of 1000 [from the term $1 - 0.001x = 1 - x/1000$] and by encounters with predators (the

term $-0.006xy$). The predator population increases only through the term $0.00008xy$; that is, by encounters with the prey

and not through additional food sources.

2. (a) $dx/dt = 0.12x - 0.0006x^2 + 0.00001xy$. $dy/dt = 0.08y + 0.00004xy$.

The xy terms represent encounters between the two species x and y. An increase in y makes dx/dt (the growth rate of x)

larger due to the positive term $0.00001xy$. An increase in x makes dy/dt (the growth rate of y) larger due to the positive

term $0.00004xy$. Hence, the system describes a cooperation model.

(b) $dx/dt = 0.15x - 0.0002x^2 - 0.0006xy = 0.15x(1 - x/750) - 0.0006xy$.

$dy/dt = 0.2y - 0.00008y^2 - 0.0002xy = 0.2y(1 - y/2500) - 0.0002xy$.

The system shows that x and y have carrying capacities of 750 and 2500. An increase in x reduces the growth rate of y due

to the negative term $-0.0002xy$. An increase in y reduces the growth rate of x due to the negative term $-0.0006xy$.

Hence, the system describes a competition model.

3. (a) At $t = 0$, there are about 300 rabbits and 100 foxes. At $t = t_1$, the number

of foxes reaches a minimum of about 20 while the number of rabbits is

about 1000. At $t = t_2$, the number of rabbits reaches a maximum of about

2400, while the number of foxes rebounds to 100. At $t = t_3$, the number of

rabbits decreases to about 1000 and the number of foxes reaches a

maximum of about 315. As t increases, the number of foxes decreases

greatly to 100, and the number of rabbits decreases to 300 (the initial

populations), and the cycle starts again.

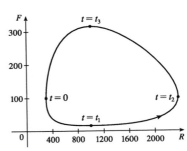

(b)

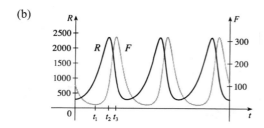

4. (a) At $t = 0$, there are about 600 rabbits and 160 foxes. At $t = t_1$, the number
   of rabbits reaches a minimum of about 80 and the number of foxes is also
   80. At $t = t_2$, the number of foxes reaches a minimum of about 25 while
   the number of rabbits rebounds to 1000. At $t = t_3$, the number of foxes
   has increased to 40 and the rabbit population has reached a maximum of
   about 1750. The curve ends at $t = t_4$, where the number of foxes has
   increased to 65 and the number of rabbits has decreased to about 950.

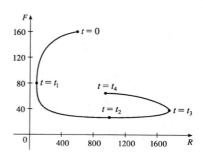

(b)

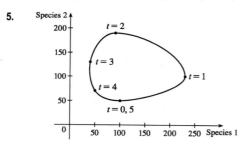

5. 6.

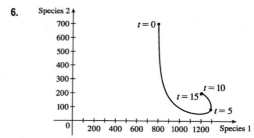

7. $\dfrac{dW}{dR} = \dfrac{-0.02W + 0.00002RW}{0.08R - 0.001RW}$ $\Leftrightarrow$ $(0.08 - 0.001W)R\,dW = (-0.02 + 0.00002R)W\,dR$ $\Leftrightarrow$

$\dfrac{0.08 - 0.001W}{W}\,dW = \dfrac{-0.02 + 0.00002R}{R}\,dR$ $\Leftrightarrow$ $\displaystyle\int\left(\dfrac{0.08}{W} - 0.001\right)dW = \int\left(-\dfrac{0.02}{R} + 0.00002\right)dR$ $\Leftrightarrow$

$0.08\ln|W| - 0.001W = -0.02\ln|R| + 0.00002R + K$ $\Leftrightarrow$ $0.08\ln W + 0.02\ln R = 0.001W + 0.00002R + K$ $\Leftrightarrow$

$\ln\left(W^{0.08}R^{0.02}\right) = 0.00002R + 0.001W + K$ $\Leftrightarrow$ $W^{0.08}R^{0.02} = e^{0.00002R + 0.001W + K}$ $\Leftrightarrow$

$R^{0.02}W^{0.08} = Ce^{0.00002R}e^{0.001W}$ $\Leftrightarrow$ $\dfrac{R^{0.02}W^{0.08}}{e^{0.00002R}e^{0.001W}} = C$. In general, if $\dfrac{dy}{dx} = \dfrac{-ry + bxy}{kx - axy}$, then $C = \dfrac{x^r y^k}{e^{bx}e^{ay}}$.

8. (a) A and L are constant $\Rightarrow$ $A' = 0$ and $L' = 0$ $\Rightarrow$ $\begin{cases} 0 = 2A - 0.01AL \\ 0 = -0.5L + 0.0001AL \end{cases}$ $\Rightarrow$ $\begin{cases} 0 = A(2 - 0.01L) \\ 0 = L(-0.5 + 0.0001A) \end{cases}$

So either $A = L = 0$ or $L = \frac{2}{0.01} = 200$ and $A = \frac{0.5}{0.0001} = 5000$. The trivial solution $A = L = 0$ just says that if there aren't any aphids or ladybugs, then the populations will not change. The non-trivial solution, $L = 200$ and $A = 5000$, indicates the population sizes needed so that there are no changes in either the number of aphids or the number of ladybugs.

(b) $\dfrac{dL}{dA} = \dfrac{dL/dt}{dA/dt} = \dfrac{-0.5L + 0.0001AL}{2A - 0.01AL}$

(c) The solution curves (phase trajectories) are all closed curves that have the equilibrium point $(5000, 200)$ inside them.

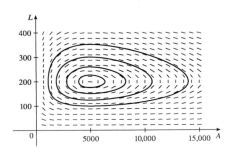

(d)

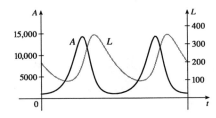

At $P_0(1000, 200)$, $dA/dt = 0$ and $dL/dt = -80 < 0$, so the number of ladybugs is decreasing and hence, we are proceeding in a counterclockwise direction. At P_0, there aren't enough aphids to support the ladybug population, so the number of ladybugs decreases and the number of aphids begins to increase. The ladybug population reaches a minimum at $P_1(5000, 100)$ while the aphid population increases in a dramatic way, reaching its maximum at $P_2(14, 250, 200)$.

Meanwhile, the ladybug population is increasing from P_1 to $P_3(5000, 355)$, and as we pass through P_2, the increasing number of ladybugs starts to deplete the aphid population. At P_3 the ladybugs reach a maximum population, and start to decrease due to the reduced aphid population. Both populations then decrease until P_0, where the cycle starts over again.

(e) Both graphs have the same period and the graph of L peaks about a quarter of a cycle after the graph of A.

9. (a) Letting $W = 0$ gives us $dR/dt = 0.08R(1 - 0.0002R)$. $dR/dt = 0$ $\Leftrightarrow$ $R = 0$ or 5000. Since $dR/dt > 0$ for $0 < R < 5000$, we would expect the rabbit population to *increase* to 5000 for these values of R. Since $dR/dt < 0$ for $R > 5000$, we would expect the rabbit population to *decrease* to 5000 for these values of R. Hence, in the absence of wolves, we would expect the rabbit population to stabilize at 5000.

(b) R and W are constant $\Rightarrow$ $R' = 0$ and $W' = 0$ $\Rightarrow$

$$\begin{cases} 0 = 0.08R(1 - 0.0002R) - 0.001RW \\ 0 = -0.02W + 0.00002RW \end{cases} \Rightarrow \begin{cases} 0 = R[0.08(1 - 0.0002R) - 0.001W] \\ 0 = W(-0.02 + 0.00002R) \end{cases}$$

The second equation is true if $W = 0$ or $R = \frac{0.02}{0.00002} = 1000$. If $W = 0$ in the first equation, then either $R = 0$ or

$R = \frac{1}{0.0002} = 5000$ [as in part (a)]. If $R = 1000$, then $0 = 1000[0.08(1 - 0.0002 \cdot 1000) - 0.001W]$ $\Leftrightarrow$

$0 = 80(1 - 0.2) - W$ $\Leftrightarrow$ $W = 64$.

Case (i): $W = 0$, $R = 0$: both populations are zero

Case (ii): $W = 0$, $R = 5000$: see part (a)

Case (iii): $R = 1000$, $W = 64$: the predator/prey interaction balances and the populations are stable.

(c) The populations of wolves and rabbits fluctuate around 64 and 1000, respectively, and eventually stabilize at those values.

(d)

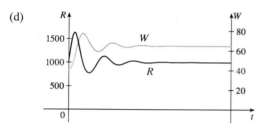

10. (a) If $L = 0$, $dA/dt = 2A(1 - 0.0001A)$, so $dA/dt = 0$ $\Leftrightarrow$ $A = 0$ or $A = \frac{1}{0.0001} = 10{,}000$. Since $dA/dt > 0$ for

$0 < A < 10{,}000$, we expect the aphid population to *increase* to 10,000 for these values of A. Since $dA/dt < 0$ for

$A > 10{,}000$, we expect the aphid population to *decrease* to 10,000 for these values of A. Hence, in the absence of

ladybugs we expect the aphid population to stabilize at 10,000.

(b) A and L are constant $\Rightarrow$ $A' = 0$ and $L' = 0$ $\Rightarrow$

$$\begin{cases} 0 = 2A(1 - 0.0001A) - 0.01AL \\ 0 = -0.5L + 0.0001AL \end{cases} \Rightarrow \begin{cases} 0 = A[2(1 - 0.0001A) - 0.01L] \\ 0 = L(-0.5 + 0.0001A) \end{cases}$$

The second equation is true if $L = 0$ or $A = \frac{0.5}{0.0001} = 5000$. If $L = 0$ in the first equation, then either $A = 0$ or

$A = \frac{1}{0.0001} = 10{,}000$. If $A = 5000$, then $0 = 5000[2(1 - 0.0001 \cdot 5000) - 0.01L]$ $\Leftrightarrow$

$0 = 10{,}000(1 - 0.5) - 50L$ $\Leftrightarrow$ $50L = 5000$ $\Leftrightarrow$ $L = 100$.

The equilibrium solutions are: (i) $L = 0$, $A = 0$ (ii) $L = 0$, $A = 10{,}000$ (iii) $A = 5000$, $L = 100$

(c) $\dfrac{dL}{dA} = \dfrac{dL/dt}{dA/dt} = \dfrac{-0.5L + 0.0001AL}{2A(1 - 0.0001A) - 0.01AL}$

(d)

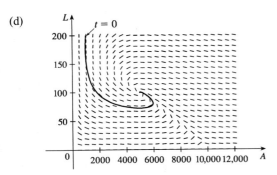

All of the phase trajectories spiral tightly around the equilibrium solution $(5000, 100)$.

(e)

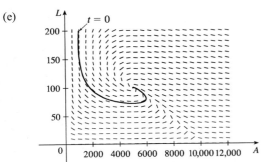

At $t = 0$, the ladybug population decreases rapidly and the aphid population decreases slightly before beginning to increase. As the aphid population continues to increase, the ladybug population reaches a minimum at about $(5000, 75)$. The ladybug population starts to increase and quickly stabilizes at 100, while the aphid population stabilizes at 5000.

(f)

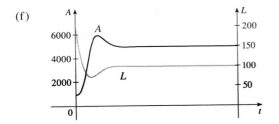

The graph of A peaks just after the graph of L has a minimum.

17

SECOND-ORDER DIFFERENTIAL EQUATIONS

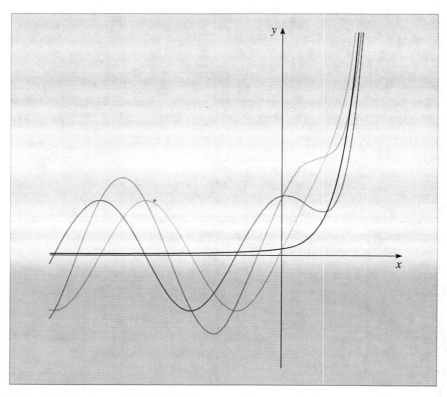

Most of the solutions of the differential equation $y'' + 4y = e^{3x}$ resemble sine functions when x is negative but they all look like exponential functions when x is large.

The basic ideas of differential equations were explained in Chapter 9; there we concentrated on first-order equations. In this chapter we study second-order linear differential equations and learn how they can be applied to solve problems concerning the vibrations of springs and the analysis of electric circuits. We will also see how infinite series can be used to solve differential equations.

A **second-order linear differential equation** has the form

$$\boxed{1} \qquad P(x)\frac{d^2y}{dx^2} + Q(x)\frac{dy}{dx} + R(x)y = G(x)$$

where P, Q, R, and G are continuous functions. We saw in Section 9.1 that equations of this type arise in the study of the motion of a spring. In Section 17.3 we will further pursue this application as well as the application to electric circuits.

In this section we study the case where $G(x) = 0$, for all x, in Equation 1. Such equations are called **homogeneous** linear equations. Thus the form of a second-order linear homogeneous differential equation is

$$\boxed{2} \qquad P(x)\frac{d^2y}{dx^2} + Q(x)\frac{dy}{dx} + R(x)y = 0$$

If $G(x) \neq 0$ for some x, Equation 1 is **nonhomogeneous** and is discussed in Section 17.2.

Two basic facts enable us to solve homogeneous linear equations. The first of these says that if we know two solutions y_1 and y_2 of such an equation, then the **linear combination** $y = c_1 y_1 + c_2 y_2$ is also a solution.

$\boxed{3}$ **THEOREM** If $y_1(x)$ and $y_2(x)$ are both solutions of the linear homogeneous equation (2) and c_1 and c_2 are any constants, then the function

$$y(x) = c_1 y_1(x) + c_2 y_2(x)$$

is also a solution of Equation 2.

PROOF Since y_1 and y_2 are solutions of Equation 2, we have

$$P(x)y_1'' + Q(x)y_1' + R(x)y_1 = 0$$

and $\qquad\qquad P(x)y_2'' + Q(x)y_2' + R(x)y_2 = 0$

Therefore, using the basic rules for differentiation, we have

$P(x)y'' + Q(x)y' + R(x)y$

$$= P(x)(c_1 y_1 + c_2 y_2)'' + Q(x)(c_1 y_1 + c_2 y_2)' + R(x)(c_1 y_1 + c_2 y_2)$$

$$= P(x)(c_1 y_1'' + c_2 y_2'') + Q(x)(c_1 y_1' + c_2 y_2') + R(x)(c_1 y_1 + c_2 y_2)$$

$$= c_1[P(x)y_1'' + Q(x)y_1' + R(x)y_1] + c_2[P(x)y_2'' + Q(x)y_2' + R(x)y_2]$$

$$= c_1(0) + c_2(0) = 0$$

Thus $y = c_1 y_1 + c_2 y_2$ is a solution of Equation 2. $\qquad\qquad\square$

The other fact we need is given by the following theorem, which is proved in more advanced courses. It says that the general solution is a linear combination of two **linearly independent** solutions y_1 and y_2. This means that neither y_1 nor y_2 is a constant multiple of the other. For instance, the functions $f(x) = x^2$ and $g(x) = 5x^2$ are linearly dependent, but $f(x) = e^x$ and $g(x) = xe^x$ are linearly independent.

> **4 THEOREM** If y_1 and y_2 are linearly independent solutions of Equation 2, and $P(x)$ is never 0, then the general solution is given by
>
> $$y(x) = c_1 y_1(x) + c_2 y_2(x)$$
>
> where c_1 and c_2 are arbitrary constants.

Theorem 4 is very useful because it says that if we know *two* particular linearly independent solutions, then we know *every* solution.

In general, it is not easy to discover particular solutions to a second-order linear equation. But it is always possible to do so if the coefficient functions P, Q, and R are constant functions, that is, if the differential equation has the form

$$\boxed{5} \qquad \boxed{ay'' + by' + cy = 0}$$

where a, b, and c are constants and $a \neq 0$.

It's not hard to think of some likely candidates for particular solutions of Equation 5 if we state the equation verbally. We are looking for a function y such that a constant times its second derivative y'' plus another constant times y' plus a third constant times y is equal to 0. We know that the exponential function $y = e^{rx}$ (where r is a constant) has the property that its derivative is a constant multiple of itself: $y' = re^{rx}$. Furthermore, $y'' = r^2 e^{rx}$. If we substitute these expressions into Equation 5, we see that $y = e^{rx}$ is a solution if

$$ar^2 e^{rx} + bre^{rx} + ce^{rx} = 0$$

or

$$(ar^2 + br + c)e^{rx} = 0$$

But e^{rx} is never 0. Thus $y = e^{rx}$ is a solution of Equation 5 if r is a root of the equation

$$\boxed{6} \qquad \boxed{ar^2 + br + c = 0}$$

Equation 6 is called the **auxiliary equation** (or **characteristic equation**) of the differential equation $ay'' + by' + cy = 0$. Notice that it is an algebraic equation that is obtained from the differential equation by replacing y'' by r^2, y' by r, and y by 1.

Sometimes the roots r_1 and r_2 of the auxiliary equation can be found by factoring. In other cases they are found by using the quadratic formula:

$$\boxed{7} \qquad r_1 = \frac{-b + \sqrt{b^2 - 4ac}}{2a} \qquad r_2 = \frac{-b - \sqrt{b^2 - 4ac}}{2a}$$

We distinguish three cases according to the sign of the discriminant $b^2 - 4ac$.

■ CASE I $b^2 - 4ac > 0$

In this case the roots r_1 and r_2 of the auxiliary equation are real and distinct, so $y_1 = e^{r_1 x}$ and $y_2 = e^{r_2 x}$ are two linearly independent solutions of Equation 5. (Note that $e^{r_2 x}$ is not a constant multiple of $e^{r_1 x}$.) Therefore, by Theorem 4, we have the following fact.

> **8** If the roots r_1 and r_2 of the auxiliary equation $ar^2 + br + c = 0$ are real and unequal, then the general solution of $ay'' + by' + cy = 0$ is
>
> $$y = c_1 e^{r_1 x} + c_2 e^{r_2 x}$$

■ In Figure 1 the graphs of the basic solutions $f(x) = e^{2x}$ and $g(x) = e^{-3x}$ of the differential equation in Example 1 are shown in blue and red, respectively. Some of the other solutions, linear combinations of f and g, are shown in black.

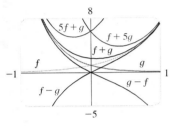

FIGURE I

EXAMPLE I Solve the equation $y'' + y' - 6y = 0$.

SOLUTION The auxiliary equation is

$$r^2 + r - 6 = (r - 2)(r + 3) = 0$$

whose roots are $r = 2, -3$. Therefore, by (8), the general solution of the given differential equation is

$$y = c_1 e^{2x} + c_2 e^{-3x}$$

We could verify that this is indeed a solution by differentiating and substituting into the differential equation.

EXAMPLE 2 Solve $3 \dfrac{d^2 y}{dx^2} + \dfrac{dy}{dx} - y = 0$.

SOLUTION To solve the auxiliary equation $3r^2 + r - 1 = 0$, we use the quadratic formula:

$$r = \frac{-1 \pm \sqrt{13}}{6}$$

Since the roots are real and distinct, the general solution is

$$y = c_1 e^{(-1+\sqrt{13})x/6} + c_2 e^{(-1-\sqrt{13})x/6}$$

■ CASE II $b^2 - 4ac = 0$

In this case $r_1 = r_2$; that is, the roots of the auxiliary equation are real and equal. Let's denote by r the common value of r_1 and r_2. Then, from Equations 7, we have

9
$$r = -\frac{b}{2a} \quad \text{so} \quad 2ar + b = 0$$

We know that $y_1 = e^{rx}$ is one solution of Equation 5. We now verify that $y_2 = xe^{rx}$ is also a solution:

$$ay_2'' + by_2' + cy_2 = a(2re^{rx} + r^2 xe^{rx}) + b(e^{rx} + rxe^{rx}) + cxe^{rx}$$
$$= (2ar + b)e^{rx} + (ar^2 + br + c)xe^{rx}$$
$$= 0(e^{rx}) + 0(xe^{rx}) = 0$$

The first term is 0 by Equations 9; the second term is 0 because r is a root of the auxiliary equation. Since $y_1 = e^{rx}$ and $y_2 = xe^{rx}$ are linearly independent solutions, Theorem 4 provides us with the general solution.

---

10 If the auxiliary equation $ar^2 + br + c = 0$ has only one real root r, then the general solution of $ay'' + by' + cy = 0$ is

$$y = c_1 e^{rx} + c_2 xe^{rx}$$

EXAMPLE 3 Solve the equation $4y'' + 12y' + 9y = 0$.

SOLUTION The auxiliary equation $4r^2 + 12r + 9 = 0$ can be factored as

$$(2r + 3)^2 = 0$$

so the only root is $r = -\frac{3}{2}$. By (10), the general solution is

$$y = c_1 e^{-3x/2} + c_2 xe^{-3x/2}$$

■ Figure 2 shows the basic solutions $f(x) = e^{-3x/2}$ and $g(x) = xe^{-3x/2}$ in Example 3 and some other members of the family of solutions. Notice that all of them approach 0 as $x \to \infty$.

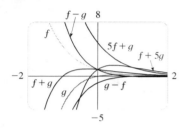

FIGURE 2

■ **CASE III** $b^2 - 4ac < 0$

In this case the roots r_1 and r_2 of the auxiliary equation are complex numbers. (See Appendix H for information about complex numbers.) We can write

$$r_1 = \alpha + i\beta \qquad r_2 = \alpha - i\beta$$

where α and β are real numbers. [In fact, $\alpha = -b/(2a)$, $\beta = \sqrt{4ac - b^2}/(2a)$.] Then, using Euler's equation

$$e^{i\theta} = \cos\theta + i\sin\theta$$

from Appendix H, we write the solution of the differential equation as

$$
\begin{aligned}
y &= C_1 e^{r_1 x} + C_2 e^{r_2 x} = C_1 e^{(\alpha + i\beta)x} + C_2 e^{(\alpha - i\beta)x} \\
&= C_1 e^{\alpha x}(\cos\beta x + i\sin\beta x) + C_2 e^{\alpha x}(\cos\beta x - i\sin\beta x) \\
&= e^{\alpha x}[(C_1 + C_2)\cos\beta x + i(C_1 - C_2)\sin\beta x] \\
&= e^{\alpha x}(c_1 \cos\beta x + c_2 \sin\beta x)
\end{aligned}
$$

where $c_1 = C_1 + C_2$, $c_2 = i(C_1 - C_2)$. This gives all solutions (real or complex) of the differential equation. The solutions are real when the constants c_1 and c_2 are real. We summarize the discussion as follows.

---

11 If the roots of the auxiliary equation $ar^2 + br + c = 0$ are the complex numbers $r_1 = \alpha + i\beta$, $r_2 = \alpha - i\beta$, then the general solution of $ay'' + by' + cy = 0$ is

$$y = e^{\alpha x}(c_1 \cos\beta x + c_2 \sin\beta x)$$

Figure 3 shows the graphs of the solutions in Example 4, $f(x) = e^{3x} \cos 2x$ and $g(x) = e^{3x} \sin 2x$, together with some linear combinations. All solutions approach 0 as $x \rightarrow -\infty$.

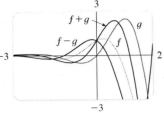

FIGURE 3

EXAMPLE 4 Solve the equation $y'' - 6y' + 13y = 0$.

SOLUTION The auxiliary equation is $r^2 - 6r + 13 = 0$. By the quadratic formula, the roots are

$$r = \frac{6 \pm \sqrt{36 - 52}}{2} = \frac{6 \pm \sqrt{-16}}{2} = 3 \pm 2i$$

By (11), the general solution of the differential equation is

$$y = e^{3x}(c_1 \cos 2x + c_2 \sin 2x)$$

INITIAL-VALUE AND BOUNDARY-VALUE PROBLEMS

An **initial-value problem** for the second-order Equation 1 or 2 consists of finding a solution y of the differential equation that also satisfies initial conditions of the form

$$y(x_0) = y_0 \qquad y'(x_0) = y_1$$

where y_0 and y_1 are given constants. If P, Q, R, and G are continuous on an interval and $P(x) \neq 0$ there, then a theorem found in more advanced books guarantees the existence and uniqueness of a solution to this initial-value problem. Examples 5 and 6 illustrate the technique for solving such a problem.

EXAMPLE 5 Solve the initial-value problem

$$y'' + y' - 6y = 0 \qquad y(0) = 1 \qquad y'(0) = 0$$

SOLUTION From Example 1 we know that the general solution of the differential equation is

$$y(x) = c_1 e^{2x} + c_2 e^{-3x}$$

Differentiating this solution, we get

$$y'(x) = 2c_1 e^{2x} - 3c_2 e^{-3x}$$

Figure 4 shows the graph of the solution of the initial-value problem in Example 5. Compare with Figure 1.

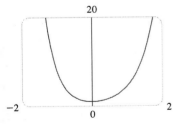

FIGURE 4

To satisfy the initial conditions we require that

$$\boxed{12} \qquad y(0) = c_1 + c_2 = 1$$

$$\boxed{13} \qquad y'(0) = 2c_1 - 3c_2 = 0$$

From (13), we have $c_2 = \frac{2}{3}c_1$ and so (12) gives

$$c_1 + \frac{2}{3}c_1 = 1 \qquad c_1 = \frac{3}{5} \qquad c_2 = \frac{2}{5}$$

Thus the required solution of the initial-value problem is

$$y = \frac{3}{5}e^{2x} + \frac{2}{5}e^{-3x}$$

EXAMPLE 6 Solve the initial-value problem

$$y'' + y = 0 \qquad y(0) = 2 \qquad y'(0) = 3$$

SOLUTION The auxiliary equation is $r^2 + 1 = 0$, or $r^2 = -1$, whose roots are $\pm i$. Thus $\alpha = 0$, $\beta = 1$, and since $e^{0x} = 1$, the general solution is

$$y(x) = c_1 \cos x + c_2 \sin x$$

Since

$$y'(x) = -c_1 \sin x + c_2 \cos x$$

■ The solution to Example 6 is graphed in Figure 5. It appears to be a shifted sine curve and, indeed, you can verify that another way of writing the solution is

$$y = \sqrt{13}\sin(x + \phi) \quad \text{where } \tan\phi = \tfrac{2}{3}$$

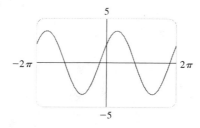

FIGURE 5

the initial conditions become

$$y(0) = c_1 = 2 \qquad y'(0) = c_2 = 3$$

Therefore the solution of the initial-value problem is

$$y(x) = 2\cos x + 3\sin x$$

A **boundary-value problem** for Equation 1 or 2 consists of finding a solution y of the differential equation that also satisfies boundary conditions of the form

$$y(x_0) = y_0 \qquad y(x_1) = y_1$$

In contrast with the situation for initial-value problems, a boundary-value problem does not always have a solution. The method is illustrated in Example 7.

EXAMPLE 7 Solve the boundary-value problem

$$y'' + 2y' + y = 0 \qquad y(0) = 1 \qquad y(1) = 3$$

SOLUTION The auxiliary equation is

$$r^2 + 2r + 1 = 0 \qquad \text{or} \qquad (r + 1)^2 = 0$$

whose only root is $r = -1$. Therefore the general solution is

$$y(x) = c_1 e^{-x} + c_2 x e^{-x}$$

The boundary conditions are satisfied if

$$y(0) = c_1 = 1$$

$$y(1) = c_1 e^{-1} + c_2 e^{-1} = 3$$

The first condition gives $c_1 = 1$, so the second condition becomes

$$e^{-1} + c_2 e^{-1} = 3$$

Solving this equation for c_2 by first multiplying through by e, we get

$$1 + c_2 = 3e \qquad \text{so} \qquad c_2 = 3e - 1$$

■ Figure 6 shows the graph of the solution of the boundary-value problem in Example 7.

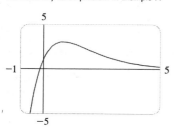

FIGURE 6

Thus the solution of the boundary-value problem is

$$y = e^{-x} + (3e - 1)xe^{-x}$$

SUMMARY: SOLUTIONS OF $ay'' + by' + c = 0$

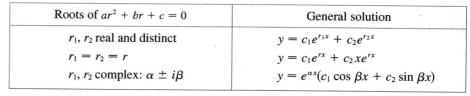

Roots of $ar^2 + br + c = 0$	General solution
r_1, r_2 real and distinct	$y = c_1 e^{r_1 x} + c_2 e^{r_2 x}$
$r_1 = r_2 = r$	$y = c_1 e^{rx} + c_2 x e^{rx}$
r_1, r_2 complex: $\alpha \pm i\beta$	$y = e^{\alpha x}(c_1 \cos \beta x + c_2 \sin \beta x)$

17.1 EXERCISES

1–13 Solve the differential equation.

1. $y'' - y' - 6y = 0$

2. $y'' + 4y' + 4y = 0$

3. $y'' + 16y = 0$

4. $y'' - 8y' + 12y = 0$

5. $9y'' - 12y' + 4y = 0$

6. $25y'' + 9y = 0$

7. $y' = 2y''$

8. $y'' - 4y' + y = 0$

9. $y'' - 4y' + 13y = 0$

10. $y'' + 3y' = 0$

11. $2\dfrac{d^2y}{dt^2} + 2\dfrac{dy}{dt} - y = 0$

12. $8\dfrac{d^2y}{dt^2} + 12\dfrac{dy}{dt} + 5y = 0$

13. $100\dfrac{d^2P}{dt^2} + 200\dfrac{dP}{dt} + 101P = 0$

14–16 Graph the two basic solutions of the differential equation and several other solutions. What features do the solutions have in common?

14. $\dfrac{d^2y}{dx^2} + 4\dfrac{dy}{dx} + 20y = 0$

15. $5\dfrac{d^2y}{dx^2} - 2\dfrac{dy}{dx} - 3y = 0$

16. $9\dfrac{d^2y}{dx^2} + 6\dfrac{dy}{dx} + y = 0$

17–24 Solve the initial-value problem.

17. $2y'' + 5y' + 3y = 0$, $y(0) = 3$, $y'(0) = -4$

18. $y'' + 3y = 0$, $y(0) = 1$, $y'(0) = 3$

19. $4y'' - 4y' + y = 0$, $y(0) = 1$, $y'(0) = -1.5$

20. $2y'' + 5y' - 3y = 0$, $y(0) = 1$, $y'(0) = 4$

21. $y'' + 16y = 0$, $y(\pi/4) = -3$, $y'(\pi/4) = 4$

22. $y'' - 2y' + 5y = 0$, $y(\pi) = 0$, $y'(\pi) = 2$

23. $y'' + 2y' + 2y = 0$, $y(0) = 2$, $y'(0) = 1$

24. $y'' + 12y' + 36y = 0$, $y(1) = 0$, $y'(1) = 1$

25–32 Solve the boundary-value problem, if possible.

25. $4y'' + y = 0$, $y(0) = 3$, $y(\pi) = -4$

26. $y'' + 2y' = 0$, $y(0) = 1$, $y(1) = 2$

27. $y'' - 3y' + 2y = 0$, $y(0) = 1$, $y(3) = 0$

28. $y'' + 100y = 0$, $y(0) = 2$, $y(\pi) = 5$

29. $y'' - 6y' + 25y = 0$, $y(0) = 1$, $y(\pi) = 2$

30. $y'' - 6y' + 9y = 0$, $y(0) = 1$, $y(1) = 0$

31. $y'' + 4y' + 13y = 0$, $y(0) = 2$, $y(\pi/2) = 1$

32. $9y'' - 18y' + 10y = 0$, $y(0) = 0$, $y(\pi) = 1$

33. Let L be a nonzero real number.
(a) Show that the boundary-value problem $y'' + \lambda y = 0$, $y(0) = 0$, $y(L) = 0$ has only the trivial solution $y = 0$ for the cases $\lambda = 0$ and $\lambda < 0$.
(b) For the case $\lambda > 0$, find the values of λ for which this problem has a nontrivial solution and give the corresponding solution.

34. If a, b, and c are all positive constants and $y(x)$ is a solution of the differential equation $ay'' + by' + cy = 0$, show that $\lim_{x\to\infty} y(x) = 0$.

17.2 NONHOMOGENEOUS LINEAR EQUATIONS

In this section we learn how to solve second-order nonhomogeneous linear differential equations with constant coefficients, that is, equations of the form

$$\boxed{1} \qquad ay'' + by' + cy = G(x)$$

where a, b, and c are constants and G is a continuous function. The related homogeneous equation

$$\boxed{2} \qquad ay'' + by' + cy = 0$$

is called the **complementary equation** and plays an important role in the solution of the original nonhomogeneous equation (1).

> **3 THEOREM** The general solution of the nonhomogeneous differential equation
> (1) can be written as
>
> $$y(x) = y_p(x) + y_c(x)$$
>
> where y_p is a particular solution of Equation 1 and y_c is the general solution of the
> complementary Equation 2.

PROOF All we have to do is verify that if y is any solution of Equation 1, then $y - y_p$ is a
solution of the complementary Equation 2. Indeed

$$a(y - y_p)'' + b(y - y_p)' + c(y - y_p) = ay'' - ay_p'' + by' - by_p' + cy - cy_p$$
$$= (ay'' + by' + cy) - (ay_p'' + by_p' + cy_p)$$
$$= g(x) - g(x) = 0 \qquad \square$$

We know from Section 17.1 how to solve the complementary equation. (Recall that the
solution is $y_c = c_1 y_1 + c_2 y_2$, where y_1 and y_2 are linearly independent solutions of Equation 2.) Therefore Theorem 3 says that we know the general solution of the nonhomogeneous equation as soon as we know a particular solution y_p. There are two methods for
finding a particular solution: The method of undetermined coefficients is straightforward
but works only for a restricted class of functions G. The method of variation of parameters
works for every function G but is usually more difficult to apply in practice.

THE METHOD OF UNDETERMINED COEFFICIENTS

We first illustrate the method of undetermined coefficients for the equation

$$ay'' + by' + cy = G(x)$$

where $G(x)$ is a polynomial. It is reasonable to guess that there is a particular solution
y_p that is a polynomial of the same degree as G because if y is a polynomial, then
$ay'' + by' + cy$ is also a polynomial. We therefore substitute $y_p(x) =$ a polynomial (of the
same degree as G) into the differential equation and determine the coefficients.

☑ EXAMPLE 1 Solve the equation $y'' + y' - 2y = x^2$.

SOLUTION The auxiliary equation of $y'' + y' - 2y = 0$ is

$$r^2 + r - 2 = (r - 1)(r + 2) = 0$$

with roots $r = 1, -2$. So the solution of the complementary equation is

$$y_c = c_1 e^x + c_2 e^{-2x}$$

Since $G(x) = x^2$ is a polynomial of degree 2, we seek a particular solution of the form

$$y_p(x) = Ax^2 + Bx + C$$

Then $y_p' = 2Ax + B$ and $y_p'' = 2A$ so, substituting into the given differential equation, we
have

$$(2A) + (2Ax + B) - 2(Ax^2 + Bx + C) = x^2$$

or
$$-2Ax^2 + (2A - 2B)x + (2A + B - 2C) = x^2$$

Polynomials are equal when their coefficients are equal. Thus

$$-2A = 1 \qquad 2A - 2B = 0 \qquad 2A + B - 2C = 0$$

The solution of this system of equations is

$$A = -\tfrac{1}{2} \qquad B = -\tfrac{1}{2} \qquad C = -\tfrac{3}{4}$$

A particular solution is therefore

$$y_p(x) = -\tfrac{1}{2}x^2 - \tfrac{1}{2}x - \tfrac{3}{4}$$

and, by Theorem 3, the general solution is

$$y = y_c + y_p = c_1 e^x + c_2 e^{-2x} - \tfrac{1}{2}x^2 - \tfrac{1}{2}x - \tfrac{3}{4} \qquad \square$$

■ Figure 1 shows four solutions of the differential equation in Example 1 in terms of the particular solution y_p and the functions $f(x) = e^x$ and $g(x) = e^{-2x}$.

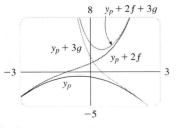

FIGURE 1

If $G(x)$ (the right side of Equation 1) is of the form Ce^{kx}, where C and k are constants, then we take as a trial solution a function of the same form, $y_p(x) = Ae^{kx}$, because the derivatives of e^{kx} are constant multiples of e^{kx}.

EXAMPLE 2 Solve $y'' + 4y = e^{3x}$.

SOLUTION The auxiliary equation is $r^2 + 4 = 0$ with roots $\pm 2i$, so the solution of the complementary equation is

$$y_c(x) = c_1 \cos 2x + c_2 \sin 2x$$

For a particular solution we try $y_p(x) = Ae^{3x}$. Then $y_p' = 3Ae^{3x}$ and $y_p'' = 9Ae^{3x}$. Substituting into the differential equation, we have

$$9Ae^{3x} + 4(Ae^{3x}) = e^{3x}$$

so $13Ae^{3x} = e^{3x}$ and $A = \tfrac{1}{13}$. Thus a particular solution is

$$y_p(x) = \tfrac{1}{13}e^{3x}$$

and the general solution is

$$y(x) = c_1 \cos 2x + c_2 \sin 2x + \tfrac{1}{13}e^{3x} \qquad \square$$

■ Figure 2 shows solutions of the differential equation in Example 2 in terms of y_p and the functions $f(x) = \cos 2x$ and $g(x) = \sin 2x$. Notice that all solutions approach ∞ as $x \to \infty$ and all solutions (except y_p) resemble sine functions when x is negative.

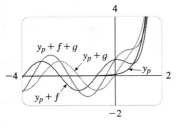

FIGURE 2

If $G(x)$ is either $C \cos kx$ or $C \sin kx$, then, because of the rules for differentiating the sine and cosine functions, we take as a trial particular solution a function of the form

$$y_p(x) = A \cos kx + B \sin kx$$

✓ **EXAMPLE 3** Solve $y'' + y' - 2y = \sin x$.

SOLUTION We try a particular solution

$$y_p(x) = A \cos x + B \sin x$$

Then
$$y_p' = -A \sin x + B \cos x \qquad y_p'' = -A \cos x - B \sin x$$

so substitution in the differential equation gives

$$(-A \cos x - B \sin x) + (-A \sin x + B \cos x) - 2(A \cos x + B \sin x) = \sin x$$

or
$$(-3A + B) \cos x + (-A - 3B) \sin x = \sin x$$

This is true if

$$-3A + B = 0 \qquad \text{and} \qquad -A - 3B = 1$$

The solution of this system is

$$A = -\tfrac{1}{10} \qquad B = -\tfrac{3}{10}$$

so a particular solution is

$$y_p(x) = -\tfrac{1}{10} \cos x - \tfrac{3}{10} \sin x$$

In Example 1 we determined that the solution of the complementary equation is $y_c = c_1 e^x + c_2 e^{-2x}$. Thus the general solution of the given equation is

$$y(x) = c_1 e^x + c_2 e^{-2x} - \tfrac{1}{10}(\cos x + 3 \sin x)$$

□

If $G(x)$ is a product of functions of the preceding types, then we take the trial solution to be a product of functions of the same type. For instance, in solving the differential equation

$$y'' + 2y' + 4y = x \cos 3x$$

we would try

$$y_p(x) = (Ax + B) \cos 3x + (Cx + D) \sin 3x$$

If $G(x)$ is a sum of functions of these types, we use the easily verified *principle of superposition*, which says that if y_{p_1} and y_{p_2} are solutions of

$$ay'' + by' + cy = G_1(x) \qquad \qquad ay'' + by' + cy = G_2(x)$$

respectively, then $y_{p_1} + y_{p_2}$ is a solution of

$$ay'' + by' + cy = G_1(x) + G_2(x)$$

☑ **EXAMPLE 4** Solve $y'' - 4y = xe^x + \cos 2x$.

SOLUTION The auxiliary equation is $r^2 - 4 = 0$ with roots ± 2, so the solution of the complementary equation is $y_c(x) = c_1 e^{2x} + c_2 e^{-2x}$. For the equation $y'' - 4y = xe^x$ we try

$$y_{p_1}(x) = (Ax + B)e^x$$

Then $y'_{p_1} = (Ax + A + B)e^x$, $y''_{p_1} = (Ax + 2A + B)e^x$, so substitution in the equation gives

$$(Ax + 2A + B)e^x - 4(Ax + B)e^x = xe^x$$

or
$$(-3Ax + 2A - 3B)e^x = xe^x$$

Thus $-3A = 1$ and $2A - 3B = 0$, so $A = -\frac{1}{3}$, $B = -\frac{2}{9}$, and

$$y_{p_1}(x) = \left(-\tfrac{1}{3}x - \tfrac{2}{9}\right)e^x$$

For the equation $y'' - 4y = \cos 2x$, we try

$$y_{p_2}(x) = C \cos 2x + D \sin 2x$$

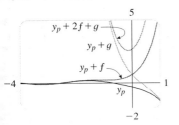

In Figure 3 we show the particular solution $y_p = y_{p_1} + y_{p_2}$ of the differential equation in Example 4. The other solutions are given in terms of $f(x) = e^{2x}$ and $g(x) = e^{-2x}$.

FIGURE 3

Substitution gives

$$-4C \cos 2x - 4D \sin 2x - 4(C \cos 2x + D \sin 2x) = \cos 2x$$

or

$$-8C \cos 2x - 8D \sin 2x = \cos 2x$$

Therefore $-8C = 1$, $-8D = 0$, and

$$y_{p_2}(x) = -\tfrac{1}{8} \cos 2x$$

By the superposition principle, the general solution is

$$y = y_c + y_{p_1} + y_{p_2} = c_1 e^{2x} + c_2 e^{-2x} - \left(\tfrac{1}{3}x + \tfrac{2}{9}\right)e^x - \tfrac{1}{8} \cos 2x$$

Finally we note that the recommended trial solution y_p sometimes turns out to be a solution of the complementary equation and therefore can't be a solution of the nonhomogeneous equation. In such cases we multiply the recommended trial solution by x (or by x^2 if necessary) so that no term in $y_p(x)$ is a solution of the complementary equation.

EXAMPLE 5 Solve $y'' + y = \sin x$.

SOLUTION The auxiliary equation is $r^2 + 1 = 0$ with roots $\pm i$, so the solution of the complementary equation is

$$y_c(x) = c_1 \cos x + c_2 \sin x$$

Ordinarily, we would use the trial solution

$$y_p(x) = A \cos x + B \sin x$$

but we observe that it is a solution of the complementary equation, so instead we try

$$y_p(x) = Ax \cos x + Bx \sin x$$

Then

$$y_p'(x) = A \cos x - Ax \sin x + B \sin x + Bx \cos x$$

$$y_p''(x) = -2A \sin x - Ax \cos x + 2B \cos x - Bx \sin x$$

Substitution in the differential equation gives

$$y_p'' + y_p = -2A \sin x + 2B \cos x = \sin x$$

■ The graphs of four solutions of the differential equation in Example 5 are shown in Figure 4.

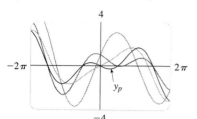

FIGURE 4

so $A = -\frac{1}{2}$, $B = 0$, and

$$y_p(x) = -\tfrac{1}{2}x \cos x$$

The general solution is

$$y(x) = c_1 \cos x + c_2 \sin x - \tfrac{1}{2}x \cos x$$

We summarize the method of undetermined coefficients as follows:

SUMMARY OF THE METHOD OF UNDETERMINED COEFFICIENTS

1. If $G(x) = e^{kx}P(x)$, where P is a polynomial of degree n, then try $y_p(x) = e^{kx}Q(x)$, where $Q(x)$ is an nth-degree polynomial (whose coefficients are determined by substituting in the differential equation).

2. If $G(x) = e^{kx}P(x) \cos mx$ or $G(x) = e^{kx}P(x) \sin mx$, where P is an nth-degree polynomial, then try

$$y_p(x) = e^{kx}Q(x) \cos mx + e^{kx}R(x) \sin mx$$

where Q and R are nth-degree polynomials.

Modification: If any term of y_p is a solution of the complementary equation, multiply y_p by x (or by x^2 if necessary).

EXAMPLE 6 Determine the form of the trial solution for the differential equation $y'' - 4y' + 13y = e^{2x} \cos 3x$.

SOLUTION Here $G(x)$ has the form of part 2 of the summary, where $k = 2$, $m = 3$, and $P(x) = 1$. So, at first glance, the form of the trial solution would be

$$y_p(x) = e^{2x}(A \cos 3x + B \sin 3x)$$

But the auxiliary equation is $r^2 - 4r + 13 = 0$, with roots $r = 2 \pm 3i$, so the solution of the complementary equation is

$$y_c(x) = e^{2x}(c_1 \cos 3x + c_2 \sin 3x)$$

This means that we have to multiply the suggested trial solution by x. So, instead, we use

$$y_p(x) = xe^{2x}(A \cos 3x + B \sin 3x)$$

THE METHOD OF VARIATION OF PARAMETERS

Suppose we have already solved the homogeneous equation $ay'' + by' + cy = 0$ and written the solution as

$$\boxed{4} \qquad y(x) = c_1y_1(x) + c_2y_2(x)$$

where y_1 and y_2 are linearly independent solutions. Let's replace the constants (or parameters) c_1 and c_2 in Equation 4 by arbitrary functions $u_1(x)$ and $u_2(x)$. We look for a particular solution of the nonhomogeneous equation $ay'' + by' + cy = G(x)$ of the form

$$\boxed{5} \qquad y_p(x) = u_1(x)\,y_1(x) + u_2(x)\,y_2(x)$$

(This method is called **variation of parameters** because we have varied the parameters c_1 and c_2 to make them functions.) Differentiating Equation 5, we get

$$\boxed{6} \qquad y_p' = (u_1'y_1 + u_2'y_2) + (u_1 y_1' + u_2 y_2')$$

Since u_1 and u_2 are arbitrary functions, we can impose two conditions on them. One condition is that y_p is a solution of the differential equation; we can choose the other condition so as to simplify our calculations. In view of the expression in Equation 6, let's impose the condition that

$$\boxed{7} \qquad u_1'y_1 + u_2'y_2 = 0$$

Then $$y_p'' = u_1'y_1' + u_2'y_2' + u_1 y_1'' + u_2 y_2''$$

Substituting in the differential equation, we get

$$a(u_1'y_1' + u_2'y_2' + u_1 y_1'' + u_2 y_2'') + b(u_1 y_1' + u_2 y_2') + c(u_1 y_1 + u_2 y_2) = G$$

or

$$\boxed{8} \qquad u_1(ay_1'' + by_1' + cy_1) + u_2(ay_2'' + by_2' + cy_2) + a(u_1'y_1' + u_2'y_2') = G$$

But y_1 and y_2 are solutions of the complementary equation, so

$$ay_1'' + by_1' + cy_1 = 0 \qquad \text{and} \qquad ay_2'' + by_2' + cy_2 = 0$$

and Equation 8 simplifies to

$$\boxed{9} \qquad a(u_1'y_1' + u_2'y_2') = G$$

Equations 7 and 9 form a system of two equations in the unknown functions u_1' and u_2'. After solving this system we may be able to integrate to find u_1 and u_2 and then the particular solution is given by Equation 5.

EXAMPLE 7 Solve the equation $y'' + y = \tan x$, $0 < x < \pi/2$.

SOLUTION The auxiliary equation is $r^2 + 1 = 0$ with roots $\pm i$, so the solution of $y'' + y = 0$ is $c_1 \sin x + c_2 \cos x$. Using variation of parameters, we seek a solution of the form

$$y_p(x) = u_1(x) \sin x + u_2(x) \cos x$$

Then $$y_p' = (u_1' \sin x + u_2' \cos x) + (u_1 \cos x - u_2 \sin x)$$

Set

$$\boxed{10} \qquad u_1' \sin x + u_2' \cos x = 0$$

Then
$$y_p'' = u_1' \cos x - u_2' \sin x - u_1 \sin x - u_2 \cos x$$

For y_p to be a solution we must have

|11| $$y_p'' + y_p = u_1' \cos x - u_2' \sin x = \tan x$$

Solving Equations 10 and 11, we get

$$u_1'(\sin^2 x + \cos^2 x) = \cos x \tan x$$

$$u_1' = \sin x \qquad u_1(x) = -\cos x$$

(We seek a particular solution, so we don't need a constant of integration here.) Then, from Equation 10, we obtain

$$u_2' = -\frac{\sin x}{\cos x} u_1' = -\frac{\sin^2 x}{\cos x} = \frac{\cos^2 x - 1}{\cos x} = \cos x - \sec x$$

So
$$u_2(x) = \sin x - \ln(\sec x + \tan x)$$

(Note that $\sec x + \tan x > 0$ for $0 < x < \pi/2$.) Therefore

$$y_p(x) = -\cos x \sin x + [\sin x - \ln(\sec x + \tan x)] \cos x$$

$$= -\cos x \ln(\sec x + \tan x)$$

and the general solution is

$$y(x) = c_1 \sin x + c_2 \cos x - \cos x \ln(\sec x + \tan x)$$

▨ Figure 5 shows four solutions of the differential equation in Example 7.

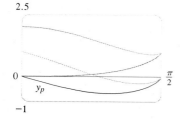

FIGURE 5

17.2 EXERCISES

1–10 Solve the differential equation or initial-value problem using the method of undetermined coefficients.

1. $y'' + 3y' + 2y = x^2$

2. $y'' + 9y = e^{3x}$

3. $y'' - 2y' = \sin 4x$

4. $y'' + 6y' + 9y = 1 + x$

5. $y'' - 4y' + 5y = e^{-x}$

6. $y'' + 2y' + y = xe^{-x}$

7. $y'' + y = e^x + x^3, \quad y(0) = 2, \quad y'(0) = 0$

8. $y'' - 4y = e^x \cos x, \quad y(0) = 1, \quad y'(0) = 2$

9. $y'' - y' = xe^x, \quad y(0) = 2, \quad y'(0) = 1$

10. $y'' + y' - 2y = x + \sin 2x, \quad y(0) = 1, \quad y'(0) = 0$

▨ **11–12** Graph the particular solution and several other solutions. What characteristics do these solutions have in common?

11. $y'' + 3y' + 2y = \cos x$ **12.** $y'' + 4y = e^{-x}$

13–18 Write a trial solution for the method of undetermined coefficients. Do not determine the coefficients.

13. $y'' + 9y = e^{2x} + x^2 \sin x$

14. $y'' + 9y' = xe^{-x} \cos \pi x$

15. $y'' + 9y' = 1 + xe^{9x}$

16. $y'' + 3y' - 4y = (x^3 + x)e^x$

17. $y'' + 2y' + 10y = x^2 e^{-x} \cos 3x$

18. $y'' + 4y = e^{3x} + x \sin 2x$

19–22 Solve the differential equation using (a) undetermined coefficients and (b) variation of parameters.

19. $4y'' + y = \cos x$

20. $y'' - 2y' - 3y = x + 2$

21. $y'' - 2y' + y = e^{2x}$

22. $y'' - y' = e^x$

23–28 Solve the differential equation using the method of variation of parameters.

23. $y'' + y = \sec^2 x, \ 0 < x < \pi/2$

24. $y'' + y = \sec^3 x, \ 0 < x < \pi/2$

25. $y'' - 3y' + 2y = \dfrac{1}{1 + e^{-x}}$

26. $y'' + 3y' + 2y = \sin(e^x)$

27. $y'' - 2y' + y = \dfrac{e^x}{1 + x^2}$

28. $y'' + 4y' + 4y = \dfrac{e^{-2x}}{x^3}$

17.3 APPLICATIONS OF SECOND-ORDER DIFFERENTIAL EQUATIONS

Second-order linear differential equations have a variety of applications in science and engineering. In this section we explore two of them: the vibration of springs and electric circuits.

VIBRATING SPRINGS

We consider the motion of an object with mass m at the end of a spring that is either vertical (as in Figure 1) or horizontal on a level surface (as in Figure 2).

In Section 6.4 we discussed Hooke's Law, which says that if the spring is stretched (or compressed) x units from its natural length, then it exerts a force that is proportional to x:

$$\text{restoring force} = -kx$$

where k is a positive constant (called the **spring constant**). If we ignore any external resisting forces (due to air resistance or friction) then, by Newton's Second Law (force equals mass times acceleration), we have

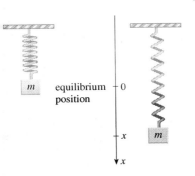

FIGURE I

$$\boxed{1} \qquad m\frac{d^2x}{dt^2} = -kx \quad \text{or} \quad m\frac{d^2x}{dt^2} + kx = 0$$

This is a second-order linear differential equation. Its auxiliary equation is $mr^2 + k = 0$ with roots $r = \pm\omega i$, where $\omega = \sqrt{k/m}$. Thus the general solution is

$$x(t) = c_1 \cos \omega t + c_2 \sin \omega t$$

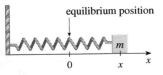

equilibrium position

FIGURE 2

which can also be written as

$$x(t) = A \cos(\omega t + \delta)$$

where

$$\omega = \sqrt{k/m} \quad \text{(frequency)}$$

$$A = \sqrt{c_1^2 + c_2^2} \quad \text{(amplitude)}$$

$$\cos \delta = \frac{c_1}{A} \qquad \sin \delta = -\frac{c_2}{A} \quad (\delta \text{ is the phase angle})$$

(See Exercise 17.) This type of motion is called **simple harmonic motion**.

☑ **EXAMPLE 1** A spring with a mass of 2 kg has natural length 0.5 m. A force of 25.6 N is required to maintain it stretched to a length of 0.7 m. If the spring is stretched to a length of 0.7 m and then released with initial velocity 0, find the position of the mass at any time t.

SOLUTION From Hooke's Law, the force required to stretch the spring is

$$k(0.2) = 25.6$$

so $k = 25.6/0.2 = 128$. Using this value of the spring constant k, together with $m = 2$ in Equation 1, we have

$$2\frac{d^2x}{dt^2} + 128x = 0$$

As in the earlier general discussion, the solution of this equation is

2 $$x(t) = c_1 \cos 8t + c_2 \sin 8t$$

We are given the initial condition that $x(0) = 0.2$. But, from Equation 2, $x(0) = c_1$. Therefore $c_1 = 0.2$. Differentiating Equation 2, we get

$$x'(t) = -8c_1 \sin 8t + 8c_2 \cos 8t$$

Since the initial velocity is given as $x'(0) = 0$, we have $c_2 = 0$ and so the solution is

$$x(t) = \tfrac{1}{5} \cos 8t$$ ☐

FIGURE 3

DAMPED VIBRATIONS

We next consider the motion of a spring that is subject to a frictional force (in the case of the horizontal spring of Figure 2) or a damping force (in the case where a vertical spring moves through a fluid as in Figure 3). An example is the damping force supplied by a shock absorber in a car or a bicycle.

We assume that the damping force is proportional to the velocity of the mass and acts in the direction opposite to the motion. (This has been confirmed, at least approximately, by some physical experiments.) Thus

$$\text{damping force} = -c\frac{dx}{dt}$$

where c is a positive constant, called the **damping constant**. Thus, in this case, Newton's Second Law gives

$$m\frac{d^2x}{dt^2} = \text{restoring force} + \text{damping force} = -kx - c\frac{dx}{dt}$$

or

3 $$m\frac{d^2x}{dt^2} + c\frac{dx}{dt} + kx = 0$$

Equation 3 is a second-order linear differential equation and its auxiliary equation is $mr^2 + cr + k = 0$. The roots are

$$\boxed{4} \qquad r_1 = \frac{-c + \sqrt{c^2 - 4mk}}{2m} \qquad r_2 = \frac{-c - \sqrt{c^2 - 4mk}}{2m}$$

According to Section 17.1 we need to discuss three cases.

■ CASE I $c^2 - 4mk > 0$ **(overdamping)**
In this case r_1 and r_2 are distinct real roots and

$$x = c_1 e^{r_1 t} + c_2 e^{r_2 t}$$

Since c, m, and k are all positive, we have $\sqrt{c^2 - 4mk} < c$, so the roots r_1 and r_2 given by Equations 4 must both be negative. This shows that $x \rightarrow 0$ as $t \rightarrow \infty$. Typical graphs of x as a function of t are shown in Figure 4. Notice that oscillations do not occur. (It's possible for the mass to pass through the equilibrium position once, but only once.) This is because $c^2 > 4mk$ means that there is a strong damping force (high-viscosity oil or grease) compared with a weak spring or small mass.

■ CASE II $c^2 - 4mk = 0$ **(critical damping)**
This case corresponds to equal roots

$$r_1 = r_2 = -\frac{c}{2m}$$

and the solution is given by

$$x = (c_1 + c_2 t)e^{-(c/2m)t}$$

It is similar to Case I, and typical graphs resemble those in Figure 4 (see Exercise 12), but the damping is just sufficient to suppress vibrations. Any decrease in the viscosity of the fluid leads to the vibrations of the following case.

■ CASE III $c^2 - 4mk < 0$ **(underdamping)**
Here the roots are complex:

$$\left.\begin{array}{c} r_1 \\ r_2 \end{array}\right\} = -\frac{c}{2m} \pm \omega i$$

where

$$\omega = \frac{\sqrt{4mk - c^2}}{2m}$$

The solution is given by

$$x = e^{-(c/2m)t}(c_1 \cos \omega t + c_2 \sin \omega t)$$

We see that there are oscillations that are damped by the factor $e^{-(c/2m)t}$. Since $c > 0$ and $m > 0$, we have $-(c/2m) < 0$ so $e^{-(c/2m)t} \rightarrow 0$ as $t \rightarrow \infty$. This implies that $x \rightarrow 0$ as $t \rightarrow \infty$; that is, the motion decays to 0 as time increases. A typical graph is shown in Figure 5.

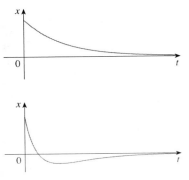

FIGURE 4
Overdamping

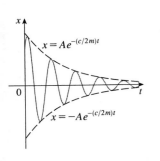

FIGURE 5
Underdamping

☑ EXAMPLE 2 Suppose that the spring of Example 1 is immersed in a fluid with damping constant $c = 40$. Find the position of the mass at any time t if it starts from the equilibrium position and is given a push to start it with an initial velocity of 0.6 m/s.

SOLUTION From Example 1, the mass is $m = 2$ and the spring constant is $k = 128$, so the differential equation (3) becomes

$$2\frac{d^2x}{dt^2} + 40\frac{dx}{dt} + 128x = 0$$

or

$$\frac{d^2x}{dt^2} + 20\frac{dx}{dt} + 64x = 0$$

The auxiliary equation is $r^2 + 20r + 64 = (r + 4)(r + 16) = 0$ with roots -4 and -16, so the motion is overdamped and the solution is

$$x(t) = c_1 e^{-4t} + c_2 e^{-16t}$$

We are given that $x(0) = 0$, so $c_1 + c_2 = 0$. Differentiating, we get

$$x'(t) = -4c_1 e^{-4t} - 16c_2 e^{-16t}$$

so

$$x'(0) = -4c_1 - 16c_2 = 0.6$$

Since $c_2 = -c_1$, this gives $12c_1 = 0.6$ or $c_1 = 0.05$. Therefore

$$x = 0.05(e^{-4t} - e^{-16t})$$

▨ Figure 6 shows the graph of the position function for the overdamped motion in Example 2.

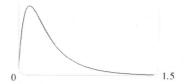

0.03

0   1.5

FIGURE 6

FORCED VIBRATIONS

Suppose that, in addition to the restoring force and the damping force, the motion of the spring is affected by an external force $F(t)$. Then Newton's Second Law gives

$$m\frac{d^2x}{dt^2} = \text{restoring force} + \text{damping force} + \text{external force}$$

$$= -kx - c\frac{dx}{dt} + F(t)$$

Thus, instead of the homogeneous equation (3), the motion of the spring is now governed by the following nonhomogeneous differential equation:

5

$$m\frac{d^2x}{dt^2} + c\frac{dx}{dt} + kx = F(t)$$

The motion of the spring can be determined by the methods of Section 17.2.

A commonly occurring type of external force is a periodic force function

$$F(t) = F_0 \cos \omega_0 t \qquad \text{where} \quad \omega_0 \ne \omega = \sqrt{k/m}$$

In this case, and in the absence of a damping force ($c = 0$), you are asked in Exercise 9 to use the method of undetermined coefficients to show that

$$\boxed{6} \qquad x(t) = c_1 \cos \omega t + c_2 \sin \omega t + \frac{F_0}{m(\omega^2 - \omega_0^2)} \cos \omega_0 t$$

If $\omega_0 = \omega$, then the applied frequency reinforces the natural frequency and the result is vibrations of large amplitude. This is the phenomenon of **resonance** (see Exercise 10).

ELECTRIC CIRCUITS

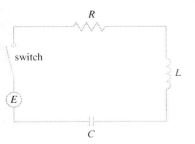

FIGURE 7

In Sections 9.3 and 9.5 we were able to use first-order separable and linear equations to analyze electric circuits that contain a resistor and inductor (see Figure 5 on page 582 or Figure 4 on page 605) or a resistor and capacitor (see Exercise 29 on page 607). Now that we know how to solve second-order linear equations, we are in a position to analyze the circuit shown in Figure 7. It contains an electromotive force E (supplied by a battery or generator), a resistor R, an inductor L, and a capacitor C, in series. If the charge on the capacitor at time t is $Q = Q(t)$, then the current is the rate of change of Q with respect to t: $I = dQ/dt$. As in Section 9.5, it is known from physics that the voltage drops across the resistor, inductor, and capacitor are

$$RI \qquad L\frac{dI}{dt} \qquad \frac{Q}{C}$$

respectively. Kirchhoff's voltage law says that the sum of these voltage drops is equal to the supplied voltage:

$$L\frac{dI}{dt} + RI + \frac{Q}{C} = E(t)$$

Since $I = dQ/dt$, this equation becomes

$$\boxed{7} \qquad \boxed{L\frac{d^2Q}{dt^2} + R\frac{dQ}{dt} + \frac{1}{C}Q = E(t)}$$

which is a second-order linear differential equation with constant coefficients. If the charge Q_0 and the current I_0 are known at time 0, then we have the initial conditions

$$Q(0) = Q_0 \qquad Q'(0) = I(0) = I_0$$

and the initial-value problem can be solved by the methods of Section 17.2.

A differential equation for the current can be obtained by differentiating Equation 7 with respect to t and remembering that $I = dQ/dt$:

$$L\frac{d^2I}{dt^2} + R\frac{dI}{dt} + \frac{1}{C}I = E'(t)$$

EXAMPLE 3 Find the charge and current at time t in the circuit of Figure 7 if $R = 40\ \Omega$, $L = 1$ H, $C = 16 \times 10^{-4}$ F, $E(t) = 100 \cos 10t$, and the initial charge and current are both 0.

SOLUTION With the given values of L, R, C, and $E(t)$, Equation 7 becomes

$$\boxed{8}\qquad\qquad \frac{d^2Q}{dt^2} + 40\frac{dQ}{dt} + 625Q = 100 \cos 10t$$

The auxiliary equation is $r^2 + 40r + 625 = 0$ with roots

$$r = \frac{-40 \pm \sqrt{-900}}{2} = -20 \pm 15i$$

so the solution of the complementary equation is

$$Q_c(t) = e^{-20t}(c_1 \cos 15t + c_2 \sin 15t)$$

For the method of undetermined coefficients we try the particular solution

$$Q_p(t) = A \cos 10t + B \sin 10t$$

Then
$$Q_p'(t) = -10A \sin 10t + 10B \cos 10t$$

$$Q_p''(t) = -100A \cos 10t - 100B \sin 10t$$

Substituting into Equation 8, we have

$$(-100A \cos 10t - 100B \sin 10t) + 40(-10A \sin 10t + 10B \cos 10t)$$
$$+ 625(A \cos 10t + B \sin 10t) = 100 \cos 10t$$

or $\qquad (525A + 400B) \cos 10t + (-400A + 525B) \sin 10t = 100 \cos 10t$

Equating coefficients, we have

$$525A + 400B = 100 \qquad\qquad\qquad 21A + 16B = 4$$
$$\text{or}$$
$$-400A + 525B = 0 \qquad\qquad\qquad -16A + 21B = 0$$

The solution of this system is $A = \frac{84}{697}$ and $B = \frac{64}{697}$, so a particular solution is

$$Q_p(t) = \frac{1}{697}(84 \cos 10t + 64 \sin 10t)$$

and the general solution is

$$Q(t) = Q_c(t) + Q_p(t)$$
$$= e^{-20t}(c_1 \cos 15t + c_2 \sin 15t) + \frac{4}{697}(21 \cos 10t + 16 \sin 10t)$$

Imposing the initial condition $Q(0) = 0$, we get

$$Q(0) = c_1 + \tfrac{84}{697} = 0 \qquad c_1 = -\tfrac{84}{697}$$

To impose the other initial condition, we first differentiate to find the current:

$$I = \frac{dQ}{dt} = e^{-20t}[(-20c_1 + 15c_2)\cos 15t + (-15c_1 - 20c_2)\sin 15t]$$

$$+ \tfrac{40}{697}(-21\sin 10t + 16\cos 10t)$$

$$I(0) = -20c_1 + 15c_2 + \tfrac{640}{697} = 0 \qquad c_2 = -\tfrac{464}{2091}$$

Thus the formula for the charge is

$$Q(t) = \frac{4}{697}\left[\frac{e^{-20t}}{3}(-63\cos 15t - 116\sin 15t) + (21\cos 10t + 16\sin 10t)\right]$$

and the expression for the current is

$$I(t) = \tfrac{1}{2091}[e^{-20t}(-1920\cos 15t + 13{,}060\sin 15t) + 120(-21\sin 10t + 16\cos 10t)]$$

NOTE 1   In Example 3 the solution for $Q(t)$ consists of two parts. Since $e^{-20t} \to 0$ as $t \to \infty$ and both $\cos 15t$ and $\sin 15t$ are bounded functions,

$$Q_c(t) = \tfrac{4}{2091}e^{-20t}(-63\cos 15t - 116\sin 15t) \to 0 \qquad \text{as } t \to \infty$$

So, for large values of t,

$$Q(t) \approx Q_p(t) = \tfrac{4}{697}(21\cos 10t + 16\sin 10t)$$

and, for this reason, $Q_p(t)$ is called the **steady state solution**. Figure 8 shows how the graph of the steady state solution compares with the graph of Q in this case.

NOTE 2   Comparing Equations 5 and 7, we see that mathematically they are identical. This suggests the analogies given in the following chart between physical situations that, at first glance, are very different.

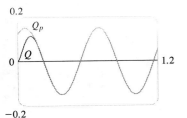

0.2

Q_p

Q

0   1.2

−0.2

FIGURE 8

$$\boxed{5} \quad m\frac{d^2x}{dt^2} + c\frac{dx}{dt} + kx = F(t)$$

$$\boxed{7} \quad L\frac{d^2Q}{dt^2} + R\frac{dQ}{dt} + \frac{1}{C}Q = E(t)$$

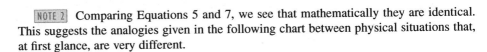

Spring system		Electric circuit	
x	displacement	Q	charge
dx/dt	velocity	$I = dQ/dt$	current
m	mass	L	inductance
c	damping constant	R	resistance
k	spring constant	$1/C$	elastance
$F(t)$	external force	$E(t)$	electromotive force

We can also transfer other ideas from one situation to the other. For instance, the steady state solution discussed in Note 1 makes sense in the spring system. And the phenomenon of resonance in the spring system can be usefully carried over to electric circuits as electrical resonance.

17.3 EXERCISES

1. A spring has natural length 0.75 m and a 5-kg mass. A force of 25 N is needed to keep the spring stretched to a length of 1 m. If the spring is stretched to a length of 1.1 m and then released with velocity 0, find the position of the mass after t seconds.

2. A spring with an 8-kg mass is kept stretched 0.4 m beyond its natural length by a force of 32 N. The spring starts at its equilibrium position and is given an initial velocity of 1 m/s. Find the position of the mass at any time t.

3. A spring with a mass of 2 kg has damping constant 14, and a force of 6 N is required to keep the spring stretched 0.5 m beyond its natural length. The spring is stretched 1 m beyond its natural length and then released with zero velocity. Find the position of the mass at any time t.

4. A force of 13 N is needed to keep a spring with a 2-kg mass stretched 0.25 m beyond its natural length. The damping constant of the spring is $c = 8$.
   (a) If the mass starts at the equilibrium position with a velocity of 0.5 m/s, find its position at time t.
   (b) Graph the position function of the mass.

5. For the spring in Exercise 3, find the mass that would produce critical damping.

6. For the spring in Exercise 4, find the damping constant that would produce critical damping.

7. A spring has a mass of 1 kg and its spring constant is $k = 100$. The spring is released at a point 0.1 m above its equilibrium position. Graph the position function for the following values of the damping constant c: 10, 15, 20, 25, 30. What type of damping occurs in each case?

8. A spring has a mass of 1 kg and its damping constant is $c = 10$. The spring starts from its equilibrium position with a velocity of 1 m/s. Graph the position function for the following values of the spring constant k: 10, 20, 25, 30, 40. What type of damping occurs in each case?

9. Suppose a spring has mass m and spring constant k and let $\omega = \sqrt{k/m}$. Suppose that the damping constant is so small that the damping force is negligible. If an external force $F(t) = F_0 \cos \omega_0 t$ is applied, where $\omega_0 \neq \omega$, use the method of undetermined coefficients to show that the motion of the mass is described by Equation 6.

10. As in Exercise 9, consider a spring with mass m, spring constant k, and damping constant $c = 0$, and let $\omega = \sqrt{k/m}$. If an external force $F(t) = F_0 \cos \omega t$ is applied (the applied frequency equals the natural frequency), use the method of undetermined coefficients to show that the motion of the mass is given by $x(t) = c_1 \cos \omega t + c_2 \sin \omega t + (F_0/(2m\omega))t \sin \omega t$.

11. Show that if $\omega_0 \neq \omega$, but ω/ω_0 is a rational number, then the motion described by Equation 6 is periodic.

12. Consider a spring subject to a frictional or damping force.
    (a) In the critically damped case, the motion is given by $x = c_1 e^{rt} + c_2 t e^{rt}$. Show that the graph of x crosses the t-axis whenever c_1 and c_2 have opposite signs.
    (b) In the overdamped case, the motion is given by $x = c_1 e^{r_1 t} + c_2 e^{r_2 t}$, where $r_1 > r_2$. Determine a condition on the relative magnitudes of c_1 and c_2 under which the graph of x crosses the t-axis at a positive value of t.

13. A series circuit consists of a resistor with $R = 20\ \Omega$, an inductor with $L = 1$ H, a capacitor with $C = 0.002$ F, and a 12-V battery. If the initial charge and current are both 0, find the charge and current at time t.

14. A series circuit contains a resistor with $R = 24\ \Omega$, an inductor with $L = 2$ H, a capacitor with $C = 0.005$ F, and a 12-V battery. The initial charge is $Q = 0.001$ C and the initial current is 0.
    (a) Find the charge and current at time t.
    (b) Graph the charge and current functions.

15. The battery in Exercise 13 is replaced by a generator producing a voltage of $E(t) = 12 \sin 10t$. Find the charge at time t.

16. The battery in Exercise 14 is replaced by a generator producing a voltage of $E(t) = 12 \sin 10t$.
    (a) Find the charge at time t.
    (b) Graph the charge function.

17. Verify that the solution to Equation 1 can be written in the form $x(t) = A \cos(\omega t + \delta)$.

18. The figure shows a pendulum with length L and the angle θ from the vertical to the pendulum. It can be shown that θ, as a function of time, satisfies the nonlinear differential equation

$$\frac{d^2\theta}{dt^2} + \frac{g}{L} \sin\theta = 0$$

where g is the acceleration due to gravity. For small values of θ we can use the linear approximation $\sin\theta \approx \theta$ and then the differential equation becomes linear.
    (a) Find the equation of motion of a pendulum with length 1 m if θ is initially 0.2 rad and the initial angular velocity is $d\theta/dt = 1$ rad/s.
    (b) What is the maximum angle from the vertical?
    (c) What is the period of the pendulum (that is, the time to complete one back-and-forth swing)?
    (d) When will the pendulum first be vertical?
    (e) What is the angular velocity when the pendulum is vertical?

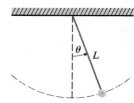

17.4 | SERIES SOLUTIONS

Many differential equations can't be solved explicitly in terms of finite combinations of simple familiar functions. This is true even for a simple-looking equation like

$$\boxed{1} \qquad y'' - 2xy' + y = 0$$

But it is important to be able to solve equations such as Equation 1 because they arise from physical problems and, in particular, in connection with the Schrödinger equation in quantum mechanics. In such a case we use the method of power series; that is, we look for a solution of the form

$$y = f(x) = \sum_{n=0}^{\infty} c_n x^n = c_0 + c_1 x + c_2 x^2 + c_3 x^3 + \cdots$$

The method is to substitute this expression into the differential equation and determine the values of the coefficients $c_0, c_1, c_2, \ldots$. This technique resembles the method of undetermined coefficients discussed in Section 17.2.

Before using power series to solve Equation 1, we illustrate the method on the simpler equation $y'' + y = 0$ in Example 1. It's true that we already know how to solve this equation by the techniques of Section 17.1, but it's easier to understand the power series method when it is applied to this simpler equation.

EXAMPLE 1 Use power series to solve the equation $y'' + y = 0$.

SOLUTION We assume there is a solution of the form

$$\boxed{2} \qquad y = c_0 + c_1 x + c_2 x^2 + c_3 x^3 + \cdots = \sum_{n=0}^{\infty} c_n x^n$$

We can differentiate power series term by term, so

$$y' = c_1 + 2c_2 x + 3c_3 x^2 + \cdots = \sum_{n=1}^{\infty} n c_n x^{n-1}$$

$$\boxed{3} \qquad y'' = 2c_2 + 2 \cdot 3c_3 x + \cdots = \sum_{n=2}^{\infty} n(n-1) c_n x^{n-2}$$

In order to compare the expressions for y and y'' more easily, we rewrite y'' as follows:

■ By writing out the first few terms of (4), you can see that it is the same as (3). To obtain (4), we replaced n by $n + 2$ and began the summation at 0 instead of 2.

$$\boxed{4} \qquad y'' = \sum_{n=0}^{\infty} (n+2)(n+1) c_{n+2} x^n$$

Substituting the expressions in Equations 2 and 4 into the differential equation, we obtain

$$\sum_{n=0}^{\infty} (n+2)(n+1) c_{n+2} x^n + \sum_{n=0}^{\infty} c_n x^n = 0$$

or

$$\boxed{5} \qquad \sum_{n=0}^{\infty} [(n+2)(n+1) c_{n+2} + c_n] x^n = 0$$

If two power series are equal, then the corresponding coefficients must be equal. Therefore the coefficients of x^n in Equation 5 must be 0:

$$(n + 2)(n + 1)c_{n+2} + c_n = 0$$

$$\boxed{6} \qquad c_{n+2} = -\frac{c_n}{(n + 1)(n + 2)} \qquad n = 0, 1, 2, 3, \ldots$$

Equation 6 is called a *recursion relation*. If c_0 and c_1 are known, this equation allows us to determine the remaining coefficients recursively by putting $n = 0, 1, 2, 3, \ldots$ in succession.

Put $n = 0$: $\qquad c_2 = -\dfrac{c_0}{1 \cdot 2}$

Put $n = 1$: $\qquad c_3 = -\dfrac{c_1}{2 \cdot 3}$

Put $n = 2$: $\qquad c_4 = -\dfrac{c_2}{3 \cdot 4} = \dfrac{c_0}{1 \cdot 2 \cdot 3 \cdot 4} = \dfrac{c_0}{4!}$

Put $n = 3$: $\qquad c_5 = -\dfrac{c_3}{4 \cdot 5} = \dfrac{c_1}{2 \cdot 3 \cdot 4 \cdot 5} = \dfrac{c_1}{5!}$

Put $n = 4$: $\qquad c_6 = -\dfrac{c_4}{5 \cdot 6} = -\dfrac{c_0}{4! \, 5 \cdot 6} = -\dfrac{c_0}{6!}$

Put $n = 5$: $\qquad c_7 = -\dfrac{c_5}{6 \cdot 7} = -\dfrac{c_1}{5! \, 6 \cdot 7} = -\dfrac{c_1}{7!}$

By now we see the pattern:

$$\text{For the even coefficients,} \quad c_{2n} = (-1)^n \frac{c_0}{(2n)!}$$

$$\text{For the odd coefficients,} \quad c_{2n+1} = (-1)^n \frac{c_1}{(2n + 1)!}$$

Putting these values back into Equation 2, we write the solution as

$$y = c_0 + c_1 x + c_2 x^2 + c_3 x^3 + c_4 x^4 + c_5 x^5 + \cdots$$

$$= c_0\left(1 - \frac{x^2}{2!} + \frac{x^4}{4!} - \frac{x^6}{6!} + \cdots + (-1)^n \frac{x^{2n}}{(2n)!} + \cdots\right)$$

$$+ c_1\left(x - \frac{x^3}{3!} + \frac{x^5}{5!} - \frac{x^7}{7!} + \cdots + (-1)^n \frac{x^{2n+1}}{(2n + 1)!} + \cdots\right)$$

$$= c_0 \sum_{n=0}^{\infty} (-1)^n \frac{x^{2n}}{(2n)!} + c_1 \sum_{n=0}^{\infty} (-1)^n \frac{x^{2n+1}}{(2n + 1)!}$$

Notice that there are two arbitrary constants, c_0 and c_1.

NOTE 1 We recognize the series obtained in Example 1 as being the Maclaurin series for $\cos x$ and $\sin x$. (See Equations 11.10.16 and 11.10.15.) Therefore we could write the solution as

$$y(x) = c_0 \cos x + c_1 \sin x$$

But we are not usually able to express power series solutions of differential equations in terms of known functions.

☑ **EXAMPLE 2** Solve $y'' - 2xy' + y = 0$.

SOLUTION We assume there is a solution of the form

$$y = \sum_{n=0}^{\infty} c_n x^n$$

Then

$$y' = \sum_{n=1}^{\infty} n c_n x^{n-1}$$

and

$$y'' = \sum_{n=2}^{\infty} n(n-1) c_n x^{n-2} = \sum_{n=0}^{\infty} (n+2)(n+1) c_{n+2} x^n$$

as in Example 1. Substituting in the differential equation, we get

$$\sum_{n=0}^{\infty} (n+2)(n+1) c_{n+2} x^n - 2x \sum_{n=1}^{\infty} n c_n x^{n-1} + \sum_{n=0}^{\infty} c_n x^n = 0$$

$$\sum_{n=0}^{\infty} (n+2)(n+1) c_{n+2} x^n - \sum_{n=1}^{\infty} 2n c_n x^n + \sum_{n=0}^{\infty} c_n x^n = 0$$

$$\sum_{n=0}^{\infty} [(n+2)(n+1) c_{n+2} - (2n-1) c_n] x^n = 0$$

This equation is true if the coefficient of x^n is 0:

$$(n+2)(n+1) c_{n+2} - (2n-1) c_n = 0$$

7     $$c_{n+2} = \frac{2n-1}{(n+1)(n+2)} c_n \qquad n = 0, 1, 2, 3, \ldots$$

We solve this recursion relation by putting $n = 0, 1, 2, 3, \ldots$ successively in Equation 7:

Put $n = 0$: $$c_2 = \frac{-1}{1 \cdot 2} c_0$$

Put $n = 1$: $$c_3 = \frac{1}{2 \cdot 3} c_1$$

Put $n = 2$: $$c_4 = \frac{3}{3 \cdot 4} c_2 = -\frac{3}{1 \cdot 2 \cdot 3 \cdot 4} c_0 = -\frac{3}{4!} c_0$$

Put $n = 3$: $$c_5 = \frac{5}{4 \cdot 5} c_3 = \frac{1 \cdot 5}{2 \cdot 3 \cdot 4 \cdot 5} c_1 = \frac{1 \cdot 5}{5!} c_1$$

Put $n = 4$: $\quad c_6 = \dfrac{7}{5 \cdot 6} c_4 = -\dfrac{3 \cdot 7}{4! \, 5 \cdot 6} c_0 = -\dfrac{3 \cdot 7}{6!} c_0$

Put $n = 5$: $\quad c_7 = \dfrac{9}{6 \cdot 7} c_5 = \dfrac{1 \cdot 5 \cdot 9}{5! \, 6 \cdot 7} c_1 = \dfrac{1 \cdot 5 \cdot 9}{7!} c_1$

Put $n = 6$: $\quad c_8 = \dfrac{11}{7 \cdot 8} c_6 = -\dfrac{3 \cdot 7 \cdot 11}{8!} c_0$

Put $n = 7$: $\quad c_9 = \dfrac{13}{8 \cdot 9} c_7 = \dfrac{1 \cdot 5 \cdot 9 \cdot 13}{9!} c_1$

In general, the even coefficients are given by

$$c_{2n} = -\frac{3 \cdot 7 \cdot 11 \cdot \,\cdots\, \cdot (4n - 5)}{(2n)!} c_0$$

and the odd coefficients are given by

$$c_{2n+1} = \frac{1 \cdot 5 \cdot 9 \cdot \,\cdots\, \cdot (4n - 3)}{(2n + 1)!} c_1$$

The solution is

$$y = c_0 + c_1 x + c_2 x^2 + c_3 x^3 + c_4 x^4 + \cdots$$

$$= c_0 \left(1 - \frac{1}{2!} x^2 - \frac{3}{4!} x^4 - \frac{3 \cdot 7}{6!} x^6 - \frac{3 \cdot 7 \cdot 11}{8!} x^8 - \cdots \right)$$

$$+ c_1 \left(x + \frac{1}{3!} x^3 + \frac{1 \cdot 5}{5!} x^5 + \frac{1 \cdot 5 \cdot 9}{7!} x^7 + \frac{1 \cdot 5 \cdot 9 \cdot 13}{9!} x^9 + \cdots \right)$$

or

$$\boxed{8} \qquad y = c_0 \left(1 - \frac{1}{2!} x^2 - \sum_{n=2}^{\infty} \frac{3 \cdot 7 \cdot \,\cdots\, \cdot (4n - 5)}{(2n)!} x^{2n} \right)$$

$$+ c_1 \left(x + \sum_{n=1}^{\infty} \frac{1 \cdot 5 \cdot 9 \cdot \,\cdots\, \cdot (4n - 3)}{(2n + 1)!} x^{2n+1} \right) \qquad \square$$

NOTE 2 In Example 2 we had to assume that the differential equation had a series solution. But now we could verify directly that the function given by Equation 8 is indeed a solution.

NOTE 3 Unlike the situation of Example 1, the power series that arise in the solution of Example 2 do not define elementary functions. The functions

$$y_1(x) = 1 - \frac{1}{2!} x^2 - \sum_{n=2}^{\infty} \frac{3 \cdot 7 \cdot \,\cdots\, \cdot (4n - 5)}{(2n)!} x^{2n}$$

and $\qquad y_2(x) = x + \displaystyle\sum_{n=1}^{\infty} \frac{1 \cdot 5 \cdot 9 \cdot \,\cdots\, \cdot (4n - 3)}{(2n + 1)!} x^{2n+1}$

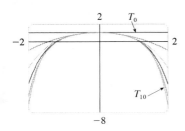

FIGURE I

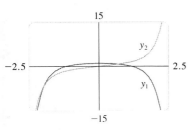

FIGURE 2

are perfectly good functions but they can't be expressed in terms of familiar functions. We can use these power series expressions for y_1 and y_2 to compute approximate values of the functions and even to graph them. Figure 1 shows the first few partial sums $T_0, T_2, T_4, \ldots$ (Taylor polynomials) for $y_1(x)$, and we see how they converge to y_1. In this way we can graph both y_1 and y_2 in Figure 2.

NOTE 4 If we were asked to solve the initial-value problem

$$y'' - 2xy' + y = 0 \qquad y(0) = 0 \qquad y'(0) = 1$$

we would observe from Theorem 11.10.5 that

$$c_0 = y(0) = 0 \qquad c_1 = y'(0) = 1$$

This would simplify the calculations in Example 2, since all of the even coefficients would be 0. The solution to the initial-value problem is

$$y(x) = x + \sum_{n=1}^{\infty} \frac{1 \cdot 5 \cdot 9 \cdot \cdots \cdot (4n - 3)}{(2n + 1)!} x^{2n+1}$$

17.4 EXERCISES

1–11 Use power series to solve the differential equation.

1. $y' - y = 0$

2. $y' = xy$

3. $y' = x^2 y$

4. $(x - 3)y' + 2y = 0$

5. $y'' + xy' + y = 0$

6. $y'' = y$

7. $(x - 1)y'' + y' = 0$

8. $y'' = xy$

9. $y'' - xy' - y = 0, \quad y(0) = 1, \quad y'(0) = 0$

10. $y'' + x^2 y = 0, \quad y(0) = 1, \quad y'(0) = 0$

11. $y'' + x^2 y' + xy = 0, \quad y(0) = 0, \quad y'(0) = 1$

12. The solution of the initial-value problem

$$x^2 y'' + xy' + x^2 y = 0 \qquad y(0) = 1 \qquad y'(0) = 0$$

is called a Bessel function of order 0.
(a) Solve the initial-value problem to find a power series expansion for the Bessel function.
(b) Graph several Taylor polynomials until you reach one that looks like a good approximation to the Bessel function on the interval $[-5, 5]$.

17 REVIEW

CONCEPT CHECK

1. (a) Write the general form of a second-order homogeneous linear differential equation with constant coefficients.
(b) Write the auxiliary equation.
(c) How do you use the roots of the auxiliary equation to solve the differential equation? Write the form of the solution for each of the three cases that can occur.

2. (a) What is an initial-value problem for a second-order differential equation?
(b) What is a boundary-value problem for such an equation?

3. (a) Write the general form of a second-order nonhomogeneous linear differential equation with constant coefficients.

(b) What is the complementary equation? How does it help solve the original differential equation?
(c) Explain how the method of undetermined coefficients works.
(d) Explain how the method of variation of parameters works.

4. Discuss two applications of second-order linear differential equations.

5. How do you use power series to solve a differential equation?

TRUE-FALSE QUIZ

Determine whether the statement is true or false. If it is true, explain why.
If it is false, explain why or give an example that disproves the statement.

1. If y_1 and y_2 are solutions of $y'' + y = 0$, then $y_1 + y_2$ is also a solution of the equation.

2. If y_1 and y_2 are solutions of $y'' + 6y' + 5y = x$, then $c_1 y_1 + c_2 y_2$ is also a solution of the equation.

3. The general solution of $y'' - y = 0$ can be written as

$$y = c_1 \cosh x + c_2 \sinh x$$

4. The equation $y'' - y = e^x$ has a particular solution of the form

$$y_p = A e^x$$

EXERCISES

1–10 Solve the differential equation.

1. $y'' - 2y' - 15y = 0$

2. $y'' + 4y' + 13y = 0$

3. $y'' + 3y = 0$

4. $4y'' + 4y' + y = 0$

5. $\dfrac{d^2 y}{dx^2} - 4\dfrac{dy}{dx} + 5y = e^{2x}$

6. $\dfrac{d^2 y}{dx^2} + \dfrac{dy}{dx} - 2y = x^2$

7. $\dfrac{d^2 y}{dx^2} - 2\dfrac{dy}{dx} + y = x \cos x$

8. $\dfrac{d^2 y}{dx^2} + 4y = \sin 2x$

9. $\dfrac{d^2 y}{dx^2} - \dfrac{dy}{dx} - 6y = 1 + e^{-2x}$

10. $\dfrac{d^2 y}{dx^2} + y = \csc x, \quad 0 < x < \pi/2$

11–14 Solve the initial-value problem.

11. $y'' + 6y' = 0, \quad y(1) = 3, \quad y'(1) = 12$

12. $y'' - 6y' + 25y = 0, \quad y(0) = 2, \quad y'(0) = 1$

13. $y'' - 5y' + 4y = 0, \quad y(0) = 0, \quad y'(0) = 1$

14. $9y'' + y = 3x + e^{-x}, \quad y(0) = 1, \quad y'(0) = 2$

15. Use power series to solve the initial-value problem

$$y'' + xy' + y = 0 \qquad y(0) = 0 \qquad y'(0) = 1$$

16. Use power series to solve the equation

$$y'' - xy' - 2y = 0$$

17. A series circuit contains a resistor with $R = 40\ \Omega$, an inductor with $L = 2$ H, a capacitor with $C = 0.0025$ F, and a 12-V battery. The initial charge is $Q = 0.01$ C and the initial current is 0. Find the charge at time t.

18. A spring with a mass of 2 kg has damping constant 16, and a force of 12.8 N keeps the spring stretched 0.2 m beyond its natural length. Find the position of the mass at time t if it starts at the equilibrium position with a velocity of 2.4 m/s.

19. Assume that the earth is a solid sphere of uniform density with mass M and radius $R = 3960$ mi. For a particle of mass m within the earth at a distance r from the earth's center, the gravitational force attracting the particle to the center is

$$F_r = \frac{-GM_r m}{r^2}$$

where G is the gravitational constant and M_r is the mass of the earth within the sphere of radius r.

(a) Show that $F_r = \dfrac{-GMm}{R^3}\, r$.

(b) Suppose a hole is drilled through the earth along a diameter. Show that if a particle of mass m is dropped from rest at the surface, into the hole, then the distance $y = y(t)$ of the particle from the center of the earth at time t is given by

$$y''(t) = -k^2 y(t)$$

where $k^2 = GM/R^3 = g/R$.

(c) Conclude from part (b) that the particle undergoes simple harmonic motion. Find the period T.

(d) With what speed does the particle pass through the center of the earth?

| **E** | **ANSWERS TO ODD-NUMBERED EXERCISES**

CHAPTER 1

Exercises 1.1 □ **page 8**

1. (a) -2 (b) 2.8 (c) $-3, 1$ (d) $-2.5, 0.3$
(e) $[-3, 3], [-2, 3]$ (f) $[-1, 3]$
3. No **5.** Yes, $[-3, 2], [-3, -2) \cup [-1, 3]$
7. Diet, exercise, or illness
9.

11.

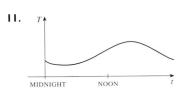

13.

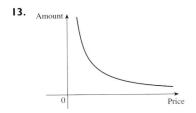

15.

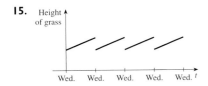

17. $12, 16, 3a^2 - a + 2, 3a^2 + a + 2, 3a^2 + 5a + 4,$
$6a^2 - 2a + 4, 12a^2 - 2a + 2, 3a^4 - a^2 + 2,$
$9a^4 - 6a^3 + 13a^2 - 4a + 4, 3a^2 + 6ah + 3h^2 - a - h + 2$
19. $-3 - h$ **21.** $-1/(ax)$
23. $\left\{ x \mid x \neq \frac{1}{3} \right\} = \left(-\infty, \frac{1}{3}\right) \cup \left(\frac{1}{3}, \infty\right)$
25. $[0, \infty)$ **27.** $(-\infty, 0) \cup (5, \infty)$
29. $(-\infty, \infty)$ **31.** $(-\infty, \infty)$

33. $[5, \infty)$ **35.** $(-\infty, 0) \cup (0, \infty)$

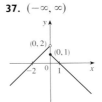 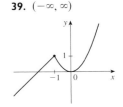

37. $(-\infty, \infty)$ **39.** $(-\infty, \infty)$

41. $f(x) = -\frac{7}{6}x - \frac{4}{3}, -2 \leq x \leq 4$ **43.** $f(x) = 1 - \sqrt{-x}$
45. $A(L) = 10L - L^2, 0 < L < 10$
47. $A(x) = \sqrt{3}x^2/4, x > 0$ **49.** $S(x) = x^2 + (8/x), x > 0$
51. (a)

(b) $400, $1900
(c)

53. f is odd, g is even
55. (a) $(-5, 3)$ (b) $(-5, -3)$
57. Odd **59.** Neither **61.** Even

Exercises 1.2 □ **page 21**

1. (a) $y = 2x + b$,
where b is the y-intercept

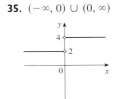

(b) $y = mx + 1 - 2m$,
where m is the slope.
See graph at right.
(c) $y = 2x - 3$

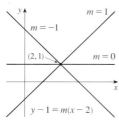

3. Their graphs have slope -1.

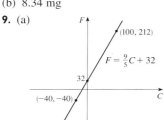

5. $f(x) = -3x(x + 1)(x - 2)$
7. (a) 8.34, change in mg for every 1 year change
(b) 8.34 mg
9. (a)

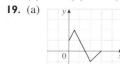

(b) $\frac{9}{5}$, change in °F for every 1°C change; 32, Fahrenheit temperature corresponding to 0°C

11. (a) $T = \frac{1}{6}N + \frac{307}{6}$ (b) $\frac{1}{6}$, change in °F for every chirp per minute change (c) 76°F
13. (a) $P = 0.434d + 15$ (b) 196 ft
15. (a) $y = f(x) + 3$ (b) $y = f(x) - 3$ (c) $y = f(x - 3)$
(d) $y = f(x + 3)$ (e) $y = -f(x)$ (f) $y = f(-x)$
(g) $y = 3f(x)$ (h) $y = \frac{1}{3}f(x)$
17. (a) 3 (b) 1 (c) 4 (d) 5 (e) 2
19. (a)

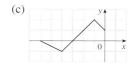

(b)

(c) (d)

21.

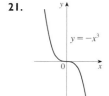

23.

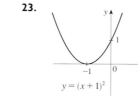

25.

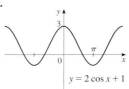

$y = 2\cos x + 1$

27.

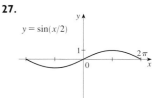

$y = \sin(x/2)$

29.

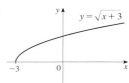

$y = \sqrt{x + 3}$

31.

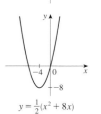

$y = \frac{1}{2}(x^2 + 8x)$

33.

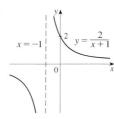

$x = -1$ $y = \frac{2}{x + 1}$

35. $(f + g)(x) = x^3 + 5x^2 - 1, (-\infty, \infty)$
$(f - g)(x) = x^3 - x^2 + 1, (-\infty, \infty)$
$(fg)(x) = 3x^5 + 6x^4 - x^3 - 2x^2, (-\infty, \infty)$
$(f/g)(x) = (x^3 + 2x^2)/(3x^2 - 1), \{x \mid x \neq \pm 1/\sqrt{3}\}$
37. (a) $(f \circ g)(x) = 4x^2 + 4x, (-\infty, \infty)$
(b) $(g \circ f)(x) = 2x^2 - 1, (-\infty, \infty)$
(c) $(f \circ f)(x) = x^4 - 2x^2, (-\infty, \infty)$
(d) $(g \circ g)(x) = 4x + 3, (-\infty, \infty)$
39. (a) $(f \circ g)(x) = \sin(1 - \sqrt{x}), [0, \infty)$
(b) $(g \circ f)(x) = 1 - \sqrt{\sin x}$,
$\{x \mid x \in [2n\pi, \pi + 2n\pi], n \text{ an integer}\}$
(c) $(f \circ f)(x) = \sin(\sin x), (-\infty, \infty)$
(d) $(g \circ g)(x) = 1 - \sqrt{1 - \sqrt{x}}, [0, 1]$
41. (a) $(f \circ g)(x) = (2x^2 + 6x + 5)/[(x + 2)(x + 1)]$,
$\{x \mid x \neq -2, -1\}$
(b) $(g \circ f)(x) = (x^2 + x + 1)/(x + 1)^2, \{x \mid x \neq -1, 0\}$
(c) $(f \circ f)(x) = (x^4 + 3x^2 + 1)/[x(x^2 + 1)], \{x \mid x \neq 0\}$
(d) $(g \circ g)(x) = (2x + 3)/(3x + 5), \{x \mid x \neq -2, -\frac{5}{3}\}$
43. $(f \circ g \circ h)(x) = \sqrt{x^2 + 6x + 10}$
45. $g(x) = x^2 + 1, f(x) = x^{10}$ **47.** $g(t) = \cos t, f(t) = \sqrt{t}$
49. $h(x) = x^2, g(x) = 3^x, f(x) = 1 - x$
51. $h(x) = \sqrt{x}, g(x) = \sec x, f(x) = x^4$
53. (a) 4 (b) 3 (c) 0 (d) Does not exist; $f(6) = 6$ is not in the domain of g. (e) 4 (f) -2
55. (a) $r(t) = 60t$ (b) $(A \circ r)(t) = 3600\pi t^2$; the area of the circle as a function of time
57. (a)

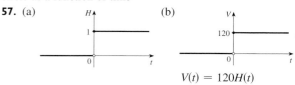

(b)

$V(t) = 120H(t)$

(c)

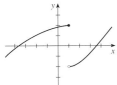

$V(t) = 240H(t - 5)$

59. Yes; $m_1 m_2$
61. (a) $f(x) = x^2 + 6$ (b) $g(x) = x^2 + x - 1$
63. (a) Even; even   (b) Odd; even
65. Yes

Exercises 1.3 □ page 33

1. (a) (i) -32 ft/s   (ii) -25.6 ft/s   (iii) -24.8 ft/s
(iv) -24.16 ft/s   (b) -24 ft/s
3. (a) 2   (b) 3   (c) Does not exist   (d) 4
(e) Does not exist
5. (a) -1 (b) -2 (c) Does not exist   (d) 2   (e) 0
(f) Does not exist   (g) 1   (h) 3
7.   **9.**

11. $\frac{2}{3}$ **13.** $\frac{1}{2}$ **15.** $\frac{1}{4}$ **17.** $\frac{3}{5}$ **19.** (a) 4
21. (a) 0.998000, 0.638259, 0.358484, 0.158680, 0.038851,
0.008928, 0.001465; 0
(b) 0.000572, -0.000614, -0.000907, -0.000978,
-0.000993, -0.001000; -0.001
23. $\frac{4}{7}$ (or any smaller positive number)
25. 0.6875 (or any smaller positive number)
27. (a) $\sqrt{1000/\pi}$ cm   (b) Within approximately 0.0445 cm
(c) Radius; area; $\sqrt{1000/\pi}$; 1000; 5; ≈ 0.0445
45. (a) 0.093   (b) $\delta = (B^{2/3} - 12)/(6B^{1/3}) - 1$, where
$B = 216 + 108\varepsilon + 12\sqrt{336 + 324\varepsilon + 81\varepsilon^2}$

Exercises 1.4 □ page 43

1. (a) 5   (b) 9   (c) 2   (d) $-\frac{1}{3}$ (e) $-\frac{3}{8}$ (f) 0
(g) Does not exist   (h) $-\frac{6}{11}$
3. 59   **5.** 390   **7.** $\frac{1}{8}$ **9.** $\pi/2$ **11.** 5
13. Does not exist   **15.** $\frac{6}{5}$ **17.** 8   **19.** $\frac{1}{12}$ **21.** $\frac{1}{6}$
23. $-\frac{1}{16}$ **25.** (a), (b) $\frac{2}{3}$ **29.** 7   **33.** 6
35. Does not exist
37. (a) (i) 0   (ii) 0   (iii) 1   (iv) 1   (v) 0
(vi) Does not exist
(b)

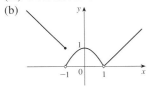

39. (a) (i) -2 (ii) Does not exist   (iii) -3
(b) (i) $n - 1$ (ii) n (c) a is not an integer.
43. 3   **45.** 3   **47.** $\frac{1}{2}$ **55.** 15; -1

Exercises 1.5 □ page 54

1. $\lim_{x \to 4} f(x) = f(4)$
3. (a) -4 (removable), -2 (jump), 2 (jump), 4 (infinite)
(b) -4, neither; -2, left; 2, right; 4, right
5.

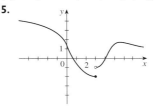

7. (a)

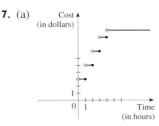

(b) Discontinuous at $t = 1, 2, 3, 4$
9. 6
13. $f(1)$ is not defined   **15.** $\lim_{x \to 1} f(x)$ does not exist

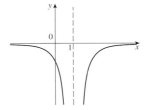 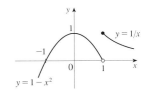

17. $\{x \mid x \neq -3, -2\}$ **19.** $\left[\frac{1}{2}, \infty\right)$ **21.** $[0, \infty)$
23. $x = (-\pi/2) + 2n\pi$, n an integer

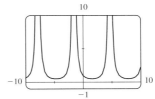

25. $\frac{7}{3}$ **29.** 0, right; 1, left

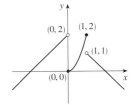

31. $\frac{2}{3}$
33. (a) $g(x) = x - 4$ (c) $g(x) = x^2 - 4x + 16$
(d) $g(x) = 1/(3 + \sqrt{x})$
41. (b) $(0.86, 0.87)$
43. (b) 1.434   **45.** Yes

Exercises 1.6 □ page 66

1. (a) ∞ (b) ∞ (c) $-\infty$ (d) 1 (e) 2
(f) $x = -1, x = 2, y = 1, y = 2$
3. 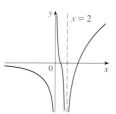 **5.**

7.

9. 0 **11.** $x \approx -1.62, x \approx 0.62, x = 1; y = 1$
13. $-\infty$ **15.** ∞ **17.** $-\infty$ **19.** $\frac{1}{2}$ **21.** 2
23. $\frac{1}{6}$ **25.** Does not exist **27.** ∞ **29.** $-\infty$
31. ∞ **33.** $y = 2; x = -2, x = 1$ **35.** (a), (b) $-\frac{1}{2}$
37. $y = 3$ **39.** $f(x) = \dfrac{2 - x}{x^2(x - 3)}$
41. (a) 0 (b) $\pm\infty$ **43.** 4
45. (b) It approaches the concentration of the brine being pumped into the tank.
47. Within 0.1 **51.** $N \geqslant 13$ **53.** (a) $x > 100$

Chapter 1 Review □ page 70

True-False Quiz

1. False **3.** True **5.** False **7.** True **9.** False
11. True **13.** True **15.** False **17.** True **19.** True

Exercises

1. (a) 2.7 (b) 2.3, 5.6 (c) $[-6, 6]$ (d) $[-4, 4]$
(e) $[-4, 4]$ (f) Odd; its graph is symmetric about the origin.
3. $\left[-\frac{2}{3}\sqrt{3}, \frac{2}{3}\sqrt{3}\right], [0, 2]$ **5.** $\mathbb{R}, [0, 2]$
7. (a) Shift the graph 8 units upward.
(b) Shift the graph 8 units to the left.
(c) Stretch the graph vertically by a factor of 2, then shift it 1 unit upward.
(d) Shift the graph 2 units to the right and 2 units downward.
(e) Reflect the graph about the x-axis.
(f) Reflect the graph about the line x-axis, then shift it 3 units upward.
9.

11. 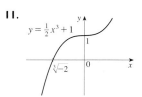 **13.**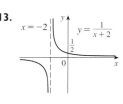

15. (a) Neither (b) Odd (c) Even (d) Neither
17. (a) $(f \circ g)(x) = \sqrt{\sin x}$,
$\{x \mid x \in [2n\pi, \pi + 2n\pi], n \text{ an integer}\}$
(b) $(g \circ f)(x) = \sin \sqrt{x}, [0, \infty)$ (c) $(f \circ f)(x) = \sqrt[4]{x}, [0, \infty)$
(d) $(g \circ g)(x) = \sin(\sin x), \mathbb{R}$
(e) $(g \circ g)(x) = (x^2 - 9)^2 - 9, (-\infty, \infty)$
19. All have domain $\mathbb{R}$. The range is $[-1, 1]$ for n odd and $[0, 1]$ for n even. The spikes become sharper as $n \to \infty$.
21. (a) (i) 3 (ii) 0 (iii) Does not exist (iv) 2
(v) ∞ (vi) $-\infty$ (vii) 4 (viii) -1
(b) $y = 4, y = -1$ (c) $x = 0, x = 2$ (d) $-3, 0, 2, 4$
23. 1 **25.** $\frac{3}{2}$ **27.** 3 **29.** ∞ **31.** $-\frac{1}{8}$ **33.** $-\frac{1}{2}$
35. 2 **37.** $\frac{1}{2}$ **39.** $x = 0, y = 0$ **41.** 1
47. (a) (i) 3 (ii) 0 (iii) Does not exist (iv) 0 (v) 0
(vi) 0 (b) At 0 and 3 (c)

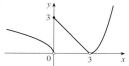

CHAPTER 2

Exercises 2.1 □ page 80

1. (a) -4 (b) $y = -4x - 9$
(c)

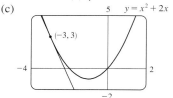

3. $y = -x + 5$ **5.** $y = \frac{1}{2}x + \frac{1}{2}$
7. (a) $8a - 6a^2$ (b) $y = 2x + 3, y = -8x + 19$
(c)

9. (a) 0 (b) C (c) Speeding up, slowing down, neither
(d) The car did not move.
11. -24 ft/s
13. $-2/a^3$ m/s; -2 m/s; $-\frac{1}{4}$ m/s; $-\frac{2}{27}$ m/s
15. $g'(0), 0, g'(4), g'(2), g'(-2)$

17.

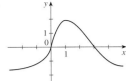

19. $7; y = 7x - 12$

21. (a) $-\frac{3}{5}; y = -\frac{3}{5}x + \frac{16}{5}$ (b)

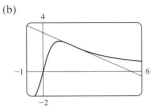

23. $-2 + 8a$ **25.** $5/(a+3)^2$ **27.** $-1/[2(a+2)^{3/2}]$
29. $f(x) = x^{10}, a = 1$ or $f(x) = (1+x)^{10}, a = 0$
31. $f(x) = 2^x, a = 5$
33. $f(x) = \cos x, a = \pi$ or $f(x) = \cos(\pi + x), a = 0$
35.

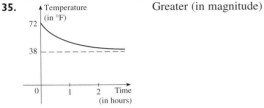

Greater (in magnitude)

37. (a) (i) 11 percent/year (ii) 13 percent/year
(iii) 16 percent/year
(b) 14.5 percent/year (c) 15 percent/year
39. (a) (i) $20.25/unit (ii) $20.05/unit (b) $20/unit
41. (a) The rate at which the cost is changing per ounce of
gold produced; dollars per ounce
(b) When the 800th ounce of gold is produced, the cost of
production is $17/oz.
(c) Decrease in the short term; increase in the long term
43. The rate at which the temperature is changing at 10:00 AM;
$4°F/h$
45. (a) The rate at which the oxygen solubility changes with
respect to the water temperature; $(mg/L)/°C$
(b) $S'(16) \approx -0.25$; as the temperature increases past 16°C,
the oxygen solubility is decreasing at a rate of 0.25 $(mg/L)/°C$.
47. Does not exist

Exercises 2.2 □ **page 91**
1. (a) 1.5 (b) 1
(c) 0 (d) -4
(e) 0 (f) 1
(g) 1.5

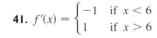

3. (a) II (b) IV (c) I (d) III

5.

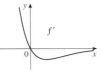

7.

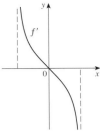

9.

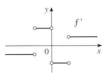

11.

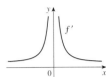

13.

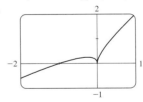

The derivative is negative
for the years 1963 to 1971.

1950 1960 1970 1980 1990

15. (a) 0, 1, 2, 4 (b) $-1, -2, -4$ (c) $f'(x) = 2x$
17. $f'(x) = \frac{1}{2}, \mathbb{R}, \mathbb{R}$ **19.** $f'(x) = 3x^2 - 3, \mathbb{R}, \mathbb{R}$
21. $g'(x) = 1/\sqrt{1 + 2x}, [-\frac{1}{2}, \infty), (-\frac{1}{2}, \infty)$
23. $G'(t) = 4/(t + 1)^2, (-\infty, -1) \cup (-1, \infty)$,
$(-\infty, -1) \cup (-1, \infty)$
25. (a) $f'(x) = 4x^3 + 2$
27. -4 (corner); 0 (discontinuity)
29. -1 (vertical tangent); 4 (corner)
31.

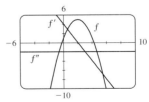

Differentiable at -1;
not differentiable at 0

33. $a = f, b = f', c = f''$
35. $a = $ acceleration, $b = $ velocity, $c = $ position
37.

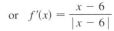

$f'(x) = 4 - 2x,$
$f''(x) = -2$

39. (a) $\frac{1}{3}a^{-2/3}$

41. $f'(x) = \begin{cases} -1 & \text{if } x < 6 \\ 1 & \text{if } x > 6 \end{cases}$

or $f'(x) = \dfrac{x - 6}{|x - 6|}$

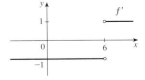

45. 63°

Exercises 2.3 □ page 104

1. $f'(x) = 0$ **3.** $f'(x) = 5$ **5.** $f'(x) = 3x^2 - 4$
7. $f'(x) = 1 - 3\cos x$ **9.** $f'(t) = t^3$
11. $y' = -\frac{2}{5}x^{-7/5}$ **13.** $V'(r) = 4\pi r^2$ **15.** $F'(x) = \frac{5}{32}x^4$
17. $y' = 0$ **19.** $y' = \frac{3}{2}\sqrt{x} + (2/\sqrt{x}) - 3/(2x\sqrt{x})$
21. $v' = 2t + \dfrac{3}{4t\sqrt[4]{t^3}}$ **23.** $z' = -10A/y^{11} - B\sin y$
25. $y = -3\sqrt{3}x + 3 + \pi\sqrt{3}$, $y = \dfrac{x}{3\sqrt{3}} + 3 - \dfrac{\pi}{9\sqrt{3}}$
27. $y = \frac{3}{2}x + \frac{1}{2}$

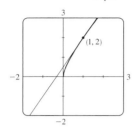

29. $f'(x) = 4x^3 - 9x^2 + 16$, $f''(x) = 12x^2 - 18x$
31. $g'(t) = -2\sin t - 3\cos t$, $g''(t) = -2\cos t + 3\sin t$
33. $-\cos x$ **35.** $(2n + 1)\pi \pm \frac{1}{3}\pi$, n an integer
39. $y = \frac{1}{3}x - \frac{1}{3}$
41. (a) $v(t) = 3t^2 - 3$, $a(t) = 6t$ (b) 12 m/s^2
(c) $a(1) = 6 \text{ m/s}^2$
43. (a) $3t^2 - 24t + 36$
(b) -9 ft/s   (c) $t = 2, 6$
(d) $0 \le t < 2, t > 6$
(e) 96 ft
(f) See graph at right.

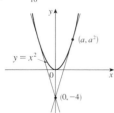

45. (a) $t = 4$ s
(b) $t = 1.5$ s; the velocity has a minimum.
47. (a) 5.02 m/s   (b) $\sqrt{17}$ m/s
49. (a) $C'(x) = 3 + 0.02x + 0.0006x^2$
(b) $\$11$/pair, the rate at which the cost is changing as the 100th pair of jeans is being produced; the cost of the 101st pair
(c) $\$11.07$
51. (a) $8\pi \text{ ft}^2$/ft   (b) $16\pi \text{ ft}^2$/ft   (c) $24\pi \text{ ft}^2$/ft
The rate increases as the radius increases.
53. (a) $dV/dP = -C/P^2$ (b) At the beginning
57. $A = -\frac{3}{10}$, $B = -\frac{1}{10}$
59. $(\pm 2, 4)$

61. $a = -\frac{1}{2}, b = 2$ **63.** $y = \frac{3}{16}x^3 - \frac{9}{4}x + 3$
65. 1000 **67.** $3; 1$

Exercises 2.4 □ page 111

1. $y' = 5x^4 + 3x^2 + 2x$ **3.** $g'(t) = 3t^2\cos t - t^3\sin t$
5. $F'(y) = 5 + 14/y^2 + 9/y^4$

7. $f'(x) = \cos x - \frac{1}{2}\csc^2 x$
9. $h'(\theta) = \csc\theta - \theta\csc\theta\cot\theta + \csc^2\theta$
11. $g'(x) = 5/(2x + 1)^2$
13. $y' = 2t(1 - t)/(3t^2 - 2t + 1)^2$ **15.** $y' = 2v - 1/\sqrt{v}$
17. $y' = \dfrac{r(4 + 3\sqrt{r})}{2(1 + \sqrt{r})^2}$ **19.** $y' = \dfrac{\cos x + x\sin x}{\cos^2 x}$
21. $f'(\theta) = \dfrac{\sec\theta\tan\theta}{(1 + \sec\theta)^2}$ **23.** $y' = (x\cos x - 2\sin x)/x^3$
25. $f'(x) = 2cx/(x^2 + c^2)^2$
27. $y = \frac{1}{2}x + \frac{1}{2}$ **29.** $y = 2x + 1 - \frac{1}{2}\pi$
31. (a) $y = \frac{1}{2}x + 1$ (b)

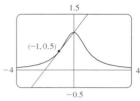

33. $\frac{1}{4}$ **35.** $\theta\cos\theta + \sin\theta$; $2\cos\theta - \theta\sin\theta$
41. (a) -16 (b) $-\frac{20}{9}$ (c) 20 **43.** (a) 0 (b) $-\frac{2}{3}$
45. (a) $y' = xg'(x) + g(x)$ (b) $y' = [g(x) - xg'(x)]/[g(x)]^2$
(c) $y' = [xg'(x) - g(x)]/x^2$
47. (a) $v(t) = 8\cos t$, $a(t) = -8\sin t$
(b) $4\sqrt{3}, -4, -4\sqrt{3}$; to the left; speeding up
49. -0.2436 K/min   **51.** Two, $\left(-2 \pm \sqrt{3}, \frac{1}{2}(1 \mp \sqrt{3})\right)$
53. (b) $y' = \sin x\cos x + x\cos^2 x - x\sin^2 x$
55. (b) $y' = -2x(2x^2 + 1)/(x^4 + x^2 + 1)^2$

Exercises 2.5 □ page 119

1. $4\cos 4x$ **3.** $-20x(1 - x^2)^9$ **5.** $\dfrac{\cos x}{2\sqrt{\sin x}}$
7. $F'(x) = \dfrac{2 + 3x^2}{4(1 + 2x + x^3)^{3/4}}$ **9.** $g'(t) = -\dfrac{12t^3}{(t^4 + 1)^4}$
11. $y' = -3x^2\sin(a^3 + x^3)$ **13.** $y' = -\frac{1}{2}\csc^2(x/2)$
15. $g'(x) = 4(1 + 4x)^4(3 + x - x^2)^7(17 + 9x - 21x^2)$
17. $y' = 8(2x - 5)^3(8x^2 - 5)^{-4}(-4x^2 + 30x - 5)$
19. $y' = 3x^2\cos nx - nx^3\sin nx$
21. $y' = (\cos x - x\sin x)\cos(x\cos x)$
23. $F'(z) = 1/[(z - 1)^{1/2}(z + 1)^{3/2}]$
25. $y' = (r^2 + 1)^{-3/2}$ **27.** $y' = -\sin x\sec^2(\cos x)$
29. $y' = (x\cos\sqrt{1 + x^2})/\sqrt{1 + x^2}$
31. $y' = -12\cos x\sin x(1 + \cos^2 x)^5$
33. $y' = 4\sec^2 x\tan x$
35. $y' = -2\cos\theta\cot(\sin\theta)\csc^2(\sin\theta)$
37. $y' = \cos(\tan\sqrt{\sin x})(\sec^2\sqrt{\sin x})\dfrac{1}{2\sqrt{\sin x}}(\cos x)$
39. $y = 20x + 1$
41. (a) $y = \pi x - \pi + 1$ (b)

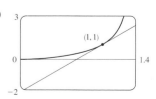

43. $F'(t) = -42(1 - 7t)^5$, $F''(t) = 1470(1 - 7t)^4$

45. $y' = \dfrac{2x^2}{(x^3 + 1)^{1/3}}$, $y'' = \dfrac{4x}{(x^3 + 1)^{1/3}} - \dfrac{2x^4}{(x^3 + 1)^{4/3}}$

47. 24   **49.** (a) 30   (b) 36

51. (a) $\frac{3}{4}$ (b) Does not exist   (c) -2

53. (a) $F'(x) = -\sin x \, f'(\cos x)$

(b) $G'(x) = -\sin(f(x))f'(x)$

55. 120

57. $((\pi/2) + 2n\pi, 3)$, $((3\pi/2) + 2n\pi, -1)$, n an integer

59. $v(t) = \frac{5}{2}\pi \cos(10\pi t)$ cm/s

61. (a) $dB/dt = \frac{7}{54}\pi \cos(2\pi t/5.4)$ (b) 0.16

63. dv/dt is the rate of change of velocity with respect to time; dv/ds is the rate of change of velocity with respect to displacement

65. (b) $-n \cos^{n-1}x \sin[(n + 1)x]$

Exercises 2.6 □ page 125

1. (a) $y' = -(y + 2 + 6x)/x$

(b) $y = (4/x) - 2 - 3x$, $y' = -(4/x^2) - 3$

3. $y' = -x(3x + 2y)/(x^2 + 8y)$

5. $y' = (3 - 2xy - y^2)/(x^2 + 2xy)$

7. $y' = (-2xy^2 - \sin y)/(2x^2y + x \cos y)$

9. $y' = \tan x \tan y$

11. $y' = \dfrac{y \sec^2(x/y) - y^2}{y^2 + x \sec^2(x/y)}$ **13.** $y' = \dfrac{4xy\sqrt{xy} - y}{x - 2x^2\sqrt{xy}}$

15. $-\frac{16}{13}$ **17.** $y = -x + 2$ **19.** $y = x + \frac{1}{2}$

21. $y = -\frac{9}{13}x + \frac{40}{13}$ **23.** $-81/y^3$ **25.** $-2x/y^5$

27. (a) $y = \frac{9}{2}x - \frac{5}{2}$ (b)

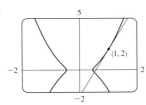

29. (a)

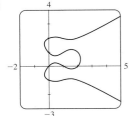

Eight; $x \approx 0.42$, 1.58

(b) $y = -x + 1$, $y = \frac{1}{3}x + 2$ (c) $1 \mp \sqrt{3}/3$

31. $\left(\pm\frac{5}{4}\sqrt{3}, \pm\frac{5}{4}\right)$

33.

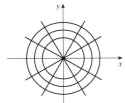

35.

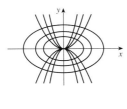

39. $\left(\pm\sqrt{3}, 0\right)$ **41.** $(-1, -1)$, $(1, 1)$ **43.** (a) 0   (b) $-\frac{1}{2}$

Exercises 2.7 □ page 131

1. $dV/dt = 3x^2 \, dx/dt$ **3.** 48 cm²/s   **5.** 70   **7.** $\pm\frac{46}{13}$

9. (a) The rate of decrease of the surface area is 1 cm²/min.
(b) The rate of decrease of the diameter when the diameter is 10 cm

(c)

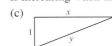

(d) $S = \pi x^2$

(e) $1/(20\pi)$ cm/min

11. (a) The plane's altitude is 1 mi and its speed is 500 mi/h.
(b) The rate at which the distance from the plane to the station is increasing when the plane is 2 mi from the station

(c)

(d) $y^2 = x^2 + 1$

(e) $250\sqrt{3}$ mi/h

13. 65 mi/h   **15.** $837/\sqrt{8674} \approx 8.99$ ft/s

17. -1.6 cm/min   **19.** $\frac{720}{13} \approx 55.4$ km/h

21. $10/\sqrt{133} \approx 0.87$ ft/s   **23.** $\frac{4}{5}$ ft/min

25. $6/(5\pi) \approx 0.38$ ft/min   **27.** 0.3 m²/s   **29.** 80 cm³/min

31. $\frac{107}{810} \approx 0.132$ Ω/s   **33.** (a) 360 ft/s   (b) 0.096 rad/s

35. $1650/\sqrt{31} \approx 296$ km/h   **37.** $7\sqrt{15}/4 \approx 6.78$ m/s

Exercises 2.8 □ page 137

1. $L(x) = -10x - 6$ **3.** $L(x) = -x + \pi/2$

5. $\sqrt{1 - x} \approx 1 - \frac{1}{2}x$;

$\sqrt{0.9} \approx 0.95$,
$\sqrt{0.99} \approx 0.995$

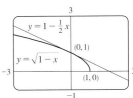

7. $-1.204 < x < 0.706$ **9.** $-0.045 < x < 0.055$

11. 32.08   **13.** 4.02

17. (a) $dy = 2x(x \cos 2x + \sin 2x) \, dx$

(b) $dy = 5/(2\sqrt{4 + 5x}) \, dx$

19. (a) $dy = \sec^2x \, dx$ (b) $dy = -0.2$, $\Delta y = -0.18237$

21. (a) 270 cm³, 0.01, 1%   (b) 36 cm², 0.006, 0.6%

23. (a) $84/\pi \approx 27$ cm²; $\frac{1}{84} \approx 0.012$

(b) $1764/\pi^2 \approx 179$ cm³; $\frac{1}{56} \approx 0.018$

25. A 5% increase in the radius corresponds to a 20% increase in blood flow.

27. (a) 4.8, 5.2   (b) Too large

Chapter 2 Review □ page 138

True-False Quiz

1. False   **3.** False   **5.** True   **7.** False

9. True   **11.** False

Exercises

1. $f''(5)$, 0, $f'(5)$, $f'(2)$, 1, $f'(3)$
3. (a) The rate at which the cost changes with respect to the interest rate; dollars/(percent per year)
(b) As the interest rate increases past 10%, the cost is increasing at a rate of $1200/(percent per year).
(c) Always positive

5.

7. $a = f$, $c = f'$, $b = f''$

9. The rate at which the total value of US currency in circulation is changing in billions of dollars per year; $22.2 billion/year

11. $f'(x) = 3x^2 + 5$ **13.** $6x(x^4 - 3x^2 + 5)^2(2x^2 - 3)$

15. $\dfrac{1}{2\sqrt{x}} - \dfrac{4}{3\sqrt[3]{x^7}}$ **17.** $\dfrac{2(2x^2 + 1)}{\sqrt{x^2 + 1}}$ **19.** $\dfrac{(t^2 + 1)}{(1 - t^2)^2}$

21. $-\dfrac{\sec^2\sqrt{1-x}}{2\sqrt{1-x}}$ **23.** $\dfrac{1 - y^4 - 2xy}{4xy^3 + x^2 - 3}$

25. $\dfrac{2 \sec 2\theta\,(\tan 2\theta - 1)}{(1 + \tan 2\theta)^2}$ **27.** $-(x - 1)^{-2}$

29. $\dfrac{2x - y\cos(xy)}{x\cos(xy) + 1}$ **31.** $-6x\csc^2(3x^2 + 5)$

33. $\cos(\tan\sqrt{1 + x^3})(\sec^2\sqrt{1 + x^3})\dfrac{3x^2}{2\sqrt{1 + x^3}}$

35. $2\cos\theta\,\tan(\sin\theta)\sec^2(\sin\theta)$

37. $\frac{1}{5}(x\tan x)^{-4/5}(\tan x + x\sec^2 x)$ **39.** $-\frac{4}{27}$

41. $-5x^4/y^{11}$ **43.** $y = 2\sqrt{3}x + 1 - \pi\sqrt{3}/3$

45. $y = 2x + 1$ **47.** $(\pi/4, \sqrt{2}), (5\pi/4, -\sqrt{2})$

49. (a) 2   (b) 44   **51.** $f'(x) = 2xg(x) + x^2g'(x)$

53. $f'(x) = 2g(x)g'(x)$ **55.** $f'(x) = g'(g(x))g'(x)$

57. $f'(x) = g'(\sin x)\cdot\cos x$

59. $h'(x) = \dfrac{f'(x)[g(x)]^2 + g'(x)[f(x)]^2}{[f(x) + g(x)]^2}$

61. -4 (discontinuity), -1 (corner), 2 (discontinuity), 5 (vertical tangent)

63. (a) $v(t) = 3t^2 - 12$, $a(t) = 6t$
(b) Upward when $t > 2$, downward when $0 \le t < 2$ (c) 23

65. $\frac{4}{3}$ cm²/min   **67.** 13 ft/s   **69.** 400 ft/h

71. (a) $L(x) = 1 + x$; $\sqrt[3]{1 + 3x} \approx 1 + x$; $\sqrt[3]{1.03} \approx 1.01$
(b) $-0.23 < x < 0.40$

71. $12 + 3\pi/2 \approx 16.7$ cm²   **75.** $\frac{1}{32}$ **77.** $\frac{1}{4}$

CHAPTER 3

Exercises 3.1 □ page 147

1. (a) $f(x) = a^x$, $a > 0$ (b) $\mathbb{R}$ (c) $(0, \infty)$
(d) See Figures 6(c), 6(b), and 6(a), respectively.

3.
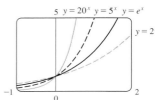
All approach 0 as $x \to -\infty$, all pass through $(0, 1)$, and all are increasing. The larger the base, the faster the rate of increase.

5.
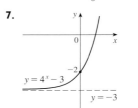
The functions with base greater than 1 are increasing and those with base less than 1 are decreasing. The latter are reflections of the former about the y-axis.

7.
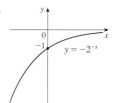

9.
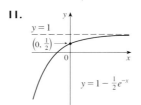

11.
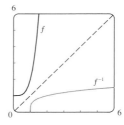

13. (a) $y = e^x - 2$ (b) $y = e^{x-2}$ (c) $y = -e^x$
(d) $y = e^{-x}$ (e) $y = -e^{-x}$
15. (a) $(-\infty, \infty)$ (b) $(-\infty, 0) \cup (0, \infty)$
17. $f(x) = 3\cdot2^x$ **21.** At $x \approx 35.8$
23. ∞ **25.** 1   **27.** 0   **29.** 0

Exercises 3.2 □ page 158

1. (a) See Definition 1.
(b) It must pass the Horizontal Line Test.
3. No   **5.** Yes   **7.** No   **9.** No   **11.** Yes
13. No   **15.** 2   **17.** 0
19. $F = \frac{9}{5}C + 32$; the Fahrenheit temperature as a function of the Celsius temperature; $[-273.15, \infty)$
21. $f^{-1}(x) = -\frac{1}{3}x^2 + \frac{10}{3}$, $x \ge 0$ **23.** $f^{-1}(x) = \sqrt[3]{\ln x}$
25. $y = e^x - 3$
27. $f^{-1}(x) = \sqrt[4]{x - 1}$ **29.**
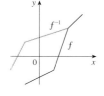

31. (b) $\frac{1}{12}$
(c) $f^{-1}(x) = \sqrt[3]{x}$,
domain $= \mathbb{R} =$ range
(e)

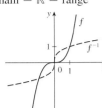

33. (b) $-\frac{1}{2}$
(c) $f^{-1}(x) = \sqrt{9 - x}$,
domain $= [0, 9]$,
range $= [0, 3]$
(e)

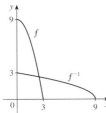

35. 1   **37.** $2/\pi$ **39.** $\frac{3}{2}$

41. (a) It's defined as the inverse of the exponential function
with base a, that is, $\log_a x = y \Longleftrightarrow a^y = x$.
(b) $(0, \infty)$ (c) $\mathbb{R}$ (d) See Figure 13.

43. (a) 6   (b) -2 **45.** (a) 2   (b) 2

47. $3 \log_2 x + \log_2 y - 2 \log_2 z$ **49.** $10 \ln u + 10 \ln v$

51. $\ln 8$ **53.** $\ln \dfrac{(1 + x^2)\sqrt{x}}{\sin x}$

55.

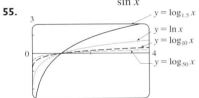

All graphs approach
$-\infty$ as $x \to 0^+$, all
pass through $(1, 0)$,
and all are increas-
ing. The larger the
base, the slower the
rate of increase.

57. About 1,084,588 mi

59. (a)

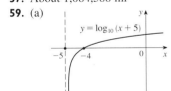

(b)

61. (a) $\sqrt{e}$ (b) $-\ln 5$

63. (a) $5 + \log_2 3$ or $5 + (\ln 3)/\ln 2$ (b) $\frac{1}{2}(1 + \sqrt{1 + 4e})$

65. (a) $x < \ln 10$ (b) $x > 1/e$

67. (a) $(-\infty, \frac{1}{2} \ln 3]$ (b) $f^{-1}(x) = \frac{1}{2} \ln(3 - x^2)$, $[0, \sqrt{3})$

69. $-\infty$ **71.** 0   **73.** ∞

75.

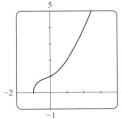

The graph passes the
Horizontal Line Test.

$f^{-1}(x) = -\dfrac{\sqrt[3]{4}}{6}\left(\sqrt[3]{D - 27x^2 + 20} - \sqrt[3]{D + 27x^2 - 20} + \sqrt[3]{2}\right)$,
where $D = 3\sqrt{3}\sqrt{27x^4 - 40x^2 + 16}$;
two of the expressions are complex.

Exercises 3.3 □ page 166

1. $f'(x) = \dfrac{3}{(3x - 1) \ln 2}$ **3.** $f'(\theta) = -\tan \theta$

5. $f'(x) = \dfrac{1}{5x \sqrt[5]{(\ln x)^4}}$ **7.** $f'(x) = \dfrac{\sin x}{x} + \cos x \ln(5x)$

9. $g'(x) = -\dfrac{2a}{a^2 - x^2}$ **11.** $F'(t) = \dfrac{6}{2t + 1} - \dfrac{12}{3t - 1}$

13. $f'(u) = \dfrac{1 + \ln 2}{u[1 + \ln(2u)]^2}$ **15.** $y' = \dfrac{10x + 1}{5x^2 + x - 2}$

17. $f'(x) = x(x + 2)e^x$ **19.** $y' = (x - 2)e^x/x^3$

21. $y' = e^{-x^2}(1 - 2x^2)$ **23.** $y' = (\cos x - x \sin x)e^{x \cos x}$

25. $h'(t) = 3t^2 - 3^t \ln 3$ **27.** $y' = \dfrac{(ad - bc)e^x}{(ce^x + d)^2}$

29. $y' = 2^{\sin \pi x}(\pi \ln 2) \cos \pi x$ **31.** $f'(u) = (-1/u^2)e^{1/u}$

33. $y' = -x/(1 + x)$ **35.** $F'(t) = e^{t \sin 2t}(2t \cos 2t + \sin 2t)$

37. $y' = e^{\alpha x}(\beta \cos \beta x + \alpha \sin \beta x)$;
$y'' = e^{\alpha x}[(\alpha^2 - \beta^2) \sin \beta x + 2\alpha\beta \cos \beta x]$

39. $y' = 1 + \ln x$, $y'' = 1/x$ **41.** $x - ey = e$

43. $f'(x) = \dfrac{2x - 1 - (x - 1) \ln(x - 1)}{(x - 1)[1 - \ln(x - 1)]^2}$;
$(1, 1 + e) \cup (1 + e, \infty)$

45. $y' = (2x + 1)^5(x^4 - 3)^6\left(\dfrac{10}{2x + 1} + \dfrac{24x^3}{x^4 - 3}\right)$

47. $y' = \dfrac{\sin^2 x \, \tan^4 x}{(x^2 + 1)^2}\left(2 \cot x + \dfrac{4 \sec^2 x}{\tan x} - \dfrac{4x}{x^2 + 1}\right)$

49. $y' = x^x(1 + \ln x)$

51. $y' = (\cos x)^x(-x \tan x + \ln \cos x)$

53. $y' = (\tan x)^{1/x}\left(\dfrac{\sec^2 x}{x \tan x} - \dfrac{\ln \tan x}{x^2}\right)$

55. $y' = \dfrac{1 - 2xye^{x^2 y}}{x^2 e^{x^2 y} - 1}$ **57.** $y' = \dfrac{2x}{x^2 + y^2 - 2y}$

59. $v(t) = 2e^{-1.5t}(2\pi \cos 2\pi t - 1.5 \sin 2\pi t)$

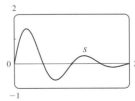
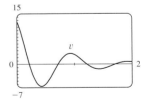

63. $f^{(n)}(x) = 2^n e^{2x}$ **65.** $f^{(n)}(x) = (-1)^{n-1}(n - 1)!/(x - 1)^n$

67. $\frac{1}{2}$

Exercises 3.4 □ page 173

1. About 235

3. (a) $100(4.2)^t$ (b) ≈ 7409 (c) $\approx 10,632$ bacteria/h
(d) $(\ln 100)/(\ln 4.2) \approx 3.2$ h

5. (a) 1508 million, 1871 million   (b) 2161 million
(c) 3972 million; wars in the first half of century, increased life
expectancy in second half

7. (a) $Ce^{-0.0005t}$ (b) $-2000 \ln 0.9 \approx 211$ s
9. (a) $100 \times 2^{-t/30}$ mg (b) ≈ 9.92 mg
(c) ≈ 199.3 years
11. ≈ 2500 years **13.** (a) $\approx 137°F$ (b) ≈ 116 min
15. (a) $13.\overline{3}°C$ (b) ≈ 67.74 min
17. (a) ≈ 64.5 kPa (b) ≈ 39.9 kPa
19. (a) $3828.84 (b) $3840.25 (c) $3850.08
(d) $3851.61 (e) $3852.01 (f) $3852.08

Exercises 3.5 □ page 180

1. (a) $\pi/3$ (b) π **3.** (a) $\pi/3$ (b) $-\pi/4$
5. (a) 0.7 (b) $\pi/3$ **9.** $x/\sqrt{1 + x^2}$
17. $y' = \dfrac{1}{2\sqrt{x}(1 + x)}$ **19.** $y' = \dfrac{1}{\sqrt{-x^2 - x}}$
21. $H'(x) = 1 + 2x \arctan x$ **23.** $y' = -2e^{2x}/\sqrt{1 - e^{4x}}$
25. $y' = -\dfrac{\sin \theta}{1 + \cos^2\theta}$ **27.** $h'(t) = 0$
29. $y' = \sqrt{a^2 - b^2}/(a + b \cos x)$
31. $g'(x) = \dfrac{2}{\sqrt{1 - (3 - 2x)^2}}$; $[1, 2], (1, 2)$
33. $\pi/6$ **35.** $-\pi/2$ **37.** $\pi/2$ **39.** $\frac{1}{4}$ rad/s

Exercises 3.6 □ page 185

1. (a) 0 (b) 1 **3.** (a) $\frac{3}{4}$ (b) $\frac{1}{2}(e^2 - e^{-2}) \approx 3.62686$
5. (a) 1 (b) 0
17. $\coth x = \frac{5}{4}$, $\operatorname{sech} x = \frac{3}{5}$, $\cosh x = \frac{5}{3}$, $\sinh x = \frac{4}{3}$, $\operatorname{csch} x = \frac{3}{4}$
19. (a) 1 (b) -1 (c) ∞ (d) $-\infty$ (e) 0 (f) 1
(g) ∞ (h) $-\infty$ (i) 0
27. $f'(x) = x \sinh x + \cosh x$ **29.** $h'(x) = 2x \cosh(x^2)$
31. $h'(t) = -\dfrac{t \operatorname{csch}^2\sqrt{1 + t^2}}{\sqrt{1 + t^2}}$ **33.** $H'(t) = e^t \operatorname{sech}^2(e^t)$
35. $y' = 3e^{\cosh 3x} \sinh 3x$ **37.** $y' = \dfrac{1}{2\sqrt{x}(1 - x)}$
39. $y' = \sinh^{-1}(x/3)$ **41.** $y' = -\dfrac{1}{x\sqrt{x^2 + 1}}$
43. (a) 0.3572 (b) 70.34°
45. (b) $y = 2 \sinh 3x - 4 \cosh 3x$ **47.** $\left(\ln(1 + \sqrt{2}), \sqrt{2}\right)$

Exercises 3.7 □ page 193

1. -2 **3.** $-\infty$ **5.** ∞ **7.** p/q **9.** $-\infty$ **11.** $\ln\frac{5}{3}$
13. $\frac{1}{2}$ **15.** 1 **17.** $-1/\pi^2$ **19.** $\frac{1}{2}a(a - 1)$ **21.** 0
23. 3 **25.** 0 **27.** 1 **29.** ∞ **31.** 1 **33.** e^{-2}
35. $1/\sqrt{e}$ **37.** 5 **45.** $\frac{16}{9}a$ **47.** 56 **51.** (a) 0

Chapter 3 Review □ page 195

True-False Quiz

1. True **3.** False **5.** True **7.** True **9.** False
11. False **13.** False **15.** True

Exercises

1. No **3.** (a) 7 (b) $\frac{1}{8}$
5.

7.

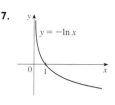

9.

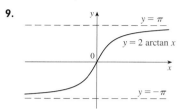

11. (a) 9 (b) 2 **13.** $e^{1/3}$ **15.** $\ln \ln 17$
17. $\sqrt{1 + e}$ **19.** $\tan 1$ **21.** $f'(t) = t + 2t \ln t$
23. $h'(\theta) = 2 \sec^2(2\theta)e^{\tan 2\theta}$ **25.** $y' = 5 \sec 5x$
27. $y' = (1 + c^2)e^{cx} \sin x$ **29.** $y' = 2 \tan x$
31. $y' = e^{-1/x}(1 + 1/x)$ **33.** $y' = -(2 \ln 2) t2^{-t^2}$
35. $H'(v) = \dfrac{v}{1 + v^2} + \tan^{-1}v$
37. $y' = 2x^2 \cosh(x^2) + \sinh(x^2)$
39. $y' = \cot x - \sin x \cos x$ **41.** $y' = -\dfrac{1}{x}\left(1 + \dfrac{1}{(\ln x)^2}\right)$
43. $y' = 3 \tanh 3x$ **45.** $y' = \dfrac{\cosh x}{\sqrt{\sinh^2 x - 1}}$
47. $f'(x) =$
$\dfrac{6x}{x^2 + 1} \sin^2(\ln(x^2 + 1)) \cdot \cos(\ln(x^2 + 1)) \cdot e^{\sin^3(\ln(x^2 + 1))}$
49. $f'(x) = g'(x)e^{g(x)}$ **51.** $f'(x) = g'(x)/g(x)$
53. $2^x(\ln 2)^n$ **57.** $y = -x + 2$ **59.** $(-3, 0)$
61. (a) $y = \frac{1}{4}x + \frac{1}{4}(\ln 4 + 1)$ (b) $y = ex$
63. (a) $200(3.24)^t$ (b) $\approx 22,040$
(c) $\approx 25,910$ bacteria/h (d) $(\ln 50)/(\ln 3.24) \approx 3.33$ h
65. (a) C_0e^{-kt} (b) ≈ 100 h **67.** 0 **69.** 0 **71.** $-\infty$
73. -1 **75.** π **77.** 8 **79.** 0 **81.** $\frac{1}{2}$ **83.** $\frac{2}{3}$

CHAPTER 4

Exercises 4.1 □ page 203

Abbreviations: abs., absolute; loc., local; max., maximum;
min., minimum

1. Absolute minimum: smallest function value on the entire
domain of the function; local minimum at c: smallest function
value when x is near c
3. Abs. max. at b, loc. max. at b and e, abs. min. at d,
loc. min. at d and s
5. Abs. max. $f(4) = 4$; abs. min. $f(7) = 0$; loc. max. $f(4) = 4$
and $f(6) = 3$; loc. min. $f(2) = 1$ and $f(5) = 2$

7.

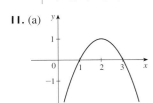

9.

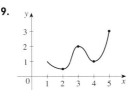

11. (a)

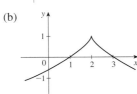

(b)

(c)

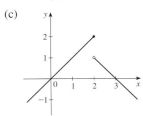

13. (a)

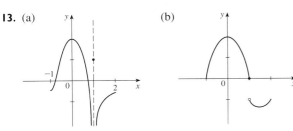

(b)

15. Abs. max. $f(1) = 5$ **17.** None
19. Abs. and loc. max. $f(\pi/2) = f(-3\pi/2) = 1$;
abs. and loc. min. $f(3\pi/2) = f(-\pi/2) = -1$
21. Abs. max. $f(0) = 1$ **23.** $-\frac{2}{5}$ **25.** $-4, 2$
27. $0, \frac{1}{2}(-1 \pm \sqrt{5})$ **29.** $0, 2$
31. $0, \frac{8}{7}, 4$ **33.** $n\pi$ (n an integer)   **35.** $1/e$
37. $f(0) = 5, f(2) = -7$ **39.** $f(-1) = 8, f(2) = -19$
41. $f(3) = 66, f(\pm1) = 2$ **43.** $f(\sqrt{2}) = 2, f(-1) = -\sqrt{3}$
45. $f(\pi/4) = \sqrt{2}, f(0) = 1$
47. $f(2) = 2/\sqrt{e}, f(-1) = -1/\sqrt[8]{e}$
49. $f\left(\dfrac{a}{a+b}\right) = \dfrac{a^a b^b}{(a+b)^{a+b}}$
51. (a) $2.19, 1.81$ (b) $\frac{6}{25}\sqrt{\frac{3}{5}} + 2, -\frac{6}{25}\sqrt{\frac{3}{5}} + 2$
53. (a) $0.32, 0.00$ (b) $\frac{3}{16}\sqrt{3}, 0$ **55.** $\approx 3.9665°C$
57. Cheapest, $t = 10$; most expensive, $t \approx 5.1309$
59. (a) $r = \frac{2}{3}r_0$ (b) $v = \frac{4}{27}kr_0^3$

(c)

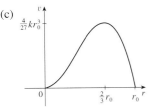

Exercises 4.2 □ page 210

1. 2   **3.** $\pm\frac{1}{4}, \pm\frac{3}{4}$
5. f is not differentiable on $(-1, 1)$ **7.** $0.8, 3.2, 4.4, 6.1$
9. (a), (b)   (c) $2\sqrt{2}$

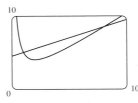   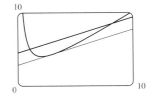

11. 0   **13.** $-\frac{1}{2}\ln\left[\frac{1}{6}(1 - e^{-6})\right]$
15. f is not differentiable at 1   **23.** 16
25. No   **31.** No

Exercises 4.3 □ page 217

Abbreviations: inc., increasing; dec., decreasing; CD, concave
downward; CU, concave upward; HA, horizontal asymptote;
VA, vertical asymptote; IP, inflection point

1. (a) Inc. on $(-\infty, -2), (2, \infty)$; dec. on $(-2, 2)$
(b) Loc. max. $f(-2) = 17$; loc. min. $f(2) = -15$
(c) CU on $(0, \infty)$; CD on $(-\infty, 0)$; IP $(0, 1)$
3. (a) Inc. on $(\pi/3, 5\pi/3), (7\pi/3, 3\pi)$;
dec. on $(0, \pi/3), (5\pi/3, 7\pi/3)$
(b) Loc. max. $f(5\pi/3) = 5\pi/3 + \sqrt{3}$;
loc. min. $f(\pi/3) = \pi/3 - \sqrt{3}, f(7\pi/3) = 7\pi/3 - \sqrt{3}$
(c) CU on $(0, \pi), (2\pi, 3\pi)$; CD on $(\pi, 2\pi)$; IP $(\pi, \pi), (2\pi, 2\pi)$
5. (a) Inc. on $(-1, \infty)$; dec. on $(-\infty, -1)$
(b) Loc. min. $f(-1) = -1/e$
(c) CU on $(-2, \infty)$; CD on $(-\infty, -2)$; IP $(-2, -2e^{-2})$
7. (a) Inc. on $(0, e^2)$; dec. on (e^2, ∞)
(b) Loc. max. $f(e^2) = 2/e$
(c) CU on $(e^{8/3}, \infty)$; CD on $(0, e^{8/3})$; IP $\left(e^{8/3}, \frac{8}{3}e^{-4/3}\right)$
9. Loc. max. $f\left(\frac{3}{4}\right) = \frac{5}{4}$
11. (a) f has a local maximum at 2.
(b) f has a horizontal tangent at 6.
13. (a) $3, 5$ (b) $2, 4, 6$ (c) $1, 7$
15.   **17.**

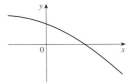   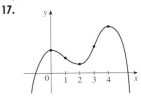

19.

   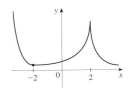

21. (a) Inc. on $(0, 2)$, $(4, 6)$, $(8, \infty)$;
dec. on $(2, 4)$, $(6, 8)$
(b) Loc. max. at $x = 2, 6$;
loc. min. at $x = 4, 8$
(c) CU on $(3, 6)$, $(6, \infty)$;
CD on $(0, 3)$
(d) 3   (e) See graph at right.

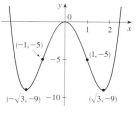

23. (a) Inc. on $(-\infty, -1)$, $(2, \infty)$;
dec. on $(-1, 2)$
(b) Loc. max. $f(-1) = 7$;
loc. min. $f(2) = -20$
(c) CU on $\left(\frac{1}{2}, \infty\right)$; CD on $\left(-\infty, \frac{1}{2}\right)$;
IP $\left(\frac{1}{2}, -\frac{13}{2}\right)$
(d) See graph at right.

25. (a) Inc. on $\left(-\sqrt{3}, 0\right)$, $\left(\sqrt{3}, \infty\right)$;
dec. on $\left(-\infty, -\sqrt{3}\right)$, $\left(0, \sqrt{3}\right)$
(b) Loc. min. $f\left(\pm\sqrt{3}\right) = -9$;
loc. max. $f(0) = 0$
(c) CU on $(-\infty, -1)$, $(1, \infty)$;
CD on $(-1, 1)$; IP $(\pm 1, -5)$
(d) See graph at right.

27. (a) Inc. on $(-\infty, -1)$, $(1, \infty)$;
dec. on $(-1, 1)$
(b) Loc. max. $h(-1) = 5$;
loc. min. $h(1) = 1$
(c) CU on $\left(-1/\sqrt{2}, 0\right)$, $\left(1/\sqrt{2}, \infty\right)$;
CD on $\left(-\infty, -1/\sqrt{2}\right)$, $\left(0, 1/\sqrt{2}\right)$;
IP $(0, 3)$, $\left(\pm 1/\sqrt{2}, 3 \mp \frac{7}{8}\sqrt{2}\right)$
(d) See graph at right.

29. (a) Inc. on $(-2, \infty)$;
dec. on $(-3, -2)$
(b) Loc. min. $A(-2) = -2$
(c) CU on $(-3, \infty)$
(d) See graph at right.

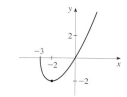

31. (a) Inc. on $(-1, \infty)$;
dec. on $(-\infty, -1)$
(b) Loc. min. $C(-1) = -3$
(c) CU on $(-\infty, 0)$, $(2, \infty)$;
CD on $(0, 2)$;
IP $(0, 0)$, $\left(2, 6\sqrt[3]{2}\right)$
(d) See graph at right.

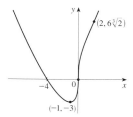

33. (a) Inc. on $(0, \pi/3)$, $(\pi, 5\pi/3)$;
dec. on $(\pi/3, \pi)$, $(5\pi/3, 2\pi)$
(b) Loc. max. $f(\pi/3) = f(5\pi/3) = \frac{3}{2}$; loc. min. $f(\pi) = -3$
(c) Let $\alpha = \cos^{-1}\left(\frac{1}{8}\left(1 + \sqrt{33}\right)\right)$, $\beta = \cos^{-1}\left(\frac{1}{8}\left(1 - \sqrt{33}\right)\right)$,
$y_1 = \frac{3}{16}\left(1 + \sqrt{33}\right)$, and $y_2 = \frac{3}{16}\left(1 - \sqrt{33}\right)$.

CU on $(0, \alpha)$, $(\beta, 2\pi - \beta)$,
$(2\pi - \alpha, 2\pi)$;
CD on (α, β), $(2\pi - \beta, 2\pi - \alpha)$;
IP (α, y_1), (β, y_2), $(2\pi - \beta, y_2)$,
$(2\pi - \alpha, y_1)$
(d) See graph at right.

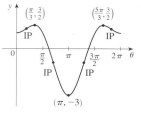

35. (a) HA $y = 1$, VA $x = -1$, $x = 1$
(b) Inc. on $(-\infty, -1)$, $(-1, 0)$;
dec. on $(0, 1)$, $(1, \infty)$
(c) Loc. max. $f(0) = 0$
(d) CU on $(-\infty, -1)$, $(1, \infty)$;
CD on $(-1, 1)$
(e) See graph at right.

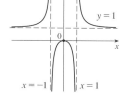

37. (a) HA $y = 0$
(b) Dec. on $(-\infty, \infty)$
(c) None
(d) CU on $(-\infty, \infty)$
(e) See graph at right.

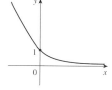

39. (a) VA $x = 0$, $x = e$
(b) Dec. on $(0, e)$
(c) None
(d) CU on $(0, 1)$; CD on $(1, e)$;
IP $(1, 0)$
(e) See graph at right.

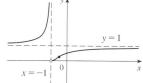

41. (a) HA $y = 1$, VA $x = -1$
(b) Inc. on $(-\infty, -1)$, $(-1, \infty)$
(c) None
(d) CU on $(-\infty, -1)$, $\left(-1, -\frac{1}{2}\right)$;
CD on $\left(-\frac{1}{2}, \infty\right)$; IP $\left(-\frac{1}{2}, 1/e^2\right)$
(e) See graph at right.

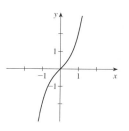

43. $(3, \infty)$
45. (a) Loc. and abs. max. $f(1) = \sqrt{2}$, no min.
(b) $\frac{1}{4}\left(3 - \sqrt{17}\right) \approx -0.28$
47. When $t \approx 7.94$
49. $f(x) = \frac{1}{9}\left(2x^3 + 3x^2 - 12x + 7\right)$

Exercises 4.4 □ page 225

Abbreviation: SA, slant asymptote

1. A. $\mathbb{R}$ B. y-int. 0; x-int. 0
C. About $(0, 0)$ D. None
E. Inc. on $(-\infty, \infty)$ F. None
G. CU on $(0, \infty)$; CD on $(-\infty, 0)$;
IP $(0, 0)$
H. See graph at right.

3. A. $\mathbb{R}$ B. y-int. 2; x-int. 2, $\frac{1}{2}(7 \pm 3\sqrt{5})$

C. None   D. None

E. Inc. on $(1, 5)$;

dec. on $(-\infty, 1)$, $(5, \infty)$

F. Loc. min. $f(1) = -5$;

loc. max. $f(5) = 27$

G. CU on $(-\infty, 3)$;

CD on $(3, \infty)$; IP $(3, 11)$

H. See graph at right.

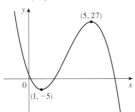

5. A. $\mathbb{R}$ B. y-int. 0;

x-int. $-4, 0$

C. None   D. None

E. Inc. on $(-3, \infty)$;

dec. on $(-\infty, -3)$

F. Loc. min. $f(-3) = -27$

G. CU on $(-\infty, -2)$, $(0, \infty)$;

CD on $(-2, 0)$; IP $(0, 0)$,

$(-2, -16)$

H. See graph at right.

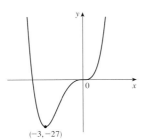

7. A. $\mathbb{R}$ B. y-int. 1

C. None   D. None

E. Inc. on $(-\infty, 0)$, $(1, \infty)$;

dec. on $(0, 1)$

F. Loc. max. $f(0) = 1$;

loc. min. $f(1) = -2$

G. CU on $(1/\sqrt[3]{4}, \infty)$; CD on

$(-\infty, 1/\sqrt[3]{4})$;

IP $(1/\sqrt[3]{4}, 1 - 9/(2\sqrt[3]{16}))$

H. See graph at right.

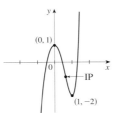

9. A. $\{x \mid x \neq 1\}$

B. y-int. 0; x-int. 0

C. None

D. VA $x = 1$, HA $y = 1$

E. Dec. on $(-\infty, 1)$, $(1, \infty)$

F. None

G. CU on $(1, \infty)$; CD on $(-\infty, 1)$

H. See graph at right.

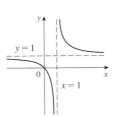

11. A. $\{x \mid x \neq \pm 3\}$

B. y-int. $-\frac{1}{9}$

C. About y-axis

D. VAs $x = \pm 3$, HA $y = 0$

E. Inc. on $(-\infty, -3)$, $(-3, 0)$;

dec. on $(0, 3)$, $(3, \infty)$

F. Loc. max. $f(0) = -\frac{1}{9}$

G. CU on $(-\infty, -3)$, $(3, \infty)$;

CD on $(-3, 3)$

H. See graph at right.

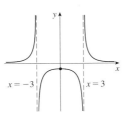

13. A. $\mathbb{R}$ B. y-int. 0; x-int. 0

C. About $(0, 0)$ D. HA $y = 0$

E. Inc. on $(-3, 3)$;

dec. on $(-\infty, -3)$, $(3, \infty)$

F. Loc. min. $f(-3) = -\frac{1}{6}$;

loc. max. $f(3) = \frac{1}{6}$;

G. CU on $(-3\sqrt{3}, 0)$, $(3\sqrt{3}, \infty)$;

CD on $(-\infty, -3\sqrt{3})$, $(0, 3\sqrt{3})$;

IPs $(0, 0)$, $(\pm 3\sqrt{3}, \pm\frac{1}{12}\sqrt{3})$

H. See graph at right.

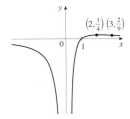

15. A. $(-\infty, 0) \cup (0, \infty)$

B. x-int. 1   C. None

D. HA $y = 0$; VA $x = 0$

E. Inc. on $(0, 2)$;

dec. on $(-\infty, 0)$, $(2, \infty)$

F. Loc. max. $f(2) = \frac{1}{4}$

G. CU on $(3, \infty)$;

CD on $(-\infty, 0)$, $(0, 3)$; IP $(3, \frac{2}{9})$

H. See graph at right

17. A. $(-\infty, 5]$ B. y-int. 0; x-int. 0, 5

C. None   D. None

E. Inc. on $(-\infty, \frac{10}{3})$; dec. on $(\frac{10}{3}, 5)$

F. Loc. max. $f(\frac{10}{3}) = \frac{10}{9}\sqrt{15}$

G. CD on $(-\infty, 5)$

H. See graph at right.

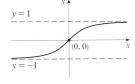

19. A. $\mathbb{R}$ B. y-int. 0; x-int. 0

C. About the origin

D. HAs $y = \pm 1$

E. Inc. on $(-\infty, \infty)$ F. None

G. CU on $(-\infty, 0)$;

CD on $(0, \infty)$; IP $(0, 0)$

H. See graph at right.

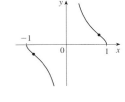

21. A. $\{x \mid |x| \leq 1, x \neq 0\} = [-1, 0) \cup (0, 1]$ B. x-int. ± 1

C. About $(0, 0)$ D. VA $x = 0$

E. Dec. on $(-1, 0)$, $(0, 1)$ F. None

G. CU on $(-1, -\sqrt{2/3})$, $(0, \sqrt{2/3})$;

CD on $(-\sqrt{2/3}, 0)$, $(\sqrt{2/3}, 1)$;

IPs $(\pm\sqrt{2/3}, \pm 1/\sqrt{2})$

H. See graph at right.

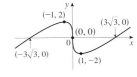

23. A. $\mathbb{R}$ B. y-int. 0; x-int. 0, $\pm 3\sqrt{3}$ C. About the origin

D. None   E. Inc. on $(-\infty, -1)$, $(1, \infty)$; dec. on $(-1, 1)$

F. Loc. max. $f(-1) = 2$;

loc. min. $f(1) = -2$

G. CU on $(0, \infty)$; CD on $(-\infty, 0)$;

IP $(0, 0)$

H. See graph at right.

25. A. $\mathbb{R}$ B. y-int. 0; x-int. -1, 0
C. None   D. None
E. Inc. on $(-\infty, -\frac{1}{4})$, $(0, \infty)$;
dec. on $(-\frac{1}{4}, 0)$
F. Loc. max. $f(-\frac{1}{4}) = \frac{1}{4}$;
loc. min. $f(0) = 0$
G. CD on $(-\infty, 0)$, $(0, \infty)$
H. See graph at right.

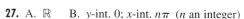

27. A. $\mathbb{R}$ B. y-int. 0; x-int. $n\pi$ (n an integer)
C. About the origin, period 2π D. None
E. Inc. on $(2n\pi - \pi/2, 2n\pi + \pi/2)$;
dec. on $(2n\pi + \pi/2, 2n\pi + 3\pi/2)$
F. Loc. max. $f(2n\pi + \pi/2) = 2$;
loc. min. $f(2n\pi + 3\pi/2) = -2$
G. CU on $((2n-1)\pi, 2n\pi)$;
CD on $(2n\pi, (2n+1)\pi)$;
IPs $(n\pi, 0)$
H. See graph at right.

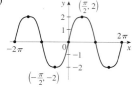

29. A. $(-\pi/2, \pi/2)$ B. y-int. 0; x-int. 0
C. About y-axis
D. VA $x = \pm\pi/2$
E. Inc. on $(0, \pi/2)$;
dec. on $(-\pi/2, 0)$
F. Loc. min. $f(0) = 0$
G. CU on $(-\pi/2, \pi/2)$
H. See graph at right.

31. A. $(0, 3\pi)$ B. No y-int.   C. None   D. None
E. Inc. on $(\pi/3, 5\pi/3)$, $(7\pi/3, 3\pi)$;
dec. on $(0, \pi/3)$, $(5\pi/3, 7\pi/3)$
F. Loc. min. $f(\pi/3) = (\pi/6) - \frac{1}{2}\sqrt{3}$,
$f(7\pi/3) = (7\pi/6) - \frac{1}{2}\sqrt{3}$;
loc. max. $f(5\pi/3) = (5\pi/6) + \frac{1}{2}\sqrt{3}$
G. CU on $(0, \pi)$, $(2\pi, 3\pi)$;
CD on $(\pi, 2\pi)$; IP $(\pi, \pi/2)$, $(2\pi, \pi)$
H. See graph at right.

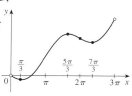

33. A. All reals except $(2n+1)\pi$ (n an integer)
B. y-int. 0; x-int. $2n\pi$ C. About the origin, period 2π
D. VAs $x = (2n+1)\pi$
E. Inc. on $((2n-1)\pi, (2n+1)\pi)$ F. None
G. CU on $(2n\pi, (2n+1)\pi)$; CD on $((2n-1)\pi, 2n\pi)$;
IPs $(2n\pi, 0)$
H.

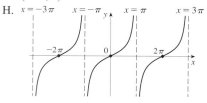

35. A. $\mathbb{R}$ B. y-int. $\frac{1}{2}$ C. None
D. HAs $y = 0$, $y = 1$
E. Inc. on $\mathbb{R}$ F. None
G. CU on $(-\infty, 0)$; CD on $(0, \infty)$;
IP $(0, \frac{1}{2})$ H. See graph at right.

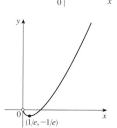

37. A. $(0, \infty)$ B. x-int. 1
C. None   D. None
E. Inc. on $(1/e, \infty)$; dec. on $(0, 1/e)$
F. Loc. min. $f(1/e) = -1/e$
G. CU on $(0, \infty)$
H. See graph at right.

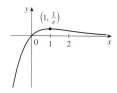

39. A. $\mathbb{R}$ B. y-int. 0; x-int. 0
C. None   D. HA $y = 0$
E. Inc. on $(-\infty, 1)$; dec. on $(1, \infty)$
F. Loc. max. $f(1) = 1/e$
G. CU on $(2, \infty)$; CD on $(-\infty, 2)$;
IP $(2, 2/e^2)$ H. See graph at right.

41. A. All x in $(2n\pi, (2n+1)\pi)$ (n an integer)
B. x-int. $\pi/2 + 2n\pi$ C. Period 2π D. VAs $x = n\pi$
E. Inc. on $(2n\pi, \pi/2 + 2n\pi)$;
dec. on $(\pi/2 + 2n\pi, (2n+1)\pi)$
F. Loc. max. $f(\pi/2 + 2n\pi) = 0$
G. CD on $(2n\pi, (2n+1)\pi)$
H.

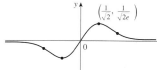

43. A. $\mathbb{R}$ B. y-int. 0; x-int. 0   C. About $(0, 0)$
D. HA $y = 0$ E. Inc. on $(-1/\sqrt{2}, 1/\sqrt{2})$;
dec. on $(-\infty, -1/\sqrt{2})$, $(1/\sqrt{2}, \infty)$
F. Loc. min. $f(-1/\sqrt{2}) = -1/\sqrt{2e}$;
loc. max. $f(1/\sqrt{2}) = 1/\sqrt{2e}$
G. CU on $(-\sqrt{3/2}, 0)$, $(\sqrt{3/2}, \infty)$;
CD on $(-\infty, -\sqrt{3/2})$, $(0, \sqrt{3/2})$;
IPs $(\pm\sqrt{3/2}, \pm\sqrt{3/2}\, e^{-3/2})$, $(0, 0)$
H.

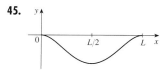

45.

47. A. $\left(-\infty, \frac{1}{2}\right) \cup \left(\frac{1}{2}, \infty\right)$
B. y-int. 1; x-int. $\frac{1}{4}\left(5 \pm \sqrt{17}\right)$
C. None **D.** VA $x = \frac{1}{2}$;
SA $y = -x + 2$
E. Dec. on $\left(-\infty, \frac{1}{2}\right)$, $\left(\frac{1}{2}, \infty\right)$
F. None
G. CU on $\left(\frac{1}{2}, \infty\right)$; CD on $\left(-\infty, \frac{1}{2}\right)$
H. See graph at right.

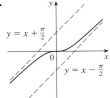

49. A. $\{x \mid x \neq 0\}$ **B.** None
C. About $(0, 0)$
D. VA $x = 0$; SA $y = x$
E. Inc. on $(-\infty, -2)$, $(2, \infty)$;
dec. on $(-2, 0)$, $(0, 2)$
F. Loc. max. $f(-2) = -4$;
loc. min. $f(2) = 4$
G. CU on $(0, \infty)$; CD on $(-\infty, 0)$
H. See graph at right.

51.

53. Inc. on $(0.92, 2.5)$, $(2.58, \infty)$;
dec. on $(-\infty, 0.92)$, $(2.5, 2.58)$;
loc. max. $f(2.5) = 4$; loc. min. $f(0.92) \approx -5.12$,
$f(2.58) \approx 3.998$; CU on $(-\infty, 1.46)$, $(2.54, \infty)$;
CD on $(1.46, 2.54)$; IPs $(1.46, -1.40)$, $(2.54, 3.999)$

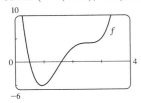 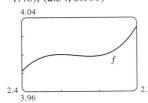

55. Inc. on $(-1.49, -1.07)$, $(2.89, 4)$; dec. on $(-4, -1.49)$,
$(-1.07, 2.89)$; loc. max. $f(-1.07) \approx 8.79$; loc. min.
$f(-1.49) \approx 8.75$, $f(2.89) \approx -9.99$; CU on $(-4, -1.28)$,
$(1.28, 4)$; CD on $(-1.28, 1.28)$; IPs $(-1.28, 8.77)$, $(1.28, -1.48)$

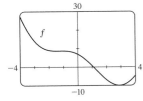 

57. Inc. on $\left(-8 - \sqrt{61}, -8 + \sqrt{61}\right)$;
dec. on $\left(-\infty, -8 - \sqrt{61}\right)$, $\left(-8 + \sqrt{61}, 0\right)$, $(0, \infty)$;
CU on $\left(-12 - \sqrt{138}, -12 + \sqrt{138}\right)$, $(0, \infty)$;
CD on $\left(-\infty, -12 - \sqrt{138}\right)$, $\left(-12 + \sqrt{138}, 0\right)$

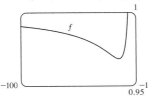 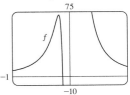

59. For $c \geq 0$, there is no IP and only one extreme point, the
origin. For $c < 0$, there is a maximum point at the origin, two
minimum points, and two IPs, which move downward and away
from the origin as $c \to -\infty$.

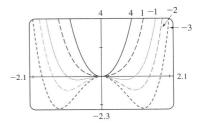

61. There is no maximum or minimum, regardless of the
value of c. For $c < 0$, there is a vertical asymptote at $x = 0$,
$\lim_{x \to 0} f(x) = \infty$, and $\lim_{x \to \pm\infty} f(x) = 1$.
$c = 0$ is a transitional value at which $f(x) = 1$ for $x \neq 0$.
For $c > 0$, $\lim_{x \to 0} f(x) = 0$, $\lim_{x \to \pm\infty} f(x) = 1$, and there are
two IPs, which move away from the y-axis as $c \to \infty$.

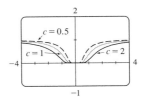 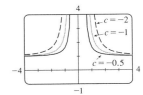

63. For $|c| < 1$, the graph has local maximum and minimum
values; for $|c| \geq 1$ it does not. The function increases for $c \geq 1$
and decreases for $c \leq -1$. As c changes, the IPs move vertically but not horizontally.

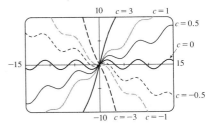

Exercises 4.5 □ page 232

1. (a) 11, 12   (b) 11.5, 11.5   **3.** 10, 10
5. 25 m by 25 m
7. (a)

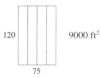

(b)

(c) $A = xy$
(d) $5x + 2y = 750$
(e) $A(x) = 375x - \frac{5}{2}x^2$
(f) $14{,}062.5 \text{ ft}^2$

9. 4000 cm^3 **13.** $\left(-\frac{1}{3}, \pm\frac{4}{3}\sqrt{2}\right)$ **15.** $L/2, \sqrt{3}\,L/4$
17. $4\pi r^3/(3\sqrt{3})$
19. Width $60/(4 + \pi)$ ft; rectangle height $30/(4 + \pi)$ ft
21. (a) Use all of the wire for the square
(b) $40\sqrt{3}/(9 + 4\sqrt{3})$ m for the square
23. $V = 2\pi R^3/(9\sqrt{3})$ **27.** $E^2/(4r)$
29. (a) $\frac{2}{3}s^2 \csc\theta\,(\csc\theta - \sqrt{3}\cot\theta)$ (b) $\cos^{-1}(1/\sqrt{3}) \approx 55°$
(c) $6s\left[h + s/(2\sqrt{2})\right]$
31. $10\sqrt[3]{3}/(1 + \sqrt[3]{3})$ ft from the stronger source
33. $y = -\frac{5}{3}x + 10$
35. (b) (i) $342{,}491$; $342/\text{unit}$; $390/\text{unit}$
(ii) 400   (iii) $320/\text{unit}
37. (a) $p(x) = 19 - \frac{1}{3000}x$ (b) \$9.50
39. (a) $p(x) = 550 - \frac{1}{10}x$ (b) \$175   (c) \$100
41. $(a^{2/3} + b^{2/3})^{3/2}$ **45.** $x = 6$ in.
47. $\frac{1}{2}(L + W)^2$ **49.** At a distance $5 - 2\sqrt{5}$ from A

Exercises 4.6 □ page 240

1. (a) $x_2 \approx 2.3, x_3 \approx 3$ (b) No   **3.** $\frac{4}{5}$ **5.** 1.1797
7. -1.25 **9.** 3.10723251   **11.** 0.876726
13. $-1.39194691, 1.07739428, 2.71987822$
15. -0.44285440 **17.** $-1.97806681, -0.82646233$
19. 0.52026899   **21.** (b) 31.622777
27. $(0.904557, 1.855277)$ **29.** 0.76286%

Exercises 4.7 □ page 246

1. $F(x) = 2x^3 - 4x^2 + 3x + C$
3. $F(x) = 4x^{5/4} - 4x^{7/4} + C$
5. $F(x) = \frac{3}{4}x^{3/4} - x^{-5} + C_1$ if $x < 0$,
$F(x) = \frac{3}{4}x^{3/4} - x^{-5} + C_2$ if $x > 0$
7. $F(u) = \frac{1}{3}u^3 - 6u^{-1/2} + C$
9. $G(\theta) = \sin\theta + 5\cos\theta + C$
11. $F(x) = x^2 + 5\sin^{-1}x + C$ **13.** $F(x) = x^5 - \frac{1}{3}x^6 + 4$
15. $x^3 + x^4 + Cx + D$ **17.** $\frac{1}{2}x^2 + \frac{25}{126}x^{14/5} + Cx + D$
19. $4x^{3/2} + 2x^{5/2} + 4$ **21.** $2\sin t + \tan t + 4 - 2\sqrt{3}$

23. $2x^4 + \frac{1}{3}x^3 + 5x^2 - 22x + \frac{59}{3}$
25. $-\sin\theta - \cos\theta + 5\theta + 4$
27. $-\ln x + (\ln 2)x - \ln 2$ **29.** 10   **31.** b
33. $s(t) = 1 - \cos t - \sin t$
35. $s(t) = -10\sin t - 3\cos t + (6/\pi)t + 3$
37. (a) $s(t) = 450 - 4.9t^2$ (b) $\sqrt{450/4.9} \approx 9.58$ s
(c) $-9.8\sqrt{450/4.9} \approx -93.9$ m/s   (d) About 9.09 s
41. 225 ft   **43.** $\frac{130}{11} \approx 11.8$ s
45. $\frac{88}{15} \approx 5.87 \text{ ft/s}^2$ **47.** $62{,}500 \text{ km/h}^2 \approx 4.82 \text{ m/s}^2$
49. (a) 22.9125 mi   (b) 21.675 mi   (c) 30 min 33 s
(d) 55.425 mi

Chapter 4 Review □ page 248

True-False Quiz

1. False   **3.** False   **5.** True   **7.** False   **9.** True
11. True   **13.** False   **15.** True   **17.** True

Exercises

1. Abs. min. $f(0) = 10$; abs. and loc. max. $f(3) = 64$
3. Abs. max. $f(0) = 0$; abs. and loc. min. $f(-1) = -1$
5.

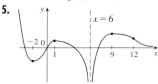

7.

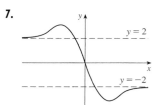

9. (a) None
(b) Dec. on $(-\infty, \infty)$
(c) None
(d) CU on $(-\infty, 0)$; CD on $(0, \infty)$;
IP $(0, 2)$
(e) See graph at right.

11. (a) None
(b) Inc. on $(2n\pi, (2n + 1)\pi)$, n an integer;
dec. on $((2n + 1)\pi, (2n + 2)\pi)$
(c) Loc. max. $f((2n + 1)\pi) = 2$; loc. min. $f(2n\pi) = -2$
(d) CU on $(2n\pi - (\pi/3), 2n\pi + (\pi/3))$;
CD on $(2n\pi + (\pi/3), 2n\pi + (5\pi/3))$; IPs $\left(2n\pi \pm (\pi/3), -\frac{1}{4}\right)$
(e)

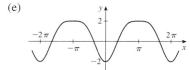

13. (a) None
(b) Inc. on $\left(\frac{1}{4}\ln 3, \infty\right)$,
dec. on $\left(-\infty, \frac{1}{4}\ln 3\right)$
(c) Loc. min.
$f\left(\frac{1}{4}\ln 3\right) = 3^{1/4} + 3^{-3/4}$
(d) CU on $(-\infty, \infty)$
(e) See graph at right.

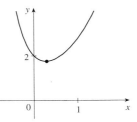

15. A. $\mathbb{R}$ B. y-int. 0; x-int. 0, 1
C. None   D. None
E. Inc. on $\left(\frac{1}{4}, \infty\right)$; dec. on $\left(-\infty, \frac{1}{4}\right)$
F. Loc. min. $f\left(\frac{1}{4}\right) = -\frac{27}{256}$
G. CU on $\left(-\infty, \frac{1}{2}\right)$, $(1, \infty)$;
CD on $\left(\frac{1}{2}, 1\right)$; IPs $\left(\frac{1}{2}, -\frac{1}{16}\right)$, $(1, 0)$
H. See graph at right.

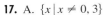

17. A. $\{x \mid x \neq 0, 3\}$
B. None   C. None
D. HA $y = 0$; VAs $x = 0$, $x = 3$
E. Inc. on $(1, 3)$;
dec. on $(-\infty, 0)$, $(0, 1)$, $(3, \infty)$
F. Loc. min. $f(1) = \frac{1}{4}$
G. CU on $(0, 3)$, $(3, \infty)$; CD on $(-\infty, 0)$
H. See graph at right.

19. A. $[-2, \infty)$
B. y-int. 0; x-int. -2, 0
C. None   D. None
E. Inc. on $\left(-\frac{4}{3}, \infty\right)$, dec. on $\left(-2, -\frac{4}{3}\right)$
F. Loc. min. $f\left(-\frac{4}{3}\right) = -\frac{4}{9}\sqrt{6}$
G. CU on $(-2, \infty)$
H. See graph at right.

21. A. $\{x \mid |x| \geq 1\}$
B. None   C. About $(0, 0)$
D. HA $y = 0$
E. Dec. on $(-\infty, -1)$, $(1, \infty)$
F. None
G. CU on $(1, \infty)$; CD on $(-\infty, -1)$
H. See graph at right.

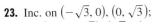

23. Inc. on $\left(-\sqrt{3}, 0\right)$, $\left(0, \sqrt{3}\right)$;
dec. on $\left(-\infty, -\sqrt{3}\right)$, $\left(\sqrt{3}, \infty\right)$;
loc. max. $f\left(\sqrt{3}\right) = \frac{2}{9}\sqrt{3}$,
loc. min. $f\left(-\sqrt{3}\right) = -\frac{2}{9}\sqrt{3}$;
CU on $\left(-\sqrt{6}, 0\right)$, $\left(\sqrt{6}, \infty\right)$;
CD on $\left(-\infty, -\sqrt{6}\right)$, $\left(0, \sqrt{6}\right)$;
IPs $\left(\sqrt{6}, \frac{5}{36}\sqrt{6}\right)$, $\left(-\sqrt{6}, -\frac{5}{36}\sqrt{6}\right)$

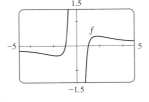

25. Inc. on $(-0.23, 0)$, $(1.62, \infty)$; dec. on $(-\infty, -0.23)$, $(0, 1.62)$;
loc. max. $f(0) = 2$; loc. min. $f(-0.23) \approx 1.96$,
$f(1.62) \approx -19.2$; CU on $(-\infty, -0.12)$, $(1.24, \infty)$;
CD on $(-0.12, 1.24)$; IPs $(-0.12, 1.98)$, $(1.24, -12.1)$

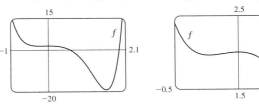

27.

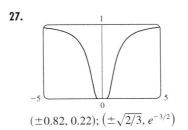

$(\pm 0.82, 0.22)$; $\left(\pm\sqrt{2/3}, e^{-3/2}\right)$

29. Max. at $x = 0$, min. at $x \approx \pm 0.87$, IPs at $x \approx \pm 0.52$
31. For $C > -1$, f is periodic with period 2π and has local
maxima at $2n\pi + \pi/2$, n an integer. For $C \leq -1$, f has no
graph. For $-1 < C \leq 1$, f has vertical asymptotes. For $C > 1$,
f is continuous on $\mathbb{R}$. As C increases, f moves upward and its
oscillations become less pronounced.
37. 500, 125   **39.** $3\sqrt{3}\,r^2$ **41.** $4/\sqrt{3}$ cm from D; at C
43. $L = C$ **45.** \$11.50   **47.** 1.16718557
49. $F(x) = e^x - 4\sqrt{x} + C$ **51.** $2\arctan x - 1$
53. $\frac{1}{2}x^2 - x^3 + 4x^4 + 2x + 1$
55. $s(t) = \frac{1}{6}t^3 - t^2 + 3t + 1$ **57.** No
59. (b) About 8.5 in. by 2 in.   (c) $20/\sqrt{3}$ in. by $20\sqrt{2/3}$ in.

CHAPTER 5

Exercises 5.1 □ page 260

1. (a) 40, 52

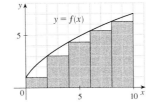
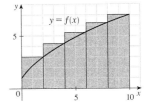

(b) 43.2, 49.2

3. (a) $\frac{77}{60}$, underestimate (b) $\frac{25}{12}$, overestimate

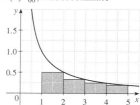
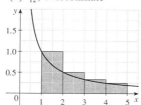

5. (a) 8, 6.875

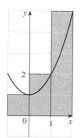

(b) 5, 5.375

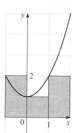

(c) 5.75, 5.9375

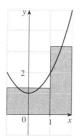

(d) M_6

7. 34.7 ft, 44.8 ft **9.** 63.2 L, 70 L **11.** 155 ft

13. $\lim\limits_{n\to\infty} \sum\limits_{i=1}^{n} \sqrt[4]{1 + 15i/n} \cdot (15/n)$

15. The region under the graph of $y = \tan x$ from 0 to $\pi/4$

17. (a) $\lim\limits_{n\to\infty} \dfrac{64}{n^6} \sum\limits_{i=1}^{n} i^5$ (b) $\dfrac{n^2(n+1)^2(2n^2+2n-1)}{12}$

(c) $\frac{32}{3}$

19. $\sin b$, 1

Exercises 5.2 □ page 272

1. 0.25

The Riemann sum represents the sum of the areas of the two rectangles above the x-axis minus the sum of the areas of the two rectangles below the x-axis.

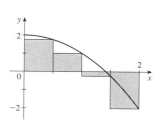

3. −0.856759

The Riemann sum represents the sum of the areas of the two rectangles above the x-axis minus the sum of the areas of the three rectangles below the x-axis.

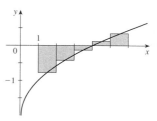

5. −0.028 **7.** (a) 4 (b) 6 (c) 10 **9.** −475, −85
11. 124.1644 **13.** 0.3084 **15.** $\int_0^\pi x \sin x\, dx$
17. $\int_1^8 \sqrt{2x + x^2}\, dx$ **19.** 42 **21.** $\frac{4}{3}$

23. 3.75 **25.** $\lim\limits_{n\to\infty} \sum\limits_{i=1}^{n} \dfrac{2 + 4i/n}{1 + (2 + 4i/n)^5} \cdot \dfrac{4}{n}$

27. $\lim\limits_{n\to\infty} \sum\limits_{i=1}^{n} \left(\sin \dfrac{5\pi i}{n} \right) \dfrac{\pi}{n} = \dfrac{2}{5}$

29. (a) 4 (b) 10 (c) −3 (d) 2

31. $-\frac{3}{4}$ **33.** $3 + \frac{9}{4}\pi$ **35.** 2.5 **37.** $-\frac{38}{3}$

39. $\int_{-1}^{5} f(x)\, dx$ **41.** 122 **43.** 3

47. $\frac{1}{2} \leq \int_1^2 dx/x \leq 1$ **49.** $\dfrac{\pi}{12} \leq \int_{\pi/4}^{\pi/3} \tan x\, dx \leq \dfrac{\pi}{12}\sqrt{3}$

51. $\int_0^1 x^4\, dx$

Exercises 5.3 □ page 282

1. $\frac{364}{3}$ **3.** 18 **5.** $\frac{5}{9}$ **7.** $-2 + 1/e$ **9.** 52
11. $-\frac{63}{4}$ **13.** $\frac{55}{63}$ **15.** 1 **17.** ln 3 **19.** π
21. $\frac{256}{5}$ **23.** $e^2 - 1$ **25.** $1 + \pi/4$ **27.** $\frac{1}{2}e^2 + e - \frac{1}{2}$
29. The function $f(x) = 1/x^2$ is not continuous on the interval $[-1, 3]$, so the Evaluation Theorem cannot be applied.
31. 2 **33.** 0, 1.32; 0.84
35. 3.75

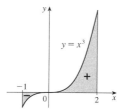

39. $\frac{2}{5}x^{5/2} + C$

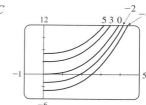

41. $2t - t^2 + \frac{1}{3}t^3 - \frac{1}{4}t^4 + C$ **43.** $\sec x + C$ **45.** $\frac{4}{3}$
47. Increase in the child's weight (in pounds) between the ages of 5 and 10
49. Number of gallons of oil leaked in the first 2 hours
51. Increase in revenue when production is increased from 1000 to 5000 units

53. Newton-meters   **55.** (a) $-\frac{3}{2}$ m   (b) $\frac{41}{6}$ m

57. (a) $v(t) = \frac{1}{2}t^2 + 4t + 5$ m/s   (b) $416\frac{2}{3}$ m

59. 1.4 mi   **61.** 1800 L   **63.** 3

Exercises 5.4 □ page 291

1. (a) 0, 2, 5, 7, 3
    (b) (0, 3)
    (c) $x = 3$

(d)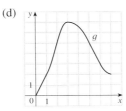

3. 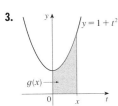 $g'(x) = 1 + x^2$

5. $g'(x) = \sqrt{1 + 2x}$ **7.** $g'(y) = y^2 \sin y$

9. $h'(x) = -\dfrac{\arctan(1/x)}{x^2}$ **11.** $y' = \dfrac{\cos \sqrt{x}}{2x}$

13. $g'(x) = \dfrac{-2(4x^2 - 1)}{4x^2 + 1} + \dfrac{3(9x^2 - 1)}{9x^2 + 1}$ **15.** $\frac{1}{3}$

17. $2/\pi$

19. (a) 1   (b) 2, 4   (c)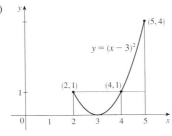

21. $38\frac{1}{3}$ **23.** $\sqrt{257}$

25. (a) Loc. max. at 1 and 5; loc. min. at 3 and 7

(b) 9

(c) $\left(\frac{1}{2}, 2\right)$, $(4, 6)$, $(8, 9)$

(d) See graph at right.

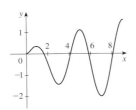

27. 29

29. (a) $-2\sqrt{n}$, $\sqrt{4n - 2}$, n an integer > 0
(b) $(0, 1)$, $\left(-\sqrt{4n - 1}, -\sqrt{4n - 3}\right)$, and $\left(\sqrt{4n - 1}, \sqrt{4n + 1}\right)$, n an integer > 0 (c) ≈ 0.74

31. $f(x) = x^{3/2}$, $a = 9$

33. (b) Average expenditure over $[0, t]$; minimize average expenditure

Exercises 5.5 □ page 298

1. $\frac{1}{3} \sin 3x + C$ **3.** $\frac{2}{9}(x^3 + 1)^{3/2} + C$

5. $-1/(1 + 2x)^2 + C$ **7.** $\frac{1}{5}(x^2 + 3)^5 + C$

9. $\frac{1}{63}(3x - 2)^{21} + C$ **11.** $\frac{1}{3}(\ln x)^3 + C$

13. $-\frac{1}{3} \ln|5 - 3x| + C$ **15.** $\frac{2}{3}\sqrt{3ax + bx^3} + C$

17. $-(1/\pi) \cos \pi t + C$ **19.** $\frac{2}{3}(1 + e^x)^{3/2} + C$

21. $\frac{1}{7} \sin^7\theta + C$ **23.** $-\frac{2}{3}(\cot x)^{3/2} + C$

25. $\ln|\sin^{-1}x| + C$ **27.** $\frac{1}{3} \sec^3 x + C$

29. $x - e^{-x} + C$ **31.** $-\ln(1 + \cos^2 x) + C$

33. $\tan^{-1}x + \frac{1}{2} \ln(1 + x^2) + C$

35. 0   **37.** $\frac{182}{9}$ **39.** 4   **41.** $2(e^2 - e)$ **43.** $\frac{16}{15}$

45. $\ln(e + 1)$ **47.** 0   **49.** 2   **51.** $\frac{1}{10}(1 - e^{-25})$

53. $2/(5\pi)$ **55.** 6π **57.** All three areas are equal.

59. $\dfrac{5}{4\pi}\left(1 - \cos\dfrac{2\pi t}{5}\right)$ L   **61.** 5

Chapter 5 Review □ page 300

True-False Quiz

1. True   **3.** True   **5.** False   **7.** True   **9.** True

11. False   **13.** True

Exercises

1. (a) 8   (b) 5.7

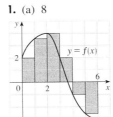   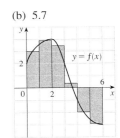

3. $\frac{1}{2} + \pi/4$ **5.** $f = c$, $f' = b$, $\int_0^x f(t)\, dt = a$

7. 37   **9.** $\frac{9}{10}$ **11.** -76 **13.** $\frac{21}{4}$ **15.** $\frac{1}{3} \sin 1$

17. $(1/\pi)(e^\pi - 1)$ **19.** $\ln 2 - \frac{7}{4}$ **21.** $\sqrt{x^2 + 4x} + C$

23. $(1/2\pi)(\sin \pi t)^2 + C$ **25.** $2e^{\sqrt{x}} + C$

27. $-\frac{1}{2}[\ln(\cos x)]^2 + C$ **29.** $\frac{1}{4} \ln(1 + x^4) + C$

31. $\ln|1 + \sec \theta| + C$ **33.** $\frac{64}{5}$

35. $F'(x) = \sqrt{1 + x^4}$ **37.** $y' = (2e^x - e^{\sqrt{x}})/(2x)$

39. $4 \leq \int_1^3 \sqrt{x^2 + 3}\, dx \leq 4\sqrt{3}$ **41.** 1.11

43. Number of barrels of oil consumed from Jan. 1, 2000, through Jan. 1, 2003

45. 72,400   **47.** $f(x)$ **49.** $c \approx 1.62$ **51.** $\dfrac{e^{2x}(1 + 2x)}{1 - e^{-x}}$

CHAPTER 6

Exercises 6.1 □ page 309

1. $\frac{1}{2}x^2 \ln x - \frac{1}{4}x^2 + C$ **3.** $\frac{1}{5}x \sin 5x + \frac{1}{25} \cos 5x + C$

5. $2(r - 2)e^{r/2} + C$

7. $-\dfrac{1}{\pi}x^2 \cos \pi x + \dfrac{2}{\pi^2}x \sin \pi x + \dfrac{2}{\pi^3} \cos \pi x + C$

9. $\frac{1}{2}(2x + 1)\ln(2x + 1) - x + C$

11. $t \arctan 4t - \frac{1}{8}\ln(1 + 16t^2) + C$

13. $\frac{1}{13}e^{2\theta}(2 \sin 3\theta - 3 \cos 3\theta) + C$

15. $\pi/3$ **17.** $\frac{1}{2} - \frac{1}{2}\ln 2$ **19.** $\frac{1}{4} - \frac{3}{4}e^{-2}$

21. $\frac{1}{12}(\pi - 12 + 6\sqrt{3})$ **23.** $2(\ln 2)^2 - 4 \ln 2 + 2$

25. $2(\sin\sqrt{x} - \sqrt{x}\cos\sqrt{x}) + C$ **27.** $-\frac{1}{2} - \pi/4$

29. (b) $-\frac{1}{4}\cos x \sin^3 x + \frac{3}{8}x - \frac{3}{16}\sin 2x + C$

31. (b) $\frac{2}{3}, \frac{8}{15}$

37. $x[(\ln x)^3 - 3(\ln x)^2 + 6 \ln x - 6] + C$

39. $\frac{9}{2}\ln 3 - \frac{13}{9}$ **41.** $2 - e^{-t}(t^2 + 2t + 2)$ m   **43.** 2

Exercises 6.2 □ page 319

1. $\frac{1}{5}\cos^5 x - \frac{1}{3}\cos^3 x + C$ **3.** $-\frac{11}{384}$

5. $\pi/4$ **7.** $3\pi/8$ **9.** $\frac{3}{2}\theta + 2 \sin\theta + \frac{1}{4}\sin 2\theta + C$

11. $\frac{1}{192}(3\pi - 4)$ **13.** $\frac{1}{2}\cos^2 x - \ln|\cos x| + C$

15. $\ln(1 + \sin x) + C$ **17.** $\frac{1}{2}\tan^2 x + C$

19. $\tan x - x + C$ **21.** $\frac{1}{5}\tan^5 t + \frac{2}{3}\tan^3 t + \tan t + C$

23. $\frac{117}{8}$ **25.** $\frac{1}{3}\sec^3 x - \sec x + C$

27. $\frac{1}{4}\sec^4 x - \tan^2 x + \ln|\sec x| + C$

29. $\sqrt{3} - (\pi/3)$

31. $\frac{1}{3}\csc^3\alpha - \frac{1}{5}\csc^5\alpha + C$ **33.** $\ln|\csc x - \cot x| + C$

35. (b) $\frac{1}{6}\sin 3x - \frac{1}{14}\sin 7x + C$

37. $\dfrac{\sqrt{x^2 - 9}}{9x} + C$ **39.** $\frac{1}{3}(x^2 - 18)\sqrt{x^2 + 9} + C$

41. $\pi/24 + \sqrt{3}/8 - \frac{1}{4}$

43. $-\dfrac{\sqrt{25 - x^2}}{25x} + C$ **45.** $\ln(\sqrt{x^2 + 16} + x) + C$

47. $\frac{1}{4}\sin^{-1}(2x) + \frac{1}{2}x\sqrt{1 - 4x^2} + C$

49. $\frac{1}{6}\sec^{-1}(x/3) - \sqrt{x^2 - 9}/(2x^2) + C$

51. $\dfrac{x}{\sqrt{a^2 - x^2}} - \sin^{-1}\left(\dfrac{x}{a}\right) + C$ **53.** $\sqrt{x^2 - 7} + C$

55. $\ln\left|\dfrac{\sqrt{1 + x^2} - 1}{x}\right| + \sqrt{1 + x^2} + C$

57. $\frac{1}{4}\sin^{-1}x^2 + \frac{1}{4}x^2\sqrt{1 - x^4} + C$

59. $\frac{1}{3}\ln|3x + 1 + \sqrt{9x^2 + 6x - 8}| + C$

61. $\dfrac{1}{2}\left[\tan^{-1}(x + 1) + \dfrac{x + 1}{x^2 + 2x + 2}\right] + C$

63. $s = (1 - \cos^3\omega t)/(3\omega)$ **65.** $\frac{1}{6}(\sqrt{48} - \sec^{-1}7)$

Exercises 6.3 □ page 327

1. (a) $\dfrac{A}{x + 3} + \dfrac{B}{3x + 1}$ (b) $\dfrac{A}{x} + \dfrac{B}{x + 1} + \dfrac{C}{(x + 1)^2}$

3. (a) $\dfrac{A}{x + 4} + \dfrac{B}{x - 1}$ (b) $\dfrac{A}{x - 1} + \dfrac{Bx + C}{x^2 + x + 1}$

5. (a) $1 + \dfrac{A}{x - 1} + \dfrac{B}{x + 1} + \dfrac{Cx + D}{x^2 + 1}$

(b) $\dfrac{At + B}{t^2 + 1} + \dfrac{Ct + D}{t^2 + 4} + \dfrac{Et + F}{(t^2 + 4)^2}$

7. $x + 6 \ln|x - 6| + C$ **9.** $2 \ln|x + 5| - \ln|x - 2| + C$

11. $\frac{1}{2}\ln\frac{3}{2}$ **13.** $a \ln|x - b| + C$ **15.** $2 \ln 2 + \frac{1}{2}$

17. $\frac{27}{5}\ln 2 - \frac{9}{5}\ln 3$ (or $\frac{9}{5}\ln\frac{8}{3}$)

19. $-\frac{1}{36}\ln|x + 5| + \dfrac{1}{6(x + 5)} + \frac{1}{36}\ln|x - 1| + C$

21. $2 \ln|x| + 3 \ln|x + 2| + (1/x) + C$

23. $\ln|x - 1| - \frac{1}{2}\ln(x^2 + 9) - \frac{1}{3}\tan^{-1}(x/3) + C$

25. $\frac{1}{2}\ln(x^2 + 1) + (1/\sqrt{2})\tan^{-1}(x/\sqrt{2}) + C$

27. $\frac{1}{2}\ln(x^2 + 2x + 5) + \frac{3}{2}\tan^{-1}\left(\dfrac{x + 1}{2}\right) + C$

29. $\frac{1}{3}\ln|x - 1| - \frac{1}{6}\ln(x^2 + x + 1) - \dfrac{1}{\sqrt{3}}\tan^{-1}\dfrac{2x + 1}{\sqrt{3}} + C$

31. $\dfrac{1}{x} + \frac{1}{2}\ln\left|\dfrac{x - 1}{x + 1}\right| + C$

33. $\dfrac{-1}{2(x^2 + 2x + 4)} - \dfrac{2\sqrt{3}}{9}\tan^{-1}\left(\dfrac{x + 1}{\sqrt{3}}\right) - \dfrac{2(x + 1)}{3(x^2 + 2x + 4)} + C$

35. $2 + \ln\frac{25}{9}$ **37.** $\frac{3}{10}(x^2 + 1)^{5/3} - \frac{3}{4}(x^2 + 1)^{2/3} + C$

39. $\ln\left[\dfrac{(e^x + 2)^2}{e^x + 1}\right] + C$

41. $\left(x - \frac{1}{2}\right)\ln(x^2 - x + 2) - 2x + \sqrt{7}\tan^{-1}\left(\dfrac{2x - 1}{\sqrt{7}}\right) + C$

43. $t = -\ln P - \frac{1}{9}\ln(0.9P + 900) + C$, where $C \approx 10.23$

Exercises 6.4 □ page 333

1. $\pi/4$

3. $\dfrac{1}{2\pi}\sec(\pi x)\tan(\pi x) + \dfrac{1}{2\pi}\ln|\sec(\pi x) + \tan(\pi x)| + C$

5. $-\dfrac{\sqrt{4x^2 + 9}}{9x} + C$ **7.** $\pi^3 - 6\pi$

9. $-\frac{1}{2}\tan^2(1/z) - \ln|\cos(1/z)| + C$

11. $\dfrac{2y - 1}{8}\sqrt{6 + 4y - 4y^2} + \frac{7}{8}\sin^{-1}\left(\dfrac{2y - 1}{\sqrt{7}}\right)$
$- \frac{1}{12}(6 + 4y - 4y^2)^{3/2} + C$

13. $\frac{1}{9}\sin^3 x[3 \ln(\sin x) - 1] + C$

15. $\dfrac{1}{2\sqrt{3}}\ln\left|\dfrac{e^x + \sqrt{3}}{e^x - \sqrt{3}}\right| + C$

17. $\frac{1}{5}\ln|x^5 + \sqrt{x^{10} - 2}| + C$

19. $\frac{1}{2}(\ln x)\sqrt{4 + (\ln x)^2} + 2 \ln[\ln x + \sqrt{4 + (\ln x)^2}] + C$

21. $\sqrt{e^{2x} - 1} - \cos^{-1}(e^{-x}) + C$

25. $-\frac{1}{4}x(5 - x^2)^{3/2} + \frac{5}{8}x\sqrt{5 - x^2} + \frac{25}{8}\sin^{-1}(x/\sqrt{5}) + C$

27. $-\frac{1}{5}\sin^2 x \cos^3 x - \frac{2}{15}\cos^3 x + C$

29. $\frac{1}{10}(1 + 2x)^{5/2} - \frac{1}{6}(1 + 2x)^{3/2} + C$

31. $-\ln|\cos x| - \frac{1}{2}\tan^2 x + \frac{1}{4}\tan^4 x + C$

33. $\dfrac{2^{x-1}\sqrt{2^{2x} - 1}}{\ln 2} - \dfrac{\ln(\sqrt{2^{2x} - 1} + 2^x)}{2 \ln 2} + C$

Exercises 6.5 □ page 343

1. (a) $L_2 = 6, R_2 = 12, M_2 \approx 9.6$
(b) L_2 is an underestimate, R_2 and M_2 are overestimates.
(c) $T_2 = 9 < I$ (d) $L_n < T_n < I < M_n < R_n$
3. (a) $T_4 \approx 0.895759$ (underestimate)
(b) $M_4 \approx 0.908907$ (overestimate)
$T_4 < I < M_4$
5. (a) $5.932957, E_M \approx -0.063353$
(b) $5.869247, E_S \approx 0.000357$
7. (a) 2.413790 (b) 2.411453 (c) 2.412232
9. (a) 0.146879 (b) 0.147391 (c) 0.147219
11. (a) 4.513618 (b) 4.748256 (c) 4.675111
13. (a) -0.495333 (b) -0.543321 (c) -0.526123
15. (a) 1.064275 (b) 1.067416 (c) 1.074915
17. (a) $T_{10} \approx 0.881839, M_{10} \approx 0.882202$
(b) $|E_T| \leq 0.01\overline{3}, |E_M| \leq 0.00\overline{6}$
(c) $n = 366$ for T_n, $n = 259$ for M_n
19. (a) $T_{10} \approx 1.719713, E_T \approx -0.001432$;
$S_{10} \approx 1.718283, E_S \approx -0.000001$
(b) $|E_T| \leq 0.002266, |E_S| \leq 0.0000016$
(c) $n = 151$ for T_n, $n = 107$ for M_n, $n = 8$ for S_n
21. (a) 2.8 (b) 7.954926518 (c) 0.2894
(d) 7.954926521 (e) The actual error is much smaller.
(f) 10.9 (g) 7.953789422 (h) 0.0593
(i) The actual error is smaller. (j) $n \geq 50$

23.

n	L_n	R_n	T_n	M_n
4	0.140625	0.390625	0.265625	0.242188
8	0.191406	0.316406	0.253906	0.248047
16	0.219727	0.282227	0.250977	0.249512

n	E_L	E_R	E_T	E_M
4	0.109375	−0.140625	−0.015625	0.007813
8	0.058594	−0.066406	−0.003906	0.001953
16	0.030273	−0.032227	−0.000977	0.000488

The observations are the same as after Example 1.
25. (a) 11.5 (b) 12 (c) $11.\overline{6}$
27. $37.7\overline{3}$ ft/s   **29.** $10,177$ megawatt-hours
31. (a) 23.44 (b) $0.341\overline{3}$ **33.** 59.4
35.

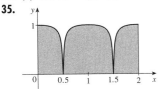

Exercises 6.6 □ page 352

Abbreviations: C, convergent; D, divergent

1. (a) Infinite interval (b) Infinite discontinuity
(c) Infinite discontinuity (d) Infinite interval

3. $\frac{1}{2} - 1/(2t^2)$; $0.495, 0.49995, 0.4999995$; 0.5
5. $\frac{1}{12}$ **7.** D **9.** $2e^{-2}$ **11.** D **13.** 0 **15.** $\frac{1}{25}$
17. D **19.** 1 **21.** $\pi/9$ **23.** D **25.** $\frac{32}{3}$
27. $\frac{75}{4}$ **29.** D **31.** $\frac{8}{3} \ln 2 - \frac{8}{9}$
33. e **35.** $2\pi/3$

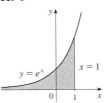

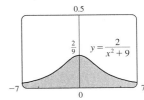

37. Infinite area

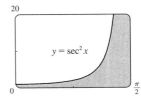

39. (a)

t	$\int_1^t [(\sin^2 x)/x^2]\, dx$
2	0.447453
5	0.577101
10	0.621306
100	0.668479
1,000	0.672957
10,000	0.673407

It appears that the integral is convergent.

(c)

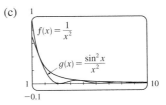

41. C **43.** C **45.** D **47.** π **49.** $p < 1, 1/(1-p)$
53. (a)

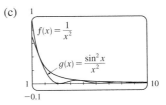

(b) The rate at which the fraction $F(t)$ increases as t increases
(c) 1; all bulbs burn out eventually
55. 8264.5 years   **57.** 1000 **61.** $C = 1$; $\ln 2$

Chapter 6 Review □ page 354

True-False Quiz

1. False   **3.** False   **5.** False   **7.** False
9. (a) True   (b) False   **11.** False   **13.** False

Exercises

1. $5 + 10 \ln \frac{2}{3}$ **3.** $\ln 2$
5. $\frac{1}{9}\sec^9 x - \frac{3}{7}\sec^7 x + \frac{3}{5}\sec^5 x - \frac{1}{3}\sec^3 x + C$
7. $-\cos(\ln t) + C$ **9.** $\frac{64}{5}\ln 4 - \frac{124}{25}$ **11.** $\sqrt{3} - (\pi/3)$
13. $\ln|x| - \frac{1}{2}\ln(x^2 + 1) + C$
15. $\frac{1}{3}\sin^3\theta - \frac{2}{5}\sin^5\theta + \frac{1}{7}\sin^7\theta + C$
17. $x \sec x - \ln|\sec x + \tan x| + C$
19. $\frac{1}{18}\ln(9x^2 + 6x + 5) + \frac{1}{9}\tan^{-1}\left(\frac{1}{2}(3x + 1)\right) + C$
21. $\ln\left|x - 2 + \sqrt{x^2 - 4x}\right| + C$
23. $-\frac{1}{12}(\cot^3 4x + 3\cot 4x) + C$
25. $\frac{3}{2}\ln(x^2 + 1) - 3\tan^{-1}x + \sqrt{2}\tan^{-1}(x/\sqrt{2}) + C$
27. $\frac{2}{5}$ **29.** 0   **31.** $6 - 3\pi/2$
33. $\dfrac{x}{\sqrt{4 - x^2}} - \sin^{-1}\left(\dfrac{x}{2}\right) + C$
35. $4\sqrt{1 + \sqrt{x}} + C$ **37.** $\frac{1}{2}\sin 2x - \frac{1}{8}\cos 4x + C$
39. $\frac{1}{8}e - \frac{1}{4}$ **41.** $\frac{1}{36}$ **43.** D
45. $4\ln 4 - 8$ **47.** D   **49.** $\pi/4$
51. $\frac{1}{2}\left[e^x\sqrt{1 - e^{2x}} + \sin^{-1}(e^x)\right] + C$
53. $\frac{1}{4}(2x + 1)\sqrt{x^2 + x + 1} + \frac{3}{8}\ln\left(x + \frac{1}{2} + \sqrt{x^2 + x + 1}\right) + C$
55. No
57. (a) 1.090608 (overestimate)
(b) 1.088840 (underestimate)   (c) 1.089429 (unknown)
59. (a) $0.00\overline{6}$, $n \geq 259$ (b) $0.00\overline{3}$, $n \geq 183$
61. 8.6 mi
63. (a) 3.8   (b) 1.7867, 0.000646   (c) $n \geq 30$

CHAPTER 7

Exercises 7.1 □ page 361

1. $\frac{32}{3}$ **3.** $e - (1/e) + \frac{10}{3}$ **5.** 19.5   **7.** $\frac{1}{6}$ **9.** 72
11. $\frac{9}{8}$ **13.** $\frac{32}{3}$ **15.** $\ln 2$ **17.** 0, 0.90; 0.04
19. 0, 0.70; 0.08
21. $\frac{1}{2}$

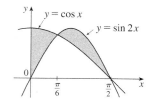

23. 118 ft   **25.** 84 m²
27. 8868; increase in population over a 10-year period
29. $r\sqrt{R^2 - r^2} + \pi r^2/2 - R^2 \arcsin(r/R)$ **31.** ± 6
33. $4^{2/3}$ **35.** $f(t) = 3t^2$ **37.** $0 < m < 1$; $m - \ln m - 1$

Exercises 7.2 □ page 370

1. $\pi/2$

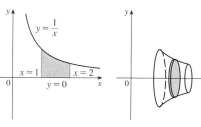

3. 162π

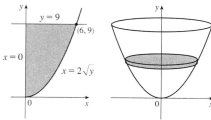

5. $4\pi/21$

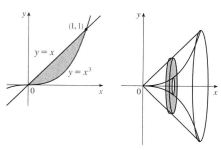

7. $64\pi/15$

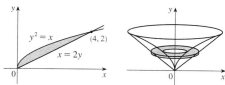

9. $\pi/6$

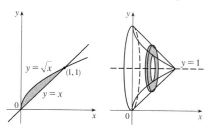

11. $29\pi/30$

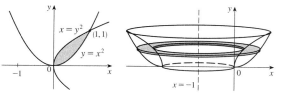

13. $13\pi/30$ **15.** $\pi \int_0^{\pi/4} (1 - \tan^3 x)^2\, dx$
17. 0, 0.747; 0.132   **19.** $\frac{11}{8}\pi^2$

21. (a) Solid obtained by rotating the region $0 \leqslant y \leqslant \cos x$, $0 \leqslant x \leqslant \pi/2$ about the x-axis (b) Solid obtained by rotating the region $y^4 \leqslant x \leqslant y^2$, $0 \leqslant y \leqslant 1$ about the y-axis
23. 1110 cm³ **25.** $\frac{1}{3}\pi r^2 h$ **27.** $\pi h^2\left(r - \frac{1}{3}h\right)$
29. $\frac{2}{3}b^2 h$ **31.** 10 cm³ **33.** 24 **35.** 2 **37.** 3
41. (a) $8\pi R \int_0^r \sqrt{r^2 - y^2}\, dy$ (b) $2\pi^2 r^2 R$ **43.** (b) $\pi r^2 h$
45. $\frac{5}{12}\pi r^3$ **47.** $8\int_0^r \sqrt{R^2 - y^2}\sqrt{r^2 - y^2}\, dy$

Exercises 7.3 ◽ page 376

1. Circumference $= 2\pi x$, height $= x(x-1)^2$; $\pi/15$

3. 2π **5.** $\pi(1 - 1/e)$ **7.** 16π **9.** $21\pi/2$
11. $768\pi/7$ **13.** $250\pi/3$ **15.** $17\pi/6$ **17.** $67\pi/6$
19. 24π **21.** $\int_1^2 2\pi x \ln x\, dx$
23. $\int_0^1 2\pi(x+1)[\sin(\pi x/2) - x^4]\, dx$
25. $\int_0^\pi 2\pi(4-y)\sqrt{\sin y}\, dy$ **27.** 1.142
29. Solid obtained by rotating the region $0 \leqslant y \leqslant x^4$, $0 \leqslant x \leqslant 3$ about the y-axis
31. Solid obtained by rotating the region bounded by (i) $x = 1 - y^2$, $x = 0$, and $y = 0$, or (ii) $x = y^2$, $x = 1$, and $y = 0$ about the line $y = 3$
33. $81\pi/10$ **35.** $8\pi(3 - \ln 4)$ **37.** $4\pi/3$
39. $\frac{4}{3}\pi r^3$ **41.** $\frac{1}{3}\pi r^2 h$

Exercises 7.4 ◽ page 383

1. $3\sqrt{10}$ **3.** $\frac{2}{243}(82\sqrt{82} - 1)$ **5.** $\frac{1261}{240}$ **7.** $\frac{32}{3}$
9. $\ln(\sqrt{2} + 1)$ **11.** $\sinh 1$
13. $\sqrt{1 + e^2} - \sqrt{2} + \ln(\sqrt{1 + e^2} - 1) - 1 - \ln(\sqrt{2} - 1)$
15. $\int_0^{2\pi} \sqrt{1 + \sin^2 x}\, dx$ **17.** $\int_1^4 \sqrt{9y^4 + 6y^2 + 2}\, dy$
19. 5.115840 **21.** 1.569619 **23.** $\ln 3 - \frac{1}{2}$
25. 6

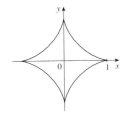

27. $s(x) = \frac{2}{27}\left[(1 + 9x)^{3/2} - 10\sqrt{10}\right]$ **29.** 209.1 m
31. 29.36 in.

Exercises 7.5 ◽ page 394
1. 9 ft-lb **3.** 180 J **5.** $\frac{15}{4}$ ft-lb
7. (a) $\frac{25}{24} \approx 1.04$ J (b) 10.8 cm
9. (a) 625 ft-lb (b) $\frac{1875}{4}$ ft-lb

11. 650,000 ft-lb **13.** 3857 J **15.** 2450 J
17. (a) $\approx 1.06 \times 10^6$ J (b) 2.0 m
21. (a) $Gm_1 m_2\left(\dfrac{1}{a} - \dfrac{1}{b}\right)$ (b) $\approx 8.50 \times 10^9$ J
23. 6.5×10^6 N **25.** 3.5×10^4 lb **27.** 5.27×10^5 N
29. (a) $\approx 5.63 \times 10^3$ lb (b) $\approx 5.06 \times 10^4$ lb
(c) $\approx 4.88 \times 10^4$ lb (d) $\approx 3.03 \times 10^5$ lb
31. 2.5×10^5 N **33.** 10; 1; $\left(\frac{1}{21}, \frac{10}{21}\right)$ **35.** (0, 1.6)
37. $\left(1/(e-1), \frac{1}{4}(e+1)\right)$ **39.** $\left(\frac{2}{5}, \frac{1}{2}\right)$
41. $\left(\dfrac{\pi\sqrt{2} - 4}{4(\sqrt{2} - 1)}, \dfrac{1}{4(\sqrt{2} - 1)}\right)$
43. $\frac{4}{3}$, 0, $\left(0, \frac{2}{3}\right)$ **47.** $\left(0, \frac{1}{12}\right)$ **49.** $\frac{1}{3}\pi r^2 h$

Exercises 7.6 ◽ page 404
1. $y = Kx$ **3.** $y = K\sqrt{x^2 + 1}$
5. $y + \ln|\sec y| = \frac{1}{3}x^3 + x + C$ **7.** $u = Ae^{2t + t^2/2} - 1$
9. $u = -\sqrt{t^2 + \tan t + 25}$
11. $\cos x + x \sin x = y^2 + \frac{1}{3}e^{3y} + \frac{2}{3}$
13. $y = \dfrac{4a}{\sqrt{3}} \sin x - a$ **15.** $y = 7e^{x^4}$
17. (a) $\sin^{-1}y = x^2 + C$
(b) $y = \sin(x^2)$, $-\sqrt{\pi/2} \leqslant x \leqslant \sqrt{\pi/2}$

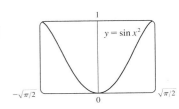

(c) No
19. $\cos y = \cos x - 1$

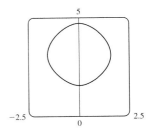

21. III **23.** IV

25.

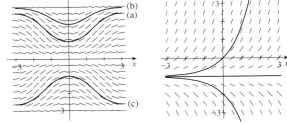

27.

29.

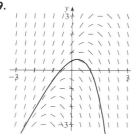

31.

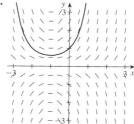

33. (b) $P(t) = M - Me^{-kt}$; M

35. (a) $C(t) = (C_0 - r/k)e^{-kt} + r/k$
(b) r/k; the concentration approaches r/k regardless of the value of C_0

37. $P(40) \approx 732$, $P(80) \approx 985$; $t \approx 55$

39. (a) $dy/dt = ky(1 - y)$

(b) $y = \dfrac{y_0}{y_0 + (1 - y_0)e^{-kt}}$ (c) 3:36 PM

43. (a) $15e^{-t/100}$ kg   (b) $15e^{-0.2} \approx 12.3$ kg

45. About 4.9%   **47.** g/k

49. (a) $dA/dt = k\sqrt{A}\,(M - A)$

(b) $A(t) = M\left(\dfrac{Ce^{\sqrt{M}kt} - 1}{Ce^{\sqrt{M}kt} + 1}\right)^2$, where $C = \dfrac{\sqrt{M} + \sqrt{A_0}}{\sqrt{M} - \sqrt{A_0}}$

and $A_0 = A(0)$

Chapter 7 Review ▫ **page 408**

Exercises

1. $\frac{125}{6}$ **3.** $e - \frac{11}{6}$ **5.** $64\pi/15$

7. $1656\pi/5$ **9.** $\frac{4}{3}\pi(2ah + h^2)^{3/2}$

11. $\int_0^1 \pi[(1 - x^3)^2 - (1 - x^2)^2]\,dx$

13. (a) $2\pi/15$ (b) $\pi/6$ (c) $8\pi/15$

15. (a) 0.38   (b) 0.87

17. Solid obtained by rotating the region $0 \leqslant y \leqslant \cos x$, $0 \leqslant x \leqslant \pi/2$ about the y-axis

19. Solid obtained by rotating the region in the first quadrant bounded by $x = 4 - y^2$ and the axes about the x-axis

21. 36   **23.** $\frac{125}{3}\sqrt{3}$ m^3 **25.** $\frac{15}{2}$

27. 3.292287   **29.** 3.2 J

31. (a) $8000\pi/3 \approx 8378$ ft-lb   (b) 2.1 ft

33. ≈ 458 lb   **35.** $\left(-\frac{1}{2}, \frac{12}{5}\right)$ **37.** $2\pi^2$

39. $y^3 + y^2 = \cos x + x \sin x + C$

41. $r(t) = 5e^{t - t^2}$

43. (a)

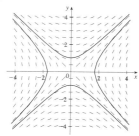

(b) The pair of lines $y = \pm x$, for $C = 0$; the hyperbola $x^2 - y^2 = -C$ for $C \neq 0$.

CHAPTER 8

Exercises 8.1 ▫ **page 418**

Abbreviations: C, convergent; D, divergent

1. (a) A sequence is an ordered list of numbers. It can also be defined as a function whose domain is the set of positive integers.
(b) The terms a_n approach 8 as n becomes large.
(c) The terms a_n become large as n becomes large.

3. $\frac{1}{3}, \frac{2}{5}, \frac{3}{7}, \frac{4}{9}, \frac{5}{11}, \frac{6}{13}$; yes; $\frac{1}{2}$ **5.** $a_n = \left(-\frac{2}{3}\right)^{n-1}$

7. $a_n = 5n - 3$ **9.** 5   **11.** 0

13. D   **15.** 0   **17.** 0   **19.** 0   **21.** 0

23. e^2 **25.** D   **27.** ln 2

29. (a) 1060, 1123.60, 1191.02, 1262.48, 1338.23   (b) D

31. Convergent by the Monotonic Sequence Theorem; $5 \leqslant L < 8$

33. Decreasing; yes   **35.** Not monotonic; yes   **37.** 2

39. $(3 + \sqrt{5})/2$ **41.** (b) $(1 + \sqrt{5})/2$ **43.** 62

Exercises 8.2 ▫ **page 427**

1. (a) A sequence is an ordered list of numbers whereas a series is the *sum* of a list of numbers.
(b) A series is convergent if the sequence of partial sums is a convergent sequence. A series is divergent if it is not convergent.

3. 3   **5.** 15   **7.** D   **9.** D   **11.** D   **13.** $\frac{5}{2}$

15. D   **17.** D   **19.** $\frac{3}{2}$ **21.** $\frac{11}{6}$ **23.** $\frac{2}{9}$ **25.** $\frac{1138}{333}$

27. $-3 < x < 3$; $x/(3 - x)$

29. All x; $\dfrac{2}{2 - \cos x}$

31. $a_1 = 0$, $a_n = 2/[n(n + 1)]$ for $n > 1$, sum $= 1$

33. (a) $S_n = D(1 - c^n)/(1 - c)$ (b) 5

35. $(\sqrt{3} - 1)/2$ **37.** $1/[n(n + 1)]$

39. The series is divergent.

45. $\{s_n\}$ is bounded and increasing.

47. (a) $0, \frac{1}{9}, \frac{2}{9}, \frac{1}{3}, \frac{2}{3}, \frac{7}{9}, \frac{8}{9}, 1$

49. (a) $\frac{1}{2}, \frac{5}{6}, \frac{23}{24}, \frac{119}{120}$; $[(n + 1)! - 1]/(n + 1)!$ (c) 1

Exercises 8.3 ▫ **page 436**

1. C

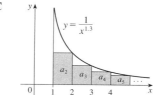

3. (a) Nothing   (b) C

5. p-series; geometric series; $b < -1$; $-1 < b < 1$

7. C   **9.** C   **11.** C   **13.** C   **15.** D   **17.** C

19. C   **21.** D   **23.** C   **25.** D   **27.** $p > 1$

31. (a) 1.54977, error $\leqslant 0.1$ (b) 1.64522, error $\leqslant 0.005$
(c) $n > 1000$

37. Yes

Exercises 8.4 □ page 446

Abbreviations: AC, absolutely convergent;
CC, conditionally convergent
1. (a) A series whose terms are alternately positive and negative
(b) $0 < b_{n+1} \le b_n$ and $\lim_{n\to\infty} b_n = 0$, where $b_n = |a_n|$
(c) $|R_n| \le b_{n+1}$
3. C **5.** C **7.** D **9.** 7 **11.** 5 **13.** 0.9721
15. 0.0676 **17.** An underestimate **19.** D
21. AC **23.** CC **25.** AC **27.** AC **29.** AC
31. D **33.** AC **35.** AC **37.** D
39. (a) and (d)

Exercises 8.5 □ page 451

1. A series of the form $\sum_{n=0}^{\infty} c_n(x-a)^n$, where x is a variable and a and the c_n's are constants
3. $1, [-1, 1)$ **5.** $1, [-1, 1]$ **7.** $\infty, (-\infty, \infty)$
9. $\frac{1}{2}, \left(-\frac{1}{2}, \frac{1}{2}\right]$ **11.** $4, (-4, 4]$ **13.** $2, (-4, 0]$
15. $b, (a-b, a+b)$ **17.** $0, \left\{\frac{1}{2}\right\}$
19. (a) Yes (b) No **21.** k^k
23. (a) $(-\infty, \infty)$
(b), (c)

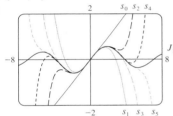

25. $(-1, 1), f(x) = (1+2x)/(1-x^2)$ **29.** 2

Exercises 8.6 □ page 456

1. 10 **3.** $\sum_{n=0}^{\infty} (-1)^n x^n, (-1, 1)$ **5.** $\sum_{n=0}^{\infty} x^{3n}, (-1, 1)$
7. $-\sum_{n=0}^{\infty} \frac{1}{5^{n+1}} x^n, (-5, 5)$ **9.** $\sum_{n=0}^{\infty} (-1)^n \frac{1}{9^{n+1}} x^{2n+1}, (-3, 3)$
11. $\sum_{n=0}^{\infty} \left[\frac{(-1)^{n+1}}{2^{n+1}} - 1\right] x^n, (-1, 1)$
13. (a) $\sum_{n=0}^{\infty} (-1)^n(n+1)x^n, R = 1$
(b) $\frac{1}{2} \sum_{n=0}^{\infty} (-1)^n(n+2)(n+1)x^n, R = 1$
(c) $\frac{1}{2} \sum_{n=2}^{\infty} (-1)^n n(n-1)x^n, R = 1$
15. $\ln 5 - \sum_{n=1}^{\infty} \frac{x^n}{n5^n}, R = 5$
17. $\sum_{n=3}^{\infty} \frac{n-2}{2^{n-1}} x^n, R = 2$
$\ln 3 + \sum_{n=1}^{\infty} \frac{(-1)^{n-1}}{n3^n} x^n, R = 3$

19.

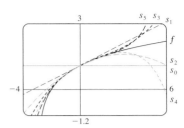

21. $\sum_{n=0}^{\infty} \frac{2x^{2n+1}}{2n+1}, R = 1$

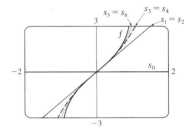

23. $C + \sum_{n=0}^{\infty} \frac{t^{8n+2}}{8n+2}, R = 1$
25. $C + \sum_{n=1}^{\infty} (-1)^{n+1} \frac{x^{2n-1}}{4n^2-1}, R = 1$
27. 0.199989 **29.** 0.000983 **31.** 0.09531
33. (b) 0.920 **37.** $[-1, 1], [-1, 1), (-1, 1)$

Exercises 8.7 □ page 469

1. $b_8 = f^{(8)}(5)/8!$ **3.** $\sum_{n=0}^{\infty} (n+1)x^n, R = 1$
5. $\sum_{n=0}^{\infty} (-1)^n \frac{x^{2n}}{(2n)!}, R = \infty$ **7.** $\sum_{n=0}^{\infty} \frac{5^n}{n!} x^n, R = \infty$
9. $\sum_{n=0}^{\infty} \frac{x^{2n+1}}{(2n+1)!}, R = \infty$
11. $7 + 5(x-2) + (x-2)^2, R = \infty$
13. $\sum_{n=0}^{\infty} \frac{e^3}{n!} (x-3)^n, R = \infty$
15. $\sum_{n=0}^{\infty} (-1)^{n+1} \frac{1}{(2n)!} (x-\pi)^{2n}, R = \infty$
17. $\sum_{n=0}^{\infty} (-1)^n \frac{1 \cdot 3 \cdot 5 \cdot \cdots \cdot (2n-1)}{2^n \cdot 3^{2n+1} \cdot n!} (x-9)^n, R = 9$
23. $1 + \frac{x}{2} + \sum_{n=2}^{\infty} (-1)^{n-1} \frac{1 \cdot 3 \cdot 5 \cdot \cdots \cdot (2n-3)}{2^n n!} x^n, R = 1$
25. $\sum_{n=0}^{\infty} (-1)^n \frac{(n+1)(n+2)}{2^{n+4}} x^n, R = 2$
27. $\sum_{n=0}^{\infty} (-1)^n \frac{\pi^{2n}}{(2n)!} x^{2n}, R = \infty$
29. $\sum_{n=0}^{\infty} (-1)^n \frac{1}{2n+1} x^{2n+2}, R = 1$
31. $\sum_{n=0}^{\infty} (-1)^n \frac{1}{n!} x^{n+2}, R = \infty$

33. $\frac{1}{2}x + \sum\limits_{n=1}^{\infty} (-1)^n \dfrac{1 \cdot 3 \cdot 5 \cdot \,\cdots\, \cdot (2n - 1)}{n!\,2^{3n+1}} x^{2n+1}$, $R = 2$

35. $\sum\limits_{n=1}^{\infty} \dfrac{(-1)^{n+1}2^{2n-1}x^{2n}}{(2n)!}$, $R = \infty$

37. $\sum\limits_{n=0}^{\infty} (-1)^n \dfrac{1}{(2n)!} x^{4n}$, $R = \infty$

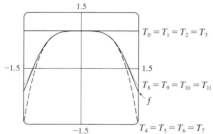

39. 0.81873

41. (a) $1 + \sum\limits_{n=1}^{\infty} \dfrac{1 \cdot 3 \cdot 5 \cdot \,\cdots\, \cdot (2n - 1)}{2^n n!} x^{2n}$

(b) $x + \sum\limits_{n=1}^{\infty} \dfrac{1 \cdot 3 \cdot 5 \cdot \,\cdots\, \cdot (2n - 1)}{2^n n!} \dfrac{x^{2n+1}}{2n + 1}$

43. $C + \sum\limits_{n=0}^{\infty} (-1)^n \dfrac{x^{6n+2}}{(6n + 2)(2n)!}$

45. $C + x + \dfrac{x^4}{8} + \sum\limits_{n=2}^{\infty} (-1)^{n-1} \dfrac{1 \cdot 3 \cdot 5 \cdot \,\cdots\, \cdot (2n - 3)}{2^n n!(3n + 1)} x^{3n+1}$

47. 0.440　　**49.** 0.09998750　　**51.** $\frac{1}{3}$　　**53.** $\frac{1}{120}$

55. $1 - \frac{3}{2}x^2 + \frac{25}{24}x^4$　　**57.** $1 + \frac{1}{6}x^2 + \frac{7}{360}x^4$

59. e^{-x^4}　　**61.** $1/\sqrt{2}$　　**63.** $e^3 - 1$

65. (a) $\sum\limits_{n=1}^{\infty} nx^n$　(b) 2

67. (a) $1 + \dfrac{x^2}{2} + \sum\limits_{n=2}^{\infty} (-1)^{n-1} \dfrac{1 \cdot 3 \cdot 5 \cdot \,\cdots\, \cdot (2n - 3)}{2^n n!} x^{2n}$

(b) 99,225

Exercises 8.8 □ page 476

1. (a) $T_0(x) = 1 = T_1(x)$, $T_2(x) = 1 - \frac{1}{2}x^2 = T_3(x)$,
$T_4(x) = 1 - \frac{1}{2}x^2 + \frac{1}{24}x^4 = T_5(x)$,
$T_6(x) = 1 - \frac{1}{2}x^2 + \frac{1}{24}x^4 - \frac{1}{720}x^6$

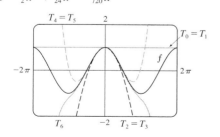

(b)

x	f	$T_0 = T_1$	$T_2 = T_3$	$T_4 = T_5$	T_6
$\dfrac{\pi}{4}$	0.7071	1	0.6916	0.7074	0.7071
$\dfrac{\pi}{2}$	0	1	−0.2337	0.0200	−0.0009
π	−1	1	−3.9348	0.1239	−1.2114

(c) As n increases, $T_n(x)$ is a good approximation to $f(x)$ on a larger and larger interval.

3. $\dfrac{1}{2} + \dfrac{\sqrt{3}}{2}\left(x - \dfrac{\pi}{6}\right) - \dfrac{1}{4}\left(x - \dfrac{\pi}{6}\right)^2 - \dfrac{\sqrt{3}}{12}\left(x - \dfrac{\pi}{6}\right)^3$

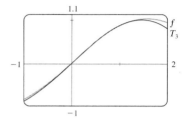

5. $x + \frac{1}{6}x^3$

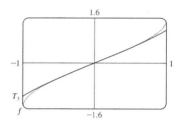

7. $x - 2x^2 + 2x^3$

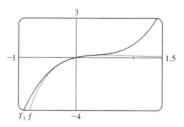

9. (a) $1 + \frac{1}{2}x$　(b) 0.00125

11. (a) $x + \frac{1}{3}x^3$　(b) 0.06

13. (a) $1 + x^2$　(b) 0.00006

15. (a) $8 + \frac{3}{8}(x - 16) - \frac{3}{1024}(x - 16)^2 + \frac{5}{65,536}(x - 16)^3$
(b) 0.0000034

17. 0.57358　　**19.** Four

21. $-1.037 < x < 1.037$　　**23.** 21 m, no

27. (c) They differ by about 8×10^{-9} km.

Chapter 8 Review □ page 479

True-False Quiz

1. False **3.** True **5.** False **7.** False **9.** False
11. True **13.** True **15.** False **17.** True

Exercises

1. $\frac{1}{2}$ **3.** D **5.** 0 **7.** e^{12} **9.** C **11.** C
13. D **15.** C **17.** C **19.** C **21.** CC **23.** AC
25. 8 **27.** $\pi/4$ **29.** e^{-e} **33.** 0.9721
37. $4, [-6, 2)$ **39.** 0.5, [2.5, 3.5)

41. $\frac{1}{2}\sum_{n=0}^{\infty}(-1)^n\left[\frac{1}{(2n)!}\left(x-\frac{\pi}{6}\right)^{2n}+\frac{\sqrt{3}}{(2n+1)!}\left(x-\frac{\pi}{6}\right)^{2n+1}\right]$

43. $\sum_{n=0}^{\infty}(-1)^n x^{n+2}, R=1$ **45.** $-\sum_{n=1}^{\infty}\frac{x^n}{n}, R=1$

47. $\sum_{n=0}^{\infty}(-1)^n\frac{x^{8n+4}}{(2n+1)!}, R=\infty$

49. $\frac{1}{2}+\sum_{n=1}^{\infty}\frac{1\cdot 5\cdot 9\cdot\,\cdots\,\cdot(4n-3)}{n!\,2^{6n+1}}x^n, R=16$

51. $C+\ln|x|+\sum_{n=1}^{\infty}\frac{x^n}{n\cdot n!}$

53. (a) $1+\frac{1}{2}(x-1)-\frac{1}{8}(x-1)^2+\frac{1}{16}(x-1)^3$
(b) (c) 0.000006

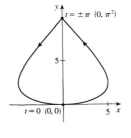

55. $-\frac{1}{6}$

CHAPTER 9

Exercises 9.1 □ page 486

1.
3.

5. (a) (b) $y=\frac{2}{3}x+\frac{13}{3}$

7. (a) (b) $y=1-x^2, x\geqslant 0$

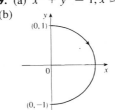

9. (a) $x^2+y^2=1, x\geqslant 0$ **11.** (a) $y=1/x, y>1$
(b) (b)

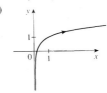
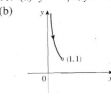

13. (a) $y=\frac{1}{2}\ln x+1$
(b)

15. Moves counterclockwise along the circle
$(x-3)^2+(y-1)^2=4$ from $(3,3)$ to $(3,-1)$
17. Moves 3 times clockwise around the ellipse
$(x^2/25)+(y^2/4)=1$, starting and ending at $(0,-2)$
19.

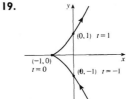

21. **23.**

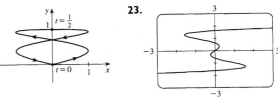

25. (b) $x=-2+5t, y=7-8t, 0\leqslant t\leqslant 1$
27. (a) $x=2\cos t, y=1-2\sin t, 0\leqslant t\leqslant 2\pi$
(b) $x=2\cos t, y=1+2\sin t, 0\leqslant t\leqslant 6\pi$
(c) $x=2\cos t, y=1+2\sin t, \pi/2\leqslant t\leqslant 3\pi/2$
31. The curve $y=x^{2/3}$ is generated in (a). In (b), only the portion with $x\geqslant 0$ is generated, and in (c) we get only the portion with $x>0$.
35. $x=a\cos\theta, y=b\sin\theta; (x^2/a^2)+(y^2/b^2)=1$, ellipse

EXERCISES 9.6 ■ PAGE 612

1. (a) $x =$ predators, $y =$ prey; growth is restricted only by predators, which feed only on prey.
(b) $x =$ prey, $y =$ predators; growth is restricted by carrying capacity and by predators, which feed only on prey.

3. (a) The rabbit population starts at about 300, increases to 2400, then decreases back to 300. The fox population starts at 100, decreases to about 20, increases to about 315, decreases to 100, and the cycle starts again.

(b)

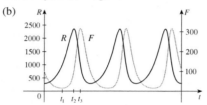

5.

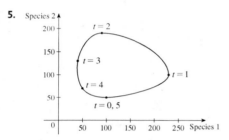

9. (a) Population stabilizes at 5000.
(b) (i) $W = 0, R = 0$: Zero populations
(ii) $W = 0, R = 5000$: In the absence of wolves, the rabbit population is always 5000.
(iii) $W = 64, R = 1000$: Both populations are stable.
(c) The populations stabilize at 1000 rabbits and 64 wolves.

(d)

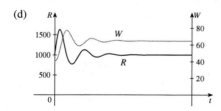

5.

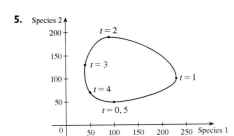

Species 2

9. (a) Population stabilizes at 5000.
(b) (i) $W = 0$, $R = 0$: Zero populations
(ii) $W = 0$, $R = 5000$: In the absence of wolves, the rabbit population is always 5000.
(iii) $W = 64$, $R = 1000$: Both populations are stable.
(c) The populations stabilize at 1000 rabbits and 64 wolves.

(d)

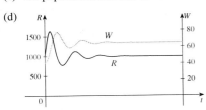

True-False Quiz

1. True   **3.** False   **5.** True   **7.** True

Exercises

1. (a)

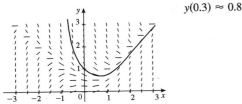

(b) $0 \leqslant c \leqslant 4$;
$y = 0$, $y = 2$, $y = 4$

3. (a)

$y(0.3) \approx 0.8$

(b) 0.75676
(c) $y = x$ and $y = -x$; there is a local maximum or minimum
5. $y = (\frac{1}{2}x^2 + C)e^{-\sin x}$ **7.** $y = \pm\sqrt{\ln(x^2 + 2x^{3/2} + C)}$
9. $r(t) = 5e^{t-t^2}$ **11.** $y = \frac{1}{2}x(\ln x)^2 + 2x$ **13.** $x = C - \frac{1}{2}y^2$

15. (a) $P(t) = \dfrac{2000}{1 + 19e^{-0.1t}}$; ≈ 560 (b) $t = -10 \ln \frac{2}{57} \approx 33.5$

17. (a) $L(t) = L_\infty - [L_\infty - L(0)]e^{-kt}$ (b) $L(t) = 53 - 43e^{-0.2t}$

19. 15 days   **21.** $k \ln h + h = (-R/V)t + C$

23. (a) Stabilizes at 200,000
(b) (i) $x = 0$, $y = 0$: Zero populations
(ii) $x = 200{,}000$, $y = 0$: In the absence of birds, the insect population is always 200,000.
(iii) $x = 25{,}000$, $y = 175$: Both populations are stable.
(c) The populations stabilize at 25,000 insects and 175 birds.
(d)

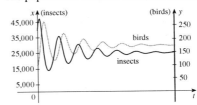

25. (a) $y = (1/k) \cosh kx + a - 1/k$ or
$y = (1/k) \cosh kx - (1/k) \cosh kb + h$ (b) $(2/k) \sinh kb$

1. $f(x) = \pm 10e^x$ **5.** $y = x^{1/n}$ **7.** $20°C$

9. (b) $f(x) = \dfrac{x^2 - L^2}{4L} - \frac{1}{2}L \ln\left(\dfrac{x}{L}\right)$ (c) No

11. (a) 9.8 h   (b) $31{,}900\pi \approx 100{,}000$ ft^2; 6283 ft^2/h
(c) 5.1 h
13. $x^2 + (y - 6)^2 = 25$

CHAPTER 10

1.

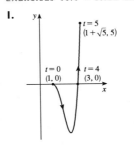

3.

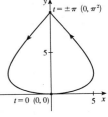

5. (a)

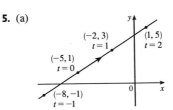

(b) $y = \frac{2}{3}x + \frac{13}{3}$

CHAPTER 17

1. $y = c_1 e^{3x} + c_2 e^{-2x}$ **3.** $y = c_1 \cos 4x + c_2 \sin 4x$
5. $y = c_1 e^{2x/3} + c_2 x e^{2x/3}$ **7.** $y = c_1 + c_2 e^{x/2}$
9. $y = e^{2x}(c_1 \cos 3x + c_2 \sin 3x)$
11. $y = c_1 e^{(\sqrt{3}-1)t/2} + c_2 e^{-(\sqrt{3}+1)t/2}$
13. $P = e^{-t}\left[c_1 \cos(\frac{1}{10}t) + c_2 \sin(\frac{1}{10}t)\right]$

15.

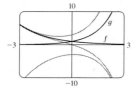

All solutions approach either 0 or $\pm\infty$ as $x \to \pm\infty$.

17. $y = 2e^{-3x/2} + e^{-x}$ **19.** $y = e^{x/2} - 2xe^{x/2}$
21. $y = 3 \cos 4x - \sin 4x$ **23.** $y = e^{-x}(2 \cos x + 3 \sin x)$
25. $y = 3 \cos(\frac{1}{2}x) - 4 \sin(\frac{1}{2}x)$ **27.** $y = \dfrac{e^{x+3}}{e^3 - 1} + \dfrac{e^{2x}}{1 - e^3}$
29. No solution
31. $y = e^{-2x}(2 \cos 3x - e^{\pi} \sin 3x)$
33. (b) $\lambda = n^2\pi^2/L^2$, n a positive integer; $y = C \sin(n\pi x/L)$

1. $y = c_1 e^{-2x} + c_2 e^{-x} + \frac{1}{2}x^2 - \frac{3}{2}x + \frac{7}{4}$
3. $y = c_1 + c_2 e^{2x} + \frac{1}{40} \cos 4x - \frac{1}{20} \sin 4x$
5. $y = e^{2x}(c_1 \cos x + c_2 \sin x) + \frac{1}{10}e^{-x}$
7. $y = \frac{3}{2} \cos x + \frac{11}{2} \sin x + \frac{1}{2}e^x + x^3 - 6x$
9. $y = e^x(\frac{1}{2}x^2 - x + 2)$
11.

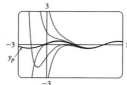

The solutions are all asymptotic to $y_p = \frac{1}{10} \cos x + \frac{3}{10} \sin x$ as $x \to \infty$. Except for y_p, all solutions approach either ∞ or $-\infty$ as $x \to -\infty$.

13. $y_p = Ae^{2x} + (Bx^2 + Cx + D) \cos x + (Ex^2 + Fx + G) \sin x$
15. $y_p = Ax + (Bx + C)e^{9x}$
17. $y_p = xe^{-x}[(Ax^2 + Bx + C) \cos 3x + (Dx^2 + Ex + F) \sin 3x]$
19. $y = c_1 \cos(\frac{1}{2}x) + c_2 \sin(\frac{1}{2}x) - \frac{1}{3} \cos x$
21. $y = c_1 e^x + c_2 x e^x + e^{2x}$
23. $y = c_1 \sin x + c_2 \cos x + \sin x \ln(\sec x + \tan x) - 1$
25. $y = [c_1 + \ln(1 + e^{-x})]e^x + [c_2 - e^{-x} + \ln(1 + e^{-x})]e^{2x}$
27. $y = e^x\left[c_1 + c_2 x - \frac{1}{2} \ln(1 + x^2) + x \tan^{-1}x\right]$

1. $x = 0.35 \cos(2\sqrt{5}\,t)$ **3.** $x = -\frac{1}{5}e^{-6t} + \frac{6}{5}e^{-t}$ **5.** $\frac{49}{12}$ kg

7.

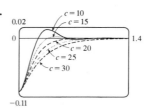

13. $Q(t) = (-e^{-10t}/250)(6 \cos 20t + 3 \sin 20t) + \frac{3}{125}$, $I(t) = \frac{3}{5}e^{-10t} \sin 20t$
15. $Q(t) = e^{-10t}\left[\frac{3}{250} \cos 20t - \frac{3}{500} \sin 20t\right]$ $- \frac{3}{250} \cos 10t + \frac{3}{125} \sin 10t$

1. $c_0 \displaystyle\sum_{n=0}^{\infty} \frac{x^n}{n!} = c_0 e^x$ **3.** $c_0 \displaystyle\sum_{n=0}^{\infty} \frac{x^{3n}}{3^n n!} = c_0 e^{x^3/3}$
5. $c_0 \displaystyle\sum_{n=0}^{\infty} \frac{(-1)^n}{2^n n!} x^{2n} + c_1 \displaystyle\sum_{n=0}^{\infty} \frac{(-2)^n n!}{(2n+1)!} x^{2n+1}$
7. $c_0 + c_1 \displaystyle\sum_{n=1}^{\infty} \frac{x^n}{n} = c_0 - c_1 \ln(1 - x)$ for $|x| < 1$
9. $\displaystyle\sum_{n=0}^{\infty} \frac{x^{2n}}{2^n n!} = e^{x^2/2}$
11. $x + \displaystyle\sum_{n=1}^{\infty} \frac{(-1)^n 2^2 5^2 \cdot \cdots \cdot (3n-1)^2}{(3n+1)!} x^{3n+1}$

True-False Quiz

1. True   **3.** True

Exercises

1. $y = c_1 e^{5x} + c_2 e^{-3x}$ **3.** $y = c_1 \cos(\sqrt{3}x) + c_2 \sin(\sqrt{3}x)$
5. $y = e^{2x}(c_1 \cos x + c_2 \sin x + 1)$
7. $y = c_1 e^x + c_2 x e^x - \frac{1}{2} \cos x - \frac{1}{2}(x + 1) \sin x$
9. $y = c_1 e^{3x} + c_2 e^{-2x} - \frac{1}{6} - \frac{1}{5}xe^{-2x}$
11. $y = 5 - 2e^{-6(x-1)}$ **13.** $y = (e^{4x} - e^x)/3$
15. $\displaystyle\sum_{n=0}^{\infty} \frac{(-2)^n n!}{(2n+1)!} x^{2n+1}$
17. $Q(t) = -0.02e^{-10t}(\cos 10t + \sin 10t) + 0.03$
19. (c) $2\pi/k \approx 85$ min   (d) $\approx 17,600$ mi/h

index

# #

#, # definition of a limit , 31,64

A

absolute maximum and minimum , 651

absolute maximum and minimum values ,
654,658,662

absolute value function , 5

absolutely convergent series, 446

acceleration
   vector components of . 588

addition of vectors , 529

Airy function , 457

Airy, Sir George , 457

alternating harmonic series , 444

alternating series , 442

Alternating Series Estimation Theorem , 445

Alternating Series Test , 443

angle(s)
   between vectors . 537,538

angular momentum , 593

angular speed , 586

antiderivative
   general vs. particular . 333

antidifferentiation formulas , 244

aphelion , 517

approximate integration , 336

approximating cylinder , 369

approximation
   by Taylor polynomials . 476

approximation, linear
   to a tangent plane . 625,629

arc curvature , 578,579,580,582

arc length
   of a space curve . 576,577

arc length formula , 383

arc length function , 577

Archimedes , 394

area
   of a surface . 777,778

Area Problem , 253

arrow diagram for a function , 2

astroid , 499

asymptote(s)
   of a hyperbola . 515

average cost function , 235

average rate of change
   units for . 80

average speed of molecules , 356

average value of a function , 679,708

average velocity , 584

axes, coordinate , 523

axis of a parabola , 514

B

Barrow, Isaac , 286

base
   change of . 158

base of a cylinder , 366

basis vectors , 533

Bernoulli, James , 402

Bernoulli, John , 491

Bessel function , 453,457

Bessel, Friedrich , 453

binomial coefficient , 470

binomial series , 469,470,471

binormal vector , 580,581,582

blood flow , 137

boundary curve , 792

bounded sequence , 418

bounded set , 655

Boyle's Law , 5

Brache, Tycho , 590

brachistochrone problem , 491

branches of a hyperbola , 515

bullet-nose curve , 120

C

C1 transformation , 720

cable, hanging , 182

calculator, graphing , 489,507

calculus, differential vs. integral , 286

cancellation equations , 151

Cantor set , 433

Cantor, Georg , 433

cardioid , 504

carrying capacity , 405

CAS
   See computer algebra system.

Cassini, Giovanni , 509

catenary , 182

Cauchy, Augustin-Louis , 676

Cauchy-Schwarz Inequality , 543

Cavalieri's Principle , 376

Cavalieri, Bonaventura , 343

center of gravity , 394

center of mass

of a wire . 739

centripetal force , 586

centroid
   of a solid . 705

Chain Rule
   for several variables . 631,633,634

change of base in a logarithm , 158

change of variables:
   in a triple integral . 725,726

charge density , 694

charge, electric , 694,705

circle
   area of . 319

circle of curvature , 582

circular cylinder , 366

circulation of a velocity field , 795

Cissoid of Diocles , 508

Clairaut's Theorem , 619

Clairaut, Alexis , 619

closed curve , 750

Closed Interval Method , 203

closed set , 655

closed surface , 786

Cobb-Douglas production function , 664

cochleoid , 521

coefficient
   of a power series . 452

combinations of functions , 18

common ratio , 426

comparison properties of the integral , 273

Comparison Test , 438

comparison tests for series , 437

Comparison Theorem for integrals , 354

Completeness Axiom , 423

component function , 732

component of b along a, 540

components of a vector , 530

composite function
   continuity of . 612

composition of functions , 19

compound interest , 173,174,194

computer algebra system
   for plotting a vector field . 733

concavity , 215

Concavity Test , 216

conchoid , 508

conductivity (of a substance) , 789

cone

index

index

index

TABLE OF INTERVALS

Notation	Set description	Picture	Notation	Set description	Picture
(a, b)	$\{x \mid a < x < b\}$		(a, ∞)	$\{x \mid x > a\}$	
$[a, b]$	$\{x \mid a \leq x \leq b\}$		$[a, \infty)$	$\{x \mid x \geq a\}$	
$[a, b)$	$\{x \mid a \leq x < b\}$		$(-\infty, b)$	$\{x \mid x < b\}$	
$(a, b]$	$\{x \mid a < x \leq b\}$		$(-\infty, b]$	$\{x \mid x \leq b\}$	
			$(-\infty, \infty)$	$\mathbb{R}$ (set of all real numbers)	

SPECIAL FUNCTIONS

POWER FUNCTIONS $f(x) = x^a$

(i) $f(x) = x^n$, n a positive integer

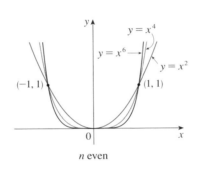

n even

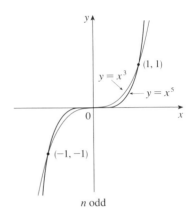

n odd

(ii) $f(x) = x^{1/n} = \sqrt[n]{x}$, n a positive integer

(iii) $f(x) = x^{-1} = \dfrac{1}{x}$

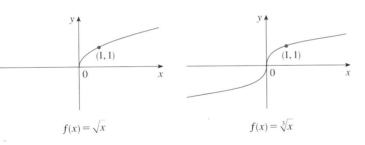

$f(x) = \sqrt{x}$ $f(x) = \sqrt[3]{x}$

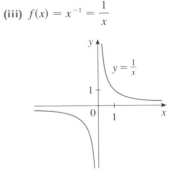

INVERSE TRIGONOMETRIC FUNCTIONS

$\arcsin x = \sin^{-1}x = y \iff \sin y = x$ and $-\dfrac{\pi}{2} \leq y \leq \dfrac{\pi}{2}$

$\arccos x = \cos^{-1}x = y \iff \cos y = x$ and $0 \leq y \leq \pi$

$\arctan x = \tan^{-1}x = y \iff \tan y = x$ and $-\dfrac{\pi}{2} < y < \dfrac{\pi}{2}$

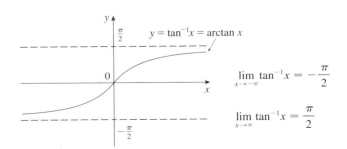

$\displaystyle\lim_{x \to -\infty} \tan^{-1}x = -\dfrac{\pi}{2}$

$\displaystyle\lim_{x \to \infty} \tan^{-1}x = \dfrac{\pi}{2}$

SPECIAL FUNCTIONS

EXPONENTIAL AND LOGARITHMIC FUNCTIONS

$\log_a x = y \iff a^y = x$

$\ln x = \log_e x, \quad \text{where} \quad \ln e = 1$

$\ln x = y \iff e^y = x$

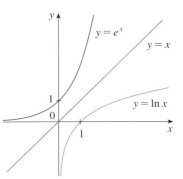

$$\lim_{x \to -\infty} e^x = 0 \qquad \lim_{x \to \infty} e^x = \infty$$

$$\lim_{x \to 0^+} \ln x = -\infty \qquad \lim_{x \to \infty} \ln x = \infty$$

Cancellation Equations	Laws of Logarithms
$\log_a(a^x) = x \qquad a^{\log_a x} = x$	**1.** $\log_a(xy) = \log_a x + \log_a y$
$\ln(e^x) = x \qquad e^{\ln x} = x$	**2.** $\log_a\left(\dfrac{x}{y}\right) = \log_a x - \log_a y$
	3. $\log_a(x^r) = r \log_a x$

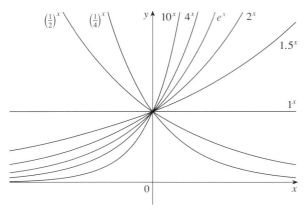

Exponential functions

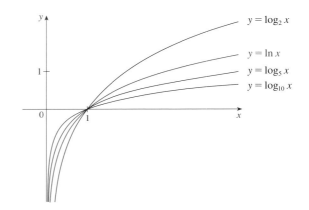

Logarithmic functions

HYPERBOLIC FUNCTIONS

$\sinh x = \dfrac{e^x - e^{-x}}{2}$ $\qquad$ $\operatorname{csch} x = \dfrac{1}{\sinh x}$

$\cosh x = \dfrac{e^x + e^{-x}}{2}$ $\qquad$ $\operatorname{sech} x = \dfrac{1}{\cosh x}$

$\tanh x = \dfrac{\sinh x}{\cosh x}$ $\qquad$ $\coth x = \dfrac{\cosh x}{\sinh x}$

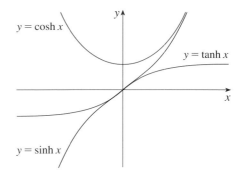

INVERSE HYPERBOLIC FUNCTIONS

$y = \sinh^{-1} x \iff \sinh y = x$ $\qquad$ $\sinh^{-1} x = \ln\left(x + \sqrt{x^2 + 1}\right)$

$y = \cosh^{-1} x \iff \cosh y = x \quad \text{and} \quad y \geq 0$ $\qquad$ $\cosh^{-1} x = \ln\left(x + \sqrt{x^2 - 1}\right)$

$y = \tanh^{-1} x \iff \tanh y = x$ $\qquad$ $\tanh^{-1} x = \frac{1}{2} \ln\left(\dfrac{1 + x}{1 - x}\right)$

4

DIFFERENTIATION RULES

GENERAL FORMULAS

1. $\dfrac{d}{dx}(c) = 0$

2. $\dfrac{d}{dx}[cf(x)] = cf'(x)$

3. $\dfrac{d}{dx}[f(x) + g(x)] = f'(x) + g'(x)$

4. $\dfrac{d}{dx}[f(x) - g(x)] = f'(x) - g'(x)$

5. $\dfrac{d}{dx}[f(x)g(x)] = f(x)g'(x) + g(x)f'(x)$ (Product Rule)

6. $\dfrac{d}{dx}\left[\dfrac{f(x)}{g(x)}\right] = \dfrac{g(x)f'(x) - f(x)g'(x)}{[g(x)]^2}$ (Quotient Rule)

7. $\dfrac{d}{dx}f(g(x)) = f'(g(x))g'(x)$ (Chain Rule)

8. $\dfrac{d}{dx}(x^n) = nx^{n-1}$ (Power Rule)

EXPONENTIAL AND LOGARITHMIC FUNCTIONS

9. $\dfrac{d}{dx}(e^x) = e^x$

10. $\dfrac{d}{dx}(a^x) = a^x \ln a$

11. $\dfrac{d}{dx}\ln|x| = \dfrac{1}{x}$

12. $\dfrac{d}{dx}(\log_a x) = \dfrac{1}{x \ln a}$

TRIGONOMETRIC FUNCTIONS

13. $\dfrac{d}{dx}(\sin x) = \cos x$

14. $\dfrac{d}{dx}(\cos x) = -\sin x$

15. $\dfrac{d}{dx}(\tan x) = \sec^2 x$

16. $\dfrac{d}{dx}(\csc x) = -\csc x \cot x$

17. $\dfrac{d}{dx}(\sec x) = \sec x \tan x$

18. $\dfrac{d}{dx}(\cot x) = -\csc^2 x$

INVERSE TRIGONOMETRIC FUNCTIONS

19. $\dfrac{d}{dx}(\sin^{-1}x) = \dfrac{1}{\sqrt{1 - x^2}}$

20. $\dfrac{d}{dx}(\cos^{-1}x) = -\dfrac{1}{\sqrt{1 - x^2}}$

21. $\dfrac{d}{dx}(\tan^{-1}x) = \dfrac{1}{1 + x^2}$

22. $\dfrac{d}{dx}(\csc^{-1}x) = -\dfrac{1}{x\sqrt{x^2 - 1}}$

23. $\dfrac{d}{dx}(\sec^{-1}x) = \dfrac{1}{x\sqrt{x^2 - 1}}$

24. $\dfrac{d}{dx}(\cot^{-1}x) = -\dfrac{1}{1 + x^2}$

HYPERBOLIC FUNCTIONS

25. $\dfrac{d}{dx}(\sinh x) = \cosh x$

26. $\dfrac{d}{dx}(\cosh x) = \sinh x$

27. $\dfrac{d}{dx}(\tanh x) = \text{sech}^2 x$

28. $\dfrac{d}{dx}(\text{csch}\, x) = -\text{csch}\, x \coth x$

29. $\dfrac{d}{dx}(\text{sech}\, x) = -\text{sech}\, x \tanh x$

30. $\dfrac{d}{dx}(\coth x) = -\text{csch}^2 x$

INVERSE HYPERBOLIC FUNCTIONS

31. $\dfrac{d}{dx}(\sinh^{-1}x) = \dfrac{1}{\sqrt{1 + x^2}}$

32. $\dfrac{d}{dx}(\cosh^{-1}x) = \dfrac{1}{\sqrt{x^2 - 1}}$

33. $\dfrac{d}{dx}(\tanh^{-1}x) = \dfrac{1}{1 - x^2}$

34. $\dfrac{d}{dx}(\text{csch}^{-1}x) = -\dfrac{1}{|x|\sqrt{x^2 + 1}}$

35. $\dfrac{d}{dx}(\text{sech}^{-1}x) = -\dfrac{1}{x\sqrt{1 - x^2}}$

36. $\dfrac{d}{dx}(\coth^{-1}x) = \dfrac{1}{1 - x^2}$

TABLE OF INTEGRALS

BASIC FORMS

1. $\displaystyle\int u\, dv = uv - \int v\, du$

2. $\displaystyle\int u^n\, du = \frac{u^{n+1}}{n+1} + C, \quad n \neq -1$

3. $\displaystyle\int \frac{du}{u} = \ln|u| + C$

4. $\displaystyle\int e^u\, du = e^u + C$

5. $\displaystyle\int a^u\, du = \frac{a^u}{\ln a} + C$

6. $\displaystyle\int \sin u\, du = -\cos u + C$

7. $\displaystyle\int \cos u\, du = \sin u + C$

8. $\displaystyle\int \sec^2 u\, du = \tan u + C$

9. $\displaystyle\int \csc^2 u\, du = -\cot u + C$

10. $\displaystyle\int \sec u \tan u\, du = \sec u + C$

11. $\displaystyle\int \csc u \cot u\, du = -\csc u + C$

12. $\displaystyle\int \tan u\, du = \ln|\sec u| + C$

13. $\displaystyle\int \cot u\, du = \ln|\sin u| + C$

14. $\displaystyle\int \sec u\, du = \ln|\sec u + \tan u| + C$

15. $\displaystyle\int \csc u\, du = \ln|\csc u - \cot u| + C$

16. $\displaystyle\int \frac{du}{\sqrt{a^2 - u^2}} = \sin^{-1}\frac{u}{a} + C$

17. $\displaystyle\int \frac{du}{a^2 + u^2} = \frac{1}{a}\tan^{-1}\frac{u}{a} + C$

18. $\displaystyle\int \frac{du}{u\sqrt{u^2 - a^2}} = \frac{1}{a}\sec^{-1}\frac{u}{a} + C$

19. $\displaystyle\int \frac{du}{a^2 - u^2} = \frac{1}{2a}\ln\left|\frac{u + a}{u - a}\right| + C$

20. $\displaystyle\int \frac{du}{u^2 - a^2} = \frac{1}{2a}\ln\left|\frac{u - a}{u + a}\right| + C$

FORMS INVOLVING $\sqrt{a^2 + u^2}$, $a > 0$

21. $\displaystyle\int \sqrt{a^2 + u^2}\, du = \frac{u}{2}\sqrt{a^2 + u^2} + \frac{a^2}{2}\ln\left(u + \sqrt{a^2 + u^2}\right) + C$

22. $\displaystyle\int u^2\sqrt{a^2 + u^2}\, du = \frac{u}{8}(a^2 + 2u^2)\sqrt{a^2 + u^2} - \frac{a^4}{8}\ln\left(u + \sqrt{a^2 + u^2}\right) + C$

23. $\displaystyle\int \frac{\sqrt{a^2 + u^2}}{u}\, du = \sqrt{a^2 + u^2} - a\ln\left|\frac{a + \sqrt{a^2 + u^2}}{u}\right| + C$

24. $\displaystyle\int \frac{\sqrt{a^2 + u^2}}{u^2}\, du = -\frac{\sqrt{a^2 + u^2}}{u} + \ln\left(u + \sqrt{a^2 + u^2}\right) + C$

25. $\displaystyle\int \frac{du}{\sqrt{a^2 + u^2}} = \ln\left(u + \sqrt{a^2 + u^2}\right) + C$

26. $\displaystyle\int \frac{u^2\, du}{\sqrt{a^2 + u^2}} = \frac{u}{2}\sqrt{a^2 + u^2} - \frac{a^2}{2}\ln\left(u + \sqrt{a^2 + u^2}\right) + C$

27. $\displaystyle\int \frac{du}{u\sqrt{a^2 + u^2}} = -\frac{1}{a}\ln\left|\frac{\sqrt{a^2 + u^2} + a}{u}\right| + C$

28. $\displaystyle\int \frac{du}{u^2\sqrt{a^2 + u^2}} = -\frac{\sqrt{a^2 + u^2}}{a^2 u} + C$

29. $\displaystyle\int \frac{du}{(a^2 + u^2)^{3/2}} = \frac{u}{a^2\sqrt{a^2 + u^2}} + C$

TABLE OF INTEGRALS

FORMS INVOLVING $\sqrt{a^2 - u^2}$, $a > 0$

30. $\displaystyle\int \sqrt{a^2 - u^2}\, du = \frac{u}{2}\sqrt{a^2 - u^2} + \frac{a^2}{2}\sin^{-1}\frac{u}{a} + C$

31. $\displaystyle\int u^2\sqrt{a^2 - u^2}\, du = \frac{u}{8}(2u^2 - a^2)\sqrt{a^2 - u^2} + \frac{a^4}{8}\sin^{-1}\frac{u}{a} + C$

32. $\displaystyle\int \frac{\sqrt{a^2 - u^2}}{u}\, du = \sqrt{a^2 - u^2} - a\ln\left|\frac{a + \sqrt{a^2 - u^2}}{u}\right| + C$

33. $\displaystyle\int \frac{\sqrt{a^2 - u^2}}{u^2}\, du = -\frac{1}{u}\sqrt{a^2 - u^2} - \sin^{-1}\frac{u}{a} + C$

34. $\displaystyle\int \frac{u^2\, du}{\sqrt{a^2 - u^2}} = -\frac{u}{2}\sqrt{a^2 - u^2} + \frac{a^2}{2}\sin^{-1}\frac{u}{a} + C$

35. $\displaystyle\int \frac{du}{u\sqrt{a^2 - u^2}} = -\frac{1}{a}\ln\left|\frac{a + \sqrt{a^2 - u^2}}{u}\right| + C$

36. $\displaystyle\int \frac{du}{u^2\sqrt{a^2 - u^2}} = -\frac{1}{a^2 u}\sqrt{a^2 - u^2} + C$

37. $\displaystyle\int (a^2 - u^2)^{3/2}\, du = -\frac{u}{8}(2u^2 - 5a^2)\sqrt{a^2 - u^2} + \frac{3a^4}{8}\sin^{-1}\frac{u}{a} + C$

38. $\displaystyle\int \frac{du}{(a^2 - u^2)^{3/2}} = \frac{u}{a^2\sqrt{a^2 - u^2}} + C$

FORMS INVOLVING $\sqrt{u^2 - a^2}$, $a > 0$

39. $\displaystyle\int \sqrt{u^2 - a^2}\, du = \frac{u}{2}\sqrt{u^2 - a^2} - \frac{a^2}{2}\ln\left|u + \sqrt{u^2 - a^2}\right| + C$

40. $\displaystyle\int u^2\sqrt{u^2 - a^2}\, du = \frac{u}{8}(2u^2 - a^2)\sqrt{u^2 - a^2} - \frac{a^4}{8}\ln\left|u + \sqrt{u^2 - a^2}\right| + C$

41. $\displaystyle\int \frac{\sqrt{u^2 - a^2}}{u}\, du = \sqrt{u^2 - a^2} - a\cos^{-1}\frac{a}{|u|} + C$

42. $\displaystyle\int \frac{\sqrt{u^2 - a^2}}{u^2}\, du = -\frac{\sqrt{u^2 - a^2}}{u} + \ln\left|u + \sqrt{u^2 - a^2}\right| + C$

43. $\displaystyle\int \frac{du}{\sqrt{u^2 - a^2}} = \ln\left|u + \sqrt{u^2 - a^2}\right| + C$

44. $\displaystyle\int \frac{u^2\, du}{\sqrt{u^2 - a^2}} = \frac{u}{2}\sqrt{u^2 - a^2} + \frac{a^2}{2}\ln\left|u + \sqrt{u^2 - a^2}\right| + C$

45. $\displaystyle\int \frac{du}{u^2\sqrt{u^2 - a^2}} = \frac{\sqrt{u^2 - a^2}}{a^2 u} + C$

46. $\displaystyle\int \frac{du}{(u^2 - a^2)^{3/2}} = -\frac{u}{a^2\sqrt{u^2 - a^2}} + C$

TABLE OF INTEGRALS

FORMS INVOLVING $a + bu$

47. $\displaystyle \int \frac{u\,du}{a + bu} = \frac{1}{b^2}\left(a + bu - a \ln|a + bu|\right) + C$

48. $\displaystyle \int \frac{u^2\,du}{a + bu} = \frac{1}{2b^3}\left[(a + bu)^2 - 4a(a + bu) + 2a^2 \ln|a + bu|\right] + C$

49. $\displaystyle \int \frac{du}{u(a + bu)} = \frac{1}{a}\ln\left|\frac{u}{a + bu}\right| + C$

50. $\displaystyle \int \frac{du}{u^2(a + bu)} = -\frac{1}{au} + \frac{b}{a^2}\ln\left|\frac{a + bu}{u}\right| + C$

51. $\displaystyle \int \frac{u\,du}{(a + bu)^2} = \frac{a}{b^2(a + bu)} + \frac{1}{b^2}\ln|a + bu| + C$

52. $\displaystyle \int \frac{du}{u(a + bu)^2} = \frac{1}{a(a + bu)} - \frac{1}{a^2}\ln\left|\frac{a + bu}{u}\right| + C$

53. $\displaystyle \int \frac{u^2\,du}{(a + bu)^2} = \frac{1}{b^3}\left(a + bu - \frac{a^2}{a + bu} - 2a \ln|a + bu|\right) + C$

54. $\displaystyle \int u\sqrt{a + bu}\,du = \frac{2}{15b^2}(3bu - 2a)(a + bu)^{3/2} + C$

55. $\displaystyle \int \frac{u\,du}{\sqrt{a + bu}} = \frac{2}{3b^2}(bu - 2a)\sqrt{a + bu} + C$

56. $\displaystyle \int \frac{u^2\,du}{\sqrt{a + bu}} = \frac{2}{15b^3}(8a^2 + 3b^2u^2 - 4abu)\sqrt{a + bu} + C$

57. $\displaystyle \int \frac{du}{u\sqrt{a + bu}} = \frac{1}{\sqrt{a}}\ln\left|\frac{\sqrt{a + bu} - \sqrt{a}}{\sqrt{a + bu} + \sqrt{a}}\right| + C, \quad \text{if } a > 0$

$\displaystyle \qquad\qquad\quad = \frac{2}{\sqrt{-a}}\tan^{-1}\sqrt{\frac{a + bu}{-a}} + C, \qquad \text{if } a < 0$

58. $\displaystyle \int \frac{\sqrt{a + bu}}{u}\,du = 2\sqrt{a + bu} + a\int \frac{du}{u\sqrt{a + bu}}$

59. $\displaystyle \int \frac{\sqrt{a + bu}}{u^2}\,du = -\frac{\sqrt{a + bu}}{u} + \frac{b}{2}\int \frac{du}{u\sqrt{a + bu}}$

60. $\displaystyle \int u^n\sqrt{a + bu}\,du = \frac{2}{b(2n + 3)}\left[u^n(a + bu)^{3/2} - na\int u^{n-1}\sqrt{a + bu}\,du\right]$

61. $\displaystyle \int \frac{u^n\,du}{\sqrt{a + bu}} = \frac{2u^n\sqrt{a + bu}}{b(2n + 1)} - \frac{2na}{b(2n + 1)}\int \frac{u^{n-1}\,du}{\sqrt{a + bu}}$

62. $\displaystyle \int \frac{du}{u^n\sqrt{a + bu}} = -\frac{\sqrt{a + bu}}{a(n - 1)u^{n-1}} - \frac{b(2n - 3)}{2a(n - 1)}\int \frac{du}{u^{n-1}\sqrt{a + bu}}$

TABLE OF INTEGRALS

TRIGONOMETRIC FORMS

63. $\int \sin^2 u \, du = \frac{1}{2}u - \frac{1}{4}\sin 2u + C$

64. $\int \cos^2 u \, du = \frac{1}{2}u + \frac{1}{4}\sin 2u + C$

65. $\int \tan^2 u \, du = \tan u - u + C$

66. $\int \cot^2 u \, du = -\cot u - u + C$

67. $\int \sin^3 u \, du = -\frac{1}{3}(2 + \sin^2 u)\cos u + C$

68. $\int \cos^3 u \, du = \frac{1}{3}(2 + \cos^2 u)\sin u + C$

69. $\int \tan^3 u \, du = \frac{1}{2}\tan^2 u + \ln|\cos u| + C$

70. $\int \cot^3 u \, du = -\frac{1}{2}\cot^2 u - \ln|\sin u| + C$

71. $\int \sec^3 u \, du = \frac{1}{2}\sec u \tan u + \frac{1}{2}\ln|\sec u + \tan u| + C$

72. $\int \csc^3 u \, du = -\frac{1}{2}\csc u \cot u + \frac{1}{2}\ln|\csc u - \cot u| + C$

73. $\int \sin^n u \, du = -\frac{1}{n}\sin^{n-1} u \cos u + \frac{n-1}{n}\int \sin^{n-2} u \, du$

74. $\int \cos^n u \, du = \frac{1}{n}\cos^{n-1} u \sin u + \frac{n-1}{n}\int \cos^{n-2} u \, du$

75. $\int \tan^n u \, du = \frac{1}{n-1}\tan^{n-1} u - \int \tan^{n-2} u \, du$

76. $\int \cot^n u \, du = \frac{-1}{n-1}\cot^{n-1} u - \int \cot^{n-2} u \, du$

77. $\int \sec^n u \, du = \frac{1}{n-1}\tan u \sec^{n-2} u + \frac{n-2}{n-1}\int \sec^{n-2} u \, du$

78. $\int \csc^n u \, du = \frac{-1}{n-1}\cot u \csc^{n-2} u + \frac{n-2}{n-1}\int \csc^{n-2} u \, du$

79. $\int \sin au \sin bu \, du = \frac{\sin(a-b)u}{2(a-b)} - \frac{\sin(a+b)u}{2(a+b)} + C$

80. $\int \cos au \cos bu \, du = \frac{\sin(a-b)u}{2(a-b)} + \frac{\sin(a+b)u}{2(a+b)} + C$

81. $\int \sin au \cos bu \, du = -\frac{\cos(a-b)u}{2(a-b)} - \frac{\cos(a+b)u}{2(a+b)} + C$

82. $\int u \sin u \, du = \sin u - u \cos u + C$

83. $\int u \cos u \, du = \cos u + u \sin u + C$

84. $\int u^n \sin u \, du = -u^n \cos u + n \int u^{n-1} \cos u \, du$

85. $\int u^n \cos u \, du = u^n \sin u - n \int u^{n-1} \sin u \, du$

86. $\int \sin^n u \cos^m u \, du = -\frac{\sin^{n-1} u \cos^{m+1} u}{n+m} + \frac{n-1}{n+m}\int \sin^{n-2} u \cos^m u \, du$
$\qquad = \frac{\sin^{n+1} u \cos^{m-1} u}{n+m} + \frac{m-1}{n+m}\int \sin^n u \cos^{m-2} u \, du$

INVERSE TRIGONOMETRIC FORMS

87. $\int \sin^{-1} u \, du = u \sin^{-1} u + \sqrt{1-u^2} + C$

88. $\int \cos^{-1} u \, du = u \cos^{-1} u - \sqrt{1-u^2} + C$

89. $\int \tan^{-1} u \, du = u \tan^{-1} u - \frac{1}{2}\ln(1+u^2) + C$

90. $\int u \sin^{-1} u \, du = \frac{2u^2-1}{4}\sin^{-1} u + \frac{u\sqrt{1-u^2}}{4} + C$

91. $\int u \cos^{-1} u \, du = \frac{2u^2-1}{4}\cos^{-1} u - \frac{u\sqrt{1-u^2}}{4} + C$

92. $\int u \tan^{-1} u \, du = \frac{u^2+1}{2}\tan^{-1} u - \frac{u}{2} + C$

93. $\int u^n \sin^{-1} u \, du = \frac{1}{n+1}\left[u^{n+1}\sin^{-1} u - \int \frac{u^{n+1} \, du}{\sqrt{1-u^2}} \right], \quad n \neq -1$

94. $\int u^n \cos^{-1} u \, du = \frac{1}{n+1}\left[u^{n+1}\cos^{-1} u + \int \frac{u^{n+1} \, du}{\sqrt{1-u^2}} \right], \quad n \neq -1$

95. $\int u^n \tan^{-1} u \, du = \frac{1}{n+1}\left[u^{n+1}\tan^{-1} u - \int \frac{u^{n+1} \, du}{1+u^2} \right], \quad n \neq -1$

TABLE OF INTEGRALS

ONENTIAL AND LOGARITHMIC FORMS

96. $\displaystyle\int ue^{au}\,du = \frac{1}{a^2}(au-1)e^{au} + C$

100. $\displaystyle\int \ln u\,du = u\ln u - u + C$

97. $\displaystyle\int u^n e^{au}\,du = \frac{1}{a}u^n e^{au} - \frac{n}{a}\int u^{n-1}e^{au}\,du$

101. $\displaystyle\int u^n \ln u\,du = \frac{u^{n+1}}{(n+1)^2}[(n+1)\ln u - 1] + C$

98. $\displaystyle\int e^{au}\sin bu\,du = \frac{e^{au}}{a^2+b^2}(a\sin bu - b\cos bu) + C$

102. $\displaystyle\int \frac{1}{u\ln u}\,du = \ln|\ln u| + C$

99. $\displaystyle\int e^{au}\cos bu\,du = \frac{e^{au}}{a^2+b^2}(a\cos bu + b\sin bu) + C$

HYPERBOLIC FORMS

103. $\displaystyle\int \sinh u\,du = \cosh u + C$

108. $\displaystyle\int \operatorname{csch} u\,du = \ln\left|\tanh\tfrac{1}{2}u\right| + C$

104. $\displaystyle\int \cosh u\,du = \sinh u + C$

109. $\displaystyle\int \operatorname{sech}^2 u\,du = \tanh u + C$

105. $\displaystyle\int \tanh u\,du = \ln\cosh u + C$

110. $\displaystyle\int \operatorname{csch}^2 u\,du = -\coth u + C$

106. $\displaystyle\int \coth u\,du = \ln|\sinh u| + C$

111. $\displaystyle\int \operatorname{sech} u\tanh u\,du = -\operatorname{sech} u + C$

107. $\displaystyle\int \operatorname{sech} u\,du = \tan^{-1}|\sinh u| + C$

112. $\displaystyle\int \operatorname{csch} u\coth u\,du = -\operatorname{csch} u + C$

FORMS INVOLVING $\sqrt{2au - u^2}$, $a > 0$

113. $\displaystyle\int \sqrt{2au-u^2}\,du = \frac{u-a}{2}\sqrt{2au-u^2} + \frac{a^2}{2}\cos^{-1}\left(\frac{a-u}{a}\right) + C$

114. $\displaystyle\int u\sqrt{2au-u^2}\,du = \frac{2u^2-au-3a^2}{6}\sqrt{2au-u^2} + \frac{a^3}{2}\cos^{-1}\left(\frac{a-u}{a}\right) + C$

115. $\displaystyle\int \frac{\sqrt{2au-u^2}}{u}\,du = \sqrt{2au-u^2} + a\cos^{-1}\left(\frac{a-u}{a}\right) + C$

116. $\displaystyle\int \frac{\sqrt{2au-u^2}}{u^2}\,du = -\frac{2\sqrt{2au-u^2}}{u} - \cos^{-1}\left(\frac{a-u}{a}\right) + C$

117. $\displaystyle\int \frac{du}{\sqrt{2au-u^2}} = \cos^{-1}\left(\frac{a-u}{a}\right) + C$

118. $\displaystyle\int \frac{u\,du}{\sqrt{2au-u^2}} = -\sqrt{2au-u^2} + a\cos^{-1}\left(\frac{a-u}{a}\right) + C$

119. $\displaystyle\int \frac{u^2\,du}{\sqrt{2au-u^2}} = -\frac{(u+3a)}{2}\sqrt{2au-u^2} + \frac{3a^2}{2}\cos^{-1}\left(\frac{a-u}{a}\right) + C$

120. $\displaystyle\int \frac{du}{u\sqrt{2au-u^2}} = -\frac{\sqrt{2au-u^2}}{au} + C$

WEB PROJECTS

These projects can be completed anytime after you have studied the corresponding section in the textbook. To select a project, go to **www.stewartcalculus.com** and click on **PROJECTS**.

2 DERIVATIVES

2.1 WRITING PROJECT ▪ Early Methods for Finding Tangents

2.3 APPLIED PROJECT ▪ Building a Better Roller Coaster

2.5 APPLIED PROJECT ▪ Where Should a Pilot Start Descent?

2.8 LABORATORY PROJECT ▪ Taylor Polynomials

3 INVERSE FUNCTIONS

3.7 WRITING PROJECT ▪ The Origins of L'Hospital's Rule

4 APPLICATIONS OF DIFFERENTIATION

4.1 APPLIED PROJECT ▪ The Calculus of Rainbows

4.5 APPLIED PROJECT ▪ The Shape of a Can

5 INTEGRALS

5.3 DISCOVERY PROJECT ▪ Area Functions

5.4 WRITING PROJECT ▪ Newton, Leibniz, and the Invention of Calculus

APPLIED PROJECT ▪ Where To Sit at the Movies

APPLIED PROJECT ▪ Calculus and Baseball

6 TECHNIQUES OF INTEGRATION

6.4 DISCOVERY PROJECT ▪ Patterns in Integrals

7 APPLICATIONS OF INTEGRATION

7.2 DISCOVERY PROJECT ▪ Rotating on a Slant

7.4 DISCOVERY PROJECT ▪ Arc Length Contest

7.6 APPLIED PROJECT ▪ How Fast Does a Tank Drain?

APPLIED PROJECT ▪ Which Is Faster, Going Up or Coming Down?

8 SERIES

8.1 LABORATORY PROJECT ▪ Logistic Sequences

8.7 LABORATORY PROJECT ▪ An Elusive Limit

WRITING PROJECT ▪ How Newton Discovered the Binomial Series

8.8 APPLIED PROJECT ▪ Radiation from the Stars

9 PARAMETRIC EQUATIONS AND POLAR COORDINATES

9.1 LABORATORY PROJECT ▪ Running Circles Around Circles

9.2 LABORATORY PROJECT ▪ Bézier Curves

10 VECTORS AND THE GEOMETRY OF SPACE

10.4 DISCOVERY PROJECT ▪ The Geometry of a Tetrahedron

10.5 LABORATORY PROJECT ▪ Putting 3D in Perspective

10.9 APPLIED PROJECT ▪ Kepler's Laws

11 PARTIAL DERIVATIVES

11.7 APPLIED PROJECT ▪ Designing a Dumpster

DISCOVERY PROJECT ▪ Quadratic Approximations and Critical Points

11.8 APPLIED PROJECT ▪ Rocket Science

APPLIED PROJECT ▪ Hydro-Turbine Optimization

12 MULTIPLE INTEGRALS

12.5 DISCOVERY PROJECT ▪ Volumes of Hyperspheres

12.6 DISCOVERY PROJECT ▪ The Intersection of Three Cylinders

12.7 LABORATORY PROJECT ▪ Families of Surfaces

APPLIED PROJECT ▪ Roller Derby

13 VECTOR CALCULUS

13.8 WRITING PROJECT ▪ Three Men and Two Theorems